The Man Who Loved Children

By the Same Author

The Salzburg Tales
Seven Poor Men of Sydney
The Beauties and the Furies
House of All Nations
For Love Alone
Lettie Fox, Her Luck
A Little Tea, a Little Chat
The People with the Dogs

Christina Stead / The Man Who Loved Children

Introduction by Randall Jarrell

Holt, Rinehart and Winston

New York   Chicago   San Francisco

88107-0115
Printed in the United States of America

AN UNREAD BOOK

BY RANDALL JARRELL

A MAN ON A PARK BENCH has a lonely final look, as if to say: "Reduce humanity to its ultimate particles and you end here; beyond this single separate being you cannot go." But if you look back into his life you cannot help seeing that he is separated off, not separate—is a later, singular stage of an earlier plural being. All the tongues of men were baby-talk to begin with: go back far enough and which of us knew where he ended and Mother and Father and Brother and Sister began? The singular subject in its objective universe has evolved from that original composite entity—half-subjective, half-objective, having its own ways and laws and language, its own life and its own death—the family.

The Man Who Loved Children knows as few books have ever known—knows specifically, profoundly, exhaustively—what a family is: if all mankind had been reared in orphan asylums for a thousand years, it could learn to have families again by reading *The Man Who Loved Children*. Tolstoy said that "each unhappy family is unhappy in a way of its own—" a way that it calls happiness; the Pollits, a very unhappy family, are unhappy in a way almost unbelievably their own. And yet as we read we keep thinking: "How can anything so completely itself, so completely different from me and mine, be, somehow, me and mine?" The book has an almost frightening power of remembrance; and so much of our earlier life is repressed, forgotten, both in the books we read and the memories we have, that this seems friendly of the book, even when what it reminds us of is terrible. A poem says, "O to be a child again, just for tonight!" As you read *The Man Who Loved Children* it is strange to have the wish come true.

When you begin to read about the Pollits you think with a laugh, "They're wonderfully plausible." When you have read fifty or a hundred pages you think with a desperate laugh, or none, that they are wonderfully implausible—implausible as mothers and fathers and children, in isolation, *are* implausible. There in that warm, dark, second womb, the bosom of the family, everything is carried far past plausibility: a family's private life is as immoderate and insensate, compared to its public life, as our thoughts are, compared to our speech. (O secret, satisfactory, shameless things! things that, this side of Judgment Day, no stranger ever will discover.) Dostoevsky wrote: "Almost every reality, even if it has its own immutable laws, nearly always is incredible as well as improbable. Occasionally, moreover, the more real, the more improbable it is." Defending the reality of his own novels, he used to say that their improbable extremes were far closer to everyday reality than the immediately plausible, statistical naturalism of the books everyone calls lifelike; as a proof he would read from newspaper clippings accounts of the characters and events of a Dostoevsky novel. Since Christina Stead combines with such extremes an immediately plausible naturalism, she could find her own newspaper clippings without any trouble; but the easiest defense of all would be simply for her to say, "Remember?" We do remember; and, remembering, we are willing to admit the normality of the abnormal—are willing to admit that we never understand the normal better than when it has been allowed to reach its full growth and become the abnormal.

I I

Inside the Pollit family the ordinary mitigated, half-appreciative opposition of man and woman has reached its full growth. Sam and his wife Henny are no longer on speaking terms; they quarrel directly, but the rest of the time one parent says to a child what the child repeats to the other parent. They are true opposites: Sam's blue-eyed, white-gold-haired, pale fatness is closer to Henny's haggard saffron-skinned blackness than his light general spirit is to her dark particular one. The children lean to one side of the universe or the other and ask for understanding: "Sam's answers were always to the point, full of facts; while the more one heard of Henny's answer, the more intriguing it was, the less was understood. Beyond Sam stood the physical world, and beyond Henny—what?"

Like Henny herself are Henny's *treasure drawers*, a chaos of laces, ribbons, gloves, flowers, buttons, hairpins, pots of rouge, bits of mascara, foreign coins, medicines (Henny's own "aspirin, phenacetin, and pyramidon"); often, as a treat, the children are allowed to *look in the drawers.* "A musky smell always came from Henrietta's room, a combination of dust, powder, scent, body odors that stirred the children's blood, deep, deep." At the center of the web of odors is their *Mothering, Moth, Motherbunch,* "like a tall crane in the reaches of the river, standing with one leg crooked and listening. She would look fixedly at her vision and suddenly close her eyes. The child watching (there was always one) would see nothing but the huge eyeball in its glove of flesh, deep-sunk in the wrinkled skull-hole, the dark circle round it and the eyebrow far above, as it seemed, while all her skin, unrelieved by brilliant eye, came out in its real shade, burnt olive. She looked formidable in such moments, in her intemperate silence, the bitter set of her discolored mouth with her uneven slender gambler's nose and scornful nostrils, lengthening her sharp oval face, pulling the dry skinfolds. Then when she opened her eyes there would shoot out a look of hate, horror, passion, or contempt."

To the children she is "a charming, slatternly witch; everything that she did was right, right, her right: she claimed this right to do what she wished because of all her sufferings, and all the children believed in her rights." She falls in a faint on the floor, and the accustomed children run to get pillows, watch silently "the death-like face, drawn and yellow under its full black hair," the "poor naked neck with its gooseflesh." She is nourished on "tea and an aspirin"; "tea, almost black, with toast and mustard pickles"; a "one-man curry" of "a bit of cold meat, a hard-boiled egg, some currants, and an onion"—as her mother says, "All her life she's lived on gherkins and chilies and Worcestershire sauce. . . . She preferred pickled walnuts at school to candy." She sews, darns, knits, embroiders. School had taught her only three things, to play Chopin ("there would steal through the listening house flights of notes, rounded as doves, wheeling over housetops in the sleeping afternoon, Chopin or Brahms, escaping from Henny's lingering, firm fingers"), to paint watercolors, and to sew. It is life that has taught her to give it "her famous *black look*"; to run through once again the rhymes, rituals, jokes, sayings, stories— inestimable stones, unvalued jewels—that the children beg her for; to drudge at old tasks daily renewed; to lie and beg and borrow and sink deeper into debt; to deal the cards out for the game she cheats at and has never won, an elaborate two-decked solitaire played "feverishly, until her mind was a darkness, until all the memories and the ease had long since drained away . . . leaving her sitting there, with blackened eyes, a yellow skin, and straining wrinkles." Marriage, that had found Henny a "gentle, neurotic creature wearing silk next to the skin and expecting to have a good time at White House receptions," has left her "a thin, dark scarecrow," a "dirty cracked plate, that's just what I am." In the end, her black hair swiftly graying, she has turned into "a dried-up, skinny, funny old woman" who cries out: "I'm an old woman, your mother's an old woman"; who cries out, "Isn't it rotten luck? Isn't every rotten thing in life rotten luck?"

All Henny's particularities, peculiarities, sum themselves up
into a strange general representativeness, so that she somehow
stands for all women. She shares helplessly "the natural outlawry
of womankind," of creatures who, left-handed, sidelong in the
right-handed, upright world of men, try to get around by hook or
by crook, by a last weak winning sexual smile, the laws men have
made for them. Henny "was one of those women who secretly
symphathize with all women against all men; life was a rotten
deal, with men holding all the aces." Women, as people say,
take everything personally—even Henny's generalizations of all
existence are personal, and so living. As she does her "microscopic
darning," sometimes a "small mouse would run past, or even
boldly stand and inquisitively stare at her. Henny would look
down at its monstrous pointed little face calmly and go on with
her work." She accepts the "sooty little beings" as "house guests"
except when she wakes to smell the "musky penetrating odor of
their passage"; or when she looks at one and sees that it is a
pregnant mother; or when the moralist her husband says that
mice bring germs, and obliges her to kill them. She kills them;
"nevertheless, though she despised animals, she felt involuntarily
that the little marauder was much like herself, trying to get by."
Henny is an involuntary, hysterical moralist or none; as her
creator says, "Henny was beautifully, wholeheartedly vile: she
asked no quarter and gave none to the foul world." And yet, and
so, your heart goes out to her, because she is miserably what life
has made her, and makes her misery her only real claim on existence. Her husband wants to be given credit for everything, even
his mistakes—especially his mistakes, which are always well-meaning, right-minded ones that in a better world would be unmis-
taken. Henny is an honest liar; even Sam's truths are ways to
get his own way.

But you remember best about Henny what is worst about
Henny: her tirades. These are too much and (to tell the truth)
too many for us; but if anything so excessive is to be truthfully
represented, that is almost inevitable. These tirades are shameful,
insensate, and interminable, including and exaggerating all that

[ix]

there is; looking at the vile world, her enemy, Henny cries: "Life is nothing but rags and tags, and filthy rags at that. Why was I ever born?" Before long the reader has impressed upon his shrinking flesh the essential formula of Henny's rhetoric. A magnifying word like *great* is followed by an intensive like *vile, filthy, rotten, foul:* Henny's nose has been shoved into the filth of things, so that she sees them magnified, consummately foul, as Swift saw the bodies and the physiological processes of the people of Brobdingnag. At the "mere sight of the great flopping monster" her stepdaughter, Henny cries out: "She's that Big-Me all over again. Always with her eyes glued to a book. I feel like snatching the rotten thing from her and pushing it into her eyes, her great lolling head. . . . She crawls, I can hardly touch her, she reeks with her slime and filth—she doesn't notice! I beat her until I can't stand—she doesn't notice! When I fall on the floor, she runs and gets a pillow and at that I suppose she's better than her murderer of a father who lets me lie there."

The girl sewing a fine seam, the watercolor-painter, the piano-player has stepped from the altar into the filth of marriage and child-bearing and child-rearing; and forever after she can tell the truth about it—the naked, physiological, excremental truth—only in physiological, excremental terms. It is women who must clean up the mess men make, the mess everything makes: the hag Henny stares out at "the darn muck of existence," the foul marsh above which the dwellings of men rise on precarious stilts, and screams at it her daemonic tirades. She knows. Whatever men say, women know; as an old woman says chuckling, an accessory to the fact: "Life's dirty, isn't it, Louie, eh? Don't you worry what they say to you, we're all dirty." Sometimes even Henny absently consents to it: "she looked vaguely about, sniffing that familiar smell of fresh dirtiness which belongs to mankind's extreme youth, a pleasant smell to mothers."

When Henny is "defenceless, in one of those absences of hatred, aimless lulls that all long wars must have," she looks at us "strangely, with her great, brown eyes," and even her husband's "heart would be wrung with their unloving beauty." Our own

[x]

hearts are wrung by Henny: when, "beginning to cry like a little girl, and putting the fold of her dressing gown to her face," she cries, "Ai, ai"; when she feels "a curious, dull, but new sensation," and awakening from "a sort of sullen absence . . . knew what was happening: her heart was breaking. That moment, it broke for good and all"; when, no longer able to "stand any of this life any longer," in a sort of murderous delirium she beats her favorite child "across the head, screaming at him, 'Die, die, why don't you all die and leave me to die or to hang; fall down, die; what do I care?' "—while her son, "not thinking of defending himself," cries "brokenly, in a warm, pleading voice, 'Mother, don't, don't, Mother, Mother, Mother, Mother, Mother, don't, please, please, Mother, Mother' "; when her love affair—an affair like a piece of dirty newspaper—reaches its abject public end; when, a few days after death, "the image of Henny started to roam . . . the window curtains flapped, the boards creaked, a mouse ran, and Henny was there, muttering softly to herself, tapping a sauce pan, turning on the gas. The children were not frightened. They would say, laughing, somewhat curious, 'I thought I heard Mothering,' and only Ernie or Tommy . . . would look a bit downcast; and perhaps Chappy missed her, that queer, gypsy-like, thin, tanned, pointed face with big black eyes rolling above him"; and when, last of all, the storms of July thunder above her grave, and "it was as if Henny too had stormed, but in another room in the universe, which was now under lock and key."

I I I

There is something grand and final, indifferent to our pity, about Henny: one of those immortal beings in whom the tragedy of existence is embodied, she looks unseeingly past her mortal readers. The absurdity and hypocrisy of existence are as immortal in her husband Sam.

All of us can remember waking from a dream and uselessly longing to go back into the dream. In Sam the longing has been useful: he has managed to substitute for everyday reality an everyday dream, a private work of art—complete with its own language, customs, projects, ideology—in which, occasionally pausing for applause, he goes on happily and foolishly and self-righteously existing. As he reads about Henny the reader feels, in awe, how terrible it must be to be Henny; as he reads about Sam he blurts, "Oh, please don't let me be like Sam!" Sam is more than human; occasionally he has doubts, and is merely human for a moment—so that our laughter and revulsion cease, and we uneasily pity him—but then the moment is over and he is himself again.

Often Henny, in defeated misery, plunges to rock-bottom, and gropes among the black finalities of existence; up above, in the holy light, the busy Sam, "painting and scraping and singing and jigging from the crack of dawn," clambers happily about in the superstructure of life. There among his own children, his own speeches, his own small zoo, pond, rockery, aquaria, museum ("What a world of things he had to have to keep himself amused!"), the hobbyist, naturalist, bureaucrat, democrat, moralist, atheist, teetotaler, ideologue, sermonizer, sentimentalist, prude, hypocrite, idealist Sam can say, like Kulygin: "I am satisfied, I am satisfied, I am satisfied!" If he had not been married he would not have remembered that he was mortal. Sam "was naturally light-hearted, pleasant, all generous effusion and responsive emotion. . . . Tragedy itself could not worm its way by any means into his heart. Such a thing would have made him ill or mad, and he was all for health, sanity, success, and human love."

Sam's vanity is ultimate: the occasional objectivity or common decency that makes us take someone else's part, not our own, is impossible for Sam, who is right because he is Sam. It is becoming for Sam to love children so (Henny says in mockery, "The man who loves children!" and gives the book its title), since he himself is partly an adult and partly a spoiled child in his late thirties; even his playing with words, the grotesque self-satisfying language he makes for himself, is the work of a great child, and exactly right for children. After he has had to live among adults for eight months, he seems sobered and commonplace; but at home among the children, he soon is Sam again. At home "the children listened to every word he said, having been trained to him from the cradle." He addresses them "in that low, humming, cello voice and with that tender, loving face he had when beginning one of his paeans or dirges"; his speech has "a low insinuating humming that enchanted the sulky ear-guards and got straight to their softened brains." The children listen openmouthed; but Sam's mouth is open wider still, as he wonders at himself. "Were not his own children happy, healthy, and growing like weeds, merely through having him to look up to and through knowing that he was always righteous, faithful, and understanding?" It is wonderful to him that he originates independently the discoveries of the great: "The theory of the expanding universe . . . it came to me by myself. . . . And very often I have an idea and then find months, years later, that a man like our very great Woodrow Wilson or Lloyd George or Einstein has had it too."

Kim was the Little Friend of all the World; Sam is its Little Father. He wishes that he "had a black baby too. A tan or Chinese one—every kind of baby. I am sorry that the kind of father I can be is limited." A relative objects, to his not sending the children to Sunday school, "When they grow up they will have nothing to believe in." Sam replies: "Now they believe in their poor little Dad: and when they grow up they'll believe in Faraday, Clerk Maxwell, and Einstein." Their poor little Dad is for the Pollit children a jealous God, one who interferes with everything they do and still is not satisfied, but imports children from outside the family so that he can interfere with *them*. He makes each of the children tell him what the others are doing "in the secrecy of their rooms or the nooks they had made their own. With what surprise and joy he would seize on all this information of his loving spies, showing them traits of character, drawing a moral conclusion from everything!" Sam loves and enjoys the

[xiii]

children, the children admire and enjoy Sam; and yet there is nothing too awful for him to do to them and feel that he is right to do to them—the worst things are so mean and petty, are full of such selfishness and hypocrisy, are so *impossible,* that even as you believe you cry, "It's unbelievable!"

We can bear to read about Sam, a finally exasperating man, only because he is absolutely funny and absolutely true. He is so entirely real that it surprises the reader when an occasional speech of his—for instance, some of his *Brave New World* talk about the future—is not convincing. Perhaps different parts of his speech have different proportions of imagination and fancy and memory: it doesn't seem that the same process (in Christina Stead, that is) has produced everything. But Sam is an Anglo-Saxon buffoon, hypocrite, quite as extraordinary as the most famous of Dostoevsky's or Saltykov-Schedrin's Slavic ones. Sam asks for everything and with the same breath asks to be admired for never having asked for anything; his complete selfishness sees itself as a complete selflessness. When he has been out of work for many months, it doesn't bother him: "About their money, as about everything, he was vague and sentimental. But in a few months he would be earning, and in the meantime, he said, 'It was only right that the mother too should fend for her offspring.'" One morning there are no bananas. "Sam flushed with anger. 'Why aren't there any bananas? I don't ask for much. I work to make the Home Beautiful for one and all, and I don't even get bananas. Everyone knows I like bananas. If your mother won't get them, why don't some of you? Why doesn't anyone think of poor little Dad?' He continued, looking in a most pathetic way round the table, at the abashed children, 'It isn't much. I give you kids a house and a wonderful playground of nature and fish and marlin and everything, and I can't even get a little banana.'" Sam moralizes, rationalizes, anything whatsoever: the children feel that they have to obey, *ought* to obey, his least whim. There is an abject reality about the woman Henny, an abject ideality about the man Sam; he is so idealistically, hypocritically, transcendentally masculine that a male reader worries, "Ought I to be a man?"

Every family has words and phrases of its own; that ultimate family, the Pollits, has what amounts to a whole language of its own. Only Sam can speak it, really, but the children understand it and mix phrases from it into their ordinary speech. (If anyone feels that it is unlikely for a big grown man to have a little language of his own, let me remind him of that great grown man Swift.) Children's natural distortions of words and the distortions of Artemus Ward and Uncle Remus are the main sources of this little language of Sam's. As we listen to Sam talking in it, we exclaim in astonished veneration, "It's so!" Many of the words and phrases of this language are so natural that we admire Christina Stead for having invented them at the same instant at which we are thinking, "No, nobody, not even Christina Stead, could have made *that* up!"—they have the uncreated reality of any perfect creation. I quote none of the language: a few sentences could show neither how marvellous it is nor how marvellously it expresses Sam's nature, satisfies his every instinct. When he puts his interminable objections and suggestions and commands into the joke-terms of this unctuous, wheedling, insinuating language—what a tease the wretch is!—it is as if to make the least disagreement on the part of the children a moral impossibility.

His friend Saul says to Sam: "Sam, when you talk, you know you create a world." It is true; and the world he creates is a world of wishes or wish-fantasies. What Freud calls the primary principle, the pleasure principle, is always at work in that world —the claims of the reality principle, of the later ego, have been abrogated. It is a world of free fantasy: "Sam began to wonder at himself: why did he feel free? He had always been free, a free man, a free mind, a freethinker."

Bismarck said: "You can do anything with children if you will only play with them." All Bismarck's experience of mankind has been concentrated into knowledge, and the knowledge has been concentrated into a single dispassionate sentence. Sam has, so to

[xv]

speak, based his life on this sentence; but he has taken literally the *children* and *play* that are figurative in Bismarck's saying. Children are damp clay which Sam can freely and playfully manipulate. Yet even there he prefers "the very small boys" and "the baby girls"; the larger boys, the girls of school age, somehow cramp his style. (His embryonic love affair is an affair not with a grown-up but with the child-woman Gillian.) He reasons and moralizes mainly to force others to accept his fantasy, but the reasoning and moralizing have become fantastic in the process.

In psychoanalytical textbooks we read of the mechanism of denial. Surely Sam was its discoverer: there is no reality—except Henny—stubborn enough to force Sam to recognize its existence if its existence would disturb his complacency. We feel for Sam the wondering pity we feel for a man who has put out his own eyes and gets on better without them. To Sam everything else in the world is a means to an end, and the end is Sam. He is insensate. So, naturally, he comes out ahead of misunderstanding, poverty, Henny, anything. Life itself, in Johnson's phrase, *dismisses him to happiness:* " 'All things work together for the good of him that loves the Truth,' said the train to Sam as it rattled down towards the Severn, 'all things—work—together—for the good—of him—that loves—the TRUTH!' "

Sam is one of those providential larger-than-life-size creations, like Falstaff, whom we wonder and laugh at and can't get enough of; like Queen Elizabeth wanting to see Falstaff in love, we want to see Sam in books called *Sam at School, Sam in the Arctic, Grandfather Sam*. About him there is the grandeur of completeness: beyond Sam we cannot go. Christina Stead's understanding of him is without hatred; her descriptions of his vilest actions never forget how much fun it is to be Sam, and she can describe Sam's evening walk with his child in sentences that are purely and absolutely beautiful: "Pale as a candle flame in the dusk, tallow-pale, he stalked along, holding her hand, and Louie looked up and beyond him at the enfeebled stars. Thus, for many years, she had seen her father's head, a ghostly earth flame against the heavens, from her little height. Sam looked down on the moon

of her face; the day-shine was enough still to light the eyeballs
swimming up to him."

I V

A description of Louie ought to begin with *Louie knew she
was the ugly duckling.* It is ugly ducklings, grown either into
swans or into remarkably big, remarkably ugly ducks, who are
responsible for most works of art; and yet how few of these give
a truthful account of what it was like to be an ugly duckling!—
it is almost as if the grown, successful swan had repressed most of
the memories of the duckling's miserable, embarrassing, magical
beginnings. (These memories are deeply humiliating in two
ways: they remind the adult that he once was more ignorant and
gullible and emotional than he is; and they remind him that he
once *was,* potentially, far more than he is.) Stumbling through
creation in awful misery, in oblivious ecstasy, the fat, clumsy,
twelve- or thirteen-year-old Louie is, as her teacher tells her, one
of those who "will certainly be famous." We believe this because
the book is full of the evidence for it: the poems and plays
Louie writes, the stories she tells, the lines she quotes, the things
she says. The usual criticism of a novel about an artist is that, no
matter how real he is as a man, he is not real to us as an artist,
since we have to take on trust the works of art he produces. We
do not have to take on trust Louie's work, and she is real to us
as an artist.

Someone in a story says that when you can't think of anything
else to say you say, "Ah, youth, youth!" But sometimes as you
read about Louie there *is* nothing else to say: your heart goes out
in homesick joy to the marvellous inconsequential improbable
reaching-out-to-everything of the duckling's mind, so different
from the old swan's mind, that has learned what its interests are
and is deaf and blind to the rest of reality. Louie says, "I wish I

had a Welsh grammar." Sam says, "Don't be an idiot! What for?" Louie answers: "I'd like to learn Welsh or Egyptian grammar; I could read the poetry Borrow talks about and I could read *The Book of the Dead.*"

She starts to learn *Paradise Lost* by heart ("Why? She did not know really"); stuffs the little children full of La Rochefoucauld; in joyful amazement discovers that *The Cenci* is about her father and herself; recites,

A yellow plum was given me and in return a topaz fair I gave,
No mere return for courtesy but that our friendship might outlast
the grave,

indignantly insisting to the grown-ups that it *is* Confucius; puts as a motto on her wall, *By my hope and faith, I conjure thee, throw not away the hero in your soul;* triumphantly repeats to that little tyrant of her fields, Sam-the-Bold:

> *The desolator desolate,*
> *The tyrant overthrown,*
> *The arbiter of other's fate*
> *A suppliant for his own!*

Louie starts out on her own *Faust,* a "play, called *Fortunatus,* in which a student, sitting alone in his room in the beaming moon, lifts his weary head from the book and begins by saying,

> *The unforgotten song, the solitary song,*
> *The song of the young heart in the age-old world,*
> *Humming on new May's reeds transports me back*
> *To the vague regions of celestial space . . ."*

For the teacher whom she loves Louie creates "a magnificent project, the Aiden cycle . . . a poem of every conceivable form and also every conceivable meter in the English language," all about Miss Aiden. She copies the poems into an out-of-date diary, which she hides; sometimes she reads them to the children in the orchard "for hours on end, while they sat with rosy, greedy faces upturned, listening." As Henny and Sam shriek at each other downstairs, Louie tells the children, lying loosely in bed in the warm night, the story of *Hawkins, the North Wind*. Most of Louie's writings are so lyrically funny to us that as we laugh we catch our breath, afraid that the bubble will break. At *Hawkins,* a gruesomely satisfying story different from any story we have read before, we no longer laugh, nor can we look down at the story-teller with a grown-up's tender, complacent love for a child: the story is dark with Louie's genius and with Christina Stead's.

Best of all is *Tragos: Herpes Rom* (*Tragedy: The Snake-Man*). Louie writes it, and the children act it out, for Sam's birthday. It is written in a new language Louie has made up for it; the language-maker Sam says angrily, "Why isn't it in English?" and Louie replies, "Did Euripides write in English?" Not only is the play exactly what Louie would have written, it is also a work of art in which the relations between Louie and her father, as she understands them, are expressed with concentrated, tragic force. Nowhere else in fiction, so far as I know, is there so truthful and satisfying a representation of the works of art the ugly duckling makes up, there in the morning of the world.

Louie reads most of the time—reads, even, while taking a shower: "her wet fingers pulped the paper as she turned." Her life is accompanied, *ostinato,* by *always has her nose stuck in a book . . . learn to hold your shoulders straight . . . it will ruin your eyes.* Louie "slopped liquids all over the place, stumbled and fell when carrying buckets, could never stand straight to fold the sheets and tablecloths from the wash without giggling or dropping them in the dirt, fell over invisible creases in rugs, was unable to do her hair neatly, and was always leopard-spotted yellow and blue with old and new bruises. . . . She acknowledged her unwieldiness and unhandiness in this little world, but she had an utter contempt for everyone associated with her, father, stepmother, even brothers and sister, an innocent contempt which she never thought out, but which those round her easily recognized." The Louie who laconically holds her scorched fingers in the candle-flame feels "a growling, sullen power in herself . . . She went up to bed insulted again. 'I will repay,' she said on the stairs, halting and looking over the banisters, with a frown." When the world is more than she can bear she screams her secret at it: " 'I'm the ugly duckling, you'll see,' shrieked Louie."

Most of the time she knows that she is better and more intelligent than, different from, the other inhabitants of her world; but the rest of the time she feels the complete despair—the seeming to oneself wrong, *all* wrong, about everything, *everything*—that is the other, dark side of this differentness. She is a force of nature, but she is also a little girl. Heart-broken when her birthday play is a shameful failure, like so much of her life at home, Louie "began to squirm and, unconsciously holding out one of her hands to Sam, she cried, 'I am so miserable and poor and rotten and so vile [the words *rotten* and *vile* are natural, touching reminiscences of Henny's tirade-style] and melodramatic, I don't know what to do. I don't know what to do. I can't bear the daily misery . . .' She was bawling brokenly on the tablecloth, her shoulders heaving and her long hair, broken loose, plastered over her red face. 'No wonder they all laugh at me,' she bellowed. 'When I walk along the street, everyone looks at me, and whispers about me, because I'm so messy. My elbows are out and I have no shoes and I'm so big and fat and it'll always be the same. I can't help it, I can't help it . . . They all laugh at me: I can't stand it any more . . .' Coming to the table, as to a jury, she asked in a firmer voice, but still crying, 'What will become of me? Will life go on like this? Will I always be like this?' She appealed to Sam, 'I have always been like this: I can't live and go on being like this?' "

And Sam replies: "Like what? Like what? I never heard so much idiotic drivel in my born days. Go and put your fat head under the shower."

To Louie the world is what won't let her alone. And the world's interferingness is nothing to Sam's: Sam—so to speak—

wakes her up and asks her what she's dreaming just so as to be able to make her dream something different; and then tells her that not every little girl is lucky enough to have a Sam to wake her up. To be let alone! is there any happiness that compares with it, for someone like Louie? Staying with her mother's relatives in the summer, she feels herself inexplicably, miraculously given a little space of her own—is made, for a few weeks, a sort of grown-up by courtesy. And since Louie has "a genius for solitude," she manages to find it even at home. Henny may scold her and beat her, but Henny does leave her alone ("It is a rotten shame, when I think that the poor kid is dragged into all our rotten messes"), and Louie loves her for it—when Sam talks to Louie about her real mother, Louie retorts, "Mother is my mother," meaning Henny.

At school Louie "was in heaven, at home she was in a torture chamber." She never tells anyone outside "what it is like at home . . . no one would believe me!" To the ordinary misery of differentness is added the misery of being the only one who sees the endless awful war between Henny and Sam for what it is: "Suddenly she would think, *Who can see aught good in thee/ Soul-destroying misery?* and in this flash of intelligence she understood that her life and their lives were wasted in this contest and that the quarrel between Henny and Sam was ruining their moral natures." It is only Louie who tries to do anything about it all: with a young thing's fresh sense and ignorance and courage she tries to save the children and herself in the only way that she knows—what she does and what she can't quite make herself do help to bring the book to its wonderful climax. It is rare for a novel to have an ending as good as its middle and beginning: the sixty or seventy pages that sum up *The Man Who Loved Children*, bring the action of the book to its real conclusion, are better than even the best things that have come before.

As he looks at Louie Sam "can't understand what on earth caused this strange drifting nebula to spin." By the time we finish the book we have been so thoroughly in sympathy and in empathy with Louie that we no longer need to understand—we are used to being Louie. We think about her, as her teacher thinks: "It's queer to know everything and nothing at the same time." Louie knows, as she writes in her diary, that "everyday experience which is misery degrades me"; she mutters aloud, "If I did not know I was a genius, I would die: why live?"; a stranger in her entirely strange and entirely familiar family, she cries to her father: "I know something, I know there are people not like us, not muddleheaded like us, better than us." She knows that soon she will have escaped into the world of the people better than us, the great objective world better than Shakespeare and Beethoven and Donatello put together—didn't they all come out of it? Louie is a potentiality still sure that what awaits it in the world is potentiality, not actuality. That she is escaping from some Pollits to some more Pollits, that she herself will end as an actuality among actualities, an accomplished fact, is an old or middle-aged truth or half-truth that Louie doesn't know. As Louie's story ends she has gone for a walk, "a walk around the world"; she starts into the future accompanied by one of those Strauss themes in which a whole young orchestra walks springily off into the sunshine, as though going away were a final good.

V

As you read *The Man Who Loved Children* what do you notice first? How much life it has, how natural and original it is; Christina Stead's way of seeing and representing the world is so plainly different from anyone else's that after a while you take this for granted, and think cheerfully, "Oh, she can't help being original." The whole book is different from any book you have read before. What other book represents—tries to represent, even—a family in such conclusive detail?

Aristotle speaks of the pleasure of recognition; you read *The*

Man Who Loved Children with an almost ecstatic pleasure of recognition. You get used to saying, "Yes, that's the way it is"; and you say many times, but can never get used to saying, "I didn't know *anybody* knew that." Henny, Sam, Louie, and the children —not to speak of some of the people outside the family—are entirely real to the reader. This may not seem much of a claim: every year thousands of reviewers say it about hundreds of novels. But what they say is conventional exaggeration—reality is rare in novels.

Many of the things of the world come to life in *The Man Who Loved Children:* the book has an astonishing sensory immediacy. Akin to this is its particularity and immediacy of incident; it is full of small, live, characteristic, sometimes odd or grotesque details that are at once surprising enough and convincing enough to make the reader feel, "No, nobody could have made that up." And akin to these on a larger scale are all the "good scenes" in the book: scenes that stand out in the reader's memory as in some way remarkable—as representing something, summing something up, with real finality. There is an extraordinary concentration of such scenes in the pages leading up to the attempted murder and accomplished suicide that is the climax of the book: Ernie's lead, Louie's play, Louie's breakdown after it, Ernie's money box, Ernie's and Louie's discoveries before Miss Aiden comes, Miss Aiden's visit, Henny's beating of Ernie, the end of Henny's love affair, Henny's last game of solitaire, the marlin, Sam and the bananas, the last quarrel. That these scenes come where they do is evidence of Christina Stead's gift for structure; but you are bewildered by her regular ability to make the scenes that matter most the book's best imagined and best realized scenes.

Without its fairly wide range of people and places, attitudes and emotions, *The Man Who Loved Children* might seem too concentrated and homogeneous a selection of reality. But the people outside the Pollit household are quite varied: for instance, Louie's mother's family, Sam's and Henny's relatives, some of the people at Singapore, Henny's Bert Anderson, the "norphan" girl, Louie's friend Clare. There are not so many places—Washington, Ann Arbor, Harper's Ferry, Singapore—but each seems entirely different and entirely alive. As he reads about Louie's summers the reader feels, "So this is what Harper's Ferry looks like to an Australian!" European readers are used to being told what Europe looks like to an American or Russian of genius; we aren't, and we enjoy it. (Occasionally Christina Stead has a kind of virtuoso passage to show that she is not merely a foreign visitor, but a real inhabitant of the United States; we enjoy, and are amused at, it.) Because *The Man Who Loved Children* brings to life the variety of the world outside the Pollit household, the happenings inside it—terrible as some of them are—do not seem depressing or constricted or monotonous to the reader: "within, a torment raged, day and night, week, month, year, always the same, an endless conflict, with its truces and breathing spaces; out here were a dark peace and love." And, too, many of the happenings inside the family have so much warmth and habitual satisfaction, are so pleasant or cozy or funny, are so *interesting*, that the reader forgets for a moment that this wonderful playground is also a battlefield.

Children-in-families have a life all their own, a complicated one. Christina Stead seems to have remembered it in detail from her childhood, and to have observed it in detail as an adult. Because of this knowledge she is able to imagine with complete realism the structures, textures, and atmosphere of one family's spoken and unspoken life. She is unusually sensitive to speech-styles, to conversation-structures, to everything that makes a dialogue or monologue a sort of self-propagating entity; she knows just how family speech is different from speech outside the family, children's speech different from adults'. She gives her children the speeches of speakers to whom a word has the reality of a thing: a thing that can be held wrong-side-up, played with like a toy, thrown at someone like a toy. Children's speech-ways—their senseless iteration, joyous nonsense, incremental variation, entreaties and insults, family games, rhymes, rituals, proverbs with the force of law, magical mistakes, occasional uncannily penetrating descriptive phrases—are things Christina Stead knows as well as she knows the speech-ways of families, of people so used to each other that half the time they only half-say something, imply it with a family phrase, or else spell it out in words too familiar to be heard, just as the speaker's face is too familiar to be seen. The book's household conversations between mother and child, father and child, are both superficially and profoundly different from any conversation in the world outside; reading such conversations is as satisfying as being given some food you haven't tasted since childhood. (After making your way through the great rain-forest of the children's speech, you come finally to one poor broomstick of a tree, their letters: all the children—as Ernie says, laughing—"start out with 'Dear Dad, I hope you are well, I am well, Mother is well,'" and then they get stuck.") The children inherit and employ, or recognize with passive pleasure, the cultural scraps—everything from Mozart to *Hiawatha*—that are a part of the sounds the grown-ups make. Father and Mother are gods but (it is strange!) gods who will sometimes perform for you on request, taking part in a ritual, repeating stories or recitations, pretending to talk like a Scot or a Jew or an Englishman—just as, earlier, they would pretend to be a bear.

Christina Stead knows the awful eventfulness of little children's lives. That grown-ups seldom cry, scream, fall, fight each other, or have to be sent to bed seems very strange to someone watching children: a little child pays its debt to life penny by penny. Sam is able to love a life spent with children because he himself has the insensate busy-ness of a child. Yet, wholly familiar as he is, partly child-like as he is, to the children he is monstrous—not the singular monster that he is to us, but the ordinary monster that any grown-up is to you if you weigh thirty or forty pounds and have your eyes two feet from the floor. Again and again the reader is conscious of Christina Stead's gift for showing how different *anything* is when looked at from a really different point of view. Little Evie, "fidgeting with her aunt's great arm around her, seemed to be looking up trustfully with her brown eyes, but those deceptive eyes were full of revolt, mistrust, and dislike"; she averts her gaze from her aunt's "slab cheeks, peccary skin . . . the long, plump, inhuman thigh, the glossy, sufficient skirt, from everything powerful, coarse, and proud about this great unmated mare . . . "Oh,' thought Evie to herself, 'when I am a lady with a baby, I won't have all those bumps, I won't be so big and fat, I will be a little woman, thin like I am now and not fat in front or in the skirt.' "

One of the most obvious facts about grown-ups, to a child, is that they have forgotten what it is like to be a child. The child has not yet had the chance to know what it is like to be a grown-up; he believes, even, that being a grown-up is a mistake he will never make—when *he* grows up he will keep on being a child, a big child with power. So the child and grown-up live in mutual love, misunderstanding, and distaste. Children shout and play and cry and want candy; grown-ups say *Ssh!* and work and scold and want steak. There is no disputing tastes as contradictory as these. It is not just Mowgli who was raised by a couple of wolves; any child is raised by a couple of grown-ups. Father and Mother may be nearer and dearer than anyone will ever be again—still, they are members of a different species. God is, I suppose, what our parents were; certainly the giant or ogre of the stories is so huge, so powerful, and so stupid because that is the way a grown-up looks to a child.

Grown-ups forget or cannot believe that they seem even more unreasonable to children than children seem to them. Henny's oldest boy Ernie (to whom money is the primary means of understanding and changing the world; he is a born economic determinist, someone with absolute pitch where money is concerned) is one of Christina Stead's main ways of making us remember how mistaken and hypocritical grown-ups seem to children. Ernie feels that he sees the world as it is, but that grown-ups are no longer able to do this: their rationalization of their own actions, the infinitely complicated lie they have agreed to tell about the world, conceals the world from them. The child sees the truth, but is helpless to do anything about it.

The Pollit children are used to the terrible helplessness of a child watching its parents war. There over their heads the Sun and the Moon, God the Father and the Holy Virgin, are shouting at each other, striking each other—the children contract all their muscles, try not to hear, and hear. Sometimes, waked in darkness by the familiar sounds, they lie sleepily listening to their parents; hear, during some lull in the quarrel, a tree-frog or the sound of the rain.

Ernie feels the same helpless despair at the poverty of the family; thinking of how *many* children there already are, he implores, "Mothering, don't have another baby!" (Henny replies, "You can bet your bottom dollar on that, old sweetness.") But he does not really understand what he is saying: later on, he and the other children look uncomprehendingly at Henny, "who had again queerly become a large woman, though her hands, feet, and face remained small and narrow." One night they are made to sleep downstairs, and hear Henny screaming hour after hour upstairs; finally, at morning, she is silent. "They had understood nothing at all, except that mother had been angry and miserable and now she was still; this was a blessed relief." Their blank misunderstanding of what is sexual is the opposite of their eager understanding of what is excremental. They thrill to the inexplicably varying permissiveness of the world: here they are being allowed to laugh at, as a joke, what is ordinarily not referred to at all, or mentioned expediently, in family euphemisms!

The book is alive with their fights, games, cries of "You didn't kiss me!"—"Look, Moth, Tommy kissed you in the glass!" But their great holidays so swiftly are gone: the "sun was going down, and Sunday-Funday was coming to an end. They all felt it with a kind of misery: with such a fine long day and so many things to do, how could they have let it slip past like this?" And summer vacation is the same: the indefinite, almost infinite future so soon is that small, definite, disregarded thing, the past!

On a winter night, with nothing but the fire in the living room to warm the house, the child runs to it crying, "Oo, gee whiz, is it cold; jiminy, I'm freezing. Moth, when are we going to get the coal?" (Anyone who remembers his childhood can feel himself saying those sentences—those and so many more of the book's sentences.) And as the child grows older, how embarrassing the parent is, in the world outside: "Louie looked stonily ahead or desperately aside." And, home again, the parent moralizes, sermonizes—won't he *ever* stop talking?—to the child doing its homework, writing, writing, until finally the parent reads over the child's shoulder what is being written on the page of notebook paper: *Shut up, shut up, shut up, shut up* . . . The book follows the children into the cold beds they warm, goes with them into their dreams: when you read about Louie's hard-soft nightmare or the horseman she hears when she wakes in the middle of the night, you are touching childhood itself.

V I

There is a bewitching rapidity and lack of self-consciousness about Christina Stead's writing; she has much knowledge, extraordinary abilities, but is too engrossed in what she is doing ever to seem conscious of them, so that they do not cut her off from the world but join her to it. How literary she makes most writers seem! Her book is very human, and full of humor of an unusual kind; the spirit behind it doesn't try to be attractive and is attractive. As you read the book's climactic and conclusive pages you are conscious of their genius and of the rightness of that genius: it is as though at these moments Christina Stead's mind held in its grasp the whole action, the essential form, of *The Man Who Loved Children.*

Say that you read: "As Henny sat before her teacup and the steam rose from it and the treacherous foam gathered, uncollectible round its edge, the thousand storms of her confined life would rise up before her, thinner illusions on the steam. She did not laugh at the words 'a storm in a teacup.'" You feel an astonished satisfaction at the swift and fatal conclusiveness, the real poetry—the concentration of experience into a strange and accurate, resonant image—of such a passage. Doesn't one feel the same satisfaction with, wonder at, some of the passages I have already quoted? But quotation gives no idea of what is most important in Christina Stead's style, its simple narrative power— she tells what happens so that it happens, and to you. The direct immediate life of most of her sentences is in extraordinary contrast to the complicated uneasy life of others; as her content varies, her style varies. Ordinary styles have the rhythmical and structural monotony of a habit, of something learned and persisted in. A style like Christina Stead's, so remarkable for its structural variety, its rhythmical spontaneity, forces you to remember that a style can be a whole way of existing, so that you exist, for the moment, in perfect sympathy with it: you don't read it so much as listen to it as it sweeps you along—fast enough, often, to make you feel a blurred pleasure in your own speed. Often a phrase or sentence has the uncaring unconscious authority—how else could you say it?—that only a real style has. But few such styles have the spontaneity of Christina Stead's; its own life carries it along, here rapid and a little rough, here good-humoredly, grotesquely incisive, here purely beautiful—and suddenly, without ever stopping being natural, it is grand.

Her style is live enough and spontaneous enough to be able to go on working without her; but, then, its life is mechanical. When her style is at its worst you have the illusion that, once set in motion, it can rattle along indefinitely, narrating the incidents of a picaresque, Pollit-y universe with an indiscriminate vivacity that matches theirs. (You remember, then, that where everybody's somebody, nobody's anybody—that Christina Stead is, on her father's side, a Pollit.) But, normally, you listen to "the breeze, still brittle, not fully leaved"; see a mountain graveyard, "all grass and long sights"; have a child raise to you its "pansy kitten-face"; see a ragged girl fling out her arms in "a gesture that somehow recalled the surf beating on a coast, the surf of time or of sorrows"; see that in the world outside "clouds were passing over, swiftly staining the garden, the stains soaking in and leaving only bright light again." You read: "Bonnie stayed upstairs sobbing, thinking she had a broken heart, until she heard soft things like the hands of ghosts rubbing her counterpane and soft ghostly feet unsteadily shifting on her rug; and, looking up, she saw Evie and Isabel staring at her with immense rabbit eyes. In a little crockery voice, Isabel asked, 'What are you crying for?' " Louie's dying uncle tells her the story of *Pilgrim's Progress;* "and occasionally he would pause, the eyes would be fixed on her, and suddenly he would smile with his long dark lips; the face would no longer be the face of a man dying of consumption, with its burning eyes, but the ravishment of love incarnate, speaking through voiceless but not secret signs to the child's nature." Sometimes one of her long descriptive sentences lets you see a world at once strange and familiar, Christina Stead's and your own: the romantic Louie looks out at the shabby old Georgetown of the 1930's and sees "the trees of the heath round the Naval Observatory, the lamplight falling over the wired, lichened fence of the old reservoirs, the mysterious, long, dim house that she yearned for, the strange house opposite, and below, the vapor-blue city of Washington, pale, dim-lamped, under multitudinous stars, like a winter city of Africa, she thought, on this night at this hour." As you look at the landscapes—houses and yards and trees and birds and weathers—of *The Man Who Loved Children,* you see that they are alive, and yet you can't tell what has made them come to life—not the words exactly, not even the rhythm of the words, but something behind both: whatever it is that can make the landscapes live and beautiful, but that can make Ernie sobbing over his empty money box, and Henny beginning to cry, "Ugh-ugh," with her face in her hands, more beautiful than any landscape.

VII

Christina Stead can perfectly imitate the surface of existence—and, what is harder, recognize and reproduce some of the structures underneath that surface, and use these to organize her book. You especially notice, in her representation of life, two structural processes: (1) A series of similar events, of increasing intensity and importance, that leads to a last event which sums up, incarnates, all the events that have come before. It is easy to recognize and hard to make up such an event; Christina Stead has an uncanny ability to imagine an event that will be the necessary but surprising sum of the events before it. (2) A series of quantitative changes that leads to a qualitative change: that is, a series of events leading to a last qualitatively different event that at once sums up and contradicts the earlier events, and is the beginning of a new series. And Christina Stead depends almost as much on the conflict of opposites—for instance, of Sam with Henny, the male principle with the female principle, the children with the grown-ups, the ugly duckling with the ducks. She often employs a different principle of structure, the principle that a different point of view makes everything that is seen from that point of view different. Her book continually shows the difference between children's and adults' points of view, between men's and women's, between Henny's relatives and Sam's relatives, between Sam's and anybody else's, between Louie's and anybody else's, between Henny's and anybody else's—when Henny comes home from shopping and tells what happened on the trip, the people and events of the story seem to the children part of a world entirely different from their own, even if they have been along with Henny on the trip. A somewhat similar principle of organization is the opposition between practice and theory, between concrete fact and abstract rationalization, between what people says things are and what they are. And Christina Stead, like Chekhov, is fond of having a character tell you what life is, just before events themselves show you what it is.

The commonest and most nearly fundamental principle of organization, in serial arts like music and literature, is simply that of repetition; it organizes their notes or words very much as habit organizes our lives. Christina Stead particularly depends on repetition, and particularly understands the place of habit in our lives. If she admits that the proverb is true—*Heaven gives us habits to take the place of happiness*—she also admits that the habits *are* happiness of a sort, and that most happiness, after all, is happiness of a sort; she could say with Yeats that in Eden's Garden "no pleasing habit ends."

Her book, naturally, is full of the causal structures in terms of which we explain most of life to ourselves. Very different from the book's use of these is its use of rhythm as structure, atmosphere as structure: for instance, the series of last things that leads up to Henny's suicide has a dark finality of rhythm and atmosphere that prepares for her death as the air before a thunderstorm prepares for the thunderstorm. Kenneth Burke calls form the satisfaction of an expectation; *The Man Who Loved Children* is full of such satisfactions, but it has a good deal of the deliberate disappointment of an expectation that is also form.

A person is a process, one that leads to death: in *The Man Who Loved Children* the most carefully worked out, conclusive process is Henny. Even readers who remember themselves as ugly ducklings (and take a sort of credulous, incredulous delight in Louie) will still feel their main human-ness identify itself with Henny: the book's center of gravity, of tragic weight, is Henny. She is a violent, defeated process leading to a violent end, a closed tragic process leading to a conclusion of all potentiality, just as Louie is an open process leading to a "conclusion" that is pure potentiality. As the book ends, Henny has left, Louie is leaving, Sam stays. Sam is a repetitive, comic process that merely marks time: he gets nowhere, but then he doesn't want to get anywhere. Although there is no possibility of any real change in Sam, he never stops changing: Sam stays there inside Sam, getting less and less like the rest of mankind and more and more like Sam, Sam squared, Sam cubed, Sam to the nth. A man who repeats himself is funny; a man who repeats himself, *himself,* HIMSELF, is funnier. The book dignifies Henny in death, dismisses Sam with: *And he lived happily ever after.* The Pollits' wild war of opposites, with Henny dead, becomes a tame peace. Even Louie, the resistance, leaves, and Sam-the-Bold, the Great I-Am, the Man Who Loved Children, is left to do as he pleases with the children. *For a while:* Sam has laid up for himself treasures that moth and rust can't corrupt, but that the mere passage of the years destroys. Children don't keep. In the end Sam will have to love those hard things to love, grown-ups; and, since this is impossible for Sam, Sam won't despair, won't change, but will simply get himself some more children. He has made the beings of this world, who are the ends of this world, means; when he loses some particular means what does it matter?— there are plenty of other means to that one end, Sam.

The process the book calls Louie is that of a child turning into a grown-up, a duckling turning into a swan, a being that exists in two worlds leaving the first world of the family for the world outside. The ugly duckling loves the other pretty ducklings and tries to save them from the awful war between the father duck and the mother duck—though the war is ended by Henny's act, not Louie's. Yet Louie knows that they are not really her brothers and sisters, not really her parents, and serenely leaves them for the swan-world in which, a swan, she will at least be reunited to her real family, who are swans. Or do swans have families? Need families? Who knows? Louie doesn't know and, *for a while,* doesn't need to care.

The last fourth of the book makes Ernie, the child closest to Henny, a queer shadow or echo of Henny. The episodes of Ernie's lead, Ernie's money box, and Ernie's beating bring him to a defeated despair like Henny's, to a suicide-in-effigy: he makes a doll-dummy to stand for himself and hangs it. But all this is only a child's "as if" performance—after Henny's death the penniless Ernie is given some money, finds some more money, forgets Henny, and starts out all over again on the financial process which his life will be.

The attempted murder and accomplished suicide that are the conclusion of Henny and the climax of *The Man Who Loved Children* are prepared for by several hundred events, conversations, speeches, phrases, and thoughts scattered throughout the book. Henny's suicide- or murder-rhetoric; the atmosphere of violence that hangs around her, especially where Sam and Louie are concerned; the conversation in which she discusses with her mother and sister the best ways to kill oneself, the quickest poisons: these and a great many similar things have established, even before the sixty or seventy pages leading directly to Henny's death, a situation that makes plausible—requires, really—her violent end. And yet we are surprised to have it happen, this happening as thoroughly prepared for as anything I can remember in fiction.

It is no "tragic flaw" in Henny's character, but her character itself, that brings her to her end: Henny is her own fate. Christina Stead has a Chinese say, "Our old age is perhaps life's decision about us—" or, worse, the decision we have made about ourselves without ever realizing we were making it. Henny's old age may be life's decision about Henny; her suicide is the decision she has made about herself—about life—without ever knowing she was making it. She is so used to thinking and saying: *I'll kill myself! Better kill myself!* that when Louie gives her the chance she is fatally ready to take it. The defeated, despairing Henny has given up her life many times, before that drinking of the breakfast cup of tea with which she gives it up for good. What life has made of Henny, what Henny most deeply is, drinks —she is never more herself than when she destroys herself.

Many things in her life are latent or ultimate causes of Henny's death; but its immediate, overt causes—the series of extraordinarily imagined and accomplished finalities that leads to this final finality, that demands as its only possible conclusion Henny's death—all occur in the sixty or seventy pages before that death. At the beginning of the series, there is finality in the episode in which Henny feels her heart break "for good and all"; in the episode in which the aging Henny becomes, suddenly, "a dried-up, skinny, funny old woman." Miss Aiden's visit makes the reader see that this family sinking into poverty has become, without his realizing it, *poor,* abjectly, irretrievably poor. Everything valuable is gone, Henny's dearest possessions have been sold or pawned: the treasure drawers are empty.

Next day Ernie finds his money box empty, blankly sobs, and Henny, who has stolen the money, cries "Ugh-ugh" and tries to comfort him. She has stolen, from the child she loves most, the one thing that is indispensable to him. When Henny, later on, begins to beat Ernie over the head, and goes on hysterically beating him until she faints, it is as if she felt so guilty about him that it is unbearable to her to have him exist at all. The life in which what has happened can happen is more than Henny can endure—she tries to obliterate Ernie and life, and then faints, momentarily obliterating herself.

The awful end of her affair with Bert Anderson is a kind of final, public, objective degradation of Henny; she begs for a last trifle, nothing almost, and the world refuses her even that. The long nightmare-ish episode of the rendering of the marlin into oil is the final incarnation of all the senseless busy-nesses with which Sam has tormented her: "one marlin had been enough, with their kneading, manuring, trotting about, plastering, oiling, and dripping, to give Spa House a scent of its own for many years to come." But nothing else in *The Man Who Loved Children* has the empty finality of Henny's last game of solitaire. She has played it her whole life and never once won; now she wins. "The game that she had played all her life was finished; she had no more to do; she had no game." And, a little later, Henny breaks down as she has never broken down before: " 'Ai, ai,' cried Henny, beginning to cry like a little girl, and putting the dressing gown to her face, 'ai, ai' " The world has been too much for Henny, the old woman has changed back into a child. As there has never before been anything child-like about Henny, the scene has a pitiable finality. The quarrel with Sam which follows (a quarrel monotonous with Henny's repetitions of *kill every-*

body, kill myself) is the last, the worst, and the most violent of their quarrels. The next morning Henny admits to Ernie that she will never be able to pay him back, and says with a perplexed, wondering conclusiveness: "I don't know what to do." Ernie is Henny's main connection to life, her only connection to hope and to the future: when life makes her steal his money, beat him until she faints, and then tell him that she can never pay him back, what is there left to her but the "All right, I will!" that is her last word to life?

VIII

After you have read *The Man Who Loved Children* several times you feel that you know its author's main strengths and main weakness. The weakness is, I think, a kind of natural excess and lack of discrimination: she is most likely to go wrong by not seeing when to stop or what to leave out. About most things—always, about the most important things—she is not excessive and does discriminate; but a few things in *The Man Who Loved Children* ought not to be there, and a few other things ought not to be there in such quantities.

When you look at these passages that—it seems to you—ought not to be there, it is as if you were seeing an intrusion of raw reality into the imagined reality of the book: some actual facts are being rapidly, scrappily, and vivaciously described. You don't feel that these had to go into the book, nor do you feel that they have been through the process of being created all over again that the rest of the material of the book has been through. They are, so to speak, God's creation, not Christina Stead's; and Christina Stead's fairly effective reporting of this first creation is a poor substitute for her own second creation. Such accidental realities seem to have slipped into the book unquestioned—or perhaps, when a part of the author questioned them, another part answered, "But that's the way it really was." (One of the most puzzling things about a novel is that "the way it really was" half the time is, and half the time isn't, the way it ought to be in the novel.) Another sort of unrequired and consequently excessive passage seems to be there because the author's invention, running on automatically, found it easy to imagine it that way; such a passage is the equivalent, in narrative, of a mannered, habitual, easily effective piece of rhetoric.

Isn't there a little too much of the Pollits' homecoming party, of Henny's tirades, of Sam's dream-sermons? Aren't these slightly excessive representations of monstrously excessive realities? Aren't there a few too many facts about Annapolis and Harper's Ferry, about Henny's more remote relatives? When Christina Stead is at her worst—in *The Man Who Loved Children* she never is—you feel that there is just too much of Christina Stead. At its worst her writing has a kind of vivacious, mechanical over-abundance: her observation and invention and rhetoric, set into autonomous operation, bring into existence a queer picaresque universe of indiscriminate, slightly disreputable incidents. Reading about them is like listening to two disillusioned old automata gossiping over a cup of tea in the kitchen.

Ruskin says that anyone who expects perfection from a work of art knows nothing of works of art. This is an appealing sentence that, so far as I can see, is not true about a few pictures and statues and pieces of music, short stories and short poems. Whether or not you expect perfection from them, you get it; at least, there is nothing in them that you would want changed. But what Ruskin says is true about novels: anyone who expects perfection from even the greatest novel knows nothing of novels. Some of the faults of *The Man Who Loved Children* are the faults a large enough, live enough thing naturally has; others (those I have been discussing) are the faults a book of Christina Stead's naturally has—they are, really, the other side of her virtues. An occasional awkwardness or disparity is the result of her having created from an Australian memory an American reality; but usually you are astonished at how well acclimated, recreated, these memories are. Two or three Joyce-ish sentences—one seems consciously and humorously Joyce-ish—make you remember that the rest of the sentences in the book are pure Stead. What Louie reads and quotes and loves is more what she would have read in 1917 than in 1937; but objecting to *that* is like objecting to Tolstoy's making the characters in *War and Peace* his own contemporaries, not Napoleon's—Christina Stead understands that it is only her own realities, anachronistic or not, that can give Louie the timeless reality that Louie has.

A reader of *The Man Who Loved Children* naturally will want to know something about Christina Stead. I know only what I have found in reference books or guessed from her novels. Let me repeat some of the first: it will have for the reader the interest of showing where Sam and Louie (and, no doubt, Henny) began.

Christina Stead was born in Australia, in 1902. Her mother died soon afterwards, her father remarried, and she "became the eldest of a large family." Her father was a rationalist, a Fabian socialist, and a naturalist in the Government Fisheries Department. As a girl she was particularly interested in "fish, natural history, Spencer, Darwin, Huxley . . . the sea . . . I had plenty of work with the young children, but I was attached to them, and whenever I could, told them stories, partly from Grimm and Andersen, partly invented."

She went to Teachers' College, disliked teaching, took a business course at night, went to London in 1928 and worked there, went to Paris in 1929 and worked there for several years. She had been a public school teacher, a teacher of abnormal children, a demonstrator in the psychology laboratory of Sydney University, and a clerk in a grain company; in Paris she was a clerk in a banking house. She lived in the United States during the late '30's and early '40's, and now lives in England. Her husband is William Blake, the author of several novels and of the best and most entertaining textbook of Marxian economics that I know. In 1934 Christina Stead published *The Salzburg Tales;* in 1935, *Seven Poor Men of Sydney;* in 1936, *The Beauties and the Furies;* in 1938, *House of All Nations;* in 1940, *The Man Who Loved Children;* in 1944, *For Love Alone;* in 1946, *Letty Fox, Her Luck;* in 1948, *A Little Tea, a Little Chat;* in 1952, *The People with the Dogs.*

Her books have had varying receptions. *House of All Nations* was a critical success and a best-seller; *The Man Who Loved Children* was a failure both with critics and with the public. It has been out of print for many years, and Christina Stead herself is remembered by only a few readers. When the world rejects, and then forgets, a writer's most profound and imaginative book, he may unconsciously work in a more limited way in the books that follow it; this has happened, I believe, to Christina Stead. The world's incomprehension has robbed it, for twenty-five years, of *The Man Who Loved Children;* has robbed it, forever, of what could have come after *The Man Who Loved Children.*

I X

When we think of the masterpieces that nobody praised and nobody read, back there in the past, we feel an impatient superiority to the readers of the past. If we had been there, we can't help feeling, *we'd* have known that *Moby Dick* was a good book—why, how could anyone help knowing?

But suppose someone says to us, "Well, you're here now: what's our own *Moby Dick?* What's the book that, a hundred years from now, everybody will look down on *us* for not having liked?" What do we say then?

But if I were asked something easier—to name a good book that we don't read and that the people of the future will read—

I'd be less at a loss. In 1941 I bought two copies of *The Man Who Loved Children*, one to read and the other to lend. In the long run a borrower of one died and a borrower of the other went abroad, so that I have nothing left but a copy from the library. Lending a favorite book has its risks; the borrower may not like it. I don't know a better novel than *Crime and Punishment*— still, every fourth or fifth borrower returns it unfinished: it depressed him; besides that, he didn't believe it. More borrowers than this return the first volume of *Remembrance of Things Past* unfinished: they were bored. There is no book you can lend people that all of them will like.

But *The Man Who Loved Children* has been a queer exception. I have lent it to many writers and more readers, and all of them thought it good and original, a book different from any other. They could see that there were things wrong with it—a novel is a prose narrative of some length that has something wrong with it—but they felt that, somehow, the things didn't matter.

To have this happen with a book that was a failure to begin with, and that after twenty-five years is unknown, is strange. Having it happen has helped me to believe that it is one of those books that their own age neither reads nor praises, but that the next age thinks a masterpiece.

But I suppose I'd believe this even if every borrower had told me it was bad. As Wordsworth and Proust say, a good enough book in the long run makes its own readers, people who believe in it because they can't help themselves. Where *The Man Who Loved Children* is concerned, I can't help myself; it seems to me as plainly good as *War and Peace* and *Crime and Punishment* and *Remembrance of Things Past* are plainly great. A few of its less important parts are bad and all of its more important parts are good: it is a masterpiece with some plain, and plainly negligible, faults.

I call it a good book, but it is a better book, I think, than most of the novels people call great; perhaps it would be fairer to call it great. It has one quality that, ordinarily, only a great book has: it does a single thing better than any other book has ever done it. *The Man Who Loved Children* makes you a part of one family's immediate existence as no other book quite does. When you have read it you have been, for a few hours, a Pollit; it will take you many years to get the sound of the Pollits out of your ears, the sight of the Pollits out of your eyes, the smell of the Pollits out of your nostrils.

The Man Who Loved Children

CHAPTER ONE

1 ⚜ Henny comes home.

ALL THE June Saturday afternoon Sam Pollit's children were on
the lookout for him as they skated round the dirt sidewalks and
seamed old asphalt of R Street and Reservoir Road that bounded
the deep-grassed acres of Tohoga House, their home. They were
not usually allowed to run helter-skelter about the streets, but
Sam was out late with the naturalists looking for lizards and sala-
manders round the Potomac bluffs, Henrietta, their mother, was
in town, Bonnie, their youthful aunt and general servant, had
her afternoon off, and they were being minded by Louisa, their
half sister, eleven and a half years old, the eldest of their brood.
Strict and anxious when their parents were at home, Louisa when
left in sole command was benevolent, liking to hear their shouts
from a distance while she lay on her belly, reading, at the top of
the orchard, or ambled, woolgathering, about the house.

The sun dropped between reefs of cloud into the Virginia
woods: a rain frog rattled and the air grew damp. Mother coming home from the Wisconsin Avenue car, with parcels, was seen
from various corners by the perspiring young ones, who rushed
to meet her, chirring on their skates, and who convoyed her
home, doing figures round her, weaving and blowing about her
or holding to her skirt, and merry, in spite of her decorous irritations.

"I come home and find you tearing about the streets like mad
things!"

They poured into the house, bringing in dirt, suppositions,

questions, legends of other children, and plans for the next day, while Louie, suddenly remembering potatoes and string beans neglected, slunk in through the back door. Henrietta took a letter off the hall stand, a letter addressed to her, to "Mrs. Samuel Clemens Pollit," which she tore open, muttering, with a half-smile, "The fool!" She went into the long dining room to read it, while Saul, technically the elder of the seven-year-old twins, hung from the chair back, saying,

"Who's it from, Mother, who's it from?" and his twin, straw-headed Samuel, tried to wrest her handbag from her, meanwhile repeating, "Can I look in your bag, can I look in your bag, can I?"

When she heard him, at last, she relinquished the worn old cowhide bag and went on reading, without paying the least attention to their excited examination of her keys and cosmetics, nor to ten-year-old Ernest, her first-born, who, after counting her money and putting it into little piles, said sagely,

"Mother has two dollars and eighty-two cents: Mother, when you went out you had five dollars and sixteen cents and a stamp. What did you buy, Mother?"

They heard Louisa coming, chanting, "Hot tea, hot tea! Make way there!" and shifted a quarter of an inch on their hams. Louie picked her way carefully through their midst, carrying a large cup of tea which she put down in front of her stepmother.

"Did anyone come or telephone?"

"The paint came, Mother" Louie stopped in the doorway. "It's in the washhouse."

"Is he going to start painting and messing everything up tomorrow?" Henrietta asked.

Louie said nothing but moved slowly out.

"Mother, you spent two dollars and thirty-four cents. What did you buy?"

"What's in this parcel, Moth?" Evie asked.

"Oh, leave me alone; you're worse than your father."

Henrietta took off her gloves and began to sip her tea. This was her chair and also the one that all visitors sought. It was straight but comfortable, not too low, and set between the corner

[4]

window and that cushioned bench which ran along the west wall. The children would line up on this bench and hang entranced on the visitor's life story. Visitors looked awkward there, arrayed in the accidents of life's put-together and rough-and-tumble, laughing uncouthly, unexpectedly at imbecile jokes, giving tongue to crackpot idioms; yet they thought themselves important, and it appeared that as they ran about the streets things happened to them. They had knots of relations with whom they argued and sweethearts to whom they cooed; they had false teeth, eyeglasses, and operations. The children would sit there staring with mouth open and gulping, till Henny snapped, "Are you catching flies?"

When Henny sat there, on the contrary, everything was in order and it was as if no one was in the house; it was like the presence of a somber, friendly old picture that has hung on a wall for generations. Whenever Sam was out, particularly in the afternoon, Henny would sit there, near the kitchen where she could get her cups of tea hot, and superintend the cooking. The children, rushing in from school or from the orchard, would find her there, quiet, thin, tired, with her veined, long olive hands clasped round the teacup for warmth, or gliding, skipping through wools and needles, as she knitted *her* pattern into bonnets and bootees for infants who were always appearing in the remote world. Then she would be cheerful and say to them in her elegant, girlish, spitfire way, "A fool for luck, a poor man for children, Eastern shore for hard crabs, and niggers for dogs"; and, "I have a little house and a mouse couldn't find it and all the men in our town couldn't count the windows in it: what is it?" When she had asked the riddle she would smile archly, although they all knew the answer, for Henny knew very few riddles. But these dear little rigmaroles would only come out when Daddy was out.

At other times they would find her, ugly, with her hair pushed back and her spectacles on, leaning over a coffee-soiled white linen tablecloth (she would have no others, thinking colored ones *common*), darning holes or fixing the lace on one of her lace covers inherited from Monocacy, her old Baltimore home. Then she would growl,

[5]

"If you stand there staring at me, I'll land you one to send you flying!" or, "Don't gabble to me about the blessed snakes: it's bad luck to have snakes, and he always keeps snakes for pets."

Now Henny sent little Evie running to get her hand lotion and nail buff while she discontentedly examined her great agate nails and complained about flecks in them and an injured half-moon,

"I don't know what I go to that woman in the arcade for; she hacks my cuticle too."

"You have money on your tea, Moth!" said Saul cheerfully.

"Yes, that's good," and she carefully lifted the circle of froth to her mouth in her teaspoon, but it broke, and at this she gave an irritated cry, "Oh, there, now I won't get any." The cup was a cup that their father had seen in a junk shop near P Street, old heavy china with the word "Mother" on it, between bunches of roses: and he had made them buy it for her for her last birthday.

Henny sat dreaming, with the letter in her lap. She was not nervous and lively like the Pollits, her husband's family, who, she said, "always behaved like chickens with their heads cut off," but would sit there still, so gracefully languid, except to run her fingers over the tablecloth, tracing the design in the damask, or to alter her pose and lean her face on her hand and stare into the distance, a commonplace habit which looked very theatrical in Henny, because of her large, bright eyeballs and thin, high-curved black eyebrows. She was like a tall crane in the reaches of the river, standing with one leg crooked and listening. She would look fixedly at her vision and suddenly close her eyes. The child watching (there was always one) would see nothing but the huge eyeball in its glove of flesh, deep-sunk in the wrinkled skullhole, the dark circle round it and the eyebrow far above, as it seemed, while all her skin, unrelieved by brilliant eye, came out in its real shade, burnt olive. She looked formidable in such moments, in her intemperate silence, the bitter set of her discolored mouth with her uneven slender gambler's nose and scornful nostrils, lengthening her sharp oval face, pulling the dry skinfolds. Then when she opened her eyes, there would shoot out a look of hate, horror, passion, or contempt. The children (they were good chil-

[6]

dren, as everyone said) would creep up, so as not to annoy her and say, at her elbow, "Moth, can Whitey come in?" or some such thing, and she would start and cry,

"What do you mean sneaking up on me like that, are you spying on me like your father?" or, "Get out of my sight before I land you one, you creeper!" or, "What do you mean trying to frighten me, is it supposed to be funny?"

And at other times, as now, she would sit with her glances hovering round the room, running from dusty molding to torn curtain frill, from a nail under the transom left over from the last Christmas to a worn patch on the oilcloth by the door, threadbare under so many thousand little footsteps, not worrying about them, but considering each well-known item, almost amiable from familiarity, almost interested, as if considering anew how to fix up these things when fatigue had gone and the tea and rest had put new energy into her.

Henny had never lived in an apartment. She was an old-fashioned woman. She had the calm of frequentation; she belonged to this house and it to her. Though she was a prisoner in it, she possessed it. She and it were her marriage. She was indwelling in every board and stone of it: every fold in the curtains had a meaning (perhaps they were so folded to hide a darn or stain); every room was a phial of revelation to be poured out some feverish night in the secret laboratories of her decisions, full of living cancers of insult, leprosies of disillusion, abscesses of grudge, gangrene of nevermore, quintan fevers of divorce, and all the proliferating miseries, the running sores and thick scabs, for which (and not for its heavenly joys) the flesh of marriage is so heavily veiled and conventually interned.

As Henny sat before her teacup and the steam rose from it and the treacherous foam gathered, uncollectible round its edge, the thousand storms of her confined life would rise up before her, thinner illusions on the steam. She did not laugh at the words "a storm in a teacup." Some raucous, cruel words about five cents misspent were as serious in a woman's life as a debate on war appropriations in Congress: all the civil war of ten years

[7]

roared into their smoky words when they shrieked, maddened, at each other; all the snakes of hate hissed. Cells are covered with the rhymes of the condemned, so was this house with Henny's life sentence, invisible but thick as woven fabric. Here she sat to play solitaire, the late sun shining on the cards and on the green and red squares of the linoleum. When Sam was out, if Henny felt restless, she would take her double pack and shuffle them with a sound like a distant machine gun, and worry and reshuffle and begin to lay them out eagerly, by fours. All the children watched and showed her where to lay the cards, until she said good-humoredly,

"Oh, go and put your head in a bag!" and she taught Louie how to play, saying she must never touch them when her father was round, that was all.

Sam tried to impart everything he knew to the children and grumbled that the *mother* taught nothing at all: yet their influence on the boys and girls was equal. The children grabbed tricks and ideas according to the need of the day, without thinking at all of where they got them, without gratitude; and Henny saw this and so did not bother her head about her children. She herself belonged to a grabbing breed. Henny would also tell fortunes, by the cards, over her tea, though never for the children. While she was dealing to tell the fortune of Aunt Bonnie (Sam's twenty-five-year-old sister and their unpaid maid of all work), or Miss Spearing (Henny's old-maid friend from schooldays), she would always begin a wonderful yarn about how she went to town, "more dead than alive and with only ten cents in my purse and I wanted to crack a safe," and how, in the streetcar, was "a dirty shrimp of a man with a fishy expression who purposely leaned over me and pressed my bust, and a common vulgar woman beside him, an ogress, big as a hippopotamus, with her bottom sticking out, who grinned like a shark and tried to give him the eye," and how this wonderful adventure went on for hours, always with new characters of new horror. In it would invariably be a woman with a cowlike expression, a girl looking frightened as a rabbit, a yellow-haired frump with hair like a haystack in a fit, some woman who bored Henny with her silly gassing, and impudent flighty young girls behind counters, and waitresses smelling like a tannery (or a fish market), who gave her lip, which caused her to "go to market and give them more than they bargained for." There were men and women, old acquaintances of hers, or friends of Sam who presumed to know her, to whom she would give the go-by, or the cold shoulder, or a distant bow, or a polite good day, or a black look, or a look black as thunder, and there were silly old roosters, creatures like a dying duck in a thunderstorm, filthy old pawers, and YMCA sick chickens, and women thin as a rail and men fat as a pork barrel, and women with blouses so puffed out that she wanted to stick pins in, and men like coalheavers, and women like boiled owls and women who had fallen into a flour barrel; and all these wonderful creatures, who swarmed in the streets, stores, and restaurants of Washington, ogling, leering, pulling, pushing, stinking, overscented, screaming and boasting, turning pale at a black look from Henny, ducking and diving, dodging and returning, were the only creatures that Henny ever saw.

What a dreary stodgy world of adults the children saw when they went out! And what a moral, high-minded world their father saw! But for Henny there was a wonderful particular world, and when they went with her they saw it: they saw the fish eyes, the crocodile grins, the hair like a birch broom, the mean men crawling with maggots, and the children restless as an eel, that she saw. She did not often take them with her. She preferred to go out by herself and mooch to the bargain basements, and ask the young man in the library what was good to read, and take tea in some obscure restaurant, and wander desolately about, criticizing shopwindows and wondering if, in this street or that, she would yet, "old as I am and looking like a black hag," meet her fate. Then she would come home, next to some girl "from a factory who looked like a lily and smelled like a skunk cabbage," flirting with all the men and the men grinning back, next to some coarse, dirty workman who pushed against her in the car and smelled of sweat, or some leering brute who tried to pay her fare.

[9]

Louie would sit there, on the end of the bench, lost in visions, wondering how she would survive if some leering brute shamefully tried to pay her fare in a public car, admiring Henny for her strength of mind in the midst of such scandals: and convinced of the dreary, insulting horror of the low-down world. For it was not Henny alone who went through this inferno, but every woman, especially, for example, Mrs. Wilson, the woman who came to wash every Monday. Mrs. Wilson, too, "big as she was, big as an ox," was insulted by great big brutes of workmen, with sweaty armpits, who gave her a leer, and Mrs. Wilson, too, had to tell grocers where they got off, and she too had to put little half-starved cats of girls, thin as toothpicks, in their places. Mrs. Wilson it was who saw the ravishing Charlotte Bolton (daughter of the lawyer, who lived in a lovely bungalow across the street), she saw "my lady, standing with her hands on her hips, waggling her bottom and laughing at a man like a common streetgirl," and he "black as the inside of a hat, with dark blood for sure." Louie and Evie, and the obliging little boys, tugging at the piles of greasy clothes on Mondays, puffing under piles of new-ironed linen on Tuesdays, would be silent for hours, observing this world of tragic faery in which all their adult friends lived. Sam, their father, had endless tales of friends, enemies, but most often they were good citizens, married to good wives, with good children (though untaught), but never did Sam meet anyone out of Henny's world, grotesque, foul, loud-voiced, rude, uneducated, and insinuating, full of scandal, slander, and filth, financially deplorable and physically revolting, dubiously born, and going awry to a desquamating end.

After Henny had talked her heart out to her sister, Aunt Hassie, or to Bonnie even (though she despised a Pollit), or to her bosom friend, Miss Spearing, she would sometimes go, and after a silence, there would steal through the listening house flights of notes, rounded as doves, wheeling over housetops in the sleeping afternoon, Chopin or Brahms, escaping from Henny's lingering, firm fingers. Sam could be vile but always as a joke. Henny was beautifully, wholeheartedly vile: she asked no quarter and gave none to the foul world, and when she told her children tales of the villainies they could understand, it was not to corrupt them, but because, for her, the world was really so. How could their father, said she, so fool them with his lies and nonsense?

The chair, and the slanting of the light, the endless insoluble game of solitaire, were as comfortable to Henny's ravaged nerves as an eiderdown. In the warmth of the late afternoon, some time before she expected to hear the rush of feet, she would sit there at her third or fourth game and third or fourth cup of tea. So sitting she would seem to herself to be bathing in the warm moisture of other summers. She would see the near rush or distant slow-moving glitter on the steeps of North Charles Street, see the half-dry fountain with a boat in Eutaw Place, which could be seen from the front windows of the brownstone house Hassie had there, and the hot-smelling, rose-colored stoops flowing down and up the gully: see the masts of little boats and the barges, the sole twinkle of a car on the bridge; see the hot, washed windows of dressmakers and the tasseled curtains of a club, the dormant steps of little night bars, the yellow and pink of some afternoon-tea place where she had gone with Hassie when she was a schoolgirl. Or if the wind was high and her headache had not yet come on, she could smell the brackish .and weakly salt streams of the Chesapeake, scudding in her cousin's twelve-footer, or her father's motorboat; feel the sounds and scents of Saturdays long swept away on the long rollers of years, when she was a thin-blooded, coquettish girl, making herself bleed at the nose for excitement, throwing herself on the lawns of Monocacy in a tantrum, spitting fire at the servants, coaxing her father, waiting for the silly toys her father would buy her—engagement to a commercial fortune, marriage to a great name, some unexpected stroke of luck in blue-blooded romance, social fun, nursemaids, two fashionable children in pink and blue. These things surged out of the past, as she sat there, but faintly, no more distinct than a wind that is blowing ten mile off and sometimes sends a puff of air. If she became conscious of these streams on the rainbow fringe of memory, she would bite her lip and flush, perhaps angry at her indulgent father for getting her the man he had got, angry at herself for having been so weak.

"Sadie was a lady," she would suddenly say in the stillness, and, "Hrmph!" or, "If I had a ladida like that to deal with I'd drown her when a pup." Besides, she could not even now forget the humiliation of having her name five or six years in old social calendars among the "eligibles": nor of having married a man who was after all a mere jog-trot subaltern bureaucrat, dragged into the service in the lowest grades without a degree, from mere practical experience in the Maryland Conservation Commission, and who owed his jealousy-creating career to her father's influence in the lobbies of the capital.

Soon Ernie, her favorite, would rush in, saying breathlessly, "Did it come out, Moth?" This kept her sitting there. While she sat and played or did her microscopic darning, sometimes a small mouse would run past, or even boldly stand and inquisitively stare at her. Henny would look down at its monstrous pointed little face calmly and go on with her work, while it pretended to run off, and took another stand, still curious, behind another chair leg. The mice were well fed. They regularly set traps, but there was no coming to the end of the mice in that house. Henny accepted the sooty little beings as house guests and would only go on the warpath at night, when she woke up suddenly to smell in the great hall, or even in her own bedroom, the musky penetrating odor of their passage: or when she looked at her little spectator and saw that it was a pregnant mother. She would have accepted everything else, too, the winds, the rattlings and creaking of the old house, the toothaches and headaches, the insane anxieties about cancer and t.b., too, all house guests, if she could have, and somewhere between all these hustlers, made herself a little life. But she had the children, she had a stepdaughter, she had no money, and she had to live with a man who fancied himself a public character and a moralist of a very saintly type. The moralist said mice brought germs and so she was obliged to chase the mouse and all its fellow guests. Nevertheless, although she despised animals, she felt involuntarily that the little marauder was much like herself, trying to get by: she belonged to the great race of human beings who regard life as a series of piracies of all powers.

She would play on and on till her cheeks got hot and then call for another cup of tea, or else go and get herself some store cheese and Worcestershire sauce in a plate, pushing the cards aside.

"I wish your mother would stop playing patience, it makes her look like an old witch or an old vixen possum," Sam would say in a gently benevolent voice, in some offstage colloquy, if he ever came home and found her still at it. It did exhaust her in the end. She played feverishly, until her mind was a darkness, until all the memories and the ease had long since drained away. And then when the father came home, the children who had been battling and shuttling around her would all rush off like water down the sink, leaving her sitting there, with blackened eyes, a yellow skin, and straining wrinkles: and she would think of the sink, and mutter, as she did at this moment,

"A dirty cracked plate: that's just what I am!"

"What did you say, Mummy?" asked little Sam. She looked at him, the image of his father, and repeated, "I'm a greasy old soup plate," making them all laugh, laughing herself.

"Mother, you're so silly," Evie said.

Henny got up and moved into her room. It was a large room taking up a quarter of the original ground-floor plan, with two windows facing the east, and one window on the front lawn but screened from R Street by the double hedges. Although the room was furnished with the walnut suite that she had brought from home, and the double bed which she now used alone, there was plenty of room for their play.

Henny sat down at the dressing table to take off her hat. They clustered round the silver-littered table, picked up her rings.

"What did you buy, Mother?" someone persisted.

"Mother, can I have a nickel?"

Henny said, fluffing out the half-gray curls round her face, "I asked my mother for fifty cents to see the elephant jump the fence. Shoo, get out! You wretched limpets never give me a minute to myself."

"Mother, can I have a nickel, please?"

"Mother, what did you buy-uy?" chanted Henny's baby, Tommy, a dark four-year-old boy with shining almond eyes and a skullcap of curls. Meanwhile he climbed on the dressing table and, after studying her reflection for a long time in the mirror, kissed it.

"Look, Moth, Tommy kissed you in the glass!" They laughed at him, while he, much flattered, blushed and leaned over to kiss her, giving her a hearty smack-smack while he watched himself in the mirror.

"Oh, you kissing bug! It's unlucky for two to look in the same glass. Now get down and get out! Go and feed the darn animals and then come and wash your hands for dinner."

The flood receded, leaving Henny high and dry again. She sighed and got out the letter she had received that afternoon, reading it carefully.

At the end she folded it again, said with a sneer, "And a greasy finger mark from his greasy hypocritical mauler right in the middle: the sight of his long pious cheeks like suet and her fat red face across the table from each other——"

She looked at the letter thoughtfully for a while, turning it over, got out her fountain pen, and started a reply. But she tore her sheet of paper across, spat on the soiled letter, and, picking it up with a pair of curling tongs, burned it and her few scratchings in a little saucepan which had boiled dry on the radiator.

The letter was from her eldest brother, Norman Collyer. It refused to lend her money and said, somewhere near the offensive finger mark,

You should be able to manage. Your husband is making about $8,000 yearly and you always got lucky dips anyhow, being Father's pet. I can only give you some good advice, which doubtless you will not follow, knowing you as I do. That is, draw in your horns, retrench somehow, don't go running up accounts and don't borrow from moneylenders. I've seen my own family half starving. What do you think I can make out of the job Father gives me?

You must get out of your own messes. The trouble is you never had to pay for your mistakes before.

Henny opened her windows to let the smoke out, and then began taking trinkets out of her silver jewel case and looking at them discontentedly. She threw open the double doors of her linen closet and rummaged amongst the sheets, pulling out first a library book and then two heavy silver soup ladles and six old silver teaspoons. She looked at them indifferently for a moment and then stuck them back in their hiding place.

She let Louie give the children their dinner, and ate hers on a tray in her bedroom, distractedly figuring on a bit of envelope. When she brought her tray out to the kitchen, Louie was slopping dishes about in the sink. Henny cried,

"Take your fat belly out of the sink! Look at your dress! Oh, my God! Now I've got to get you another one clean and dry for Monday. You'll marry a drunkard when you grow up, always wet in front. Ernie, help Louie with the washing-up, and you others make yourselves scarce. And turn off the darn radio. It's enough when Mr. Big-Me is at home blowing off steam."

They ran out cheerfully while Louie drooped her underlip and tied a towel round her waist. Henny sighed, picked up the cup of tea that Louie had just poured out for her, and went into her bedroom, next door to the kitchen. She called from there,

"Ernie, bring me your pants and I'll mend them."

"There's time," he shouted considerately, "you don't need to tonight. Tomorrow's Sunday-Funday, and we're painting the house—I'll wear my overalls."

"Did you hear what I said?"

"O.K." He shed his trousers at once and rushed in to her holding them out at arm's length. He stood beside her for a moment, watching her pinch the cloth together. "I bet I could do that easy, Mum: why don't you teach me?"

"Thank you, my son; but Mother will do it while she has the strength."

"Are you sick today, Mother?"

"Mother's always sick and tired," she said gloomily.

"Will I bring you my shawl, Mother?" This was his baby shawl that he always took to bed with him when he felt sick or weepy.

"No, Son." She looked at him straight, as if at a stranger, and then drew him to her, kissing him on the mouth.

"You're Mother's blessing; go and help Louie." He cavorted and dashed out, hooting. She heard him in half a minute, chattering away affectionately to his half sister.

"But I should have been better off if I'd never laid eyes on any of them," Henny grumbled to herself, as she put on her glasses and peered at the dark serge.

2 ✖ Sam comes home.

STARS DRIFTED in chinks of the sky as Sam came home: the lamps were clouded in leaves in this little island of streets between river and parks. Georgetown's glut of children, issue of streets of separate little houses, went shouting, colliding downhill, while Sam came up whistling, seeing the pale faces, flying knees, lights and stars above, around him. Sam could have been home just after sunset when his harum-scarum brood were still looking for him, and he had meant to be there, for he never broke his word to them. He could have taken Shank's ponies, which, he was fond of saying, "take me everywhere, far afield and into the world of marvels which lies around us, into the highways and byways, into the homes of rich and poor alike, seeking the doorstep of him who loves his fellow man—and fellow woman, of course—seeking every rostrum where the servants of evil may be flagellated, and the root of all evil exposed."

On Shank's ponies he could have got home that afternoon in less than an hour, crossing the Key Bridge from Rosslyn, when the naturalists left the new bird sanctuary on Analostan Island. But today Sam was the hero of his Department and of the naturalists because he had got the long-desired appointment with the

Anthropological Mission to the Pacific, and not only would he have his present salary plus traveling expenses, but his appointment was a bold step forward on his path of fame.

Sam looked, as he passed, at a ramshackle little house, something like the wretched slum he had once boarded in with his brother at Dundalk, out of Baltimore, and a smile bared his teeth.

"Going to glory," said Sam: "I've come a long way, a long, long way, Brother. Eight thousand a year and expenses—and even Tohoga House, in Georgetown, D.C., lovely suburb of the nation's capital; and the children of poor Sam Pollit, bricklayer's son, who left school at twelve, are going to university soon, under the flashing colonnades of America's greatest city, in the heart of the democratic Athens, much greater than any miserable Athens of the dirt grubbers of antiquity, yes—I feel sober, at rest. The old heart doesn't flutter: I must be careful not to rest on my laurels now—haste not, rest not! I feel free!" Sam began to wonder at himself; why did he feel free? He had always been free, a free man, a free mind, a freethinker. "By Gemini," he thought, taking a great breath, "this is how men feel who take advantage of their power."

Sam looked round him—just ahead was Volta Place, where Dribble Smith, his friend in the Treasury, lived. He chuckled, hearing Dribble practicing his scales inside, to his daughter's accompaniment. Passing Smith's hedge, Sam said half aloud,

"What it must be, though, to taste supreme power!"

He thought of his long-dead mother, who came from the good old days when mothers dreamed of their sons' being President, *Poor woman, good woman: she little thought when she dropped a tear at my being sent to work in the fish market that in the fish market I would meet my fate.* Ahead of him, not far uphill, was his harbor and his fate.

"Another thing," said Sam to himself, "is that going away now, Madeleine and I will have time to use our heads, get things straight: the love that harms another is not love—but what desires beset a man! They are not written in the calendar of a man's duty; they are part of the secret life. Some time the secret life rises and overwhelms us—a tidal wave. We must not be carried away. We have each too much to lose." He strode on, "Forget, forget!" He struggled to remember something else, something cheerful. They had taken him to Dirty Jack's house to celebrate his appointment; there they had made merry, Sam being at the top of his form. There was a young creature there, timid, serious, big-eyed, with a black crop who turned out to be Dirty Jack's (that is, Old Roebuck's) only daughter, the one who did the charming flower painting. What an innocent, attentive face! It positively flamed with admiration; and the child-woman's name was Gillian. He had made up a poem on the spur of the moment:

> Gillian, my Gillian,
> He would be a villy-un,
> Who would be dally-dillyin'
> About a Lacertilian
> When he could look at you!

"By Jiminy!" ejaculated Sam, who had strange oaths, since he could never swear foul ones, "genius burns: nothing succeeds like success! And did Dirty Jack jerk back his head and give me one of those looks of his with his slugs of eyes, to intimidate me; whereas, no one noticed him at all, at all, poor old Dirty Jack." He began to hum with his walking, "Oh, my darling Nelly Gray, they have taken you away."

"By Gee," he exclaimed half aloud, "I am excited! A pity to come home to a sleeping house, and what's not asleep is the devil incarnate; but we're a cheerful bunch, the Pollits are a cheerful bunch. But wait till my little gang hears that they're going to lose their dad for a nine-month! There'll be weeping and wailing and gnashing of teeth!" and Sam clapped his hands together. He loved this Thirty-fourth Street climb, by the quiet houses and under the trees. He had first come this way, exploring the neighborhood, a young father and widower, holding his year-old Louisa in his arms, with her fat bare legs wagging, and, by his side, elegant, glossy-eyed Miss Henrietta Collyer, a few months before their marriage; and that was ten years ago. Then afterwards, with each and all of the children, up and down and round about, taking them to the Observatory, the parks, the river, the woodland by the Chesapeake and Ohio Canal, or walking them out to Cabin John, teaching them birds, flowers, and all denizens of the woodland.

Now Old David Collyer's Tohoga House, Sam's Tohoga House, that he called his island in the sky, swam above him. A constellation hanging over that dark space midmost of the hill, which was Tohoga's two acres, was slowly swamped by cloud.

He came up slowly, not winded, but snuffing in the night of the hot streets, looking up at the great house, tree-clouded. Now he crossed P Street and faced the hummock. On one side the long galvanized-iron back fence of his property ran towards Thirty-fifth Street and its strip of brick terrace slums. Over this fence leaned the pruned boughs of giant maples and oaks. The old reservoir was away to the right. A faint radiance showed Sam that the light in the long dining room was on. He ran up the side steps and stole across the grass behind the house, brushing aside familiar plants, touching with his left hand the little Colorado blue spruce which he had planted for the children's "Wishing-Tree" and which was now five feet high.

He was just on six feet and therefore could peer into the long room. It ran through the house and had a window looking out at the front to R Street. A leaved oak table stood in the center and at the table, facing him, sitting in his carving chair, was his eldest child, Louisa, soon twelve years old, the only child of his dead first wife, Rachel. Louie was hunched over a book and sat so still that she seemed alone in the house. She did nothing while he looked at her but turn a page and twist one strand of her long yellow hair round and round her finger, a trick of her father's. Then without Sam having heard anything, she lifted her head and sat stock-still with her gray eyes open wide. She now rose stiffly and looked furtively at the window behind her. Sam heard nothing but the crepitations of arboreal night. Then he noticed that the window was sliding gently down. Louisa advanced jerkily to this magically moving window and watched it as it fitted itself into the sill. Then she shook her head and turning to the room as if it were a person she laughed soundlessly. It was nothing but the worn cords loosening. She opened the window and then shut it again softly, but leaned against the pane looking up into the drifting sky, seeking something in the street. She had been there, and Sam, whistling softly *Bringing Home the Sheaves,* was about to go inside, when a thin, dark scarecrow in an off-white wrapper —Henrietta, his wife—stood in the doorway. Through the loose window frame he heard her threadbare words,

"You're up poring over a book with lights flaring all over the house at this hour of the night. You look like a boiled owl! Isn't your father home yet?"

"No, Mother."

"Why is your knee bleeding? Have you been picking the scab again?"

Louie hung her head and looked at her knee, crossed with old scars and new abrasions and bruises: she flushed and the untidy hair fell over her face.

"Answer, answer, you sullen beast!"

"I bumped it."

"You lie all the time."

The child straightened with wide frowning eyes, pulled back her arms insolently. Henny rushed at her with hands outstretched and thrust her firm bony fingers round the girl's neck, squeezing and saying, "Ugh," twice. Louisa looked up into her stepmother's face, squirming, but not trying to get away, questioning her silently, needing to understand, in an affinity of misfortune. Henrietta dropped her arms quickly and gripped her own neck with an expression of disgust, then pushed the girl away with both hands; and as she flounced out of the room, cried,

"I ought to put us all out of our misery!"

Louisa moved back to her chair and stood beside it, looking down at the book. Then she sank into the chair and, putting her face on both hands, began to read again.

Sam turned his back to the house and looked south, over the dark, susurrous orchard, towards the faint lights of Rosslyn. A zephyr stole up the slope as quietly as a nocturnal animal and with it all the domestic scents, wrapping Sam's body in peace. Within, a torment raged, day and night, week, month, year, always the same, an endless conflict, with its truces and breathing spaces; out here were a dark peace and love.

"Mother Earth," whispered Sam, "I love you, I love men and women, I love little children and all innocent things, I love, I feel I am love itself—how could I pick out a woman who would hate me so much!"

Surefooted he moved way down to the animal cages, heard them stir uneasily, and spoke to the raccoon,

"Procyon! Procyon! Here's little Sam!" But the raccoon refused to come to the wire. He went up the slope again, thinking, *Fate puts brambles, hurdles in my path, she even gives me an Old Woman of the Sea, to try me, because I am destined for great things.*

When Sam came into the hall there was no light anywhere on the ground floor. The saffron dark through his sitting room at the head of the first flight of stairs showed that Louie was in her bedroom. She had heard his whistle and had rushed upstairs with her book.

"Why, why?" thought Sam. "She could have waited to hear what her daddy has been doing all day. She is so dogged—and she has her little burdens." He climbed softly upstairs and peeped into the bedroom. Louie's bed stood against the back or south wall and little Evelyn's against the front wall. A brown paper shade arranged by Louie cut off the light from the smaller girl's face. Louie in her petticoat, one sock on, one off, turned towards him guiltily.

"Why you up so late, Looloo?"

"I was reading."

"Been seein' things, Looloo?"

"What do you mean?" She looked suspicious.

"So you ain't been seein' things?" He began to chuckle.

[21]

She was silent, pondering.

"My mind says to me, it says, little glumpy Looloo been seein' things and Looloo's been unhappy too."

She hung her head.

"What you see in the darkness of night, Looloo?"

"Nothing!"

"That ain't much for tuh see. Air you tellin' your poor Sam de troof?"

"I never lie," she said angrily.

"No josts [ghosts], no sperrits, no invisible hands, no nuffin?"

"No," but she began to smile shamefacedly.

"All right, Looloo: bed! Early start tomorrow." He grinned at her, white-toothed, red-lipped, blue eyes bright.

"The paint came, Dad. Are you going to paint?" she asked excitedly.

"Sure thing. Fust thing you know! And Looloo—the big news, the big news has come! Shh! I'm going!"

"When?" She started towards him. He was very happy.

"You're going to be months and months without your poor little Sam."

"Who'll look after us?"

"Your mother and Auntie Bonnie: same as now. And you yourself, Loolook! You'll be in high school after the holidays!"

She reluctantly gave her book into his firm persuasive fingers. It was *The Legend of Roncesvalles*. He poked through it for a while and then handed it back, saying,

"Yes, you'll learn from that, Loolook, that where there are kings there will be wars; don't let it give you the idea, Loo, that there's romance in those old savages: but you know better than that. I know my girl."

So saying, he moved out and dropped downstairs, congratulating himself, "She said nothing about the little scene! Good girl! Nothing morbid there! Well, least said, soonest mended!"

He sat down to the covered tray that Henny had left for him as usual, and began to drink his milk and eat thinly cut sandwiches. He sat in the chair Louie had just vacated.

"To a certain extent," he continued ruminating, "to a child of mine, these negative early experiences are aids in the formation of character, will prove of great value in penetrating human nature and human motives later on: perhaps she will go far, like myself, on the path of human understanding. Self-control; and a penetration of the springs of human action. It's a pity she's not a good-looker," he finished hastily. He forgot Louie, and went on about Madeleine.

Madeleine was his secretary, Madeleine Vines, and he had only got her by a little gentle pressure, a little friendly smile in the right place, for she was the Helen of the Department of Commerce, and her admirers weekly predicted a siege by the Treasury, or State, War, and Navy, to get her. They made a splendid pair, handsome man and lovely woman; but months had gone by before Sam had suddenly seen the light pouring forth from her. On that day, a Tuesday morning in late winter, she had said these simple words, "Mr. Pollit, I just love to hear you talk!"

"That did it," said Sam rapturously now, "yes, that did it. But what a slowpoke that same Samuel Pollit is!"

Suddenly there was a tapping at the back window and Sam started out of his delicious reverie. The shower had come; and it was very late.

Sam let the shower pass, but it came again. He, waking through the night, saw through the panes the tussle of cloud streak and sky spark, leaf blot and lamp flake, and smelled the damp cedar. Some marauder fluttered the nestlings. Sam looked out his window with "Hist, Hist!" and reduced the twig world to silence. Then, shutting the windows in his study, in the girls' room and the twins' room next to his and in the attic room, sometime towards morning, he woke some of his children and through their half-dreams they heard him say, Fine day, tomorrow, kids! I told it to stop raining by sunup! and tomorrow Sunday-Funday.

Louie, who had spent several hours already in an incommunicable world, woke to hear riding again the night rider in the street outside. For years now at night she had heard him riding his horse up and down, sometimes galloping faintly down the street but generally exercising around their very house, and for hours, as long as she could stay awake, Ker-porrop! Ker-porrop! Ker-porrop! he went. She had looked out before she went to bed, for the horseman, many nights, as tonight, and had not seen him. He only began to ride late after other folk were abed, Ker-porrop! Ker-porrop! on a thin-limbed, bay filly, as she imagined. Once she had asked, "Who is the horseman?" and been laughed at, "It's only a dream!" But it was no dream for she heard it only when awake, and sometimes faint and sometimes near, he rode tonight again, in the summer swelter. She could almost see him as he passed and repassed under the lamplight and the dapple of leaves. She got up and leaned out of the southward window, her plait tumbling over the window sill; but the sound had ceased, he must have turned the corner. Yes, when she went back to bed, there he was again. She liked to wake in the night and hear the friendly rider: so perhaps, she thought, went Paul Revere, tumbling through the night, alone, a man when all others lay like logs. Louie and the rider on the red mare were wakers.

3 ♲ Sunday a Funday.

ON SUNDAY MORNING the sun bolted up brash and chipper from the salad beds of the Atlantic and with a red complexion came loping towards them over the big fishing hole of the Chesapeake. Before it was light the dooryard thrush began to drop his song, *quirt-quirt,* hesitant, fretful, inquiring, angelically solitary, from the old elm across the street. Sam whistled to him and then nestlings fluttered, a beast fell to the ground, the early birds got to work, and presently, by hearty creaking and concerted peeping, they and Sam made the sky pale and flagged the daystar. Sam was always anxious for morning. He was greedy for the daylight world, because the fevers of the dark, and the creatures real to man's sixth, inward, dark sense, which palpitates in such an agony about three o'clock in the morning, all disappeared at the dark's first fading. When the first ray came, he stood on feet of clay in a world of clay; the dread other worlds of dreams were gone beyond comparison. In these fresh summer mornings (it was fresh on the hill) when the earth perspired profusely, Sam would often get up before daybreak, patter downstairs in bare feet, just wearing bathing pants, and would go out on to the lawn, getting ready for some job, getting the animals up, or standing under the trees, whistling to the birds. But not today, because he had stayed awake most of the night.

It was six-thirty by the alarm clock. Sam began whistling softly through his teeth the tune of,

> *One evening in the month of May*
> *(Johnny get your gun, get your gun!)—*

and waited. There was a grunt next door in the twins' room. The twins were turning over, trying to dig shuteye out of their pillows, closing their ears. Upstairs, Ernie's voice joined in,

> *I met ole Satan by the way.*

There was a slippery sound like a little fish flopping on the stairs: that was four-year-old Tommy hurrying down to his mother's room. Louisa, from her bed across the sitting room, said sleepily, "Shh! Shh! It's early!"

Sam waited a moment, thinking, Will I whistle up the Gemini or my Darkeyes? Of all these little affections, he was most sure of Evelyn, his pet, a queer little dove, who in her eight years had never been naughty and who bubbled with laughter when he grinned at her, hung her head, cried, when he scowled. He called her his little woman, *Little-Womey*. He began,

"Little-Womey, Little-Womey, git-up, git-up!"

"Sh, sh!" said Louie in whose room Evie slept. No answer.

"Is you awake, Little-Womey, or is you in the arms of Morpheus?"

[25]

No answer: but by almost imperceptible noises Sam could tell that everyone was awake now, listening. There was an exclamation in his wife's room downstairs. Henrietta had been awake for hours, as long as Sam himself, knitting, reading, waiting for her morning tea.

"Womey, Womey, c'mon, c'mon, giddap for your pore little Sam."

Evelyn giggled. He heard it all right and insisted, "C'mon, Womey: come on: do my head, come, scratch my head. Come, do m'head: do m'yed, do m'yed. Come on, Penthestes; co-ome on, Penthestes."

His voice had fallen to the lowest seductive note of yearning. Evie chuckled with doubt, pleasure. She had many petnames, any, in fact, that occurred to Sam, such as Penthestes (a chicka-dee) or Troglodytes (the house wren), names of engaging little dusky birds or animals. Saul, the more self-possessed of the twins, shouted to Evelyn, while the other, Little-Sam, who was his father's copy, shouted out that he was awake. Their mother, in her bed, grumbled again. Sam was enjoying himself and now began to whine,

"Womey won't come en scratch m'yed: Womey is mean to her pore little dad."

Evie jumped out of the covers and ran across Sam's sitting room. At his bedroom door she giggled, eyes flying, fat brown star-fish hands together on the dark mouth.

"I heard you the first time, Taddy."

"C'mon," he begged, full of love for her. She jumped onto his bed and crouched on his pillow behind his head: there she began to massage his head and twist his thick silky hair. He closed his eyes in ease and asked in an undertone,

"Is Looloo up yet?"

"No, Taddy."

Sam whistled an ascending chromatic scale which was Louisa's whistle, and the same scale descending, which was Ernest's whistle. Evie, imitating her mother, protested,

"She is asleep, Taddy: let her sleep. She needs it." Sam took no notice but went on in an insinuating, teasing voice,

"Loobyloo! Loo-oobyloo! Loozy! Tea!"

Although Louisa did not answer she was at that moment crawling soundlessly out of bed. She heard him urging Evie, "Go on, Womey, call her Loozy."

"No, Taddy, she doesn't like it."

"Go on, when I tahzoo [tells you]."

"No, Taddy, she can hear."

"Loo-hoozy! Loozy! Tea-heehee!"

Out of the tail of her eye Evelyn saw Louisa flash across the landing to the stairs. "She went," she chanted soothingly, "she went."

"This Sunday-Funday has come a long way," said Sam softly: "it's been coming to us, all day yesterday, all night from the mid-Pacific, from Peking, the Himalayas, from the fishing grounds of the old Leni Lenapes and the deeps of the drowned Susquehanna, over the pond pine ragged in the peat and the lily swamps of Anacostia, by scaffolded marbles and time-bloodied weather-board, northeast, northwest, Washington Circle, Truxton Circle, Sheridan Circle to Rock Creek and the blunt shoulders of our Georgetown. And what does he find there this morning as every morning, in the midst of the slope, but Tohoga House, the little shanty of Gulliver Sam's Lilliputian Pollitry—Gulliver Sam, Mrs. Gulliver Henny, Lugubrious Louisa, whose head is bloody but unbowed, Ernest the calculator, Little-Womey—" Evie laughed. "—Saul and Sam the boy-twins and Thomas-snowshoe-eye, all sun-tropes that he come galloping to see."

"He doesn't come to see us," deprecated Evie.

"No, he could live without us," Sam agreed. He opened his eyes, "Whar my red book?" His bedside table was littered with pamphlets from the Carnegie Peace Foundation, scientific journals, and folders from humanitarian leagues. On top lay three magazines. Sam picked out one which was folded back and laid his forefinger on the pretty, sober woman pictured above the title.

"Bin readin' fine stor-wy, Little Womey," he said, " 'bout a fine woman en a fine little girl. Good sweet story—makes your pore little Sam bust into tears."

"Is it sad, Taddy?"

"It is sad and glad. It is just like our poor little silly, funny human life, but it comes to a good end because they are good people underneath all their poor willfulnesses and blindnesses. They really love each other, although they *do* show a tendency to scratch out each other's eyes at moments: en then they find they don't hate each other as much as they thought. People are like that, my *Troglodytes minor*. Love people, little Darkeyes, always be in love with human beings and you will be happy. And what is more, much more, you will do good."

"Taddy," she began, hesitating, "can Isabel come in today?"

"Mebbe," said Sam. "Oh, mwsk, mwsk!" He kissed a girl figured in a corset advertisement, "I'll marry her! Hello, beautiful! Look at the girl with da spaghett'—mwsk, mwsk, mwsk! I love her. I'll marry her too. Mwsk!

> *Oh, woman in our hours of ease*
> *Uncertain, coy and hard to please:*
> *But when the time comes round for chow*
> *A ministering angel thou.*

Look at this one with the mayonnaise. Mwsk! Here's a knockout. Mwsk!"

"You missed that one, Taddy."

"Not her! She's a fright: she's a holy terror. No ma'am: I like my girls often and I likes 'em pretty. En look at this one. Holy Methusalem! He must have had his mother-in-law staying with him. This one would frighten a screech owl at midnight on Bear Mountain. The question is, how bare? Mwsk! Oh, raccoons and rattlesnakes! This one knocks my eyes out! I only got one eye. I can't stand it. I must marry her at once and get back my eye."

Evie giggled, giggled, shivering with pleasure. The twin boys and Ernest had crowded into the room, and craned and gleamed round the bed, saying, "Oo, not that one, she's ugly."

[28]

"Here's a peach," said Ernest. Ernest was nearly ten.

"This one's a peacherino, though, she's mine," Sam said. He kissed the cocktail heroine several times, "young and juicy, a ripe tomato," he continued wickedly, grinning at the boys, while Evie pored over the picture. "Mwsk! Here's a little ducky, she looks naughty but she's a good girl really."

"How do you know?" Evie stared at the girl with thin legs in silk stockings and flying crayon billows.

Sam teased, "They don't write stories about really bad girls, Little-Womey, remember that. And they never make a really bad girl pretty, even if they do write about her for the sake of the truth. That's because they really want people to be happy and good, and want us to believe that the beautiful are the good and vice versa. Because, if we believe it, it will come true——"

"Here's one you can kiss, Dad," cried Saul, excitedly.

"Aren't we going to scrape and paint this morning, Pad?" Ernest wanted to know.

"When the tea comes—big news, big news," said Sam, raising himself in bed and looking round at them. They fawned round his bed, expectant.

"You're going to get a new car?" Saul hazarded; but Ernest knew it was no such thing.

From there they could hear the kettle lid hopping madly on the stove. Sam whistled Louie's whistle and shouted,

"Loozy! Water's a-bilin!"

This was followed by another shout from below, his wife's, and a third, a soprano hail came from the attic floor, where Sam's youngest sister, Bonnie, was still abed; she sang, "Hold everything! I'm coming down."

"In the sweet by-and-by," said Sam to the children and winked. The kettle stopped bobbing. Bonnie shouted,

"Ki-hids? Louie?"

"Stay in bed, Bon," Sam replied: "Looloo's making the tea." He explained to the children, "Bonniferous might as well snooze an hour longer da fornin [this morning]: Sunday a funday for all hands."

[29]

"But Looloo is working," objected Ernest.

"Looloo is asleep too, on her feet," grinned Sam. Now there was another shout from belowstairs,

"Tea up or down?"

"Up."

In a minute they heard the jingle of tea-things and Louie's grunting. She was a heavy girl, overgrown for her years. She came in with her large fat face pink, but glum. She put the tray down on the bed beside Sam's calves and poured out all round. When she came down from the attic, where she had carried Aunt Bonnie's, Sam sang out,

"Whar's yourn, Loogoobrious?"

"In the kitchen."

"Whyn't you bring it along? Ernest-Paine-Pippy! Go and get Louie's tea for her."

"I've got to make the porridge," she cried; and so got away. She tripped on the oilcloth at the head of the stairs.

"Johnny-head-in-air!" called Sam, "c'mere a minute: be here with your father when he tahzem [tells them] the great news! Kids, your Sam's going to Malaya with the Smithsonian Expedition, like I always told you I would."

"When?" asked Louie morosely.

"Don't know yet," he said: "will you be glad, Looloo, to see your poor little Sam go away to furrin parts?"

"No."

"Will you miss your poor little dad?"

"Yes," she lowered her eyes in confusion.

"Bring up your tea, Looloo-girl: I'm sick, hot head, nedache [headache], dot pagans in my stumjack [got pains in my stomach]: want my little fambly around me this morning. We'll have a corroboree afterwards when I get better. Mother will make the porridge." He was begging her, yearning after her.

"Mother told me to make it," she said obstinately.

He gave a sudden impatient glance,

"Go ahead then! I've never met anyone so cussed in all my born days!"

[30]

Lowering, she turned and trudged out. Halfway downstairs a smile flashed into her face—she was free! Upstairs her father was singing and chattering with her brothers and sister; her mother and aunt were in bed reading; the morning was beginning in slow time, and her book for which she had an unconquerable passion, the same *Legend of Roncesvalles* which she was now reading for the third time, was open on the washtub beside the stove. She could read it as she sifted in the oatmeal. It was a glorious hot morning; the birds were now in the full middle of their music. The shadows were diluted light; the air was hot and moist; sweet air from flowers and humus and pines drifted in. The old wood of the house smelled precious, and even the smell of oatmeal slowly coming to the boil was wholesome.

When the porridge was made, Louie took her book in to the showerhouse built at the end of the veranda, and propped it on a crossbeam while she took her cold shower. She stood under the water, stirring gently, and her wet fingers pulped the pages as she turned. Outside the house already resounded to their shouts.

Bonnie, with her silver-gilt hair in a pageboy bob, skipped round the kitchen getting breakfast and singing *"Deh, vieni, non tardar."* Sam and the boys were in the washhouse, mixing the paint, and Evie was laying the table in the long dining room. A burst of song came from out of doors, the father and his fledglings starting up with "Mid pleasures and palaces"; and when they came to the chorus, Evie could be heard fluting away, "Home, home, sweet, sweet home!" The birds, cheered by all this, began to sing madly like a thousand little harmless brass devils under the leaves; hearing which, Louie at once put on the record that always made the birds begin to cheep, "Papageno, Papagena!" Henrietta sang out,

"He can't open an eye without having the whole tribe jigging and buzzing round him."

Coming from the shower, Louie saw through the door Tommy sitting in his mother's armchair, playing with her solitaire cards. A musky smell always came from Henrietta's room, a combination of dust, powder, scent, body odors that stirred the children's blood, deep, deep. It had as much attraction for them as Sam's jolly singing, and when they were allowed to, they gathered in Henrietta's room, making hay, dashing to the kitchen to get things for her, asking her if she wanted her knitting, her book, tumbling out into the hall and back, until it was as if she had twenty children, their different voices steaming, bubbling, and popping, like an irrepressible but inoffensive crater. Henrietta would not have them on the bed with her, though. She sat there by herself, in the center, propped on two or three pillows, in an old dressing gown, with her glasses on and her gray-speckled black hair drawn tightly back in a braid. Beside her would be some darning, or a library book sprawling halfway down the bed where she had thrown it in disgust, with a "Such rot!"

But she sometimes let them snuggle into the shawls, old gowns, dirty clothes ready for the wash, and blankets thrown over her great easy chair, hold their small parliament on the flowered green carpet, or look at all the things in her dressing table, and in what they called her *treasure drawers*. All Henny's drawers were treasure drawers. In them were spilled and tossed all sorts of laces, ribbons, gloves, flowers, jabots, belts, and collars, hairpins, powders, buttons, imitation jewels, shoelaces, and—wonder of wonders!—little pots of rouge, bits of mascara, anathema to Sam, but to them a joyous mystery. Often, as a treat, the children were allowed to *look in the drawers* and then would plunge their hands into this mess of textures and surfaces, with sparkling eyes and rapt faces, feeling, guessing, until their fingers struck something they did not recognize, when their faces would grow serious, surprised, and they would start pulling, until a whole bundle of oddments lay on the floor and their mother would cry,

"Oh, you pest!"

There were excitement, fun, joy, and even enchantment with both mother and father, and it was just a question of whether one wanted to sing, gallop about, and put on a performance ("showing off like all Pollitry," said Henny), or look for mysteries ("Henny's room is a chaos," said Sam). A child could question both father and mother and get answers: but Sam's answers were always to the point, full of facts; while the more one heard of Henny's answer, the more intriguing it was, the less was understood. Beyond Sam stood the physical world, and beyond Henny —what? A great mystery. There was even a difference in the rooms. Everyone knew everything that was in Sam's rooms, even where the life-insurance policy and the bankbook were, but no one (and least of all Sam, that know-all and see-all) knew for certain what was in even one of Henrietta's closets and tables. Their mother had locked cabinets with medicines and poisons, locked drawers with letters and ancient coins from Calabria and the south of France, a jewel case, and so on. The children could only fossick in them at intervals, and Sam was not even allowed into the room. Thus Henny had at times, even to Louie, the air of a refuge of delight, a cave of Aladdin, while Sam was more like a museum. Henrietta screamed and Samuel scolded: Henny daily revealed the hypocrisy of Sam, and Sam found it his painful duty to say that Henny was a born liar. Each of them struggled to keep the children, not to deliver them into the hands of the enemy: but the children were not taking it in at all. Their real feelings were made up of the sensations received in the respective singsongs and treasure hunts.

Louisa was Henny's stepchild, as everyone knew, and no one, least of all Louie, expected Henny to love this girl as she loved her own. But though Henny's charms had perceptibly diminished, Henny's treasures, physical and mental, the sensual, familiar house life she led, her kindness in sickness, her queer tags of folklore, boarding-school graces, and femininity had gained on Louie. Uncritical and without knowledge of other women, or of mother's love, she was able to like Henny's airs, the messes of her linen and clothes closets, her castoff hats and shoes, the strange beautiful things she got secondhand from rich cousins, her gifts, charities, and the fine lies to ladies come to afternoon tea. As for affection, Louie did not miss what she had never known. Henny, delicate and anemic, really disliked the powerful, clumsy, healthy child, and avoided contact with her as much as she could. It happened that this solitude was exactly what Louie most craved.

[33]

Like all children she expected intrusion and impertinence: she very early became grateful to her stepmother for the occasions when Henny most markedly neglected her, refused to instruct her, refused to interpret her to visitors.

Henny, in the clouded perspectives of Louie's childish memory, had once been a beautiful, dark, thin young lady in a ruffled silk dressing gown, mother of a very large red infant in a ruffled bassinet, receiving in state a company of very beautiful young ladies, all in their best dresses. After this particular day, Louie's memory was blacked out, and only awoke some years later to another Henny. The dark lady of the ruffles had disappeared and in her place was a grubby, angry Henny, who, after screeching, and crying at them all, would fall in a faint on the floor. At first, Sam would run to get cushions; later, when they reached the epoch where Sam habitually said, "Don't take any notice, Looloo, she is foxing!" Louie still ran for the cushions, and would puff and struggle over the deathlike face, drawn and yellow under its full black hair; and would run to the kitchen to ask Hazel, the thin, bitter maid, for Henny's tea. When quite small, she had been trusted to go to the forbidden medicine chest, to get out Henny's medicine—phenacetin, aspirin, or the tabu pyramidon—or her smelling salts; and even once had brought the bottle of spirits hidden behind all those bottles at the back, which all the children knew was there, and which none of them would ever have revealed to their father. None of them thought there was cheating in this: their father was the tables of the law, but their mother was natural law; Sam was household czar by divine right, but Henny was the czar's everlasting adversary, household anarchist by divine right.

But here came Louie observing them both fitfully and with difficulty, since her last birthday. There did not seem to be any secrets in her parents' life. Henny was very free of comments on her husband, and Sam, in season, took each of his children aside, but most particularly the eldest, and told, in simple language, the true story of his disillusionment. In this light, Louie and clever Ernie, who observed and held his tongue, saw, in a strange

Punch-and-Judy show, unrecognizable Sams and Hennys moving in a closet of time, with a little flapping curtain, up and down.

"The night of our marriage I knew I was doomed to unhappiness!"

"I never wanted to marry him: he went down on his knees!"

"She lied to me within three days of marriage!"

"The first week I wanted to go back home!"

"Oh, Louie, the hell, where there should have been heaven!"

"But he stuck me with his brats, to make sure I didn't get away from him."

The children tried to make head or tail of these fatal significant sentences, formed in the crucible of the dead past, and now come down on their heads, heavy, cold, dull. Why were these texts hurled at them from their parents' Olympus: Louie tried to piece the thing together; Ernie concluded that adults were irrational.

On her eleventh birthday in February, Henny had given Louisa the old silver mesh bag that her stepdaughter had desired for years. Love and gratitude welled up in Louie; the more so that Sam made an especially poor showing on the same occasion, giving an exercise book that Louie needed for school. Since then Louie had passed on to an entirely original train of thought which was, in part, that Henny was perhaps not completely guilty towards Sam, that perhaps there was something to say on Henny's side. Was she always a liar when she spoke of her pains and miseries, always trying to make a scene when she denounced Sam's frippery flirtations and domestic crimes? Henny was gradually becoming not a half-mad tyrant, whose fits and maladies must be cared for by a stern, muscular nurse; not all a hysteric, the worthless, degenerate society girl whom Sam had hoped to reform despite vitiated blood and bad habits of cardplaying, alcohol, and tobacco; but she was becoming a creature of flesh and blood, nearer to Louisa because, like the little girl, she was guilty, rebellious, and got chastised. Louie had actually once or twice had moments when she could listen to Henny's scoldings and (although she trembled and cried bitterly) could recognize that they came from some illness, her neuralgias, or cold hands and feet, or the accumulation of bills, or from Sam's noisy joys with the children, and perennial humanitarian orations.

Although Louisa was on the way to twelve and almost a woman, Sam had not suspected this veering. He went on confiding in her and laying the head of his trouble on her small breasts. But Henny, creature of wonderful instinct and old campaigner, had divined almost instantly. No, it was deeper. Henny was one of those women who secretly sympathize with all women against all men; life was a rotten deal, with men holding all the aces. The stepmother did nothing extraordinary to bring out Louisa's sympathy, because she had left too much behind her and gone too far along her road to care about the notions of even the flesh of her own flesh, but this irresistible call of sex seemed now to hang in the air of the house. It was like an invisible animal, which could be nosed, though, lying in wait in one of the corners of this house that was steeped in hidden as well as spoken drama. Sam adored Darwin but was no good at invisible animals. Against him, the intuitions of stepmother and stepdaughter came together and procreated, began to put on carnality, feel blood and form bone, and a heart and brain were coming to the offspring. This creature that was forming against the gay-hearted, generous, eloquent, goodfellow was bristly, foul, a hyena, hate of woman the house-jailed and child-chained against the keycarrier, childnamer, and riothaver. Sometimes now an involuntary sly smile would appear on Henny's face when she heard *that dull brute, Sam's pigheaded child,* oppose to his quicksilver her immovable obstinacy, a mulishness beyond rhyme and reason. Sam had his remedies, but Henny smiled in pity at his remedies. He would take Louie out, often in view of the street, in order to give his "lesson a social point" and say, in that splendid head tone of his,

"You see, I am not angry: I am not punishing you out of pique. I am just. You know why I am punishing you. Why is it?"

"For no reason."

He would give her a gentle flip, "Don't be obstinate! You know why!"

He would keep it up, till she began to bawl, yielded, "Yes, I know."

Then he would make her hold out her hands, and would beat her, "You will understand why I have to do this when you get a little older."

"I will never understand."

"You will understand and thank me!"—and in what a contented tone!

"I will never understand and never forgive you!"

"Looloo-girl!" this, yearning.

"I will never forgive you!"

He laughed. Henny, half indignant, half interested, behind the curtain, would think, "Wait, wait, wait: only wait, you devil!" Henny had begun to beat Louisa less; and Louie had not been wrong in seeing a distorted sympathy for her in Henny's pretense of strangling her the night before.

CHAPTER TWO

1 ❦ In the morning by the bright light.

LOUIE, PASSING her mother's door on the way to the stairs, thought nothing at all of the night scene, but went in and dawdled awkwardly at the bedside.

"Mother, do you think my neck's getting too long?" Henny peered at her as if she had not seen her for months.

"Of course not."

"Mother, my dress is so old: in that dress my neck looks so long now."

"I have no money for new dresses. Perhaps next month."

"Sing it, Moth, sing it," whined Tommy. Henrietta looked at him, pulled her glasses down on her nose, and sang,

> *Like his father, like his father,*
> *He has the cut of a kangaroo,*
> *Bandy-legged and ginger too;*
> *And his nose is very pecu-li-ar—*
> *He winds it round the back of his neck*
> *Just like his pa!*

"Sing it again, Moth!"

"Oh, go to Tokyo!"

Tommy was immensely flattered. Louie earnestly continued,

"Mother, when Miss Bundy makes my dresses next time could she make something distinguished?"

"Distinguished! Distinguished!" cried Henny, looking at her angrily.

"Sing, 'When Uncle John,' " urged Tommy.

"It has to be distinguished now, with the ten cents he gives me," cried Henny in indignation.

"Moth! Moth-er! Go on."

"Be quiet! Distinguished—some more of your Pollit swank and snobbery!"

Louie began to weep quietly and edged out.

"Mo-oth!"

"Oh, you pest!"

"Mo-o-th!"

> When Uncle John came home from sea
> He brought a parrot home to me,
> And it could laugh and it could sing
> And it could say like anything,
> "Pretty Polly, Pretty Polly, Polly-wolly-doodle,"
>   all the day.

"Mother, I love that!"

"Well, I don't. Go and annoy your father now."

"Can I have a piece of sugar, Mother?"

"Go and bring in Mother's toast, baby."

"Then can I have a piece of your sugar?"

"My name's Jimmy: take all you gimme."

"Can I, Mother?"

"You can, my son."

"But Mother, may I?"

"Mother, may I go out to swim? Yes, my darling daughter."

"Mother!"

"Ask Louie: she'll give you a piece."

"No, she wo-on't, no she won't, Mother."

"Ask her."

"No, she won-on't, Mother."

"Tell her I said so."

"All right."

Tommy rushed out of the room, where he had been getting quite bored, with his usual small trophy. Tommy had brought one piece of wisdom from the womb, *Ask and ye shall receive.* His wide, crooked, irresistible grin and nodding curls did nothing to undeceive him.

But now Aunt Bonnie was heard crying,

"Hot pog, there! Hot pog, there! Make way," and Evie and Tommy, having raced to the gong, began to wrestle about who should *bong* it. Bonnie seized the stick and authoritatively sent the separate soft notes floating all round the neighborhood. There was a rush of overalled males from the washhouse, and Sam began whistling. Each one had a special whistle: there was also a signal for sitting-down and one for come-in-a-hurry.

They were standing in the hall, answering their whistles, the rule being that no one was to enter the dining room till the signal was given. Sam asked Ernest, *sotto voce,*

"Did you tell them?"

Ernest gave him a glance, rushed to the kitchen, shouting, "Dad's going to Malaya," then to the bottom of the stairs where he shouted, "Louisa, Dad's going to Malaya!"

Louie, who was standing at the top of the stairs ready to answer her whistle, started to come down, stumbled on the oilcloth, and sat down three steps below. She had hurt herself, but at the present time she was practicing to be a Spartan and so said nothing.

"Johnny-head-in-air!" said Ernie.

Louie came downstairs with dignity. The twins, who had answered their whistles from the animal cages, burst into the hall, and jostled each other at the bottom of the stairs,

"Looloo, Looloo! Dad's going to Manila [*Malaya, you dope! Manila and Malaya!*] Louie, Dad's going with the Expedition!"

"Of course, with the Expeditionary Force," confirmed Ernest.

"I know!" said Louie, loudly. "I knew before you."

"Tell Thomas-Woodrow to tell his mother," Sam begged Ernest, in a low voice. Since Sam and his wife were not on speaking terms, even this remarkable announcement had to be made by a go-between. Ernest had dealt with many difficult situations. He now took his stand in the northern, or front, door of the hall, nearest his mother's bedroom, and shouted officially.

"Tomkins, Daddy is going to the Pacific and Malaya with the Smithsonian Expedition."

Henny, of course, understood that this was for her. They heard her say to Evie, who arrived rather anxiously at her bedside, "Tell him to go to the big bonfire for all I care."

But Sam, ever true to his intention, had cornered Tommy, so that Henny's baby boy now appeared shyly beside her also, and repeated the news.

"All right, my son," she answered dryly.

But she was nervous. She sent Evie flying to the kitchen for fresh tea and toast. Today there was a big, unexpected painting job. She hated the noise of the blowtorch, and the smell of the paint, old or new, made her sick. Usually during painting jobs she managed to pay a visit to her sister Hassie in Baltimore, or to go down to the dressmaker's and discuss the little girls' clothes, or merely to gossip. But this had been sprung on her; and then, if Sam was really going away at last, she would have to get word to him, go over money matters, and discuss the care of the children. He was a fanatic about the children's education, having ideas all his own, and everything had to be done according to his notions, to the very last detail. Her children could be vaccinated, if she chose, but Louie must not be vaccinated; he would not obey rules about dental and medical inspection, and yet he made a spectacle of himself both at the school and at the Department, if the children could not go everywhere free, because they were not earning; and all the rest of it. She wished he would not always try to show himself superior to everyone.

Then, there was the care of the large, old-fashioned house, the neglected grounds; and not only Sam's small zoo, but his other possessions and constructions, a pond, a rockery, aquaria, his museum, and so on. What a world of things he had to have to keep himself amused! And as to clothing, food, provender, and household necessaries—they were as usual down to their last stitch, ounce, grain, and bar of soap. Sam would take a blue fit when he saw the length of the bills, and at that they were bills doctored by Henny or by a conniving petty tradesman for the sake of her father's estate. He would take a blue fit, probably try to divorce her, or separate, she thought, if he ever got to know the truth.

She bit her lip, got up, put on her red dressing gown and the drugstore slippers given to her by Tommy on her last birthday, and looked impatiently for her fountain pen. It was a beautiful and expensive one given to her by her father, but it was always hidden somewhere.

"I believe he takes it and hides it himself!" she declared irrationally. At last, she called Evie from the table and sent her to fetch school pen and ink; and she sat down to write a note to her husband on a sheet of white paper embossed with her initials HCP—Henrietta Collyer Pollit. The few lines finished, she called Louie, who was carrying in the oatmeal, and said to her,

"Put that on your father's desk where he can see it."

"Pog!" Sam shouted his cant word for food. Bonnie began to bring in the remaining plates of porridge.

"Tomkins was changing the stones on the path so they could see a new view," burst out Saul; and all the children shrieked with laughter while Tommy got very red.

Sam was served first, then a plate put in Louie's empty place, then in Ernest's, and so on in order of age. The ritual was that Saul and Little-Sam were to have their plates placed on the table at the same instant.

"Orb-epp," Sam said in a tone of reproof to Louie. This was one of his words for "serviette." She brought it to him. As soon as the plates were empty, all but Little-Sam's, Ernest nudged his father, who said,

"Go ahead, Looloo!"

Louisa then stood up in her place and repeated, stonily,

"The world stands aside to let the man pass who knows whither he is going.—David Starr Jordan."

"It's a little one," observed Ernest. Sam nodded quietly at Louisa, which meant she was to go on. She continued,

> *"Perhaps there is no more important component of char-*
> *acter than steadfast resolution. The boy who is going to*
> *make a great man or is going to count in any way in*
> *after life——"*

"Or the woman," Sam commented.
"That is not in it," she countered, and finished,

> *"—must make up his mind not merely to overcome a*
> *thousand obstacles, but to win in spite of a thousand*
> *repulses or defeats.—Theodore Roosevelt, The Strenu-*
> *ous Life."*

Little-Sam was still struggling stolidly through his porridge which he found revolting. He flushed, now that the recitation was at an end. He was in line of Sam's eye (as who was not?). Sam did not fail him,

"Eat up, Little Samphire!"

The six-year-old plucked up courage to ask if he could leave the rest. He had the nerve for this at least once a week, always with the same result. Sam said solemnly,

"Waste not; want not."

Little-Sam gloomily fell to, picking up a lump of cold glue on the tip of his spoon. Sam, to cover his condition, continued cheerfully.

"Teddy was a great and good man, a good citizen, good President, naturalist, and father. He had some little wrong ideas, but he was a great American. And I can't say no handsomer than that, me lads!"

Ernest, with a malicious expression, but a modest tone, inquired, "How many sayings has Looloo learned this year?"

Sam fell in with his mood at once, "Oodles: but does she really underconstumble one of them? No: Looloo is obstinate. Loogoobrious does not appreciate her pore little dad."

[43]

Louisa went scarlet and flashed at him,

"I know more by heart than you."

Sam, with a glance of complicity round the table, giggled in an underhand style. Ernest promptly answered his own question,

"Looloo learned one hundred and sixty-five, only thirty in January because she didn't on New Year's and twenty-nine in February because it's leap year and this is June fourteenth, that is, sum total of one hundred and sixty-five sayings for 1936."

Sam smiled dazzlingly at Ernest, who continued with a comical grin, "How many balusters in the balustrade?"

They tried to guess, but of course Ernest knew.

"Feel better; hooray!" exclaimed Sam now. "Afore I had the collywobbles and pains in the lumbar region—by which I don't refer to Oregon none, lads. Here we are all reunited. You should have seen all Pollitry in the old days united round Grandpa Charlie's table, improvising their parts, singing the 'Anvil Chorus.' Now, I wish you kids would do that: your father's musical enough! Bonniferous!" he shouted, "come on in out of the kitchen and we'll have a singsong before the job."

Bonnie came running in, her eyes shining. She sat down and bubbled over before she had even sat down, "Oh, I had the funniest dream: I dreamed I was a lumberjack, and we were hauling in the savannas: I had seven elephants—or was it nine?" She paused anxiously and looked round the table. "No, nine, because the ninth fell in the mud—a sort of morass—and we were hauling and pulling away for dear life to get it out. Can you imagine anything more ridiculous, me seated on an elephant's neck? Isn't it silly, what you dream?"

"I dreamed I was in a forest of snakes," said Sam: "bad sign! Snakes mean enemies. Whenever I dream snakes, I meet one or more enemies. It's a sign. Now last night I was walking through a mangrove swamp and from every tree hung snakes, hissing at me and swaying into my path. Got to look out. Woke this morning with a hot head and the collywobbles. But never mind. Here we all are united. Looloo," he said heartily, "go and tell Pet to

[44]

come and sit down. I want the family united today. I want you round today, for I am going away," he sang.

"Across Manila Bay," chanted Little-Sam, relieved at having swallowed all the oatmeal. They all laughed in triumph at this rhyme.

Louisa could be heard in Henny's room delivering the message. They heard Henny, sharp as a rifle, "He has enough of an audience; I've eaten."

Louie came back looking foolish. "Henny!" shouted Sam indignantly.

They did not take much notice of this, but Bonnie pleaded, "If she doesn't feel well, Samuel."

"Henny!" shouted Sam.

"Tell your father to go and chase himself," shouted Henny from the kitchen.

"Samphire," said Sam, containing himself, "go and tell Mother, I order her to come and sit with us at this Sunday breakfast. I will not tolerate this everlasting schism," he finished with a shout of rage.

"Oh, I'm too tired to fight him," Henny said in the kitchen. She dawdled in, her color high and her eyes black, and sat down stiff as a poker in her armchair, which was always left vacant for her. She tossed her head in her old-fashioned style, giving him her famous *black look*.

"Let us be together, Henny," said Sam along the table, in a gentle voice. She gave him a glance more furious than before.

"Tell your father," she said to Evie, seated beside her, "that it's enough to be ordered like a dog: I don't want to listen to his mawkery." Evie turned her head toward her father and silently pleaded with him to consider this message transmitted. Sam had his eyes on his plate, trying to restrain himself, and getting redder every minute.

Ernest said at once, "Daddy, Mother says not to speak to her."

No one laughed. Bonnie said brightly, "Come on, kids, finish up your toast and your orange juice and scram! Lot to be done!"

[45]

The children obediently fell to. After a few minutes Henny got up to get herself some more tea. Sam could not prevent himself from admonishing her gently, "Henrietta, you really oughtn't to tan the inside of your stomach this way: it must be like leather."

She tossed her head and disappeared through the door. There was a brief silence of thanksgiving. Then Sam said very gently, "Singsong, boys and girls," and he gave the first notes, in which they immediately joined,

"Steal away, steal away, steal away to Jesus!"

2 ⚡ Monoman and the misfits.

AT THIS MOMENT, a quavering little voice called from the street, "Samm-ee!"

The twins and Tommy scrambled from their places and rushed to the back veranda, where they were at once followed by their father.

From where they stood, they peered at Thirty-fourth Street going downhill, barely visible through the screen of trees and bushes. Diagonally across from the bottom fence were the houses of Reservoir Road, where some of their friends and neighbors lived. These were as wonderful a collection of people as were ever got together in one manhive. Sam, that quick and malicious observer, had got them by heart, and all without contact greater than "Good morning!" and "Good evening!" on the way to the Wisconsin Avenue car. "Many a good laugh the caravanserai had over their foibles and follies," said Bonnie. They were all eccentric, touched, ill-intentioned, ignorant, superstitious, avaricious, or full members of nitwitry. Their children, however, as Sam's children found, were commonplace and amiable little beings, and Sam himself did all he could to attract the very small boys and

[46]

the girls of all ages to Tohoga House. Sam did not care for the girls of school age as much as for the baby girls.

He could often be seen spying out of the attic windows, up and down the streets, for some toddler from the neighbors' houses, who might be making for the Garden of Eden, Tohoga House, or peering up at its clifflike walls and the immense trees, full of birds and birds' nests, and at the man-high hedges and who might grin in a watery way or even wave its sea-anemone hand when it saw Sam's sunflower-colored head away up there amongst the birds and leaves. He beamed, he bloated with joy, to see how they feared and loved his great house. He had lately thought of calling it Tohoga Place, instead of Tohoga House. Through the eccentric neighbors (with smaller houses) and their worshiping children Sam loved his house more. For Sam was one of those careful, fearful men who well remember worse days, and are determined never to return to them. Once he had paid rent for the small sunless back room in his brother's jerry-built sham-Tudor ribbon dwelling in Dundalk, near the shipyards where his brother was then a painter; and even that was a step up from his father's house. Tohoga House, which this very day he purposed to call Tohoga Place, with a few scrawls of paint, and for which he paid only fifty dollars monthly, with taxes, to his father-in-law, was still all joy to Samuel, so much joy, in fact, that he could forget the black days of his marriage, Henny's early threats of infanticide, suicide, arson. For Sam was naturally lighthearted, pleasant, all generous effusion and responsive emotion. He was incapable of nursing an injustice which would cost him good living to repay, an evil thought which it would undo him to give back, or even sorrow in his bosom; and tragedy itself could not worm its way by any means into his heart. Such a thing would have made him ill or mad, and he was all for health, sanity, success, and human love.

Little-Sam was carrying on a conversation with the infant, Roger White, about the Pollits' soapbox truck, which Sam had made and had baptized *Leucosoma*. Sam called to the baby boy in his honeyed, teasing voice,

"Whitey! Whitey! C'mon in. C'mon in and yuh kin use me truck." Whitey giggled. "Hit's my kyar," wheedled Sam, "you got tuh aks me. Ain't dat de troof, boys?"

The comedy went on, rather feebly supported by the Pollit children. The truck transaction was a serious one, involving the White goat which ate the mayflower when imported into Tohoga's gardens, and their father was making a fool of himself; but they were high-minded about it, they let him amuse himself. Presently Whitey was induced to come up the steps to have some orange juice. They all sat on the homemade bench along the wall.

"Now I've got five sons," said Sam; "all I need is five more." His sons grinned with embarrassment.

"Oo, Taddy," murmured Evie, anxiously, "you'd have too many: there wouldn't be enough to eat."

"For ten sons, I'd make enough to eat. We'd grow it ourselves. We'd farm out all our land, one strip per lad, we'd grow all our own bread, veg, and everything. I'd get some more womenfolk and we'd make our own bread and everyfink. What do you fink, Whitey?"

"Sure, you could grow your own cows too and get milk too," declared Whitey excitedly. Sam was flattered.

"I wish I had a hundred sons and daughters," Sam rejoined with equal excitement, "then I wouldn't have a stroke of work to do, see. All you kids could work for me. I'd have a CCC camp for the boys and an SSS, spick-and-span settlement for the girls. No work for Mother, Dad, or Bonnie. Yes, the Mormings [Mormons] had the right idea altogether: fifty women and their children and no work for the old man." He grinned wickedly at Louisa who was staring out of the kitchen window.

"My father's going to Manila and Malaya," Little-Sam told the visitor.

Some discussion ensued as to whether he was going by bus, boat, or airplane. Sam let them spar for a while and then went into detail, dreamy-eyed, warmly describing the journey over land and sea, the peoples he would *come into contact with*. He carried them along with him, while they sat with dimmed glare of eyes and lips apart, telling that this——

"—came near to the heart of my dreams and will help me to fulfill one of my most ardent wishes—as Looloo knows and Ernie too—to know my fellow man to the utmost—as you will all, someday, and little Whitey here too, perhaps—to penetrate into the hearts of dark, yellow, red, tawny, and tattooed man. For I believe that they are all the same man at heart and that a good one; and they can be brought together sooner or later by their more advanced brothers into a world fellowship, in which all differences of nationality, creed, or education will be respected and gradually smoothed out, and eventually the religion of all men will be one and the same—world peace, world love, world understanding, based on science and the fit education of even the meanest, most wretched. Not the communism of today, which is a political doctrine—not of hate, I wouldn't say that—but of war, class war, hated sound—the doctrine of misguided but certainly well-meaning men, for I have met some of them and there are fine fellows in it, though not fitted to be leaders, because not understanding human love—but a doctrine of confusion, let us say, and confusion is not based on science. We are all, so important to ourselves, only members of a species. The species must be our concern. But we are not animals: species must not fight species for mutual extermination. We are men; we must get together for the good of the genus, indeed of the natural order, so to speak." He smiled a broad, public-meeting smile.

The children, after staring, as if at the movies, at his verbal pictures of all those colored men, had passed into a trance, but were now getting restless; and Sam stopped when he saw this.

Louisa was propping herself up against the railing. She was staring at her father absently. The morning was hot, and Sam had nothing on beneath his painting overalls. When he waved his golden-white muscular hairless arms, large damp tufts of yellow-red hair appeared. He kept on talking. The pores on his well-stretched skin were very large, his leathery skin was quite unlike the dull silk of the children's cheeks. He was not ashamed of his effluvia, thought it a gift that he sweated so freely; it was "natural." The scent that women used, he often remarked, was to cover lack of washing!

"My system," Sam continued, "which I invented myself, might be called *Monoman* or *Manunity!*"

Evie laughed timidly, not knowing whether it was right or not. Louisa said, "You mean Monomania."

Evie giggled and then lost all her color, became a stainless olive, appalled at her mistake.

Sam said coolly, "You look like a gutter rat, Looloo, with that expression. Monoman would only be the condition of the world after we had weeded out the misfits and degenerates." There was a threat in the way he said it. "This would be done by means of the lethal chamber and people might even ask for the painless death, or *euthanasia,* of their own accord."

Louisa couldn't help laughing at the idea, and declared, "They wouldn't."

"People would be taught, and would be anxious to produce the new man and with him the new state of man's social perfection."

"Oh, murder me, please, I'm no good," squeaked Ernie suddenly. Of course, he had instant success, and Sam chuckled. But nothing more happened nor was any more heard at the moment of Sam's ideal state, Manunity, or Monoman.

They heard a weird, distorted wheezing, "Phoe-bee! Phoe-bee!" and looked round startled; for it was not the Phoebe, but rather like the clanking ghost of a Phoebe, or even a very old man of a Phoebe in his last sneeze at life. But then they saw their friend, the catbird, Mr. Dumetella, back on the little naked twig of elm, where he swung all the summer: he was merely practicing the flycatcher's call for his own repertory. After a few such wheezes, the bird ceased mocking and began to trill.

"How he sings, how he loves to be heard!" cried Sam with rapture and began to whistle to the bird. It stopped and listened attentively. For months they had been teaching him songs to put into his medley. Sam and the boys were all excellent whistlers.

"And now," called Sam, "jobs, boys, jobs. Whitey can work up the putty." He lobbed off the veranda, leading them, and they all joined in his song, "I Know a Bank."

3 ⚜ What should be man's morning work?

THE WHOLE community worked. Louie was making the beds; Evie was doing the slops; Mother had decided to make some raspberry tarts, and Aunt Bonnie peeled the potatoes. It was a sizzling, pungent Sunday morning full of oven odors. Bonnie kept bursting into song, and upstairs Louie too could be heard crooning, "Bid me to live and I will live, thy protestant to be." A great chorus came from the washhouse. Henny was absorbed in her own ideas and hardly heard the jubilaum; besides which, she was so used to what she called the "Pollit buzzing" that she could bear it when the day was fine. She only opened her ears when Louie's song ceased. That usually meant that Louie was no longer working but was beginning to loiter or to read. In fact, Louie was staring out of the back attic window, southerly, where she could catch a glimpse of the stones of the capital widely tumbled through the river reek: and she was thinking—repeating rather, something from Thoreau, "Morning work! What should be man's morning work?" But she was not thinking that. She was glowing with pleasure and imagining a harlequinade of scenes in which she, Louie, was acting, declaiming (but not, not like the Pollits, nor like comic-opera Auntie Bonnie), to a vast, shadowy audience stretching away into an opera house as large as the world, with tiers of boxes as high as the Cathedral at least. She had a leading man, a shade of giant proportions, something like Mephisto, but he did not count, she only counted: she projected the shadow of her soul over this dream population, who applauded from time to time with a noise like leaves bowling over the path—as they were doing at this moment in the cement paths of Tohoga House

[51]

and on the asphalt pavements outside, which she could see at intervals, through the moving shawls of leaves.

Now, at the same time that her stepmother downstairs, conscious of the silence above, was thinking, "I must remember to write Samuel a note to speak to his daughter about her dirt and laziness (only she is so darned callous, she doesn't listen even to him—)," Louie muttered aloud to herself over the window sill, "If I did not know I was a genius, I would die: why live?"

Evie appeared in the doorway of the boys' attic. "What did you say, Louie?"

"Nothing; have you finished the slops?"

"Will you carry Auntie Bonnie's pail down?"

"All right," said Louie angrily.

Evie went back into the room, drooping, offended. "Mother said you were always to carry it."

Louie turned on her and bellowed, "I know what Mother said."

Evie shrank back, startled, her eyes wide open, the pupils enlarged with fear. She had seen an awful sight, Louie in one of her passions. In such a moment, nothing would hold her back, she knew nothing but herself, no one, and the worst thing, more terrifying, was the way she villainously held back the animal in her, while it waited to pounce. Once she had flown to Evie, started to drag her by the hair: once she had burst a boil on Ernie's temple. She went pale, her rather pale eyes on the contrary becoming dark, and her hair seeming to stiffen.

Louie, for her part, felt her heart sink. She had never seen such a look of terror on her sister's face: she felt she was a human beast of some sort. She resolved never to let Evie see her anger again. Evie might sink into a fit. One processional sunset, coming home from Baltimore, they had had to get out of the car, carrying Evie stiff and white, to a house on the roadside; and Louie might have made this happen again. She was incapable of caressing her sister, but she said gently,

"Never mind, never mind! I will."

Of course, the morning, every morning, was full of such incidents. That was family life. They were all able to get through the

[52]

day without receiving any particular wounds; every such thing left its tiny scar, but their infant skins healed with wonderful quickness.

A roaring broke out downstairs, the sound of the blowtorch with which their father was beginning on the porch handrail. The two girls hung out the window and observed a respectful group of little boys, the Pollit boys and Whitey, and Whitey's brother, Borden (who had been sent to bring him home).

Saul looked up at an airplane, saw his sisters, and yelled, "Daddy's using the blowtorch, come and see!"

Little-Sam yelled out above the blowing, "Is that Loolook? Soon time for alevena, Loolook!" *Alevena* was the eleven o'clock meal, with tea, sandwiches, and fruit, which all the children shared. They had either bananas cut up on bread or sirup-and-butter on bread. Louie hurried down to get it ready. Meantime a wonderful smell of roasting meat and cooking pastry streamed out of the kitchen, and there was in it the smell of slightly roasted linen. Bonnie was ironing blouses for her sister-in-law and herself for the afternoon. Just as Louie had got to the last three steps and had stopped to stare out at the wan, withered, and flourishing world, seen through the blue, yellow, and green panes of the pointed hall window, and at the fire-bellied newts in the aquarium, Henny's raucous shout came from the kitchen,

"Bonnie, look at you're doing!"

"Oh, heaven's sake!"

There was a rush of feet. Louie moved along too. When she got to the door, her mother turned to her at once and said, with concentrated exasperation,

"Look at your darnfool aunt's done! Look at it, my best blouse! I suppose I'm supposed to go out of this house naked; you'd think they'd put their heads together!" and she flung out of the kitchen into her bedroom. Sam was staring in the window, in consternation, his cheeks flecked with old paint, his mouth open. Bonnie, with her hair damp and tumbled, was holding helplessly in her hands, so that they could see, a blouse so badly burned that the burned piece flapped in and out like a shutter. It was a fine embroidered lawn blouse, which Henny had got from her cousin Laurie, the rich one in Roland Park.

"I just looked round for a second," Bonnie explained, frightened, looking first at her brother, then at Louie. "I looked out of the window because Pet told me she couldn't endure the smell of the blowtorch and I thought I'd say alevena—and then I seemed to smell something—I couldn't tell what, it seemed familiar. You know when there's a combination of smells, you find it hard to distinguish? When I looked back, there it was smoking up from the board. Such bad luck! I knew it. I knocked over that vase Mrs. Rowings gave me this morning. I'd better break a cup right away. And Pet's best blouse! Oh, I could cry." She was crying. "Poor Pet: you can't blame her," she pleaded with her brother. A row of little heads, like coconuts, was laid on the sill. Whitey's brother, Borden, had even come into the kitchen to stare. She was the guilty one, the cynosure of all eyes. Henny was exclaiming in her bedroom,

"Oh, God! What a pack! I'll shoot myself rather than live in the house with such fools! I must be mad!" Ernest, who had been staring solemnly, unexpectedly burst into a howl, a very comical howl, with his long black eyes shut and his mouth wide open and square: "Uh-huh, uh-huh," he sobbed.

Sam muttered, "You women are always doing such darned-fool things!" He drew his gang away from the window.

"A kitchen is a laboratory: what would anybody think of a laboratory assistant that did things like that? Women need more scientific training!" He suddenly looked away, hearing something, and lunged forward, giving Little-Sam a clip on the ear. The boy had been circling round the blowtorch, fascinated, and had picked it up, merely out of curiosity about its weight. Sam caught the torch out of his son's hands,

"You disobedient lout!" he shouted, in fear and distress. Little-Sam burst out into a faint yelping. The White boys ranged themselves side by side, entranced by the strange spectacle. Henny had not done exclaiming and now sallied into the kitchen where Bonnie was still fumbling and trying to explain everything,

"It was only a second—I don't understand myself!" Bonnie only received five dollars a month pocket money from her brother who was always in straits and she didn't see how she could get Henny such another blouse. Henny looked tragic in her long smudged dressing gown, with her hair hanging thin out of untidy braids, and she cried,

"Get upstairs and out of my sight, go on, I'm sick of putting up with you and your nonsense."

Bonnie, the survivor of many similar scenes, pleaded in a cowardly way, "Pet, I'll get you another (I don't know how) but you may be sure——"

"Don't call me Pet. I don't want you here. I only put up with you and your eternal gossiping and buzzing because you're too much of a fool to keep a job and your brother wants to keep you off the streets."

Bonnie flashed, "I work for it: I earn my keep and my—five dollars."

"Your five dollars, your five dollars, take your five dollars and ram it down your throat," cried Henny: "do I get even five dollars the months we're behind? Doesn't he punish me, the way he punishes the children and all of us? Why are you throwing it up at me? I'd give you more."

"I could bite my tongue out," said Bonnie.

"Do you think I get five dollars for slaving my head off for him and his breed, and never getting a decent bite, nor a rag to my back? Do you think I'd care about the silly, stupid thing if I had another rotten rag in my wardrobe to get on my back? You could have it and all the rest of your rot," she finished impatiently. "Get out of my sight: Louie will help me with the dinner, and then I'm going out, and let them lock me up for a lunatic if I ever set foot again in such a madhouse."

"What's the matter, Pet?" asked Bonnie, looking queer. "You're not yourself Pet: I know this is your offday."

"Go upstairs and pack," screamed Henny: "I don't want you and your filth round the house where my children can see it. Get upstairs and get out or I'll scream it out to the neighbors."

Bonnie crimsoned and huffily went into the hall while Sam, with a peculiar inquisitive and guilty air, was standing in the southern door of the hall. When Henny sped out of the kitchen, she saw him and gave him a black look. He said diffidently,

"Pet, don't make such a noise about it: you'll get another blouse: from your cousin Laurie, no doubt," he finished with a faint sneer. Henny went into action at once, glad of the provocation.

"I won't have your guttersnipe of a sister here, running after every cheap common man she meets in the gutter, staying out on the tiles till all hours, with her commercial travelers, going to their rooms and smoking. I smelled smoke in her room this morning."

Bonnie, pale with injured pride, was going upstairs without a word. Henny followed her intolerantly to the bottom of the stairs, conscious of Sam's standing there. Bonnie turned on the fifth or sixth step,

"Henny, how can you? I've always been your friend, you know that."

"Go up, go up at once, or I'll let them know what you put in the washhouse," said Henny with a spot of color under her rouge. She flung open the hall door, "I'll let that man Bannister, across the street, that you think's so fine, that you're always showing your legs to, know what I have to put up with."

Bonnie, pale, looked over the balustrade at her brother, who however said nothing, only looked foolish and helpless there in his overalls, half naked, with spots on his face. She started up the stairs again. Henny rapaciously cried out,

"You used your slip to wipe up a spilled pot; and not satisfied with that, you've brought home bedbugs from some dirty low dive you've been in, like a sloppy servant girl, and the mice go there to eat up all the greasy crumbs you've got in little bags in your dressing table. You were born in the slums and bring the slums with you into my house, you and your rotten, slave-driving brother. And the whole place looks like a slaughterhouse."

Bonnie began to bawl and they heard her tripping up the next pair of stairs. Behind her back Henny still cried out vile things, while Samuel with that intimidated but sordid expression moved away with his little tribe towards the back porch. He called out suddenly,

"Loozy! Alevena!"

He put out the blowtorch and gathered the children round him in the long dining room and looked out through the open northern window for a minute without speaking. They saw his wet eyelashes. Then he put one arm round Evie and one round the silent, mystified Tommy, drew them to him, and said,

"Let's be quiet together, kids. I wanted us to be so happy to-day, happy and rejoicing because your poor little Sam loves you and is doing what is best for everyone."

Looking at them all tenderly, he cut up the fruit himself and poured out the tea. On Sunday they were all allowed to have tea all day to be with him.

"Thick for the lads, thin for the girls," said Sam, suiting the action to the words as he handed out the slices of bread.

"Now masticate, denticate, chump, chew, and swallow." Then he fell silent again, and nothing was heard for a space but the mild breeze blowing through the hall and making the gong vibrate softly, *ton, ton!*

Gently Sam leaned over his baby, "Tomkins, here!" Tommy reached his fat face to his father. To the boy's pouted lips he joined his own, siphoning the chewed sandwich into Tommy's mouth.

"Not only for the ptyalin," Sam communicated to them, "which is now already mixed with the food and helps Tommy to digest, but also for the communization of germs. Tommy will not, I think, suffer from the dyspepsia that all you other kids do. All you other kids are like your poor little Sam—your heads go whizz, and your digestion doesn't agree! Good digestion is for the bovine. But Tomkins, though not strictly bovine, will probably be a prize fighter, and so I'm helping him along. I used to do this to Looloo when she was a little girl and lost her mother." He stopped for a moment sadly, as always when harking back to

[57]

Rachel and his short marriage with her. "I had to be mother and father too, to little Looloo. This is what parent birds sometimes do to their nestlings. We were very close then," he continued, looking Louie over intently, "and communicated by thought alone: she could hardly speak, but we each knew what the other was thinking, because she was the child of a great love!"

He passed a thin sandwich to Evie. He nodded all round the table at the exercising jaws, "Looloo still loves her father too, although she pretends to be so unfeeling and so cussed." He looked at her again and began to laugh. Very annoyed, with a stern face, Louie pretended not to hear. "Come here, my Looloo!" She got up and came to his side, rather shyly. "Right here!" Surprised, she came closer. Mottled with contained laughter, he stretched his mouth to hers, trying to force the banana into her mouth with his tongue, but she broke away, scattering the food on the floor and down the front of her much spotted smock, while everyone clamored and laughed. Sam himself let out a bellow of laughter, but managed to say,

"Get a floor cloth, Looloo-girl: you ought to do what I say!"

With a confused expression, the girl trudged to the kitchen and came back to clean the floor. When she got up she was scarlet with the exertion. She cleaned the cloth and then let herself out dreamily into the yard. Clouds were passing over, swiftly staining the garden, the stains soaking in and leaving only bright light again. Louie forgot the incident completely as a dream.

This messiness was only like all Louie's contacts with physical objects. She dropped, smashed, or bent them; she spilled food, cut her fingers instead of vegetables and the tablecloth instead of meat. She was always shamefaced and clumsy in the face of that nature which Sam admired so much, an outcast of nature. She slopped liquids all over the place, stumbled and fell when carrying buckets, could never stand straight to fold the sheets and tablecloths from the wash without giggling or dropping them in the dirt, fell over invisible creases in rugs, was unable to do her hair neatly, and was always leopard-spotted yellow and blue with old and new bruises. She shut drawers on her fingers and doors

[58]

on her hands, bumped her nose on the wall, and many a time felt like banging her head against the wall in order to reach oblivion and get out of all this strange place in time where she was a square peg in a round hole.

There was a picture of a sweet, gay, shy little girl with curls all over her head, in an old frame in her father's room. She could hardly believe that she, the legend of the family, whom everyone had a right to correct, had been that little girl. She wondered vaguely, from time to time, if she would have been any different if her mother had lived. But she did not believe it, and the picture of a yearning, tragic, sickly young woman that Sam drew did not catch her fancy. She was not like that: she felt a growling, sullen power in herself which was merely darkness to the splendid sunrise that she felt certain would flash in her in a few years. She acknowledged her unwieldiness and unhandiness in this little world, but she had an utter contempt for everyone associated with her, father, stepmother, even brothers and sister, an innocent contempt which she had never thought out, but which those round her easily recognized. It enraged Henny beyond expression: "the Pollit snobbishness!" she would say ten times a day. But it fell on deaf ears. Louie knew she was the ugly duckling. But when a swan she would never come sailing back into their village pond; she would be somewhere away, unheard of, on the lily-rimmed oceans of the world. This was her secret. But she had many other intimations of destiny, like the night rider that no one heard but herself. With her secrets, she was able to go out from nearly every one of the thousand domestic clashes of the year and, as if going through a door into another world, forget about them entirely. They were the doings of beings of a weaker sort.

Henny was annoyed to see the tribe bow before herself in the role of virago; she had not been brought up to think that she would succeed because of a mean disposition. She had been nurtured in the idea that she was to be a great lady, like the old-time beauties of the South. So now she hurried to dress herself and get out of a house where all her hopes had been ruined and

[59]

where she was forced by circumstances to slur and smut herself to herself. She was restless, full of spite, contempt, and unhappiness—what a spineless crowd, a Baltimore slum breed, the spawn of a man who had begun by taking the kicks and orders of some restaurant keeper or fish handler at the age of twelve and so had never learned independence! The worst was that they looked upon her as an heiress, and she hadn't a nickel in her purse and was forced to go into debt to keep the breed alive. She had no car she could use and was forced on a Sunday (Funday!) to rattle downtown in a streetcar, hungry and without a clean blouse. She supposed she could have forced some money out of him, but she hadn't the patience or the interest to carry on her victory. She was sunk for life. Old David Collyer would never take her back, and what other man seriously wanted a woman with five children even if the Collyer estate was free of debt? She did not care two ticks whether she won victories over such cowards or not: they had won the final victory over her.

She took a bit of cold meat, a hard-boiled egg, some currants, and an onion and made herself a one-man curry, which she ate hastily with some tea made for her by Louie. Then she swished upstairs to the attic, to find Bonnie. Bonnie was reading some old love letters and had only packed two vests in her trunk.

Henny said, with her head high, "I take back all I said: I let my temper run away with me. You can stay if you like, though I'm darned if I would! I'm going to town and I'll be late home."

"I know you didn't mean it, Pet."

"Oh, I'm a brute; but the way they drive me mad and I feel as weak as a cat through getting nothing to eat!"

"Let me make you a little bite, Pet!" Bonnie cried eagerly, rising and putting the letters back in her drawer.

"I've eaten a bit of curry," Henny unbent, and seemed pathetic and graceful to butter-hearted Bonnie. "I don't know why I jump on you."

Bonnie started to say something and bit her lip. Then, "I'll get the dinner, Pet. And I'll get you another blouse somehow."

[60]

Henny turned about and gave a hard laugh, "Don't be a fool! Where will you get the money to pay for one? Did I pay for it? I'm a mendicant from my rich relatives! Like an old washer-woman I get their out-of-date clothes, sweaty under the arms. Cheap servants like you and me can't buy decent clothes, or pay back debts. I'll wear any old thing. Who would look at an old hag like me?"

"Whatever you wear, you look so much the lady, Henny!"

She said roughly, "I look like what I am, a poor old wreck: if I'd done ten years of streetwalking I wouldn't look so weather-beaten! Well, will you look after feeding the kids and so on? I'd like to be out all day if I could."

Henny hurried downstairs again, but out of the flush of recon-ciliation, she thought, I have to smoodge her: I can't employ a girl here who would live in. I never could keep a servant. No one but a Pollit would stand me; not even an Uncle Tom. She laughed to herself and went in to finish her dressing.

Cheered by the news that Henny was going out before lunch, they all went back to work with vim.

"Little, Mother said to clean her shoes," dictated Evie to Little-Sam who was mooning on the path, on his haunches and drawing invisibly with one finger.

"Little is commooning with his thoughts and with Nature," said Sam-major in a low voice. "Leave him to it."

"Then Ernie must do them," said Evie strictly.

"You shut up!" snapped Ernest.

"What's Mothering want clean shoes for?" inquired Sam under his breath.

"She's going to meet Aunt Hassie."

"Why doesn't Hassie bring her car up and take Mother down?" continued Sam, painting with his practiced stroke.

"I don't know," Evie admitted sadly. When Hassie came she always brought something for Evie; but she did not come often.

"Why does everything have to be done in a hole-and-corner way?" said Sam without anger. "Pet simply loves deceit. It took me a long time to realize that that was part of the way she was brought up and I was rather harsh at first, I admit. I don't want deceitful ways round the home, kids! Now I know Henny doesn't look at it that way: that is the curse of the bringing-up of women to useless arts. They used to be brought up to catch men. Yes, that was the ultimate goal—to get a rich husband. Strange, in our republic! But it was so. Now, you know I'm always frank and honest myself. But women have been brought up much like slaves, that is, to lie. I don't want to teach you to criticize your mother."

Meanwhile, Evie and Ernest were whispering energetically and scowling at each other in reciprocating moods of admonition and Evie began to cry. As if a button had been pressed, Bonnie's pale head floated in the dark hall doorway and she recited,

"Dogs delight to bark and bite for 'tis their nature so!" while Louie looked out of the dining-room window where she was reading the *Legend,* and shouted,

"Stop it!"

Ernest grinned. "Who's cleaning my shoes?" called Henny.

Ernest made sham moves, while Evie, sniffling, began to trudge round to the kitchen steps.

"You do 'em," shouted Ernest after her, "I did them yesterday."

"Boy dear!" called Henny.

"Go on," said Sam, giving him a push.

"Yes, Mother!" shouted Ernest.

"Little Ernie boy," called Henny, "do Mother's shoes?"

"There's a darling, there's a good boy," crowed Bonnie: "there's a mother's boy; kiss its Bonnie. Who's a good boy? Don't use that rag, darlin'. Come, honey, give its Bonnie a big kiss."

Ernest nonchalantly brushed a kiss on her cheek, in between two rubs.

"There's a dear little man: someone's going to be a big hit with the girls, I know."

Ernest polished the shoes in an efficient style and rushed in with them, after putting away the polish and rags.

"Ten cents," he said: "that's what the shoeshine boys want, Mothering. That's all I charge."

"You go to Tokyo," said Henny: "you'll have to lend me your money box to go downtown."

"How much?" inquired he excitedly. "How much? Will you give me the usual commission, Mothering?"

"You bet your sweet life," said Henny. "Have you got a dollar, boy dear?"

"Five cents," bargained Ernest.

"Maybe ten cents, if Hassie gives me any money. And don't tell your father."

"Do you think Old David will give me five dollars for my birthday like last time?"

"Shh!" said Henny, shocked.

"Preparedness!" Ernie grinned at her. Ernie and Henny lived in an intimacy of their own, largely built up of calculations, loans, and commissions. Ernie understood her need of money; she understood why Ernie should make a profit out of her need. Twinkling at his mother, as he handed her the dollar in small change, and nodding his head carefully as he counted the residue back into the slot, Ernie concluded,

"Well, got to write it down," and he dashed upstairs to the attic to make the addition to his accounts notebook. He was a charming child, everyone's darling, he made no enemies, and he managed to remain above the domestic battle through concentration on his money matters. They ranted, but he had already defined all his relations to the world—Sam gave him a nickel every Saturday, Henny was good for at least twenty-five cents a month commissions: Louie, who loved him and knew his passion, gave him money on his birthday instead of a present, and so on. His passion interested all his relatives, and they liked to give him money to add fuel to the flames! Odd human race, thought Ernie. But he himself was no miser. At Christmas and for the various birthdays, he disbursed handsomely and strictly in order and percentage of age. He had a calculator in the back of his notebook, which now stood as follows:

[63]

New Year's Day, 1936.

Sam (father)	38, birthday on February 11—25 cents
Mother	(I don't know) August 15— 25 cents
Louisa	11, birthday on Feb. 16— 15 cents
Myself	10, birthday on Nov. 16—no present
Evie	8, birthday on Jan. 10— 10 cents
Saul and Sam	(twins) birthday on Jan. 1—10 c. (5 ea.)
Tommy	4, birthday on Nov. 15— 5 cents

Birthday presents (1936)

———

90 cents

At Christmas Ernest divided his bank money by half and divided the half pro rata amongst his family. He always begged a gift for his rich grandfather from Henny, for Henny and he understood their duty.

Sam, issue of a poor family, ignored all such duties, and had chimeric views about money, the bright, the beautiful, the leveler, the just: he called it "the root of all evil." Henny raged and Ernie smiled at this. Henny was thinking already, "That boy will get me out of a mess later on: if only Father stays alive until he grows up! I wish one of my brothers had had the *nous!*" And even Samuel would wink and grin to the others,

"Nary a word! A chip off the old Collyer block!" but at other times he would see a great chemist or physicist in Ernie.

Ernie heard things humming out at the back and, as soon as business was done, rushed out.

"Lumpkin!" shouted Bonnie. "Sweet lumpkin?"

"As she walks, she wobbles," cried Sam provokingly from the porch, craning his head to discover Ernie; "as she walks she wobbles, boys!"

"Smithy is here!" Little-Sam told Ernie. Dribble Smith's ten-year-old son had, in fact, escaped during roasting hour and climbed the side steps to view wonderful Pollitry in action. When Gregg Smith laughed, he also dribbled, or blew bubbles, the habit which

[64]

had won little tenor Smith ignoble fame amongst many bureaucrats.

"As she walks, she wobbles," chanted Sam, painting.

"Shh! That's Mrs. Bannister," said Saul from his perch on the
handrail. "She'll hear you, Pad."

Bonnie rushed to the window of the kitchen, "So it is! Old
Mother Slipperslopper."

"You hate her, don't you, Bonniferous?" teased Sam looking up.

"Sam, don't be ridiculous," said Bonnie, getting pink.

"Samsam, how will we paint the roof of the porch?" inquired
Saul thoughtfully.

"Simplicissimus! Ex-cruciatingly simplicissimus," exclaimed
Sam. "Put the board across on our two ladders. As she walks, she
wobbles, boys," he continued, taking a dip of paint.

"As she walks, she wobbles," said Tommy.

"Old Mother Bannister, sat on her canister," said his father.
Louie's face loomed in the open dining-room window, "Daddy,
don't be so rude!"

The children were giggling, repeating Sam's crack, *sotto voce,*
"Old Mother Bannister."

"You stop it; don't be so rude," cried Louie indignantly. Sam
chuckled, "Toppid, Toppid, I god a gold id by dose!"

Old Mother White, oh, what a sight
In the middle of the night!

"Don't make them do it, Daddy!" Louie shrieked, this time
from the hall doorway, where she stood book in hand.

"Don't get her mad," said Saul wickedly from above.

"Get her mad," winked Sam at Little-Sam; all the little faces
turned toward Louie.

Sam obliged, "Old Mother Jewell is a durn foo-ell!"

The children shrieked in triumph. "Looloo's as mad as a hor-
net," confided Ernest.

"Make her mad, go on!"

Sam painted away merrily, "As she walks, she wobbles, all her skirts are hobbles, she tripped up on the cobbles, and oh, what a shine!" Ernest guffawed.

"You're disgusting," said Louie, lowering.

"Go on," urged Little-Sam, "Daddy, go on!" The children and Smithy stood round with shining eyes. "Dirty Old Kydd has such greasy lapels! pooh," said Ernest.

Sam sang, "Old Man Goat and Angela Kydd stewed old cats, that's what they did: then they came to their last resource, they made potroast of a rocking horse."

Even Louie melted at this, though the Kydds, who lived in a tiny wooden house at the back, were her friends. The Kydds made toys for a living and led a cat-and-dog life. Louie laughed.

"Now she's not mad, oo-hoo," cried Little-Sam dancing; "Now she laughed. You laughed, Louie, you laughed." Louie began to giggle and bob about helplessly like a jelly.

"Say some more to make her laugh," Ernie jogged his father's elbow and whispered. Sam picked out the Boltons who lived in the expensive little brick bungalow across the road. They had one daughter, Charlotte, the seventeen-year-old brunette beauty whom Sam admired.

"Old Mother Bolton, couldn't get a holt on, old Dad Bolton, so he gave her a jolt on—the beezer."

The children writhed with joy. Ernie pulled his father's overalls, "Mareta, Mareta!" Mareta was the little Jewell girl.

"Nothing could be sweeter than Mareta when you beat her in the mo-orning!" sang Sam.

"Why do you beat her; is she an egg?" inquired Little-Sam wickedly, looking at his eldest brother.

"She's a good egg, mwsk!" said Sam throwing a kiss. "Oh, sweet Mareta, I'd like to meet her and then I'd heat her a cup of tea!"

"Ernest-Paine loves Mareta," Saul confided.

Ernie blushed but was flattered.

"John Coverdale Jewell is drunk as a roo-ell," sang Sam.

"Shut up, you fool," suddenly shouted Little-Sam to his father, with dancing eyes and an impudent lip.

"Oh, Daddy, he called you a fool!" Evie was very shocked.

"I'm tired of you," shouted Little-Sam, in a frenzy, "you make me sick!"

Sam giggled and winked at the children around him. "Say nothing," he murmured, "say nothing."

"You're an old gasbag," cried Little-Sam, a dervish.

Sam began to chant softly, a song about Little-Sam's school-teacher, "Ole Miss Jones, rattles her bones, over the stones: she's only a porpoise that nobody owns."

Little-Sam paused, eying his father.

"She has two glass eyes," contributed Ernie. "Two glass eyes and two real eyes."

"Saul is her pet," Evie said nastily.

"When Old Bebbo comes round, she certainly is scared stiff," said Ernie. "I saw her through the partition."

"Ooh, her hair, I hate it," cried Evie.

"When Old Bebbo comes in, she rushes round like a bat in hell," Ernie persevered.

"Hades," emended Sam.

"Hades."

"When Old Bebbo comes round, she falls on the ground in a fit," the father affirmed.

"But she loves Mr. McHenry," Evie chattered. "When she can she runs and talks to him and laughs and talks: she's in love with him."

"She wants to marry him," said the father coyly.

"But she can't," declared Ernie stoutly, "because she's an old maid. Oh, I hate her. She's so fat. And she's got two glass eyes."

Sam sang,

> *Two glass eyes, two glass eyes,*
> *See how they run, see how they run,*
> *Two glass eyes and a wooden leg,*
> *She's too ugly to teach and she ought to beg,*
> *And she cut off her nose with a carving knife*
> *Through two glass eyes.*

They all watched Saul softly. Saul unconcernedly began to whistle to himself, but Little-Sam scowled.

"What's her name?" whispered his father.

"Lil, Lillian," they cried at once: "Old Lil."

"She's a Red," said Ernie: "she's always talking about the union."

Sam neatly finished his section of the wall, singing,

> *Jack and Bill*
> *Wouldn't look at Lil;*
> *It went to her head*
> *And she saw red!*

Saul began to climb down off the porch roof.

"Whar you a-goin', Saul?" inquired his father, much surprised. Saul said nothing, but continued down to the ground. He put his paintbrush in the turpentine and went round to the front lawn, where he stood silently for some time waiting till the song, sung for the second time, was finished, and poking his fingers through the privet hedge, looking for any insect that might turn up. Sam watched him carefully for a while, making signs to the others. Nothing happened. Then the father nodded to himself, nodded to the others, winked and said merrily, "Not bad, not bad! Self-control!' He nodded again; and sent Little-Sam up on to the porch roof to finish Saul's job.

"Taddy, can Isabel come in?" put in Evie.

"Isabel, wasabel-hasabel-possible," Sam answered.

"Taddy!"

Sam flung his brushes in the pot, "Tired-oo. Hot head. Spell till munchtime," said he. "Knock-off time, Littla-Sam!"

"Taddy, can Isabel go round the Wishing-Tree?"

"Powwow!" said Sam wearily. He squatted in the sun, drawing the children round him. "Got to tah youse kids 'bout my Wonderful Idea. It's about Pangea, the Earth United, or what happened in the year 3000. I was in the orfus doing nothing and it all came to me clear as could be: I really saw it, kids. Little-Sam,

[68]

go and get the papers off my desk! That is what Louie and me and you others would make—if Looloo would ever be a dood dirl, with our heads, our hearts, and our hands:

"Heart and hands together, lads! Go on, Little-Sam! Ah, love could you and I with Fate conspire. . . . But the beauty of it is, kids and Looloo," he continued wildly, "is that we can, we can do so: you and I and little Tomtom can build this Pangea of mine, this Eugea, we can make it come true! Perhaps even little Tomtom will see the time when the last wars are done and we see the Federal States of Europe, and man no longer hidden under a cloud of misunderstanding, hate-engendered, from his brother man."

Little-Sam came back, "I can't find it, Pad."

"The message to Garcia," said Sam, "the message to Garcia! Where there's a will there's a way. Run along, Little-Sam. You'll find it."

"I don't know which it is," cried Little-Sam desperately: "there are millions of papers. Gee!"

"I dunno vitch I vant, a vatch or a veskit," Sam ignored him, doing one of his favorite imitations, a vaudeville Jew. Little-Sam faded into the house, grumbling.

"I give you tree per cent," continued Sam. "Vot you vant vid a veskit? Vid a veskit I kip my visky [whiskers] from flyin' away in de vind!" The children screamed with laughter.

"Mr. Goldberg," said Sam, *sotto voce,* "Mr. Goldberg!"

"Do a Frenchman, Taddy," urged Evie.

"Oo, la-la! Vair is my corsets?" He pretended to tilt his hat over one eye (apparently wearing a stovepipe hat while looking for his corsets). "Vot ave you for little-breakfast zis mornin: I can only eat frogs!" The children capered.

Little-Sam came back rebellious: "I can't find it!"

"Good-by, children!" called Henny from the hall. There was a rush for the house. Sam lay back and closed his eyes. At that moment, a little voice no bigger than two twigs creaking together on a tree, said from the side steps, "Mr. Pollit! Mr. Pollit!"

He opened his eyes on the hazy blue world, said gently, "Yiss?"

Mareta Jewell, a little dark girl, came precipitately up the steps, and approached him with the little dancing hesitations of the shy, "Can I go round the Wishing-Tree?"

"Yes, love," he smiled.

"Will I get my wish, Mr. Pollit?"

"Maybe, if you wish hard, and are a good girl and it's a good wish, you will get it, I expect."

She gurgled joyously and ran round the little spruce.

CHAPTER THREE

1 ❧ Beautiful and childlike was he.

IN THE AFTER-DINNER heat, when the dishes were dried and put away and the greasy sink was shining, Louie slipped down the orchard in her bare brown feet and, opening the unhinged back gate a trifle, looked out into the peaceful street. Just opposite were the little wooden houses of the only two neighbors who were Louie's friends—the Kydds and the Walkers. The Walkers were a middle-aged couple with a twelve-year-old boy called Mark Antony. Junius Walker, the dark, nervous father, worked in the Bureau of Engraving, and tried to teach his slow lad Latin at night. He inveigled Louisa into his parlor, from time to time, to read a Latin grammar with his boy. When the time came, blond, fat Mark Antony would go to a private school in England to learn to be a gentleman.

In between the Walkers' small lot and Middenways', the corner grocers, on a lot of the same size, was a similar wooden house, neglected and vine-grown, in which lived an old couple, John and Angela Kydd. John Kydd made toys and, to show it, had two rocking-horse heads on his gate. He left promptly at seven-thirty every morning and returned rotating on his fat legs at six every evening. In between these hours the lonely and scared old woman would often call in Louisa, who was such a big, brave girl, to keep her company. Louisa did not care for either place; they offered her nothing to eat and they reeked of eccentricity; but Junius Walker took pains to explain to her things that no one else had mentioned, ceramics, glazes, firing, and offered to teach her china painting, and as for the Kydds, no one in the neighborhood but herself had ever been invited into the frowsy, furniture-choked dwelling. Sam, always lampooning, found the Kydds and the Walkers inexhaustible sources of inspiration: every day he found new jokes about the two eccentrics. Though Louie knew them much better than he did, she saw them with his eyes, as ridiculous if not positively touched, filthy and mean-spirited to be so poor, vain to have airs and graces when so poor, superstitious to hold any religious beliefs, thickheaded to hold any political beliefs, hoity-toity to hold any esthetic beliefs, fustian to pretend to any education, when so poor. But Louie never said what was in her head and she had a kind heart; so she came down, with bare legs, and in her faded, dirty, outgrown dress, in torn underwear from her fine house on the hill, and listened for hours to the notions that these strange poor folk had about themselves. She felt at home with them. She was eccentric, ugly, and awkward, and they were quite evidently, in their lives, eccentric, ugly, and awkward. Sam had a voice, she had an ear, and these struggling, poor people, gasping just at the surface of the river, about to sink, had lives. They told her something about their lives, which were not cataclysmic, such as Pollitry lived, but lives lived in neat corpuscles, lives which only looked out, squinted-eyed, askance, dubious, through two fishy eyes. The Walkers and Kydds repelled Louie, but she was flattered that they chose her. Ernie knew all the men and women; Evie visited all the "ladies with babies," as she said, and Tommy was dangerously favored: only the two oddities wanted Louie.

Sam and the boys were resting in the deep coarse grass at the bottom of the orchard under the trees and Louie was about to join them. It was a fatty, dreamy hour. Sam's voice began behind Louie with a low insinuating humming that enchanted the sulky ear guards and got straight to their softened brains,

"Your Poor-Sam brought you up in Washington, the new Jerusalem, as I verily believe, because he wanted you to feel the blood beating through the heart of the nation. Think of the logcutters' children in Oregon and the little redskins on Indian reservations and the little tall-eared Missourians and the little frozen two-legged ears of Minnesota Swedish wheat whose only dream in life is to come and see the Great White Father—whoever he may happen to be: while my tadpoles can see not only him but me, every day that is."

"I'd like to go on an Indian reservation," said Saul, far away.

Sam began his humming again:

> *Most beloved by Hiawatha*
> *Was the gentle Chibiabos,*
> *He, the best of all musicians,*
> *He, the sweetest of all singers.*
> *Beautiful and childlike was he,*
> *Brave as man is, soft as woman . . .*
> *When he sang, the village listened:*
> *All the warriors gathered round him:*
> *All the women came to hear him:*
> *Now he stirred their souls to passion,*
> *Now he melted them to pity.*

"The passion was the passion of nature, the passion for good, not selfish human passion," Sam commented.

Bare feet appeared now and again amongst the green blond spikelets, and now a summer-burnt head appeared in the same place. Saul said, "Where's Looloo? She went out the gate." The grass bottom bloomed with heads and eyes. "She's gone to Mrs. Kydd's." They giggled.

"I have many wonderful thoughts during those times when I am sauntering about by myself (and when perhaps to the foolish or mean eyes and heads that I seem to have round me I am just mooning about). Take the theory of the expanding universe—I want to figure it out some day. It came to me by myself. The theory of wave motion came to me merely from looking at my mother's dishcloth hanging on the back veranda, when I was a little boy no bigger than Ernest-Paine here. And very often I have an idea and then find months, years later, that a man like our very great Woodrow Wilson or Lloyd George or Einstein has

[73]

had it too. Of course, I believe in a transmission of ideas, on the same principle as radio, amongst a community of minds."

The children were silent, sunk back to the grass; but Little-Sam had sneaked off to the gate to look after Louie.

"It is a pity I had handicaps which you all know about," he said hastily, "or I should have been able to accomplish all the wonderful things in my heart." He sighed, "When you kids get bigger, and have your own life dreams, you will appreciate your Poor-Sam more."

Through all the soft wind sounds came the call of bobwhites in the White Field.

"Hear in the Buzzum of my famerly I am enjoyin' myself at peas with awl mankind an dthe wiminfolks likewise," Sam quoted dreamily.

"Little-Samuel, come'n lie down," called his father. But Little-Sam, after gaping at the Kydds' house, had slid on to the foot-path to read the newest legends scrawled on the Pollit back fence. Opinions of the Pollits as well as of neighbors were written here every day by boys. Sam, used to being obeyed, did not know that Little-Sam was away still.

"Boys," said he, "boys, you soon won't have your little feyther with you. He is going away to Greenland's icy mountings and India's coral strand. You have to look after yourselves, your mother, and your sisters. I want all of you to stand together and look after the house for me, not only the female hanni-miles mentioned and aforesaid, but also the real honest-to-goodness hanni-miles, Procyon the raccoon, Gimlet the parrot, Didelpha the vixen opossum, Cocky-Andy the sulphur-crested cockatoo, Big-Me the pygmy opossum, not to mention the birds and reptilians. That will be quite a job for even you smart boys. Now we'll have to work up a schedule. And fustest, you must write to your pore little Sam ebbly week and tell him how 'tis tuh hum; and second, you must keep a record of the birds and hanni-miles wot visit Tohoga House, Tohoga Place that is. No! Momento! Loogoo-brious can do that. It will be a good thing for her, keep her mind off of her herself, on which onpleasant objeck," he continued (believing that Louie was there), "it is glued at time of speaking. But that is, no doubt, on account of her fai-hairy figuar and her bewchus face."

He waited for the boys to laugh, but they were all in a mood of indolence. Near them was only the warning chak-chak of the cat-bird.

"Yes, siree," continued Sam, "Loochus's eggspression at this yere moment eggspresses one idear, Give us Liberty or give us Death. But that is the age, that is the season; we must forgive Loochus her trespasses, or else bring in a verdick of arson in the third degree."

Little-Sam had been timidly flirting with a stray fox-terrier bitch, with a sore paw, but after a few pats from a safe distance, the dog showed such a sudden, desperate affection for the boy, that he got frightened and, darting to the gate, shut it in the fox's nose. In a surge of emotion he dashed up to his father with,

"Looloo's gone over to see Mrs. Kydd. Mrs. Kydd called her and took her inside."

"I hope Old Goat gives her a nice sardine tin to eat," said Sam.

The front gate to the Kydds' house was locked and fixed with barbed wire. The lock and hinges had rusted. The front path, unused for years, could barely be seen through the grass and weeds. Unpruned cedars lined this path. The only entrance was by the side gate, over a cinder path, covered by a trellis broken with the weight of untidy grapevines. Caterpillars dropped from this vine on to Louie's hair, but she put her hands up and deli-cately removed them. The little old woman ran in front of her, turning every few steps to smile, nod, and beckon,

"Quick, come into my kitchen: I must show you something," and again a pretty nod of complicity. Louie hoped for something sweet, even though she had never eaten in this house before. They hurried down the side passage and onto a wooden veranda, very dark with vines. There were two rockers, with faded cushions and a rain-beaten table. Old Angela raised her finger warningly and pointed down at the broken plank just by the door. They went into the narrow hall littered with bits of furniture, indistinguishable in this sudden dark, but which Louie knew from other visits, and so into the old kitchen, where a wood-and-coal stove was set in a large fireplace. Old Angela, with her quaint bright mystery, beckoned Louie again to the fireplace and, when she got there, cautiously lifted the lid of a small black stew-pot.

"Look, look," she nodded with excitement. The little girl looked and saw nothing but a meat stew with vegetables from which steam was rising.

"And something else," cried the old woman in a fit of generosity, "look! Only wait!" She scurried to the dark larder and, after struggling for a while with something, returned with a half slice of bacon which she dangled before her. "There," she said, "you watch," and she dropped the bacon into the stew. "A better taste," nodded the old woman. "My, it will be wonderful tonight! Mr. Kydd loves stew and stew with a bit of bacon in it—mm-mm, he loves that. Mr. Kydd says to me, 'Angela, you're a good cook, and just put a bit of bacon in and you're a better cook!' " She nodded at the girl full of understanding. "Come, will we go into the front room? It's brighter, eh, more cheerful for a young lady! And you have such beautiful little feet," she continued, stopping in the hallway, "such beautiful, beautiful little brown feet, a little brown maid."

"Oh," said Louie, "I forgot—at home we go about barefoot because it is healthier——"

"Such beautiful little feet: you are quite right," said the old woman, "I am sure you are a wonderful girl at home to your mother, yes I am sure of it."

Louie would not be pushed into any admission, but followed her into the parlor. They passed one closed room which Louie had never seen, and reached the parlor where John Kydd had his organ. The sunlight poured through a triple window with dust-thick panes, and cast red, blue, and green stains on the thick dust of the floor. Three doors, beside the hall door, led out of this room, but it was impossible to reach two of them, and the third could be got at only by squirming around a large drop-leaf table extended, two chairs, and an old-fashioned glass table designed for showing a tea service under glass. Near the window was a dining table, a card table, and other odds and ends.

"We have so much furniture," said Angela, "so many things! Aren't people stupid, eh? You must think us so stupid! Now sit down and let me look at you. Your hair is so lovely, isn't it, such a nice shade, and what a trouble it must be to your dear mother to wash and fix and braid and all that!" Louie became conscious of the tatters of her hair.

"I am sure you play the organ," cried the old woman. "Do try it, do play me something? Mr. Kydd loves to play to me."

"No, no," protested Louie, "I can't."

"But you have such artistic hands," protested the old lady. She looked scarcely older, perhaps younger, than Louie as she sat there, or rather like a child face fitted into a bonnet of untidy white hair and stuck on an old wrinkled neck. Her dirty brown woolen dress had lost its belt, and its hem was undone. A black petticoat hung beneath, but revealed wrinkled stockings fallen round the ankles and turned black shoes. But the little heart-shaped face that nodded so eagerly at Louie had two large soft brown eyes, well set, and deep fringed, and a supplicating, kind smile blew in and out of the old cheeks. Since Louie had come she had altered her years, she seemed ten, fifteen years younger; and she sat now on the organ stool dangling her little legs and chattering away like a little girl, poring credulously over Louie's expressions, begging for acquiescence, for information. Louie was used to her. Her dirt and the dirt of the old man were repulsive, but the old man beat her, so the story went, and Louie felt conscience-stricken. Often, Louie had seen her racing after him down the passage, as he strutted to the gate in the morning, crying,

"John, John! Don't leave me without a cent, John! What will happen to me? John, only a nickel! It's just to have. I spend nothing. What do I spend? I need nothing. But I must have money!"

Everyone knew of her and John. They sought no friends

amongst the neighbors, despising them all. But everyone knew (for Angela had confided the truth from time to time, whispering into one ear and begging some little snatch of food from another) that this same John beat her, starved her, and insulted her and that she was abandoned by all her family, though old and frail, because John had systematically alienated them. The Walkers, on one side, Middenway, the grocer, on the other, had heard her cries and his storming late at night or in the peace of some holiday.

There was a strange vileness in them and in the house which fitted their solitary lives and their dirt perfectly. Louie had an ear that always lay in wait and after the honeyed greetings, the love, and the tender stories about John, the cruelty and coarseness of their lives would prick through oftener and oftener, until Angela would come to tell her about John's habits. What habits could anyone have in that house but the most hideous?

"I wanted to ask you something," said the old woman, "but you will perhaps be angry with me. But you are so good and big and brave and strong. It is something I can't do myself. I'm so little. Look at me! Look at my arm!" She bared a frightful faggot of sinews. "Like two threads! No, my dear, I cannot, by myself, and Mr. Kydd is so busy. But perhaps you will."

"Yes," said Louisa, "what is it?"

"You are so good, and you sit there with your lovely little bare feet—" the old woman paused, as if led astray by her own cunning irrelevance. She began again, "You know, nothing is worse than to hurt an animal, eh? Cruelty to animals is—" she shook her head. "You wouldn't be cruel to animals," she pounced on the child with her great eyes.

"No," said Louie, "but you have to trap some."

"Yes," cried the old one, "yes, harmful ones: yes, mice—even cats. Kittens are nice, so soft, they play and not even a little mew! But when they get to be big tomcats, ouf!" She shuddered. "You know last Friday I found my yard full of tin cans. Who put them there? I don't know." She peered at Louie, looking very old. Louie became confused and wondered if Angela suspected the

Pollits of filling her yard with rubbish. "Who could do it?" inquired the old woman sharply.

"Who could do such a thing?" Louie asked angrily. "That is awfully mean."

The old woman sighed, "You see, I love animals. I have no food myself, but if an animal comes crying to my door, I must give it a scrap, mustn't I? What have I—spinach water, crusts, but what I have I give! (I give, I give)" she muttered angrily at the end. "I have a lovely pussycat, dear, you have seen it."

"Yes," said Louie dubiously, for now she saw daylight. The Kydds' cat was able to attract into the Kydds' back yard all the cats of the neighborhood; the cat club was there, and there they howled from moon to sun. The tin cans of Friday were the last, not the first.

"And John said," she continued, lowering her voice respectfully, "that we mustn't annoy the neighbors. Annoy!" She laughed suddenly and clearly. "Me annoy! I am so timid—like a little mouse. How can I get rid of the cat?" she demanded of Louie.

"Give it away."

"No, no!" She looked at the child for a long time, revolving something in her mind. "If someone would kill it for me—I must! I hate to. Kill a living creature! I can't kill a fly! And I haven't the strength, not to, not to get a fresh sheet out of the drawer. I tug and tug. It stays fast. What can I do? You are good, you are so strong, young, and healthy—" she paused.

"My father would kill it for you," offered Louie. The old woman refused at once: no, no, that would never do. No one must ever know she killed her cat, only someone she could trust, trust as she trusted no one. (Louie, for instance.)

"All right," said Louie.

The old woman stared, as if in astonishment, "You will."

"Yes."

The old woman began to cuddle herself, "Such a dear sweet little girl, with her little brown feet—" She paused and said in a businesslike tone, "Tom is out on the front porch." She immediately led the way to the rarely opened front door and showed the white cat sulking under a bench. Angela had tried to catch him herself. Louie said they had to have a box, and Angela at once produced a suitable box from under the kitchen table, and brought a hammer and nails, in a marvelously efficient way.

"You will have to give me a piece of your stew meat," said Louie. The little woman fetched her a piece without a murmur, like the smallest drummerboy to the largest general. And Louie managed, in a very short time, with savant caresses taught her by her animal-catching father, to get the cat and drop it in the box. They slammed down the lid. At once, the cat seemed to know its fate. It seemed to swell to twice the size, its hair stiffened, and its magnificent blue eyes shot rays of fire: its eyeballs turned to flames, and it began screaming in a horrid voice that neither had ever heard from a cat before. Louie felt a fear of the mad beast, and a wicked lust to down it and finish it, just because with all its shrieking it was helpless.

"In here," muttered the old woman. She led the way towards the locked door of the passage, unlocked it with difficulty, and put on the light by a string. There was a rusty old bath covered with dust.

"We'll fill the bath and drop the box in," said she. "You do it, my dear. You are so very kind: you do it. I can't see it," and she hurried out, leaving the girl with the cat. Louie turned the rusted tap and let the water run: the cat cowered and gleamed in the box. When the bath was full enough Louie got the box and pushed it under. The cat struggled with large floating gestures in its prison. At the first convulsion Louie felt a sort of sickness, then she pushed it hard under and, sitting on the edge of the bath, kept it under with her feet. The box heaved a little. The cat took a long time to drown. Presently she came out to the kitchen to find the old lady sitting there at the table, silent, with her great lamps glowing in her face.

"I did it," said Louie.

The old woman thanked her but rather perfunctorily. "I would give you a cake," she said, "but I have none, none at all. I will get you a little cake."

"Thank you," said Louie hungrily.

"Not now, not now. Perhaps your dear mother wants you, dear?"

"No, she's out."

"I don't like cream cakes," said the old lady politely. They had talked some fifteen minutes about cakes before Angela heard her husband's footsteps on the cinderpath. She bundled the little girl out the front door and directed her round,

"Come again, soon, soon, darling, little darling!" she whispered.

Louie was sorry that she had only been invited over for the cat, but she believed that the little woman loved her and that there was peace in her foul cottage.

2 ☲ Intrepid passengers.

IT SEEMED AT FIRST as Louie edged in through the jammed gate that there was perfect quiet in the orchard. The sun shone, there was a flip-flop of leaves, and suddenly a silvery leap of a young boy's voice. The powwow was still going on! Little-Sam jumped up,

"There's Looloo! What did you do, Looloo?"

"Looloo went without her shoes," Ernie observed. Sam's head rose through the grass too.

"Loochus, why did you go without shoes?"

"You said it would be better if the whole population went without shoes, it would harden them."

Sam looked and suddenly popped with laughter, then cried, "You're a fathead!"

He dropped down in the grass again and waited. At last a voice came, "Go on, Pad!"

"There will be anagravitational ships, a word I made up myself," said Sam, "the ease with which gravitation could be cut off is so simple to us nowadays—of course we're in the year 3001, Loo-loo!—that it seems absurd—excruciating!—that twentieth-century brains which did show some signs of awakening out of the medieval torpor could have been so slow to grasp it—in fact, it was not even hinted at till 1994. Why? Their so-called minds were preoccupied with what might be truly described as self-destruction—pansewerpipes or universal self-destruction. And a few are still seen, in museums, the cavorite ships of Wellsian cavorite, I mean, but in the main they had long been thrown into the discard even in the year of our Ford 2050, because of the simplicity with which gravitation could be cut off and taken in, to a major or minor extent at will, by a simple turn of a few levers or the pressing of buttons—the physical and practical application I will describe to you later, kids, or perhaps Ernest-Paine or Little-Sam themselves will be the ones to really work it out in some laboratory later on—and now I'm speaking of the year of our Ford 1936," he ended solemnly.

"Oh, gee, let's go and get on the job, Pad," said Saul.

"Directional Towers were then necessary for the stages of the cavorite ships," dictated Sam. "They were stationed here and there throughout the earth on high places, all done by our friends of the American Geographical Society and introducing the true Surplane Life, or Age of Surplaners. These Surplaners utilizing the Stratosphere Stations attained terrific speed—1200 mph was attained in 2050 as even little Tomtom learned in his kindergarten physics book. Our experimenters now reach 3800 mph, and we will soon supersede the need for vessels at all—it is fairly safe to predict that in ten years, say year of our Ford 3011, there will be *projection by dematerialization;* the cartridges in which the passengers will take their places will be sundered, smashed to smithereens, and so shot through space, as gas or lighter than gas, avoiding friction."

"But the passengers?" inquired Ernest, aghast.

"Also smashed to smithereens and reassembled," Sam expounded coolly.

"How?" asked Little-Sam in trepidation. His utter faith in his father made him believe that this would really take place.

"In tubes," said Sam airily. "Each passenger will be shot into a tube and decomposed."

"No one would travel," declared Ernest.

"That's what they said when the locomotive came in," Sam was contemptuous. "We are people of 3001. Each one has a formula and is reassembled according to that minutely correct formula. We haven't the freaks and neuroses of the Dark Ages. We were born according to formula: we are not a hazardous aggregation of mean genes. We approximate a mean, the mean of our intellectual class. When we are born, we are studied, and deviations, if noxious to the species, are suppressed; good deviations are preserved. And furthermore, we bear our formula on our arm band!"

"But the arm band would be decomposed in the tube," Louisa discovered triumphantly.

Sam grinned and bit his lip. "The formula for each passenger would be radiotelegraphed ahead with the notice of his having taken a ticket," said he. "Thus," he suddenly cried, "Looloo, you meant to be mean and clever, but actually you merely gave me another idea—thus, you could resurrect the dead from the residue of fires, after accidents—resurrection would be real, not a faded dream."

"That is wonderful," said Louie, much struck.

"Slightually," Sam smirked, "slightually, your poor little Sam is wonderful, but a prophet in his own mud puddle——"

After a silence of digestion, Saul said, "Let's do our job, Pad, go on." He started dragging Sam to a sitting position.

"O.K. Looloo, I been giving the boys their places in my Planned Economy. Ernest-Paine is my lieutenant while I'm away and Louie ain't a looie, she's going to run the women for me."

"I won't do what Ernie says," yelled Saul.

"You got to do what you're own legally elected chief says," gently said Sam. "And you're free to elect your own boss, you

know, boys, as long as it's Ernie; and if there's complaints you
kin throw him out en eleck another as long as it's Ernest-Paine,
just like the Bolshies."

"I won't," said Little-Sam.

"I'll make ya," Ernest was calm.

"You shut up, you rat," Saul called lazily from the orchard
path.

Sam softly admonished, "Don't call humans rats—rats are superior."

"I'll knock you into the middle of next week if you call me a
rat," Ernest replied.

Sam chuckled and winked at Louie.

"You stink," drawled Saul, "you stink like Mr. Gardner, you
stink like Mr. Kydd on ice; you stinkurate!"

"Go on," whispered Sam, letting out a kick at Ernest who was
hopping over "the grave" (a depression in the orchard where seedling boxes had once been). "Go on, Ernest-Paine!"

"I'll murder you for that," yelled Ernie at once, "I'll push in
your daylights."

Sam flattened the grass with both hands and squatted down in
a flat place, saying gleefully, "Go on, Sawbones, give it to him; go
on, Ernest-Paine, attaboy!"

Saul could never keep his temper and had flushed. Ernest came
up to him coolly and said, "C'mon, c'mon, you coward!"

"Sawbones ain't no cowyard," said Sam gently. Saul rushed up
from his position below Ernest, as if about to take flight, and
rolled into Ernest with both fists going, landing both, though, on
his chest.

"He's fightin' mad, Ernest-Paine," cried Sam, "you've got him!
Keep your temper, Sawbones! You'll never down him, Ernest!
They've gone into a clinch! They love each other! Break! Get
him on the point, or you'll never do it. Sawbones, a foul!"

The two boys separated, Saul tottering aside in his misery. He
was crimson, and tears of rage and humiliation were running
down his cheeks. Ernest kept dancing at him, a thing that infuri-
ated him. Saul had more solid muscles but always lost his temper,

[84]

so that Ernest always beat him by first goading him into a paroxysm of resentment.

"Now," cried Sam, "Sawbones, go on, bust him wide open!" He laughed genially, more like his eldest sister Jo than himself.

"Daddy, don't let him," cried Tommy, frightened. Sam laughed, putting his great arm round Tommy,

"Men must fight, Tomahawk (but only for the right). Sawbones must learn to keep his temper. Ernest must learn to hold his own."

With a great effort, Saul had for the moment held back his temper and was going at Ernest like a windmill, his eyes wide open and glaring like jellies, his red lips pressed back over his teeth. Ernest, his conceit taken by surprise, was breathing hard, somewhat flustered.

"Go it, Sawsidge, you're getting there!" cried Saul's father. "You're getting Ernie down. He's getting woozy." He turned aside to Little-Sam and remarked very audibly,

"You see, if Sawbones keeps his temper, he's got Ernie beat a million, because Sawbones has a better fighting kit!"

Saul, with a deeper flush and half a smile, lunged at Ernest's cheek, missed, and himself received a painful blow on the upper arm which made tears of pain come into his eyes.

"Good hit!" recorded Sam.

Saul lowered his eyes and began rubbing his arm and stamping his feet and bellowing miserably.

"Daddy," said Little-Sam, "make them stop now."

"Take it like a man, you fathead," cried Sam to Saul. "Fight him: what are you bawling for?" He shoved him forward. Saul automatically sent a soft blow wide, and then suddenly, with a loud bellow, turned and ran up the orchard as fast as he could. But his legs were shaking, and he stumbled at every step. Sam shouted,

"Sawbones, Sawbones!" and impulsively, yanking Tommy to his feet, Sam crowed, "Come on, boys, after him. The boy who ran away! C'mon! Give him the fright of his life!" With shrieks, they started after the fugitive, Sam in front dragging along Little-

Sam whose face was anxious. Saul gave a look behind, saw the pack after him, darted sideways through the grasses, and went sprawling behind a young pine tree. He lay there face downwards, sobbing into the earth. Sam came up, with the boys slightly astern, and stood there, for a moment, then poked his son with his toe,

"Get up, son!"

Quite broken, Saul began to pick himself up, dispersedly, as if his skeleton had become disarticulated and floated off in impossible directions. Sam got out his handkerchief and wiped Saul's eyes on it, then said,

"C'mon, kids: job! Work heals all sorrows!"

With an occasional sob, Saul tailed along, and in a quarter of an hour it seemed as if there had never been a cloud in the sky. When they were shifting their ladder so as to get on the roof itself, Sam sat down on the edge of the path and, drawing them round him into one of his powwows, said, with his arm along Saul's shoulder,

"Kidalonks! When there is bad blood in this family, I want you to get it out of your system by a man-to-man fight. Then we'll all be very happy and love one another. Nothing is worse than a nursed grudge: Our tempers are our worse natures and when they come along, we give 'em a good physical shakeup and hey, presto! we're wholesome and clean again, good citizens and good brothers." He looked round the little manhood with satisfaction. "My good boys," he said. And then began the difficult, exciting, and dangerous business of climbing on the roof. From it they saw the Cathedral and the capital city,

3 ✠ Henny downtown.

THE CAPITAL CITY, always duller than hard-working, mercantile, familiar Baltimore, is detestable on Sundays, dull and Pharisaical, thought Henny. Nothing but an emergency would have induced her to go downtown on a Sunday: the department stores were shut, there was no obsessed crowd of women on Seventh and Eighth Streets in which she could hide her garments, shabby bag, untended hair, and old skin. Her poverty was naked on the empty streets, and if no one walked abroad she felt all the more ghastly, like a wretched sinner in the sight of God. For Washington is Heaven, and Henny, disfigured, burdened with shameful secrets, felt like a human being would feel on first entering the sight of the angels. She detested perennial Heaven, Sinai's thunder, the new Jerusalem's powerful hierarchy; she felt it was the Eden of fleshpot men and ugly women striving for God knows what ugly, unhewn, worthy ends, not for the salvation of miserable creatures like herself. When she had first come to Washington, she had come with no more sense of married life or of social life than a harem-reared woman, being then a gentle, neurotic creature, wearing silk next to the skin and expecting to have a good time at White House receptions. Here she was, Collyer's youngest spoiled daughter, haggard, threadbare, over-rouged, worrying about how to indebt herself, going to meet a coarse fellow who was her lover merely because she could not get him into trouble. She rarely cried now, but she felt her eyes smart.

Where, in all the self-righteous lying world, could she turn for a friend? She even thought angrily of her children—they were simply eating up her flesh as they had when they were at the breast, no less. Did they know or would they ever know what a torture cell her life had been for them, borrowing money to buy them clothes, to avoid quarrels with their father, the quarrels already too many and already making cowards and sneaks of them? What would have happened if I'd never been born? she thought; they would never have been born. That hypocrite would have got some other woman with his yellow hair and big smile, but I should not have been responsible for their calvary, nor had even this toothache!

She thought bitterly about all men, most of all about her brother-in-law, her beautiful sister Eleanor's husband. He had loved Henny first and then discovered that Eleanor was the favorite and would get a bonus as well as her share of the estate; or that was how Henny put it to herself.

How hot it was in Washington! It was a hundred degrees in the shade, at least, thought Henny, and she seemed already to smell herself; she was no better than the painted young girls who buzzed round the journalists in the cafés. She looked in open kitchen windows, at the suits worn by little boys, at their scuffed shoes. She swept along without looking at adults, thinking of her children and the mounting cost of keeping them. They were such fine big children (as everyone said constantly) that a suit of clothes lasted a boy about three months. She thought of her big house on the hill and snickered bitterly. Even Bert Anderson, who had known her for so long, would give a lot to get inside it, to be able to say,

"I was up at Sam Pollit's the other Sunday, you know he married the Collyer clam-and-oyster money, young Henrietta, she was a Baltimore belle at one time, and they certainly have a crowd of fine little kiddies—was kidding Sam telling him his Roosevelt, the Great Democrat, would soon be the forgotten man," etc. This little preview of Bert Anderson, her stand-by from the Department of Internal Revenue, made Henny smile a little. This red-cheeked, lusty, riotous giant was not a gentleman, but he treated her as a single girl, listened to every word she had to say, always seemed eager, gave her advice, and was fascinated by money matters. He called her jocosely "young Henrietta," too, tried to improve her appearance in his brutal style, behaved like a grizzly-bear cub, and had no morality, character, ambitions, or way of life that she need respect.

Henny went upstairs when she came to the bar and restaurant near Twelfth Street and was glad to see that it was after one already. Bert would be there promptly at one-fifteen. She fiddled with the table silver and the menu, wished she had dawdled longer, muttered, "But I feel too conspicuous parading up and down the streets smirking nicely at mothers with children: and I might run into one of the Commissioner's fine friends, too. Bert is never late."

She saw Bert, shining with health, bursting in through the door, his hat still on his head to hide his thinning hair. He looked young, presentable, with a tight red skin and a thick irrepressible black beard newly ground off to skin level, jutting nose and chin, bright black eyes, and a ready grin; the lips were too red, the teeth too white in this grin, one thought, at first meeting. He bustled down to her, holding out both hands, and hailing her,

"Well, I'm not late, I'm not late. I told you one-fifteen, didn't I?" He looked round for a hook for his hat, then pressed her mouth with his cushiony lips.

"You're good to me, Bert, to come running when I get a freak and ring you up."

"Bert Anderson, always on tap," he affirmed. "I'm your guy, aren't I? If not me, then who? Maybe you've got someone else." He chuckled. "Well, what are we eating? And drinking? Cigarette? Smoking? No oysters I guess for the daughter of Paty du Clam? You don't mind if I do? Hello, hello there! How's things, Mullarkey? What's new? That's fine, that's fine!" He gave their order and then, one hand washing another, leaned over the table to Henny,

"Now then, what's new? Want to hear the latest? Did you hear about the fellow who had a nag racing out at Bowie? He kind of liked the horse and took it out a few magazines to read in the stable. The horse just looked and turned back to eat its hay. The little dog burst out laughing, and said, 'Hey, you don't think a horse can read, do you?' "

"Where's the joke?" asked Henny.

"Ha, ha, ha—ha, ha, ha," roared Bert, "you don't see it! Did you hear about the two dickybirds who were sitting on a tree and one said, 'That's Hitler!' and the other said, 'What are you waiting for?' "

"What an idiot!" said Henny, laughing. "Oh, I'll admit one thing, I get a good laugh with you. That young miss at the telephone sounded snippety. I heard what she said!"

"I know," he howled cheerfully, "I told her to cover the goddam mouthpiece when she made a silly crack like that. 'Well, how old is she, anyhow?' the kid said. I said, 'Oh, about thirty-two, thirty-three,' I told her. 'Well, what did I say? I said an old lady,' the kid said; 'what is she beefing about?' I told her, 'That's a lady, something you don't know about.' I won't tell you what she said, since you are a real lady!"

"No, but you're dying to," said Henny with a grimace, "I should like a stiff drink. I wish the churches and the smug big shots with cellars of their own hadn't passed this law."

"Good old Sinai, good old Jenkins Hill," cried Bert, "got to make the nation's capital safe for the bug-eyed tourist. I guarantee Samuel the Righteous thinks it's fine."

Henny shrugged, "Of course, he thinks that if he could get in and have half an hour's talk with President Roosevelt, he would banish alcohol for his term from the White House. The reason he knew Woodrow Wilson was God Almighty was that prohibition came in in his presidency. I sometimes think I live in the White House—or I think Samuel thinks so—" she shrugged again. "I can't understand why he never went into politics, with his gift of the gab and greensward style!"

Bert laughed interrogatively.

"Biggity style, all in the higher regions. I wish to all creation he'd picked out another woman, for his own sake, too."

"Maybe he will," Bert consoled her.

Henny laughed bitterly. "You know his favorite quotation? 'Good name in man and woman is the immediate jewel of their souls.' The children, Dad's money, his fat job, his reputation with all the high and mighty people he knows!" She laughed in an embarrassed way, "And he believes men should be virgins when they marry!"

"Holy mackerel!"

"We had our first fight over that. I simply didn't believe him! Now I do. And all the rest goes with it—no cards, no dirty jokes, no drinks, no smokes, no lively books. When I married him he had more than four thousand books and not one novel! He lectured me so when he caught me with one of Hassie's library books that I didn't dare read a novel for six months. But like all hypocrites and sneaks, it's all right if it has another label. He lets that child of his read stuff about hysteria—nuns having fits in convents and dreaming the Old One has what he might have for all I know, and animals breeding and old customs on European farms and all sorts of rot he lets that child of eleven read, because it's science! She drives me mad with her reading. She's that Big-Me all over again. Always with her eyes glued to a book. I feel like snatching the rotten thing from her and pushing it into her eyes, into her great lolling head: I'd like to stew the rotten books in one of my jam pans and make them both eat it. The feast of learning he's always talking about! I'd like to see their great bellies swell with their dirty scientific books the way he makes mine with wind and—" she stopped. Bert meekly ate his oysters and drank his wine.

"Now the mistake you make, young Henrietta, is that you think about these things all the time," said Bert, after a pause. "Now look at me," he coaxed, "suppose I started to worry over the fact that my old man never turned an honest cent in his life, but scrounged on me, his kid, eh?"

"You know, Bert," she said, trembling slightly, "the impulse to kill him becomes so strong sometimes, when I think of the way he's taken my life and trampled all over it and then thinks it's sufficient if he reads a few highbrow books, that I don't know how to get over it. I clench my fists together to keep from rushing at his greasy yellow head, or throwing something into that noisy mouth, forever boasting and screaming. If I could kill him and that child," she said, "I'd gladly do time for it. But what would the kids do? Go to an asylum? No one would stand it. No one could stand it. Hassie, who only has one kid anyhow, says, 'Compromise, compromise!' She wouldn't compromise; she has a meek little skinned rat of man who runs out all over the streets anyhow and goes to bars with queer fish, while she stays at home and runs the business; what does she know about compromise? The very one who tells me to compromise wouldn't compromise for half a minute. He talks about human equality, the rights of man, nothing but that. How about the rights of woman, I'd like to scream at him. It's fine to be a great democrat when you've a slave to rub your boots on. I have to stuff mattresses because we haven't enough money to buy new ones! Look at my hands!"

She showed him her worn hands. The skin was darkened by dirt ground in and snowy in patches, where the coarse soap had bitten it.

"And I rub in hand lotion every day," she said bitterly. "They say in the magazines, look after yourself and your husband will love you. If love was got by a woman giving her last drop of blood to wash the clothes in and her last shred of skin to carpet the house with, I wouldn't get it, and he wouldn't notice it. He is injured, if you don't mind! He boasts and screams about how cheap he buys his clothes for a man in his position, and what he gives up for the kids! He writes poems to himself on the subject: and what about me? I'm the heiress: I'm the rich woman who can stop up all the holes and darn all the tatters in her underwear and borrow old coats from her sister and beg old-fashioned jackets from her cousins, and I don't sacrifice at all. It is all on account of me. The whole thing is due to my bad management." Bert raised his eyes quizzically and held up his pencil,

"Henny, why can't you make a go of it on eight thousand a year? You pay fifty dollars a month rent to your old man, that's all."

"What?" cried Henny indignantly, "Food alone costs me three thousand and more a year. Everything is budgeted to the minimum, and it never works out. You know how much I had to spend on the two girls last year? Thirty-two dollars. Hassie gave me a dress for Evie, but she detests Louisa and will never give me a thing for her. There isn't a person in the family her size, she's so enormous, and I can't get any hand-me-downs for her. And I waste money! So says the Professor. The house is falling to pieces: there are always repairs. That's why we got it so cheap. Dad couldn't sell it. And you know the taxes we have to pay on that white elephant."

[92]

Bert pocketed his pencil helplessly. "You're right. Isn't it funny: if you get seven hundred and fifty a year or eight thousand a year, it's never enough! But—" he looked at her, "Well, what's the use? You would have all those kiddies."

"Oh, don't let's talk about it," she cried feverishly. "I didn't come here to talk about him and my troubles."

"That's right, that's right, that's a good girl! Here, we'll have a drop more wine, just to celebrate the transwafting of Samuel the Righteous to parts unknown."

"If he gives the household money to me in a lump sum," she said more thoughtfully, "you see I can pay off some of my old debts. When I was so terribly strapped after Ernie came, I just borrowed right and left—I hadn't the faintest idea how to run a house, and I only had Hazel Moore five months before Samuel quarreled with her. I blush, even in my own room, when I think I never paid Connie O'Meara the hundred. She must think I'm a cheap chiseler! I'll pay her first." She laughed excitedly, "Here I am spending it all already. How much do you think I have in my purse?"

"A buck?" His manner was a little less jovial than it had been up to now. She noticed this and flashed a look of contempt at his great curly head, bent over the plate. He was stowing food away in his usual elephantine manner, seeming to have three or four hands which were all in operation, moving quickly in different directions, seizing bread, sugar, cream, and so on. She decided to punish him,

"Ten cents!"

"How come?"

"Ernie tore his pants. *She* had to have new stuff for a dress. I hope I'll be able to palm her off on Eleanor again this summer, if her own relatives at Harpers Ferry won't take her."

"Do they use any propaganda against the stepmother out there?"

"If they did, she wouldn't know it. I don't know what passes in that girl's head, it isn't anything normal. I just know that if she makes up her mind to do a thing, she'll do it: and it isn't just her damned obstinacy, although I yell at her that it is: it's that she's deaf."

"I didn't know."

"No, not deaf! She doesn't know there's anyone else alive walking this earth but herself. So if she wants to do it, she'll do it and if you cut her fingers off, she wouldn't know it, she'd just go and do it. She's terrible. She's a horrible sort of beast, it seems to me sometimes. She crawls, I can hardly touch her, she reeks with her slime and filth—she doesn't notice! I beat her until I can't stand —she doesn't notice! When I fall on the floor, she runs and gets a pillow and at that I suppose she's better than her murderer of a father who lets me lie there. And if she whimpers a bit or bellows, she'll go right off the next minute with a face like a stone and stare and moon away at some book and forget everything I've screamed at her. I show her the veins sticking out on my hands and ask her if she isn't ashamed. But I'm waiting a bit till she gets a bit older and punishes her father for all he's made me suffer: or she'll take it out on some other man. Someone will catch a beauty."

Bert laughed, "Revenge is a wild kind of justice! Not mine, Lord Bacon's: I had no idea you were such a vengeful tiger."

"I'd drink his blood but it would make me vomit," she said, with pain. "When I think that in a few months I'm going to be the stepmother not of a child but of a woman and a woman with his nature, I want to commit suicide. Why should I go through with it?"

"Say, would you like to take a stroll?" inquired Bert. "Or how about the movies? Then we can take a drink at home after, if you like."

"Yes, you're right, Bert. It's cool there and I can have some quiet. It's just that he's painting and scraping and singing and jigging from crack of dawn and he wants to take up my bedroom floor now, so for weeks I'll have to sleep with a bed full of sand and dirt and a floor covered with old sacks. It's insane."

"Thank God I'm not a handy man," said Bert sighing.

"Yes, you are, handy," she concluded, with a queer sideways

glance. He laughed. When he got up to get his hat, she stood, pulling on her gloves, and looking up at his face which was turned from her. Suppose she lost him by yowling too much? For a moment she had a tinge of real love for the man. He was a queer sort. He would not marry anyone. He went out with, and no doubt lied to, girl after girl—nice romantic girls too; and though such a bounder, he looked like the ideal husband, stalwart, husky, bighearted, a good-time-Charlie, pretty sensible, and easy enough to handle, open to flattery, to pathos. There he was in a crisis, always helping her out in a friendly way. He even lent small amounts of money, showing her the amounts in his little vest-pocket book and saying, with a good-natured but meaningful slap, as she put it away, "It's there, it's mounting up: but you'll pay me off when the dividends come, won't you, young Henrietta?" She thought today she would get five dollars out of him.

CHAPTER FOUR

1 ✠ Scandal in Pollitry.

AT THREE in the afternoon Aunt Josephine Pollit, tall, blue-eyed, with hail-fellow-well-met dental set came through the gate at a lively pace, though she was putting on a hearty middle age. She carried herself as if she were a yellow solid valise cheerfully borne by a successful commercial traveler. She carried other things with her, a light coat, an umbrella, a purse, a book, and a package. When the twins came flying down the path, she shifted the parcel to the other hand and patted them while kissing them heartily.

"Are you glad to see your Auntie, twinnies? Where's Mother? Is your mother inside?"

"Mother's out."

"Out! Didn't anyone tell her your Auntie Jo was coming? Oh, isn't that too bad! I must see her! I must see Samuel! Where is your father? Come inside, chickies, Auntie has something for you —later on."

"Ooch!" they shrieked dutifully, and "What?"

"In a minute, must wait for Auntie to get her things off. Where's Auntie Bonnie? Is she out too? Now, who's going to get their auntie a glass of water?"

"Me, Auntie!" said Little-Sam.

" 'I,' you mean, Sammy: 'I will, Auntie.' "

He grinned bashfully and started towards the house.

"Where's your father? ('I will, Auntie!') Now!"

"I will, Auntie," he shouted from the door as he fled into the house.

"On the roof painting the roof," said Saul.

"On the roof! On Sunday afternoon! Tell him I'm here! Sam! Samuel! Tell him I'm here!" She sniffed grandly and marched into the house. But Sam had spied her from the roof top and now he cringed and whined at Saul, over the guttering.

"Ask Josie did she bring me a little bit of choc? She always brings me sumpin."

"Oo Taddy!" said Evelyn, going scarlet.

"Go on, kids," whined Sam piteously, "ask Josie if she's got anyfink for pore little Sam; I won't come down unless. En I might fall on my head, I might get sunstroke, anyfink might happen to me up here!"

"Oo, Taddy, you said never to ask for anything," Evie said very gravely.

"Gwan, kids," squeaked Sam, "tell her she's got to bribe me. Oh, oh, I'm falling: vertigo's going to get me, my head's going round. All because of no choc. Got to have some!"

"Don't say it," Louie ordered them fiercely from the veranda, "don't you go and say that."

"Gwan, boys," urged Sam more miserably and shamefully than before, "want a little bit o' choc, even one little tablet, I'll even take a crumb. She's got to send me up a bit: or she's got to send out and buy a bit."

Louie rushed out and planted herself in view of her father. "I won't let them," she shouted. The children hung about, not knowing what to do.

Jo had gone inside and taken off her hat. She shook back the dazzling yellow furze of curls that could never be smoothed down and powdered her nose. She beamed at the discussion outside, but when they came to this impasse, she strode to the veranda and shouted,

"I've got some chocolate for you, Samuel; come down! I've got to talk to you!"

"You bring it up," whined and scraped Sam, perilously over the guttering; although he suffered from vertigo and vertigo's nausea, he could never resist a comedy.

"Come down and don't be a fool," trumpeted Jo. "I have to talk to you!"

Sam grinned and started to come down the ladder,

"Josie used to yell that from the back window in Lombard Street; when I used to drag home carcasses and fishbones to make fertilizer—you remember, Jo? Phew! What a stench! Josie would bang up the window and yell down the street, 'Father, speak to that boy! Sam, don't be a fool!' And bang went the window again."

"Come down to earth," cried Jo impatiently, "Samuel, stop acting the goat!" She started to frown, but a smile broke through. She went up to her youngest brother and kissed him, saying more gently than before,

"Come in and get your chocolate and Louie will make us some coffee. Louie dear, come here, come and kiss Auntie, dear!" She looked her up and down, ran her hand through Louie's helpless waterfall of hair and proclaimed, "Louie's getting to be a big girl now: she's going to be just like me. Only straight hair! I was something like you at your age, dear! You're going to be just like me. I hope!" she sniffed cheerfully and laughed aloud. "Run along, dear!" And now this Juno frowned and demanded, "Is Bonnie here?"

"I think Bonniferous is snoozing," Sam replied.

"A most disgraceful thing," said Joe, "absolutely preposterous. Sam you must insist, absolutely insist, that she stop seeing this wretched man, that card-trick horror: it's disgraceful! To think that a sister of mine should go out with a man like that, and a married man! You must stop it! I insist upon it, Samuel!"

Sam became very grave, laid his hand on his sister's arm, and led her away from the children into the sunroom, which ran south and north and was entered from the long dining room. This was a beautiful, quiet room, with a high conservatory window looking out on the orchard, lined with books and containing Henny's piano. The children stayed outside to play, for they were tired by the heavy painting job of the day. Louie made coffee. From time to time they heard the upright Jo and austere

Sam in a passionate discussion somewhere in a corner of the house, or saw her stalking up and down in the sunroom, taking off her pince-nez, putting them on, tossing her head like a draft horse, sniffing, the sun shining through her loofah hair as she paused between the curtains, to give her nephews a good-natured look.

"Right is right, and wrong is wrong," she proclaimed through the window, "and any man, woman, or child with a sense of decency would refuse to speak to him. I won't hear any more about it; and there's an end of it. It must and will be stopped! He has a wife. If I had ever imagined that anyone in my family could so much as think of such a thing as attacking the holy bonds of matrimony—there's no excuse whatever. Be sure'that sin will find you out! And if she persists, you must send her away. I am sure Henny agrees with me. I myself will speak to Henny. When I heard of it, to my face, I nearly died of shame. And it was Miss Critchmar who told me! Suppose they want to elect me to the chapter—and a rumor like that gets round? What will I say? How could I show my face?"

"It wouldn't be your fault, Jo," said Sam seriously, "but of course we will stop it."

"Such an abomination cannot go on. She must be stopped," Jo said. "It makes me sick. And just when I had discovered that one of our ancestors, Sam, fought in the American Revolution. This genealogist assured me that there were several of our name and one certainly is a relative. And just then this bombshell comes along and hits me amidships! I was so horrified, Sam, I didn't sleep for five nights! You can imagine the state I was in! Where is the stupid girl?"

"Upstairs. I'll send for her."

"I'll go myself! Don't move! I shall give her a talking-to she'll not forget in a hurry. Disgusting. Oh, it's disgusting! A sister of mine! How could she! What is the matter with her, Sam? Mother was such a splendid character and you and I have never committed a sin in our lives. I believe that. I am not a Pharisee! I wish that you would go to church, Sam, but I must say that for a nonbeliever you lead an exemplary life. But of course, Father's example—" she stopped, seeing Louie with the coffee, and then continued nobly, "Father could have been a better man."

"Well, that's not to the point now," Sam said quietly. "Perhaps you'd better leave it to me, Jo. I'll find out how things stand. Don't accuse without evidence. An evil tongue can do more harm than two foolish people—probably no more than foolish, remember! Make allowance for mere harmless folly, Jo."

"That's a lot of bosh and you know it! A married man! What must he be thinking about Bonnie, your sister, Sam? If you think I'm going to put up with it, you're much mistaken. I'm surprised at your being so weak-kneed, Sam, you so decent; you were always so decent. I always do my duty. Some people don't like me for it, but I know why."

Sam interjected, "Jo, you are not the avenging angel, you must be human in these matters. I have more experience than you."

"More? How more? You mean you're married. Rubbish! I have to deal with mothers and their problems all day long, too. They confide in me. I have a big following among the mothers. My opinion is objective just because I do not deal with compromise. Not that you do, Sam; I know you've always been good—the best; I don't say that. You're the best boy that ever was. You're too soft, that's all, so you can't handle this."

Sam motioned to her to sit down; and she did so, "You see, Jo, I used to be like you, I thought just the same way. I understand how you feel. But you are wrong, believe me; you cannot dragoon human beings even in the name of morality. It is kindness, human love, and patience with human weakness that is necessary. Remember this is your own sister, ten years my junior, and I know little enough how to run my own affairs! Be kind to her. Go and speak to her—I admit it's a woman's place: but be kind."

"I will never be kind to weak wickedness," cried Jo, bouncing up and tossing back her head; "be sure of that, Samuel."

"Run out, Looloo," said Sam, to the little girl who had just brought in the coffee tray.

"And another thing," cried Jo, more moderately, "I want to

ask you about my income tax, Sam, about the deductions. A man came to ask me questions. I'm perfectly sure I'm overassessed; and I can't sleep at night with the pneumatic drilling in the streets; and I couldn't get half that price if I really tried to sell it. I'm going to get a loan to put in improvements—but what's the use really? I ought to lease it to a boardinghouse keeper who would give me my rents regularly and I shouldn't have to worry. It all keeps me awake and I can't afford to lose sleep over a lot of irresponsible people. That old woman with the rosary on her bed only comes once a fortnight to get her relief, or when she had a fight with her son-in-law. That nice German, such a decent fellow and a good tenant, is going to his homeland to see his parents. Such a studious man, nice and quiet; and those two awful Italians didn't work for four days. They went out on a beer party and got stinking drunk and didn't work. My house is simply going down, and I haven't time to do it up, put them out, and get decent tenants. That horrible little thing on the first floor is going to have *another* baby and the first one hardly with a tooth, she doesn't get through washing the dishes till eleven o'clock or twelve and then another bedraggled girl comes with her baby carriage and there they sit in the dark, in the damp, and chatter and cook a bit of spaghetti, and that shiftless tramp with a cigarette stuck between his lips when he hasn't enough to eat even and the rent not paid. It makes me sick, such shiftless horrible people in the world, and they are the ones the government supports! Can you understand it, Sam? I can't. And in the house next to mine is a woman with a piece of land in the country, who gets relief. Isn't it wicked, Sam? Oh, you don't know what's going on, Sam, because you're in a government department and you don't meet people as I do. I have to meet them face to face, I have to actually speak to these awful creatures, because they are my tenants, and I have to worry about the plumbing for them. Do you think they're pleased with anything? No, you don't know a lot yourself, Sam. That's what I say. Don't throw it up at me that I'm not married; for I could easily have been married, but I just said, 'No, no, I'm waiting for Mr. Right.' What do you think of that, Sam? Another baby, with one nine months old, it just makes me sick."

"Maybe they like children," said Sam, grinning.

"Tommyrot, it's sheer improvidence and shiftlessness!" said Jo, indignantly, staring at her brother. "They owe me three weeks' rent now! Stop being a giddy goat, Sam. Now, there, I've had my coffee and I'm going up to speak to that girl. I'll bring her to her senses."

Jo went upstairs boiling with self-respect. Henny referred to her agreeably as that "great blond beast, deaf, dumb, and blind to all but self, self, self"; and Sam said that "Jo was a very good woman, but not broadminded"; and Bonnie always said, with a laugh, "Jo's a good soul, poor thing!" Bonnie had been taking forty winks in her room, drunk with the heat, when Jo's irruption into the house had wakened her. She had at once applied her ear to the stairway well and heard most of what had been said to Sam by Jo. If she could have got out of the house, she would have, but it was impossible; the foot of the stair was at the dining-room door. Bonnie even considered climbing out of her window and trying to reach the porch and shin down the porch posts, a thing that she surely would have done ten years ago. But she could not do it here. With relief she had heard the voices of two little girls in the room opposite hers. Evie and Isabel were playing Mothers, Evie's favorite and perpetual game. Evie was a lady with a baby, and Isabel was her little girl going to school, a distribution of roles which had never varied. Isabel went to school (in the corner), put up her hand, scribbled on the floor, and after a surprisingly short morning came home for lunch. At lunch she was invariably rude to her mother and had to be slapped. After lunch she always refused to go back to school and had to be ordered out of the house in a cranky voice. While she was in afternoon school, the mother would change her baby's diaper, croon to it, smack it, teach it, and repeat infinitely the little attentions that Evie really had had to give to Tommy. Evie often asked her mother to have a new baby so that she could look after it, and in the meantime, she had become the occasional nursemaid for most of the mothers on the opposite side of the street. Evie was doing up Isabel's braid for the third time in the course of three fleeting days of motherhood, "and now you've got to go to school and I'll cook the dinner for my husband," said Evie, tying a rag round her waist.

"But you haven't got a husband," Isabel cried disconsolately; "you have two children but no husband. No lady has that. Let me be the mother."

The doe-eyed Evie showed a surprising forensic turn while she convinced Isabel that it was utterly unsuitable for her to be a mother; but she agreed, with a rather lost and disgruntled expression, to allow a phantom husband to share the honors of householding with her. Isabel insisted on a real husband, and Evie was obliged to hang out the back window and yell, "Little-Sam, I want you." Her brother argued. Evie yelled, "You must be my husband." "No," yelled Little-Sam. Evie turned hastily to Isabel and said sternly, "My husband is at the office; now you must go to school." Isabel vanquished, picked up her schoolbag, and went to school again while Evie, muttering happily to herself, busied herself over her doll and imaginary housework.

Jo, halted by the little scene, had let her face of stern rectitude crease grimly to release a smile for "the kiddies," and then she went in to the flabbergasted Bonnie. Jo stopped a few paces from Bonnie, who was sitting on her bed, and said sternly,

"Well, I heard a nice thing on Friday! What are you and that man Holloway doing going about together and in broad day all over Baltimore; and in a barroom too. I can't imagine you doing such a thing! You'll stop it at once, that's all. I'm not going to have my name ruined, if you don't care about yours."

"Mind your own business," said Bonnie flushing and springing up. On the bed were scattered collars, letters, and paper patterns.

Jo seemed surprised by this resistance. "What do you mean? It is my business. Do you know what you're doing? You're going out with a man with a legal wife; you know what that means?"

[103]

"Go and put your head in a bag," said Bonnie. "If I like to have an innocent friendship with a married man, it's none of your affair."

Jo burst out that there was no innocence with a married man and what was Bonnie coming to? Did she know where the primrose path was leading her and that being seen all over the place with a married man and drinking spirits in bars didn't look like innocence; and that she should think of her brothers and sisters if not of herself, and of what Henny's friends would think if they knew that that was Sam's sister running round the streets openly and brazenly with a married man? What did she think she looked like?

"A sight for sore eyes," said Bonnie.

"What?" shouted Jo. "Such brazenness!"

"Honi soit qui mal y pense," Bonnie told her, curling her lip. This was too much for Jo who rushed up and, shaking her by the shoulders, in a great passion, cried that she must write a letter at once, this very afternoon, in fact now ("Now, if not sooner," said Bonnie coolly) to the Horror and tell him that he would never see her again.

"His positively final appearance on all stages," said Bonnie, pettishly, which showed Jo that she was losing her temper (it never held very long).

"Stop acting the goat," cried Jo, therefore, "and think of the way he's treating you; what can he think of you?"

"He understands me," said Bonnie. "I'm naturally vivacious and though I love Sam's kiddies, I must have friends of my own: and he's a real gentleman besides."

"Fiddlesticks!" said Jo, "you behave like a child. Now sit down and write the man a letter and I'll post it myself. Sam agrees with me that it has got to stop."

"Anyone would think I was pickled in crime," Bonnie complained; "he's sweet on me and he's separated from his wife and he's going to get a divorce."

"I know for certain she won't divorce him," said Jo.

"He told me she would, she hates him and they're unhappy

and they wanted to separate a long time ago, but he just jogged along till he met me, that's what he said."

But Jo told her to never mind, she knew all about it and she told Bonnie that far from hating his wife, he was now living with her again—everyone knew it; there had been a reconciliation, and so forth, and that the horrible man simply went, straight from giving Bonnie a good time, to his wife's table and that everyone was talking and that there would be a frightful scandal and she, Bonnie, might be the cause of another separation: "Whom God hath joined let no man put asunder," said Jo, solemnly.

Bonnie began to cry. "I didn't know, I can't believe it; he said to me, 'Why should we wait forever on a woman's whim?' That's what he said; can you blame me?"

"You let the cat out of the bag that time, didn't you?" asked Jo; and the end of it was that she forced Bonnie to write the letter then and there and, after reading it severely, she carried it downstairs with the intention of posting it.

Bonnie stayed upstairs sobbing, thinking she had a broken heart, until she heard soft things like the hands of ghosts rubbing her counterpane and soft ghostly feet unsteadily shifting on her rug; and looking up, she saw Evie and Isabel staring at her with immense rabbit eyes. In a little crockery voice, Isabel asked,

"What are you crying for?" and Evie at once piped up with the same question. Affectionate Bonnie threw her arms round the two little girls and dragged them to her, while she sobbed, "Auntie Jo came and took all the gilt off my gingerbread, that's why, darlings; there, you lump of sweetness!" (she kissed Evie). "Bless you, kittycat, bless its kind loving heart; there, darling" (she kissed Isabel), "you're a dear little girl too, never mind about poor Bonnie. I'm a poor lone, lorn crittur, that's why I'm crying; now don't you worry about the troubles of grownups, your little lives must be all sunshine, dear; you will have trouble enough when you grow up, because we all do; now, there, there, kiss poor Bonnie again, now, there there, look, look; Evie has a tear in her eye, there, my darling lump," she ravished Evie's head with kisses, parting her soft, glossy black hair in a fever of love, "there, let its Bonnie hug it for a minute to make me feel better!" Evie looked up lovingly at Bonnie's shining hair and periwinkle-blue eyes,

"You are pretty, Auntie," she said.

"Other people think so, too," said Bonnie nodding, with a faint smile; she was already beginning to see that "all was not lost," as she put it to herself. She got up and began to collect her bits of paper and lace, trying a collar on one little girl and the other and saying cheerfully, "Fear not: all will be well!" and "Never say die!" and "A merry heart goes all the way," and "Sticks and stones will break my bones but names will never hurt me!" and "Oh, don't you look perfectly, mm-mm! now, look in the glass, darlin'," until she was as chipper as a canary; and, bundling everything suddenly into the drawer, she pushed them out, "Now go and play, you two young puppies," and ran downstairs, humming a tune and determined to be "the gayest of the gay," to show them she "was not broken nor even badly bent."

When she got down Sam and Jo were talking confidentially about Jo's salary, retirement allowance, and an income-tax inquiry. There was some distribution of chocolate going on, and Ernie was hanging on to the bench, drinking in Auntie Jo with his eyes and ears. Jo was full of her summer holidays—she and Miss Critchmar, her other self, would go to Atlantic City, but not for long on account of her worries with her tenants in Lombard Street, Baltimore; and she went on to discuss these troubles again, the new bathroom, the new house she would like to take over on a five-years' lease, but always envisaging the difficulty of getting responsible people to live in it and a good furnace man. The children lounged or sat and stared at Auntie Jo with admiration. She was a marvel to be able to tell off a bank manager, a landlord, and to own two houses of her own. Auntie Jo was neither a married woman nor an old maid, nor a schoolma'am, she was a landlord.

"You were wrong, Samuel," said Jo, "to let that house go in P Street."

Sam put up his hand to silence her: he never talked about

money or property before the children, thinking it a vile thing.

"What rot!" exclaimed Jo. "A man is none the worse for getting rent! You'd be better off today."

Louie spoke up, however, "It was my house and Daddy sold it to buy mother her ring and the dining-room suite."

"It was not your house," said Sam sadly to her.

"You said so," she answered timidly, "once, one time."

"Do you want to live there?"

"No, there are Negroes living in it. I went to look at it."

"You have a house to live in: of what use would it be to you?"

"I could sell it—if I had it," she said humbly.

"What for? What do you want to buy?"

She was silent: a rage of desire rushed through her, but she couldn't think of what she wanted to buy; she muttered, "I could buy a boat, I could go sailing."

"We must never think about money or of owning things," said Sam kindly, bending a rather dewy eye on her. "Greed, the desire to possess, money, the currency of greed, is the root of all evil, it is the means of devouring others, and the lives of others: you know how I feel about that." Silently Louie took her place beside Ernie, while Auntie Jo, with a beaming eye, smiled on them both, saying, "That is not for you little ones yet awhile: let us work and worry for you; you play and learn."

Ernie smiled faintly between his hands and looked at father and aunt with deep appreciation. His father earned $666 monthly, his aunt $200 monthly or more. His aunt got rent out of families in two houses, each with three stories and basement, and his father, though no longer a landlord, would make extra expenses going abroad on this expedition. His father was thirty-eight years old, though, while Auntie Jo was, as near as he could make out, at least forty-eight. But again, she was head of the kindergarten department, much in the same relative position as her brother, who was head of his department, and even a kind of superhead invented for himself alone. Auntie Jo had no car, but was saving the money to go to England and see the seat of the Calverts, even though they were Catholics, and the cathedrals of England. Who would manage her houses while she was away? he pondered. If she put it off long enough he would like to reside there and look after the tenants. On the other hand, his grandfather, Old David Collyer, would be more likely to give him a better job.

As soon as he could, Ernie wanted to open a bank account and put money into it. To put money into it, one had to make money by inducement of people who did not care so much for money or who needed it and would pay for it, or who were fools or who did not see the money in odd things, or who were simply like fruit trees growing wild to have the fruit picked off them. Ernie often thought of making money, but never by putting on a performance himself, say: only by manipulation of objects or of other persons. The idea of selling himself, which was, on the whole, Louie's idea, of selling her talents on a stage, seemed strange to Ernie. He sometimes figured that if Louie grew up to be an actress, he would sell photographs of her, or would take the money at the door. His father had stopped him from delivering groceries from the small, independent store at the corner. This did not worry him at all. He picked the eyes out of every conversation, for he knew there were hundreds of other ways of getting a living. Once for fun, Sam had let him black boots outside Tohoga House. To Sam it was an immense joke; but Henny, on this occasion, flew out of her muteness in a storm cloud and made such a bluster round Sam's ears that Sam had had to call off the joke. That time Henny had threatened to leave him and take the children home to Roland Park. People gave him money (though not Auntie Jo, who was very careful, even with chocolate); and people allowed him to earn money by services. He made money lending nickels to boys of good standing, charging them one penny, or interest in kind. He dealt fairly by them and did a good business. Only he himself knew (Henny had not guessed) how much money he had in his money box when, at Christmas, he left himself the half of his takings.

Ernie thought Louie lacked sagacity but calculated that after all she was putting her best foot forward, when she spoke of going on the stage. He himself also looked years ahead and saw himself making his way in the world, handling, changing money, cautiously getting the best of bargains, finding out how others made money. They had secrets, he thought, though no more intellect than himself. He watched and listened day by day for those secrets. He knew he was a child and that children had no rights, but he did not fret since time would cure him. In the meantime he did business with children and relatives who were his natural guardians if not warders. He knew he could not go to law and win suits, nor go into business; he knew his word would not be taken against that of an adult, and that adults, if they so wished, could do him great harm, give him great insults and injuries and never be punished, nor even perhaps suspected; that was their power, the right they grew into, one of the privileges of manhood. He smiled at them, though, not as enemies, but as persons of privilege, and he really liked power and privilege, he had a zest for it. Ernie listened to all that everyone said about himself, finding it truly fascinating to know how each sucked a living from the earth. He rarely lost his head but had no criticism of the temperaments of others. Above all, he understood and was curious about the relations of people. Auntie Jo was Samuel's eldest sister and the head of the family as she often proclaimed. Samuel usually obeyed her in matters of relation, morality, for example, but she came to Samuel with her financial matters. Father and Mother fought because there was not enough money forthcoming. Mother wasted her money, and Sam was unable to understand how expenses could be so large. If there were only two children, himself and Louie, they would live in clover, but there were six. What if another ever came? That would be difficult. One morning, after thinking about this in bed, Ernie had gone to his Mother and said, "Mothering, don't have another baby!"

Henny had said, "You can bet your bottom dollar on that, old sweetness."

Ernie did not like this feverish phrase of Henny's, for the idea of his bottom dollar ever coming to light at all (from under the heap of other dollars) did not appeal to him.

"We must never think about money," said both Auntie Jo and Daddy. Ernie knew that this was one of the pious precepts handed down by people in power to smaller people in subjection, since both Auntie Jo and Samuel constantly thought about bills, salaries, and getting on, and always had money in their purses. Ernie knew that parents and guardians handed down many other wise saws for the same purpose, which was to prevent the young ones from getting into their game too soon. Get a piece of filet steak for your father—and don't eat the pie that's for your Aunt, and those almonds are for Mother; and don't quarrel—though we do; go to bed—though we stay up, going to the movies is not good for children—though I go; and don't talk whilst I talk; all commands enforced by power alone and obeyed by weakness alone—for as Louie grew up, she obeyed less and less, not letting things slip by inadvertence or sly disobedience, but refusing to do things in open revolt—"I will not because it is not right!" Now, Louie had her own right and wrong, she was already entering their world of power. Ernie studied their conflicts and made up his mind about things. Here was Auntie Jo always in conflicts, in which, by the way, she generally lost. She was deep into one of her favorite jeremiads,

"I didn't sleep a wink all night four nights in succession on account of the noise, the noise, their picks clinking all night. There ought to be some regard for taxpayers. Why can't they work in the daytime? I nearly fell asleep on the bus coming over." Jo sniffed and nodded her bright-colored head, "It's a scandal!"

"Why don't you get a little car?" inquired Sam greedily. "Then you could come and see us often—and bring me choc," he winked at the children, "and you could take us all out for a ride."

Jo smiled at him, "I would, Sam, only I'm putting by, you know, for my trip; I've got other relatives to visit besides you, Sam," she grinned at him. "You're not my only brother, you know!"

Auntie Jo sat in the chair bubbling and boiling, and Samuel, listening to her, rested from his labors until they heard Bonnie's brisk song on the stairs, *"Voi che sapete!"*

Jo drew herself up and looked matronly at Bonnie, while Sam said reproachfully, "Jo has been telling me something, Bonniferous, that I never would have believed about you. We'll have a little talk afterwards."

Bonnie looked at her brother silently, while her blue eyes filled with tears. Sam said gently, "It's all right, Bonniferous, I know it's all right."

"Good heavens, I should think so!" cried Jo. Then she rose and strode to the sunroom and began to twirl downwards the piano stool, while Sam flung himself happily on the settee amongst the cushions and the children poured through the bars of sun and window shadows, nodding in the winds of jollity. Jo began to strum masterfully, *Marching through Georgia*. She stopped brusquely and asked over her shoulder with her hands poised,

"Another thing! Why didn't you go to Jinny's when you said you would? Besides you wrote to Jinny that you were looking for a job in Baltimore. I suppose on account of that man!"

"Play, Jo, play!" said Sam indolently. " 'Ta-ra, ta-ra, we bring the Jubilee!' Go on! Don't hector, Jo, go on!"

"Nonsense," cried Jo, swinging round and shaking indignant bright pince-nez at him, "hectoring indeed! Don't be silly! Here she stays writing letters all over the place and carrying on as she likes, and trying to get to Baltimore where she can be near that card-trick scoundrel. I know all about him. A fine thing for a sister of mine to be taken in by a——"

"Jo!" warned Sam, nodding and grinning at the fascinated children. "A sister of mine too!" He laughed, "Go on, Jojo, play: never mind the curtain lecture!"

"Curtain lecture," cried Jo. "Nonsense! I intend to speak my mind. I'm perfectly honest, and honest people need not be afraid to hear what I have to say. I always speak the truth!"

"A good principle," said Sam dryly, "but——"

"Let me play, Jo," broke in Bonnie heedlessly, "the kids love the musical monologues I give them, don't you, kids? How's

[111]

abouts 'The Big Bad Wolf,' or the 'Gunny-Wolf,' or 'Mr. Possum and Mr. Dog'?"

The children began to clamor, while Bonnie blushed and explained to Jo, as if nothing had happened, "I make them up as I go along, the music I mean—listen! Jo! Let me have the piano a minute!"

"Who can't do it?" inquired Jo jealously.

"The 'Gunny-Wolf,' " cried the children.

"Listen, children," Jo said in her best kindergarten manner, " 'The first Noel that the angels did say.' "

"No nims [hymns]," said Sam.

"You should be ashamed of yourself," cried Jo, "such prejudice!"

"No nims," said Sam firmly.

"You're not giving the children a chance to choose for themselves: is that impartiality?" inquired Jo. "You should at least allow them to hear about God."

"Why? When there ain't no sich animal?" said Sam comfortably.

"Sammy!" implored Bonnie. Jo burst out, though, "You'll regret it later on, if you don't: you distort their minds with fairy tales, absurdities: Hans Andersen but not the Bible! When they grow up they will have nothing to believe in."

Sam laughed very comfortably, "Now they believe in their poor little dad: and when they grow up they'll believe in Faraday, Clerk Maxwell, and Einstein; and snakes alive!" he cried indignantly, getting up into a sitting posture, "if my children can't distinguish between Grimm and Clerk Maxwell, let them go and jump in the lake, for sweet nuthatch's sake!"

"They are forced to go to school and they should be forced to go to church," cried Jo indignantly. "A nice set of citizens!"

Sam laughed, "It's not even right they should be forced to go to school when they have a father like me: I can teach my children. I don't need schoolma'ams!" And he grinned evilly at his sister.

"They need more women in the state legislature," said Jo, "and

[112]

irresponsible fathers like you would be forced to: I know Henny thinks as I do."

"Yiss, but you ain't in it," said Sam, "and what's more you never will be. En if I had my way no crazy shemales would so much as git the vote! Becaze why? Becaze they is crazy! Becaze they know nuffin! Becaze if they ain't got childer, they need childer to keep 'em from goin' crazy; en if they have childer the childer drive em crazy."

Jo scorned him, "I'm as good as any man I ever met." She sniffed cheerfully, "Pollits for Politics, say I."

Sam turned to the children and said, "Did you notice the stones in this yere wall rock when Jo sniffed, kids? When Jo was a girl, Father used to say he wished he could have Jo's nose stuffed with silver dollars, he'd pay the year's rent."

"Don't be rude, Sam!" shouted Jo above her strumming. "Noses mean character: I've got a nobody nose!"

"Nobody knows the sniffles she got," sang Sam. Jo laughed. "You wish you had a nose like mine; only Father had one like mine and he looked like Charles Dickens. Sam and I are the only ones with the real Pollit nose."

"Jo's nose pickled in brine would make two sides of bacon for a week," said Sam. Bonnie, who had a tiptilted nose, by the way, laughed till she cried.

"Louie will beat you though," continued Sam. Louie smiled down her nose.

"Nonsense!" cried Jo gaily. "A big nose means a generous nature. Anyhow, don't you mind, Louie! Be like me! Let her have one."

"A big nose means a big cold," said Bonnie.

"A big nose means big lungs," declared Sam, vainly heaving his chest up and down, uff-puff. "Big lungs mean a big voice, big voice means reaching the hearts of your countrymen, even without the radio and with, my friends, with, you become a Roosevelt, than which is none whicher. I'm always glad I'm not a squib, like Crazy-Daisy down at the Department. He squeaks through lack of nose." Sam imitated the squeak of Craven Day, an old clerk down at the Bureau of Fisheries, politely called, by about one hundred intimates, Crazy-Daisy. He was a rusty, tall, round-backed permanent functionary, who became more eccentric as he approached the age of fifty. Sam went by the name of Softsoap-Sam. The children's eyes danced with excitement; they could never get enough of Crazy-Daisy, the accountant, or of Ratty-Atty (Mr. George Atson), another accountant, or of Skinny, or Finny, or Dirty Jack, or Dribble Smith, or Hohnenlinden, or Alphabetical Davies (Skinner, Finigan, John Roebuck, Bertrand Smith, Max Hohnen, and A. B. C. Davies), all Sam's inferiors by grades in the branches of the Department. Less interesting were the Moguls, the bosses, who, however, had respectable names, Mr. Virgen, Mr. J. Cappie Larbalestier, and Mr. Murphy, all Sam's superiors in the Department. Mr. Virgen had three beautiful daughters, all Virgens (said Sam), who moved through rose gardens, gave parties, and possessed three blue Persian kittens—Sam adored them all: he adored Iris, Penelope, and Maisie Virgen and had written a ditty to them one Saturday afternoon at tea, as follows:

> *What I most admire is—Iris:*
> *But would have envelope me—the web*
> *of Penelope:*
> *Though the one that drives me crazy—is Maisie.*

Now the children had no need of a Punch-and-Judy show as their gifted and possessed father went through his antics, gibbering and hunching his shoulder, scolding and squawking, fawning and groveling, imitating Crazy-Daisy, talking to a Negro cleaner, talking to Sam. What a circus it was down at the Department! When the children, severally, taken down by Sam to the Department, chanced to see one of these grotesque and marvelous creatures, they at once burst out laughing or else devoured the fable with their eyes. This was Crazy-Daisy! This, Dirty Jack. The best thing was that Crazy-Daisy really hunched his shoulder and Dirty Jack really had grease on his coat and soup on his tie. Of Crazy-

Daisy's goings-on, though, they could get no evidence—his stargazing, zodiac-fixed horse races at Bowie and his predictions about salary aspirations, lawsuits, and wills were all done in the secrecy of his own office, on his little office stool, or else in his faraway bungalow in Hyattsville. But here was something new.

Sam said, "The other day Crazy-Daisy was asking the Department of Agriculture for a bedbug."

There was a whoop of joy. Jo exclaimed, "Samuel!"

"But none was forthcoming, so he sent one of the messengers out to catch one, and the messenger had to go to Skinny's Hotel in Thirteenth Street and catch one and at first he got a black eye. Then the messenger brought it back, and Crazy-Daisy put it in a little Sen-Sen box with borated cotton. Then he took it home——"

"For a pet, oh, for a pet," gasped Bonnie, collapsing on a chair.

"No, he let it out of the shutter in the box and put it on his old coat. Then when the woman who has the bungalow saw it, she chased him out of his room without asking him for the rent. So he saved a week's rent!"

"Samuel!" said Jo, "you ought to be ashamed."

"I don't see you crying," said Sam, "I don't see you busting in two tears!"

Jo, grinning faintly, turned back to the piano, gave a sniff to settle her features, and struck a note.

Bonnie continued, "What did he do with the bedbug, oh, he-ha!"

"Ate it," suggested Ernie.

"Married it," said Sam, "got it a wife."

"It takes two bedbugs to make a world of trouble," said Jo from the piano, playing softly, "Ladybird, ladybird, fly away home."

"Quiet, kids," said Sam, "perpend, give ear: Jo will play us a toon, a little moozic." Sam lay back looking at the ceiling, while Bonnie tapped her foot and shifted uneasily, ready at any minute to point out the wrong notes. At last she burst out, when Jo struck out into the *Marche Hongroise*, "Jo, excuse me, but you're out of practice, I think! Your timing's wrong. You were never good at time. You ought to have had a metronome," she ended unhappily.

"What!" roared Jo. "What cheek! I play every day of the week at school and for my own pleasure on Saturdays. Mrs. Ogden always says she loves to hear the music drifting across the yard from my flat. How absurd!" She played louder and faster than ever. Bonnie persisted gloomily, "Let me show you how that bit goes, Jo: don't be so obstinate!"

"Obstinate! What?" cried Jo. "What nonsense. I'm never obstinate! You're itching to get at the piano. You know nothing about it! You never play. Oh, don't annoy me! I didn't get a wink of sleep last night. I shall get a headache. Don't irritate me." She turned to the keyboard and played with even more mistakes to the end. "You see, you put me out," she said indignantly to Bonnie.

"You should be above criticism," said Bonnie nastily.

"Kiddies, dance, round in a ring now," Jo cried, brightly ignoring her and determined to keep the piano at all costs.

Louie gravely came into the middle of the carpet, lifted her skirts slightly, and began to practice ballet steps, positions one to six.

Sam stared and burst into a roar of laughter. "Our fairy! Look at our fairy!"

Louie smiled slightly, thinking it a compliment, and began to skip about childishly. Jo chuckled; Bonnie took it all seriously and commanded, "Left foot, right foot, go on (there's no harm in improvisation—let me play for her, Jo!)."

The children began to skip around at will, and Bonnie, pulling up a chair to the piano, tried to play a little tune in the bass.

"You can't dance, Looloo, and don't try," said Sam nastily.

"Go on, darlin'," begged Bonnie, tapping away. Evie had stopped, looking from one to the other. Louie obstinately kept twirling farther off, in a corner of the carpet.

"Stop it, you fathead, you silly fathead," cried Sam wrathfully, "do you want to make an idiot of yourself? You don't know what you look like, you great fat lump. I don't want to see your legs: keep your dress down. And please tell Henny to lengthen it." With a sort of sacred horror he looked aghast at her fat thighs half revealed. Louie flushed and, moving down the room, towards the south window, did a few steps to herself, hesitating and quiet as a meditation.

"Stop it, you—mule!" cried Sam, half laughing, "or I'll give you a flip. I can't bear to see Looloo making a fool of herself," he explained to his sisters. "So cussed a child I've never seen." He looked at her sideways, taunting, charming, "You'll find your place in the world, Looloo, but whatever we eventually find in that mountain of fat, it isn't going to be a Pavlova!" Even Bonnie held her tongue. "Your head's big enough to hold a fair mess of brains, if they're not addled, always, of course," said Sam, in high good humor. He turned away from her altogether, frowning again, "I don't know where Looloo, though, gets the foolish, flighty notions she's been getting lately." He explained to every one present, "Bonniferous was an awful nitwit when she was a kid, always thinking she would be a stage or cinema star and darned if silly Looloo hasn't been bitten by the same bug." He began to laugh and there were some more silly jokes about the adventure of Crazy-Daisy.

Meanwhile, no one had noticed Henny return home and go into her room, leaving the door slightly ajar. Thus Henny heard that Sam, going into the men's room, had come into a discussion between Craven Day and a messenger, from which he learned that Craven Day lent money secretly and at usurious rates to empty pockets, miseries, and follies in the Department. Samuel had been most irate and had reported this to the chief of Day's division, as was only his duty: "to think of an officer of the Department battening on the wretchedness or improvidence of his fellow being," said Sam, though less hotly than at that other time.

"Is he a Jew?" asked Jo.

"No more than you," Sam replied. "And it's just possible that you'll become one in time, Jo, collecting rents and grinding the noses of the poor."

"I keep my nose to the grindstone," said Jo bitterly.

"It doesn't do it much good," Bonnie hastened to say.

"Jo the Jew," said Ernie thoughtfully. Jo flashed a look at him by no means friendly. But this inspired Louie to remark that she had personally seen the stewed cats at the Kydds' place today. Bonnie was all eyes and ears and wanted to know the details. Louie, giggling, informed them that she had dropped a piece of bacon in the stewed cats, and that she had escaped in the nick of time from Old Goat, who had returned early to beat Angela and eat his cats. Up till this minute she had forgotten the drowning; and suddenly she flushed and said no more. Sam was grinning at this improvement on his morning fancy and asked in a mean, driveling tone what the stew smelled like. Immediately, Henny's door, which had been standing open, flew shut. Everyone started, "What was that?" The wind? No, no wind. Ernie drawled,

"It was Mothering: she's been home for ages!"

"Oh, I must see Henny," declared Jo in excitement and jumped up. No sooner had she quit the piano stool than Bonnie flew to it and began to sing and play in her best style, *"L'amour est un oiseau."*

The children, after knocking, rushed in ahead of their aunt and found Evie already there, asking,

"Do you want a cup of tea, Mother?"

"Would you care for——?"

"Would you care for a cup of tea?"

"Yes, I should be very glad of it." She rooted Tommy out of the armchair, saying, "You and your everlasting messing," and flopped into the chair sighing. She turned with a smile to the twins standing side by side and gave one of her queer little recitations that they all knew by heart but loved to hear:

"Have a cup of tea, sir? No, sir! Why, sir? Because I have a cold, sir! Let me hear you cough, sir! Hm, hm, hm!"

Louie, arriving at this moment, said with a silly smile, "Say, *Piccadilly*, Mother."

Henny obliged with "Offal baw the R.A. Show and yet a chappie has to go: the only thing in Piccadilleh I wegard as being silleh."

When they asked for *The Bath Bun,* her good temper evaporated, and she told them to clear out and shut the door.

"Aren't you coming out to see Auntie Jo?" inquired Tommy, who was new to life.

"I'd like to see her at the bottom of the sea," Henny replied genially (and Jo, on the other side of the door, hearing this, sniffed good-humoredly and prepared a smile); "and all the fool Pollits with her: now get out."

"We're Pollits, Moth," Ernest reminded her as usual.

"And I might screw your necks too," Henny agreed. They all laughed and scampered out, finding Auntie Jo at the door. She sniffed honorably to signal that she was there and called cheerfully,

"Henny, my dear, may I come in?" She carefully shut the door, and at this sound Bonnie stopped playing. After a moment, hearing Jo talking "nineteen to the dozen," she sighed and went on with her music, but with less verve. It was a mystery, thought Bonnie, that Jo was so wonderful with little kiddies and knew so little about all other kinds of people. As soon as children crossed the threshold of the elementary schoolroom they became forever incomprehensible and alien to Jo.

Evie, standing now between her mother and her aunt, fidgeting with her aunt's great arm round her, seemed to be looking up trustfully with her brown eyes, but those deceptive eyes were full of revolt, mistrust, and dislike. Evie saw only the peccary skin, long blond hair strewn on her aunt's slab cheeks, the powder and rouge (light as it was) caked with moisture, the loofah hair; she shrank from the long, plump, inhuman thigh, the glossy, sufficient skirt, from everything powerful, coarse, and proud about this great unmated mare. She shrank from her caresses and from the undulations of a voice intended to be full of honey: she understood that Jo was wooing her mother. The thin, dark mother seemed, as she grew more insolent, more polished, more ladylike, to be more enchanting to little dark Evie. "Oh," thought Evie to herself, "when I am a lady with a baby, I won't have all those bumps, I won't be so big and fat, I won't croak and shout, I will be a little woman, thin like I am now and not fat in front or in the skirt." She was very much ashamed of Auntie Jo's waggling; she feared that when her aunt went down the street, people would stop and begin to laugh, until the whole street would point at her aunt and shriek, "As she walks she wobbles." Evie gradually, politely, drew away from Auntie Jo and laid her thin brown arms over her mother's slender thighs.

"Run away and play, mother's pet," said Henny, now as elegant and sweet as she could possibly be. As Evie closed the door, she heard Aunt Jo say,

"Well, I found out all about that man! Bonnie has been carrying on with him as I thought. I can't get over it! A sister of mine! But then, I suppose I should realize that Bonnie lost her mother when very young," and Jo's voice, becoming sentimental and womanly, was lost to Evie, though she had closed the door as slowly as possible.

Presently Jo had to go, saying good-by all round, patting heads, waving very cheerfully and lovingly to Henny, even though once again she had to trample on her feelings and forbid the question that always came up in her mind, "Why won't Henny ask me just once to stay to a meal?" Henny, not even waiting till Jo had got safely out of earshot, ran out to the kitchen to get some more tea, exclaiming,

"Frowsy, blowsy old hen! I wonder I put up with her as much as I do! Why does she sit gabbling in my ear for an hour? Does she think I like her company? Why on earth doesn't she put a comb through that bristling ugly yellow haystack of hers. I can't stand it: it's like a birch broom in a fit. I wish she would stop pawing and mugging me. Ugh!" And the children pondered once more over this mystery; why was Jo's fine corn-silk hair so ugly?

Meanwhile, Sam, after a long and merry afternoon, at last

declared that it was knock-off time and went upstairs to rest before dinner. He did close his eyes for half an hour before a bright idea unfolded itself to him and he got up to knock out a program for his Pacific trip on the portable. But during this half-hour he had been thinking about his little sister, Bonnie, for whom he had a great tenderness. She had always opened an eager ear to all his little-boy projects and schoolboy boastings and adolescent discoveries. When he was away, would she fall a prey to the card-trick màn, the wolf Holloway? She knew nothing of the world, Sam thought, and he wished again that his mother had lived, if only for Bonnie's sake. This led him to think of Henny and her occupations during his absence. Although Henny was now old and leathery, scraggy and haggard, she had a large acquaintance in her old home town, Baltimore, amongst immoral and worthless men and women, who went in for alcohol and smoking.

Sam had discussed this intimate question at lunch yesterday with Saul Pilgrim, his oldest friend; Saul had given the world-old advice, had dug up the plan that had already served since antiquity. For the tenth time, he told Saul Pilgrim about the second year of his marriage to Henny. He had brought a man to the house who had been the codlin-moth of marriage. He had told him never to darken his door again, but the mischief was done. A woman that Sam had loved, wooed, and given his name to, and had a child by, could in such a short space of time look at another man and perhaps worse! Only Henny's vicious upbringing, that of a rich wastrel, could explain it. Sam, like all men who have the traits of a man, had not failed to do, in the second year of marriage and ever since, what all real men do: he had confided his secret sorrow to a great many of his bosom friends, calling upon truth to witness that never was a more faithful, long-suffering husband than he, or a lighter-headed, vainer, more pernicious woman, than this that he, good soul, had innocently joined himself to. There were plenty of women, said Sam, yes, he knew it, with his views of loyalty; he believed in, loved the sex; but all the Collyers were corrupt.

Sam had told Saul about the delights of his first marriage. The first true joy he had known on earth, even greater than his first love, Louie's mother, was the education of his baby daughter Louisa. He had kept a journal from the first day, supervised her education from the first week. As a reward, he one day heard her say his name, "Tamma, Tamma!"

Thinking of the delight he had each time, to see the new inchoate mind burst from the womb, to see the clouds of larval imbecility disperse from the infant face, to watch that horrible throbbing patch close in the cranium and try to devise from its round forehead what its future would be, Sam got up with a sibylline smile and went to his desk to write out a prospectus of his Pacific trip. Though far away, he would carry his children with him in his heart and he would be with them too.

It was then that Sam found Henny's note, left since this morning, and till now covered by papers, for Little-Sam, looking for "The Year 3000," had scrambled up everything. A minute later came the lusty shout,

"Henrietta! Come up here!"

Henny muttered in her room; it was like the rusty stirring of some weed-grown sea animal, bottom-prisoned by blindness.

"Henrietta! Henrietta!" shouted Sam. Henny muttered. Then, suddenly, she was in the door of the kitchen, tossing her head and rolling her eyes back so that her pale olive eyeballs glared—a bizarre trick of hers, saying loudly to Bonnie,

"Tell the children's father that he can come down to me if he wants to speak to me. I'm not a servant!" She then retreated as hastily to her bedroom. Bonnie looked discomfited at Louie and whispered,

"You go and tell Daddy he ought to go and talk to your mother when she wants him to; oh, dear," and she gave Louie a plaintive glance and nodded.

"Henrietta, speak to me, you devil," cried Sam.

Like a genie of smoke Henny again stood in the kitchen door; and said firmly, "Louisa, don't stand there like a stuck pig! Go and tell your father that if he wants to speak to me he can come downstairs to do it, even if he is the Great I Am." The little girl, hangdog, bowed under the guilt of both, stumped upstairs, as Sam continued to call and Henny continued to blackguard him. At the top of the stairs, in his sitting room, Sam was standing, holding a piece of paper in his hand and trembling with rage. He shouted at Louisa,

"Tell that accurst devil to come and say what she has to say, not to write letters!"

Louie mumbled, "She said to go to her, Daddy; she said she won't come up. She said she couldn't walk upstairs." Louie looked at his red face and whispered hastily, "Don't shout at her, Daddy, it makes her angry." Desperately she looked up into his face: but he was beyond her. However, he mastered himself and brushed past Louisa towards the stairs. At the head of the stairs, he turned towards her roughly and said,

"Go and look at yourself in the glass! You'd better clean up your face." While he was running downstairs, Louisa hastened to his shaving glass and saw that her nose was running with her crying, and she had brushed her face into smudges. She wept while she was rubbing her cheeks on his shaving towel. Everyone heard the birds outside.

Samuel found Henny standing, in her outdoor dress, waiting stiffly, and—as he admitted in a moment of surprise—attractive with her proud expression, high color, and curled hair. He handed her the note with a glance of contempt, and she mechanically read through what she had herself written:

> *Samuel Pollit: I have to talk to you about finances and about that child of yours. I cannot be left stranded with a houseful of children and no servant. I must have Hazel Moore back and be able to pay her. You must agree to this and also make regular payments. You can starve me but not your children.*
>
> *HCP.*

She threw it on the bed.

"What's the meaning of this, Henny?" he asked, pointing to

the crushed bit of paper. "Don't send me notes. I ordered you not to do it."

Her voice rattled in her throat and she rolled her lids down over her large eyes and compressed her mouth, looking as ugly and bitter as she could,

"You take a jaunt whenever you like, and expect me to stay here when I'm sick with a great windy house gone to seed, full of little children. How am I to look after them? I do all the work and get all the blame while you streel off whenever it suits you and get your name in the papers. You cut a big figure with your friends, but I know what's behind it." She tossed her head, "I suppose you think I don't know how you tell everyone everything about me! What can you expect——?"

But Sam was taking hold of himself, and a surge of compassion, not only for himself, nor for Henny, but for the misery of all such souls wedded to bondage, rushed up,

"What do you want to see me about, Pet? As for the money, you'll get all I have: you'll get it regularly. I understand that it's not easy for you to be left alone here and you'd better make up your mind either to live amicably with Bonnie, or else to get a general servant. But I absolutely forbid you to have Hazel Moore in this house. She's a Bible thumper and hates me; she's a desiccated virgin and hates the children, and I won't have a cabal of women setting my children against me."

Henny threw her head back and laughed, the artificial, society laugh never heard in Tohoga House except in stresses, a gesture which showed all the cords and wrinkles in her early-aged neck and her saffron skin. She went on,

"I suppose you want me to bring up two little girls with a woman like your sister Bonnie in the house? Hazel is the only one who'll stand by me and she's the only one who would stand your insults and the poverty and dirt of this house, and the noise. I've got to have her. I won't, I can't undertake it by myself. You plant me in a charity house on the top of a windy hill and expect me to bring up six children without money, or heat, or proper clothes, or decent food, and in a town that's the most expensive in the country, where everyone has a car and servants. Why, I wonder you don't notice that everyone laughs in your face. Well, there's just one thing for it—either I have Hazel, and money to pay her, or I'll go home and take the children with me, and if you try to take them, I'll sue you and let out all the rotten bag of tricks you pull. I'll take the grin off your face and the flattering smile and the softsoaping handshake, and I'll wipe the great big, mealy words out of your mealy mouth."

He bent a little, baffled by her rowdiness, but replied, "I won't have Hazel, she puts my children against me. I haven't forgotten," he ended in a low voice, eying Henny accusingly. She gave a ringing laugh,

"She threw your stupid books on the floor and that's an injury for life; don't you think a woman gets sick of your jawing, and calling you to your meals, while she's got the dirty work to do?"

"Books are sacred to me," Sam said in a self-commiserating voice: "who would hurt them, would hurt a human being; it is more and worse, because they are the thoughts of people."

"And for one of your dirty books you would kill me," Henny cried, getting up. "Let's stop this. You have her or you don't have me, that's all. You can go now and make up your mind."

He softened his voice, "Pet, don't let's get into a conflict again: try to help me. This is for you and the children. Even if you hate me, you know this job is a good thing. I have a better position and better pay. You could have done much better and had social life if you had been willing. I can get a job anywhere after an appointment like this. If you are tired of Washington, we can go elsewhere perhaps."

She was silent for a while and relaxed slightly so that one could see that for him she had once had charm. At last she said,

"Don't be so pigheaded: you think of no one but yourself. You know I can't manage the children. I haven't the force of character of a Pollit. I won't let Hazel say anything against you. You ought to know that. As for her religious mumbo jumbo—do I go to church? You weaned me from that! You can rest assured."

He began to hector, "I won't have any negative talk round my

[125]

children. I love my children: they are with me day and night."
She cried, "Oh, Samuel, don't be such a fool. What humbug! Do
you think I can't manage Hazel! She's been with me since I was
a girl—and if I can't, Mother can. Let's talk about other things.
Louisa's getting too big to beat. I don't know what to do with
her. Her stupid great-aunt didn't ask her to her for the holidays
today, and I'm darned if I'll have her round the house all the
time. I want a little peace and to have my children to myself. She
has your high-and-mighty ways. Another thing, she's over eleven
and she's getting to be a woman already. It makes me sick to
think that I have to tell her what's coming to her, what she has
to go through. Why should I do it? Why should I go through the
rigmarole with another woman's girl? I'm not going to speak to
her. It's your place or the place of one of her aunts. I couldn't
drag her into all the darn muck of existence myself."

Sam flushed, with an expression of excited curiosity,

"Why, already——?"

Henrietta tapped her foot with impatience, "You've got to talk
to her and tell her how to behave. I'm not going to beat such a
big girl any more. My veins swell and I nearly faint every time
I have to face her. And you shouldn't beat her either. It's not
right at her age. You don't know what you're doing, that think
yourself so clever. Write to her mother's sister and tell her she
has to take her and do the business too. I won't."

Sam lowered his head, "Henrietta, you must do that: you are
her mother."

"Her mother!" cried Henrietta, looking scornful. "If you
weren't what you are you'd see what a rotten beastly thing I am.
If you weren't what you are you wouldn't drag her through this:
but anything to suit your book. I detest the child but I'm sorry
for her, which is more than you are. Take her away. I can't face
it. Oh, God," she turned away from him, "when I think that whoever she is, she has to do what I have done, and know what I
have known, and find out all the beastly lies." She looked up at
him, "That's why I don't care what she hears or knows about our
marriage. Let her know for herself what it is: then she won't look

back to me as the one who tricked her. I beat her, but I don't lie to her."

Sam sighed; and, after a silence, he said, "Well, Pet, I'll, of course, speak to Louie and tell her to behave and help you all she can and to work at school and so on. But I'm no fit person and I'm afraid you have to act as mother to her. That is the duty you took on in the beginning and you must perform it. She is young yet anyhow. Let us hope—we'll let it go for a while!"

Henny shrieked with impatience, "Let it go! Why don't you send the miserable sulky wretch to boarding school, while you're away? What can I do with another woman's girl? Isn't it enough to have one of my own? When I think of the years ahead of her I want to drown myself."

Sam said in his deep, sympathetic tone, "Why don't you try mothering Louie a bit?"

Henny gave him a sulky look, "You try it!"

Sam bit his lip, "I've been hard on her, Pet, hoping you would soften. I taught her not to coax me or kiss me, or climb on my lap as the others do because in the beginning it made you so angry—but I hope she still looks to me for righteousness and justice! I thought she would turn to the woman for affection and love. It is natural. If I had been soft to her you would have turned against us both." His voice trembled.

"What's the use of going into that? How am I to get the household money? You know we need a new boiler."

He began to explain to her that she would get her money monthly, almost all his salary, and that he would exist on his expenses as much as he could and that he would get invitations from friends abroad which would stretch the money farther.

As soon as she understood the number of persons going, she sneered, "I suppose you fine scientists can't get along without secretaries; I suppose you're taking some of those eighteen-year-old high-class women along."

His face became stern, "Henrietta!"

"Well, are you?"

"I won't answer such insinuations."

She let out a howl of laughter, "I hear your answer. I know your breed; all your fine officials debauch the young girls who are afraid to lose their jobs: that's as old as Washington." He clenched his fist and brought it down on her dressing table; then, controlling himself, he turned to her, with a paling face and said quietly,

"Perhaps I have made a mistake, but Heaven knows I have been faithful to my marriage vows."

She chuckled, "The more fool you!"

He flushed and rushed to her, taking her by the shoulder and shaking her hard. She turned her face awkwardly to look up at him, "You know you're lying!"

He struck her hard on the shoulder, saying, "You are tempting me to do it!"

She at once let out a loud cry, "Don't you hit me, you devil; don't you dare strike your wife; I'll let everyone know!"

She struggled up from the chair and ran to the side window that looked out on Thirty-fourth Street and faced an empty paddock. There were no houses within hailing distance from this window since their house took up the side of that block, and she was gratified when she felt Sam's hand over her mouth. She spat and pushed it away, cried feebly,

"Help, help! Murder!"

Sam dropped behind her. She waited for him to speak, but he said nothing. She turned and walked to her chair. "Get me my smelling salts," she said to him. "You're killing me." She opened her purse and took out a bottle of pyramidon.

"Pet, don't take that dreadful thing!"

She laughed and pushed past him to the washstand from which she took a glass of water. Raising it, she asked him, "How do you know what's in this?" She looked at him through the water as she drank it and slowly closed her eyes. "Now get out," she said through the water.

Sam, turning away, saw Louie, a figure of condemnation, in the doorway. The look of concern she turned on her mother changed to rebuke when she looked at him. Sam put out his hand

and said quietly, "Looloo," but she ducked ably by him and went to Henrietta, "Mother, can I get you anything?"

"Leave me alone," said Henrietta, "your father has done enough. Go out and close the door." Louie did so. Sam stood irresolute in the hall. When Louie came out, he said under his breath,

"Looloodirl!"

Louie looked at him, and turning, began to walk towards the kitchen.

"Looloodirl!"

She slowed up, but entered the kitchen at this pace. He called sharply, "Louie!"

She reappeared and footed the journey towards him unwillingly.

He demanded, "Why don't you come when your poor little Samuel calls?"

"I don't know."

"I know," he said with sudden bitterness, "because your mother's game is working after all. She is turning you against me."

"No," said Louie.

He looked at her pityingly, "No, I know you don't know it, Looloo."

"Why do you torment her?" Louie burst out blindly.

"Come into the sunroom," he said, "I want to talk to you; no, better you and I should go and have a little talky-walky. Comb your hair and put on your shoes, and we'll go and look at the dear old Plenty-Fish perhaps." Plenty-Fish was what he sometimes called the Potomac.

To make her farewells, Louie went back to the veranda where the children were sitting, waiting for her. Saul said,

"Go on, Louie, the story!"

"I can't, I've got to go for a walk."

"The story, oh, finish it first," said Evie.

Louie hesitated and then began in a husky voice, "When they

[129]

came to the inn, he who had the pig's heart could not sit down to table, but went to snuffle in a dish in the corner."

She felt and heard without seeing the shudder of delight that went through them. Saul, who had been doing "Hrork, hrork!" like a pig, stopped, transfixed, looking ugly and comical, with a green velvet band tied round his head, holding up his short, stiff yellow hair. Ernie's brown face was merry and shining.

"Looloodirl!"

Ernie groaned, "Pad, let her finish, let her finish first!"

"Da seevo [this evening]!" Samuel sang out, "da seevo; now Loolabulloo and Sam-the-Bold have to have a little talky-walky." The children groaned but in a minute dashed off to other occupations. The sun was going down, and Sunday-Funday was coming to an end. They all felt it with a kind of misery: with such a fine long day and so many things to do, how could they have let it slip past like this? Tomorrow was schoolday, brief, snipped up into lessons, full of playground clashes, nasty, and without fun. There was no day going like Sunday-Funday with Sam at home.

2 ⚓ The meridian of murder.

As THEY WALKED OUT, the sun went down in yellow pulp and Sam's New Jerusalem was dissolved in a milk soup, but there was a faint air on Georgetown Heights. The clouds were rising higher, but plenty of stars lay inanimate beyond the filmy sky.

"Judge not, Looloo," said Sam in an undertone: "who knows all forgives all. I knew before marriage to Henrietta Collyer that she and I should never have come together, but a young man's sense of honor, so often mistaken, misplaced as medieval chivalry, prevented me from making the break." He put his arm along her shoulders.

"But Mother said she didn't want to marry you," Louie remarked maliciously.

Sam ignored this.

"I say, frankly, Looloo, that I believed that I could remold her life and with my wife and children make a little nucleus of splendid men and women to work for the future. That was, is, my only dream, my life hope: for I am only a dreamer in realities. I want you to understand me, Looloo: she did not even try to."

Pale as a candle flame in the dusk, tallow-pale, he stalked along, holding her hand, and Louie looked up and beyond him at the enfeebled stars. Thus, for many years, she had seen her father's head, a ghostly earth flame against the heavens, from her little height. Sam looked down on the moon of her face; the day-shine was enough still to light the eyeballs swimming up to him.

"You will never understand, Looloo-dirl, what I suffered: but I have battled my way through. Fate puts stones in the path of those she wants to try; she found I had stuffing in me and is satisfied." He told her what he had suffered, tantrums, screams, fainting fits, lies, slander, the running to neighbors and family with tales, the planting in his household of an enemy and spy, Hazel Moore.

"One day she found some of my books on the table she wanted for luncheon, and she pushed them off on to the floor, hating me and them: this cut me to the heart, Looloo, because it showed me how both of them were in league against me and all that stands for man's progress and the freedom of his spirit. Don't think I was stiff-necked—I spoke to both of them gently, argued with the Devil—as the old Christians would say." He told her about the "tyranny of tears": "Men call it the tyranny of tears, it is an iron tyranny—no man could be so cruel, so devilish, as a woman with her weakness, recrimination, convenient ailments, nerves, and tears. We men are all weak as water before the primitive devices of Eve. I was patient at first, many years. You were too young then, Looloo: you did not see how kind I was, hoping for an improvement: constant dropping wears away a stone, and it was only much later that I found out hardness worked better than love. It broke my heart, nearly, to find it out. It would have broken my heart only that I had other interests. When you grow up, Looloo-dirl, you will understand what I mean, though you, Looloo, will never use those treacherous devices."

"No," said Louie, very good.

He pressed her hand, "You can never know the hell I have been through: you do not know what she did not only to me but to the little children. She has tortured them, turned them against me, lied to them, pretended I lied, I, who never told a lie in my life, Looloo: I want you to believe that and remember it always," he said sternly.

"Yes," Louie said solemnly.

"I do not know how I got through without breaking down, without my heart bursting from sorrow and shame. These heads and hearts I have come from that."

Louie became confidential, looking up trustingly into his shadowed face, "I saw things too, Daddy: I remember those things."

He said rather briskly, "Yes, you have seen things, too; but you cannot appreciate what I mean and will not for years to come, perhaps never. My sorrows, while all the time I was struggling upward, were more than man should bear."

"I had sorrows too," she piped up.

"I know, Looloo, I know," he said hastily, squeezing her hand. "We are close to each other: you are nearly of an age to begin to understand me. I wished to live only in the regions of thought and I was forced back, dragged down to earth—no, into the slime, by a woman who is—without knowing it, I believe, poor woman —as vicious as it is possible to be, without committing crimes. But there are crimes against the spirit of man." There was suppressed thunder in his voice. "Who tarnishes, assaults, threatens, hates the spirit of man is guilty of crime." After a pause he said gloomily, "Even at that I am not sure she did not want to commit actual crimes. Many is the time I have gone to the Department not knowing whether I would come home to find you butchered! Yes, Looloo, that is what she would say to me when I left for work, knowing it would torture me all through the day; she would ring me up at work to say it, knowing it would prevent me from working."

"I know," said Louie.

"She told me she would kill you and bury you in 'the grave' in the orchard, not to get rid of you, so much as to go to jail and get away from me: she said she would welcome hanging to get away from me. Can you imagine what my life was, Looloo?" he asked in a tone of horror, far away from his daughter, in the grisly past. "Murder! And she used to threaten to write insulting letters to the women I knew, noble-minded women—she said she would poison me and herself. She said she hated my children—her own children, Looloo-dirl, her own children!"

"She tried to choke me," said Louie sulkily.

Sam said, sharp as a whip, "What does this mean?"

"Last time when Tommy had convulsions, when I came in with the other blanket, I nearly fell into the bath of hot water, and Mother tried to choke me and then Tommy, and then she said she would drown us rather in the hot water and then she tried to choke herself."

After a short pause, Sam abruptly told her not to be melodramatic, that she could defend herself against a weak woman like Henny, and her brother too, "Your mother is not strong."

Louie sulked; then she said hotly, "You said it depends where it is whether it's murder."

"What are you talking about?"

"The Polynesians don't think it's murder: you said so. Old women collect money, then they get a young man to murder them and bury them. You said so. You said, it doesn't matter if the people in the country don't mind it."

His voice had cleared, "Oh! Yes, I did say that, Looloo, murder depends upon the meridian, so to speak: the thousand and one tables of morality (when we objectively consider the facts of ethnic mores), teach us not to be hidebound about our own particular little prejudices, even in law. Consider what is supposed to be a heinous offense, murder. Now, call it war, and it becomes a patriotic duty to urge other people to go and murder and be murdered. Foolish old Jo, who is a goodhearted woman, sent dozens of white feathers during the Late Unpleasantness or, in other words, desired young men to go and be murdered. En she could hev done with a young man herself: it was a combination of the sacred folly of race suicide, willful sterility, and murder. En ebblyone thought Jo was a big gun of patriotism: I bleeve your little foolish Aunt Jo will get herself 'lected to the D.A.R.'s yet—she's bin and discovered a Pollit what had no more sense than to go and fight long time ago: ten to one he was a redcoat— oh, what a joke on Jo!"

"Mother said to ask you for some money for a new dress, Dad," said Louie, after Sam had finished laughing. Sam chuckled again. "This one is all spots," said Louie.

"Now, wimmin is prone to murder," said Sam. "In wicked old Europe still, you get the village witch planning to murder husbings for them wives what is a bit tired of making coffee for the old man."

"Do they?" asked Louie, entranced.

"Yiss, and fum what I know of some wimminfolk what I know," continued Sam chuckling, "they would very much like to get to know them there witches. En some husbings too would like to know such witches." Louie giggled. "We could get rid of our old wives which is always mad at us and we could get sweet little beauts what is seventeen years old," said Sam. Louie giggled.

Louie and Sam chattered for a while on this interesting subject of countenanced murder, and then Sam told Louie that they must be serious, for murder was really a serious thing, because it meant hate, and hate produced all the wickedness of the world.

"If your own dear mother had lived, for example, my life would have been fulfilled and it would have been a paradise for me. I would not have minded if her mind had not developed, if she had just remained my own dear wife, for I should have been heartened to go on. Your dear mother understood my aims—or, let us say, she understood me and urged me on, in everything. She was anxious for me to study and get on, not for vulgar success, but because she was a true woman whose home was dear to her and because I was dear to her and you too, little Ducky she called you, and then because she knew of my high ambitions, through my so often having told them to her."

"What was your ambition?" asked Louie, full of interest. She too was very ambitious. She wished to be a Spartan, for example: if she could go to the dentist and never make a squeak, she felt she would make a great impression. Then she wished to become great. At present she only read about men of destiny.

"You know it, Looloo," he replied in a deep voice. "It is to be of those who spread the light, the children of light."

On the way back, he was soulfully happy. To amuse her he told her some more about permitted murder, for he could see it amused her. In some secret societies, it was understood that a traitor would be murdered by a member of the society: this was the understanding on which he entered the fraternity. Suicide ought to be recognized and permitted, for a person was captain of his own life. Murder of the unfit, incurable, and insane should be permitted. Children born mentally deficient or diseased should be murdered, and none of these murders would really be a crime, for the community was benefited, and the good of the whole was the aim of all, or should be.

"Murder might be beautiful, a self-sacrifice, a sacrifice of someone near and dear, for the good of others—I can conceive of such a thing, Looloo! The extinction of one life, when many are threatened, or when future generations might suffer—wouldn't you, even you, think that a fine thing? Why, we might murder thousands—not indiscriminately as in war now—but picking out the unfit and putting them painlessly into the lethal chamber. This alone would benefit mankind by clearing the way for a eugenic race. I am glad to say that some of our states have already passed laws which seem to point to a really scientific view of these things, in the near future. But you are right, Looloo, the old savages went us one better—the Polynesians got there before us, in a way."

When they got home, Louie was full of excitement. She had never come so near to talking about her own ambitions, and Sam was in a comradely mood.

"You will be all right, Looloo," concluded Sam, kissing her good night. "You are myself; I know you cannot go astray."

"I won't be like you, Dad."

He laughed, "You can't help it: you are myself."

She sulked; she wanted to be like Eleanora Duse, not like Sam.

"I wish I had a Welsh grammar," she said swiftly.

"Don't be an idiot! What for?" He laughed.

"I'd like to learn Welsh or Egyptian grammar; I could read the poetry Borrow talks about, and I could read *The Book of the Dead*."

"Learn good American grammar," he said, good-humoredly, giving her a flip on the cheek.

"I know that," said Louie; "there's no one as good as me."

"And learn to hold your shoulders straight," he said, turning away from her and turning on the radio. "You know, Looloo, I'd like to get half an hour on a station and get direct contact with a broader audience: imagine talking to your fellow man from coast to coast!"

She went up to bed insulted again.

"I will repay," she said, on the stairs, halting and looking over the banisters, with a frown. "Vengeance is mine, saith the Lord, I will repay, no, vengeance is mine, I will repay."

She dreamed she had a large scythe, suspended in space, and in this dusky space was God, softly thundering with the rhythm of a pendulum, but the pendulum was the scythe. The scythe, which she was somehow operating, swung closer to the earth and began there to mow the grass. The heartbeats of God grew louder with long rollings, like the gong in the hall, and she thought, "It is the last day." She woke. The gong was being beaten in the hall as if to get them up for the morning, but it was dark still. Down in the hall Henny cried,

"I'll bring people in; help! Louie, your father's beating me!"
Louie heard Bonnie rushing downstairs.

3 ❧ Conversation.

"HE LIVES," said Henny to herself, in her bed, "in a golden cloud
floating about over a lot of back alleys he never sees; and I'm a
citizen of those back alleys, like a lot of other sick sheep. I'd like
to pull the wool off his eyes, but I don't dare. He'd take the children away from me; I'd be branded, hounded—I know his Lordship. I'm steaming with this heat and the pain I'm in. I suppose
he's too good to notice that, because he keeps making Dr. Doe
itemize the bill, the tooth patchings are getting few and far between. Connie O'Meara thinks she's a modern woman; and I
have a vote too. But the fact remains that a man can take my
children from me if he gets something on me; and a lot of fat old
maids and scrawny hags in their fifties stand back of every darn
man-made law in this and any other state. I have to be pure and
chaste before getting married and after—for whom please?—for
Samuel Pollit; otherwise, I'm no good before and he can take my
children after. He's dying to do it, too, and have them brought
up by that monster Jo Pollit, I suppose, or his beautiful Louisa,
in memory of dear Rachel, the great love: anyone, as long as he
grabs them away from me, because I'm no good."

Henny tossed and turned, trying to make some plans about her
finances in Sam's absence. Would she get her own family together
and arrange a kind of unofficial moratorium with her creditors
so that either she could pay them off by economy and reform, or
her father or Hassie could be eventually moved to pay them off?
What would she do if Sam's stern nature or perfect morality
should weaken or if, by any freak of scientific curiosity or middle-
aged humanity, he might start looking into her life and asking
himself what sort of a person he was married to? It would be all
up with Henny and her children. Yet she daily trembled before
the wild plunge of confessing herself to him and letting him
know the worst; with rage, envy, malice, she thought of his ignorance of all her troubles. He thought she was a sort of ignorant
servant, and so he paid her almost nothing. He hankered after

women with degrees and time to run to committee meetings. "It is easy," thought Henny, "to worry about peace conferences when you have servants, a car, and new hats; yes, then you give teas and so forth at home, to show off your new Persian mat and cocktail table. I thought of doing the same: I understand. But it is easy to get a little flutter out of the latest anti-alien bill out of New Mexico and the fate of peons when a man hasn't the courage to get a mistress, or incur a debt, or take a drink of whisky!"

Henny got up and started to play patience on her dressing table, brushing aside the extensive toilet set and looking at herself occasionally in the mirror. She liked to do this: it refreshed and encouraged her. "Good God, what an old hag!" she said as she sat down; "really, that Bert is a good soul! I must do something, dye my hair or something—but I hate it! Especially with my wrinkles! A young wig on an old face—very convincing. Why with his prudery and chastity the wretch has used me up more than four husbands." She began to laugh, "But here he lives like a Mormon with women all round him, sister, wife so-called, servant at times, daughters to work for him, to say nothing of secretaries and public women to admire him and hold his hand, distant relations visiting him—and yet no one in his bed!" She slapped down the cards irritably, "Anything rather than lose my expectations! Poor wretches, poor miserable wretches! And to think the poor creature, his sister, that washes his floors for him can't even kiss her knave of hearts because it doesn't suit his name." She threw back her head and laughed fully but falsely to herself in the mirror. The pack was out. She lifted two or three cards and peeped, then abstracted a card and put it in its place. But after two or three more moves, she suddenly began to gather them in and shuffle them. As usual, she had cheated without the game's coming out. She began to lay the cards out again, then said, "Who the dickens cares if it comes out or not?" and, pulling her gown round her, went out to make herself some tea. First, she shut the door, because she had left the cards lying on the table. Louie and Sam both heard familiar noises in the kitchen. Louie dropped off at once again, but Sam had been restless and now lay awake thinking. Perhaps, now, in the middle of the night, he should go down and talk to her (or would she wake the children with her woman's hysterics?). He turned and tossed while the teamaking was in progress; he was afraid of her execrations, afraid of her hardness and misery. He called a spade the predecessor of modern agriculture, she called it a muck dig: they had no words between them intelligible. At last he rolled out of bed and stood dubiously on his bedside mat shuffling his toes into each other, and then at the head of the stairs, shilly-shallying. At last he padded downstairs. There was a curious rumpling noise in the kitchen. In the great hall below it was cooler. He stood just outside the fall of light trying to see what she was doing. He was startled to see her leaning backwards on a loose-jointed kitchen chair, fixing a roller blind. He waited until she had regained her balance and then cried,

"Pet, why couldn't it wait till the morning? Of all the fool things!"

"Oh, my God!" she cried, turning quickly with her hand on her chest; then furiously, "How you frightened me! Was that your idea? Why didn't you let me hear you coming instead of sneaking up on me, spying on me in the middle of the night? What do you want? Are you spying on me as usual?"

"Pet, why the deuce do you do these fool things? Half the accidents are caused by fool women in homes doing stupid things."

"If you think I care if I break my neck!" She laughed, all the deep smudges and lines in her face coming out. "A broken arm, and I'd have a holiday perhaps; a broken back, and I'd have a holiday forever."

"Henny, drink your tea. I came to talk to you quietly while the others are in bed—about my trip!"

"I should think so! But why at this unearthly hour? Are you afraid of their hearing what I have to say to you?"

"Let's talk, Pet, while we have the chance. We are bringing up a family and we haven't exchanged words for years."

"Whose fault is it, I'd like to know," she said tossing her head and her poor naked neck with its goose flesh. "Every word you say to me is an insult. I used to go out with you till you insulted me in public. I used to have friends here till you insulted them. I won't let my children hear their mother insulted. When they get sense what will they think of you treating their mother that way?"

"I'm not going into the black past——"

She interrupted him, turning her back, "If you have something to say, out with it and leave me alone."

"I am going away for six or eight months—that depends on funds and results," Sam said deliberately, "and during that time you are, of course, my lieutenant, and have to run the house and bring up the children. I hope you will try to do it on a proper budget and without unnecessary waste. The remuneration is good, and we can perhaps save something. We will need it, Henny. I have heard that your father, with all his obligations and his keeping of your weak-kneed brothers and their big families, is not doing well. It's pouring money into a quicksand to give it to your brothers. I wish there had been more like Hassie in the family. But let that pass. I want you to take thought to the future. And perhaps we can come to a better understanding. You know yourself that we can't go on like this."

"I wish to God we could not," said Henny desperately, "but we can, that's the devil of it——"

"It's on account of this language," Sam exclaimed impatiently, "that I have to come down like this in the middle of the night. My children ought not to hear such expressions. They hear nothing like that from their father. And I must insist on your controlling your language while I'm away. You know if I could I would take them from your influence—I cannot. The law keeps me in bondage and so I see them daily being filched from me, sneaked away by a hundred kinds of mean tricks and bitter expressions and my own home life run in the Collyer style——"

"The Collyer style," she repeated twice: "where would you be without the Collyer style? You Dr. Know-All! You don't know where your bread and butter comes from. You know everything but that!"

Sam gave her a hard look, "You know I cannot provide for two homes, or I would."

"You probably do as it is," Henny teased. "No, I know you; you haven't the guts for it. You just keep them tailing along." He kept his temper, "Well, I see you're not in a proper mood. I'll wait till the morning. Get some sleep. Don't stay up brooding and fixing your facial muscles into those hag lines: you look like a woman of forty-five!"

She gave him a fierce look, "Just as you please!" She turned to pour out another cup of tea, her hands trembling more and more. She realized that he was still standing there. Swiftly she turned to him, "I might as well tell you now; why should I drag through another sleepless night? It's beyond my endurance. It will kill me. Sam, let us separate! I can't stand it. You're not happy. I'll go back to Mother and take the children while you're away, and when you come back we can fix things up without anyone noticing particularly. Your going away makes just the right opportunity. We can close this damn-fool rackety old barn, and I'll live at Monocacy. I'll even take your stinking animals along and let the man look after them, if you want the kids to have them. And Father can let Tohoga House, if he's as hard up as he seems."

Anger and balking gleamed in Sam's eyes,

"You will never break up my home. I know that's been your object for years and the aim of all your secret maneuvers. I love my children as no man ever loved his before. I know men love their children, but mine are bound up in me, part of me—" he paused breathless for a moment. "In all my misery they are my great consolation; there could be no joy in the world like my home to me. Men wreck their lives, endure backbreaking toil for years for their children. Some women cannot even understand such love as man feels in his strength for those weak ones playing round him who—" He paused again, much moved. "The light of the years to come, to me; and the law would give them into your charge because you are their mother, no matter what kind of a woman you are."

"How dare you say that! How dare you——"

"Silence!" he said very sternly. "I'll say no more now. Get to bed. I see there are some things to be thrashed out. I might have known you had some such devilish scheme to work as soon as your chance came. You have no respect for my work; you only look meanly on this absence of mine as a chance to wreak all your spite and vengeance. When a woman hates, she will wreck a dozen lives to pay back what she conceives to be some injury. You only see in this a chance to further your own work of disintegration. You devil of rust and rot and boring. You will not smash my family life. You will carry your bargain through to the end. You will look after my children—" his voice trembled, and he said very bitterly,—"ours!" He collected himself and turned towards the door. "Good night! I'll speak to you in the morning."

"I'll divorce you," cried Henny. "I'll find a way. There must be a way. And I'll take my children from you. The man who loves children! You can have your own. That's all you really care about, anyway. You and she can go and live together and think about your rotten fine thoughts and you can weep over that sweet woman that would have made your life a paradise. Poor wretch! She died."

Sam turned and shouted, "Don't try to smear my past happiness." The house no longer contained snores either fantastic, light, and querulous, or determined and snorty, but Louie still slept well.

Henny said, "When you come back there'll be no home. You'll have to find another way to provide for me and them."

"Shut up," shouted Sam, "shut up or I'll shut you up."

"You took me and maltreated me and starved me half to death because you couldn't make a living and sponged off my father and used his influence, hoisting yourself up on all my aches and miseries," Henny began chanting with fury, "boasting and blowing about your success when all the time it was me, my poor body that was what you took your success out of. You were breaking my bones and spirit and forcing your beastly love on me: a brute, a savage, a wild Indian wouldn't do what you did, slobbering round me and calling it love and filling me with children month after month and year after year while I hated and detested you and screamed in your ears to get away from me, but you wouldn't let me go. You were quite certain in your heart of hearts where your marvelous success came from, forcing me to stay here in this rotten old molar of a house to suit yourself, making me go down on my hands and knees to scrub floors and wash your filthy linen and your torn old bed sheets, your blankets, and even your suits—I've stuffed mattresses for you and your children and cooked dinners for the whole gang of filthy, rotten, ignorant, blowing Pollits that I hate. I've had the house stinking like a corpse cellar with your formalin that you're proud of and had to put up with your vile animals and idiotic collections and your blood-and-bone fertilizer in the garden and everlasting talk, talk, talk, talk, talk," she screamed in a hoarse voice, "boring me, filling my ears with talk, jaw, jaw, till I thought the only way was to kill myself to escape you and your world of big bluffs and big sticks, saving the whole rotten world with your talk. I've stood you and your rotten stinking little brat combing lice from her hair from the public school and her green teeth falling from the roots with dirt and your sweat and you know nothing all the time. It's ten years and it's too much, I'm through; you can pack your things and get out with your filthy brat. This is my house and you can go and find the tenement house you lived in, in Baltimore, before you slipped about in the slime in my father's fishshop, with the slum brats you were raised with; find the house and stay in it with your loud-mouth, dung-haired sister and take your whore sister with you."

Sam hit her, with his open hand, across the mouth. Looking back madly at him over her shoulder, she raced into the hall, groped and found the stick in the dark and struck the gong, shrieking for the children to come downstairs and saying she would rouse the neighbors, that the beast was at her again. When she heard Bonnie on the stairs, she ran into the kitchen, seized the bread knife, and rushed at him, slashing him backwards and forwards across the arm and shoulder, and began slashing at his face before he had the presence of mind to knock it out of her hand and push her away. She stumbled and fell to the floor, where she lay exhausted and trembling.

Bonnie and Louisa, who had been brought up short in the hall, petrified with horror, rushed into the kitchen, crying and begging the man and woman to come to their senses. Blind with her tears, and sobbing loudly, Louie, tripping over her night-dress, went to help her mother, who was resting on her elbow as she got up slowly, weeping dejectedly. Louie began tugging at her, but Henrietta pushed her away, saying, "Don't touch me, I've had enough of everything!" while Bonnie was wiping the blood off Sam's face and arm with a damp cloth, crying and saying, "What happened, Henny? Whatever happened, Sam? Oh, it wasn't because of me? What did you do to her, Sam? The children——!"

Sam was unable to articulate, full of rage, fear, and astonishment. He pushed Bonnie away and finished the wiping himself. Then as he watched Henny, leaning, like the dying gladiator, on her arm, and brushing her hand across her mouth, he said in a strange, distant voice, "Leave us; go to bed and leave us!"

Bonnie looked at him, terrified, but said nothing.

Henny looked up at him, "I don't want to be left with the likes of you; I'm afraid for my life." She began to move like a creature broken with pain, and sniffing, still feeling her mouth with a drooping wrist, she stood up and pushed back her hair.

Sam said automatically, "The gas is on full!" and Henny turned to it, and turned it down under the bubbling kettle.

"Go to bed," Sam admonished Louie in an undertone. Louie and Bonnie moved out, full of doubt, but not daring to intervene, realizing that this was a conflict on another plane. Bonnie, pausing on the stairs, sent the little girl to bed, whispering to her, "I'll just wait for a while, darlin'; don't you fret: Bonnie will watch."

"Henny!" Sam said.

"Oh, what do you want?" she murmured mournfully.

"Look at me!" He held out his arm and turned his face, showing the cuts which were still bleeding.

She gave a swift glance and picked up the damp dishcloth which she handed to him again, "Here, wipe yourself off: don't stand there with that blessed martyred air like a saint in church!" She looked at him awkwardly and with much difficulty wrenched her ashamed gaze away.

He dropped the rag in the sink, dried his hands, and, looking at her sideways from the towel, said evenly, "The worst part of it is, Pet, that you love me still in a way; everything you do—even this!—shows me that. I know it!"

Henny, after tightening all the taps on the stove, stood hunched, with her arms folded tightly gripping her forearms, her head bent towards her right shoulder; and in a moment she noticed the frosty glare of the wedding ring on her left fist. As she looked dully at the band of gold that was with her night, day, in her washings and cleanings, in the children's sickness and at their birthday parties, that went into the bath water, the dough bowl, and the folds of new cotton print running over the sewing machine, that went to the maternity ward with her and to the manicurist and fortuneteller's, that she saw when drinking cocktails with Bert and when signing away her every cent on some scrap of paper at the moneylender's, that stayed with her as stayed the man she had taken it from, she took a grip on herself. If this plain ugly link meant an eyeless eternity of work and poverty and an early old age, it also meant that to her alone this potent breadwinner owed his money, name, and fidelity, to her, his kitchen-maid and body servant. For a moment, after years of scamping, she felt the dread power of wifehood; they were locked in each other's grasp till the end—the end, a mouthful of sunless muckworms and grass roots stifling his blare of trumpets and her blasphemies against love. The timid, fame-loving wretch would never dare to shake her off; and that was how she had him still.

Sam was saying, "—I had long shuddering days, Henny, when it was as if the north wind was blowing all day, when I thought of our home here on the heights, exposed to all the winds of our anger and hate, those winds raging every hour of the day and night through our rooms and corridors. What would I find when

I reached home? You will never know—because you do not care in that way for me—what I suffered in the early days of our marriage. You talk of your own sufferings, Henny. I know, for instance, that that is why Hassie does not come here. But what about me? I loved you. Can you imagine the hours of horror I spent before I reached home, wondering if I would find my children slaughtered, as you promised, and yourself weltering in your own blood? One day I came home and looked everywhere for you. I called you. There was no answer. Nearly fainting, I rushed from room to room; and all the time, enjoying my exhaustion and horror, perhaps, you were hiding in the closet in the staircase. When I opened the door, I found you moaning and spent in the corner, worn out by your own dramatics! I never knew when you meant it, nor that you were always shamming so shamefully. I saw my entire life a waste, a desert of shame and unspeakable sorrow, and behind me, a suicided wife! I spent those years in fever and agony, those years that I would have gladly given to my country alone. The man with a peaceful nest to fly home to, has everything; there is no effort he will not make for his mate and offspring. A public office is a public trust; and yet above me I had this sword of Damocles. I could have gone farther, Henny. You could have been the wife of a bigger man, a better one. But I, the most natural and loving of husbands and fathers, have been denied this simple pleasure, the only reward, besides public esteem and the love of friends, that I ever wanted."

Henny, meanwhile, had been quietly busy at the stove and now pushed towards him, over the sink cover, a little white cup full of hot coffee.

"Take some coffee, Samuel; the sugar's on the dresser."

"I made long trips," said Sam, in a warmer voice. "I visited the hatcheries and the foreshores and even went with the investigation vessel so that you would have time to settle down."

Henny said nothing but sat with her back to him, taking gulps of tea. Her face flushed slightly, and her eyes brightened.

Sam broke the silence with a lamentable note, "And instead you flirted with Mark Colefax; I take your word it was no more."

[146]

Henny broke a biscuit and said nothing, though she slewed an impatient look in his direction. He missed it. "I have never forgiven him. It is against my nature. I love to forgive, let bygones be bygones, but a man who betrays his friend's most sacred trust and essays to foul his home is no ordinary man. I am sorry to say that I pass on the other side of the street and avoid the streets he takes. No man with the feelings of a man could forgive!"

These remarks brought up an expression of rage on Henny's face, but she was careful not to let Sam see it. Sam felt her silence and assured her that goodness knew he did not mean to bring up all the black past; perhaps they had weathered the storm now; perhaps this appointment would bring a change of life for them both. They were older, their children were growing up; in the joys and interests of an adolescent family, they might lose themselves and think of others, of young ones, the citizens of the future.

"I have done nothing in all these years to justify such dislike as you seem to show, or pretend to feel," continued Sam, "but perhaps we both understand whence such feelings spring; we are both poor human creatures, and in this understanding of ourselves may be, perhaps, the origin of a better life together."

"I don't know," Henny at last murmured, "exactly what you're driving at. What is the good of fooling ourselves? It has never worked—it never will. I don't know what you want to hang on to me for. You should have let me go at the beginning. Why did you beg me to marry you at Frederick that day? I would have got another man."

"Though I am not religious, marriage seems to me sanctified," Sam protested. "Even our marriage, Henny, is somehow above the tumult of life, if only because of our children. Could I see our children scattered, divided, with divided loyalties, trying to understand a sentence against father or mother! What a shocking thing! It is impossible," and he shuddered. "No, home is the place for the fledglings till their wings are grown and they can flit to their own place in the world. I hope that you and I have turned out some splendid minds and souls among them, Pet;

your father is a fine fellow. I hope there is at least one, perhaps another, great man of science amongst the boys, and the two girls will be fine women. I have shown them the way. If they be not as bright as I could wish, they can at least work in their country's service, in the government employ, working with me and after me, when they understand my ideals, towards that superstate builded on ideals which are seeded in the oldest blood of our countrymen—scientists, socialists of a new socialism, leaders of men! Pet, you could not see our children divided. It has been my fondest hope that I would produce mighty children, a tribe of giants to come after me. And that is the sole reason, since you ask me, for my having dragged you through these years of discontent, yet years of ferment. I did it, ungrudgingly, despite my own sorrow, and without your love, you know that: no one who knows me could doubt my motives."

Henny preserved her silence and hung over her empty cup, her head on her hand.

"I hope that at last, Henny," said Sam gently, "you are beginning to understand me."

Silence brooded; the hot air stagnated.

"Pet," said Sam gently, after a long pause, "look at me; don't let me see only the back of your head."

Through the rest of the house was the breathing of sleep; Bonnie had long abandoned her post on the stairs. Henny, defenseless, in one of those absences of hatred, aimless lulls that all long wars must have, turned towards him, looking at him strangely with her great, brown eyes. These eyes, fringed with jet, long and well formed under the high, thin penciled brows, had always stirred Sam deeply; and even when he came on her in a mood he detested, when she was sitting staring into space, communing with her disillusion, his heart would be wrung by their unloving beauty.

"Pet," said Sam, reaching out his left hand, large and shapely, "come here; come to me. Don't sit there, forever a stranger, a stranger on my hearth."

She did not move but continued to look at him speculatively, her mouth moving uncertainly. Sam tempted her, "You will be alone here a long time; come to me now: you must want to."

In the end, he rose and came towards her; she put up her hands but kissed him when he bent over her.

"My dear girl," he said passionately, "let us have another child, the seal of all our sorrows. Let us start a new life with it! I feel so much before me: nothing can stop me now. If you knew how to take the strength in me and use it for our good. I want to be happy. Kiss me, my girl: let this be our fortress against the world. I will make you understand me. You see, Pet," he said very low, "I need a woman to understand me. That is my softness. I want you to understand me."

She started up, trembling; but his long fidelity to her, of which she felt sure, moved her beyond all her resolutions. She began to gather up the cups and saucers and, to justify herself, she thought,

"I'll wring every penny of my debts out of him some way, before he goes; I'll find a way, anyway. I won't suffer," and a small trickle of courage came back into her veins.

CHAPTER FIVE

1 ☙ No more forsaken.

IN THE FIRST WEEK of every summer vacation, Louie went quickly and mysteriously to her mother's people, who lived along the Shenandoah, some in the bloody stand of hills at Harpers Ferry and some along the slopes of the upper river, near Charlestown and Winchester, in mixed orchard farms. One, Reuben Baken, kept a needy store in Frederick; one kept a large store, ships' chandler's and general grocery, in the market place in Baltimore, opposite the fishmarket (and it was here that Sam Pollit had met Rachel Baken fourteen years before). They were Virginians and Marylanders but all of Maryland origin, the root strain having settled there soon after the Revolutionary War, coming from the West of England, the Welsh Marches, and all, since the Reformation, left-wing dissenters, independent, lovers of the Lamb of God, pale-skinned, black-bearded, tall, inbred people, the greater part apathetic or infirm with the antiquity of their race, small farmers, artisans, or shopkeepers, milky-natured, music-voiced, gentle but enduring, with the quiet natures and sweet intonations of Worcester and Shrewsbury still in them. The family was full of queer aberrations, but there were no ghosts in the cupboard, for everything was told with Biblical simplicity. The Pollits fiercely guarded with the red blood of children all manner of commonplace miseries; Henny was lying, hypocritical, and ashamed before "the other woman's child," but the Bakens never saw any reason to be more secret than Isaiah. The grandfather, Israel Baken, was a boy of seven on that doomsday of December in 1859 and had never forgotten it: the family had seen the history of the Union as a history of the curtailment and abolition of involuntary servitude, and Israel's father, fighting against the slaveholders, fell, in the taking of Winchester by the Union men, December, 1862, a week before the Emancipation. Israel, eldest of three boys, himself had eight boys and three girls: Reuben, Simeon, Judah, Beulah, Joseph, Benjamin, Leah, Rachel, Dan, Jacob, and Zachariah. Henny had a convention for her children that Louie had an aunt to whose house she went for the summer, and this aunt was Aunt Beulah, who came, once a year, for an afternoon tea of polite constraint with Henny, at the beginning of the school holidays, to take Louie away.

Rachel dying, when Louie was six months old, had whispered to her eldest sister, "Look after the little girl; he is a good man, Beulah, but he knows nothing about children," and Beulah had promised to watch out for the child. This maternal duty became more difficult each year. In those fat years, Beulah's boarding-house at the top of the rise at Harpers Ferry had been full all the summer, and on Sundays automobile parties from Washington had come out all through the day to eat Beulah's chicken dinners. Her husband, Charlie, had stayed all day in the closed-in back veranda, killing, cleaning, and preparing chickens, sometimes to the number of two hundred, for the car parties. But Harpers Ferry ceased to be fashionable, people took the skyride, the fashion changed; even Harper's Ferry people all started moving away to Charlestown and elsewhere, everyone's children got jobs in the Government, the river rose and drowned the lower town, and, long before the railroad yards had been shifted, Harpers Ferry was no longer the gateway to the South, the great strategic point for holidaymakers as for warmakers, and business died. Now Aunt Beulah no longer attempted to give Sunday dinners, and merely kept her large, clean, airy house open for occasional visitors. Her two sons were in government service, and her husband, crippled with arthritis, could do no more than a little gardening round the place, sometimes relieving at the garage, but not for cash. They owned a house in the street behind the house

[151]

that led to the cemetery, but rarely rented it. Times had changed. But as times grew leaner, Louie grew larger and fatter and ate more and grew lazier. The rich Pollits (so they were to Aunt Beulah) had never paid a cent for Louie's vacation, nor for her trip back home at the end of two months, or three; and Aunt Beulah, irritated from time to time, would try to make the big girl help her in the house, but she was ashamed to do so: the child was yellow as light honey and yet she reminded her of the blue-black Rachel, long dead, but whose long eyelashes, rebellious little mouth, and high cheekbones survived in young Louie. Everyone knew that Louie had rather a thin time with that basket of young puppies and most of the time, no servant to help "the stepmother."

When Beulah's anemic, YMCA sons came home, they were kind to their little cousin, rigged up a hammock for her, showed her books to read, showed her how to make knots, to plant trees, and so on: and she would follow them naïvely, confidingly, and be sorry when they had gone.

At other times, Beulah would rouse her from her dreaming and eternal reading and repeating of verses or scenes to herself, in some sheltered corner of the garden, to go and visit the other Bakens. First, there was Uncle Dan, who lived in Charlestown and who would come to fetch them in his car. All the Baken men were tall (Grandfather Israel was six feet four, in stockings with heel holes, and straight as an iron stake), but most were spare, willowy, and ham-backed. The only one of medium size was Dan. All the Baken men had busy, discontented wives (Grandfather Israel had one, Mary, who pleaded, begged, wooed him the one livelong day to get one bitter word from him), but Uncle Dan's wife, Rose, was a mitigated shrew. All the Baken men were religious (though Grandfather Israel was too proud in his cruel, revolutionary religion to join their holy-holies), and Uncle Joseph was shut up in an asylum where he recited to himself the livelong day, but none was as nauseatingly sweet in his Christianity as Uncle Dan. Uncle Dan had traveled in groceries for thirty years and believed in the family life of breakfast foods, but he was sweet as sugar, sweet beyond belief to the forsaken Louie, and was always the first (after the sensible Beulah) to welcome Louie to this Israel of the meeting of the waters. The first time she ever went, and wondered at the irritable kindness of Aunt Rose, she had supper with them. There was a large table, with Dan at the head and Rose at the foot; next to Dan, young Dan, two years Louie's senior, and next to Rose, young Rose, Louie's junior, and, in between them, young children, two boys. Beside Louie sat Aunt Beulah. When the soup was served, Uncle Dan stood up, and the children, now, Rose, Dan, little Nellie and David, began to kneel down round their chairs. Aunt Rose, meanwhile, was bustling out to the kitchen where a young woman was cooking. "Now, Rose," said Uncle Dan kindly, and Rose, angrily untying her apron, came back and sat in her place; and then Uncle Dan said, "You need not kneel, dear Louie, but if you like to, you can," and Louie at once knelt down, but with open eyes, looking round, and saw Rose and Dan smile and look expectantly at her. Now the unctuous, undulating voice of Uncle Dan began (as he stood with eyes closed, their long lashes on the cheeks, and his fine buttery oval of a face uplifted to the ceiling), "Psalm Twenty-eight, nine: 'Save thy people and bless thine inheritance: feed them also: and lift them up forever.' Amen." He then went on to pray, mentioning all their names, "But first our dear Beulah who is with us again and especially our dear little cousin Louisa whom we all love though we see her so seldom, daughter of my dear sister Rachel, and who will surely 'also be a crown of glory in the hand of the Lord.'"

He broke off, to say to the little girl who was peering through her fingers at her cousins (while they peered through their fingers at her), "Yes, dear Louisa, we are so, so glad to have you with us," and then to go on to pray for them and her, and then to sit down, with a joke, "Now we are in the soup," to the table, and eat heartily, while Aunts Beulah and Rose hurried out to the kitchen again, to begin to chatter at once, about "Eva getting up two days after the child was born and who ever heard of such a thing?" After supper, the little girl, Rose, went and climbed on her father's knee, and wreathed his neck with her arms, laughing and coaxing, asking to go to the movies on Saturday, and fourteen-year-old Dan came, with the same dulcet tones as his father, to invite Louie to go up the garden to see his pigeons; and the little boy, David, brought Louie a box, his peepshow, which he had made himself, which caused little blond Nellie to show Louie her doll. Meanwhile the women kept bustling, clearing away and chattering about family affairs: "And you know what I'd do if she was mine? I'd cut off those horrible yards of hair, and she would lose her headaches." Afterwards they both went and sat on the porch, rocked, and did crochet and darning, while Nellie hung around her mother's skirts, and Father Dan and Son Dan went for a walk with their arms round each other. Whenever Louie came in sight they called her "dear Louie," and when bedtime came, there was another prayer, which Aunt Rose read from the place marked by Dan, " 'Oh, that men would praise the Lord for his goodness and for his wonderful works to the children of men! For he satisfieth the longing soul, and filleth the hungry soul with goodness.' Amen"; then there was kissing good night all round, so that even Louie and young Dan kissed good night without giggling, and Louie got into bed in the girls' room, feeling a little self-conscious, because the two girls said prayers and she did not. But though she felt they were foolish, with their singing tones and sweetness, their climbing on knees and kissing, prayers and family love, weakminded and backward, the air of the low-ceilinged wooden bedroom, which flowed between four shuttered windows and which was filled with shadows from moonshine and trees, seemed pure as the water of a river over sandstone. She was again (as each summer) one of the children of Israel; she was unquestioned in the house of Jacob, no more called forsaken.

In the morning the sun shone, and breakfast began merrily with smiling Uncle Dan and fretful Aunt Rose coming to the table after the children, Uncle Dan fixing his tie and saying, "Good morning, dear Louie! (Did you say good morning to your little cousin Louie who came to us again?) Louisa, I always say at breakfast the first text that I think of when I get out of bed in the morning," and smiling, birdlike, on them all, he continued, "Children!" and when they had closed their eyes and folded their hands, he recited the text, " 'And one cried unto another, and said Holy, holy, holy, is the Lord of hosts; the whole earth is full of his glory.' " Hereupon Dan had to recite the text he had learned before going to bed (his looking glass was stuck full of texts), which was from St. Matthew 5, and then they ate, though David first asked, impudently, "Can't Louie say a text?" at which Uncle Dan asked, forever singing, if she would say one, and she replied that she did not know texts. No sooner did she say this than the children laughed (having discussed the marvelous atheism of Louie overnight) and asked if she was not a sinner and whether God was not angry with her. Dan scolded them and they easily subsided. After this household, they went to Uncle Reuben's in Frederick. The young stout blond woman, plain and off-hand, whom Louie resented under the name of Aunt Jeannette, came in for a moment to see them and then retreated to the front of the store with Aunt Beulah, leaving Louie with Reuben.

Reuben was over six feet, bowed with his chest trouble, with a pale face planted with large dark eyes, wide set, and dark spare curling hair. He was the handsomest man that Louie had ever seen, and the gentlest. Aunt Jeannette came in two or three times, with a contemptuous cranky voice, asking questions to which Reuben replied with infinite patience and understanding, if not love. Then he would go back to showing the few books he had, *The Pilgrim's Progress, Paradise Lost,* and Redpath's 1860 edition of *The Public Life of Captain John Brown,* all with steel engravings. "His leg is hurting him today," Aunt Jeannette explained to Aunt Beulah in the passage after one of her sallies. Reuben did not show any suffering; he talked hesitatingly, telling her the story of *The Pilgrim's Progress* again, his face serious; and occasionally he would pause, the eyes would be fixed on her, and suddenly he would smile with his long dark lips; the face would no longer be the face of a man dying of consumption, with its burning eyes, but the ravishment of love incarnate, speaking through voiceless but not secret signs to the child's nature. He had no daughter of his own and loved the only child of his favorite sister. He thought that when he entered Heaven (if he was found worthy), he would first see his sister Rachel and give her the last news about the child she left in babyhood; so he now devoured the child with the eyes of death-to-be. Though the place was of the poorest, and the back room where the sick man sat, dark, untidy, and airless, and they could not even spare the broken biscuits from the dirty shop in the front, Louie did not want to go.

They completed the round of the four or five Baken men who had households (not counting the religious maniac and the poetic maniac) and, after six days, went back to the house in Harpers Ferry to find that Grandfather Israel had arrived with his soft, scuttling wife to stay two months. Israel was over eighty years old now. He had no money and lived on the circuit of his sons and daughters: and his arrival was always announced thus (in a whisper), "Father has come!" and his stay thus, "Father is still with me!" and the answer to this whisper was either a nod or an understanding glare of the eyes. Even at eleven or twenty-four miles' distance, "Father has come" was said in a whisper. Israel had never spoken to Louisa, for she was the seed of a disobedient daughter and an atheist. Mary, diligent, delicate, would bring her in each year (this year, Louie was as tall as the old grandmother and broader) and say, "Israel, here is Louie, Rachel's daughter," and the black panther of a man, always pacing, always pacing, would not even cease in his pacing, but would brush them aside (if they stood in his way) and say nothing, only lift his small-boned head higher.

This year, Grandmother Mary said, pushing the child forward, and a little querulous, "Israel, here is Louisa; Israel, remember, we are old, who knows if we will see her again!" The old man paused for a moment and looked down at the girl, and she, looking up, and not so alien from him as on the other days, saw his black-streaked hair, the long nose, firm, bitten, mouth and broad square chin, the unequal eyebrows over straight-staring gray eyes, the broad, filled, low forehead, with animal determination constricting the temples and the set of the head—villainously vain, yes, proud, disappointed but unyielding, on the wiry, stiff shoulders. She felt bashful with most adults, but when she looked at this old man who disliked her and thought her hideous, revolting, Louisa stared coolly, and saw no force in the gray eyes passionate for self. The old woman watched them both eagerly, saying not a word. After a minute, the old man threw back his shoulders and began his walking up and down again, ignoring the girl completely; then he said, fretfully, "Mary, what is all that noise?" which made his wife leap and run to the kitchen, taking the child with her. Those were the only words that Louisa ever heard from Israel of the cast-iron face.

He lived with his sons and daughters, commanded them from the fastnesses of spare bedrooms, but he was not of them, whether he lived with Beulah, a freethinker, or praise-God Dan, or stern Simeon (Reuben was too poor to have him). He would not sit down with them, or talk, or walk with them. He would do nothing but sit with one of his wife's shawls round him on the bed, dejected, staring at something, or pace up and down, looking intensely bitter, ready to bite, like a dog left in charge of some property. They knew his nature so well that they left him alone at all times, to preserve themselves, and so gave him no opportunity to rave, storm, and cry woe. He wanted to be angry, his mission was to be angry, and he had nothing to be angry about; the world would not let him rave, this was the great injustice he suffered from: he stalked up and down being angry, in futility; but this anger, little spent, had kept him young, black-haired, and strenuous for over eighty years. For the rest, they all secretly sighed for his death. They did not think of Scripture's injunctions in his regard, because to himself he was the Bible, the Bible was himself: what he willed was the Bible and so it had always been. He had built up an army against himself and liked hate and despised that army which was only his own children. He was a hearty despiser, hater, cynic, a surly, battling, sinewy creature. He lived a month in the house with his daughter Beulah while Louie was there and no one ever heard a living word out of him, though they heard Mary hastily mumbling to him at all hours of the day; no doubt, on his side, he conversed by signs and glances. Then, because Beulah could not keep them any more, with Louie too, Beulah wrote a letter which was answered, and there was a tearful scene in which Beulah explained that Rose would have them. The poor old woman, crying, said that they were tossed about like a ball and no one wanted them, no, not even the daughters she had brought out of her bowels; not the women who should know what she had to put up with, no one would have her. Then Beulah cried, and Louie, sitting at the head of the table, cried too; and the three women, after crying, felt united in a love. But this did not stop the grandmother from going. Beulah, ashamed but firm, went to pack the things and then there were heard sounds from the old man, who was at last angry with cause; but what was said, and if anything was said in human words, Louie never knew, for all this was behind closed doors. When the old people went, Louisa was given their room.

Dan's children, young Rose and young Dan, would come to Harpers Ferry, once a week or so, to visit Louisa. There was plenty of room for them in the tree-shaded upstairs rooms. Louie did not care for Rose, a brown-haired, restless, thin little spitfire, but hung round with Dan and, when Rose was out of the way, would go for a walk with him, sheltered at first from the radiant, moist heat when the clouds bowled over, or the clear heat of midsummer, by the old trees of the back road, and then would come out into the old graveyard, all grass and long sights, like the house of the Lord on the mountaintops, like the mountain where Dan's Lord of hosts would make unto all people a feast of fat things. Then they would either go down by the little path behind the Jefferson Rock, overhanging the river road, to sit down and stare across the water gap, or up the Shenandoah, or, sliding down by the other side of the weather-stained caretaker's cottage, find a path looking out over the Potomac, that goes down from the heights by solemn shades and rusted gates, by the steps to the bottom of the hill, the street of little poplars and the flood-ruined houses, with jagged rents and sagging beams, by lush worthless gardens and back yards with fat, sun-struck pigs to the old armory emplacement and the rowboat ferry. Sometimes they went on from there, under the Jefferson Rock, whence they would climb perilously up and back to their starting point. Dan said little, but he liked what she liked; he was merry-hearted and would bubble out confidences, in his double-stopped voice. Aunt Beulah laughed, and Uncle Charlie called them Black and White, "Well, I see Black and White have been for another walk to look for the Cutpaper Tree." He would pretend that no one could find the cut-paper tree, and then would tell them one of his tales.

One day, when they were building one of the houses on the hill, an old wooden house with carved wooden posts (it happened to be Christmas Eve), a man drove up in a carriage with two horses and said that if they would take the carriage and horses and take him in with them, he would help them build the house. He had no money and no home. They took him in. He carved for them the four posts of the veranda, and lived with the family a year, and on the Christmas morning of the following year, he took his hat, said good-by and went his way, saying that each had fulfilled his contract. There stands the house, dilapidated, but with its four posts: and that is the story. Uncle Charlie would ask them to tell him the names of the trees in his garden, English walnut, Japanese plumage cedar, and two Colorado blue spruces, one flour-powdered blue and one plain green, a catalpa, a persimmon; and then they would walk up slowly through the deeply green streets to the Negro college, with its splendid trees, and look far out into blue, chalky, smoky valleys. Dan sometimes put his arm round Louie's waist, sometimes held her hand behind her waist, and what with the Baken strictness of speech (they were without circumlocutions), their directness of gospeling villagers, all to her, in this land, all, with the meeting of the waters, and the Southern sun pouring over the hills and their burning silky heads, John Brown's Fort, the starry nights, skirlings downhill on skates from this haunted and embattled siege rock, the quiet, deserted streets, the frank worries about the death of the town and its real estate, made the Harpers Ferry of her summers a retort of revelation to Louie: the placid, high-minded heavens of Pollitry were rolled up and there was a landscape to the far end of the sky—an antique, fertile, yeoman's country, where, in the shelter of other customs and tribal gods, people believing themselves to be the children of God stuck to their occupations, gave praise, and accompanied their humblest deeds with the thunder of mystic song.

The day came when Louie had to go home. Grandmother was there, separated from tyrannical Israel for a day or two, and there was much huffy muttering in the kitchen while Aunt Beulah and Grandmother wondered why Louie's father and mother did not send the money for her fare, nor anything more than a letter asking for her. But Louie was fat and spoiled by two months of ease, she floated in a cloud, wreathed in smiles; and not noticing their complaints which were made, in fact, in a low tone of voice, she also begged them for money so that she could take home presents to all the children. She now looked forward eagerly to seeing the children and their excitement when they undid the wrapping papers: she never went home in her life without taking them something. The two women made grim faces, but said sharply, "You'll get your money," and then went on conversing low and crankily; but Louie wondered how much money she would get. She had no pocket money, except at these times.

Then the little journey through the bluffs to Point of Rocks, leaving Reuben, and Dan, and all Israel in the hills, and sulky Aunt Beulah mastering her feelings to greet a Henny all honey, and the children tumbling in; Louie rushing to her valise, the children pawing the ground, and Tommy asking, "Where did she go, Mother?" and hearing the traditional reply, "To her aunt's in the country." In the house of Pollit the people of the house of Baken remained unnamed.

2 ✥ Monocacy.

THE TREES WERE TURNING in the gullies beyond, the day they came up by hired car along Cold Spring Lane, and, turning slowly into the rising drive, jumped out at the glassed-in porch of Monocacy. Henny's family home was named not after the village but after Frederick's serpentine stream. The two little girls, in new coats, were joyous: they loved the old home with its trees, lawns, wildernesses, old barnyards, old cow and horse paddocks, and dependencies; they loved the autumn, with its blotched valleys, the rivers of warm and cold temperature flowing in the air, the smell of burning leaves, the half-raked lawns, and the stilling brooks. A creek ran through the bottom of Monocacy's grounds, and out along the railway. Opposite was an old mansion on a hill, surrounded by noble trees and a weather-beaten fence, existing from the early days of the district; and on farther hills, hidden from the road, were other old family places, dating from Henny's childhood when this had been a distant plantation of wealthy Baltimore homes; now apartment houses and new dark-brick, gabled bungalows stepped down hill towards the creek, two-family houses opened gaping plackets on the unbuilt greens, and overdone artistic modern houses were stringing along the Lane.

In Monocacy's gardens the standard roses were too heavy with flowers, the ornamental shrubs were untrimmed, the grass grew thick on the lawns, one door of the hothouse swung open, and the sun dropping spidery into the arboretum showed a jungle of weeds. "There's no gardener," cried Louie, shocked. The wind hissing in the tall grass sang abandonment; the sun smudged on unpolished windows placarded the big house with rooms vacant, dusty, and shut up. Henny, in her big fur coat, lent to her by Hassie, paid the taxi and turned into the house, biting her lips. *Everywhere money needed,* was what this spelled to her. She knew that since Hazel Moore had left Monocacy in July, to come to help her, during Sam's absence, there had been no work done in the old house, except by a little reformatory schoolgirl from a

Baltimore slum, "some love child of some horrible other Bert," thought Henny, disgusted with everything, as she came into the dusty hall, "oh, what is the world all about?"

They found Old Ellen Collyer in the housekeeper's room, buttoned to the full, sagging throat, in black, stout and placid, doing coarse crochet. The little girls ran forward and kissed her, "Hello, Old Ellen," and "Hello, Old Ellen" (for, she said, with all her grandchildren, she would think she was grandma of the whole world, if she let them say, *Grandma*); and Henny, pouting, "Hello, Mother, isn't it a beastly day?" threw her coat on the sideboard and sank into a chair, after pulling the old-fashioned bellpull.

The little girls at once ran out, while Old Ellen was saying, "Oh, only this same old shell stitch," and Henny fretted, "I hate it, it looks like an old Irish Biddy's petticoat," and asked for tea, and an aspirin, and damned the world and said, Yes, she had letters and money from Sam; when he was away she could stand him, and the farther he was away the more she could stand him! Now, the little girls were allowed to roam freely over the house, into the round room, the nursery, all the shut family bedrooms, no longer used, the billiard room, and even the dark trunk room in which was the foot of the winding stair which led to the roof and the lookout. They went into the kitchens, the closets; Evie ended up in the drawing room full of closed cabinets of china dolls, with china lace petticoats: and Louie ended in the empty stables, still sweet with hay and clean flagstones, where the sun explored the cracks of old greased halters hanging from the beams. Blowsy, tall, dusk cherry in complexion with the long summer's sun was Louie, fresh from running up and down the rock at Harpers Ferry and getting herself confused with Christian meandering upwards Beulah, she and Dan with Christian and Hopeful freed from Doubting Castle, seeing somewhere in the air (over the greens of West Virginia), the Celestial City, freed by the golden key Promise—but what promise? The promise of reaching the grass uplands of youth and understanding the world. No one asked her any questions about her summer any year, and so this world was her own secret Mesopotamia and angel-guarded pleasure, the valley of rocs and the land shadowing with wings, all strange countries, skies, spheres, and songs rolled into one small rock of the earth, known to others as Bolivar Heights, but to her as Louie's dreams which have put on flesh. For nine months of the year were trivial miseries, self-doubts, indecisions, and all those disgusts of preadolescence, when the body is dirty, the world a misfit, the moral sense qualmish, and the mind a sump of doubt: but three months of the year she lived in trust, confidence, and love.

With some dim idea of the golden stair, Louie climbed up the dusty wooden staircase between stable and barn to the lofts above the stables. There were two doorways without doors. In the right-hand loft was an army bed, and on this Uncle Barry lay on his back, with his mouth open and a yellow beam on his tired cheek. He was slender, dark, like Henny, thirty-five, one year her junior, and Old Ellen's last child. Within reach of his dangling hand were two empty whisky bottles, the like of those bottles which Louie at various times and years in her explorations of Monocacy had discovered in Barry's room, the billiard room, the round room, on the lookout, in the dung heap, in the tree guards of the cow paddock, and in the groom's toilet, which was situated behind the potting shed. The gardener and groom had gone: and here in the sweet-smelling dusty loft Barry had established his new playground, an inebriate's holy of holies, where he lay in pleasure, king of solitude. Louie pored over the snoring man. He was tall and had been handsome, but was putting on a little paunch. Louie liked Barry. He was usually out, as they said: even Louie sensed somehow that he had *a woman* in Baltimore, *like the old man, a chip off the old block*. Who had heard it said? But the children knew it, without wonder. He liked the drink. He had large, absorbed eyes, he lurched slightly, he would smile in his dark mustache, with meaningless satire, and would murmur and mutter, in his sweet Baltimore inaudibility, something or other to Louie. He did not detest her; he even took an interest in her, faintly, as if from a great distance; and occasionally would show

[163]

her things. Once, in some webby past, he had studied the dyeing of textiles with the idea of going into a hat factory downtown; and then he had collaborated with a Johns Hopkins man in a little idea—the printing of obscene books after hours, on a little press, and they made a bit of money, and then he had given up the effort altogether and devoted himself to drink, which was now his only occupation. He had charm, he could not be affronted: Louie liked him. After watching him for a while, Louie got bored, because nothing happened, he did not shriek, or see snakes, or get up. She wandered back over the saddling paddock, through the now-empty kitchens, to the housekeeper's room.

"—and said she was going to take permanganate," said Old Ellen, "because Barry wouldn't marry her to get her out of trouble. I had enough trouble with them."

"Remember that poor unfortunate—what was her name, you know, the Sleighs'—Delia!—they found her on the floor in a terrible state and she had taken Lysol?"

"They found that woman last year under a bush, you remember, who had taken about two hundred aspirins—Heavenly Father!"

Henny said impatiently, "There are so many ways to kill yourself, they're just old-fashioned with their permanganate: do you think I'd take permanganate? I wouldn't want to burn my insides out and live to tell the tale as well; idiots! It's simple. I'd drown myself. Why not put your head in a gas oven? They say it doesn't smell so bad. I don't know. I thought of asking my dentist, Give me some of that stuff, you know, nitrate, no, nitrous oxide, too much and you go out sweetly, or too much ether, eh? Permanganate, or carbolic acid, or arsenic, who would take it? There are so many things. Why, Sam has cyanide in the house any time: that's what they kill vermin with, you blow it in the holes. Why? Barry could get me some: anyone can get the easy things. Catch me eating two hundred aspirins—my heart would kill me; I couldn't stand that. I don't think much of drowning. I've thought of opening a vein in a warm bath, I heard of a woman who did that, but I think I'd feel too weak. Why be in misery at the last?

[164]

There must be plenty of things. I've thought of getting too friendly with a doctor, you know, and getting him to give me something. Get in with him, and let him get too friendly with you, then he gets sick of you, you begin to bother him, tell him you're pregnant or something, or ask him for drugs, and he'll give you something quick enough. Or you go to his consulting rooms, and he trusts you and leaves you alone—or he leaves the stuff unlocked purposely—foo, I've thought of a hundred ways. It's only a stupid servant girl would do that carbolic-acid trick. And rat poison is too nasty and they can always trace it. I couldn't touch a revolver —your hand would shake! I'm sure I'd be a poor shot, and then you wouldn't know where to do it. Oh, in labor pains, it's different: you want to die, but you want to see the kid too. I don't have such a bad time, and just about the time I start to tell them to take me and drown me and it too, it comes, and then you begin to wonder about it. And apart from that, I can't get sick enough. Anyone would think a thin stick like me, weak and miserable, would go down with everything: do you think I get more than my old cough every winter? I bet I live till ninety, with all my aches and pains. To think that's fifty more years of the Great I-Am. No wonder I want to make away with myself. Who wouldn't? You grumble, but at least Dad left you alone, he didn't try to talk you to death."

"Eleanor had none, Hassie had only one miserable shrimp, and you had all those," said the old woman, "and look at you—you were never any different! Just a cornstalk. You were a nice-looking girl, though! I thought you'd marry that Albert!"

"Oh, shut up!"

"Look at Wally," said the old woman, laughing: "what's the matter with you? Why don't you get another? You're slow, that's all. You can pick up a king yet at your age."

"I have a fine king, a god. One king is enough. Next time I pick an I.W.W.; better than the Professor at any rate. I'd rather wash for a drunk than let a high-and-mighty work for me. At least I'd have a lively time. Yes, you know I was sure of it. I'm gone. Think of it. Isn't it a disgrace? What am I to do with another one and I owe what I owe already? I've been feeling wretched and I got sick on the taxi over. God, what we women have to put up with; and I'm not even allowed to complain."

"You know the story of the doctor who found the man walking up and down in the lobby of the hospital and said, 'What's the matter?' 'My wife's having a baby upstairs,' said the man. 'Well, why don't you go upstairs?' asked the doctor. 'No,' the man said, 'we're not speaking, I don't want to show interest, we haven't spoken for two years.' 'But, well,' the doctor said, 'explain to me, will you?' 'Oh,' said the husband, 'I'm not as mad at her as that.' Reminds me of the woman with six children who told the census taker she was an old maid but not the fussy sort. Did you hear about the woman who kept going to Dr. Uno for operations and he asked her, 'Who's the father?' and she kept on saying, 'Mr. Whosthis,' until the doctor said, 'Why don't you marry the man?' and she said, 'I don't like him, doctor.' That's like you, Henny, that's just like you!" She slapped her crochet down on her knee, laughing, "Oh, you're a case, you take the cake. What for? You can't blame the man for——"

"All men are dogs," said Henny.

"Stop eating bread and sauce now, if you love me," said Old Ellen, "is that the proper thing to eat? No wonder you feel bad. You always did it when you were growing up too, and that's what made you such a namby-pamby girl. If you'd had a bit of flesh on you you could have got that——"

"Oh, do stop harping on Albert every time I come," Henny said impatiently. "When's Archie coming? I think I'll go and lie down. Where's Hassie? I hope she'll drive me back, I can't afford taxi fares, and I can't afford a new tire, so here I am."

"Will you stop flouncing round?" asked Old Ellen.

"I'm getting sick of this pattern," grumbled Henny. "But everyone admires it. I made three bonnets last month."

"You were always soaping and sighing," said Old Ellen, "and making cow eyes at the boys, you had no reserve. Remember the time Dunne Legge kissed you and you told me you were going to get married. Oh, ha-ha!"

"If you think that was a joke," said Henny; "I was wild about Dunne—all the crushes I had."

"Well—well—well, it's all over now."

"That time Dunne was in the hospital and I sent him a pair of bed socks and he said he wanted girls to have fun with, he wasn't after a sick nurse! The sneak! That's the second stitch I've dropped; I'm all to pieces. Father was in a hurry. A fisheries inspector!"

At this moment there was a rush in the hall, Evie tearing in to announce Aunt Hassie's arrival in the car. Henny and her mother went out to see Harriet, and Hassie came in saying cheerfully, "Guess who I ran into? Of all people—Dunne! You know what he told me? Poor Connie died at last. It's a good thing. I heard she kept asking the doctor to put her out."

"What was it, I didn't hear that?" Old Ellen asked.

"Cancer, intestinal cancer——"

"Oh, why didn't he give her an overdose and put her out of her misery? You'd do it for an animal, but we have to suffer!" Henny shivered. "It makes me sick. I'd do it for one of mine, I don't mind telling you. Poor girl!"

"She wasn't a girl any more—she was a great big bouncing woman, like me, with shoulders broader than me," said Hassie: "and she wasted away, she looked like a ghost. I couldn't have borne to have seen it. I've had bad luck myself! That boy of mine in the shop ran a bone into his finger and got blood poisoning, and just five weeks after Pete got his finger into the sausage machine."

"Nothing but trouble," declared Old Ellen; "there have been a lot of accidents round here lately, isn't it funny? It goes in seasons."

"Connie was thirty-six, I think," said Henny slowly, "and she was a beauty when she was a girl: she never got married—I can't understand why. She was stuck on that Senator fellow. Well, if she'd married she'd be leaving some man and children miserable at this minute. Did she linger long? How long was it? I hope not." After a silence she added, "I didn't want to earn $100 that way—

[167]

I owed her that and she went to her grave thinking I was a cheat, I don't doubt."

"She was such a big jolly girl," said Hassie: "she was on the hockey team. Then she went to Washington to get a job, and there was that man in the Post Office, and then this friend of her father's, the Senator, a married man even then, but—there was something—I never heard——"

"It was her lookout," said Henny angrily, "a woman who tries to take a man away has it coming to her: but I didn't think Connie was that sort, to take another woman's man—you can never tell, when they get the itch, but mind, I liked her: she was a decent sort; and perhaps he went after her——"

The talk fell into murmurs, although the women had no idea that anyone was listening, but soon rose again with Henny retailing her part of it, "She got into trouble, money troubles, I heard every word about it, from—a man I know, I saw her going into a moneylender's, to tell the honest truth though I never let her see, and he wouldn't leave her at home, she had to travel round with him as Mrs. if you like! Then the wife got to hear of it and tore down the house; and she went round with him. Then they used to throw them out of hotels in the country, for brawling at night. I saw her once in Washington in my younger days, at a *conversazione:* she had a breath like a salt mine and a great belly like a foaling mare, floating and bloating and talking about her medicine and when she went to the toilet. Then she died, and what does he do? Turns round and writes a book of poetry about his angel and I don't know what not, the greasy hypocrite, crying and tearing his hair and pretending: and of course he couldn't marry Connie then. Some other excuse. It was her own fault, but in a way I pitied her. And see now! Isn't it rotten luck? Isn't every rotten thing in life rotten luck? When I see what happens to girls I'd like to throttle my two, or send them out on the streets and get it over with."

"Don't be a fool," said Hassie, "don't let anyone hear you talk like that, people would misunderstand."

"What?" asked Henny with a short laugh. "Where the devil is

that custard pie, Archie? I'm going mad with my debts, and he stays away, higgles and haggles and pulls a parson's nose and looks through his spectacles. I don't wonder Eleanor is sick of him."

"Shh," said Hassie, "you don't know that!"

Old Ellen laughed. "And did you hear the latest about My Lord? Barry saw me burrowing into the dirty-clothes basket and thought it was the washerwoman and started to feel my sitdown! Did I turn round like a fury and give him something to think about!"

"Mother," said Hassie.

"Mother, Mother, Mother. Stick up for your brother Barry."

"I'm not sticking up for him, Mother."

"He'll end by hanging," said Henny coolly: "he would have been fruit on a peculiar tree before this if he'd lived in a decent country, the Casanova; is he still with that woman? I've no patience with men and their tricks."

"Is it true that when men hang they give a last kick?" asked Old Ellen. "I often thought I'd like to go to a hanging to see."

"You know that Jenny fell down the cellar stairs and nearly brought it on?" Hassie said severely.

"I know a man that went to see an electrocution," Henny said, through half-closed mouth, "I don't know what he went to see. You broke your glasses, Mother?"

"Yes, Barry's friend, that old eye man, was on a bend since last Thursday and I wouldn't let anyone but him fix them, drunk or sober: someone saw him lying on the sidewalk dead to the world, in Aliceanna Street, poor old coot. Last time, he went down to Mahogany Hall, and when he came to his senses there he was with a nice one, 'a sweet little bit,' he called her to me, shameless, and he says, 'Where am I? I got to get to work.' She put her arms round him and said, 'Don't you go, you're my man.' 'Oh, I'm sorry, but I've got to go.' But she still kept holding on to him and hollering, 'You're my man!' "

"If I thought that child was spying round and eavesdropping with her ear at the door," said Henny.

[169]

"For the love of Mike," cried Hassie, "where is she then?"

"I haven't the strength to keep her in order," said Henny.

At this Louie retreated quietly, step by step, corner by door ajar, until she reached the back veranda which lay between the housekeeper's room and the upper kitchen; just at this minute, the bell rang in the kitchen and the little new maid dragged her chair. Louie hopped into the pantry, up one step, and pretended to be studying the preserves. When the maid returned and began to fuss at the stove, Louie tiptoed back to her post and heard the end of a discussion about varicose veins, girls in factories with unwanted babies, and clots in the brain and the heart, and then suddenly they were back to the romantic Barry again, and the two young women scolded their mother for spoiling him.

"I know he's a ne'er-do-well. But if I don't look after him, who will?" says the old woman; and the two others began to laugh, especially Hassie.

"Why, what's the matter with you, Hassie? I've never seen you so gay!" said Henny laughing too, "You're always messing in politics and too good to laugh at people's jokes."

"Didn't you know she fell down the cellar steps?" said Old Ellen in an uproar. "She cracked open her head."

Hassie began to tell it rapidly, "Pete was up all night with a toothache and he was taking forty winks when he heard me scream. He never heard me scream before; he jumped out of bed with only his pajama coat on and appeared at the head of the cellar steps . . ."

"She knew she was seeing stars!" said Old Ellen.

"I thought it was an angel," said Hassie, laughing coyly.

"Perhaps it was worth it," remarked Old Ellen.

"Don't be two such fools," Henny said angrily.

"She was so surprised," said Old Ellen, holding her sides, "oh, a great experience."

"And then he yelled at me, instead of helping me up, and he went out to give the man a clip on the jaw for leaving the trap door open."

"And left you lying there," said Henny roughly.

Old Ellen was still laughing. "What harm did it do her? Perhaps she needed it all along. She's been laughing ever since."

"You ought to go to a doctor, Hassie," Henny said earnestly, "perhaps it's serious. The way I worry about the kids' heads when they fall down, I know it's no joke. I never hit them on the head. Samuel wouldn't allow it. I used to flip his marvelous offspring on the head and maybe I turned her stupid, who knows?"

"I don't understand what he keeps her there for," said Hassie.

"Why do you worry about her; she'll grow up like the rest of us," said Old Ellen.

"She's so pigheaded she drives me crazy. Her father should keep her with her own family. She always comes back from them like a stuffed pig, fat as butter. She took the car out of the garage the other day. I'd rather something happened to one of mine than to her. Her father would never let me hear the end of it." Henny choked on something.

"Much ado about nothing," said the old woman. "What do you care now?"

"I care and so would you. The child's father nags me morning, noon, and night about her looks, her future, her skirts, her fat, her yellow rattails, her filth, and her lessons."

"Henny, don't eat all that sauce," said Hassie, "in your condition, you know, you'll be ill."

"All her life she's lived on gherkins and chilies and Worcestershire sauce; it won't kill her. She preferred pickled walnuts at school to candy. Ugh! I kicked myself on the leg of this darn table. Why don't you take it, Henny? I've got no use for it. I eat my breakfast in the upper kitchen. It's sunny. You take it, Henny. You know what I'd like to do? Give all the furniture away before next time He comes! Ha-ha! Some joke! I'll bet my bottom dollar it's mortgaged. Will you take it, Hassie, then?"

"I'll probably need it," said Henny dryly, "she doesn't. Pete eats in the garage as far as I can make out. He never ate in the house that I saw."

[171]

"He's always in the refrigeration plant; it's his mania," Hassie exploded. "I don't mind: when he's at home, he gabs so much my jaws ache."

Old Ellen began to laugh healthily, "It's dangerous not to talk to your husband. Now Samuel didn't talk to Henny for four years and more——"

"I didn't talk to him; do you think anything on earth would stop the Great Mouthpiece from talking?"

"—and your Dad didn't talk to me for twenty-two years, and I had fourteen youngsters as a result."

"It isn't necessary to talk," said Henny bitterly. "Can't we get some more to eat? This is old and cold."

Louie heard the bell ringing. The young maid Nellie, sloppy and cheerful, came in suddenly from the kitchen. She went to the room and got their order for new toast, but on the way back she swerved into the pantry room and said in a fresh, childish voice to Louie,

"Why don't you come out into the kitchen? I'll give you a bit of cake."

"All right." Flustered, grinning, the child followed her. The windows were open on the lawns. Tea roses grew unpruned outside and sometimes dropped in to see them. While waiting for the kettle to boil, the new little maid sat down again in her chair by the window and took up a sock on which she was turning the heel. She pointed to a chair at the table and said to Louie, "Pull it over by me."

Louie hurried to obey and sat opposite the blond, lank-haired girl, much pleased.

"Can you knit?"

"No." Louie writhed.

"Can you talk French?"

"No." Louie looked blank.

"Say, parlayvoo fraongsay."

"What did you say?"

"That's French. Parlayvoo fraongsay. Say it." The little girl blurted it out, with blind eyes: *povvloo frossay*. Very severely, the little maid repeated her French and made Louie repeat it.

"That means, can you speak French. Then you say, wee, wee. Go on."

"Uh?"

"Wee wee."

With much giggling and blushing they got it right; and then the toast was burning.

Putting on a new slice, Nellie continued, "Voozett jolly."

Louie stared meekly at her, blushing to ear lobes.

"Say, voozett jolly."

"What does it mean?" asked Louie cautiously, for there had been a rash of dirty sayings lately; e.g., *Polly, polish it in the corner.*

"You are pretty."

Louie turned scarlet and gaped at the girl, eyes popping from their sockets.

"That's what it means," said the girl in a practical tone, after cocking half an eye at her. To cover her embarrassment, Louie got out quickly, "Fazette jolly!"

"Very good, very good: you could speak good French," the girl approved her. Louie was much encouraged. The girl went away, stayed some time, and when she came back Louie was fumbling with the needles trying to work out the how of a stitch.

"I'll show you," offered the obliging creature, "then you can knit your own tennis socks; wouldn't that be nice?"

"Yes."

"See, come and sit by me."

A long interval followed during which Louie learned to make one clumsy great hole of a plain stitch.

"And now I must undo it and do it myself," said the girl. "See, this is for Mr. Barry. He will only wear handmade socks."

"Uncle Barry will?"

"Yes, they're the best. He isn't your Uncle Barry, you know."

"Yes, he is," Louie assured her, thinking she was a stranger to the place.

"No; he's your little brothers' uncle and Evie's uncle, but not your uncle."

"No," confessed Louie.

"Well, don't say he's your uncle."

Louie was irritated and said nothing.

"That's a lie," said the girl, "because your mother is dead."

Louie studied her with a puzzled expression.

"If you lie you are a bastard," said the girl.

"I'm not a bastard."

"Yes, you are. A bastard has no father or mother."

"I have a father," said Louie angrily.

"He's gone away and left you," the girl said calmly, "and you're a norphan. A bastard is a norphan."

"You're not telling the truth."

"Yes, I am; you ask Miss Hassie. You ask Old Mrs. Collyer. That ain't your mother, that's your stepmother. You've got a stepmother. So that proves you're a bastard."

Louie was silent.

"And no one likes you," said the girl, without malice, "that's because you're a norphan. Nobody likes you."

"Yes, they do," said Louie.

"Who?"

"Everyone; a lot of people."

"Who?" continued the maid, calm in her demonstration.

Louie hesitated. "My father and my mother."

"Your brothers and Evie have a mother, but you are a norphan. And your father doesn't like you because he beats you. I know. I heard. A little bird told me. I know. You're a bastard. You get beaten."

Louie was perplexed and ashamed.

"Your father doesn't want you; he sends you to your uncle's at Harpers Ferry. They're poor. Someone told me," the young girl said with conviction. "I know; you can't fool me. You're just a norphan. They send you away. You're no good. They're going to send you to work soon."

"I'm going to high school this month," Louie said.

"You're going to the reform school for children," Nellie said sharply. "That's where they send bastards. You see. Someone told me. You stole a cooky at the grocer's."

"I'm not, I'm not," Louie said, very stormy. "That's not true."

"You stole some cookies. The grocer sent a note to your mother and she told that other maid, Hazel, and she told Mrs. Collyer. You're a thief." Louie was silent. The girl pounced, "You're a thief; you stole."

"I had a right to," said Louie angrily, "he gave it to me: I had a right to."

"You're a liar," said the girl happily. "He wrote to your stepmother. And you stole flowers from Mrs. Bolton's."

Louie was thunderstruck. One day she had picked some flowers through the fence, in fact, and then taken them inside and offered them to Mrs. Bolton to conciliate her. But how did anyone know it?

"You steal everything and they'll send you to reform school. I'm a norphan and I know all about it," said the little maid calmly. "You're a norphan too: they're going to make you go out and work like me."

Louie stared at her glumly and rebelliously. The little maid ran on cheerfully,

"Near where my folks live there's a family with two pianos. When they moved, I seen two pianos in the street. And the girls moved them out themselves. They're strong. They've got big iron muscles like men. They moved everything out themselves."

Narrowing her eyes, Louie watched her with distrust.

"You don't believe me?" said the girl sharply.

"No."

"That's calling me a liar. You called me a liar; I'll tell your stepmother on you."

"No, I believe you," said Louie hastily. The girl rattled on at once, "And they don't wear any stockings, or anything under their dresses, just bare skin, pink. One time I thought they had on pink pants, then I saw they had nothing. And they were doing high kicking on the front porch."

Louie was silent, disbelieving her.

"You heard what I said? They wore nothing on under their skirts. Nothing."

"What about it?" said Louie with contempt. At home the children ran about naked, or with only overalls on.

"It ain't right. It's wrong. You take it from me. They're fast," said the girl solemnly to Louie. "They go dancing naked with boys, you know that."

Louie was silent.

"Eh?" the girl nudged her. "Eh? What do you say to that?"

"Let them if they want to," said Louie, embarrassed.

"They go for a swim and take off their things as soon as they get in," said the young girl, very mysteriously. "What do you think of that? Is that right? I bet that makes you blush."

"No," said Louie, "why shouldn't they? If no one sees them."

"But people do see them," said Nellie. "Of course, I've never seen them; but I know people," she nodded at Louie. "I know plenty of things, plenty of things. And what I don't know won't hurt me." She laughed her infantine brittle laugh. "What do you know?"

"What do you mean?"

"Don't you know anything?"

Louie hesitated, "I know——

> *Rebellious subjects, enemies to peace,*
> *Profaners of this neighbor-stained steel,—*
> *Will they not hear? What ho! you men, you beasts——"*

Nellie began to smile, "That's nice. Can you recite?"

"Yes," said Louie. *"That quench the fire of your pernicious rage;* but it's a long one. Do you want to hear it? Besides I don't know much more."

"What else do you know, kid?"

"Lars Porsena of Clusium by the nine gods he swore."

"You say that at school?"

"Yes," said Louie.

"But you're a norphan," said the girl, shaking her head. "You got to go to work."

Neither of them had heard wistful Evie come pussy-footing into the kitchen. She now stood at the door, staring at them, in their wonderful intercourse. But espied, she came up and proffered herself, "I can dance."

"You run away, little Evie," said Nellie.

"I better go," Louie said hastily. The company of the norphan-obsessed young person was palling and she felt uneasy about the thefts. "Don't go," said Nellie quickly, "stay here. I got no one to talk to here from one day's end to another."

"You didn't tell me the truth," said Louie getting up courage.

"I did so; and they wear pink socks when they go to bed too," Nellie gabbled, with a sneer. "They do all sorts of things; but I couldn't tell them to little girls like you."

With a severe expression, Louie left the kitchen, drawing Evie after her. Louie was deeply puzzled and sin-filled. But at once she began inventing, in the cockles of her heart, a hocus-pocus of denial, and explanation, about the cookies and the flowers. But how, in the name of everything under the sun, did anyone find out about them? She began to feel that the Boltons and Middenways were little better than creeping spies and callous slanderers trying to gnaw away her reputation. She had a right to the cookies and flowers, she calculated; whatever she did for herself, on her own initiative, was right and she would defy the world: but what about the miserable insect souls and minds of adults who spied on children and tattled? Louie was full of righteous indignation, and ready to battle her way through anything. But (mystery added to mystery) no one ever mentioned the strange thefts to her: and in due time she began to think that little Nellie, the norphan, had lied, too.

3 ✤ Does Fate avenge Louie?

THE TWO LITTLE GIRLS sat side by side on the third step, Evie impatient to get back to her stuffed birds and musical box, but Louie, afraid of her footsteps, and selfishly sinking into a daydream, while her hair mingled with Evie's chestnut mane.

"Where are those girls, I wonder?"

"They can't come to any harm here. Give yourself some rest."

Hassie said, "You know Molly's poor boy spoke the other day? She heard him calling and couldn't believe her ears: she flew like the wind. He had his eyes open and seemed to be trying to lift his poor great lolling head. When he saw her, he said, 'Mother, Mother!' Then in the night she heard him again and she woke Albert and Albert heard him too. Then he said no more. After twelve years of punishment, poor Molly heard her boy speak to her. I'm sorry for poor Molly."

"It's going to die," Old Ellen declared; "that's a sign."

"Better it should die! Only the poor wretch would have nothing in her life. If it died, she would die. Imagine twelve years tied to an idiot lying on its back." Henny sighed.

"She's had her punishment on this earth," said Hassie.

"It's her own fault," cried Henny, "leaving a baby on a table while she goes to the door."

"Only a minute," sighed Hassie, "just one minute."

"One minute! I'll guarantee she was gabbing fifteen minutes."

"They will never forget that one minute all their lives. I think it's tragic," sighed Hassie. "He's very good to her."

"Men are always good to fools and perfect idiots," cried Henny impatiently. "A man will run ten miles from a woman with sense. I wonder where those kids are now. I'll have to go and look for them."

"Oh, you're like a hen with chickens," said Hassie.

"To think," said Henny, after a pause, referring to something else, "that a woman like that will probably get a slice of the estate, and the law allows it. Oh, life is too vile. If it happens, I'll go and see that woman and show her the six kids I have to feed and clothe and show her my rags. Even if she throws me downstairs, I'll give her something to think about; I'd rather scream her house down than let her get away with it. She may be a mistress, but she's the lowest of the low if she sees my six children starve because of her frills and flounces."

"I won't have her discussed in this house," Old Ellen said violently.

"And she's taking the bread out of your mouth! Don't be a fool, Mother; make a scandal. Tell Father you'll write to his club."

"I won't," said Old Ellen. "I'm through with fighting, I'm through with scolding and shouting, I'm through with thinking I'll get my rights. I'm through with your father, I'm through with the estate. If they give me a little corner to go and live with Barry when he's dead, that's all I ask. Let her get it and enjoy it: she's got life before her. Let her enjoy life over my old stringy carcass."

"But can you imagine Archie standing for it?"

"He told me he fought the old man bitterly on that," said Hassie in a low voice, "but—you know—" she stopped.

"I know," said Old Ellen suddenly.

"You can't let a kid starve even if it's beyond the pale," grumbled Henny.

"I'm too old for argy-bargying after all these years of not speaking," said Old Ellen.

"I'd fight for money to my last drop of blood," said Henny indignantly. "Can you live on air? Father comes smiling at my children, and all with that beau-of-the-nineties air, and smelling of lotion, and I know he's come from and going to his love nest."

"And your little tin Jesus," said Old Ellen suddenly, "what is he doing when your back's turned. Ha-ha! Your little tin Jesus."

"Shut up, Mother," said Henny, "don't be stupid. I wish to God you were right. I'd get a divorce. No such luck. You know who I saw the other day as large as life? Dunne Legge and his wife. She was hurrying into Woodward, Lothrop's, and he was meekly sitting there at the wheel. She's not fat, but beefier than ever in the hips, you know how she was, well ten times more so and great big shoulders lolloping, but well corseted, and there he sat grinning calfishly like a lap dog after her. She always heckled him and hackled him and that's what he wanted. I didn't know that! I took his word for what he wanted. But when I saw her the first time, I knew I'd been a fool to take his word! She bossed him and he took it in big gobs: it got him. It would have been a bad mistake. It's enough to wave the big stick over the kids without a great big bear of a man. He saw me and I bowed to him very quietly, but he got out of the car and came over to me and stood talking, and I don't mind telling you he made a sort of gentlemanly pass at me, but I wasn't having any. I know the fine monsieur. If he thinks I have no memory! It gave me a sort of satisfaction, I tell you, to be so distant with him. Then she bustled up and just ran over, sirupy and saccharine and I skedaddled: I can't stand such falsity! The last thing I saw her struggling to get that great body of her into the car door. But there she sits, a ton of beef, and has cars and servants and everything. Oh, it all makes me sick. It all makes me sick: what's the use of struggling? You fall madly in love with one man and nearly break your heart because he throws you over and years later you find out you would have been miserable with him; and you go to a man you don't care for and it's just the same with him too. Life is nothing but rags and tags and filthy rags at that. Why was I ever born?"

"It's too late to ask me that," said Old Ellen. "But you mightn't have been." She began to laugh, "Your old man sent me anonymous letters himself to make me divorce him." She rippled with he-hes. "I hung on to spite him. I didn't want him. It's my only pleasure left." She laughed. "All I've got left is to sit in the sun and watch Barry booze and sometimes give him a kick in the pants. Sit in the sun and watch barflies, huh?"

"I'll bet that child is hanging around somewhere spying and listening," Henny worried.

At that Louie got up and pulled Evie silently up after her. The two of them started to tiptoe into the long dining room, but Evie, who didn't know the reason for this maneuver, broke away and ran to the door of the breakfast room calling,

"Mother, where's Uncle Barry?"

"Evie, Evie," Louie called.

"Just as I thought, I was sure," said Henny.

"Send the child away," Hassie said.

"Let her stay," Old Ellen commanded comfortably. "She's a big girl now, and Evie's too little a girl, eh, my dears? What do you fret yourself so much for?" she asked Henny. "Wait till you've had as many as I've had. They know more or less, it makes no difference in the end of the book. Sure, let her stay, you want to stay, don't you, Louie?"

"Yes—no," Louie looked from one to the other. Henny laughed with irritation, "Let her stay, let her hear the dirt." Old Ellen laughed, "You want to hear the dirt?"

"She's got her ears stuffed with dirt," said Henny. They all laughed good-naturedly. Old Ellen affected to disregard the child's blush and cried,

"Well, I've got a head full of dirt. You could comb it out. These windy days I don't wash it for a sixmonth. Life's dirty, isn't it, Louie, eh? Don't you worry what they say to you, we're all dirty."

Louie lifted her head, her eyes opened gladly, and she began to laugh while Evie moved slowly into Hassie's skirts. Old Ellen said loudly,

"Only it's all over now; I'm clean now. The worst was when they were all at school and running to the stables and dirtying up the house and worrying about women with that hang-dog, up-and-down-day, blue-Monday look, tramping through the house, dirtying it all up with cigars and cigarettes and stealing your father's keys and getting at his lordship's decanters." She laughed uproariously, "Oh, I used to listen at night for Barry creeping down, the way you listen for a mouse to squeak. There I would find him tasting and nipping with an electric torch! What a lad!" She laughed. "Now, it's different. I'm a decent

[181]

body, fit to talk to my washerwoman. No more milk on my bodices, mud on my skirts, only snuff on my mustache."

With utter repugnance, the two little girls looked at the well-filled old parchment face with its corrugated lips.

"Mother! Louie, run out onto the lawn. Mother, I wish you wouldn't talk that way before the children. Evie, run and play in the drawing room! Will you stop it, Mother! You're disgusting."

The old woman laughed, "Oh, let her stay. One day she'll get married, won't you, Louie?"

Louie looked shyly at her, filled with gratitude.

"And I'll have a baby," said Evie.

"You'll have a man in your skirts soon enough," said Old Ellen.

"Mother, for shame! You ought to blush!" cried the two women. "Before babies!"

"Baby me no babies!" cried Old Ellen. "They're grown women. When I was Evie's age I was looking after cows and horses and listening to the bellowing, with the cows a-bulling in the great big yellow summer moons. Kids grow up in the country. You keep them in bibs, you're child spoilers. Louie's a big sensible girl. Teach your grandmother to suck eggs, eh, Louie?"

Louie simpered vaguely.

"Mother, be quiet!"

Old Ellen had the devil in her. "Do you know that old joke that you brought home from school, and did I give you a smack-bottom then, though I remember the day with a laugh this many years gone. Mrs. Jones had a black baby. Mr. Jones died of fright when he had to explain it."

"Mother! Louie, leave the room. Mother, she'd do better to go and talk to that poor miserable creature from Highlandtown in your kitchen than to you. Go at once, Louie!"

The old woman gabbled on, ignoring her daughters' frowns, and Louie lingered. "Then the baby died and they buried it in one coffin and everyone saw that the little thing was black. Haugh!"

Hassie flushed and bounced up. But Henny sat in her place and merely commanded harshly, "Leave the room at once, or I'll make you."

Louie, struggling for a foothold, said quickly, with a whine, "Mother, Nellie says I am a bastard."

They all thoroughly enjoyed the cries and questions that followed. But Old Ellen herself bounced in her seat, saying, "I'll put salt on my lady's tail," while Hassie cried that she must get rid of the wicked little faggot and Henny told her this was what came of letting Barry choose the kitchenmaids. At that moment, there was a sound of a car honking plaintively, and they saw Archie's big sedan behind Hassie's car on the gravel drive. At the same time, Henny violently tugged at the bellpull and there came Nellie's running footsteps.

Archibald Lessinum came up the drive with a fretful expression which changed to polite pleasure when he saw the ladies. Mother and Hassie and Henny were all greeted and kissed, and he already noted their trouble and anger—three matrons with tumbled laps and Henny still carrying her serviette and wiping her lips.

"Did I alarm you, ladies?"

Archie was a short, neat, small-boned blond of a family of decayed officials whose money had gone during the war. Old David Collyer, self-made man who loved struggling talent, picked out Archie Lessinum and made him his clerk, then lawyer, then son-in-law, just as he had picked out Samuel Pollit and made him son-in-law and advanced him. Archie, thin and weak, had first liked a little the sprightly, spoiled young Henny with her dark great eyes; but after a few months of feeding, he felt the power rise up in him to cope with noble fleshly Eleanor, her father's pet, who fell romantically in love with him. This passion held for seven years when they were married.

Hassie, who expected to be named executrix of her father's will, treated Archie very seriously and confidentially as man to man; Henny saw him with a twinge of pain even now. Eleanor had no children. As for Old Ellen, she could hardly distinguish him from the rest of the world or her sons; having produced so many after pregnancies of identical length and after so many identical childhood illnesses, she could hardly tell one man from another. She was as glad to see young Archie as anyone else.

"Here you come as usual in the nick of time, young Archie," said she. "A young puss I have here has been giving lip again. I want you to speak to her. She must be sick of listening to women's jaw."

"Certainly, Mother," he said, taking it to heart, and fixing his little round glasses at the girl who was retreating through the back hall.

"Nellie! Come here at once."

The women looked very serious. He planted himself a little to the side of the three women, all taller than he. "What is it?" he muttered to Hassie. Hassie told him the offense.

"What did you say, Nellie?" he asked. "Repeat the word. You told Louie something." When he said "Louie," he winced slightly, for he detested the child as well as her father. It pained him to have to be compared with this other hand-picked son-in-law. The harum-scarum little creature looked worried; but she was frightened and told all. Archie said,

"You will go up to your room and pack, Nellie."

Immediately there was a movement amongst the women, Henny saying, "Quite right; I'd do the same," but Hassie looking doubtful and Old Ellen taking the apron from Nellie's hands,

"Well, if she's going, I have to get the supper."

"She can have her notice, but she must wait till tomorrow," said Hassie, "Mother can't be left alone and Barry is out."

Louie started forward to help, "No, Uncle Barry is in the stables."

"How do you know?" cried Henny.

"I saw him; he's asleep on the bed up there." There was another cat's-paw of emotion, Henny declaring, "You had no right to go sneaking up there, haven't I told you not to," and, Hassie fervently ejaculating that Henny should look after a young girl better, both tweaked hold of poor Louie's dress and urged her out on to the veranda, "Now go and play and don't cause any more trouble." Too much was going on, however, for them to notice her, and Evie, who remained sitting all the time on the bottom shelf of the big hall stand, saw everything unrebuked.

In the end Nellie went up to pack, Hassie driving her before her like a heifer to market, through the kitchens and to the enclosed stairs. Old Ellen going up the front stairs, arrived heavily and flatfooted in her room at the same time, going through the billiard room to say,

"Stop blubbering, my girl, and get your things together unless you want us to pack for you, and it mighn't be a bad idea. I'm sorry to see you go: you were a good girl in your way."

Meanwhile, in the breakfast room, where Archie sat with Henny and Hassie had returned, a violent conversation had arisen about Nellie's bags. All servant girls stole, said Archie; and Hassie said that where they didn't it was the exception that proved the rule.

"I'd steal if I had only her threadbare rags, and rich rotters swanked their things under my nose," said Henny viciously, irritated by Archie's pious look and cautionary notions. Archie did not deign to answer this; but he gave Henny a secret glance which seemed to mean that he wouldn't put it past her; and she replied with a black look.

"But I feel embarrassed," confessed Hassie, "when I look through and find nothing. It is like a slap in the face."

"You must not think of yourself," Archie assured her severely, "it has a demoralizing effect on the girls if they think they can get away with anything. If they don't steal this time, then they will next, provided they fancy they will not be searched."

The upshot of it was that Archie's male authority won. No sooner had Nellie brought down her old-fashioned trunk and valise than they had to be set down in the great hall and opened again. Henny poh-pohed and declared she would not stay there poking her nose into any slovenly, filthy Highlandtown rags, and went out of the hall, while Archie held up his small white hand, trying to frown down Henny of whom he now violently disap-

[185]

proved, and sternly told the girl not to touch the things but to let her mistress go through them.

"Then she must get the potstick or the copper stick," said Henny, from the door. "If she touches the mess, she's a fool; I'd rather be boiled in oil than put a finger to it; who knows what dirt is there—bugs or some disease, who knows what dirt? Here," said she, and stuck out between Hassie and Old Ellen towards Archie a pair of brass-handled tongs that she had seized from the fireplace in the breakfast room, "here, Archie, lift her things out with these!" But it was an insult to Archie, not the girl. He turned away and said,

"Mother, will you look through, please."

Henny shrugged and gave the tongs to Evie to put back. "Of all the dam foolery," said Henny.

Meanwhile Old Ellen was puffing over the trunk and pushing her fingers under old stockings and the remains of a dark apricot outfit bought for Nellie's last Easter, and presently hauled out a photograph of Barry, from Barry's room.

"What is this, my lady?" she asked, as she held out her hands.

"You are a thief," said Hassie, horrified.

"You know what we could do to you for this?" inquired Archie, solemnly.

She looked around at them, frowning. It ended by her having to unpack everything before their eyes and then repacking and trudging out with both packets to Hassie's car where she had to sit. Hassie would take her downtown when she went. Meanwhile, Henny was very angry with them all, because this meant that Louie or she would have to stay overnight and get their own food, and that Hassie would have to engage a new servant by tomorrow; and Henny was more angry still because now it could not be put off any longer and they would have to sit down at once and discuss Henny's financial position. The family was to make Henny a loan, in order to pay off bills she had run up for the children's clothes and dentistry, unknown to Sam, and she was to pay Archie back each time she received money from Sam. At her own urgent, exasperated request, after many threats of suicide and tears, Archie had agreed not to tell Sam about these debts.

"He would make it an excuse for taking my children away from me," said Henny, and related how Samuel struck her when he found out about the $102 owing at Middenway's, the corner grocer's. There was some talk about speaking to Samuel about striking his wife, but secretly they all felt that it would not do their spoiled sister any harm. Old David had paid Henny's bills so long after they each had had to struggle for every cent they used.

4 🜨 Shoes.

THE CLEAR AUTUMN WEATHER was with them, fresh as spring; and for the children it was always spring anyway: shriveling summer was spring, the blight of the leaves was spring, the frozen gutter was spring, and spring waiting for the buds to glisten and the birds to break eggshells was early spring too, spring so young and foolish that no poems yet applied to it, spring just born, spring with throbbing head, spring babbling and spilling, spring with jelly backbone.

Louie, going to the eastern veranda, to hang out the dish-cloths and dish mop after washing up, saw the strange girl, Olive Burchardt, going down beside the fence, between the thinning lower branches of the trees.

Olive, who was fourteen already, looked at her and smirked, "You wash the dishes."

Louie grinned and blushed, but the rictus of embarrassment pleased Olive.

"You wash up; I seen you hanging out the dishcloth," Olive elaborated.

"Yes, I know."

"You do the work," Olive continued, sidling along up the

street, towards the back steps, her dark, famished face never to be fed, looking backwards over the paling tops. Louie watched her intently. Olive laughed.

"Mr. Middenway said you passed lowest in all the school."

"How does he know?"

"He went down to ask why his kids didn't pass and he found out everything."

Olive sidled down the street again and, without another word, but with a few backward grins and grimaces, made towards the Middenway store. Louie stared after her as painfully as if Olive was dragging some piece of her living flesh and blood over the fence tops with her. She knew Olive was going to chat about her and her mother with the Middenways and that everyone knew they owed a huge bill to the Middenways: she knew that to owe a huge bill was both a distinction and a disgrace. Then there was the hushed-up theft mystery. Olive bought from cheap Murchison, the butcher. Although the Burchardts lived just down the block, Mrs. Pollit knew nothing of them.

Hazel Moore, the maid from Monocacy, looked between the curtains of Henny's room and called, "Your mother wants you."

"Yes, Hazel."

She went reluctantly indoors, giving a last stretch after Olive, now out of sight. Henny was continuing to Hazel,

"Lord, I hate to go and get the kids shoes: I can't keep them in shoes the way they scuff and kick and shuffle along. In summer they play football and skate, and in winter they tramp in the wet till the leather is sodden and rotten."

Louie called from the staircase, "What dress will I put on, Mother?"

"Don't ask silly questions. I hate her to go into Washington, in that old thing: she looks like a sack of potatoes. Tell Toddy [Ernest] to clean my shoes. A-ah, deuce take it. I burned my neck again; where's the cold cream? Don't I look foul? I look like a half-breed."

Hazel, the tall-boned, blue-tinged Catholic maid, called from the bedroom,

"Toddy, Toddy: clean Mother's shoes."

Evie called, "Ernest is feeding the animals."

Hazel went to the south hall door calling, "Toddy, Toddy."

"Yippills?" Ernest answered.

"Clean Mother's shoes, darling."

"Momento, zecond; Little-Sam has the snake out."

"What do you say? What is that you said?" Yes, this was followed by a shriek of horror, "Henny, that boy has the snake out of the cage."

"Momento," shouted Ernest soothingly. "Smart's the word and cool's the action: snako, go back."

Little-Sam said nothing during this excitement, but picked up the cold, sulky snake by the head behind the ears, and as it began to wreathe itself slowly round his arm, he offered it the cage door. The snake put out its forked tongue tentatively, hesitated, and began to penetrate the cage, moving slowly over the dried grass. Meanwhile Henny had burned herself again, under the ear, an ugly burn that she could not afford, for her hair scarcely fell there. But the slot door fell to, and the snake was home again, sitting in the eleven o'clock sun, grudgingly awake on this cold day.

"Hurry up," shouted Henny.

"Ya'm: come nup," Ernest answered, bolting into view over the steep lawn, now rough with grass and weeds of all summer. He appeared breathless, under the back veranda, cheerfully anxious and conciliatory.

"Naughty boy," cried Hazel, "to let the snake out."

"I was cleaning the box," said Ernest. "Dad-pad told me to clean it. Gee, I didn't know Mothering was going already. O.K."

Louie loomed on the second floor south and leaned over, "Ernie, hay! Toddy, Ernesto!"

Ernest craned upwards, "Whappills?"

"How's the possum?"

"Mean, she hissed at me."

"Are any of the snakes asleep yet?"

"Sure, one and there's another shutting her eyes. Gee, they

are torpid, gee are they sleepy!" He jubilated. He ran back into the kitchen to finish the half-blacked shoes. Louie went slowly into her father's room, which she now occupied alone, and finished dressing at a snail's pace, pondering over the possum's meanness and the snake's hibernation. On her father's open roll-top desk was a book on parthenogenesis, a fertile and beautiful book of metaphysics, as it seemed to Louie, a lens on Life and its transparent secrets. Spreading glass but subtle wings, wide as the world, Louie, meandering through flowery mazes of metaphysics, was walking out with beauty and destiny. This made the process of dressing very slow, and Henny was powdered, curled, pressed, and had her hat on before Louie had buttoned her dress down the back.

"Louie, Louie!"

She fastened on her sailor and went downstairs. Her shoes were old and down at heel, but it was a happy day today, for they were going to get new ones. Henny and Hazel stood in the hall with a tinge of acrimony in their remarks to each other; something had been blowing up for days past. Hazel, twelve years older than Henny, strict, sober, and religious, made no bones about lecturing her on her wasteful ways; and Mr. Middenway, the grocer, had made some tart remarks around the district about the Pollit bills, which Hazel had picked up coming out of Mass the Sunday before. Another Sunday loomed, and Hazel wished to pay the bill in time.

"I have you and the children to look after," said Hazel, standing very stiff.

"Go to Tokyo!" Henny answered, continuing to Louie humorously, "Can't you shift your great haunches faster than that? The great fat lump drives me crazy. I suppose you were mooning over some book?"

Coming downstairs, Louie was wondering whether Olive Burchardt was still running round the streets doing the errands, for if so, she might see her. She began to run downstairs headlong and tumbled over the last three steps, falling straight on her nose and finishing in a heap at the bottom. She picked herself up, crying. Henny said,

"Oh, she's black and blue: I'm ashamed to be seen out with her —they'll think I beat her: everyone knows I'm the kid's step-mother"; and to Hazel, tossing her head, "I'll give the order to Mr. Hankin myself, and pay him; and I'll pay Middenway on the way back. Please stop bothering about it."

"I should if I were you," Hazel remarked stiffly.

Although the day was mild, Henny was wearing the heavy fur coat lent to her by Hassie, and fur-rimmed boots.

"That's so pretty, Mother," Louie said.

"Help your mother and see she doesn't slip on the snow," Hazel warned her.

Ernie whooped and dashed out to help Henny down the steps, which he had just swept, and to the gate. The flurry of children's good-bys set in again, and left them in a drift across the path and veranda.

"Good-by, Motherbunch," shouted Ernest, at her ear. The twins were struggling together in an upstairs window, squeaking urgently, "Mothering, Mothering!"

"What is it?" She turned back. Louie was hopping from one foot to another, craning her neck to see if Olive was anywhere in the neighborhood.

"Good-by, Mothering," the twins cried.

"Good-by," said Evie, on the verge of tears.

"Oh, good-by, for the love of Mike," but she waved and smiled at them. Evie rushed down the path unexpectedly, sweeping Tommy and Ernie out of her way in her passion, and her break-ing voice was lifted,

"You didn't kiss me!" Henny blew her a kiss, saying between her teeth, immediately,

"The whole caboosh busting into tears because I don't go round mugging them. I'll go to Hankin's first and pay him and he can send the order. You can get the sugar, six pounds of granulated, on the way back, and tell him I'll be over to pay him this afternoon without fail."

Louie's heart gave a painful throb. Olive Burchardt had just dawdled round the corner of R Street, from the Avenue. She saw Louie and her mother at once and made the same smirk and gesture as before; she meant to say,

You do work, you wash up.

"Can I talk to Olive, Mother, while you go to the butcher's?"

"What on earth for?"

"I want to ask her, tell her—something."

When Henny said yes, she ran across the street and yet she knew it was all aimless; she did not really like Olive. Olive waited for her. Louie was much taller this year, tall for twelve, but Olive was weedy, and what Henny called a skinny gutter rat.

"What did you come over for?" asked Olive. "Your mother's gone into the butcher's."

"I know."

"I just seen Middenway: I was talkin' to him. He said you passed lowest in the school."

"I didn't."

"You did."

"How does he know?"

"He went and asked at the school about Dorothy, his silly kid. And they told him you were the worst."

"They wouldn't tell him about me."

"They would."

There was a pause, during which Louie with flustered face picked at the curb with her shabby shoes.

"Haven't you got any other shoes?" inquired Olive.

"I'm going to get some today," she waved vaguely in the direction of the butcher's.

"You're a liar," said Olive enviously, anxious to be contradicted, greedily contemplating Louie's face; but Louie was absorbed. After a pause, Louie said, "Perhaps I can walk home from school with you on Monday; I'm in the same school with you."

Olive waited a moment and then said evilly, "I'm not goin' to school on Monday and no day. I'm leavin'."

Something seemed to hit Louie. A new sort of pain, sharp and quick as lightning, tore out of its swaddling clothes of flesh, inside Louie. For a moment, she was conscious only of her wrung bowels and the cause of misery beside her, the dark spindly creature. I can't bear this, something said very audibly inside her. It was like the first stab of an abscess; the sufferer knew it would come back. I can't bear it. She looked at Olive, "Oh, Olive, don't go."

Olive could not have known anything about this little girl. Louie had never walked home from school with her, had never been allowed to play with her, and, being clumsy where Olive was spry, had never got into Olive's athletic, knowing circle in the playground. Louie knew nothing about Olive, had only seen her from a distance, and once, a few mornings ago, in the light falling from a classroom window, a queer light making her complexion greenish. But Olive had the instinctive strike of the cat,

"I'm going away, you'll never see me again."

"Oh! Where? Don't go."

"I'm goin to work: I'm sick of school."

"Oh, where, Olive?"

"You couldn't go there. In Baltimore."

"I could go to Baltimore."

"What for?" drawled the wretch, eying her oddly.

"I don't know."

They began to cross the street, towards the butcher's, Olive enlarging on her new life and Louie drearily trying to take an interest in it. Outside the butcher's they paused,

"Well, so long, got to shove off," said Olive, but not going.

"So long."

Louie took one step towards the door and stopped, "Perhaps you could leave on Tuesday?"

"I'm going on Monday to get my books; otherwise I wouldn't go. You'll be in school," said Olive.

"All right."

"So long."

Olive dawdled off, while Louie, standing in the butcher's door, gaped after her miserably. It was a relief that Olive had moved away: but ideas began to pour frantically through Louie's brain; perhaps something would happen and Olive wouldn't go, her parents would not move till the end of the week, or at least Tuesday, or they would decide to make her go back to school, or Olive would call by to say good-by, or even give Louie one of her books. But a minute later, Louie, looking down the street at Olive's pleated blue back and ankle socks, knew that that was the last she would see of her.

"Come inside and help me, Louie," called Henny in a sweet voice. She was on excellent terms again with the butcher, who, even when the debt fell deepest, still respected her father's business reputation. Henny was not rude, sharp, and overbearing with storekeepers or their assistants, although most women of her sort think they are obliged to be so; but never failed to "butter them up," as she put it, and was always recounting the compliments paid to her by them.

Two women standing inside, with red specks of sawdust on their suede shoes, and wearing respectable felt hats, one mustard and one red, were beaming like two bowls of peaches and cream at Henny, and then turned faces like two bowls of prunes and prisms at Louie. One said the expected thing,

"I'm sure she is a great help to you, Mrs. Pollit," while the other nodded sagely at Louie, "I'm sure you love children, dear: you must be a great help."

Louie stood stony before these old lines.

"Is she fond of the children?" inquired the second lady turning to Henny with a twitch, for like all ladies she prided herself on getting on well with the little ones. The wide-eyed Louie gave no answer. Henny shifted impatiently,

"I don't know, I'm sure; I don't know what she likes. She's a secretive child."

"But I hope you can trust her with the little ones," said the first severely, "such a big girl!"

"Oh, you could trust her if she didn't always have her nose stuck in a book," Henny exclaimed, getting out of patience with the women who were worrying one of their favorite subjects.

"Too much poring over books is bad for the eyes," confided the mustard-hatted woman demurely.

"Oh, we take great care of the children's eyes," Henny assured her with sudden insolence. "Come along, Louie," and with two dignified nods and a sweet "thank you" to the butcher, she swept out of the shop, saying, "Let's hurry along: I've no time to waste." A few steps away she cried, "Silly old gobblers with their dirty hair like a haystack in a fit. Imagine a woman that age with a yellow hat perched on her bun. Making up to me and making eyes, Mrs. Pollit this and that. I don't want their sticky beaks prying into my children. And it makes me mad I have to drag a monster girl like you round with me in that outfit because your father won't let me dress you properly. Now they're probably cackling behind my back and calling me a stepmother. It makes me sick. What were you doing all that time with that skinny gutter rat?"

"Can we look in the animal shop, Mother?"

"As if you didn't have enough stinking beasts at home. This afternoon."

The river gleamed at the bottom, as they walked down the avenue to the next car stop; at the foot of the street was a bare tree. They saw the blue-painted pet shop from across the street, because Henny wanted to see what was on at the cinema, and, yielding to the child's fever, Henny crossed the street and allowed her to pore over the animals until the car came in sight. Getting into the car, Louie slipped on her turned heel and went sprawling "in full sight of the whole car, covering me with embarrassment," as Henny put it; and a pleasant-faced, middle-aged gentleman came to the rescue, taking off his hat to Henny. In the car Henny met a neighbor, whom she detested and called an old upholstered frump, Mrs. Bolton, in fact; but each woman at once became tenderly confidential with the other, and a long discussion ensued about the awkwardness of young girls, and yet the impossibility of sending "young girls" about the city alone. This was but a prelude to Mrs. Bolton's searching questions about Mr. Pollit in his absence; and Henny, with a great degree of wifely pride and modesty, retailed all Sam's political opinions and described his work with the Anthropological Mission in the Pacific.

"You must be very proud of your husband," the woman remarked with affectation.

"Oh, I am," Henny answered, with perfect good grace, "I think he is a remarkable man, he works so hard, and no one can shake him from his opinions. He would not change his opinion for anyone, once he had one. Samuel does not really care for success, but for science and getting at the truth of things. I think he is a really remarkable man; but I suppose that's foolish of me."

Mrs. Bolton's cheerfulness shriveled perceptibly, but they went on "la-di-da-ing," as Henny called it, until Henny unexpectedly got out at the White House. This enchanted Louie, who at once started looking for the squirrels.

"I could have slapped her face," cried Henny, "old upholstered busybody, prying and poking, 'What is Mr. Pollit doing now?'" she mimicked. "She had better find out what her daughter is doing now, running round with other women's husbands: I wonder she dares to look me in the face, or any woman. If my daughter did that, I'd stay at home. A woman with a daughter like that pawing my daughter. I was simply fuming and it was all I could do to be decent to her."

The morning was full of excitement, with its infinite and mysteriously varied encounters, Henny giving battle on great provocation and invariably coming off victorious. This glorious, mettlesome morning was capped by Henny's being very charming and disarming to a shoe salesman and getting Louie a new pair of scuffless shoes. In her new shoes, Louie was allowed to go to the Museum to study the exhibit of local fauna and flora, in order to get up a satisfactory nature report to send to the greedy Sam, far off in foreign jungles.

After assiduous scribbling in a new five-cent notebook, a deadly horror overcame her, the nausea of museums, and the "nature record" had to stop there, where she was taken by sickness. But after that, in obedience to Sam's further desires, she dropped in at

[196]

the Bureau of Fisheries to see Dr. Philibert, her father's other self, in the well-known cave of aquaria, where she ran across various characters of the legend; for instance, Crazy-Daisy, who stared at her very hard but did not acknowledge her, and Dear Old Ratty, who rushed up to her babbling, to pump her hand and ask after "my old friend Sam." His thin neck wobbled in its loose halter, just as Sam showed them in mimicry. Then, having "come into contact with people," according to Sam's orders, and "having begun her little life journey through the highways and byways," as he put it, having borne Sam's messages of high good will and cheer to various officers in his Department (while thoroughly convinced of the absurdity of these verbiages), Louie went home satisfied, walking to the old Rock Creek double bridge, along Pennsylvania Avenue, thick strewn with leaves. At home she was in command until six, when Hazel came home in a good temper.

Hazel, though forty-eight, had a young man; though a vixen (in Louie's opinion), she had been loved by this young man for nearly twenty years and had been engaged to him for fifteen years. But, as it was explained carefully to everyone who came to the house, Hazel was obliged to wait until she could not have children before she could marry Mr. Gray, because Mr. Gray was a Protestant and Hazel's priest would not let her children be Protestants.

When Henny came home, she and Hazel discussed the whole thing again; and Hazel, flushed, announced that she had agreed to marry Mr. Gray this year. They would go back to Charlestown, whence Hazel had come many, many years ago, to be the Collyer kitchenmaid, and live on Mr. Gray's apple orchard. The evening buzzed with visions of Hazel's future happiness and old evening of life as Mrs. Gray amidst fat apple trees.

"Perhaps you will be sorry you waited so long," Henny said rather mournfully to her old crony.

"No," Hazel shook her still black head. "When I see what you've been through with that man and his parcel of children, Henny, I think I'm better off. It's no deprivation."

[197]

"You won't always think so," said Henny, "you wait and see."

"With Mr. Gray I will have everything I want," said Hazel firmly.

"And what about me? I'll have to wrestle with these children alone again," said Henny, "and me half gone to another one. Hazel, you must wait at least till I'm up and about. What difference does it make to you? You've waited so long."

Hazel colored a little and it looked as though a tiff were blowing up, but Hazel cooled down again and told Henny she was a selfish girl, but that she would wait until Pollit came home.

"But Pollit and his Pollit relations I can't abide," declared Hazel with a spot on her cheeks, "and if I'm obliged to live in the house with that man, I'll say something we'll all be sorry for. He's ruined your life."

Between Hazel and Henny, though, the stream ran deep and still: Henny only felt a little aggrieved that Hazel looked forward so eagerly to leaving her.

CHAPTER SIX

1 ⚘ Letters to Malaya.

It was a cold and windy March night. Four of the children sat round a wood fire in the long dining room on stools and hassocks, with Henny who had again queerly become a large woman, though her hands, feet, and face remained small and narrow. Ernest sat at the oak dining table bent over his schoolbooks, very industrious, and Louisa, excused from drying the dishes, was copying the last of her "Georgetown Record" of birds, insects, and plants, which was supposed to be a daybook of observations, closed each month and sent on, but which she had again got from the Museum. The house was cold away from the fire and the children's bodies made a fire screen; they were toasted in front while chills ran down their spines. Louie had on her now shabby coat as she worked. Henny, sitting at the end of the table nearest the fire, had before her a child's mattress newly covered with ticking which she was tacking and tufting with a great steel needle. As she worked she execrated the work still to do, the coldness of the house, her poverty, her fatigue, and the infinite household tasks that lay before her. The children used to this running commentary, pegged away at the letters they were writing to their father. Henny groaned and cursed Sam's orders from afar, the squeaking pens, and cried, "Darn it!" whenever she stabbed her finger by mistake.

"Will you put my letter in with yours, Moth?" asked Evie.

"I'm afraid to write to your father: he criticizes my spelling," sneered Henny. "And it appears I know nothing about geography. Hang his stuck-up conceit."

Louisa restlessly rose again from her writing to go and look through the grimy curtains of her mother's bedroom at the every-night scene which was wild and brilliant now—the trees of the heath round the Naval Observatory, the lamplight falling over the wired, lichened fence of the old reservoir, the mysterious, long, dim house that she yearned for, the strange house opposite, and below, the vapor-blue city of Washington, pale, dim-lamped, under multitudinous stars, like a winter city of Africa, she thought, on this night at this hour. After a little while, she came back and began to drag her pen over the sheet of paper again.

"Darn it!" cried Henny again. "For the love of Mike, tell Hazel to give me some tea and an aspirin, my eyes are burning out my skull."

The dishes stopped rattling in the kitchen. They heard Hazel hang the big washbowl on its high nail; and then Evie came running in, holding the silver tight in two hands. She thrust it into the drawers of the old scratched sideboard and came bursting into the semicircle round the fire, saying,

"Oo, gee whiz, is it cold; jiminy, I'm freezing. Moth, when are we going to get the coal?"

"Your father thinks I can heat it over here from the lurid tales he puts in his letters," Henny chattered. "I'll get the coal, don't worry. Oh, that's enough for tonight."

"I wish you'd let me do it," said Louie; "let me try."

"You're not strong enough, my girl: you need my tough old arms to do this," Henny exclaimed. "Wait till you've washed and scrubbed for a man for ten or twelve years. Until that time, I won't let you turn into a drudge. You do the darn birds, that's all you're asked to do. Ernie, boy, go and get Mother's tea, I hear it being poured out."

Henny edged in close to the fire and placed her bony hands to warm them on the hot, silky heads of the twins. They turned towards her, inwards, two similar red and yellow apples, and Saul began to sing falsetto,

[200]

I would not marry a butcher, I'll tell you the reason why;
He'd chop me up for mincemeat and put me in a pie.

"Let Mother sing it," they clamored.

"Let Mother alone," said Henny.

Hazel sat in the kitchen in the cold, wrapped in a black, crocheted shawl brooding. During the last month or two she and Henny had quarreled much, and it was always over money. Henny ignored her maid's sulking in the kitchen and, to show her indifference, consented to sing, very low for them, "I wouldn't marry a butcher," a song she had dug up for the Düsseldorf scandal.

"Have you finished your father's letter, Louie?"

"Nearly."

"It's about time; you've been all night at it, and you haven't touched your homework. I don't know why you leave it to the last moment. You know he looks for it and you know if your father doesn't get it, he blames me. You don't want me forever to be the scapegoat, do you? And if you don't get through this rotten homework they pile on you, at your age, he'll blame me too. I'll write to the principal."

Louie was silent, in dread; but passed over the two-page letter she had written. Henny read it with distaste, jerked it back to her, and said, "Get the letters together and let's post them tonight; then I'll have no more of this trash round the dining room."

Hazel, looking bitter and neglected, stalked in from the kitchen, untying her dark blue apron, emphatically, from her waist. In a sergeant's voice, she demanded, "Has Louie written to her father?"

"Yes," Louie answered dryly.

"Have the others written?"

"Yes, they've written. Thank God, there's another mail off. I simply dread mailing days; I can never get the kids to write to their father."

Ernest, great favorite of Hazel, lifted his soft, wide-eyed face and shot at her, "All the 'varmints' start out with, 'Dear Dad, I hope you are well, I am well, Mother is well,' and then they get stuck."

"Evie put 'Dead Dad,' " Saul informed them.

> *Tattletale tit, your tongue will be split,*
> *And all the little puppy dogs will get a little bit,*

Hazel recited. She stroked down Evie's hair, "There, my kittycat is Hazel's baby; never mind what they say: it's all right."

"That child can't spell a word, and her father blames it on me," said Henny irritably.

The little dark girl mourned amongst them, looking abashed and melancholy from one to the other.

The letters were piled on the table, each addressed in the awkward writing of the author. Each envelope had been long and proudly fingered, and tears and smuts were strewn over them.

Just when they had all forgotten Ernie's cleverness, Evie bleated, "Ernie hasn't got any homework tonight: his class didn't have homework; I heard Miss Morrin say."

"I have, too," Ernie declared.

Louie looked at his book for a minute and decided, "It's made-up homework."

"I can do it," Ernie said angrily.

"You're screwing up your eyes there and you don't have to do it?" Henny demanded, much put out. "I've been letting you sit there half an hour longer because I thought you had to do it: you told me that, you wretched little fibber."

"It's some problems the teacher told us to do."

"Told you you could do," corrected Louie. Ernie stuck out his lower lip rebelliously.

"Ernie's nuts," said Little-Sam, "he's always studyin'; he's a fairy."

"What did you say?" cried Henny. Little-Sam grinned foolishly while the other boys (except Ernie) looked pleased. After a devious discussion which revealed that Little-Sam used the word for anyone but a football hero, Henny suddenly cried,

"Now pack up, kids, and go to bed. I've never seen such pests," while Ernie's voice was suddenly heard, contemptuous,

"Is there a law sayin' I can't do homework?"

Tommy whimpered, "Oo, my itti-gutties [itchy-scratchies]" and started to scratch at the large pink welts appearing on his legs.

"Don't scratch, and get away from the fire," Hazel commanded. Tommy jerked up his head, said, "I go bed," and scrambled off his stool. Then he burst into tears.

It was hard to get away from the hot fire and plunge into the icy air that waited for them just outside the hearth and that got colder and colder as they went to their rooms upstairs. The central heating had been off for some days, since the coal and some remains of wood blocks had given out. Little-Sam stopped at the door, whined,

"Willya tell's a story, Louie?"

"No, I've got my homework."

"Oh, go on, Louie," both the twins whined disagreeably, and Evie got up expectantly, "I'll get into Saul's bed."

Hazel's voice came over the stairhead, "Children!"

"Louie!"

"Oh, all right."

They scampered upstairs like iron nuts and bolts falling downstairs. Suddenly the noise halted. They started to come down again, "Mothering, Mothering!"

"I wish they wouldn't call me that idiotic name," Henny said, over the white wool she had begun to knit.

"Mothering, you will come up and say good night, Ernie says," Evie's figure reappeared in the doorway.

"No, I will not. Go upstairs before I chase you."

"It's so co-old," said Little-Sam, reappearing. "It's so mizz [miserable]." He shuddered.

"You go upstairs before I fan your pants," said Henny. They whinnied with fun and scampered for the stairs again. Ernie came and stood before his mother in his winter bunnyhug pyjamas, round, rosy, eager, to begin their private ritual, made up accidentally, in Ernie's second year of life, by them both,

Good night, Mother.
Good night, my son.
Will I see you in the morning?
You will if you've got any luck.
Well, I've got heaps of luck and loads
of luck, so will I?
You will, my son.
Good night, Mother.
Do you love me, Son?
Yes, Mother.
How much do you love me?
Lots and lots of love.
But how much is lots?
More than all the money in all the world
in all the years and all there is.
That's good. Well, good night now.
Good night, Mother.

It was Ernie who first insisted on repeating this, each night before going to sleep, to his mother, and on having her solemn assurance that she would be there when he woke up; and even sometimes he had insisted, "But you will be there when I wake up?" Nor had he gone to bed one night without saying it with her except when, as she said, she took a busman's holiday and went for two weeks to the maternity ward.

Ernie dashed a kiss off on his mother's cheek and sprinted for the stairs, crowing, "I wonder what story Looloo's going to tell us? I hope a story about Malaya."

There was a dive and scramble for the beds. When they had all snuggled in, sheets and blankets up to their ears, whimpering and giggling at the heat and cold, Louie, sitting in an armchair, in her winter overcoat, between the two doors, after waiting for silence and hearing all the hisses and gigglings die down, said solemnly,

"I'll tell you a story about Daddy, Sam-the-Bold. When he was just outside of Kuala Tokang, in Kelantan, he met a Korinchi-man."

There was a speechless silence.

"Although it was midafternoon, they noticed when they came near to the village on struts, in a clearing in the jungle——"

"Who noticed?" asked Ernie.

"Daddy and his men. They noticed that all the doors and windows were shut. They have no windows, only shutters in wood. The only thing they could see was a small kid tied in a rough cage."

"A kid in a cage?"

"Goat kid," explained Ernie dreamily, "like Whitey's."

"The cage was made of rough stripped saplings with its door held open by a long sapling. The kid was tied to a notched stick in the inside of the cage. 'Tiger expected,' said Wan Hoe."

"Who's Hoe?" asked Evie.

"Daddy's secretary, dumfie," said Little-Sam, while the others said "shh!"

"The Malays began to shin up trees," said Louie. "Daddy and Wan Hoe went and knocked at one of the cabins, and Wan Hoe and one of the Malays talked to them. 'They will not answer,' said the Malay. 'Ask them what it is all about, friend,' said Daddy."

"Why did he say 'friend'?" asked Evie. Solemn as a church, Louie replied,

"Because Daddy wishes all men white and black to be his friends. And he tells people when he says that that it is because he is American and he came from the great white city of brotherhood, Washington."

"And he says he is with the American Smithsonian Field Expedition," said Ernie.

"Yes. Eventually, however, there was a babble from inside the hut which burst out like a packet of crackers and then stopped. The Malay, although he was a Mohammedan and had been to Mecca, a traveled man, and was called Awang Haji, seemed afraid and kept looking everywhere over his shoulders, into the trees and undergrowth, and he kept looking at his companions, too, who were scattered around. 'Korinchi-man about here,' Wan Hoe explained to Daddy." Louie waited. The children waited. Then Little-Sam said slowly,

"What is a Korinchi-man?"

"The Korinchi-men are a wandering breed of Malays who are supposed to be weretigers, that is, they are men by day and turn into tigers at night."

"Oo-hoo-hoo-oo!" they shuddered.

"When night falls, they come and knock at a door. People open the door and ask them what they want. Then the Korinchi-man says, 'Please let me stay for the night, because tigers are prowling round. Who is so cruel as to shut out a naked man without a gun?' So the Korinchi-man asks and gains admittance to the household and when they are asleep he turns into a tiger and eats them all."

"Wheese!" Little-Sam exclaimed.

"But is it true? Do they turn into tigers?"

"Of course not," said Louie. "That is just what they think."

"Who think?"

"The other natives who live in the cabins."

"But haven't the Korinchi-men got cabins?"

"No. They are too poor."

"Why can't they chop down trees," Tommy wanted to know.

"I don't know," said Louie, "they are just a kind of gypsy; but people hate them because they have no cabins."

"If—" said Ernie, but Louie promptly jumped into the breach, "If the natives think he is a Korinchi-man they won't let him in, but make him stay out in the jungle all night. When morning comes, very often they find a tiger's tracks and no man at all; and no man comes back the next night."

They waited. Louie waited.

"Or," said Louie, "they see by the marks on the ground that the tiger has dragged a body off into the jungle."

Evie and Little-Sam shivered and hid their faces for a moment.

"So they think it is the best thing to kill Korinchi-men if they can, if they catch one alone in the daylight," said Louie, "at least some think that. Because it happened amongst Daddy's Malays there was a Korinchi-man, no one would let them in, and they were obliged to pitch tents in the open. The others, I tell you, did not like sleeping with the Korinchi, but Daddy said they would have a fire all night, and watches kept."

"Go on," said Little-Sam, "go on!"

Louie waited cunningly.

"Go on," said Ernie to oblige her. They had all heard the story several times before and yet their interest was more passionate now than at first.

"In the night Sam-the-Bold heard a giant harsh breathing just outside the tent, near his bed. He heard soft movements, and later the kid screamed. In the morning, though, the kid had gone and the bad Malay, the Korinchi-man, too. The trap had fallen, but this was one of those cunning tigers that eat up natives for years and are too smart to be caught. They were going back to their launch anyhow and they could not wait to look for Tong——"

"—the bad Malay," said Saul.

"—and no one wanted them because people thought they had brought along a weretiger with them. So they had to get back without Tong who had gone back to the jungle, perhaps to his death, for if he had the mark of the Korinchi-man he was wanted nowhere and had to go straight to the tiger's claws."

"Oo-hoo-hoo-hoo," cried Evie in a little emotional convulsion.

"Tell another story, not creepy," said Saul promptly, "so Evie won't get a dream."

They all laughed and, more sleepily, more relaxed, slid into the bedclothes.

"The golden box with the glass key," Louie announced. "Oh, goodness! Oh, I've got to go. Go to bed. I forgot to give Mother the letter. There's a registered letter from Malaya."

She rushed to her schoolbag with Ernie at her heels and drew out from a slot between books a long, much-stamped, blue-penciled letter addressed to Mrs. Samual C. Pollit. With this she ran downstairs, with Henny calling out,

"What's happened now: is the house on fire? At least we'd get warm," while Hazel continued her yarn, "And because Barry wouldn't marry her she drank iodine and they gave her white of eggs, but she was in a state—what have you got there, Louisa?"

"A letter from Daddy, Mother!" called Ernie.

"Give that to me! Where did you get it?" Henny rose from her seat, sliding her work onto the floor. "Where did you get it? Why did you hide it from me?"

"The postman brought it and I put it in my bag to keep it safe and forgot it——"

The children had tumbled downstairs again and were gathering like soft-footed, eel-haired ghosts round the fire.

"Go upstairs and get into bed," called Henny harshly. "You'll hear what you have to hear in the morning." The children trailed back again regretfully, calling questions down to her all the way up.

"This is a most important letter, this is the letter I have been sitting up for to put me out of all my misery," said Henny stormily to Louie, "and you go and hide it; what did you do it for? Are you a devil or a girl? Here I have been suffering and pricking my fingers and going through agony for hours waiting for this letter and wondering what on earth had happened. Do you like to see me suffer? Do you do it purposely? You great, woodenheaded idiot: oh, go up to bed and take that great moon-face out of my sight, and stop your sniveling."

"Is it from Daddy, Mother?" Louie could not resist asking.

"Of course, don't be an idiot. Go up to bed quickly before I hit you. When I think of the hours of agony I put in because you were too lazy and stupid to give me my letter, I want to beat you till I fall down. Oh, stop that bawling. Good night, good night."

Louie, on the stairs, heard her say, "He sent money: look—five hundred dollars. Now, thank God, the children can eat."

"You'd better give it to me," Hazel said grimly. "I don't understand how you get into such a hole."

"There's a lot you don't understand!"

Louie flushed with joy. The twins were reciting,

> *I went up one pair of stairs* (Just like me!)
> *I went up two pair of stairs* (Just like me!)
> *I opened the door* (Just like me!)
> *And looked out the window* (Just like me!)
> *And there I saw a donkey* (Just like me!)

Louie smiled to herself and went to stand in their doorway. Said she,

> *Will you kindly stop your hollers?*
> *Daddy sent five hundred dollars!*

Pandemonium broke out of bed and the anvil chorus standing at the head of the stairs shrieked, "Mummy, did Daddy send five hundred dollars?"

Henny rushed to the foot of the stairs, her old red dressing gown flying from her in the black of the hallway.

"Louisa, mind your own business! Kids, go to bed, and if one of you mentions it, I'll beat you till I can't stand up! What will I do with that child?" she moaned, going back into the warm room.

"Now we can get the new tubes for the radio," Ernie whispered to Louie.

"Hooray, hooray, hooray!" Evie capered in a slipper dance. But Louie succeeded in getting them all to bed in a few minutes. It was not long before Tommy was steaming away in sleep, and the twins, with their moon complexions, were glimmering quietly on their pillows, and Evie, with hair wild and clenched dark face, was tossing in sleep too; but Ernie was awake, calculating what they could get tomorrow; and as for Louie, in a few minutes she had entirely forgotten the five hundred dollars and, lying on her back, was halfway to sleep, thinking dizzily,

"I thought it was a horseman and it's only the blood beating through my temples when I lie down: it was a horseman, riding

[209]

up and down and—wampum, purple strings of shells, fimbriate horsemane shell and the ctenidium deep, deep down in this dusty —red—" She woke up with a start, trying to remember the beautiful thoughts she had been having; and tried to thread back, but could not. She fell asleep really and woke up shrieking, dreaming another old nightmare that she often tried to describe to them, "Hard-soft, hard-soft," a dream without sight or name, which her hands dreamed by themselves, swelling and shriveling, hard-soft. She turned on her side, and the friendly horseman (she still thought of him riding, though he was now only a phantom) lulled her to sleep with his *ker-porrop!*

2 ꕔ Sam in Malaya.

IT WAS NOT RAINING, but it should have rained. No fresh breeze had cleared away the exhalations since the evening before, and the air stuck to them like a wet rag. There were bucketfuls of water hanging in the air over their heads. Sam, towhead bare, panama in hand, all in crumpled white, with his Indian secretary, a Madrasi Kerani, trotting, walking hurriedly a step in the rear, went pushing his way along the busy five o'clock street. The immense open gutters, pitfalls, were spanned every few feet by large flagstones, and Sam and Naden had to keep dodging over these into the open street to avoid crushes and social affairs on the pavement—a family with its mattresses and rags preparing to sleep out during the steaming night, a wedding feast, with its tables and benches and hundred guests taking up several frontages, the thirteen-year-old bridegroom bedizened and bedaubed, in white cap, posing with father and uncles for his photograph. All the traffic of the pavement as well as Sam and Naden had to serpentine around these knots. Chinese lanterns and naked bulbs were strung across the pavement, and open flares lighted the tables. A Chinese peddler with a small basket was selling noisemakers, a whirring whistle very loud and highly painted, and red, white, and blue trumpets, but he could hardly make himself heard, even though Sam and Naden were thrusting along right beside him. A peddler somewhere in the throng was shouting "choklets-choklets," but all they saw were two sandaled feet sticking out of a globular swarm of market baskets of all sorts—no head was visible, nor a body, but through the rattan and pandanus solar system came the voice.

Sam was head and shoulders above most of the people. Not so Naden, his clerk, the Indian. Here and there a giant Sikh policeman, with bearded face and turban on his uncut hair, dominated the throng of torn, patched, ragged, turbaned, and capped heads. Many of these heads had no business whatever, but had so lounged and mournfully, vacantly gazed from morning to night for many months, unemployed and disorganized, hopeless and without any shelter save those of a few charities, sleeping in filth and eating garbage. The employed were scarcely better off; the smallest frontages, back rooms, passageways, holes in the wall, served for shops, businesses, and schools; and a good many businessmen kept their merchandise in their cap, pocket, lap, in the sole of their shoe or the palm of their hand. Some used the pavement, with ready-cooked food spread out before them; there were public scribes and pavement shoemakers. It was a raving, wild, thirsting, vain, money-loving, patriotic city, its own pride, the gateway of the East to the West, and the West to the East, the key of the Golden Chersonese.

"And all of these," shouted Sam, "squashed flat as pancakes under the well-oiled, deep-wrinkled, naked-naveled bellies of yellow Greed: running on the futile messages of Greed and his two secretaries of the Treasury, British Government and the Chinese Chamber of Commerce!"

"I beg pardon, sah," shouted Naden.

"Mammon," shouted Sam, "Mammon, Naden, Greed, Briton and the Yellow Peril on top of the heap!"

"Yessah."

"That's a bit of irony," yelled Sam, putting his hand between his mouth and his secretary's ear: "he can't make himself heard to sell his noisemakers."

Naden looked swiftly at the merchant, "Those are trash, tuan: I should not buy them."

"I told you not to call me 'tuan,' Naden."

"Yessah." Naden smiled and bowed slightly, "You see, I can't help myself, and I assure you, sah, it is the regular thing. My wife, sah, would be very, very much ashamed if she did not hear that: she would be afraid I should lose my job."

Sam laughed, "You have a very young wife, you must teach her differently. Tell her there is no difference between you and me, or you and the moneylenders, or you and the men of money."

Naden, not hearing very well, bowed slightly again, "Yessah! Only two streets more, please," he pointed. "You will not mind if my friends are there," he asked in the tone of one repeating a question.

"Your friends are my friends, only they probably like you better," said Sam.

The thick, moist Singapore night closed round them. In many parts it seemed to Sam that he alone could be seen amongst those dark myriads, thick as migrant birds twittering and jostling on a cornice, struggling for a foothold in this notch of the universe. Here and there the gleams of eyes and teeth could be seen, lemon faces, hadji caps, laundered coats, pale garments. As they turned out of the thoroughfare, they jostled some stretcher-bearers who were jog-trotting along with a corpse announced by bells. Merchants of live birds and lizards, merchants of fishballs and sweetmeats they left behind them, as well as the ordinary foot passengers, and a little surge of trouble that was merely a native policeman arresting someone suspected of murder.

"Good heavens, Naden," exclaimed Sam indignantly, "how can they tell one dark face from another in this light?"

"Ofttimes they can't," said Naden, "but they arrest someone. Someone they know. It is fair enough. It is certain he has already committed a murder. They would all murder if they got a chance."

[212]

"They're your people!" cried Sam.

"No, tuan, they are not," said Naden, "we have passed through a lot of scum. I am a government servant, however humble."

But Sam misunderstood the ambitious fellow entirely and considered him abject. "If that is the justice of Government," said Sam, "would you not be better without it?"

"No, tuan."

"Do you believe in masters' justice, imperialist justice?"

"You have great experience, sah: you have seen more than me."

"No, Naden, do not overrate me. I am nobody. If I seem strange to you, it is because I am not a socialist, as Colonel Willets, my boss, was once (though now, you may be sure, he is for millionaires and not the millions), nor a Laborite, nor a Democrat, nor any party man, but I look forward to the Union of Democratic Republics of the World, the United States of Mankind. Look at this poor old world as we see it today—you may look at home, Abishegenaden, for all Europe, Asia; and the Pacific World is no better nor wiser; the men of money, the bankers, the evil ones have been coming together and torturing this poor old world for a long time now, Naden. We must get rid of them, by wisdom, by spreading the light amongst these dark, dark masses. You are dark, Naden, but you are light: you are an educated man. You, too, though you are poor, must think you are rich, because you have millions—behind you! Millions of poor men who would be your brothers."

"You are a very good man," said Naden. They had now turned into the quiet streets of dwelling houses, with trees, and an occasional car, where the better-paid government servants and junior clerks lived. It was a brilliant, black tropical night, swimming with powerful scents landwards and with vapors skywards. There was still a restlessness of birds in all the trees, and insects flew round the lamps.

"Look at my poor Lai Wan Hoe in shackles because he owes money to a Sikh moneylender," mourned Sam. "That is terrible, Naden. I am afraid some harm will come to my wonderful Wan

Hoe, all because of extravagance, and the awful power of money, like a great hairy foul spider with a million eyes, as this night, sucking the blood of us poor humans. Yes, it sucks the life from the rich too, but they can stand it." He laughed heartily into Naden's eyes.

Naden laughed, but could not help remarking, "He is a ne'er-do-well, I fear, sah, speaking privately, sah."

"And that wedding feast, Naden," Sam caught him up warmly, "in the open tumult, with its gay little bridegroom sitting on his father's shoulders, and the admiring relations, the cheerful drinks —little as I approve of them!—the cakes and candies, Naden; that was a fine sight, a human sight, wasn't it?"

"Yes it was, sah!"

"It was for that that Wan Hoe got himself indebted, friend: because his brother is away in China, and he must marry his brothers and sisters and keep his old father and bury his mother. It was for pure goodness of heart and kindness and duty that he got himself indebted; perhaps they will throw him into prison— all for being profuse with the milk of human kindness. Is that bad?"

"One is obliged to consider ways and means," said Naden, unshaken. "Who goes to the moneylender, indebts his grandchildren."

Naden had been melting and glinting through his glasses, smiling, and now bowed Sam to a little house behind a lush garden. There were lights in the house which glowed through glassless windows. In that climate windows would collect mildew.

"This way," said Naden, bursting with pride and joy; and with great dignity, he stepped into the square sitting room, where a number of people were sitting and standing, and he said,

"Here is Special Field Commissioner Samuel Pollit, my most honored chief."

Sam swam up to the surface of the river of moisture that was drowning, suffocating him, and looking at all these happy or inquisitive dark faces, flashed smiles at them, talked to them all, felt the great urge of love of man rise up in his throat. What a gift he had been given, he thought, to love and understand so many races of man!—and why? His secret was simple. They were all alike: they all longed for love and understanding.

In a bed near the window hole was the timorous black girl, Naden's young wife, whose new firstborn was a son. The sick woman tried to rise, out of respect and fright, but Sam waved her back to the pillow and bent over the bed, shook the tiny hand of the baby, and kissed its head; and then put into its hand the little necklace of silver shells he had got at a friendly curio dealer's that day. The mother nearly fainted with emotion. Then Sam, smiling graciously once more, withdrew. He could not speak one word of any of their languages, and he had to go home, change, address a Y.M.C.A. meeting, and then go to an evening at a friend's house. He suffered without respite from the tropical heat, and his principles prevented him from ever taking the solace or strength of alcoholic drinks. The room of the weatherboard house smelled of mildew and sweat; snakes coiled under the floor, bats lived in the attic, and swallows squeaked in the air or in the eaves, all this without mentioning the thousand kinds of insects, all new and unpleasant, even for a naturalist, to live with.

As he stepped into the street, Sam wiped his neck with his handkerchief already wringing wet, "You have a sweet wife and child, Naden."

"No, indeed, sah, I am ashamed: they are not worthy of your kind visit. You are so kind, sah."

Naden, naturally severe, became wet-eyed and soft with emotion. Sam told Naden how lucky he was, again. He himself, Sam, had had the pleasure of being a father, five times already, and imagine the joy when he found that at one birth he had twins! He could never have it enough. Each time, he explained to Naden, he felt an immense pride, a belief in a limitless future, in an unfolding universe, a hope for the proliferating human race in that shadow of dust, and infinitesimal corner of dimensionless space, even so.

"We were monkeys, we were men: what will be men in the time to come, Naden?"

"Gods perhaps, tuan. Who knows?"

"You are right: men like gods. A great white writer wrote a book about that once. But you see, you have the same idea. Ideas unite us, Naden. I am so tired, Naden. I wish I was at home with a new little baby to cheer me up. Soon I will have a seventh child. I myself am a seventh child. You know, Naden, though, I wish I had a black baby too. A tan one, a Chinese one—every kind of baby. I am sorry that the kind of father I can be is limited." He laughed in a tired way and ran his finger round inside the collar. "Men have thought of schemes for fathering many children," he continued faintly, still laboring to bring the ideas of the west to the cultured Indian, "for preserving man's seed in tubes and fertilizing selected mothers."

"And there would be a marriage ceremony?" inquired Naden politely.

Sam smiled, "I don't think so! But that is a detail. But now we are very backward. A man who knows he is a good father of good stock may still only have one wife."

"It is a pity, sah?" inquired Naden politely.

"I am not so sure it is a good thing," said Sam, shaking his head, but very dubious about his own idea, "either for man or woman, especially for women. Many fine women would make good mothers—" he shook his head.

Naden nodded but he said merely, "Will you work late tonight, sah, when you get back?"

Sam said briefly, "No." After a moment he laughed generously, "If I had the money, do you know what I should do, Naden? You remember that orphan asylum I addressed the other day? I should adopt them all—well, not all. I should have a little Chinese baby, an Indian one, out of the asylum and take them home with me."

"And your wife, too, she likes that too, tuan?"

"The women have to wash the diapers: they are not quite so generous as ourselves, it is not mankind, but little Sam and little

Naden," said Sam. "But if one could have many wives, wives too would get the idea of the community perhaps. That would be splendid—godlike, eh, Naden?"

Naden laughed, "You are joking, I know, tuan."

"Then you do not think that I could manage all those wives?"

"Any man can," said Naden calmly. "Sah, if you will permit me: you take a great risk going down all those streets at night alone."

"I was not alone: I was with my fellow men."

"No, no, Tuan Pollit, you must never do that again. When I saw you last night, my throat jumped into my mouth, my heart, I mean."

"Man must never be afraid of man, friend."

Naden looked up at him soberly, "You are very full of ideals, sah: you are a good man. God protects goodness."

"But I keep my feet on earth, Naden."

Naden smiled at this. Sam, looking keenly at him, because there was no reply, saw the smile and asked, "Do you think I have feet of clay?"

"That is the only safe thing to have, sah. But, pardon me, you really should not go down so far into the streets at night. Every one sees you. You are so very much the white man with your fine, white hair, too, sah. There are men from the west, dark, with dark hair, but you are everything that is the white man. It is not done, I assure you, sah. Pardon me a thousand times."

"Ah," said Sam, "my natural love, Naden, my friend, of the study of mankind, man's proper study, and my real longing—it is a prodigious yearning, a passion beyond all other passions in me, Naden, for the time of the One Great Nation to come, when we will all be joined, man to man, regardless of color and creed, has given me a prodigious disregard for what is *not done*. What is not done, man can do."

"I beg your pardon," said Naden.

"And a wonderful regard for what is done, by the people."

Naden said nothing.

"And particularly by your own people or peoples, Naden,

whom I love, respect, and wish to understand. How otherwise can we teach them the few things we ourselves know in human progress? And we have something to learn from the ancient civilization you represent, the antique cultures of India."

"We are children, tuan. Thank you very much; we do not know very much; what we had we have forgotten. We are not modern."

"I wish you could come to my country and visit it: I should like you as my guest," Sam sighed. "You would see my children, and you would bring your little fellow."

"You are good, sah: you are as a god."

"No, Naden: just a man looking for the right and for the happiness of others."

"Sah, you are as the gods."

"I do not believe in gods, only in good," said Sam. "Gods demand sacrifices: good gives to all."

Naden smiled a little to himself, in his small, dark mustache and felt kindly towards the pale man wrapped in his dreams. He became a little more serious.

"I believe in God. I am sure God is coming soon, and if you are here, you will see him: then you will believe. And he will see you."

Sam said fretfully, "You know, my friend, I would rather be at home, with my children, and hear the elms and sycamores and the cedars rustle, and hear dear little Mareta, with her thin voice, asking if she will get her wish, and keeping my record of Georgetown birds, than even be near the throne of a God. And if I had to choose between such a Him, and them, I would choose them at once. And so would you, Naden. There never was a father would sacrifice his son to God, as the wicked old story has it: there never was."

Naden was silent, astonished by this idea. Sam felt he might have been rude to his believing secretary, so he added, wearily, but whimsically,

"Perhaps there is a black god and a white one." They were now crossing the little Cavanagh Bridge and under the sky, paling before moonrise, could see the flotilla of barges tied up in the river at the left hand. Sam halted to get the thin currents of coolness which were heavily moving through tons of wet air, like trickles pushing and nosing against a leviathan and gradually persuading the sleepy bulk to move an inch or so.

"I have not thought about the color of God," came the Indian's tricky, two-toned voice out of the dark.

"Abishegenaden, you are very black!"

"Yessah," he said firmly.

"Wouldn't you like to be light-colored like me?"

"No, tuan: I am not Heaven-born as you are."

"You must not say that to a poor mortal like me," said Sam. Again Sam misunderstood the Indian clerk but was happy in his error, "You know the white man, the stupid white man feels superior to those of other colors. How do you feel about that?"

"They feel, sah, that the darkest races are the oldest; it is not so long since the white man became powerful. He thinks what he thinks because he is young in the world, as a child, as my child will feel when he is a two-year-old and will be butting me with his head. That cannot last very long. The Kings of Egypt were dark; all the world was dark until a very little while ago. Then the white man came from some little crack in the earth. He does not know about the times before he came. That is how we feel, sah; he is an accident."

This surprising answer quieted Sam for a space; at length he answered (they were walking through a garden, planted with old trees, and beside high white walls),

"This is a wrong idea you have, Abishegenaden; the Egyptians were pale (coppery at best); even the very darkest among you are descended long ago from whitish or pale people like the ancient Persians. The Chinese are almost white, too, for the most part. The black man is rather rare. Do you really think, Naden," he asked, "that primitive man was black? Do you think he was black and got white?"

"Perhaps there were two or three primitive men," said Naden. Singapore is all native quarter, with the exception of small

[219]

parts given over almost entirely to Europeans. The dark and mustard skins are of many races from the mainland of Malaya, from India and China, from Tanah Bugis (Celebes), Negeri Jawa, and Malays from the Menangkabau districts of Sumatra and natives from Burma, Siam, Cochin China and even dark-eyed men from Turkey, Armenia, Portugal, with a few sons of Nippon. The British direct, with the aid of white British Empire and American overseers and bosses, but the Chinese are bosses, too, and are the machinery of the place: Malaya is strung together by the Chinese chambers of commerce. Sam's heart seemed to expand at the contact of so many alien peoples and the generous feeling that he called love of man and worship of mankind had grown up like a puffball in Singapore. He tried to learn the greetings of each race, to distinguish them and their accents, if not their languages. Very different was Abishegenaden the clerk, who, on a precarious footing in the government service, like all bureaucrats, moreover, despised not only all other races, but all grades inferior to himself. His affection for Sam was temporary and had something patronizing in it—Sam had come from outside the service and by no means could understand the niceties, strict taboos of the service. There were flabby men from outside the service, a strange sort of Yahoo, and the white man of the East, who was on the inside: Naden smiled in his sleeve,—what can a white man in a country of white men know about anything of that sort? Naden forbore to make further remarks to his superior about dark skins in America, but he thought to himself—this also is a man who—Washington or no Washington—knows nothing about how his own country is run. As they mounted the steps of the boardinghouse where Sam was staying and where his Chinese secretary was still working over his notes, Sam said with good intent,

"You are but an ebonized Aryan, Naden, and I am the bleached one that is fashionable at present."

Naden pretended not to hear this.

*   .   *   .   *

Lai Wan Hoe, a Baba Chinese (Singapore-born Chinese), his polyglot secretary, was still transcribing out of a notebook of beautiful, endlessly flowing shorthand. He was Sam's right-hand man and, in fact, did most of the work for him; without him Sam could never have done anything at all in the fainting climate. Sam sank into a chair, laughing ruefully,

"Wan Hoe, I wonder why the white man is so screwy as to worry about what is in the tropics, man, beast, or mildew! We should leave it to you and your wonderful people."

"And so you will, sir, one day," said Wan Hoe affectionately, knowing that this was one of Sam's favorite ideas, for he had become wholly enamored of all things Chinese, Chinese manners, intellects, polish, capacity for work and for living in the heat.

Naden, after seeing his white man back, had gone home again. He did not wish to work after hours, and he left the two outcasts talking together. If Sam was not a government man, Wan Hoe, who was, was just the same riding for a fall. Naden knew all about his money affairs, which every minute went from bad to worse. In fact, Wan Hoe, after drawing ahead on his salary, had got himself into debt to the moneylenders to the extent of nearly one thousand Straits dollars. Everyone in the service knew about it and whispered that Wan Hoe had stolen government money. It was a question not of who would peach first (for they had told on him long ago) but of how long the Pathan moneylender would wait for his money.

This money waste was to Sam, the only bad spot in his noble Wan Hoe.

"Sweet little woman, Naden's wife, and sweet little tar baby too," murmured Sam. He laughed, "I asked him if he liked being very black and he said, 'Yes.' "

"Yes, sir, very likely." Wan Hoe smiled. "Should you like some tea, sir? You look all in."

"Dead to the world, Wan Hoe, dead to the world," said Sam. "Any telephone calls?"

"Colonel Willets rang up, sir, and wished you to come to his hotel immediately," he said as if it were of no account.

[221]

"Good heavens! Now I'm a messenger boy to run to his hotel when he gets petulant. The white man in the tropics degenerates every day," grumbled Sam.

Wan Hoe was sympathetically silent.

"Did he say anything else?"

"He asked when you were going to address the meeting; and seemed quite angry, sir: he said they should have asked him, and further, he thinks it is a compromising subject."

"Trade-unionism is taboo, I suppose."

"He thought it improper for an American, sir."

"The old billy goat's jealous, that's all," declared Sam. "They asked me because I'm a good speaker." After a while he relented and said coaxingly to Wan Hoe, "Colonel Willets is only interested in making up to the English official set and attending the Governor's Sunday service with special italic-script invitations, and taking stengahs at the Raffles or Lady Modore's. How could anyone suspect that he would be interested in the Y.M.C.A.? He sits there making Hitlerist jokes: it is time the melting pot melted, and I wish it wouldn't melt on me. He's been here four months and he has learned to treat the syces in just the right British way. Could the Y.M.C.A. guess he was interested in spreading human knowledge?"

"He is not interested in that; he said he is the head of the Expedition."

Sam flared up, "He arrogates it to himself: we are all here on an equal footing. Dictators amongst scientists and men of mind! About the orphanage, too—and because I wrote a little thing for *The Straits Times* and because he thought I was trying to get out of paying my seat in the automobile, the time I flew to Kuala Lumpur, and, in short, friend, because he is against me. I represent the young service, and he represents the gerontocracy that is on its last legs. Shame on the old intriguer! He sent a letter about me back to Washington by the last mail. Oh, Wan Hoe, how tired I am! I don't like to complain, but I am in pain most of the day; and I have terrible insomnia. I don't know how the others get through, because, after all, I take no drink, I have no poison in my system."

"Will I now telephone Colonel Willets, sir, or will I leave it till the morning?"

Sam was thinking about the night ahead of him. He would sink on his fresh pillow and at once sweat would start from him, a Niagara of sweat, and drown the pillow and the bedding and his pajamas. Shutters, cool floors, open verandas, baths, and changes of clothes twice daily did nothing against the exhausting sweating and the heat. He would drowse and wake up any moment, any hour, with fear in him, his heart yawing and plunging into some small but bottomless pit, his head full of lead. All he could do, if it was near morning, would be to call to the boy, "Syce, tea," and swing slowly up and out, balancing himself and his head carefully. The tea would help him for a while, making him sweat profusely, and he would have half an hour in which to hope that one of his heat headaches was not going to arrive and stay with him till the four-o'clock breeze or the next nightfall.

Wan Hoe, seeing that Sam did not answer, left him to reverie and went on transcribing in his clear handwriting. His face was dark and, though fleshy, drooped with fatigue. He paused several times and laid down his pen, looked at Sam Pollit as if about to broach a new and personal subject to him; but on observing Sam's drained, drooping cheeks and his mouth loose from the long day, he quietly took up his pen again and went on writing.

When Sam had come first to British Malaya a few months ago he had been shocked by the white man of the tropics and had made up his mind not to go the way others went. He would take exercise every day, walk wherever he could, to find out how the people lived and what they were; he would speak to the dark skin and strange nether garment as a brother, and he would never fall under the sodden spell of alcohol. He struggled unaided except by iced water, through the drowsiness of the siesta hours, trying to write his impressions and articles for papers back home (he very much admired the profession of the journalist, think-

[223]

ing him a good retail purveyor of enlightenment); and about five or six would go home to take a shower and would sit with a bath towel round his loins, or with nothing on at all but a clout, while he wrote up his diary or his mail for the day. But in this climate everything had become a weariness of the flesh, even writing and speaking. He, a man capable of doing walks of twenty miles on Sundays, at home, here could hardly make ten paces without feeling weak. Still he kept it up, walking round Singapore, or the other towns, or struggling through the jungle without a moan, avoiding the European streets and shops, finding the poorest, immigrant and native-born people, the ones with no home, the ones that walked the streets all night, even after nightfall and against all warnings roaming the congested streets, through dark throngs whose faces he could not see but only suspect in the flashing of an eyeball, tooth, or trinket, in the light of a shop lamp, or electric sign hanging downwards, or the frosted bleary sparkle of some miserable shopwindow, perhaps mildewgrown.

Both Naden and Wan Hoe were worried about this habit of Sam's and warned him often, but he walked on, tall amongst the small people, protected by his humane folly. He walked bareheaded; he believed that his wonderful white-gold hair, rarely seen except in Friesland or Norway, protected him, that these childhearted people took him for something next to a god. When Naden told him he was like a god, he saw no humor in it. He thought that to the poor Indian clerk he must seem something like a god; he knew their superstition (he said to others) and how easily reverence and love passed into worship. Quietly, he would explain, "I believe in myself, because I know I love the good, and as that old sinner Thoreau said, 'I will never let the vestal fire go out in my innermost recesses': people feel that vestal fire and they feel that its possessor is sacred: they will not harm him. He walks unharmed amongst people reputed savage because they honor what is most good in man."

To whatever argument they made against this strange talk, he merely replied that he did come back unharmed and that he had

[224]

ventured, on the upper parts of wild rivers in innermost Malaya where no white man had been before, and had never been harmed or hated. Only once a wicked little urchin in far Trengganu had hooted him, a boy with a mean rat face. But at Kemaman and elsewhere they had all been his friends and followed him around, the women first laughing and much embarrassed and then praising him, admiring his white hair and white bare narrow feet, or so he heard. The streets of some of these towns were almost like the back streets of a quiet Southern town where the Negroes live, the houses standing side by side, cabins and huts with occasional weatherboard houses, a hard dirt road, and, instead of telegraph posts, the tall palms clashing in the breeze, partly shutting out the blasting blue sky and the dazzling shadows and furnace lights on the road. But the Southern Negroes would never have made friends with Sam as these people did. His heart was flooded with a blue sea of hope; it was his own experience with the cheerful, good-natured people that made him hope that the progress of friendship between nations would be as easy—it merely required a little good will, such as he had and the thing would be done in half a day.

In a short time he had fallen madly in love with Malaya and saw her as a great country, unplundered, untouched, undreamed of, brimming with natural wealth, which would make all of its soft-skinned people rich and happy. All that was needed was understanding and the eviction of the People of Greed. He himself was helping mightily the people, he believed, by getting to know them and finding out their different types and entirely addled strains. He could tell the indigenous Malays from the new imports from India, Hailam from Canton, Hohkien from Teochiew, and he tried to have a friend in each of these and many other strains. He felt like a kind of Livingstone going into the heart of the darkest unknown, as he put it, the heart of man. Some day, with the help of believers like himself, the pure souls of the earth would get together, the good and energetic who understood men, like, say, Woodrow Wilson, Franklin D. Roosevelt, and Ramsay MacDonald, Upton Sinclair, Nicholas Murray

Butler, H. G. Wells, and even himself, Samuel Pollit, and it would not be too soon for Eden, "the time of the internation," to arrive. If such a concourse of great souls could have been got together five hundred years back, Sam believed, the world would have been saved from its sorrows, wars, hate, misunderstanding, class wars, Hitler, and moneylenders; and the Golden Age, permeated by simple jokes and ginger-ale horseplay, tuneful evenings, open-air theaters and innumerable daisy chains of naturalists threading the earth and looking, looking, would have already produced a good-hearted, mild human race. Were not his own children happy, healthy and growing like weeds, truth-loving and inventive, merely through having him to look up to and through knowing that he was always righteous, faithful, understanding?

"Have you heard from your children, sir?" asked Wan Hoe, pausing.

"That is wonderful," cried Sam, "telepathy, Wan Hoe; that was telepathy," and he proceeded to tell him the chain of thought which at that moment had caused him to think of his children. He told his Chinese friend about them once more, "I suffer from the heat, the humidity, and the strangeness—not of black, but of white men—but I suffer most because when I wake, under the pressure of the heavy waves of moisture in the foredawn, before the stabbing light can get to my eyeballs I cannot call to them as I do at home, to my little dark-eyed, smudge-eyed Evie, my Little-Womey. You know what I do, Wan Hoe? I call, 'Sedgewing, Sedgewing, Sedgewing!' (Sedgewing is a made-up word that reminds me of her.) 'Sedgewing, come en do me yed.' Then she rolls out of bed grumbling gently, a thing I love to hear, and trots in in her long pink cotton nightdress, pouting gently, saying, 'Daddy, lemme lone, I wanna sleep!' But when I put out my hand, she trudges over and then hops onto my pillow and thrusts her soft finger into my hair to stroke the scalp; then my headache goes away, if I have one. Then I call up my eldest girl, Louie, a girl with a great head, perhaps too many troubles, but it makes her wiser in time to come, and she makes the morning tea, and then I get the boys out, Ernie and the Gemini, to go whistling round the place with me, sizing up carpentering jobs and bits of stonemasonry required. That is the happy life, Wan Hoe. Little-Sam sits there thinking on the path, thinking the strange, long thoughts of childhood, pondering over things which he will fashion into thoughts of science one day: and Saul, sensible and cool, goes his way poking and deducing; while Ernie, my little wonder-boy, who will certainly be a great mathematician, or (I hope not quite a dryasdust, not altogether a blue stocking) a physicist."

Sam suddenly cried, with a smile, "Bless you, Wan Hoe, you're such a good friend to me! I never had better friends than the Chinese friends I have met here in half a year, and you principally. No one understands friendship like the wise, the good and ancient People of the Middle Kingdom."

Wan Hoe's sensitive face, a soft boy's face thinning into sorrowful manhood, changed several times and his eyes smiled at Sam, "I am glad you like us very much."

"In the Chinese are great treasures of wisdom and good subtlety, craftsmanship and labor that we could do with in our country," said Sam stoutly. "I think you are the most wonderful people in the world."

Wan Hoe listened intently; and after a moment he said almost cautiously, "If you had no children, sir, I would think that you were coming to live amongst us."

"How happy that would make me! But I couldn't stand the climate and I could not bring all my children up here, Wan Hoe. No, you will have to contrive to come and visit me."

Wan Hoe shook his head, smiling pitifully. Just as Sam, guessing his troubles partly, began to speak to him about his great debts, the telephone rang again and there was Colonel Willets, irate, asking where was the s.o.b. and did he think he was going to sit round there twiddling his thumbs, and telephoning forty times in that heat. Wan Hoe said that Sam would soon be back and would no doubt go over to Willets' hotel at once. He put it down and looked regretful again that he had not spoken to

[227]

Pollit about his own affairs. But Sam had quite forgotten about it.

Wan Hoe looked round cautiously. Sam's temper was wasting. Sam confirmed Wan Hoe in his view that people born and living outside the Asiatic world were children in the world. Other men were indiscreet through temper, brutality, or contempt of their subordinates; Sam was indiscreet through trust of his subordinates. Wan Hoe speculated on the American government service and wondered for a moment if Sam had been sent to Malaya to get him out of the way. But now Sam had to swallow another mouthful of gall and trot off to Colonel Willets' room. Who was he, he asked Wan Hoe, but a vain old man who had cast his Socialist skin twenty years ago, after he had made money in real estate? All had gone by the board for Mammon, and now he thought everyone admired his boots of gold: he wanted to be cock of the walk everywhere. "May I never be an old man!" said Sam.

"Our old age is perhaps life's decision about us," said Wan Hoe, "but I hope there is no living god we may blame for the invention. Everyone remembers himself as a child and cannot recognize himself in the tatters and wrinkled, dirty flesh, in the stench and hairy moles he is forced to inhabit. He wants to cry out, 'Look, I am not like this, I am a fairy little child with peach skin and sky-blue eyes, I am like a sun gem, I sing, dance, skip; I am not this old relic of the ragbag, cadging, cheating, scolding, whining, faking, dying.' The Chinese are a knowing people; and I daresay that is why they once made a religious odor about old age; to prevent their sons seeing their own future. They sealed their eyes. You see when a man knows he will be old, he is afraid: when he becomes old, he cares for nothing—love does not count, only comfort; honor does not count, only cheating for a niche."

"How queer," said Sam smiling, "I am not Chinese, but I honor old age: I hope I will have a happy one. My sons will be grown up, men of science, my daughters married with grandchildren: my hair will be silver, not much different from now.

You are rather morbid, aren't you, Wan Hoe? I hope to have a long and happy life."

"Do you think that is possible nowadays?" asked the secretary.

Sam looked at him but said nothing. He had gathered from some vague hints that this native-born Singapore Chinese was a revolutionary, belonged to the Kuomintang frowned upon equally by the British and the rich Chinese. He could not be sent back to China, however, as immigrants could. Sam knew that Wan Hoe was on the verge of disgrace. However, he made it a rule not to inquire into a man's political actions, especially into his dangers; and he got up quickly to go out and see his colleague. He had first to strip off his soaking clothes, bathe, and get fresh ones. One of his coats put away damp, by accident, was hanging in the closet spotted with mildew. The smell of mildew could not be got out of the closet.

* . * . *

Sam had a quarrel with Colonel Willard Willets at the Raffles, but it ended as all their quarrels had to date in a sort of querulous capitulation on the part of the old man. He said Sam had engaged a seat in an automobile with him to visit a village of pygmies. Pygmies usually wander about in search of their food, but these pygmies, about forty in number, had been in this spot for a number of years. In the meantime, Sam had been taken up by the Governor and his wife, and it was arranged by them that he was to go with a visiting British scientist on the same expedition, but in a private car for which he would not pay. Now Colonel Willets thought Sam had let him down again and that he would have the whole expense of the trip himself.

Sam, who could ill afford it, however, said he would pay his share of the trip, but he would go with the English visitor as arranged: this was an anthropologist from Cambridge, and Sam cherished the opportunity of meeting him. While the Colonel was somewhat mollified at hearing that Sam would pay, Sam had got under his skin by refusing to ride with him.

But Sam had no sooner got back to the house than Colonel Willets was on the wire again, and began pulling his ears like an office boy, "And besides I don't like the catalogue of the Photographic Exhibition," he screamed.

"That's not my business," said Sam, "ring them up yourself."

"But you're in it, your name," said Willets. "Here it says: '*Anak Melayu, Menangkabau punya*—Samuel K. Pollit—Smithsonian Expedition! You are not the leader of the Smithsonian Expedition: I am. What do you mean by that?"

Sam flushed, "You refused them any photographs: you wanted to keep them for your own book. They applied to me, and I gave them some. It's a very successful photograph. I gave it on my own account. I didn't tell them to put in the Smithsonian, and it doesn't say I'm the chief."

"I won't have it," said Willets' little screaming voice made moist by tears of wrath. "Tell them to take it out. You won't get away with it: you're always the same, taking glory to yourself. They'll hear about it. Don't think I'll keep quiet about it. No sooner do you get with the British, than you start with their airs. Damn you all." He raved on, in that thin, hissing trickle of a tenor that Sam's ears could barely stand. Sam put down the telephone. He plunged his hands in his pockets and took two or three impetuous steps, to work off his rage. He felt his head begin to swell and ache again, and the thick fumes of sweat rose —he must take a bath at once. Then—a lemon drink and then dinner, and then he would be drenched again.

While he was drying himself he noticed that his hands had grown to be just like his dead mother's, the same long fingers, square tips, and veins. He thought of her with love again. Until he had married Louie's mother, Rachel, he had known no woman, because of the promise to his mother, dying.

He went into his room to dress; and, dressing in fresh linen, felt with pleasure a cool, wet wind blow; relief was rain and the eternal wet blanket of the night air, but it was a relief. He let it blow away his thoughts of the distant past. He did not think of it very often now, for he did not want to be sentimental; but sometimes, the last few weeks, these thoughts rushed in on him and fastened in his flesh, devoured him, as an invisible but rapacious creature. He had once prayed (to himself, the powers of darkness, to the unknown) to see Rachel's ghost; he had tried to see her. Now he felt as if the ghost of his own mastered desires, potency that had sunk into the earth, had grown up, a genie that was surrounding him, seizing him, thrusting him out of his honest path into the flame-leafed tropic jungle of desire. He thought of Rachel, and then suddenly his tender thoughts transformed themselves into the love of woman: he stood appalled, for a minute, feeling his heart beating fast, mad with the love of woman.

He suddenly knew himself—he had seen at least half a dozen women since he came to Malay that he wanted to kiss, embrace and even that he could conceive becoming more intimate with.

"What is this," he asked himself, with dismay, "middle age?"

But to become obscenely middle-aged in one's thirty-eighth year, he instantly realized, is not common.

"Therefore," he reasoned with himself, "it is love coming to claim me: I have been so long without love, hated at home, living in terror of my children's lives: it is pure, tender, normal love."

He began to think of other things, his daughter Louie, who would soon be a woman and who would be able to create new life, to have her own children.

"Poor, motherless girl," he sighed.

Certainly Louie would grow up to be like her own sweet, womanly mother, a blessing to some man. Thus he dismissed Louie and went to dinner thinking of the divinely good, charming expression which made him want to kiss Lady Modore. He was such a good fellow, although he knew nothing about women. One evening, for instance, after dinner, he thought it appropriate to lecture her about superfluous hair. Hair under the arms, for example, he said, should never be removed, for nature had put it there, and evidently it had some use. She had suddenly said, "You have too many children, Mr. Pollit."

"I could never have too many," he cried earnestly and began

to tell her how he would like to have a Malay wife, a beauty like he had seen with her baby this day, a Chinese wife, and an Indian wife—"there are so many little lovely dears—" even a strange pygmy wife with her immense bust, belly, and buttocks— he laughed, "and the most beautiful women in the world, for example, are the Cingalese. . . ."

"You wouldn't go native, suddenly?" she teased him.

"I would indeed," he said seriously and began again to outline his ideas, return to nature, phalanstery, peace, industry, love, law-abiding.

"Darling, call the boy."

Sam, of course, took only ginger ale. He would leave in a few days for a trip to Kuala Lumpur again, a place he loved despite his sufferings there, from heat and humidity. During the rest of the evening, he told her about his native land, its democracy, its liberty, its possibility of rebirth from generation to generation: a Thomas Jefferson, whom he was always quoting, had said, it seemed,

"There should be a revolution every twenty years."

She said coldly, "How uncomfortable! I think if I were an American I would live in the British West Indies."

Wonderful how these women could seem so disdainful!

He said playfully, "Why don't you come and visit our wonderful country? Washington is a paradise. It is all flashing walls and long avenues of trees such as would keep off the sun of Seville (only I don't want to drag in the dogs of Seville), and the people there are really interested in international affairs."

"What are the women in Washington like, tell me?"

"Oh, that's what I like about it; it is full of high-minded public women."

She looked astounded, "Really! Oh, I see what you mean," she laughed.

"And does your wife like the people there?" she asked with curiosity, having found out before that his wife was a Baltimore heiress.

He looked grave. "No, I am sorry to say. But let us not talk

[232]

about that. In our early days she went with me to the eugenics meetings, but that period soon ended."

She gave him an inquisitive sidelong glance and returned to her stengah. She was glad he was going to Kuala Lumpur to-morrow. He was presentable and even handsome. He knew how to ingratiate himself, quite unconsciously, with only the best people; but how serious! Never a blink of humor and always relating how he had had a serious talk with a priest or a minister or a missionary, and how he had told the press that they were venal, and how he had addressed this and that body of high-minded public women. Dull; but for the moment, one of their class, and so to be borne.

When he returned from the meeting there were waiting for him at the house letters delivered from the office by Lai Wan Hoe on his way home. Lai had come out of his way. There was a budget—for a wonder, everyone had written—and even a letter from his wife which read:

> *Tohoga Place,*
> *Georgetown, D.C.*
> *March 15, 1937*

To Samuel Pollit:

I acknolledge receipt of five one-hundred dollar bills for household expenses.

Henrietta Pollit

Then there were big envelopes with letters from all the little ones, covered by a long letter from his eldest, Louie.

Sam hungrily seized on this letter.

In her painful handwriting, Louie had written,

> *Our Place.*
> *Georgetown, D.C.*
> *15th March, 1937*

Dear Father,

I am enclosing the children's letters and also my George-town Record, which I hope you will like. Everyone is all right. The children miss you. Mother is not very well. It has

[233]

been cold, but tonight is a night of high moonshine over all the knolls and trees that I can forget the cold, at least. However, the little ones feel it and no doubt would like some of your Malayan heat. I hope your headaches are better. Tom said today, "Where is my little brother?" I said, "Which little brother?" and he answered, "My little brother Evie." Of course, we laughed and said, "Evie is your little sister; Saul and Sam are your little brothers." Just then Evie called him to get his face washed for lunch and he shouted, "All right, little sister." Isn't that pretty? But there was a sequel. This afternoon Tomkins said, "Saul and Sam and Ernie are my little brothers, aren't they?" I said, "Yes, Limpopo, they are." He said gravely, "I have other little brothers." I said, "What little brothers?" thinking he meant the boys across the street. Then he said very quickly, "Hutzler Brothers," and suddenly held his stomach with both hands and rolled all round on his legs the way he does, you know, screaming with laughter. Oh, they are full of tricks, and they are not naughty, even though it is some job getting them all clean for school, etc.

I have some homework to do, English composition, "get goyn lazybone."

LooLoo

Sam read this three times and put it to one side while he read the others.

Ernie's said:

DEAR SAM-THE-BOLD,

I hope I am not disrespectfull. I hope you have many boys, syces, and secretaries to wait on you all the time, like you said in your last letter. We went down last Saturday and saw the new Treasury building under construction. Also I like going down along the Reflecting Pool, and I found out how it mirrors. We are all going to see the expiriments in the Academy of Sciences, I mean with the teacher, Mr.

Blake. I have homework to do. I swan I best be getting on: giddy-ap, Napolyun, it looks like rain.

> *Lovingly,*
> *Your stupid son,*
> ERNEST-PAYNIM-PIGSNEY-PRINCEPS

Next in proper order of age came Evelyn's in large, clear, round writing like her Mother's:

> *Home.*
> *16.3.37*

DEAD DAD,

I hope you are well, Everyone is well except Mother. I am glad you are staying with a nice lady. I am glad you are going soon to Kuala. Will there be tigers in that part of the jungle? I am afraid a tiger will get you. I hope you have someone to shot the tiger. Can you shoot? I am well.

> *Your loving dauhter* EVIE
> (kisses) xxxxxxxxxxxxxxxxxxxxxx

"Dead Dad," he muttered and then shouted it with laughter. Then miserably he said, "Dead Dad, it's almost telepathic: I bet little Smudge knows how her poor Dad really feels."

The twins had two sheets of paper pinned together and written in straggling, broken-backed letters:

From Saul (said the first).

> *Homealome.*
> *Tha sixteenth.*

DEAR DAD,

I hope you are well. We are well. Mother is not well. She has a cold. Samulam and me have good games. The shaits are waking up and are hungry. We gave them some meat. I found a young spug. It died. This is all now.

> *Your loving son,*
> SAWBONES
> xxxxxxxxxxxxxxxxxx

From Sam (said the second).

[235]

Homealome.
Tha siteenth.

DEAR DAD,

I hop you are well. We are well. Mother is not well. She is sick. Sawbones found a little sparrow that could not fly. Looloo put it in the stove. But it died. We are tired because the Hams and the Eggs played this afternoon and the Hams one.

Your loving son,
SAMOLUS
xxxxxxxxxxxxxxxxx

The letter of Tom, the four-year-old, Sam looked at without interest. It was written in a surprisingly clear, round hand—his mother's, just a little shaky, to show where the infant hand had stumbled under her fist.

Home.
16th March

DEAR DAD,

I hope you are well. I am well. We are all well. It is cold. We have a fire. I am sorry you are so hot. When will you be home. The snakes are awake.

Your loving son,
TOM

The letter he opened last was from Dirty Jack's daughter, Gillian Roebuck. Gillian had started to write Sam letters about their naturalist's interests and, suddenly getting fed up with her home, had taken a position as governess with a senator's family in Washington. The typed page said,

DEAR MR. POLLIT:

Sorry not to have answered before this—the explanation is that the Wellbeens have been staying in St. Augustine, Fla., and I with them of course. It was nice; the beach is wonderful and I like the strong sea air better than the inland air.

We motored to the beach every day and all over the place. You would like the place. Of course the mental atmosphere could be better: but that is partly me, I know. The weather has improved somewhat since our return: most days have been bright and sunny, but unfortunately lack any warmth yet. We came back too soon for me. I go riding once a week as before, tho found the country interesting now. As you suggested, I am taking one tree and studying it: mine is the yellow poplar, that lovely tree *Liriodendron tulipifera*. I suppose I chose that because it is so beautiful—or else because it is our oldest Liberty Tree. Daffodils and hyacinths are beginning to come up from the South. I know you don't like the South because of the racial situation, but it is part of our lovely country just the same and so lovely. There were flocks of *Bombycilla cedrorum* and of course jays and robins by the *million* (that isn't scientific) and so many throngs of birds on their way north. They take it so easily. How I should love to have a pet; I should not feel so lonely. I envy you your wonderful collection of pets at Tohoga House and of course wish I could see them; but when I feel too blue I go to the Zoo just as you recommended and you are quite right! It's a pickmeup. I was thrilled at finding a *Rana sylvatica* the other day, heard the typical clucking-of-chickens call and there he was, leaf-brown to gray. Spring is here. I have rather a handful at present: one of the children is sick—but that didn't make me lose any weight. I am still a bit on the pudgy side and am afraid it augurs ill for the future. However, hard work—as you say, clean living and high thinking—and I may slim down. Yes, I am serious about Wild Life: it gives me a wonderful feeling for nature and has expanded my interests: I really *love nature* now, thanks to your teaching: I mean real love. It was just something to do before. It is wonderful to realize how much there is in the world.

Yours sincerely,
GILLIAN ROEBUCK

The letter shocked him in a strange way. He had a kind of awakening and saw how interesting was this youthful freshness turning to him from its dark old home, moldy with prejudice and tobacco smoke and this frank belief in his ideals. He believed he could be of some help to the girl who had started out on life's journey on her own account.

Sam read them all two or three times, but presently the leaden air pressed him down, and he put out the light, crept under the mosquito nets, and lay on his pillow. In a little while it was sweat-drenched: his blood beat feverishly and his head ached, ached. Meanwhile the birds outside the window, perched on the trees, fences, and the telephone wire outside the gate, twittered and squabbled for places. Every night they took up their footing there to sleep and not an inch of wire would be left. Some even slept perching on the backs of others. Every new wire that was put up was likewise utilized by the metropolitan and therefore homeless myriads. The night was not quiet at any time. Outside in the streets, too, even in this pleasant district, there would sometimes pass one of Singapore's giant population of waifs and hungry, strayed out from the steaming chowder of the streets, to the small European settlement.

*   *   *

He woke up in an hour or two, eyes burning, head throbbing, ready to weep with the continual pain and fever of the heat. If he could only have got to high ground it would have been better. He did not want to disturb anyone and went himself to get some iced water. He found the kitchen, which had a refrigerator, and opening the door, he leaned his head into the cold air for a while. It refreshed him a little, and then he came back to bed. But the reeking pillow, already drenched with sweat and steaming, and the moist sheets did not invite him. He opened his wardrobe to find a sarong that he usually wore when he was writing, a long strip of red, black, and yellow linen which he tucked in round his waist. The stench of clothes which could never be got dry and of the endemic mildew greeted him. Destroying and breeding nature reached in everywhere here, could not be banished, made man ridiculous.

He sat down, naked except for the linen cloth, sanguine, broad, muscular, and hairless, and after fanning himself for a few minutes and leaning his head on his hand, sighed and pulled the little portable typewriter towards him. His busy small click did not make any appreciable difference in the noises of the night.

"Singapore," he wrote, "and twelve o'clock of a night decocted in Hades."

DEAR LOOLOO-DIRL,

Lai Wan Hoe brought my budget of mail home to me tonight and so I have all your un-news.

Well, I don't mean the Georgetown Record and the story about the shaits [snakes] waking up—that *is* news. Anything to do with old Mother Nature, the mother of us all, is news; and I know you kids know it. So that's one good thing.

Now here is something for you, Loobeck, fir you always did love blood and thunder and here it is. I went into a Buddhist temple just outside Singapore and though I was an infidel they were glad to see me because I paid the right amount for propitiation at the entrance to the temple, also took some of their holy water. It was a wondrous temple and in it, besides a lot of heathen gods engaged in horrid activities, truly human activities and truly godlike too, if it is true that we humans are so poor as to be copies of the gods —for example, cheating, fighting, and making the most awful grimaces when not pleased. There was one appalling wall painting showing the sufferings of the damned and the resources of hell, and it was no slouch, I can tell you. It was certainly done by a male painter (but there aren't any others here in this land of domesticated woman-animals), and to placate a male god. There were two women who wouldn't do what their husbands told them. They were tied down on a bench and two demons (men-demons of course) were hacking their heads off. In fact, one is off already and is hanging up on the wall and the other is nearly off. It is just a Buddhist Bluebeard tale. And the expressions on the heads! I saw one poor Chinese woman looking and she had turned very pale—pale ivory, but not natural ivory—so I guess her husband, who was with her and had perhaps brought her just there, for his own reasons, will have no trouble with her for a while.

Then there is a man who wouldn't contribute to the gods; what a rascal! He is very neatly tied up inside a frame of wood, in an erect position and two demons with the most horrible grins on their faces are sawing him down from the top of his head to his toes. They are sawing him across so that his back is being separated from his front. Judging by the man's expression, he doesn't like it, but the demons do, judging from *their* expressions. They have just got down as far as his stomach. A great jagged crosscut saw with teeth about two inches long and wide.

There is a man being thrown into a great fire off a high place, a man who looks very worried, being boiled in a pan. As only a bit of him can be boiled at a time, the attendant demons are getting much pleasure out of turning him round and over so that all parts will get a fair, democratic boiling. Then one is being boiled in a deep pot of boiling oil—I don't know *what* for—but the Buddhists seem to take an interest in cooking. The one in the deep pot is a woman, perhaps she is in a deep one for more decency. As she squirms about and tries to get out of the pot the demons laugh at her and push her back again. It is a case of the clam who wouldn't be chowder. Then, in the same chowder department is a woman being held upside down in a very deep pot, almost a bottle—of boiling oil. She is held firmly by two demons, one to a leg. There is also more activity in the same department. A man is being sawn across the middle this time and right next door, in the hook-and-eye division, a man is having his stomach pulled out with great hooks and some (petty offenders, I suppose) are having their tongues yanked out, red-hot irons pushed into their eyes, which are sizzling, and there are others, quite venial, with hands and ears being lopped off with large and apparently specialized lopping knives. But these folks are specialized in knives, as you will see when I get home, with my collection of swords and scimitars and the like. So much art into such wicked weapons! And perhaps, says I, we should suspect all art capable of being applied to such a use. Think of that, Looloo-dirl, when you are reading your *Styles of Ornament* and all those funny, dopey things you read, godfather knows why!

Well, back to the joyful scene, for I know you: I bet you are enjoying it in your solemn, poker-face way. There is a particularly joyful little act—for the demons, I mean. Three men are chained to a tall metal funnel (there must be modernism), and a great fire is raging inside and being kept up by a demon stoker. The victims are being frizzled and grilled against the heated funnel, and turned round at the right time, so that they will be the right shade all round.

There are quite a lot impaled on spears put close together, and there is a man being flattened between two stone slabs; his blood and innards are oozing through in a very natural fashion. There are many other inventions—all in natural colors and blood, blood everywhere. This is all for Chinese Buddhists: I don't know whether they are tougher than other people and like this, or whether they are weaker than other people and have to have more awful warnings.

The whole thing is quite a nice little business and the priests being successful businessmen look no different from the chetties and the big fat Chinese butchers and bankers, perhaps better-humored because of the pictures they have on their walls. At the entrance to their little place of business, there are big figures of the Chinese Buddha and his pink-white marble wives and all sorts of demon gods, some of them crushing little demons under their feet, just like the advertisement for backache pills. There must be at least fifty little gods of different sorts: you can choose your god, as your pills, in the druggist's—it is rather a good, comforting idea, for surely the gods go in for competition and try to do a little better than the next god.

There is a sacred snake in a cage that attracted me. You can worship it too, if you are scared enough. Of course I went and hissed at him, but he took no notice; he knew he had no power over the rational, I suppose.

There is much burning of joss sticks and firing-off of crackers; that is the great way of worshiping because you get something for your money. I gave the priest one Straits dollar which he put in a bowl as an offering to the Lord Buddha, though I wondered how the high and mighty, suave and grand Lord Buddha should want one Straits dollar. Then the priest gave me a packet of crackers which I let off in front of the Lord Buddha, and the great god looked down on me and seemed to grin at me through the curls of smoke. It seems that now the demons of the sea and forest will let me pass—all on account of the packet of crackers, and the silver dollar. So tell my little foolish dark-eyed Smudge-Sedgewing that the tigers can't get me now, for the great Lord Buddha is watching me.

Am tired-tired with the heat and my head. Will write later. Meanwhile keep-up your Georgetown Record, Looloo, and work at your schoolwork. I expect great things of you later on, even if you do seem a little dopey now.

Your loving father,

SAMUEL POLLIT

P.S. I am not sending these notes from the ordinary tourist's love of the sensational: but because one might say truly that these are the—horrors of superstition, from which, Looloo, may you ever stay free!

DAD

P.P.S. Ask your cousin Leslie to put off getting hitched till I get back so I can join the jubilaum. I'll bring her some peachblow Chinese silk if they let me.

DAD

Sam went back to bed and slept soundly, and it was not till the next evening that, borrowing Wan Hoe's typewriter at the office, he wrote to Gillian Roebuck.

The Holy Lion City.
15th April, 1937

DEAR MISS ROEBUCK,

(Because I may only call you My Little Gillian before a host of witnesses, because you are a young lady now):

I am very, very glad you got away at last to such a wonderful place. Yes, it is wonderful to have something to love, something that will last a lifetime, or many lifetimes, and if it's nature and man in nature, that is the best thing of all.

It isn't such fun seeing things here. You have an ever-present and all-pervading conscious and subconscious sensation that it—is—HOT. You see a lovely vista of palms and wonderful trees: it is too hot to walk down to them. You see a wonderful mountain clear in air, floating in crystal and it is too hot to even attempt to go even a hundred yards towards it on foot; I'm not thinking of the dense jungle which you would have to cut your way through. You see the glorious foreshores, with their four tiers of trees, the fifty feet, the hundred, the hundred and fifty, and the two hundred, all shades of green, all fronds and foliages laced together; and it is too hot to take a boat to go there. (There is such a lovely stretch behind Singapore in the Strait.) Then you see a lovely sheet of water; but it is too hot to so much as go down to it. You are invited to tea by a lovely lady, and it is too hot to go. You try to keep your temper with a foolish, vain gnat of a human being, and it is too hot to do so. Because it is TOO HOT everywhere. The heat wilts you like a soft leaf, just like the pumpkin leaf goes in our place

[243]

on a very hot day at Tohoga. You put on nice clean clothes and they wilt when you touch them and they are full of perspiration before you finish dressing. You sweat at breakfast, you sweat at tiffin, and you sweat at eight o'clock dinner.

You don't want to go anywhere; you don't want to see anything; you don't want to know anybody. You just have one paramount thought, again conscious and subconscious, "Let's strip Jack naked!" You refuse invitations to afternoon tea because politeness prevents you from taking your clothes off in your host's house; and your tea's no sooner in than it's out quicker than in, through your skin. You can't go out to tiffin or dinner unless you sit under a punkah and then you get a chill in your back. You go for a walk in the evening to study the many interesting types of humans and their funny ways—for they live, boil, stew quite cheerfully in their infernal temperature—and you sweat and sweat and sweat and all you study is THE HEAT.

And your clothes reek and everything goes moldy in one day—hats fuzzy, boots furry, bag leprous, spectacle cases blanched, books diseased, coats blotched. Your bed reeks with the sweat of ages (an age is a week here), and the pillow at about midnight is just a sponge.

And just think, my little Gillian (yes, I will say it and call up a host of invisible witnesses as I have none visible), all that would be unnecessary if we wore shorts or a sarong like sensible people do and didn't try to be gents: you don't mind sweat pouring out of you when you've no clothes on; and the great Chinese rich men go about happily in their automobiles naked to the waist with great shining free bellies, ready to catch any breeze that kindly blows to our relief.

And now, Miss Roebuck and Miss Gillian, good-by to both of you; and I'll be seeing my dear naturalists soon in dear old Washington, our new Jerusalem, the one sane, great city, built on a definite plan for a definite purpose and not by the worst cases in a madhouse. (And with the naturalists, my little naturalist!)

Yours sincerely,
SAMUEL C. POLLIT

When they got back at last and the work was about done, Sam set to work to get his notes in order and present his section of the report. He was at first too ill and too overworked to notice that Lai Wan Hoe, his senior clerk, was more harassed than usual; and when he did notice it, he thought that it was because of the pile of work to be got through in a short time. Colonel Willets had decided to close the mission at once, being sick and tired of the Malayan heat, habits, and company. Sam had a pile of notes without end but would have been unable to get up his report without the lifetime knowledge of his Chinese secretary.

"I'll get you an assistant," said Sam, though he was cutting expenses as much as possible himself in order to take as much money home as possible to clean up accounts at home and pay for the new baby that was coming. Sam himself had urged Willets as subtly as he could to get through the work and sail for home, for he wanted above all to be there when the baby came. He also felt himself on the verge of a physical breakdown. Wan Hoe merely asked for a holiday of one day, "Only one day, sir, please!"

Sam sighed, "All right, Wan Hoe, though I can't really spare you."

But Wan Hoe took two days and on the day following, Sam found a note that had been left mysteriously on his desk;

DEAR SIR,

Please find it in your kind heart to forgive me. I had to run away. I am in trouble. Do not be angry with me. I could not help it. You were right about the moneylenders; but I was unable to take your advice. When we came back from Port Swettenham I found everything had come out into

[245]

the open; and for several days I have been trying to avoid this shameful expedient. A disgraced man in hiding.

It was in Wan Hoe's fluent handwriting but not signed. The same day the police called to apprehend Wan Hoe who was wanted for immense sums owed to moneylenders and for a relatively small sum embezzled through someone in the treasurer's office. Sam, who usually hid nothing and who regarded the police as his friends, good, stout fellows with a difficult job, acted on impulse, gave terse replies, and concealed the note. The loss of Wan Hoe struck him down. There were thousands of notes scattered about the office in good order which Wan Hoe had read, but not Sam: it would be torture for Sam, with his head-aches and bloodshot eyes, to try to get through them here. He was obliged to go to Colonel Willets and say that his section of the report would be turned in later, either on board ship or in Washington. This default pleased the Colonel greatly.

When Sam took his walks at night, he kept seeing Wan Hoe, it seemed to him. Whenever he saw the police taking up a man, he was afraid it was he. He saw many a Chinese with Wan Hoe's pleasant, sensual face and even spoke to one, but in error. Where was he hiding? Was he rotting in some shameful cell, without help? Sam tossed far into the night, thinking of Wan Hoe and discreetly made inquiries about him in the daytime, but nothing came to his ears. He was questioned by several seniors about Wan Hoe's behavior and political ideas and also was politely interviewed by the chief of police, but he replied that he knew Wan Hoe was a Chinese patriot, nothing more; he assumed every man was for his country as he, Pollit, was for his. Wan Hoe was the best secretary that ever lived since the world began. And when they suggested that Wan Hoe had gone off on the spree, Sam's hackles rose; it was a personal insult.

Just as Sam was packing up the last of his folios and manu-scripts, he received anonymously a small, scented, and carved chest, seven inches by five by four, containing six teacups not much larger than eggcups. Each cup was of six segments of carved chocolate wood and was lined with pure Straits silver, so soft that it was easily dented with the fingernail. The box opened out as a cabinet, and the cups stood on two shelves. The following day he received an invitation to take an assistant professorship of ichthyology at Hangkow University. He then understood that both these things came from Wan Hoe's brother, a professor in Hangkow and also a Chinese patriot, and that Wan Hoe was safe. Sam was as joyful as if the message had come from heaven on silver wings. But he wrote back to the University a characteristic letter in his fat civil-service phrases:

DEAR SIRS,

I am deeply honored and gratified by your letter of the 20th ultimo and your very kind offer. I wish to assure you that nothing would please me better than to be able to accept it and that it is with very deep regret indeed that I find myself obliged to send you a refusal. If I were able to proceed to the post, I should be gratifying a lifelong wish of mine to study at close quarters a people I have much admired, whose philosophy I find so much more exalted than our own in many ways. I would willingly be one more of the too few links between your people and our own and try to advance in my minor way the Pan-Pacific Comity of Nations. Your great country liberated, Malaya enlightened, the United States more Pacific-minded and a great Empire more deeply aware of its responsibilities in the Pacific—this is what I have worked for all my life and this is what I still hope to see in my lifetime.

What feasible excuse can I offer? One that you will, I trust, understand. I am the father of six small children, whom I love deeply and whose health I am afraid would suffer in these latitudes. If they were older I could move them here, but at present I could not dare to do so. Nor do I want them brought up in a distant land, much as I hope they will be citizens of the world, for I wish them to be American patriots in exactly the same degree as your own fervent, admirable

patriotic young men of the new China. This is my only
reason for refusing your kind offer.

Believe me to be, Sirs,
Respectfully yours,
SAMUEL C. POLLIT

After sending off this letter, Sam had little more to do but to
pack his things, get the curios he had had his eye on for months
and have them shipped, soothe old man Willets and fight with
him every day, help him with his packing, say farewell to Bar-
gong, his "gunner" from the launch, Naden, his Indian secretary, Teo Mah Seong, a self-taught naturalist, Teochiew Chinese,
in whose workshop he had spent many hours, and get to the boat
at the last minute.

"God damn it, I thought you had decided to stay behind with
those darkies," said Willets. "I've been sending messages to you
for an hour. Lady Modore was here, did you see her? Well, she
only drove down to give me a message for a friend. She didn't
ask after you, Pollit."

"And I didn't ask after her," Sam said, nettled. "It took me a
long time to say good-by to all my friends and leave my presents
for them, and get my presents *from* them." He grinned wickedly
at Colonel Willets who replied, "You'd better put the presents
in your report!"

Sam turned away to take a lingering look at Singapore, hoping
never to forget this eleven-o'clock view, the hills with Government House beyond the city, the long bund, the crowded native
craft and the steamers and warships sharing the famous crescent.
Beyond were brilliant green islets and jetties with water in every
direction, the long, low shoulders sloping towards the town and
huts on piers standing in the water. The ship was gorgeous as
ships can be in the tropics, with decks, walls, and every object
radiating heat and light, the women in colored dresses of semi-
transparent stuff or white tropical weaves, handkerchiefs on their
heads and waists, and everyone bustling and gay, glad to be going, excited by the Singapore stop.

"I loved the place," said Sam to Branders, one of the artists of the Expedition, "but never again. She is the Queen of Sheba, but she is too much for me."

"Here we are between the Gulf of Siam and the Bay of Bengal, with everything to see, and we have to go back to the Potomac: it's pretty flat, isn't it? Well, life's long. We'll all come back perhaps. How about a shandy?"

"I'll take a lemonade," said Sam.

CHAPTER SEVEN

1   Family corroboree.

Jo GOT TO Tohoga Place late. The Pollits were scattered all over the house and grounds. For five minutes the sunroom was the scene of straw-colored fireworks. Jo threw down her flowers, chocolates, her hat, while the others started to pour in around her, through doors and long, open French windows, and exclaimed, "Where's Sam? I want to give him a big hug! Where's my baby brother? Where is he, where is he, where is he? Tell him I'm here! Tell him Jo is here! Tell him Jo the Jolly Sailor has brought him his chocs! Where is he?"

With a rhinoceros bound, she burst out of the circle, looking for Sam, shouting for Sam. She bounded all over the place. She was a Golden Horde by herself. When she found Sam beside the snakes' cage, she fell on his neck,

"Old boy! Samivel! It's himself! If I could have got to the train I would have, Sam! What have you been doing to yourself? You lost weight! I cut out your picture in the paper and put it up in the kindergarten! You should have seen their little faces when I told them it was my brother! I'm proud of you, I say it who shouldn't. Father, tell that boy to stop it! Stop it, Sam, stop it! You're putting us all in the shade! Hooray, hooray: he's famous. He's a great man. How are you, Samivel?"

"Easy, easy, old girl!" said Sam, weeping a little, "don't be a fool, Jo! Easy, old girl! Dry those tears. There were others there besides myself, strange as that may seem to a big sister! I ain't the only white-haired boy in the days of the sun! Hooray your-self! Hooray for Jo!"

"You lummocks, you dumbbell," said Jo, wiping her eyes.

"Nary a lummocks," said Sam, "nary a lummocks! Where is the rest of the reception committee? How many more is a-goin' to fall weepin bitterly on my neck! Oh, these are too much! This is some doin's! Femaile, sez I, go home to your wife and chilluns, ef you hev sich! Weep not, fair made, it is but a slight contree-temps!"

"Fool!" cried Jo sniffing.

"So you went and missed me?" inquired Sam.

"Why not?" demanded Jo.

"There's a law saying no big yaller-haired cornstalks kin miss their little brothers," said Sam.

"You know Brownell's brother is Inspector now?" cried Jo. "That man you detest in the Department? He's forged ahead. He's a nice man. He came round last week and that Gray woman made up to him shamefully, to try and get that position. She sat up all night making a picture of Rumpelstiltskin and she signed it! 'Rembrandt'! She signs her charts too! A Leonardo in the kindergarten. Myrtle Gray! Hff! The Catholics help each other; it's a state within the state. It's a disgrace. Everyone is furious. A teacher wrote God with a small *g*, and she reported her! Not that I'm for atheists, but we don't want any Rome-controlled delators! Spying and snooping, with the priests behind her back. He complimented me and said, 'I enjoyed the lesson very much, Miss Pollit.' I could see he was favorably impressed. In the playground he came up to me and started making vague remarks—I could see he was hinting. So I up and told him what I thought about the Gray woman. Someone has to speak out! I said to him bluntly, 'I don't like sectarianism in the schools. I never did, I never shall. It's against my principles and it's against the Constitution. It's against the law. But there are some' (I said) 'that have a law higher than the law. Anyone whose political or religious capital is outside the U.S.A.'"

Sam had meantime sat down on the grass bank and was laughing languidly and pulling away at the rank weeds, "All right, Jo, all right: O.K., old girl, cool off!"

"Cool off," cried Jo, tossing her head. "What for?"

"Dear old Jo, on the same old warpath," said Sam.

"I prefer a hot head to cold feet," said Jo. She went on with her story. In the meantime, sounds of cheer came from the house where everyone was helping Jinny, Sam's sister-in-law, and Louie and Hazel decorate the place and get ready for the banquet to which they would sit down at six o'clock. Bonnie was there, not herself, a little sad and quiet, with a thin face. She was staying with Jinny in Baltimore and helping in the house. But Bonnie, after quietly embracing and weeping over Sam, had gone back to work for his party, just the same, and she was at present tasting her Badminton Cup, her own secret specialty, for which dear Lennie, her brother, had brought three bottles of claret and one of curaçao. As all Sam's parties hitherto had been nonalcoholic, this was to be the great surprise of the day; for certainly, everyone argued, since Sam went abroad, he had learned to be more a man of the world, and he, at least, would never object.

Everyone noticed that Sam had changed greatly. He was more restrained: he did not complain and patted his children on the head with a wise, sad smile, more like an ordinary father than the eccentric he had been. He had been eight months amongst people of his own age and had conversed only with them, although he had made a few casual friends of eight to twelve, Chinese and Malays, schoolboys, sons of his Teochiew friend, the naturalist and of the curio dealer and all the boys of the villages. But his relation to these, since he did not speak to them freely, was that of a tribal uncle, something of the older generation.

The children were gamboling all around their father, and as Jo's story went on, rising and falling with the urgencies of the storm, he beckoned his Ernest (who had grown more thoughtful and distant and had fewer smiles than Ali Mahmoud, Sam's friend in City Road, Singapore) and his twins, melancholy Little-

Sam and thoughtful Saul, towards him. It had been a great day, this day of welcome, and they were glad to sink on the grassy bank and swell his humming,

> *And thar we see a swampin gun*
> *Large as a log of maple*
> *Upon a dandy little cart*
> *A load for feyther's caytle . . .*

Jo waited till they paused and sniffed good-humoredly, "Well, you're too glad to see your Daddy back to think of me: it's Father's Day."

She left them there, a handsome buttercup garland sprawled along the lawn. After a short silence, Sam raised his eyes from the depths of the orchard, where he had plunged them, drinking in through them the green and the blue, and he said wearily,

"You kids didn't lose any dorsal vertebrae weeding the gardens while Dad-the-Bold was in furrin parts, did you?"

Ernie defended himself, "The varmints wouldn't work."

They defended themselves, "He never told us to."

Their father said miserably, as if to himself, "And the boiler wasn't fixed up; and there's no new boiler; and the possum died and a snake died. Nobuddy did nuffin. When Sam went away everybody just plain forgot him. 'Near can I forgit the surblime speckticul which met my gase as I alited from the Staige with my umbreller and verlise.' [Artemus Ward: The Atlantic Cable.] Weeds, springing up everywhere, the paths cracked and our hanni-miles dead." He did not even laugh; just went on sadly recounting to himself the default. The boys sat round with him, as miserable as himself. In all the wild, vacant months that had passed, like a stupid, shouting, windy holiday, they had never given one thought to their father's schemes and ideas. It had been nothing but Little-Sam's and Saul's and Ernie's ideas, a great savanna of opportunity in which they stumbled, ranged, hallooed, occasionally catching sight of each other, at intervals dreaming about a personage, genie of the swamp, who called

[253]

himself Sam-the-Bold, their father, and was away, his wand broken.

All the joyful Pollits were still running up- and downstairs, and the clink of plates, silver, and glasses could be heard, as well as Bonnie's gay call, "Nearly ready, folks, nearly ready: get ready! Who's going to strike up?" and Lennie's wild bagpipes (made by vibrating his long lean cheek), *The Campbells Are Coming, Hooray, Hooray!* Then the strains of the wedding march started up under Jo's tough fingers as Leslie Benbow, *née* Pollit, new-married, arrived with her short, half-bald husband, rather more flustered than is common in a twenty-six-year-old bride and plump in the waist. Leslie had not stayed her marriage for Sam. Many things had gone on without him.

But they all stayed in the house or on the porch, leaving Sam to his children at the top of the orchard, and to his thoughts which, it was evident, were not of the sweetest, not the sort a man might be expected to have on returning to the bosom of his family from a glorious trip to the Far East. Sam felt it keenly that Leslie, his favorite niece, did not come to see him, and that no one seemed to bother about him. He went on talking tiredly to the boys, with a joke from time to time, trying to regain his old style: "'The people gave me a cordyal recepshun. The press was loud in her prazes,'" but Artemus Ward fell off his tongue without a rebound.

Now the noises had quietened a little and the Pollits seemed to be conferring about something. In another minute, Bonnie sang out, "Come on, now, Samuel: we want you in the sun-room!"

Sam got up holding out his long fingers to his boys, and trailed them with him to the house. He stopped a minute, without thinking, before the back porch, staring at it, and then said mildly, "Needs a couple of coats!"

Inside they were avid for him, waiting to pounce on him.

"Here's our Sam! Samuel! Sammy, my boy! Sam!" Bonnie rushed forward and pecked him on the cheek. Her skin had yellowed through the winter; she was overrouged, and her beautiful hair new washed, full of blue lights, made her look sicklier.

"You're not the only one in the paper," cried Jinny affectionately, buxom and pretty in a blue dress, her red hair in more of a fuss than ever. "Jo was in the papers. Jo sent one of her poems to the *Sun* and they published it."

"Did you see our poetess?" asked Bonnie. "Jo's poems? Did you send it to him, Jo?"

"It's pretty," said Leslie, in a retiring way.

"You're flattering me," said Jo, "it's not so wonderful as you make out."

"It's very good, Jo," Bonnie declared reproachfully.

"Did you write a poem, Jo?" Sam asked with interest.

"In the Baltimore *Sun,*" said Ernie breathlessly; "she got paid for it."

"Josephine M. Pollit!" affirmed Jinny Pollit good-naturedly. Because it was Sam's welcome-home, she tried to cover up the quarrel between herself and Jo; but Jo did no such thing. She turned her back on Jinny in a grand manner.

"Have you got it, Jo?" Sam asked.

"I have it," said Bonnie, rushing to the settee and rummaging in her purse. She at length produced a dirty, browned scrap of paper which she unfolded and handed with pride to Sam. Jo said with bonhomie, "I just thought I'd send it in; and they accepted it at once."

"You could make money that way," said Lennie to Jo.

"Isn't it wonderful, Sam, a poetess in the family?" demanded Bonnie. "Being published? You ought to publish some of your letters, Sam. They went all round the family; we could never get enough of them. We read them aloud. Henny sent us all your letters. Henny was such a dear and so good to the little ones: but then she is a wonderful mother to the little ones, she really is."

During Bonnie's enthusiastic rattle, an uneasy silence had begun to gather over assembled Pollitry, but it was not till it was well advanced that Bonnie saw it and stopped. Henny was not present. Faintly Bonnie repeated, "Read it, Sam; it's wonderful."

"Don't be absurd," commanded Jo, frowning, "such a silly fuss!"

The children clustered round Sam, looking at Jo, this combination of Minerva and Juno.

"Read it, Deddy," said Tommy in his pretty, chipping accent.

Sam laughed ruefully, "Don't call me Deddy. And my Sedgewing who wrote to me, 'Dead Dad.'"

They all shrieked with laughter. Evie looked greatly mortified. Sam continued tenderly; "And who asked me if I could shot a tiger?"

There was wild hilarity, kind Bonnie and Jinny stuffing their hands into their mouths, kind Lennie and Peter Pollit, uncles, turning side on, because anyone could see that Evie was nearly in tears. Sam's old father, seventy-year-old Charles, sitting behind the throng on the settee, laughed consumedly, laughing at them all, delighted to have them together for once. He no more noticed little Evie than some puppy hiding in a corner. Sam held up his hand for the merriment to cease, saying,

"Listen, kids and kinfolk, Josie wrote this and it's very beautiful."

("Listen, listen," whispered the relatives on all sides. Old Charles Pollit leaned forward, laughing still. He could write poetry better than the lot of them.)

Sam read,

In Peggy's eyes
Is the blue of the skies
And innocent looks
That are more than wise.
In a garden plot
Of forgetmenot,
And water brooks
Beneath blue skies
A duplicate lies
Of Peggy's eyes.

Evie stared at her Aunt Jo in the delicious, timid, vacant admiration of the inept. Ernie slewed a look at Louie, standing behind two visitors, and saw her flash a look of contempt at Sam and Jo too. Sam raised his head and saw her too. He said pleasantly, "Isn't that pretty, Looloo?"

"It's nice."

Sam was pleased, "It's very nice, Looloo. Why don't you try to write something like that too, Looloo? All of us Pollits are a good hand at jingle: we can all turn out a rhyme. I think you could, and they might publish it too."

Louie became speechless with resentment, but none saw this but the watchful Ernie. Jo bounced and cried, "Oh, she's very like me: I know she's got a talent: Louie's all right. I bet she could do one nearly as good as that right now."

In a choking voice, Louie said quickly, "Oh, I don't think I would write one like that."

"Well, perhaps not right now: but soon, some day! And now, Father, Father! Come on and do your stunt!"

They began to clear back, leaving a wide circle into which old Charlie advanced with accomplished hesitations, pretending to be broken down with age and rheumatism. They began to clap and back farther away to leave him room for his dance. Louie, choking with rage, slipped out of the door without being noticed, and went into the quiet upstairs. Henny had retired for the day to the girls' room. She was sitting in a big, easy chair looking very bitter and pale, with the brown, mottled skin of pregnancy's end, her neck corrugated. Louie came slowly towards her,

"Everyone's here now, Mother."

Henny grunted, in contempt. "They were reading Auntie Jo's poem in the *Sun*."

Henny grunted.

"I think it's rot," pouted Louie.

"Oh, the Pollits are all so conceited," Henny said impatiently, "that if they write two lines, everyone has to take three fits and a faint. Don't you be like them, that's all I ask."

"Will I tidy the room?" asked Louie.

"No, leave me alone. No one's coming up here; I gave orders about that. I wish to God I could take a taxi and get away from their idiot party and all that buzzing and jigging that they think's so clever and funny."

The grandfather's cracked baritone chirped away to the audience below,

Slap, dash, slap, with a whitewash brush—
Talk about a county ball!
In and out the corners, round the Johnny Horners;
We were a gay old pair of gorners——

"Wouldn't you go down for a little while, Mother?"

"No, I'd rather go to the big bonfire! I suppose now the word will go round that I am sabotaging. Oh, darn everything. Go on down and help. Don't stand there fidgeting and staring at me."

"Would you like some tea, Mother?"

"Oh, I suppose I've got to take something. I'm so empty, I feel like a big barrel floating out to sea."

Louie, delighted, ran downstairs. Whenever her irritations got too deep, she mooched in to see her mother. Here, she had learned, without knowing she had learned it, was a brackish well of hate to drink from, and a great passion of gall which could run deep and still, or send up waterspouts, that could fret and boil, or seem silky as young afternoon, something that put iron in her soul and made her strong to resist the depraved healthiness and idle jollity of the Pollit clan.

It was a strange affection. It could never express itself by embraces or kisses, nothing more than a rare, cool, dutiful kiss on the withering cheek of Henny. It came from their physical differences, because their paths could never meet, and from the natural outlawry of womankind. Downstairs came Louie, for the tea, cheerfully muttering,

Moonbeam, leave the shadowy vale,
To bathe this burning brow.
(Shelley: "To the Moonbeam")

[258]

The indefatigable Jinny was stretching and puffing on the stepladder on the front porch, fixing a forgotten string of Chinese lanterns. In the dining room and the hall stood the wooden cases Sam had brought back from Malaya. None had been opened, though many a curious finger had poked them since early this afternoon. As soon as Sam knew that they were giving a surprise party, he had announced that, despite his fatigue, he would open them all and that everyone would see the Eastern treasures and carry off a present.

Grandfather Charlie, in high feather, spied Louie and called excitedly,

"The Old Gaffer's going to give another show! Come on, Granddaughter! The Old One's about to present 'Mr. Wemmick and the Aged Parent.' Come along, come along, roll up, roll up, come right in, the show's just about to begin! All star performance: manager, Charles Pollit; business manager, Charlie Pollit; stage manager, Chas. Pollit, and barker, Old Charlie. Mr. Wemmick, played by Charles Pollit, and The Aged, played by Charles Pollit. You must excuse, not stare at, the redundancy of that beautiful name, Pollit, in the caste, ladies and gentlemen, if there be any of that name here, for it's all in the family. And the play written by Charles—Dickens, the greatest Charlie!"

"Oh, Father, you're a perfect scream," declared Bonnie. "The old gaffer's all right," she assured the rest.

"Shut up, girl," said her father, "no talking in the free seats. Curtain! Lights! Action!" He gave three taps as he said the last three words. In a profound silence, he began the act that he had worked up himself from *Great Expectations*.

"'Massive? I think so. And his watch is a gold repeater, and worth a hundred pound.'"

The little ones sat round like idols in front of the throng or on their relatives' laps, with carved smiles on their faces and round, floating eyes. The old man, with nothing but a red bandanna, which he ordinarily used to brush off his snuff, became alternately Mr. Wemmick and The Aged, Old Grandfather Charlie, through some trap door of the imagination, disappeared until the act was over; when he suddenly popped up again with a here-we-are-again, crowing, and stumbling into his little buck-and-wing dance. At last they dragged him off the center of the stage. He sank into a rattan armchair near the door and drew Louie towards him,

"How did you like it, granddaughter?"

"Oh, you were very good," she exclaimed.

He twined a strand of her hair round his fingers gently, repeating with great affection,

> Blue were her eyes as the fairy flax,
> Her cheeks like the dawn of day,
> Her bosom white as the hawthorn buds
> That ope in the month of May.

She blushed to the roots of her hair and the flush crept downwards to stain the hawthorn. Her grandfather patted her and turned away, pulling Evie towards him instead, to hide her embarrassment. Then there was a bellying of the crowd at the southern end and something black dropped in through the window; and this black thing hopped into the middle of the room, grinning and rolling white eyes, Cousin Sid doing his Yacht Club Boys, Mammy-Minstrel Act. Then Uncle Leonard sang *The Two Grenadiers;* and this was followed by a hush. Ernie had stolen out, and there came the expected notes of the gong, liquid gold, bommm-bommm scarcely a sound, that rippled, spun, and spread itself through all the air.

The old man arose with a knowing air and came into the center of the carpet again, tramping, stamping, pawing.

"Snake dance," cried Saul excitedly.

All the Pollits lined up behind the old man in order of age, the children last in a long skeletal tail; and after stamping thunderously, they began to sway and weave out the long south window, singing at the top of their voices, "Oh sound a blast for freedom, boys, and send it far and wide!" They circled the animal cages and the rock garden and, circumnavigating the house, came in again by the front door, the old chief entering the long dining room where the banquet was spread, just as they came to the chorus of the second verse: "Hurrah, Hurrah, we bring the Jubilee!" roared the Pollits, and the rafters rang. Sam and the old man were weeping tears of emotion, and there were other damp eyes in the crowd. Then there was a great rumbling of chairs and scurrying of women, all wedging and hedging in, fitting of elbows and knees, groans and giggles until the great tribe was set to table. They had fitted into the table the two dust-stained, extra leaves from the attic, and yet it was hardly big enough. At one end of the table stood a broad-bottomed arm-chair empty. Old Charles, after one glance at it, wriggled out of his seat again (he was at the other end, next to Sam), saying, "Wait and see, wait and see: the Old Gaffer's going to get our Henny." Sam's head and lower lip drooped at this, but the others urged him on, saying with honest enthusiasm, "Yes, beg her to come, Father," and explaining to each other, "You see, poor thing, she's miserable in her condition," and "She hates to be seen—it's very natural: I don't blame poor Pet," and so on. There was indeed no malice in all Pollitry, for Henny. From time to time, one or other of them was inspired by the awful idol they worshiped, their Bounding Health, to go On the War-path against one of their own; and when On the Warpath, a Pollit was a strange, frightful being, a being of brawn and no human understanding, armed with a moral club; but they had no malice against them who hated them; they loved and pitied the intractable, malicious Henny.

After a little while, they heard Old Charlie's voice on the stairs descending slowly and in a moment he appeared, gallantly bending and bringing in Henny by the hand. Henny had waited to fix a bit of lace round her throat with a pearl brooch and to brush up her hair, so that as she came in swaying slowly on her hips under her new rosepink flowered smock, with a touch of rouge on her cheeks, she looked impressive. Her eyes were set into her skull and her face drawn, but her reluctance and pride gave her a matronly dignity. The men all rose except Sam who was sunk in a brown study and who anyhow despised such courtesy as "a foreign mannerism." When his father jogged him on the arm, as much as to say, "You get up too, Sammy," he merely looked round indifferently; and he refused to rise. At this, his brothers, Leonard, Peter and Saul, busied themselves, pulling out the chair for Henny, inquiring after her health, speaking sharply to one of the children in order to cover Sam's clumsiness. At the same moment there was a bustling and twitteration amongst the women to prevent remark and to make Henny feel that she was wanted. Sam sat silent till Henny was seated. From her seat she sent a look of thunder bowling along to the other end, to her morose spouse; then tossing her head slightly, affected to ignore him and began a society clatter with Lennie, her brother-in-law, a leaner edition of Sam, but a goodfellow, a Masonic brother, a cocktail mixer.

Henny had not gone to the train or been on the porch to greet Sam when he came from it, surrounded by all his children. Her sickness, the explanations she had to give about the money, and the scoldings she feared about the untidiness of the place drowned her in a nausea so deep that when Sam had come to the door of her bedroom where she sat she had only given him a look of hollow melancholy; and he, after a long look moist with angry, pitiful tears, had said, "Hullo, Henny," and looked away. There was so much to untangle, and Henny felt her hands nerveless. She would never again try to knit even one stitch in the long chain of their married life. She hated all that was to come. She was glad that the Pollits had surrounded him and put off the dark hour; and yet she resented their joy at him, when to her, he meant the day of reckoning. Lennie Pollit was handsome, a successful traveling salesman in men's shirts, and an angel to his wife, Jinny. Lennie and Jinny gave parties, liked a good time, and had a little money. Why did I have to pick the only Pollit mad and silly with ambition? Henny had often thought. But now she had swum beyond all Pollitry and their considerations: she was on the edge of the maelstrom and was about to sink down, down, circling. She put her hand on the edge of the table and looked round her for a glass of water, which Lennie hastened to pour for her. Henny said, "I felt faint, but it's all right now." Jinny asked her if she would like to lie down, but she refused, "I'm here now; I might as well stay."

There was a two-tiered iced cake made by Jinny; potato-and-egg salad with homemade mayonnaise, also made by Jinny; delicatessen and lemonade, little iced cakes with chocolate tears upon them, made by Henny; raspberry wheels, made by Henny; popovers made by Bonnie and a large box of chocolates given by Jo; contributions from the whole family in the shape of edibles; and down the table, three large pitchers, one transparent, one blue, and one pink, containing a rose-colored liquor with fruit floating in it. This mysterious drink intrigued the children beyond expression. They kept swallowing and looking at the glassware. Before the children were only lemonade glasses, but before the adults were wineglasses. The children suspected that even on this occasion the sherbet of paradise was to be drunk under their dry lips by the loudmouthed, money-pocketed monsters who had them in thrall. Why didn't these giants ravish the table, send the food flying besides, gobble, guff, grab, and gourmandize? To be bestial giants with the power of sherbet and also to exhibit such mean-spirited stinginess towards their own appetites was a conundrum the children could never solve. Let them once be such giants, let them even have the privilege of Louie, and they would not leave a crumb on a plate nor a drop in a bottle. The children sighed internally and ate as hard as they could hoping by their hunger, to soften the miserliness of their elders.

"What's that?" exclaimed Ernie, overcome by desire, pointing to the fascinating pitcher, "What's this, Auntie?" The cruelty of tyrants must be broken down somehow.

"Not for you, Tommy Tucker," said Bonnie hastily, hushing him with a grimace.

Lennie got up and, seizing the pitcher at a signal from Jinny, then went round pouring out the Badminton Cup into the wineglasses.

"What is this?" inquired Sam abstractedly.

"Badminton Cup," Lennie said. Sam said nothing, never having heard of such a thing. When the glass pitcher was empty, Lennie started on the other. No one had touched it. When Lennie got back to his place and all were provided for, he picked up his glass and said in his best Freemasons'-toastmaster voice,

"Old Oddfellow, Brothers and Sisters, Sons and Daughters, before we swallow a drop, let us drink a health to the man we celebrate—to SAM, our wanderer returned!"

All stood up but Henny, but Henny took hold of her glass out of politeness. Sam looked round at them smiling in a grave style, saying almost *sotto voce,* "No, no; you're wonderful people—no, no!"

Lennie repeated, "To Sam!" and the whole family intoned it, in a beautiful response, "To Sam!" They took mouthfuls of the claret cup and a few of the younger ones choked. Old Charles said by himself, "To my youngest son, Samuel Clemens Pollit!" and drank his at a draught. "Not a bad cup!" he nodded to Bonnie. Sam's bloodshot eyes moistened again and he fingered his own glass thoughtfully, as does a man accustomed to speeches, smiling faintly at several of them in turn. Jo, of course, shouted, "Speech, speech," stamped on the floor, beat on the table till the tableware rang again, and the little ones took it up foolishly, crying like a lot of young crows, "Speech, speech!"

"All right, boys and girls," said Sam, at which they all fell silent and sat down irregularly. Then he got up and told them how very, very glad he was to be home again, home again, jiggity-jig; gladder than they ever would know, although they might try to guess, knowing him and how much he loved them all and particularly how much he had always loved his native land and his splendid, flashing Washington, and his own Tohoga House and his tribe, flesh of his flesh, most particularly; and the work nearest to his hand. He did not object, he said, to wandering in the highways and byways of the world, as a student of men and manners, to receive enlightenment, and spread it again; and when Fate held out her hand, he made it a rule to take that hand with whatever it held, for Fate always had a lesson for him, just as every book that fell on its face open, and every scrap of muddy newsprint blowing in the wind and even every shop sign might hold a message for him, because the Word was sacred to him; and whatever that message might be, he was not one to turn his face away, but he smiled at Fate, for he believed Fate was on his side.

Then he lifted his glass and said quietly, "To you all, my friends, friends of my own tribe!" and put the glass to his lips, tasting it mildly, afraid it was one of those saccharine women's drinks. But he, as soon, put it down, looking round, affronted, and he said to Bonnie accusingly, "Bonniferous, what is in this? There is alcohol in this?"

She flushed and acknowledged petulantly, "It's claret cup, Sam; it won't do you any harm—it wouldn't do Tommy any harm, only on account of your views we didn't give it to the children. There's so little, just enough to give it a taste on this festive occasion; you can't be so ultrazealous—it's a fruit drink really!"

Sternly he said to her, "Bonnie, you know I never touch alcohol, nor allow it in my house!"

Henny's face twitched with a sarcastic smile.

"Your brothers and sisters like it!" cried Bonnie.

"I am sorry it is on my table," he told her coldly and sat down. He sulkily picked up his spoon and fork and messed up a piece of cake; but in a minute he thrust it aside, saying in a spoiled way to his father, "This has quite taken away my appetite: why can't I be obeyed? I thought this occasion was to give me pleasure?"

"A little tolerance hurts no one," Old Charlie said, with embarrassment, since his son had often rowed him about his own nipping and tasting.

"I refuse to discuss it here," Sam told him harshly.

Old Charles looked at him for a moment; but his face softened again and, with a roll of gay abandon, noticing that the others hesitated to sip their claret cup, he cried,

"Bonnie, my girl, more of the cup that cheers but not inebriates.

The Good Book says, 'Let us eat and drink, for tomorrow we shall die!' " and in his best glee-club voice he began to troll,

> *A boat, a boat, haste to the ferry!*
> *Let us go over and make merry!*
> *To laugh and quaff and drink good sherry!*

Sam began to pick at his food again, refusing to be drawn. The family took up the round and rang the changes round the table, Lennie singing seconds, Old Charles' voice growing young again as they sang. Even Sam could not resist the charm of the family singsong, oldest Pollit custom, and when his turn came, he took up the song, "A boat, a boat, haste to the ferry!" while Bonnie, at his left, was singing soprano, "Let us go over and make merry!" This removed the dampener that Sam's strong principles had put on the cheer; in any case, they knew Sam's fortes and foibles of old and easily forgave him.

Then Jinny and Bonnie started to discuss the recipe for the Badminton Cup, and jolly Lennie said, "Well, if my little brother won't drink it, Bon, I will drink it for him!" and in the general good humor even Sam recognized that he was swamped. Brother Ebby busied himself now with food and drink seeing that "one and all were in a mood to rejoice," and when Sam, seeing Henny take some of the Cup, said sternly, "Henny, don't drink that, especially in your condition!" and Henny, merely smirking, tossed off a whole glass, almost no one took any notice, for the same pebble cannot ripple the millpond twice.

Henny smirked even more, seeing this wildcat, hedgerow, wildweed, slum-artisan, cheap-Baltimore family grow more jolly; seeing Ebby, poor ship's carpenter, who had an imbecile for a wife and one doddle-headed child, and gaptoothed Benbow, with that strumpet girl, Leslie (as Henny put it), and two dumb boys, and old soak Charles, and garage-owner Peter (who had actually begun with a junk cart and three cowbells collecting old bedsprings and fat women's bulging corsets!), and Bonnie (obviously sleeping with some man who was doing her dirt) and Jinny (whose pert daughter Essie needed her face slapped) and Jo (whose hair was like a haystack in a fit) and all their weedy, rank children getting merrier and merrier on the dungheap that was their life. Born in the muck, thriving in the muck, and proud of the muck, thought Henrietta! Well, it's well to be some people and not know how badly off you are! Let them rot, for all I care. How she had fretted at these people who didn't care if they had an old automobile, and didn't care if they lived cheap, and didn't care if their daughters went to work in hat factories, and didn't care if their cousins married when they were two months pregnant, as long as they lived and crawled fatly over the earth! Despising them, she despised herself, who had been married to them, because she had been useless as a belle, too hysterical and featherbrained to be married as a possible financial catch in Baltimore. Poor Henrietta, thought the Pollits, who never doubted a moment that she felt degraded by them, after her fine upbringing. Ebby gravely brought round the jug to her shoulder while Lennie encouraged her by pushing across to her a plate of true-lovers'-knots in pastry, made by Ebby's wife, Emma, "Eat and drink, Henrietta," and he gave her a bright blue look.

"Sam," said Old Charlie, at the other end of the table, "live and let live; we don't know why we're here, and it's a good rule to let live, till we find out!" He took another swig of the claret cup, which was beginning to blush his ancient mind.

Sam was unhappy and irritable, "Father, you know what my principles are. Fermented and spirituous liquors dethrone reason, deform morals, and disgrace social gatherings. You know I stick to my principles through thick and thin. You know, you all know, I have never faltered in what I believe to be the right. Why do you cross me? Today of all days! In Singapore I saw what alcohol can do to the best of men; the white man in the East is soaked in alcohol. There isn't a decent liver goes out there but becomes a slave of his liver; as for its effect on women—our ministering angel becomes a harridan and—worse! You must forgive me."

Henny scrutinized him closely during this speech and at the end laughed shortly and put the second glass to her lips.

"Henny, put down that glass or leave the room: my children are here!"

"Samuel!" cried Bonnie, horrified. "Pet!" she pleaded, and Jinny said, "Sam, Sam, Sam, don't break up the party!"

"You heard me, Henny," Sam said with flushed face, "you all heard me."

Henny laughed on a high, artificial note. Her voice cracked as she said, "I heard! You wouldn't hear me bellowing that way across the table insulting my own guests—you and your Singapore society manners!"

She shut her eyes, rolling her head back in that ugly, incredibly theatrical way of hers, then snapped open the heavy lids, again giving them all a smoking look.

"He writes letters home about the fine ladies who befriended him while he was away, Lady Battersby, Lady Modore, Lady Muckymuck, and Sir William PatmybackandI'llscratchyours, with all his fine friends in fine feathers, and this is the real way he is at home, the great I-Am. Trying to boss me about when you've only just got off the boat. Probably you think I'm that nigger secretary you had or his nigger wife!" She laughed insolently and took another sip of the glass, "I'd be ashamed to insult my guests at my own parties, especially when it all came out of their purses—but that doesn't bother him, he can't drink your wine, he's too pure. He's so pure that he just came back from the sluts of Singapore, who have the staggers from gin-slings, and he wants to order me round the way he orders those wretched beggars, Chinks, and niggers the government gives him. The family carpetbagger."

Sam sprang up, sending his chair sprawling, "Henny, quit the room!" The brothers and sisters jumped up too, to restrain Sam, pacify Henny, and send out the children. The old father got up with his bent knees and laid his knotted, veined hand on his son's arm. Samuel did not notice him, thought it was some child.

Henny, laughing, stood up slowly, brushing the crumbs from her knees,

"Look at me! My back's bent in two with the fruit of my womb; aren't you sorry to see what happened to me because of his lust? I go about with a body like a football, fit to be kicked about by a bohunk halfback, an All-America football, because of his lust, the fine, pure man that won't look at women. Don't you regret my condition because of his lust? Didn't he fix me up, pin me down, make sure no man would look at me while he was gallivanting with his fine ladies? I guarantee, Samuel, that no man looked at me while you were away. Oh, what do I care?" she said, weeping to Jinny, who was talking to her, pleading with her, "What do I care, Jinny? You're a mother yourself. Haven't you done the horrible thing three times yourself for a man? What do you care when the time comes? What does any woman care for the man who got her that way? I am such a God-forgotten imbecile as to be going through the bloody mess again for a man like that, that's been slinking through the slime of Singapore with his high-society whores for eight months, and left me in this misery. I hope I never come back; I hope this is the last you see of such a rotten, helpless, stupid thing as I am, falling into his trap every time; I hope I die. I am sure I'll die. I pray to God I'll die. I can't fight any more. I'm not one of his tigers to fight all my life. I'm not a grenadier like a rotten old schoolma'am to squabble all my life. Look how he insults me! He no sooner gets back than he insults me before the whole swarm of them! Let me go; why do you hang on to me, all of you? What have I done? How did I get here? I know, through his sniveling, whining, get-rich-quick tricks. To you he's something wonderful; if you knew what he is to me, something filthy crawling in the sleeve of my dressing gown; something dirty, a splotch of blood or washing-up water on my skirts. That's what he is, with his fine airs and don't-touch-me and I'm-too-good-to-drink. The little, tin Jesus! Oh, let me go, Jinny! What do you know about him? Oh, let me go, I'm a damned fool to give way this way."

The old man said, "Son, son, go and speak to her: you ought to remember the condition she's in; a woman is not a man," and Bonnie whispered to her father, "Sam's dreadfully tired, let him alone too," while the gaping, frightened children stood stockstill in their places. Only Essie, Jinny's daughter, was grinning, a naughty girl who sneered at everyone, Jinny's pride. To Louie she said, poking her, "I always knew they fought like cats and dogs in your family: Aunt Henny gives Uncle Sam hell!" and Essie laughed. At this moment Jinny, red as a May Day flag, arrived behind her pride, and boxed her ears, which sent her howling and kicking into the passage, although Essie was twelve years old. Henny's attention was attracted that way, and Henny, feeling a deep shame for the scene she had brought on, cried out, to Louie, "What are you doing, you fat pig, slopping over the table like that? Take your fat belly off the tablecloth and stop looking like your greasy father!" and laughed desperately.

"Henny," said Jinny. "Henny, dear, come and lie down. I'll get you an ice bag for your headache; come and lie down, dear!" and Bonnie was frowning and crying at Sam, "Samuel, how could you, today of all days?"

"This is the home I come home to," said Sam and sank into his chair.

Soon Henny was lying down on Louie's bed upstairs and Louie came up with tea for her, to calm her and an aspirin, and the party, in Henny's absence, had made a shift to reorganize itself, and gather in the children to get them into a better state of mind and make them forget. They were now singing the "Hallelujah" Chorus, in a moderated style, round Henny's grand piano, with quick-witted Bonnie at the keyboard. Sam had wandered away from them, beside himself, ill and out of his usual mind, to look at the rock garden, wind-picked and weed-covered, and the cement fishpond, green with rags of moss, with sick-looking fish—the whole place had been given a lick and a promise in preparation for his coming, no sooner than yesterday. He took with him Ebby's boys, kindhearted, fox-snouted Cousin Sid, and Little-Sam. Of all the boys, he had thought most of

Little-Sam throughout his exile from home, the strawheaded, tempestuous, stubborn little boy of unpredictable reactions, with his shouts of mirth and shouts of rage, the boy who looked most like himself and who, Sam told himself, was a young genius, sure to be a great scientist and carry on his own work.

To him, kicking his heels round the rock garden, came Evie scurrying with a telegram in her hand, "It's for Mother; but Auntie Jinny says for you to open it."

Sam tore the paper and read:

FATHER COLLYER DIED SUDDENLY THIS MORNING CAN YOU COME TO YOUR MOTHER ARCHIBALD LESSINUM

"I will go after the opening of the boxes," said Sam. "Don't take it to your mother. Old David is dead. Dear old David is dead."

2 ⚓ Brought to light.

Now ERNEST AND TOMMY came in deputation to him, running and out of breath but with hope and embarrassment.

"Daddy, everyone wants to know if you're going to open the boxes now?"

"Deddy, are you going to show us the things you brought?"

Sam smiled, "Sure-LY," and started up the slope. They skipped round him, rushing toward the house and back towards him. Suddenly Ernie spurted off to carry the news. A movement began again, breathless and happy among all the Pollits; they had been straying, and now they began circulating slowly but regularly in groups like creatures swimming round an aquarium.

"Sam is going to open the cases; Sam is going to show us the Chinese things. Oh, isn't that grand!"

"Wow!" "Gee!" "Gee, I'm excited, aren't you?" "What has Uncle Sam got in there, Mumsy?" "Shh, you'll see."

Sam went to the tool house and came in with a hammer and

a cold chisel. Presently all the boys and men were lugging, tugging the boxes, but as gently as they were able so as not to break the flimsy and precious things inside.

Sam was rather reluctant to open the cases because, although he was generous, he had brought many things that he intended for the adornment of his own bare house with its great rooms. He was unaware of the sensuality of his own nature and of the joy he took in these porcelains, silks, and embroideries, the longing, the lust he had for them. He had always been poor and modern, and suddenly in the East he had found the treasures of the past. He had always despised the past, hated history, believed only in man today and in a sober, future commonweal; and now for the first time, through his love of the Chinese he loved the workmanship, treasures, theories, men of the past; and through his new acquaintance with white men in the East in positions of power. He had gone, stupidly, for the pomp and spreadeagle of scientific societies and human uplift associations, now for the first time, he had seen the exquisite beauty, sensibility and sensuality of the things treasured by those who put others in bondage. Poor good man, he thought that he had discovered a new principle, which was, as he told Saul Pilgrim, that the rich and powerful are human beings too. Talk to them of some innocent thing, like natural history and human advancement and they were as human, more human, tender, than the wages-obsessed workman: they had seen much and understood much. But he bore a little grudge to his raw, sensual, penurious family, at this moment, for standing there, adoring his success and his possessions so openly; there they stood, good-natured vultures, his own blood, ready to fall on his stuffs and snatch them, saying oh, and ah, and slavering for them; but he would not give them much, his own children came first. For them he would make a nest, a haven, a palace, a university, all in his own plot of ground and this phalanstery of a house: he would now be the East to his children as well as the West.

They first opened the box of ceramics and found two twenty-inch vases smashed; but there were left a dozen or so cloisonné and lacquer vases of various sizes. Everyone helped to put the things on the table, the mantelpiece and the piano. It was like a village fire brigade passing buckets. The expensive chips were shoveled out into the ash can. The second case had on its very top a mandarin gown of celestial blue with gold metallic threads, which was for Louie. Louie, who expected nothing of the shortsighted world, was baffled by this gift.

Her father raised his tired eyes upon her, "I bought that for you, Louie; it was sold by a real Chinese prince, a refugee, and my friend gave it to me for almost nothing, for my eldest daughter."

With a sullen, downcast face, but with a faint flush, she took it. As she went past the ranks of Pollits, they looked curiously, grudgingly at her, or fingered it. She laid it out on the sofa in the long dining room. When alone with it, triumph surged up—mine, she thought, mine; and grasped one of the stiff folds, mine—and she laid the other hand flat on it. She went self-consciously and stolidly back, but no one noticed her. Two ordinary Chinese silk dressing gowns, one pink and one yellow, with heavy embroidery and gold threads, lay on the chair, and Auntie Bonnie said fussily, "Those are for your Mother: why don't you ask her to come down, dear?"

"I'll take them up to her," said Louie.

Henny had already regretted her act of tempest, and she looked with melancholy softness at the dressing gowns, "Put them there and thank your father."

"They say, won't you come down, Mother?"

"No, I only want to be left alone." Louie withdrew.

Sam had emptied one box, all packed with silk suits of pajamas and gowns, scarves, and a long, feast-day banner of red, showing a woman in a multicolored gown. He broke open another case which chanced to contain small jade ornaments, in dark, pale, and white jade, snuffboxes and little pots and napkin rings. The furniture and fixtures could no longer be seen, overwhelmed with the china, bronze, brass, lacquer, and silks he had brought and with two cork pictures and some bits of embroidery. Sam made the boys bring in a light pine table from the veranda and on this he set out for show all the little *objets d'art*.

"Now," he said, clearing his throat, "there is something for everyone. Let us clear the chairs and put all the stuff in the other room: everyone will sit down and everyone will choose what he likes from the pine table."

Ernie, quickly looking round, saw the discomfiture amongst his relatives. They, the poor, were only to get the little things. They were not experts, and they loved the polished vases, the red lacquer, the silks and banners. The small things seemed of little value to them.

Sam, too, no slower than anyone, had seen the disappointment ,and embarrassment of his brothers, sisters, and their families. He looked embarrassed and gave a little grin. He hurried his boys with their bundles of stuffs. Bonnie, good girl, seeing how things were, immediately became very cheerful and rattled away, "While you're all· getting seated, I'll give you a song," and she took a flying leap into *Funiculi, Funicula*.

The distribution began. Sam made himself a dispenser of bric-a-brac, with a pin pot here, a matchbox there, a napkin ring beside, and a snuffbox neighboring, and again a pin pot, according to the choice of the men and women. He had a wonderful set of actor dolls, with a demon, a prince, a princess, and several minor fiends, and a little stage, but these were for his own children. He had Chinese instruments which he played for them in between times, to give a saving touch of grotesquerie to the whole thing. Perhaps soon they would forget the parsimony and disperse and not come together again until the memory of the pin pots was half gone.

There were seven cases to unpack. Sam, once started and sunk to his waist in a lake of treasures, with his tools and his relatives around him, worked without stopping, except once to say to Bonnie, "Bon, cawf [coffee]." Now Sam had reached the seventh case, which contained metals, knives with chased, inlaid, and beaten blades, and with carved and inlaid handles of ebony, ivory, and brass-inlaid silver and so on, a Chinese two-edged broadsword, a creese, a mace. At the bottom was something that he unwrapped with surprise and dragged out with difficulty, a Chinese bronze gong two feet in diameter, with raised figures. Struck once, it gave out a long, distant mellow roll, a sound which was never a single note, always a whole meditation of sound.

Sam said, "I see now why he packed it himself; it is a present from my friend Abdul Jamid ben Ali. Yes, now I remember, Abdul Jamid said, 'I hope nothing breaks,' and I am sure there is something that will not break. This is his gift. What friends in the east!"

Louie said,

A yellow plum was given me and in return a topaz fair I gave,
No mere return for courtesy but that our friendship might out-
*   last the grave.*

"Eh? What is that?"
"That is a poem after Confucius!"
Sam was careful to show no surprise, "I am glad you have got to Confucius and beyond Confusion. Abdul's little boy, Mahmoud," he continued, turning to his father, "I met every day going to school; he was intelligent and quick and spoke good English and had a ready smile for everyone."

Meanwhile there was a subdued chatter all over the rooms, where the Pollits were exclaiming over the stuffs and curios. Louie stood abstracted, with the peach-bloom silk, brought for Leslie, at her feet; and unexpectedly, she took a step forward, over the bolt of silk and declaimed,

A simple peach was given me, and in return a ruby gem I gave,
No mere return for courtesy, but that our friendship might out-
*   last the grave!*

Her cousin Essie, who was playing with the little wooden toys, models of water carriers and buffalo carts and sawyers' blocks, gave a sidelong glance and turned back intently to her game. No one else took the least notice, except Little-Sam, sitting near her, who kept looking up into her face questioningly. Big Sam took no notice. Encouraged by this, Louie declared,

A loquat branch was given me and in return an emerald I gave,
No mere return for courtesy, but that our friendship might out-
last the grave!

Sam paused and leaned back on his heels at the beginning of the stanza, and with long lank cheek he studied Louie, who seemed to have grown out of recognition in the eight months of his absence; or else his imagination had twinkled and transformed her memory in that hot climate. Was this tall, powerful girl with stern, hangdog face really Louie, the child of love? But now the face twitched with a clownish pleasure and grave conceit; the face was both ludicrous and lachrymose: Sam wanted to strike her across the face to obliterate that execrably bizarre tragicomic mask which disgraced him. Sam stared her into silence so that the mask settled, sad, too old by years, between the waterfall hair, and then abruptly, his mouth opened and he laughed hard,

"Ha-ha-ha-ha-ha, he-he-he; Ha-ha! A booby trap was given me and in return, a herring trail I gave; no mere return for courtesy but that our friendship might outlast the grave."

The Pollits were flocking back, grinning from ear to ear, not knowing what the joke was but glad to see Sam at last in high spirits. They saw Louie and Little-Sam, Essie and the others, and had no idea how the thing had started,

"Ha-ha-ha," shouted Sam, rocking on his haunches and pointing at Louie (at whom the newcomers looked in surprise), "an old black boot was given me and in return a herring head I gave, no mere return for courtesy but that our friendship might outlast the grave! A chamber pot was given me and in return a toilet bowl I gave, no mere return for courtesy but that our friendship might outlast the grave!"

The astonished Pollits crowded in, grinning confusedly and

peering from one to the other, while Auntie Jo ignorantly, cried, "A wedding cake was given me and in return a petticoat I gave, no mere return for courtesy but that our friendship might outlast the grave!"

Ernie, very knowing, with a narrow-eyed leer, capered and delivered himself, "A dusty pup was given me and in return an old tin can I gave, no mere return for dusty pup but that our friendship might outlast the grave!"

"Louie said it," declared Essie to everyone. "That was what Louie was reciting!"

But Sam recaptured the floor saying angrily, "If that's Confucius, I'll eat my hat."

"It is," cried Louie, "it is. You don't know. Listen:

> *Let me be reverent, be reverent,*
> *Even as the way of Heaven is evident,*
> *And its appointment easy is to mar."*

Bonnie ignored all this, calling out, "Now let's have a little song before we break up, not too loud, but not too soft."

"Yes," said the old man eagerly, "yes." He picked the snuff-box out of his knitted waistcoat with the cat's-eye buttons that he had got once when strolling round the world on a sailing vessel, from New Zealand, and offered it to his eldest son, Ebby, who was the only son to share what the girls called "father's disgusting habit."

"Yes," he repeated, "for he's a jolly good fellow, and so say all of us. What's the matter with Sammy? He's all right!"

"He's a chip off the old block," cried Bonnie beaming; and Old Charles tee-heed under his yellowed mustache.

"Samivel's all right," said he, raising the snuffbox to the level of his eyes and scrutinizing the design, vaguely scandalous, which consisted of two mermaids sitting on a beach. He raised the snuffbox higher and motioned round the family with it, beginning with a laugh, "Samivel is wery satisfactory to the old codger; 'wery' spelt with a 'wee.'"

[277]

"Father!" cried Jo indignantly, as the little ones started to giggle, "Wee, wee."

He slid the snuffbox into his pocket, "Shall I do All-of-a-Twist?"

"Oh, no, Father," said Jo. "Not now."

Old Charles appealed to the children, abstractedly picking his own pocket of the bandanna meanwhile, " 'I won't abase myself by descending to hold no conversation with him.' *replied the Dodger.*"

"For he's a jolly good fellow," sang out Bonnie, touching the piano.

"For he's a jolly good fellow," Ebby sang.

"And so say all of us," shouted Jo.

"Don't," said Sam, "don't, boys and girls," but his eyes were moist and to the children's surprise he seemed older. His eyes had new crow's-feet, and the tired upper part of the face, with sunken temples, for the hour resembled the weathered mahogany face of Old Charles.

"And why not?" shouted Jo jovially. "Aren't you our very own Smithsonian? Our family genius? No, or yes?"

"Yes, yes!"

"Our only genius," Jo continued.

Louie's face lowered. By a curious chance Jo looked straight at Louie, grinning evilly, Louie thought.

"And you, Jo, aren't you our genius too?" inquired Bonnie innocently. "Well, I guess we're all small pertaters, only we don't know it, all except Sam." She spun on the stool.

"Tune up," cried Grandfather in his trembling voice, and he began, in a furry voice full of little hidden screams or scratches, *The Gang's All Here.*

"Let Father give us a tune," said Ebby delightedly, his good gray eyes caressing his father. "What'll it be, Father?"

The old man ran to the center of the carpet, bagging his trousers, fussing his bushy gray hair, and pinching his cheeks to make them pink; so that they all answered that they wanted to hear *The Bold Fisherman*. Out of his coat pocket came the red bandanna which he tied in the open V of his blue shirt. The little boys were a bit ashamed, too, of the way his trouser band bulged, of the wrinkles in the legs, of the snuff spots on the handkerchief and the coat, and, in particular, of his eagerness to sing to them. But he was used to giving performances wherever he could, and he had far too many spawn, and spawn's spawn, to notice the greensickness of little boys in seven-inch pants. He threw himself into the song, and the shocking perpetual youth of Grandfather ceased shocking them for a while,

Oh, there was a bold fisherman and he set sail from Billingsgate
To chase the mild bloater and the gay mackeeray;
But when he arrove off Pimlico, the stormy wynds they began
*   to blow, and the little boat wibble-wobbled so,*
That smack overboard he fell!

This was followed by an adorable *parlando* with improvisations during which Grandfather performed on his accordion, "my I. W. W. pianner," as he called it, "music on the hoof." Grandfather was generous with his shows, and he went through three stanzas. They had hardly stopped laughing and got through wild, prolonged applause (during which Henny was seen bleakly rotating past the doorway into the kitchen), when Grandfather ran to a corner of the room and seemed to fall behind the settee. They were just wondering whether they should go and help him when he reappeared jubilant, holding his old banjo between his legs and hands. When they saw it, they all shouted. Old Charles positively gave a goatlike leap at this shout and himself cried, "A seat, a chair for the wandering minstrel!"

Well, there was no stopping him; the children were delighted, and only the distrait noticed Henny, during the next song, moving with elephantine grace in the dining room, carrying a silver sugar basin. Then Ebby took the banjo and played *One Eve-*

ning in the Month of May, and during this Bonnie saw Henny, with a scowl, heaving herself to the bottom of the staircase and then heard her moving slowly up.

More refreshments were served, and during the bustle Henny came downstairs again, this time in the new pink Chinese dressing gown.

"I feel full as a tick," said Henny, discouraged, "but I must take something; I know I'm empty," and she sat down to the kitchen table with Jinny, not saying much, but gulping down hot tea hungrily. Then she restlessly went upstairs again.

"We'll all be going soon," said Jinny kindly. "I'll pack them off, Pet!"

"Oh, it doesn't matter; I'm so darned restless, I don't care what they do: I hardly hear them," said Henny. "Ugh! I'm going upstairs to rest; now I have indigestion! I'm a fool to mix my drinks. Tell Louie to bring me the bicarbonate."

She labored upstairs. The Pollits below sang madly, "The flowers that bloom in the spring, tra-la, have nothing to do with the case."

"I suppose Collyer left this house to Henny and you?" inquired Lennie of Sam.

"Oh, he promised it," said Sam. "Don't talk about it, Len; I was very fond of the old boy and he of me."

"And that's what I mean when I say and I sing," sang the Pollits, leaning on each other's shoulders round the piano.

"Have you told Henrietta yet?"

"No, she's probably very tired. I telephoned the house and explained I'd tell her in the morning. I'll go to the funeral; it will be the first I ever went to. I don't like funerals, but dear Old David was different: I'm sorry I didn't see him; I bitterly regret it. I loved Old David."

They moved to the hall door.

"Pet will be very upset."

"Of course! Her father!"

Louie came downstairs quickly, "Daddy, Mother's sick, she says to call the doctor."

"Ugh, ouf!" said Henny loudly.

"She shouldn't have taken that wine," said Sam, "and overexcited herself. You see, I can't tell her tonight."

"Oh, damn it," said Henny loudly above.

Sam frowned.

"Louie!" called Henny, "Louisa! Bonnie!"

"I'll go," said Sam.

"Let Auntie Bonnie go," Louie advised. "Auntie!" The Pollits were roaring, "The music goes round and round!"

"Auntie!" called Louie, looking through the rooms. Bonnie came running, flustered but cheerful, from the bathroom, holding a newspaper in her hand and saying, "Oh, Sam, what are they saying about Wally in Singapore; I forgot to ask? What does the British Empire say about the American Beauty?"

"And it comes out here!" they shouted, groaned, whined, and squeaked at the piano, bellowing with laughter.

Louie said quickly, "Auntie, Mother says will you go up!"

"Louie!" screamed Henny, unseen, seething with exasperation. "Louie, tell that mad crowd to stop it!"

Leonard turned back, "Shh! Shh! Henny's sick!"

"I'll pack them off," cried Jinny, hurrying up to them.

Suddenly Henny screamed, "Samuel! Tell the damnfools to go," and they heard her begin to moan. Jinny rushed in and turned herself into a dozen Jinnys, patting and pulling, packing them off, telling them where their coats were, apologizing, explaining—Henny was overtired with the excitement and must be left alone with her family.

Henny shouted, hoarse with anger, "Samuel! Samuel!"

Louie rushed downstairs again, making a noise enough for a cavalry horse, "Daddy, Mother says she's too sick to stand it!"

"Nerves," said Sam, in a tired way, "but I suppose it's natural. Poor Pet is waiting; it's the waiting at the end."

Grandfather hurried up to Samuel, "What is it? The——"

"No," said Sam, "it's a fortnight too soon. Just hysteria."

Old Charles said hurriedly, with a shamed, begging face, "Samuel, they never called any of the little ones after me—

when it comes, if it's a boy, will you call it Charles? I'll ask Henny myself, dear boy, when the time comes. I haven't got long to go; I'd like to see a little rogue of a Charlie called after his worthless old gaffer."

"All right, Father," Sam laughed a little; "he's staking out his claim."

"Here's your coat, Lennie," said Jinny bustling up, already dressed for going out. "Will you go out and start the car? and I'll get the children."

Bonnie came running down, "I can't quite understand it, unless it's—" she looked worried from one to the other. "Send for the doctor, Samuel."

"Has she Doctor Rock still?" asked Sam frowning.

"Of course!"

"All right!"

Bonnie went to the telephone.

They heard Henny above.

The Pollits went scurrying, flying out by the open long windows and doors, shaking hands, backing into their coats, settling their hats, shouting, "Good-by! So long! See you in the comic supplement!" being whispered to, by their fathers and mothers, falling over people's feet, tangling up their own and streaming out to their automobiles and along the street to the streetcar. Neighbors facing Tohoga House, in the semidetached brick cottages, came out on the porches to watch them go.

No one went to say good-by to Henny, who was reported sick. Upstairs Henny heard them go, racing and tramping. She sat in a chair beside Louie's bed, with a stricken look, and when Louie reappeared after saying good-by, Henny said quietly,

"Tell your father to come up and see me!"

Samuel went upstairs reluctantly, and Louie, waiting at the foot of the staircase, heard his expostulations and Henny's angry answers,

"How could I arrange for it? I had no money. It's going to be here!"

"No money? What happened to all I sent? I denied myself for you and the children."

"Don't fight about money now, with the state I'm in! Get Doctor Rock."

"I told you not to have Doctor Rock; he has a reputation."

"I don't give a damn what reputation he has: he suits me. He's a good family doctor. Do I have to scream at you to get something! No sooner do you come home than it becomes a bedlam. Do I have to scream at you? Get him! Bonnie! Louie! Tell this idiot, tell this blockhead, tell him, Bonnie! Get him, you ugly beast! A woman in my condition has to beg and pray and explain!"

Louie rushed to the telephone and telephoned Doctor Rock again. The doctor's calm voice, insolently calm, it seemed, said, "What is it? What did she say?"

"She says to come quickly."

"I'll send the nurse."

The quarrel upstairs was being carried on in subdued tones. Sam presently came downstairs looking grave and quiet. He murmured impersonally to Louie, "Keep the children quiet: Mother's ill."

"I know," said Louie rudely.

He looked coldly at her, "If you know, keep them quiet. I'm sick myself, Looloo," he said breaking down suddenly. "I can't go much further myself."

He stumbled into the riotously littered dining room and across it, skirting every manner of grotesque and outlandish thing to the sunroom, where he threw himself on the settee.

"Looloo-dirl," he called piteously, "come and talk to me." She went in.

Upstairs they heard Henny groan with impatience.

"We have a long night ahead," said Sam. "I want you to arrange the children's beds downstairs. Mother wants to sleep upstairs."

"Is she very sick?" asked Louie, much frightened.

"All that," said Sam, "is a child trying to be born. I guess that by sunrise tomorrow we will have another child in the family."

Louie looked as if she could not believe her ears. She faltered, "Another child?"

"The groans you hear are the beginning of the greatest drama on earth, the act of birth." He looked at her with luminous eyes; his voice had taken on a tone of incantation. "With the coming of morning, Samuel Pollit will have a new son or daughter."

Louie blushed from head to foot.

"And I myself am so ill, Looloo-girl, that I can hardly rejoice as I always do at the birth of a child. The great glory of man, the great glory of the flaming forth of new stars, the glory of the expanding universe, which are all expressed in our lives by the mystery, wonder, and tragedy of birth have always thrilled me beyond expression. And here I lie, with bones of jelly. It did for me, Looloo. The last nights in Singapore I was so tired that when I shut my eyes, I saw blue and yellow flames, I saw things as clear as photographs, not ordinary visions; I dreamed there was a dragon on my bed. Don't tell anyone that, Looloo, and not Henrietta either, now. I don't want her to be worried."

Louie stared at him uncomfortably. Sam laughed, "a giant in his weakness."

Louie said,

> *The desolator desolate,*
> *The tyrant overthrown;*
> *The arbiter of other's fate,*
> *A suppliant for his own!*

Sam looked at her with a puzzled expression, "Why did you say that?"

She melted into a grin, "I just thought of it."

"Leave me to sleep; go and see if your mother wants anything."

When Louie got upstairs she found that Doctor Rock had been admitted by Bonnie.

"Get some clean towels for me, Louie," said Henny gasping.

The doctor turned to her with an angry expression.

"Go on, my dear," said poor Henny, quite kindly.

Bonnie was making Louie's bed.

"You will have to sleep downstairs tonight," said Henny grimly.

The doctor kept staring at her angrily.

"The water is beginning to drip, Doctor."

The doctor glared at Louie, "Go away, run away!"

3 ✠ Morning rise.

SANGUINE AND SUN-HAIRED Sam Pollit, waiting for the birth of his seventh child, had not slept all night. Louie, after some attendance at the door of the birth room, had slept well, downstairs, in Henny's big bed, with Evie. Kind Bonnie had stayed all night. The four boys, used to wind cries and human cries, had slept very well on mattresses on the floor in the sunroom, exactly as they had on the day of the great gale in 1933 when Sam feared the chimney pots would blow down. One or two of them woke once or twice and, hearing their mother cry out, saw nothing in it at all but an ordinary connubial quarrel between her and Sam, and turned and slept again. There were torments in the Himalayas, windspouts in the Grand Canyon, and Judges of the Supreme Court got into sacred rages. What could little boys do, too, about differences between their hearthstones, Mother and Father? They listened for a while, turned, and slept again.

At four o'clock the sky grew lighter and, one by one, the birds began to creak, some like rusty winches, some like door hinges, and some like fishing lines unreeled at a great rate.

There was one that sang joyously like the water burbling down a choked drain. At any rate, to Sam's ear, all of these were singing hymns of praise to the rising dawn, and congratulating themselves on their broods and him on his new child. "All Nature is awake," thought Sam, prowling amongst the chance-sown seedlings of pine at the bottom of the orchard, "and my latest young one, in a new suit of flesh, is trying to greet the dawn, too." At five-thirty the flame-red sun, so heralded, was kicked out of the horizon's waist and visibly jerked upwards. Not even a breeze stirred the hundred-year-old elms on the south-facing bluff of Tohoga Place. Overhead stretched an immense, tender spring sky. The budding trees, already root-hid in weeds, ran up the hill on all sides. The surrounding streets, their hollows, the lesser heights, and dome bubbles of reeking Washington were visible; the world was a milky cameo at sunup. The neglected garden thronged upwards with all its plants into the new sun, with its guava trees, peach trees, magnolia trees, apple trees, seedling pines and forsythia, and the wild double narcissus that grew so rank and green on the possums' graves.

From the girls' bedroom that looked due south into Virginia, carried on the sloping airs to Sam, his wife's screams began coming louder and closer together. No doubt their neighbors with the small, pinched brick faces, feverishly avoiding the sunspots on their spoiled sheets in bedrooms on Reservoir Street, and the encroachers on old Tohoga House Estate, slums of Thirty-fifth Street, back-bedroom dwellers, who rested their hot eyes on green Tohoga's wilderness, if they were awake, heard the sound too. The air was still and lazy. Sam plied fast his long legs and reached the house in a minute.

"It's the end," said Sam. Both leaves of the tall south door stood open letting in the moist air, and he raced from the porch through them and along the hall to Henny's bedroom where the two girls were fast asleep. Brick-colored light fell through the shutters of the French windows on to the ceiling, and moved quickly in bars farther and farther into the room. The air breathed heat and nightlong sweat mixed with the dewy morning coming through the shutter slits. The windows were open. Louie's long hair was spread out in a fan on the pillow, and the rumpled sheet was kicked to the bottom of the bed on her side, though it still half embraced Evie. Sam, standing at the foot of the bed, whistled Louie's whistle. When she opened her eyes, he said quickly, "Get the kids up and dressed, Looloo: I want 'em to hear the new baby come."

"Is it here?" asked the girl, half awake. He pointed in the direction of the noises, "Coming, coming; hurry. That means the end. I'll get the boys."

His daughter jumped out of bed, after shaking Evie.

"Little-Womey, hurry, hurry," said Sam, stooping to the level of her vague, surprised eyes, on the bed. "New bimbo, new bambino!"

Evie sat up suddenly, her face pulled into a grotesque and comical grin, "Have we got a new bimbo?"

"Not yet; coming, coming!" He bent and kissed her, "Bimbo's in a hurry; wants to see Little-Sam and Little-Womey."

Evie looked round everywhere, "Where, Taddy?"

"With Mother yet," Sam said tenderly.

He went to get up the boys. Ernie was out of bed like a shot and pulling his pajama pants off his feet. He looked interested and serious. He stopped with his day shirt half over his head, his two big eyes out like Brer Rabbit's from the mudhole, questioning Big Sam, at a noise from upstairs. But Big Sam did nothing, only put himself everywhere at once, on all sides of the mattresses. "Git-up, git-up," pulling and tugging at arms and legs, while the twins, not yet aware, groaned and muttered, "You get out, Erno, or I'll hit yer," and then at one moment shuttered up their eyes finally and gladly stared at Sam, back from Malaya and Manila.

"Daddy!" they both cried.

"Git-up, git-up!" he whispered joyously, mysteriously. They shot up and began prancing on their mattresses. The sun shone, but there was trouble above-stairs. Sam, however, instead of pulling a long face and slewing towards them woebegone eyes, was all merriment and gratulation, his eyes a playground for scores of dancing little twitching elvish smiles, here and there, come and gone; his tired, yellow, and flabby cheeks, flushed a little; his ugly bloodshot eyes, which had gone creased, half shut and Indian, in the tropical sun, squinting at them, leering at them, with every token of a good time to come.

"New bimbo," half whispered Sam, "new bimbo; get ready, get ready."

To Louie who appeared, hastily dressed, he said, laughing, "Get 'em dressed, Looloo."

Little-Sam stood up straight, his eyes and ears straining towards the stairs, as Louie knelt to fasten his sandals. The sun blushed on them all, banana yellow on the blonds and ginger on the brunets. They were all amazed and sober, examining the faces of Louie and Sam attentively. Sam was unconcerned. He smiled and, bending to kiss Evie, crooned, "Ming! Sedgewing! Smudgewing! Wat oo so sober fower? Wat oo ready to bust in two tears fower? Mummy get a new urchin, Daddy get a new shrimp, Evie get a new cradle kid, Tommo get a new brudder, Louie get a new somebuddy to make *wawa!*"

Evie raised her pansy kitten-face and pored over his lineaments, trying to make sense out of it all, trying to suck information out of him. He looked at her adoringly, and suddenly swung her up into his arms.

"My Little-Womey! Should have come to Malay with Poor-Sam to see all the—little brown, little bronze, little copper, little sulphur, little corn-cake, little waffle babbies; should have come to nurse all the little brown babbies; shouldn't have stayed so far away from her poor little Sam."

She threw back her head like Henny, and laughed provokingly, "But you wouldn't take me, you wouldn't take me!"

Three ringing cries came from the room upstairs, above the ceiling of the sunroom. Evie looked frightened. Sam's face changed. He plumped her on to the floor.

"Quick, quick, all hands on deck!"

He ran amongst them, behind them, marshaling them, like

a sheep dog, to the bottom of the stairs, where they stood with charmed expectant faces raised towards the landing.

Sam began to chant rather low, bending over them, with his hands on shoulders, bunching them together,

> *Mother's got a lot, but she bought a new cot!*
> *Daddy's got Sedgewing, but he's got a new Thing!*
> *Louie's got another little Creaker to her string!*

All the children laughed, a babble of little chuckles and crows, like a summer wave rearing on the shingle; but stopped, with their mouths open to listen, as Henrietta screamed wildly, hoarsely, such a cry as they never thought she could make: Louie turned startled eyes to Samuel, believing that she had gone mad. Evie started to cry. Sam grew solemn and held up his hand,

"Kids, I want you to listen: she's been crying all night; this is the end; soon you'll hear a new kind of cry. That will be the new baby. Listen, listen!"

The children strained their faces upwards listening. Sam said softly, "This is the first sunrise and the first day on earth for one of our family. See what time it is, Looloo."

It was six-thirty. When the baby's cry came, they could not pick it out, and Sam, eagerly thrusting his face amongst their ears, said, "Listen, there, there, that's the new baby." He was red with delight and success. They heard voices, and their mother groaning still, and then, quite free and separate, the long thin wailing, and the voices again.

"Six-forty-five," called Louie.

"Did you hear, Ming," he asked, "did you hear?"

"Yes, Taddy, I heard."

"What is it?" asked Tommy.

"The new baby, listen, the new baby."

"We heard," Saul announced, for the twins.

They were still there puzzled, but believing in him, so that they were convinced that a baby had in some miraculous way arrived by the roof; when, in the soft stir upstairs, they heard their mother's speaking voice and a man answering her.

"Who is there, Taddy?" Tommy asked.

"Go tell Bonnie," Sam commanded with a little satiric grin; for Bonnie, in tears and full of objections, had refused to be with them in their waiting and had gone off to the back porch to cool her feelings.

The next moment the door opened upstairs, and a strange, severe man came to the top of the stairs, surveyed them all with distaste and choler, and unkindly said to Sam, "Mrs. Pollit wishes to see you."

Sam instantly swarmed through his children, putting them aside with his hands, disengaged his long legs from the mass of little legs, and bounded up the stairs. The doctor disappeared. At the top of the flight, Sam stopped and, turning round to them, gave them a wide grin, a chuckle, and said softly,

"Wait and see, kids: wait and see!"

The door closed. They heard their parents' voices.

"Is it a baby?" inquired Little-Sam again, much surprised.

"Of course, silly; Daddy said," Evie corrected him. They had understood nothing at all, except that Mother had been angry and miserable and now she was still; this was a blessed relief. They began to scatter through the hall after Louie had forbidden them to follow Sam upstairs. Suddenly Sam was at the bottom of the stairs again, flustered with a new love. He grabbed the twins by the shoulders and said excitedly, "Tribe, you have a new brother."

The children looked at each other. "What's his name?" inquired the twin Sam.

"He has no name," said big Sam comically, knowing how odd that seemed to them. "We got to give him a name. What'll we call him, kids?"

"Sam," said twin Saul promptly.

The rest of them, all but the twin Sam, laughed. They began to suggest names, calling the baby after friends at school and street friends; and then a strange, unpleasant woman who had flown in, in the night, came halfway down the stairs and said agreeably, "Mrs. Pollit wants to see Tommy."

The frightened Tommy made a step and hung back.

"Can I go? Can I go?" they all babbled.

"She said me," Tommy objected and made a slow progress to the stairs. But he refused the nurse's hand and looked sullen when she remarked with professional unction that he was a big boy now and had a little brother to look after.

"Charles Franklin," said big Sam, "that's what we'll call him probably, after Grandpa and after the President, the greatest man of our time, the Daniel of our days. May little Charles-Franklin grow up to be like him."

"And like Grandpa," Ernie remarked.

"Grandpa is all right, but Grandpa is Grandpa; Grandpa had a hard row to hoe when he was a young man; but you kids have advantages. Grandpa came to this country with nothing but a tin box with his clothes in, but Charles-Franklin is going to have a better chance, and this is a better age. Things have changed since your grandpa's day. Grandpa specially asked for the baby to be called after him; it's just a little sentimental matter, you see, kids: Grandpa's old; we can't refuse him." He nodded his head over them and sent them outside to play till Bonnie and Hazel got breakfast ready.

"What's your name?" asked Evie, playing "mothers" with the twins.

"Ippa-pa-tixit!" declared Saul. "Mr. Ippa-pa-tixit!"

"Mrs. Ippa-pa-tixit," corrected Evie. "You're Sam's mother. What's your name, Ernie?"

"Oh, shut up," said Ernie, measuring himself against pencil marks on the veranda post.

"You're a lady, too, no," said Evie, ignoring the obstreperous Ernie, her usual antagonist and claiming Little-Sam. "You're his new baby. Mother has a new baby, and the lady in there has a new baby. Her name's Mrs. Arkus.

"Who's Mrs. Arkus?"

"Mrs. Ahss," said Ernie. The boys laughed, Evie frowned.

"The lady in there with the white dress, the nurse," explained Evie. "I have a new baby; and Mother's name is Mrs.—I don't know."

"Ahss," said Ernie.

"Mrs. Curling Tongs," Saul suggested.

"Mrs. Garbage," said Ernie.

"Mrs. Curling Tongs: and Aunt Bonnie is Mrs.—what, Saul?"

"Mrs. Garbage," said Little-Sam.

"Mrs. Cabbage!" said Evie.

"Mrs. Cabbage is making a cup of tea for Mrs. Curling Tongs; and she will go up and see her new baby. And Mrs. Curling Tongs says, 'How is your new little baby, Mrs. Cabbage?' "

They went on playing quietly and waiting for Sam (who had gone back to the bedroom to seek Tommy) and for their turns to see Mother. Bonnie meanwhile, with a rueful expression, was leaning out the front window, and presently she could not help interrupting them, "Why is my name Mrs. Cabbage, why not Mrs. Garlic or Mrs. Horse Manure?" They did not hear her, so intent were they, visiting each other and inquiring after the health of their respective new babies. They did not hear her complaining to Louie that, instead of being Mrs. Grand Piano or Mrs. Stair Carpet, they called her Garbage, "Greta Garbage, Toni Toilet," said she, laughing sadly, "because they always see me out there with the garbage can and the wet mop; association in children's naïve innocent minds, you see!"

"Oh, no, it isn't that," protested Louie, "Garbage is just a funny word: they associate you with singing and dancing and all those costumes you have in your trunk!"

"Do you think so?" Bonnie was tempted to believe. "Mrs. Strip Tease?"

Suddenly there was Sam racing madly up the slope and shouting,

"Gas, gas, I smell gas; Looloo, Bonniferous, GAS! Hazel! Ernie tell those dad-blamed women, GAS. All down the slope."

A breeze had arisen and trailed faintly through the house like a sick woman in a long dressing gown, and with it the odor of a blown-out jet, under the oatmeal. The sky was faintly greenish. The children had left their game and were wandering about over the buffalo-grass lawn, under the impression that, with Daddy's return and the new baby's advent, there would be no school. Breakfast would be in the back grass so that the house would be kept quiet. Meantime, the twins had gone up to see mother, but had been refused at the bedroom door; Mother was too tired to see anyone now; and back they came again, hand in hand, disconsolate because the new baby was invisible.

"Ma mither ca'd it God's pockit breeze," said Sam, for the thousandth time in their lives, in his imitation of a Scottish accent. "Ma graunmither useta caw me, Wee Saumy, coom ben the hoose; en she tawd me, 'Your mither, ma bonnie dochter Mary, hes muckle childer, but she hes ae ween ah luv en that's ma wee Saumy!' "

Thus Sam, in a sickly voice, reclining on the grass under the back porch, and he went on to other reminiscences of his babyhood, all in his idiom that he had from his grandmother, as he assured them, his grandmother being a stout and bonny woman afraid of no man, and his mother a stout, braw woman, though a bit bony, and very good and religious, but "no unco guid, but wi' a human hert." This morning reminded Sam of the dawn of life when, with the house full of monstrous brothers and sisters, he, the Benjamin, with an ailing mother, skipped about, peered, pondered on the mysteries of Nature, thinking the long, long thoughts of youth and discovering, by his lonesome, Nature's secrets; and he told how then and there, when his eyes were scarcely unsealed from babyhood's blissful ignorance, he fell in love with Nature and made up his mind never to leave her. So he hoped would they all, so little Charles-Franklin (that was to be) when he could toddle.

"It is never too soon to maunder and ponder," said Sam whimsically, "and there are few adults who give children, thoughtful children, that is, credit for the ideas they have. What is more promising than a wondering child? Preserve your wonder, kids! Lavoisier was a child once; Newton was once a child in arms; Joseph Henry once was no older than Charles-Franklin; Thomas A. Edison, that great man, once lay in his cradle and puked."

A few white clouds appeared in the sky, "It might be the childhood of a new Agassiz," said Sam.

"A gas, or a Gassy?" asked Ernie.

"Going to have a light westerly," said Sam.

The children began to skip, exhilarated by the new light and new air. Inside was a clacking of pot lids and cups. A flock of starlings flew overhead.

"Orchard oriole," shouted Ernie from the breast of the orchard slope, "Samulum, Sam-the-Bold!"

"Oh," cried Sam, with a great sigh, "boys, boys, I'm home: oh, what that means to me. You know how I love the great world; but how glad I am to be home with ma ain folk, no one will ever know."

He threw himself full length on the ground and grasped handfuls of new spring soft grass. "To Singapura to see many fat pigs; home again, home again, jiggity-jigs."

Suddenly he turned over sniffing the air loudly, "Gas, gas," he exploded, "Ernest-Paine, gas! Sawsam, run tell Looloo, gas!"

Ernest started to run towards the kitchen shouting, "Looloo, gas, Daddy says Agassiz." The smell of gas streamed out stronger. Sam started up and himself came to the kitchen window trying to crane in, "Gas, gas in the kitchen, tell Bonnie, Gas. Kids, tell them shemailes, gas." The four streamed after him, helter-skelter, laughing, shouting, "Gas, gas!" Suddenly Louisa put her head out of the kitchen window "Tea's ready."

"Gas," said Sam. "Hitting up the bills, eh? Friend of the gas company, eh? Here, Incorporated Friends and Allies of the Gas Co."

Louisa laughed, "It was too low under the oatmeal; it kept blowing out."

"Waste not, want not," said Sam. "Tea's ready, kids; Little-Womey (Big-Womey now), Mornin' tea! Syce, syce, tea!" He squirmed about looking for a nonexistent syce; then imitated,

"Yes, tuan!" He called again to his syce, "Syce, *teh pagi-pagi!* [early morning tea]. "Ya, tuan!" He grinned at the children, who were just getting used to having their big comrade and shock brigader back with them, and he chattered suddenly at them, *"Hantar-kau barang barang saya ka-Raffles Hotel* [Send my things to the Raffles Hotel]." But as they could not understand him, they looked bored.

"Whenever I went into a little village, I rattled off a few phrases to get the boys and girls friendly," explained Sam. "No master, no white man bothers with their lingo, so they loved me for trying. When I saw a little puddle, I would say, 'Are there any crocodiles in there?' Then I would say, 'Panas-nya sangat terek' [The heat is terrible]. All the kids ran after me. Wait till I go through my bags. It will take Sam-the-Bold nine months to tell you all that happened to him; no, I can't tell you the tithe; but no matter, here you all are with open eyes, mouths, and ears and I can talk to you, thank God (who isn't), thank goodness and thank goo."

Then he began himself to hand out the tea to them, counting in Malay, *satu, dua, tiga, ampat* . . . and taught them to count the same.

"Now I am home again with my Malay little friends and home again in Tohoga," he said with a broad smile. Everything had to have its Malay name; and already he was beginning to slop over, drown them with his new knowledge, bubbling, gurgling as he poured into them as quickly as possible all he had learned. When the tea was finished, he got them to their feet, marshaled them in order of age, to walk round the garden and survey the animals with him, saying,

"Ermy-Paine [Ernie], Mouse-deer [Evie], Gemini-Seltsam [the twins], Bullhead [Tommy], all follow Tuan Pollit to the hanni-miles, left-right, left-right! Hayfoot, strawfoot!"

Then when he had them swaying in different directions, he serpentined them across the backyard patch towards the animal cages, singing, "In de mornin', in de foren'n, by de brightlight, you can hear dose darkies singing, in de foren'n." Then he gave

[295]

their several whistles, making them answer; and he murmured in a weeping tone, "I used to whistle your whistles, kids, many mornings way back on the backwaters of Malaya, but you never answered; didn't you hear your poor Sam whistling to you across the waste of waters?"

He grinned and gave a jig, "Now I got to get a new whistle, one for Charles-Franklin (maybe)," and after a moment's thought, he began flutings until suddenly he heard the orchard oriole at the bottom of the slope warbling on its own; when he cried, "That's for me; the bird sends me its song and that will be Charles-Franklin's whistle," and he went through the whole range of whistles, adding last six sweet warbling notes which he now called "Charles-Franklin's whistle."

As they stood in front of the snake cage, he said anxiously, "Kids, last night I was dozing on Bonniferous's bed when Bonniferous was helping Mother, and I had my snake dream. Great snakes alive were crawling around da kitch [the kitchen] and out of one of my boxes jumped two beautiful young spotted cats, ocelots, *Felis pardalis*, which relieved me considduble, because they began to fight with the naiks [snakes], and then an ocelot with a snake curled round him and hissing at me tried to break through the netted back door here at me and I pushed with all my strength against them, crying out, but they gradually opened it, when I saw the door opened right on the city of Washington! There it was, with all its marbles like bones gleaming under me, and I hung on the edge of a precipice—it was the snake, or the bone yard!"

He laughed tiredly, "So, kidalonks, Fate is giving Poor-Sam yet another nest of enemies, for snakes mean enemies for Pollit. Fate loves me, kids, or she wouldn't give me so many hurdles to jump. Fate wants to put fight into me. Only I wish she wasn't quite such a worrying, devouring mother, sometimes."

Lowering his voice and looking towards the house, he said, "Kids, don't tell Mother, any time, or Bonniferous, but on the boat coming over I was so worried by silly Willets that at night I saw dragons round my bed," and he looked anxiously at the mansards of the house as if he expected to see a Chinese dragon flying through the robin's-egg blue sky at him any minute.

Then, mildly, he told them that poor Old David was dead at this minute, lying, waiting for his funeral, but it meant nothing, no more than when poor Vulpecula, the Australian opossum, died; and soon Old David would be in the fermenting, jolly ground. Daffy-downdillies [daffodils] would spring from the soil, the fresh winds would blow through the daffodils that were Old David and spread all that was mortal of Old David through the airs: "And there wasn't nuffin that was immortal in Old David," said Sam kindly, "only the love you have for him in your little beating hearts, for that's the only immortality we can have, loves; just as I have a little immortality already way over there in Singapore, in the heart of Law Chew Teng, my wonderful Chinese friend, the curio dealer—he gave me a queer present all right, a Chinese coffin, all carved—it's considered a treasure; and it's coming on after me; and then I have immortality in the breast of Mohammed bin Hassan, a Malay friend and his little boy, Ali, and in the breast of Lai Wan Hoe and others; and poor little Sam has achieved this little speck of immortality because he loves his fellow man. You do the same, kids. Now you see until the day you die, Old David is living in your hearts and memories; and perhaps longer, for you will tell your children, when you have them, about dear Old David."

Then he got them to sing a little song for dear Old David, the little ditty that their grandfather would always sing to them, *Always Merry and Bright!* Thus old David Collyer's painful and, for them, disastrous death passed over in a minute, like the death of a gnat or bee, less than the miserable, stragglefeathered death of some poor little bird in the long grasses of the White Field.

Sam worked hard, but he could not conceal from them that the distant and authoritarian Sam who had come home was not quite the lighthearted Sam that had gone away; he was harsher, and a European, he had the germ power, in his brain. At breakfast they had the nurse, Miss Putnam, with them; she was a bony-faced, bright-eyed woman, with long, irregular brows that jigged questioningly. She asked, with a sort of grace, "Mr. Pollit, will you pour me some more coffee, please?" too unctuous perhaps, for Sam, rising and pushing the electric coffeepot in her direction, turned his back and said rudely, "Pour for yourself, Nurse Putnam!" Everyone felt most uneasy. But not Sam. He went out into the hall and grumbled to Bonnie,

"I don't want any maternity nurse vamping me; let her try her charms on Dr. Rock. If I'd had my way, Louie would have helped Pet this time, as I intended. How better can a woman-child get her apprenticeship than helping an older woman?"

"Samuel," cried Bonnie, "you are joking."

"In Malaya, full of little bouncing healthy brown babies, the adolescent girls help their mothers in the villages: I don't want a soft, effete generation of women. If it hadn't been for Pet's darnfool belief in doctors and all the other civilized superstition, I shouldn't have had a doctor at all. Pet herself knows better than any doctor when it is coming; and her girls are little women. It's all tomfoolery, this idea of a medicine man with a degree. I detest all degrees. It's antidemocratic: a way of separating the monastic, university type from everyday life. I want my girls to be like those sweet brown women of the East. Their girls are beauties, better than mine because they are women."

Bonnie, carrying in another serving of toast, after having studied him for a minute, said briefly, "You don't know what you're talking about," and sprang into the long dining room with a high color. She bent officiously over the flustered nurse, saying, "My brother has all his own ideas; don't take any notice, Nurse."

But the nurse, a good-natured, foal-faced girl who always put her foot in it (as Bonnie later explained), after some mild laughing, said, "But I do know a man who made his eldest daughter do that; and she married very young; she had a son at eighteen years old. It didn't stop her at all. Isn't that funny?"

Bonnie sat biting her lip and trying to nod the careless nurse towards the listening children; finally she said stiffly, "Well, please don't tell my brother; or he'll take your word for it. That kid knows enough already; she had enough trouble," and she motioned towards Louisa, who was just returning flushed from viewing the new baby. She burst out without noticing anybody,

"The new baby's going to be called Albert-Charles, Mother says."

They all turned to her.

"Charles-Franklin," cried Sam appearing, where he had been lurking, at the southern door of the long dining room. "My Benjamin will be called Franklin, and I should put in Phoebus Apollo if I wanted to imitate those silly old Dagos what thought our beloved old Sol was a young man, a good-looker too; he was born at morning-rise, and I have just been giving him a serenade outside his window, not that he hears it yet. Morning is sacred; all great ideas are born in the morning or at midnight's starry clang. I have thoughts in the morning, in the new-time, in the dewtime, that I don't have the rest of the day. Most poicks [poets] write poems about sunset and that's jes why I don't read no poickry; poicks don't love nature enough to get up early. In the morning everyone is the same age, father and child, Ming-Sedgewing and Bullhead and Loogoobrious Looloo and Dad-the-Bold-Tuan-Pollit too are all the same age; yes, even Looloo here what has the burdens of the world on her shoulders, which is only right because she makes the poor old world heavier herself, and even Nurse Putnam and Bonniferous are all the same age in the morning."

"Then we're all just born," cried Evie, astonished.

"Charles-Franklin didn't get up yet, so he's old," declared Little-Sam grinning.

"Looloo never gets up early in the morning," piped Saul maddeningly, thinking thereby to earn approval.

Sam said wearily, "Kids, no sarcasm please; sarcasm is akin to hate. More coffee, Sedgewing! Get your little Paternal *subbor cawf* [some more coffee]. *Kop kopi, syce.*"

He surveyed them all, but refrained from criticizing them for various disorders he saw in them, bad manners, grins, wasteful habits. He could not conceal for a moment that he was grown a more serious man; his jokes and comic names rolled rustily off his tongue.

"I want you to listen to an idea I had today while your little brother was being born. The laws of nature are few, and she follows them inevitably; she obeys her own laws. She can't help it. The law of nature which the plant, the family, and the universe follows is expansion, growth, sometimes growth by transmutation, sometimes by acquisition."

"What about death?" asked Louie.

"Death is only transmutation. Now I believe that the universe, our universe is the same. I believe in the expanding universe, and you will find as time goes on, that great men will prove that it is so. I pick these ideas out of the air, and yet, I have proof too for all things go by analogy. That's the Mark Twain new-world spirit; horse sense and close analogy.

"Perhaps as Looloo says, it sometimes expands and sometimes contracts, for death is only recession, just as our minds do, the tide does, metals do and our fortunes do, going from richness to richness and understanding to understanding, just as the life of man does, following the law of progress.

"These things are not mystic, they follow an inexorable law. Remember my words!"

"How do you know?" asked Louie.

"When you get older and wiser," he said, "you will know your dad was always right. I make it rain, don't I, kids?"

"Yes," they said eagerly.

"When I say, 'Sun, you can shine!' doesn't it shine?"

"Yes, yes," they chorused joyfully.

"And when I say, 'Rain, you kin rain half an hour and then stop,' don't it obey me?"

"Yes."

"But Looloo thinks I don't know nuffin; Looloo only thinks of hummilatin [humiliating] her wise father."

"You don't make it rain," said Louie. The children, much interested, looked from one to the other. Sam, looking to them, saw the hesitation.

"Kids?" he inquired reproachfully.

"No, you don't," cried Ernie at once.

"Don't I, Little-Womey?"

Puzzled, she looked at the three older faces, "I dunno!"

Sam went to the window, studied the sky carefully for a while, then went out into the back yard. After feeling the air, he came in solemnly and said, "Because I have a lot of mean kids around, I just went out and told it it could rain tomorrow morning or this evening at the earliest."

Little-Womey looked scared, thinking about her own incredulity. Louie laughed, "You're just faking. You know it's going to rain, perhaps."

"The sun draws up the water, the water makes clouds and when they reach an icy layer the water is precipitated," Ernie explained. "The teacher told us, the teacher told us."

"How could you have the rainfall chart behind the door, if you could make it rain any time?" Louie said. Sam grinned self-consciously at this; but he would not give in, and to crush the influence of his two older children who had reached the age of dissent, he wickedly seized a large blowfly which he had been watching on the tablecloth for some time and putting it between finger and thumb flipped it at his elder daughter. It hit her on the nose. The children turned red with laughter. Louie gave him a glance of scorn and saying nothing, dug her nose into her glass of milk. Her father was now laughing, and singing, "Longnose Bluebeak, bluebeak Loobeck: why don't you laugh, Looloo: bluestocking Looloo got hit by a blowbloo!" Little-Sam, holding his belly, rolled backwards and forwards on the grass, yelling with laughter. Louie sat quite still, and this new sort of behavior calmed the children sooner than Sam expected.

Sam became solemn at once, "By smiling, we turn devils into

angels, enemies into friends; the cup of poison becomes the loving cup."

"I have no enemies," declared Louie sternly.

"One day you will get to know the world better," said Sam, still unable to forgive the skeptic of his blood.

"I know something," said Louie, "I know there are people not like us, not muddleheaded like us, better than us."

"What do you mean?"

"But I know something else: if it is chaos, it will not be chaos forever: 'out of chaos ye shall give birth to a dancing star!' Nietzsche said that."

Sam blushed, and he said gently, "You mean, out of confusion we will bring order."

"No," cried Louie, "no, no; you understand nothing. People like us understand nothing. I know people at school better than us, better in their minds than—" she stopped in deep embarrassment. The children were following her intently, trying to understand what she had found out, something they were dimly groping for.

"All right, Looloo," said Sam gently, "all right. All right."

Five minutes later he was singing them some more of his saga, as he fixed a red silk Chinese pajama suit on Evie and wound a sarong over her head and shoulders.

"Little *perempuan Melayu, Singapura punya,* sitting under an umbrella selling Eastern candies, black eyes moist as the antelope, oval copper face, full wide lips, my Little-Womey, Little Malay beauty!" and he sang to each of them as he busied himself with them, dressing them up in all the wonderful scarves, sarongs, a Kelantan shawl of woven silk with body of royal yellow and ends of Malay red and orange; a sarong batek made in Java of dyed cotton, blue with center bister and white; a handkerchief of Malay-red silk interwoven with gold thread, the center brocaded in heliotrope and yellow; a blue and gold silk sarong from Trengganu; and beautiful strange clothing that he had picked up wherever he went, for his women at home, for Henrietta, Louisa and Evelyn, getting to be a woman lover in the land of wealth, beauty, and color, promising himself, who had despised all sensual things, a future madness of material beauties.

Short of the old family plate he had acquired on his marriage with Henny and the wedding presents, he had had none of this world's goods and despised them with puritan alarm and scoffing; but the moment he set foot on the age-old shores of the East, where no one respected his new Western morality, he easily let slip this hardness and came out for every glorious profusion of art in artisanship that was possible to his purse or persuasive powers. He had learned to smile, beg, and collect, largely take the largesse of his friends. "My smile brings it to me," he would say contentedly, and, "They know I love them."

Mrs. Smith, from Volta Place, came to the open front door to inquire about Henrietta. Sam, who thought her a fine, upstanding woman, was delighted to bring her in and show her his treasures, which still lay in profusion in several rooms. Then the White boys came shyly ("How big you've got to be!" called Sam), with a message from their mother about Henrietta. What with the new baby and the splendors from Malaya, it was a morning of satisfactions. Sam could see, himself, that his return was considered a great event in the neighborhood. Resting on the settee, on a billow of silks and cottons, with his head on his clasped hands, he dropped a tear over the passing of Old David Collyer and began to imagine his own future now. Tohoga House would be his own, and there might be a quarterly allowance for Henrietta, or one or other of the children, from the estate.

"These are sordid considerations," he said to himself; but with the sun and fresh wind and the kindness of the climate, so different from all his Malayan mornings, he could not help being cheerful. Soon the nurse came down, smiling, and said Sam was to go up to see Mrs. Pollit, and carrying in his hand a pair of tiny red silk pajamas that he had brought specially for the baby and an exquisite little wreath of artificial orange flowers (he had hoped for a baby girl) that he now intended for Henny's dark hair, the happy father went upstairs. The new baby had hair of an almost invisible blond.

"Seventh child of a seventh child," said Sam, grinning at the nurse.

"Born with a caul," said the nurse, grinning at Sam.

When Sam went down, he telephoned his little prig of a brother-in-law, Archie Lessinum, to announce the birth to the family and to make arrangements about the funeral.

4 🜨 The wheel turns.

DAVID COLLYER was no better than other millionaires: when he died, his estate was scandalously less than anyone had supposed; and in fact, since Old David loved children too much, and had too many, and treated them too well, when he found out that their characters were weak all, he left even less than anyone could have predicted by any skimping of a mean imagination. Rather he left something very great—a great hole in his credit that it would take his executors a number of years to fill in. Monocacy, Tohoga House, a great stretch of still unsettled land along Cold Spring Lane, a row of white-stepped houses in South Baltimore, a house of dubious reputation (that is, certain reputation for evil) in Highlandtown, and all his shares and bonds were to be sold; and a certain amount of money was to be put back into the business. This part of the business alone would remain to pay small quarterly dividends to the sick, sallow, and financially suffering members of the great Collyer brood. Old Ellen received nothing but a small cottage in which to spend her last days with Barry.

Sam Pollit came home from the reading of the will with drooping shoulders. Nothing else since the death of his first wife Rachel had been able to affect his long-legged gay walk and the straightness of his backbone. It seemed to him, at moments, that this was nothing but a dream, that Old David could not have died so inconsequentially as to leave his youngest, spendthrift daughter penniless in a cold world, without a shoe or shell to house her children. This house, now named Tohoga Place, that he had painted and carpentered, where he had built his rockeries and all his dreams of the future, had to go under the hammer. It was not marketable as it was; would, at last, be cut up for a row of unhealthy, elbowing houses like those already spawned along one side of it. Sam did not know where they would go. He supposed he would have to join the great number of commuters who came in from Virginia every day, and settle in some ugly new bureaucrats' suburb without trees, with new-turned clay and garages lumbering along the landscape; live in some modern bungalow with a Dirty Jack on one side, and a Ratty-Matty on the other, himself indistinguishable from the crowd of public servants and their newfangled offspring. He felt bruised. He had always believed that he was the favorite son-in-law of Old David and that Old David liked him better than his own boys, because of his struggles.

Henny was still in bed, looking wasted, her eyes were red. Her hair was pulled back and plaited in two tails.

"I was there," said Sam.

Henny's black eyes searched his face bitterly, but it was not bitterness because of him, but because of all the blows she could feel were coming, from the family and from the world. She had been through the pains of death, and she felt that she did not care whether she ever saw outer air again or not. Many times that day she wished she had been buried with her poor "beau of the nineties," her gay, kindhearted father who had ruined her life by spoiling her so.

"Well," she said, after a sigh, "well, I suppose it's bad news, or you'd tell it to me. He was broke, of course."

"Yes. I'm afraid Old David was in deeper than we dreamed. Your mother is to have the cottage." He stopped, knowing that she would understand a great deal from this. But she flashed an angry look at him and cried,

"What? He didn't leave me the house? What are we to do with all those children? He came at a nice time," and she nodded at the new boy, "A caul and he brings nice luck to us. Poor Old David, poor Dad: with his fine air, and his flighting and floating, and his keeping fifteen homes going, I might have known. I *did* know! But everyone's too much of a darn coward to look out for himself. I knew! Why didn't I go and see him oftener before he took so ill?" She gave Sam a blue look. "I did go: but he was too ill. Before he lived with his woman. He put me off. Archie wouldn't tell me. He knew! Why didn't he tell me?"

Sam sat with his hands hanging loosely between his legs. "It's a blow, and no mistake. We've got two months to get out."

"I'd like to be able to do something to that man," said Henny, referring to Archie Lessinum. " 'The law is a divinity above justice even'! Dad was just bewitched by him. He gave him his own way in everything. He gave him Eleanor, made him executor. And he used to go round making great calf eyes at me and saying he was a mystic and the law was almost a mystic idea. I said, 'How interesting!' And here I sit now with seven children in rags, while there he sits with the mystic idea of Dad's estate in his hands."

"What's the good of this?" asked Sam pathetically. "This is sordid. Don't think about it now, Henny: wait till you're up. Meanwhile I'll look about for a house." On the mantelpiece stood the little wreath of orange flowers. He took it up absent-mindedly and said, after fingering it for a while, sighing, "I'll try this on Little-Womey's hair. It was for a little bride of fourteen; but I got the man to give it to me." He had forgotten that he had taken it as a childbed present to Henny. She watched him depart with it, with a bitter look, but said nothing.

Sam told Louie first, trailing out his misery, then Ernie, and then took the three little boys away down to the snake cages and told them they had to leave those slopes and gardens bursting up into a new spring. They were to be sold: other children would have the right to be there. One by one, the children became subdued, all except Little-Womey, who, with the orange wreath in her hair, was running to all her friends, the neighbors, showing off her beauty, with her soft deer eyes running over with mirth and excitement, while she told them they were all going away from Tohoga House and going to live in Virginia. By ten o'clock the next morning everyone knew it who knew Sam, and the Department was full of excitement. So he got nothing out of the old man at the last: so he had sold out for the fleshpots of Egypt and in the pots was nothing but dandelion salad. So Old Softsoap wasn't going from triumph to triumph; and one evil young man got up a story that it was very queer, Sam had been away from home ten months and yet he arrived home to the birth of a new son, oh, entirely in order, the result of a queer gynecological condition. Although it was a lie, everyone was delighted and by nightfall, instead of its being a joke and a tall story, it had become a bit of truthful scandal, the low-down on the private life of a social and service climber, a grinning Pharisee and rich man's pet. Twenty-four hours before, Sam had been the rising star of the service and now people skipped from desk to desk laughing about him and saying that he was a sneak, milksop, and goody-goody. Sam, for all his credo of the firm handclasp and frank smile, had made a sufficiency of enemies for all sorts of reasons—little enemies, people beneath him in grade and fortune, people he had never troubled to conciliate because they were mean. He had refused to consider religious partisanship or join any fraternities, "no phratries," he said contemptuously, and he had joined gaily, frequently, and with the naïvest faith in his luck, in all sorts of foolish campaigns against minor bureaucrats, sprinkling his talk with their insulting nicknames.

Then, when he was absent in Malaya, his rivals and enemies had a chance to work against him, and it could have been argued (it was argued) that Sam had deserted his official post for a floating, indefinable job and that he had excellent prospects anyhow, anywhere, so why need he get back his old job in the Department? To cap it all came the shoals of complaints from

Colonel Willets in Singapore. He sat in the Raffles Hotel, or in some bungalow where he was a guest, and wrote or dictated journals and letters, full of complaints about everyone but chiefly about that snake charmer and departmental meteor, Mr. Samuel Clemens Pollit. "He arrogated every honor to himself, he went out of his way to push into official circles, he sucked up to English officialdom, he was always holding an umbrella for some lady; he did what he could to oust Colonel Willets and ingratiate himself with foreign governments, he applied for jobs in foreign (Chinese) universities, he ran round with members of the Kuomintang and abetted absconding clerks." There was nothing that Colonel Willets did not know, in his spite: his correspondence with Washington made a wonderful Eastern romance of intrigue and hate. But Colonel Willets did not despise influence, nor lobbyists, nor Senators: he had a few of them in his sleeve, as he occasionally remarked to a select audience. When, by good luck, the great pillar of Sam's career, David Collyer, brother of the railroad millionaire, Bradford Collyer, died in debt, Colonel Willets decided to get rid of the irritating young man. He had no very good reason for it; Psalm-singing Sam (he called him this very unfairly) simply got under his skin. Sam ridiculed him. Sam offered him the hand of friendship when Colonel Willets would have been glad of a punch in the nose; he smiled at him when Colonel Willets wanted a row; he defied him pleasantly but firmly to ever put an obstacle in his brilliant career. Sam could go back to the strange yellow and brown men that he seemed to like the smell of so much, said Willets.

Washington papers were full of the return of the Expedition and the report being presented by Colonel Willard Willets. Other members of the Expedition were mentioned, including Samuel Pollit, originally of the Bureau of Fisheries and organizer and now head of the Conservation Bureau; and it was hinted (much to Sam's surprise) that Sam now might move to another sphere of activities. As the Conservation Bureau was Sam's beloved child, and yet coveted by numerous others who considered themselves better qualified than he, this unexpected paragraph in the *Post* gave him a sinking feeling; and he began harking back to the dreams of snakes he had had since his return home. "Shoals ahead," said Sam in a midday conference with his old friend Saul Pilgrim, "but I am on deck, they won't torpedo me. This is Crabby Willets' doing. Residents of Virginia and Maryland are allowed to crab in the Potomac, not in the Bureau."

But the local papers, being hungry at that moment for some juicy departmental scandal, seized on the romantic story of Sam, and with a show of spicy amiability told all, with that display of intuition and penetration of character told tersely, which is common in the world's journalist capital, that city from which (it is the proud boast) half a million words are telegraphed daily. Everyone kicked Sam about, had his opinion about Sam, including the respectable breakfasters in the S. & W. cafeteria, star-spangled visitors to the Occidental and eaters beneath its senator-ribanded walls, fish devourers in O'Donnell's, perpetual peaceful roomers of Franklin Square, and such lions as got to the zoo. Sam was daily accused of inefficiency, of bureaucracy, of pusillanimity; even malversation was hinted at. Sam's fair face became clouded, became scarlet, became pale: he ran from friend to chief, and ran into those he knew to be his enemies as often as possible, going up to them in corridors, holding out his hand, asking them why they pursued him, speaking to them of government service and charity, humanity, the service of the people: "A public office is a public trust." To a certain extent these tactics succeeded in that he embarrassed his enemies dreadfully, and they ran away from him, hiding their faces under hat brims and their necks under coat collars. They crossed the street from him and changed their routes to the office. But nothing stopped the log that was rolling towards his neck. As soon as Sam saw how badly it all was going and that those he called "the people of evil, the enemies of the commonweal, those in whom the devil, that wicked idea of our ancestors, was in a sort incarnate," were getting the upper hand for the moment, and heard with great wrath but great helplessness, that his suspension was hinted at, pending inquiry, he went to his brother-in-law and asked him to arrange to postpone the sale of Tohoga House for a few months till things were decided. Archie Lessinum, gravely kindhearted, now that handsome Sam Pollit was rolling in the mud, agreed to do this; and Sam, instead of looking for a house in Virginia, began to think of his prospects in his natal soil of Baltimore. Solicitous friends in the Department, amongst whom was the malicious, gleeful, but somewhat paternal J. Cappie Larbalestier, were warning Sam that his days were numbered.

"I am innocent," cried Sam, "my record is spotless; I am an exemplary officer. I defy them to pin any scandal of any sort on me."

"They will ease you out if they can," said the younger Brownell, who had become very friendly with this man under a cloud. But Sam saw in the younger Brownell an agent of evil and the spokesman of his enemies. Now nobody hesitated to take Sam aside and, with a frank pat on the back, tell him the sober truth; his faults had been such and such; so and so was a worm digging into his back, and since poor old David Collyer died, of course he was without his best support. Sam came nearer to knocking a confrere down than ever before whenever this last remark was made, for it was Sam's boast that he had had no support in all his life but had hewn his way through the granite of official indifference and public ignorance.

"Alone I did it," would he say. "God helps those who help themselves," and, "All things work together for the good of them who love the Lord," but by "the Lord" he only meant an obscure creature of his imagination, possibly "the Public Good," or even just his own will.

Things were blacker for Sam every day and, with his heart sounding hourly in bitter, secret oceans of misery, Sam faced something he had never conceived of in all his life—the triumph of calumny. He would go about repeating to his friends and children, "Truth crushed to earth shall rise again, the eternal years of God are hers," but the traitor thought crept in every day, as a mouse through a rotting door, that he had not before him the eternal years of God, but only a few of human fame. He suppressed these thoughts and resolved never to blacken his hands with the pitch being poured around him, and to try to tread the path of goodness, smile at his enemies, and proceed exactly as if nothing had happened. He would not seek partisans, not enter at the head of a flock of witnesses, only tell the plain truth: plain truth would shine through in beauty, more dazzling for the black or bedizened lies that "the evil ones" brought in. Sam gave one or two sober interviews, and refused to write to the papers to answer indignant letters from persons both official and private who seemed deeply stirred over his ways and personality.

"You are doomed with this air of Christian martyrdom," cried Saul Pilgrim wrathfully and humorously. His square-set, big-nosed face, a clownish variant on Sam's own, had long, lugubrious, creased cheeks, which came from his having been an intimate acquaintance of defeat since his boyhood. But Sam would just as wrathfully, and not at all humorously, reply that he had no churchly reek, he was merely acting for the right, and that the good would win, it must win.

"Suppose it does not win?" asked Saul. "You see, Sam, you call me a cynic; but I am a creator, I am a God myself. Here is a little world I have made up and in it beings: for years I have struggled to make the good triumph, but it is still a drawn battle."

In this way Saul referred to his serial story, *When the Day Comes,* which appeared in a little Alexandria advertising paper Saul had published himself, for the last seventeen years. *When the Day Comes* had begun, Chapter One, of Part One, in the very first edition of the paper seventeen years back, and this serial, the only serial at all competitive with the serial of the sun, was not yet finished, for the simple reason that the paper was still running. Saul had never been able to bring himself to botch up a happy, but improbable ending, yet could not resign himself

[311]

to unpopularity with a sad ending, and hence had gone on adding incident to incident, hoping the problem would solve itself accidentally.

"It is just like life," Saul would think to himself, in surprise, as he considered the latest chapter of *When the Day Comes*. So he was in a position to look at Sam's fix in a resigned and human way. He admired Sam for his glorious, messianic belief in himself, the world, and other people, and wished he had this temperament; but he now felt impelled to tell Sam some of the truths of life, just as if Sam had been one of his characters.

"Saul," said Sam, "what I am telling you may sound weak and willful, but it is not so: it is the innermost heart of my belief in myself and human nature. My silly Louie has written a motto on a piece of paper and stuck it on the side of her bookcase, 'By my faith and hope I conjure thee, throw not away the hero in thy soul.' In that, at least, she shows the power, the strength, and the glory of her poor Sam. She is beginning to see the light. But that is not what I wanted to say, my dear old Saul. There is a faith men live by; I have it in me. I cannot sully it by entering the forum of public debate, much as I believe that all things in the republic should be aired in the public eye. Yes, Saul, even aliens, people of a strange culture, feel this entity in me. Naden bin Tahir, my Indian secretary, asked me if I believed in my white God. 'No,' said I, 'friend; I do not need a God for I believe in ultimate good.' 'Tuan,' he said (though I told him many times I was no master but the servant of the people), 'I am surprised at this, for you are one of the Heaven-born.' 'No, brother,' I replied, 'I am a humble man who loves his fellow man.' 'I am sure, sir,' said my faithful black friend, 'that you will go to heaven. God is coming to earth soon,' said Naden, 'everyone can see it by the troubles that are going on. When he comes, wherever you are, sir,' he said, 'he will take you up in the hollow of his hand and place you on a celestial carpet near his own.' 'Oh, Naden,' said I, 'I would ask the Lord at Judgment Day to leave a little bit of my own earth and make me forever mortal on it; then under a great green-headed native elm I would sit and watch the little mortal birds. I do not want to go to heaven; I want my children, forever children, and other children, stalwart adults, and a good, happy wife, that is all I ask, but not paradise; earth is enough for me: it is because I believe earth is heaven, Naden, that I can overcome all my troubles and face down my enemies.' That is what I said to him, Saul: and to this poor black civil servant with nothing but a mean ambition and a superstitious belief in the immediate coming of some cruel Jehovah, I told what I really believe. This is God's footstool, my dear good mother used to say: and if it were really so, I should be glad to live forever by the little toe of God."

"Sam," said Saul fervently, "when you talk, you know you create a world. I live in a wonderful illusion: especially when we take walks at night, I can hardly believe in the workaday world! I can even hardly believe it is you talking: you have such wonderful faith."

"Faith," said Sam, "yes, I have faith: that is the great gift my dear good mother gave me: faith in the good."

"But why does faith prevent you from answering the charges made against you?" asked Saul.

"Who touches pitch is defiled," said Sam.

"You will lose everything, Sam: position, salary, pension. What about your children?"

"I'll never answer such wicked charges," Sam declared, scarlet with indignation, "and if my children have to live in utmost poverty, let them do what I have done. 'Sweet are the uses of adversity, which like a toad ugly and venomous, still has a precious jewel in its head,' said silly old Broadway Willy Shakespeare. I don't go much by what poets say, but he was a man, he had his reverses, as his verses sometimes show."

Saul laughed heartily, cast a sidelong glance at his intimate, but said nothing on this head.

CHAPTER EIGHT

1 ✕ Tohoga to Spa.

STRANGERS BEGAN to drive white surveyors' pegs into the children's own gardens at Tohoga House, and everyone was glad to go. Sam had been scouting round the district for weeks, looking for a suitable nest for his young ones. He could not bring himself (considering his dubious prospects, too) to rent or buy a house in the ugly new dormitory districts used by Washingtonians, expensive and inconvenient, and now that the Collyer glory had faded, he yearned to go home, back to the old-fashioned, heterogeneous views at the head of the Chesapeake tidewater country. Baltimore has many exiles, as near as Washington, as far as Heidelberg, who never cease reviling their native town with soft-tongued, exquisite scurrility, whose hunger to be away from Baltimore and obsession with the town create an appetite for Baltimore in the stranger. Baltimore is multifarious; has the attractive dirt of a fishing town, the nightmare horizons of a great industrial town; it is very old, sordid, traditional, and proud. It despises no sort of traffic that can be conceived of; it is not fanatical; it has a self-sufficiency as towns of old Europe, even in the hideous yellow waste bays full of abandoned shacks, the mazy sameness of its mean, white-stepped streets, its traffic in pleasures both respectable and disreputable. It is at the head of an inland sea and stands between natural sea-level parks and thick-wooded hills. It does not imprison. Nature has no states' rights in Maryland. Baltimore sees the meeting of two cultures of man, Northern and Southern. There mingle from the south-eastern sands to the Appalachian crests two regions of trees and plants, and two of birds and fish. Sam loved his state with passion. Released from what he dimly saw had been a bondage to the Collyer idea of financial success, Sam with love and longing had hurried round the residentials of Baltimore during the past few weeks, until he found a real home for his children. For him no apartments, no town slums and modern jerry-builts. He had resolved that even if he went back to his own old position as a Deputy Commissioner of the Conservation Bureau (and he was sick of it), he would motor to Washington every day, a matter of fifty minutes perhaps, and bring his children up on this waterside, where he had fished for gudgeon as a child.

Henny refused to take any interest in the house-hunting, only saying bitterly that she hoped he wasn't going to plank her down in rotten old Baltimore right next to some flossy friend of her schooldays who had done a million times better than she had. Henny still had some belief in Sam's abilities and his way of getting away with it, as she put it, but she saw bursting out in him a hothouse flower of idealism that he had kept in bud during Collyer's lifetime. He had conceived, since his Pacific trip, a gigantic plan. He had every hope of being appointed one of the American members of the International Pacific Salmon Fisheries Commission in a few months and he had views which he much regretted not being able to put before the whaling conference in London in June. Beyond that was the four-day September meeting of the North American Council, and conferences of other bodies to follow.

Sam, a great partisan of the Roosevelt works plans because of the work done in fish and forestry conservation by the W.P.A. and C.C.C. workers (hatcheries in North Carolina, Massachusetts, West Virginia, Pennsylvania, Indiana, Texas, and elsewhere), and seeing with pleasure new works being acquired from several states and placed under the surveillance or control of Federal bureaus, saw in President Roosevelt the first great socialist ruler, greater and more answerable than any European chief because serving so short a term. He favored a bureaucratic state socialism with the widest possible powers and a permanent staff, a bureaucracy intricately engineered, which would gradually engulf all the powers great and small of what Sam called, with a tinge of elegance, "govam'nt." But states having rights, the relations of states and the Federal Government must be negotiated by Interstate Commissions with their Commissioners, both full and deputy, attached. Sam had in his head this plan for the knitting together of all the state and Federal conservation services, eventually to be made into an immense North American Conference, which would foreshadow the All-American Republic; and on top of this an International Conservation League of Nations which, by regulating supplies and conserving instead of wasting, would prevent wars and feed all people.

This plan, with an infinity of councils, subcouncils, and town meetings, Sam had got down on paper before he left. He hoped it would have borne fruit in his absence; and within a year or two he hoped to be named, with others, to this Supreme Conservation Council. Roosevelt, loved of "the people," could do all. Sam believed that it was opposition to this grand socialist plan which was fermenting in the Department; and to his proposition that a quarter of a million dollars should be the petty cash at first allocated to the new branch of Federal Government therein proposed. In his mind's eye he saw internations within internations; and overnations over nations, all separate functions of Federal Government rising to one crest of supreme judgment, sitting in a room; all glass, no doubt, with windows on the world; each power of government to be independent, though interdependent. Sam had numerous codicils to add to his great scheme, after his taste of Imperial Government, not that he admired it—he thought the American system far more modern—but he liked the word *farflung*, the farflung bournes of conservation, and *public necessity's eminent domain*. Sam was a vague eclectic socialist, and some of the things he wrote were far more horrifying to his friends than he understood; not to mention that he went about proclaiming fair play in opinion and saying that there was some good, no doubt, in the U.S.S.R.'s system as well as holiness in the ideas of Confucius.

"I wish I could go to jail for my ideas," he said more than once, in a burst of fervor, "and then scoffers—there are scoffers even at my patent sincerity—would see how deeply I feel these ideas."

Sam with all this behind him, then, did not feel as anxious as his friends about the present attack on him: it was the rotten fabric woven by evil, the overnight sham bulwarks of enemies of the people; it would burn to ash at the match of truth. Besides Sam had powerful friends who loved the truth.

Some of this, indeed, all of this, he was able to tell the children while the old Pollit sedan was passing out of Washington and into the wooded areas on the road to Annapolis. But when they reached the richer part of the wooded road, he broke off and began to talk to them about the Free State of Maryland which would from now on be their home, how it was the first, finest, richest of the states and that with the most vision, how its foreshores had remained untouched because the pikes had had to go far inland to avoid the marshes and watercourses. No sight on earth was like the moonlight on the Choptank, and he made a great many other remarks which proved that it was only after a strict examination of all the other states in the Union, he had impartially chosen the Free State to be born in. Then he sang them a song of the trees of his home state, the oaks, red oak, scarlet oak, black oak, white oak, water oak and willow oak, shingle oak and post oak, mosscup oak and overcup oak, rock oak and swamp oak and all the others, elms, maples, hickories, dogwoods, persimmons, and pines, from Rising Sun to Snow Hill, Port Tobacco to Port Deposit, Liberty Town to Bohemia Manor, Fox Hill Levels to Deep Creek Lake, Spaniard's Neck to Indian Head, Love Point to West Friendship, Cole to The Bunker, Governor's Run to Cover, Humphrey to Pumphrey and Beaver Dam to Bivalve and a great many more which he had worked up into a recitative for them months and years ago, showing them the map and teaching them the counties. When they came into Anne

Arundel county, he began to show them the soils and trees of the county that would be their future home and expressed a hope that in a very short time they would beat him at distinguishing every natural feature, because they were boys at liberty to roam and he was their busy father, earning bread and lemonade for them all.

To all of this Henny, her weary face a little softened by the fresh summer air, said nothing, but held the baby in her lap and sometimes hushed one of the boys who shrieked too loudly.

But as they went along, nothing could bottle up their effervescence, and every half minute one of them asked, "Are we nearly there?" "What's the house like?" "When will the animals get there?" and "Is the first van of furniture there yet?" Sam meanwhile being very happy to answer each and all of the questions and not even once rebuking or frowning at any of his little citizens. The sun sizzled, the birds sang, they saw two baby rabbits foolishly sitting on the roadside and startled a pheasant. It was the finest holiday imaginable. They had all left school before the end of the term and would go no more till the summer was over.

Henny thought of this as she scudded along and worried about two things: how she could get help to set the house in order, and how, without Louie's help, she would manage through the summer (for she had determined to send Louisa to Harpers Ferry again). Sam was still going into the Department but himself confessed in her hearing (they were not speaking) that there was talk of his immediate suspension until the Civil Service Commission could inquire into the whole confusing business. It had all blown up out of nothing at all, out of those vague "enemies" and "evil ones" whom Sam had mentioned for many years.

Then they began to pass indications of summer camps and new houses, half finished in new clearings, and came into the older cottages settled behind Annapolis. At length, wild with excitement, experiencing disappointment, after the grandeur of Washington, they drove round State Circle, were unable to admire what Sam admired, the colonial charm of the State House, the pleasant retirement of St. John's College (though they saw quickly enough the little black kitten hiding in its bushes). But when Sam drove them slowly down College Avenue to King George Street, and they could see the Academy, they were excited, though the boys declared nothing would induce them to associate with such flossies, yet they would be glad enough to get in to see the Orioles v. Navy when they could; and suddenly thinking of this, Annapolis appeared to them a great and glorious place; it burst forth in the most brilliant colors. Having achieved his effect, Sam smiled and drove them back by cobbled Randall Street to the Market Space and saw the Dock, and so with them asking frenziedly, all the time, "Where is it, our House, Pad?" "But where do we live?" by Compromise Street to the Eastport Bridge. Until this moment, Henny had not had too many qualms about the place where she would have to bring up her brood. She had visited Annapolis so very often when a girl that she liked it, and yet because it was old and isolated, she knew she could avoid her old friends there or meet them there, as she pleased. She knew they were to have a house with two acres and a water frontage, and she had imagined one of the old, pretentious houses some distance up Spa Creek, or one of the primly coquettish little brick affairs standing in rows down to the boat basin. The view was exquisite there, at nightfall rivaling in stillness and sheen some little foreign lake of postcard fame. But they were to cross the Eastport Bridge. Eastport is a pleasant, little, hopeless, poor mudbank, level with the broad and shallow Chesapeake. The Chesapeake at this point is not picturesque and scarcely salt. The Eastport Bridge, low, awkward, and makeshift, looks as if it had been thrown across by an army in a hurry and forgotten there. Spa Creek is rimmed with modern and even expensive houses on the Annapolis side, but on the Eastport side to which they were now crossing, it is rimmed by a couple of slipways, boatsheds, dilapidated family houses with crumbling loamy banks and long grass down to the thick water. On the Bay side are jetties, gardens, yachts, and powerboats for bay and sea fishing. It is the sort of place for a fisherman, a mudstalker and hookbaiter, but seems pretty messy, wet, and penurious to any other person. Sam belonged to the first sort and Henny to the majority.

The children craned from the car like geese at Thanksgiving from their crates, gabbling about the yachts, jetties, and shrieking "Which house is it, Dad?" for they knew it was near the bridge and on the water. They fixed on a tidy house with a private jetty on the left hand but Ernie picked out a large tumble-down place, two stories with an attic, on the right hand, right on the shallow reach above the bridge.

"Yes," said Sam excitedly, "Yes, Ermy, Ermy right as per usual: it is, it is, the cannon's opening roar."

"Is it ours, Ded?" inquired Evie, viewing it with alarm because it was so different from Tohoga House, and she had pictured an identical place. Henny stared at the ugly old castle comedown, with its rooms upon rooms and unkempt grounds, and looked as if she would cry, but not a word came out of her until Charles-Franklin whimpered. Then she muttered, "No wonder!" Meanwhile the twins were shouting, "Can we sleep upstairs on the balcony?" and Ernie shrieked, "Wait till you get there, you dopes!"

" 'It is indeed a momentious event,' " said Sam softly, in the verbal tatters of Artemus Ward. "Kids, there's a marvolious old orchard full of apples, a manure heap, seedling frames, and all: we'll really have a garding here."

Evie repeated in her dolly voice, "I beg your parding, Mrs. Harding, but there's a blowfly in your garding."

Ernie looked at her with contempt, "You kill me!"

Evie looked quickly at her father for protection, but Sam was too anxious to know Henny's unexpressed feelings about the new house to bother about squabbles in Lilliput.

Sam had wheeled them quickly round by Severn Avenue, hoping they would not take too much notice of the weatherboard cottages. The house could be entered in two ways, by boat, from Spa Creek, or from the back by way of a long serpentine dirt drive, edged on one side by the creek and on the other by the orchard. Along this drive stood very tall old trees, all kinds of maples and an elm. The drive turned round to the left (they had now made a hairpin bend), and they stopped on ragged grass beside the glassed-in and viny side door. Towards the water was a pleasant half-moon of lawn with shrubs; beyond the shrubs was the fall of the bank on which grew large trees and rushes, and under that was a small sand beach. A rotted rowboat lay sunk in the beach. The children discovered all this in a minute, poured out of the car, and dashed about with cries.

"The house, kids," cried Sam, "here we are, here we are home again, home again. Spa House. We'll put up a board tomollo [tomorrow] saying 'Spa House' and 'No admittens.'"

"Are we going to live here?" inquired Evie somewhat dubiously, after surveying the porch and balcony, the old withering walls and the broken planks.

"Yes, Love, *e pluribus unum in proprietor persony!*" exclaimed Sam, more heartily than he felt, for as he unlocked the side door, he saw Henny sniffing angrily at the decaying timber and dirty panes. The house had been abandoned for a year, and Sam had got it cheaper than he expected, at a price of a little over $5000, with a mortgage, because he asked for no patching-up (he and the boys would do it, aided by Uncles Lennie and Ebby), and because, with a great many new building schemes and threats of condemnation, the despised Eastport was considered to be altogether unmarketable. All that part of town was now sniffed at by progressive residents: the town was progressing towards the west where the high school stands, with modern bungalows and new highways. The officers at the Naval Academy were soon to be taken out of their apartments in private houses in the town and housed in special buildings, and government and state officials from Baltimore were to be moved down here into special new buildings. The old town round the Academy was dying. People were dubious about the fate of St. John's College, and the old part of the town could look for nothing but visitors in June Week, visitors for the August fishing festival, and a possible revival in wartime. At all events, not a householder in Annapolis but considered Eastport a civic disgrace of deep dye, and would see it cleaned out and rebuilt. On the farther side of the Eastport flat, beside huge old houses built on neglected estates (it was once thought that Eastport would become fashionable) lived Negro families in a desperate situation and poor-white families, and in the little cove there are the most abandoned, hopeless old rat-eaten and rotten tubs in the whole of the watery world.

The first van of furniture was turning into the drive before they had explored even the second story, so the children were turned out to grass and Henny went to sit on a weather-beaten rocking chair with the seat out that had been left on the veranda. She faced Annapolis. Only a few hundred yards from her was the sheeny basin, a tiny Como. She had cast one glance into the Spa House kitchen and seen its old stoves (one iron oven built in and one old gas range), leprous sink, and wormy floor, and then gone silently to the rocking chair. For the past half hour she had felt a curious, dull, but new sensation and as she sat there she found out what it was. Across the water was a houseboat, a cabin on a raft, about which climbed two or three young plump girls in skin-tight satin bathing things and a couple of lanky boys in trunks. Cars were parked beyond in Shipwrights' Street. Casual mosquitoes buzzed in the damp silent rafters of the veranda but did not annoy her in the mild sunlight. All the children but Louie had already disappeared to the fringe of beach, and she heard their voices through the reeds. A girl took a plunge from the houseboat; a middle-aged man with a sandy fringe of hair round a bald spot rowed languidly past in a suicidal rowboat; two naval cadets had come into the Creek and were clutching at a flapping sail. Henny heard the men moving in some heavy thing, and heard her husband say wearily, "Looloo-dirl, make some cawf!" The reek of weeds forever damp and of the brackish water came up to her and the smell of the ground under the veranda. It had rained slightly in the night. Louie, who pretended not to hear Sam's call, came in a dawdle round the house and leaned against the veranda post behind the vines, chewing a grass stalk. She was droning to herself and presently she droned clearly, "Oh, the waterskin crawls shore-wards; and the leprous sky scales earthwards, from the musical moaning channel, to the dirty margin." It was halfwater; the surface was dull, and the sky was windy.

At that particular moment, Henny awoke from a sort of sullen absence and knew what was happening; her heart was breaking. That moment, it broke for good and all.

"Stop that rot," she cried madly to Louie, startling her out of her wits, "I never heard such damnfool tommyrot. Go and get the coffee. A big lumbering sheep, and on a day like this, she holds up the veranda post." Louie, with tactful soft-footing, dis-appeared from behind the vines, and presently Henny heard her saying,

"I say, Dad, this gas won't turn on; it's jammed."

The men trundled backwards and forwards and puffed. Louie soon came to the veranda with a cup of tea for her mother (Henny's heart would not stand coffee), "Mother, Daddy says, 'Where do you want things put?'"

"What the devil do I care? Put them in the orchard and make a bonfire of them. Put them where you like," she ended, less ungraciously. "Is it my home? It's your father's idea. Do what you like; all I want is a place to lie down, and get me a bed for Baby. Tell him I am not going to lift a finger to fix up his stinking tenement: the animals have better cages. Go on now, don't stand there staring."

Louie, not at all offended, and now observing more closely the many defects of the old house, the hanging window cords, un-latchable latches, and sunken floors, went in to say, "Mother says put everything where you like."

Sam, only too pleased, at once hallooed and whistled for the gang of children and consulted their tastes. It was not hard to suit most of them.

2 ✠ Sam suspended.

FOR THE NEXT MONTH, until the middle of July, in deep middle of the bee season, old Spa House rang from six in the morning till nightfall with the boys' shouting and Sam's whistling, hammering, ripping of timbers, and falling of plaster. Sam, with the boys, was taking the house apart and putting it together again on a different plan. He himself would renew the furnace system, take down the chimneys, pull out the bathroom, install a shower room, make new steps, put in timbers in the decrepit veranda, put in glass where it was broken, patch the plaster, calcimine, paint, and otherwise repair. The great project filled him with joy. "With my own labor union," said he to them, "I need nobody; no strikes, no trouble, only the work going up fast."

"You don't pay anything," Ernie said disagreeably. He felt first, after Henny, the pinched circumstances in which they were now living. His perquisites had ceased, and because (after a first visit during which Henny had remained in her room) one and all of the relatives in Baltimore had become timid or distant, he received no nickels or dimes in presents. His rich grandfather was dead, and Henny, more ferocious than ever, had absolutely forbidden him ("whatever your father says") to run errands for the grocer, black boots, or do any of the other things that his imagination suggested to him. Henny kept completely to herself, refusing to speak to any of the poor neighbors. Since the breakdown of her hopes, many things had come home to her. She was ashamed of everything, especially ashamed of her laboring husband who could be seen at any hour of the day crawling about the house and acting like a common workman. Why wasn't he at work? the neighbors might be asking. Henny, too, had suddenly become ashamed of having so many children; for now that Collyer was dead and the estate dissipated, people asked her ordinary questions.

"It's all bets off, and they think I'm one of themselves," Henny told her friend, old maid Miss Orkney. "I'm ashamed to go out

of the house with that string, I'm like a common Irish Biddy."
She was glad to hide behind the wild growths of Spa House.

Sam was being treated ignominiously in the Department. He
had been suspended without pay after receiving pay for three
months, at first; and though his case was up before the Civil
Service Commission, friends warned him that he was likely to
find himself out on his ear, in the street, penniless and cheated
of his pension.

"It is impossible," said Sam stoutly, "I am guiltless, and I will
not fight them with their own weapons. I will not excite opposition—for I do excite opposition. When they see how unselfish I
am, it somehow arouses the madness of anger, and jealousy in
my enemies. My absence serves me better than any number of
petitions and any logrolling. I have been accused of receiving
support from Old David's political friends: may that never be
said about a Pollit! I will only go to Washington to see my
friends. Their machinations are beneath the very contempt of a
man like me."

Henny, never speaking to him, heard him with fright; but
she had given herself up entirely to despair; she said nothing,
and it seemed to her that (now that the clouds had rolled away)
she saw her husband for the first time: she had married a child
whose only talent was an air of engaging helplessness by which
he got the protection of certain goodhearted people—Saul Pilgrim, who was penniless, various old Socialists, of small property,
and in the dim past, by the same means, her own father.

"Why don't I tie a stone round my neck and drown myself in
his idiotic creek?" she asked Louie with quiet sadness, when she
heard these declarations from Sam in the intervals of hammering. Money was slow coming from his pockets, and Henny's allowance (which had never been more than $10 to $20 monthly
from Sam, on account of her father's generosity to her) ceased
altogether. When Henny sent Louie with indignant messages to
her father about this, Sam coolly sent back his answer, that,
"Soon she would get her quarterly allowance from the estate,
and in the meantime, they must all pull in their belts." Henny

would reply (by the same telegraph) that "he ought to be ashamed to live off a dead man," to which Sam, with a stern expression, would answer nothing at all, or merely mutter that if it had not been for her devilish extravagance of a spoilt fool raised for the marriage market, they would have been well enough off on his savings. This was a constant source of quarreling (always by telegraph) and, because of it, the children knew almost all the ins and outs of their family society.

Louie, who was much involved in all this, was a hotheaded person easily getting indignant over the injustices of one to the other; and about her own share of injustice storing up a wealth of vengeful feeling, a tempest on a chain which she intended to let loose at some vague season in the future. But, to her great surprise, the rest of the family who were, after all, own sons and own daughter of Henny, seemed to take not the slightest interest in the obscene drama played daily in their eyes and ears, but, like little fish scuttling before the disturbing oar, would disappear mentally and physically into the open air or into odd corners of the house. When a quarrel started (Henny and Sam did speak at the height of their most violent quarrels) and elementary truths were spoken, a quiet, a lull would fall over the house. One would hear, while Henny was gasping for indignant breath and while Sam was biting his lip in stern scorn, the sparrows chipping, or the startling rattle of the kingfisher, or even an oar sedately dipping past the beach, or even the ferry's hoot. Exquisite were these moments. Then the tornado would break loose again. What a strange life it was for them, those quiet children, in this shaded house, in a bower of trees, with the sunny orchard shining, the calm sky and silky creek, with sunshine outside and shrieks of madness inside. For Sam, in his rages, had long ago forgotten all kindness and said to his wife the vilest insults, throwing up at her all that could possibly be called her life; and she retaliated, but losing, losing all the time. From the moment they came to Spa House Henny had begun to lose ground in the war. Back she went, step by step; and it seemed that Sam, as poverty closed round them, gained stride by stride. Poverty was a beautiful thing to him, something he was born to and could handle: to her it was something worse than death, degradation, and suicide. She envied every creature she saw if she did not immediately think with bitterness, "Little the poor wretch knows what is coming to it," or, "The poor dumb fool is too stupid to see what a life it leads." Of these remarks she was free to her children and to Louie. She often said to her stepdaughter, "Your father broke my heart, then he broke my body with housework, now he is breaking my children: I have no money—what do you think there is for me? How can he criticize me? The great ignorant howling fool! Let me die."

It was a beautiful summer. Sam hoped still that "truth crushed to earth would rise again" (he meant his case would succeed). He found a thousand theories to justify his changing the children's food from butter to margarine, and from meat, to beans, spaghetti, and fish. He superintended the cooking himself, reproaching his Little-Woman with her clumsy attempts at cooking and himself instructing her because her mother would not. He knew a noble woman, it appeared, in the Conservation Department, who put out pamphlets on cooking, and Sam was always chatting about her recipes and always trying them out. He imported gallons of oil, of all kinds, himself making experiments in the kitchen, peanut oil, corn oil, fish oil, and every kind of oil, which filled the wooden house with a roof-lifting stench and made Sam very gay indeed. He raged against Henny's odors, but for himself, in his own universe, concocted such powerful, world-conquering odors as could be smelled across Spa Creek and up and down the foreshores. Waiting for his case to be decided, he was able to forget the world and be happy.

"What a pity," he said a thousand times, grinning at his children, "that the Law forces you to go to school. Children with a father like you have need no school. See what I would do! You would learn everything by projects: you would learn to build houses, plaster, repair—you all do know that now—you would be bricklayers, carpenters; the womenfolk would be good cooks, seamstresses; we would get the best, most modern machines, have every household process done by modern machinery, and we would have none of the archaic, anachronistic, dirt, filth, and untidiness which Henny strews about because she comes from the stupid old world. Baltimore, my native heath, used to be famous in the world, for commerce, yes, even for banking (though you know what I think of the Greedy, the Money-Powerful)—Brown Brothers had a great reputation as far away as wicked old London, that capital of evil. But there is a secondary strain in dirty old Baltimore, and that is a shameful love of vice. Not only did all these silk-skirted 'great ladies' (as they liked to call themselves, though they were silly little chits) breed slaves and sell them down to horror and hell, but they were themselves bred for marriage to wealthy men from abroad and from home too, I am sorry to say. Baltimore loves other things much worse, a real underworld of vice, which is, strange to say (you kids will understand this later), considered the upper world, society—a wicked convention which has imposed itself on a silly world, full of drinking, cardplaying, and racing. Baltimore has beauties, but what corruption does the ugly old girl hide under her parasol too? But let us leave this. Baltimore is sweet because she is between the great pothole of Nature and the wonderful Blue Ridge. That saves her."

The children listened to every word he said, having been trained to him from the cradle. Only Louie, who had much to think about (nothing to do with Sam at home), would always seep away from the group, linger deceptively for a moment round the door, and a few seconds later would be seen shining on the brink of the slope, or would have completely disappeared, and be mooning and humming on the beach. Henny thought that she had sneaked off to avoid work (they had no servant now). Sam suspected her thoughts—if they were not thoughts she could share with him, what sort of ideas could they well be; something unpleasant and even depraved. He feared, with the shrinking of the holily clean, the turpitudes of adolescence, and although boys might go through it, he heartily wished that bright pure womanhood could leap straight from Little-Womey's innocence to the gentle sobriety of Gillian Roebuck's nineteen or twenty years. The swelling thighs and broad hips and stout breasts and fat cheeks of Louisa's years (she was getting on past thirteen and having lived entirely in the open air and been fed on Henny's rich meats, she looked fifteen, yet with uncouth childish manner) were repugnant to Sam: he wanted a slim, recessive girl whose sex was ashamed.

Louisa was his first adolescent, too: he was full of the mystery of female adolescence of which, in his prim boyhood, he had been ignorant. He poked and pried into her life, always with a scientific, moral purpose, stealing into her room when she was absent, noting her mottoes on the wall, *By my hope and faith, I conjure ye,*

> *throw not away the hero in your soul*—Nietzsche

and investigating her linen, shivering with shame when suggestive words came into her mouth. Her speech, according to his genteel ideas, was too wild, too passionate, too suggestive. He told her not to use the words "quick and the dead," because "quick" meant the unborn; and not to use the words "passionate" or "passional," which she was fond of, and not to recite certain of her favorite passages because she did not know the meaning of them; and all with a shrinking niceness, a qualmish sensibility which surprised and repelled her. His nice Louisa, brought up on sawdust excerpts from potted philosophers, intended for the holy life of science, he could see (much as he closed his eyes), was a burning star, new-torn from the smoking flesh of a mother sun, a creature of passion. This was what her years of sullenness had concealed, not a quiet and patient nature, like her mother's, but a stern, selfish, vain nature like her grandfather's, wicked Israel's angry seed.

Sam tried all the recipes. He gave her her mother's photograph to hang above her bed.

"What is a photograph to me?" asked Louie insolently, "Mother is my mother" (meaning Henny). He gave her a photograph of himself taken when he was twenty-three, just before

[329]

marriage, an incredibly mild, beaming angelic face, blond as the sun, dreamy and self-doubting. He carefully went through her books, her notebooks, and scraps of paper in order to guide her, set her right: his palpitating heart could not bear to think of her coming to shipwreck on the hidden reefs of youth: and, for her sake, he went through all the literature on adolescence, becoming more horrified every day as Satan's invisible world was revealed to him, who had been a bloodless youth living on greens and tap water. Youth was one of the beasts of Revelations, the worst, and more insolent than the Sun. He writhed within himself to think that his high-souled, sober-minded Louie had to go through all that. Why? With the proper training and abstracted from all bad companions, and carefully watched, he felt, and kept in touch with pure adult minds, she would pull through without scar or blot. He would be her constant companion: they would communicate thoughts, and she would be drawn to his side.

With mental lip-licking, he followed her in her most secret moments. She had papers and all sorts of rubbish to burn (she was always "clearing up her drawers"); she would build a fire by the side of the orchard and stand by, in a dream, smelling the smoke, differentiating the odors of burnt grass, paper, rag, and printed cardboard and so on, with the intoxication of an old drug fiend, adding things to the fire to get the smell: and then he would come creeping behind her, stealing up on her to discover what she was doing, what was in the fire, and what in heaven caused this strange drifting nebula to spin.

He did the same to the other children, particularly to Ernie, who had become withdrawn and gloomy, and Little-Sam, always an absorbed and uncannily tempestuous child, full of wild, formless agonies. He sensed that there was something going on, like an incantation perhaps, about which he knew nothing. He tried to think back to his youth, but could remember very little but quickly repressed shames and moral thoughts. He pried and pried, hoping to discover, in the love of science and youth, the mysteries about him. Suddenly, overcome with an inexplicable feeling of embarrassment, he would laugh aloud, run up to the child under observation and poke fun, or poke the boy with his toe, or poke Louie's fire with an inebriated, quizzical expression. Louie would flush, rake out the fire, and turn her back, without a word: Ernie would fling away from the intruding toe; Little-Sam would hang his head, flush dark red and sometimes hit out clumsily. This amused and intrigued the innocent father; and it became a sort of game with him to come upon his children in their silences. Once he had thought their silences full of long, lofty thoughts, but now they were too old, he knew they might be thinking dangerous, filthy thoughts. From all that, he was there, their shield, to protect them.

So now when Louie stole away, with what tricks and speed she could, she was pretty certain to find Sam at her back in a short time, or to hear one of the children calling her from the slope or the orchard lanes (if she was in one of her cubbyholes at the far end of the orchard). Very often she would take there with her one of the younger children: Saul, who remained in fair equilibrium through all the storms, or Tommy, the handsome child with the rosy cheeks and thick curls, who was very dear to her and whom she would nurse, between her loins and her breasts, feeling his sweet weight maternally. Tommy always yielded himself entirely, sinking back into her warm hard flesh, a boy to love and never to question womankind. Sam, seeing two of them there, would roam near and rove away again satisfied: or would ask in a quiet, paternal voice, "What donin, kids?" and would wait for the reply and depart.

Louie was not to go away this summer. Her own relatives at Harpers Ferry were tired of keeping her without any payment at all from the wealthy Pollits. They themselves had become poorer as the health of the various heads of families declined, and the male youths were still looking about for wives and careers. Bradford Collyer had a magnificent place in Montgomery County, half cultivated, with ancient trees and thousands of wild birds and a farm and livestock in little, prize porkers, cattle, a barnyard, blood horses, fodder crops, and fruit. Completely neglected, but fed and befriended, Louie had spent several summers here without seeing another child or even any adults in the daytime. The family was old: one daughter was in a sanitarium and one married in Baltimore. Bradford Collyer divided his time between Baltimore and Washington and the South, and Mrs. Bradford, a superannuated beauty, once an overwhelming society matron, cooled her rattled brains comfortably in retirement.

Mrs. Bradford, Henny's Aunt Phoebe, had agreed once more to take the child off Henny's hands, for the summer of 1937, when David Collyer's death occurred; but after that, sentiment languished and withered between them, and Henny's family became too scrubby for charity even. Besides this, if Louie had gone, the house would have been left to Sam's raving gang of boys and to Little-Womey's cooking! Hazel had married, and was now Mrs. Gray of Charlestown, West Virginia; and the irreplaceable Bonnie had dropped from human ken—no Pollit had heard from her for some time, and Pollits now lowered their voices and looked anxious in speaking of her. Sam had no money for a servant, and servants would rob him of the freedom of his own house where he ran about in shorts and the children ran about naked. No; all was for the best, and his two women, Louie and Little-Womey, would replace Henny, who was in her worst mood of bitterness, languor, and weakness. Try as she would, Henny could not do the work, make the children's clothes, repair mattresses, beat carpets, launder Sam's summer suits, and mend stockings. Sam never ceased to repine about his slovenly housekeepers and the bright beauty of homes of high-class public women who were friends of his in Washington. All went merry as a marriage bell; ringing the old changes. The children were happy and free. Louie was happy and as solitary as she could be —she had a real genius for solitude and could manage to have the solace of loneliness even in this community. She was lazy, said Henny: she was secretive, said Sam; but Louie, dragging herself by main force out of those frightful sloughs of despondency and doubt and uncleanness which seemed to be sucking her down, with amorous, muddy lips, saw hours of lightnings, when the universe split from heaven to hell and in the chasm writhed the delirium of glory, the saturnalia of which explained her world to her: she would stand on the beach watching the tall dry grass which stood in the moistest part of the shore and suddenly she would think,

> *Who can see aught good in thee*
> *Soul-destroying Misery?*

and in this flash of intelligence she understood that her life and their lives were wasted in this contest and that the quarrel between Henny and Sam was ruining their moral natures. Sam, once pathetically modest in his speech, now could hardly speak of Henny without using the word "devil; the foul devil, the miserable devil," said Sam, in his pain, over and over; and even in fun he had come to call the obstinate Louie "you mean devil, you pigheaded devil," though for her he had this dancing, inebriated look of the bad boy who teases the village idiot, and yet the two of them roamed about the village of Eastport together, following the motor roads and getting round to the small flat horseshoe inlets by rowing boat, like the closest of friends. There was nothing Sam had to say that Louie did not already understand.

In this new intimacy with his children and while patching up his new house, Sam was able to forget his troubles in Washington. He ceased to read the newspapers, except when some friend sent him a marked copy showing some attack upon him, or some indignant letter from a friend. If Sam thought about it at all, his heart beat so hard and his head ached so much that he could neither sleep, eat, nor work: therefore the only alternative was not to think about it at all.

Henny saw with alarm that Sam did not intend to fight: he was drifting, and no one seemed to know where their money was coming from. Sam referred vaguely to "your mother's quarterly checks," and remarked that "Henrietta must now expect to help with the household expenses." The children, who had heard so often from Henny that "these few miserable dollars were her very own," thought Sam very unjust, greedy, and even thieving. They did indeed see their mother in rags, and could not understand why their father did not go to work any more.

When the mail came in, in the morning, Sam at the breakfast table, with a bedraggled expression, would show Ernie and Louie the articles which attacked him and say, "See, see there; see how base mankind can be—but you must learn not to hate, but to understand: who understands all, forgives all." But Louie and Ernie would cry desperately, "Answer the letters: why don't you answer the letters?" Then Sam would enter into a long defense, point by point, showing them everything that was wrong in the attack, and naming the interest which inspired each separate enemy.

"Oh, why don't you write, Dad? Why don't you put it all down and send it in?" cried Louie, wringing her hands, with long, drooping cheeks, "Why do you let them say it?"

And Ernie, desperate too, anxious, fretted by his calculations (where did their money come from?), would say, "Write in, Dad! Please write in; why don't you tell them? If it's so easy to show them that they're all liars; why don't you do it? Please write in, Dad, why don't you?"

But Sam would shake his head, more mournful and pale than ever, and look at them both, and then at them all, with his big frank blue eyes, wet with tears, "At present the evil ones are in the ascendant: we must wait till they are on the run, but we will get them on the run."

"But how? But how?"

"Everything comes to him who waits," Sam would smile painfully. "Looloo, don't be impatient: we must not fight the enemy with his own weapons."

"You are not fighting at all, Dad," cried Louie. "You tell us all this: you can write it in. Look, it is in all the papers: everyone will believe them. I can't understand why you don't."

All the children, though, believed that Sam was utterly innocent, which in fact he was, innocent too, of all knowledge of men, business, and politics, a confiding and sheltered child strayed into public affairs.

The children felt more worried every day, those too old to be diverted into jobs and projects. Where was their food coming from? There were to be repairs and some new building in the Collyer Seafood business in Aliceanna Street, and Henny would get no dividends for two years at the earliest. Mother could no longer get them clothes on credit at Old David's store, for the account was closed. Already Sam had formed a complete, new project, whereby Louie was to leave school and be his secretary (attending business courses at night), and Little-Womey was to leave school as soon as she could, after attending cookery and housekeeping courses, and would look after the kitchen.

"Even if the worst comes to the worst," said Sam, rather cheerfully, "you will see, Sam-the-Bold will manage: never say die! Sam-the-Bold cannot be conquered by circumstances. The evil ones may fly, but when the sky is clear, Sam-the-Bold has a kite to fly after them."

Through the long holidays, Henny, tight-mouthed and determined, went at her work. In her poor clothes, she would take trips, be away for hours, going to Baltimore, to see her sister Hassie, or Uncle Archie. Once or twice Uncle Archie advanced her money upon her expectations, and on these days Sam would find a little pile of money on his desk, with a note beside it:

Sam Pollit: "Use this for household expenses," or *Sam Pollit:* "Get yourself a new shirt."

No one knew how they rubbed along; but when schooltime came, Louie was allowed to go to the Annapolis High School in a new flannel blouse and seedy old serge skirt which Hassie had sent her, and a cinnamon brown overcoat given her by Auntie Jo. She felt pretty wretched till she got to the school when she saw before her a flock of girls, half of them looking like a litter of puppies tied inside a sack, tumbling and rolling; and, adding herself quietly to the homely and ill-dressed section and subtracting herself, without even a twinge, from the pretty and smart section, she began to bounce about in her new sphere with stolid self-confidence.

3 ⚜ Miss Aiden.

THERE WERE SEVERAL new teachers in school, two fresh from the university. Of these two, one was a staggering beauty, black-haired, blue-eyed, and with a high fresh color; and the other, tall, limber, with deep gold hair and a fresh, sonorous voice, always wore a red swagger coat. There was a third, also new, though not glamorous, who had drab hair, a worried expression, who wore brown and gray eternally, was timid and cried when the girls made a noise. The susceptible girls at once divided into two camps—those who went for the beauty (Miss Bellmore) and those who went for the redcoat (Miss Aiden). Everyone but a few timid, uninteresting souls did her best to make the drab one (Miss Paramore) lead a life of misery. Louisa, who had done badly in elementary and seventh and eighth grades, discovered dazzling aptitudes within a few days in the new school. Several girls announced that they were Louisa Pollit's friends and insisted on her company. No sooner had Louisa opened her mouth than Miss Aiden gave her a smile of nonpareil sweetness and understanding, and no sooner did Miss Aiden or Miss Paramore or Miss Bellmore appear, moving kaleidoscopically through the leaves and paths, than all the girls fell to laughing, and thousands of suggestions, skits, and quotations reared their heads. All the girls had grown out of their clothes in a few days, or at least they looked like it, and associations formed naturally of friendly thinkers: girls who spoke freely but eschewed vileness, girls who giggled over dirty jokes and thought about men, girls who went frantic over what was in the newspapers, featherheaded girls who thought about clothes, sad grinds who thought about homework.

It was wonderful and new; it was Arcadia. No sooner did Louie see Miss Aiden, with her painted red mouth and goodhumored smile than she began sneering and inventing stories about her, and then the first time she sat in this redcoat's class, she felt obliged not to listen to the lesson but to get down on paper all the comicality in her heart; and this was what came out:

"There was a wedding at the circus! The hermaphrodite married the bearded, the giant the dwarf, the fat lady the hungry wonder, the clown in bags the lady in tights, the flea the elephant, the tiger a lily, the tent a Pole, the wind a Russian, the Hairless Mexican a hairtonic, the barfly a pony, the dollar a bill, the prophet a punched nickel, the instep a stepin, the punch a free pass, the judy a free-show, the cough a little hoarse, the neck a noose, the papal bull a chinashop, the pope's nose a tailfeather, the grille a sideburn, the kink a Jew, the fly a trapeze. Who told all this? The belle tolled. Who knelt? The bell knelled. Who opened the door? A jar. Who had a flower? The doughnut. Who baked the cake? Beg and borrow a pound. What size? Two sighs, seven tears. When was it ready? Tomorrow. What was the fruit? Henfruit, cockscombs, larkspurs, chickpeas, crabapple, passionfruit, breadfruit, deadseafruit. What came in on two legs? A breadbasket. Who drew the carriage? Shanks' ponies. Who paid the money? Pneumonia. Who was there? You-all. When was it? When time was a pup."

This production, which left Louie astounded (for she had no idea how she had written it, nor why with such ease), followed the tracks of all the other notes and scraps of paper which were passing round the class, and caused such gales of idiot laughter, beginning with chuckles, sniggers, and ending in uncontrollable spasms, that within a few minutes Miss Pollit found herself on the floor, the cynosure of neighboring eyes, while Miss Aiden, frowning, and then grinning, read it through.

"Did you write this, Louisa?"

"Yes, Miss Aiden." (Giggles.)

"When?"

"Just now." (Whispering.)

"Is that what you come to class for?"

"No, Miss Aiden."

("No, Miss Aiden," confirmed the class in varying tones, groans, and flutes.)

"Go back to your seat," said the mistress firmly. Louie expected the worst: she would be late home again, but to her intense surprise, she was not punished, and she sat there blushing badly, thinking of the handsome and agreeable creature in possession of her paper and able to see to the vacuous center of her silliness.

"I'll never do it again," thought Louisa a thousand times, more miserable than she had ever been before, as if one of those dreams had come true, those dreams where she found herself walking down the street in a hat and a bodice without any skirt or shoes. She did not dare to look at Miss Aiden, but sulked and blushed till the end of the lesson, when Miss Aiden with divine pity gave it back to her.

At home the domestic agony was intense. Everything that happened, a nail forgotten and left to tear the children's bare feet, set Henny screaming at them. The short entente between Louie and her stepmother was at an end. Now "the mere sight of the great flopping monster" made Henny want to tear her own eyes out, and the "mere sight" of Ernie going around with "his lumps of lead" made her want to jump in the creek, and the "mere sound of the boys snarling at Evie for their breakfast" made their mother want to pack up her traps and leave them all forever. It was not easy at home, and being kept in was a pleasure to Louie. It gave her a chance to dawdle along the road home instead of going by the bus and to chat with one or other of her friends. She had been adopted by two girls, Leana and Edie: and in the meantime, her appetites were excited by a classmate named Clare who described herself as a "Kind of Wobbly" (whatever that was), a tall, vigorous, yellow-haired girl with boy's curls and a splendid medallion face. Clare was dressed like a ragpicker's girl, and slouched and scuffled along, partly out of good-humor and partly because she wore ragpicker's shoes, from which either the toe, the heel, the upper, or the sole was always missing. Her lisle stockings of a washed-out dung color were wrinkled, dirty, and in holes; her blouse would be on inside-out, rough-dry, her skirt spotted and with hem hanging. Her shapely artisan's hands would be dirty, and even her face, if she cried (she cried sometimes, frankly), would show clean traces. For lunch she would have a sandwich or some dry bread, and she never had any money for school contributions.

"You ought to know Clare Meredith," girls would say, watching her, in a disinterested tone. Clare forever wasted time, was always chatting with her large shapely curly head laid just above the top of the desk, next to some other head, always making up skits and sending them round the class, little bits of paper written in an exquisite, fantastic small hand. She had never done her homework, nor was ever ready for a question, but would laugh up at the teacher with a gay, good-natured sloven's laugh.

One day, Louie received a note in class, sent by desk express, "I'll kiss thy foot; I'll swear myself thy subject," and there was Clare, giggling and grinning at the far end of the room like a curly mooncalf, bobbing and hawhawing, showing all her strong white teeth, a blue-eyed female Caliban. Louie at once seized her pen and, with a most serious look, wrote back, by the same post,

"By this good light, this is a very shallow monster. I am afeard of him! a very weak monster."

Clare's yell of laughter brought down the house, and even the mistress, on this occasion the Bellmore, laughed, and said in her distant silvery voice, "Gals, gals!"

Louie became chief flatterer of Miss Aiden. As soon as Louie got home (she went slower and slower as she neared the gate of Spa House and stayed a long time in the shadowed drive, for now the storms were more than could be borne), and had done the vegetables, she would pretend she had homework and, rushing upstairs, shut herself in her room, where she would go on with her poem, or scene, for the next day. She made a point of never going to school without a poem or scene (in a play) in Miss Aiden's honor. Leana, Edie, and (soon) even Clare, laughing but loyal, would wait for her at the gate and ask, "Have you got a

[339]

sonnet today?" Louie had formed a magnificent project, the Aiden Cycle. The Aiden Cycle would consist of a poem of every conceivable form and also every conceivable meter in the English language, each and every one, of course, in honor of Miss Aiden. Part of the Aiden Cycle was to be *The Sonnets,* dedicated to The Onlie Begetter, a little thing which would occupy but a brief time in that life which was entirely for Aiden. The high school contained only one such fanatic, and thus Louie became chief of all the Aiden men. Clare inclined towards Bellmore, and even wrote one sonnet (a comic one) in her favor, but she bowed before the enraptured Louie, and this intensity of feeling brought her to Louie. In a short time, though, she would chat with her old friend or lie down on a bench with her torn straw hat over her head, taking the sun. She was mostly to be seen with Louie holding long and earnest discussions. She tried to get Louie to be a socialist and to read *Progress and Poverty,* but all other passions, at this moment, meant nothing to Louie. At school, when she saw the red coat come weaving up the path, she was joyful, all triumphant love; at home, she had her hands full, using up all the spare hours to learn her plays and write her Cycle. She recognized that the Cycle was a lot of work, and she never dropped it. She began to learn *Paradise Lost* by heart. Why? She did not know really: it was a spectacular way of cele- brating Aiden.

Sam and Henny complained bitterly of the amount of home- work given to a growing girl and thought the teachers must be mad; they were always threatening to write to the school; and then Sam decided that all Louie's homework must be done in the family dining room, under the eye of one and all—it would prevent dawdling, and enable her to learn to concentrate—for if one can work when bedlam is loose, then one can work anywhere at all. This was Sam's theory. Furthermore, when the others had gone to bed, Sam was full of little speculations and homilies, trying to draw her out, trying to get in touch with her. Following her bad example, Ernest too was drawing away from Sam, and

Sam felt that he must fight it out with Louie; it was now or never in the struggle for power.

The children soon knew all about Miss Aiden, and tried to tease their eldest about her love, but she was too serious, and too enthusiastic, and she would recite to them for hours on end, while they sat with rosy, greedy faces upturned, listening. Then Louie would act, and tell them how it would be done on the stage, thus and thus; and she would try to get them to act with her. Sometimes, Sam would creep in, unexpected, in this verdant theater at the orchard's end, and would stand quietly at the back, rather surprised at his daughter. On these occasions only did a kind of humility creep into him; and Louie, seeing it, would strike at him verbally, or flash a look which said, plainer than speaking, "I am triumphant, I am king."

4 ⚹ Clare.

IF MISS ROSALIND AIDEN was the heavenly love, Clare was the alter ego. Everyone knew about her: the older ones thought her a crazy kid, while the younger ones wondered who was that dirty, ragged girl full of shouts and horseplay. When she came in through the school gate, without a hat (her hat had at last fallen to pieces), she would rip off the ragged overcoat and, showing its ripped lining and hanging seams, she would begin to sell it, ducking and grinning solicitously, smoothing down its burst seams and expatiating on its beauty, and she would offer it at auction for a dollar, fifty cents, ten cents. One day a youngster offered her ten cents for it, and she sold it, took the ten cents, and refused to take the coat back; no, it had gone under the hammer and been parted with fair and square, said this tragic muse. She trudged home to her home in a yard in Compromise Street, in Annapolis, without a coat, although it was a gray

November day, with a sneaking, damp breeze and snow threatening, and the next day came in a man's coat that a neighbor, an old man, had lent her. She herself had gone in and borrowed the coat till he should ask for it. She turned out the pockets before half the school, finding string, tickets, and a mucus-streaked handkerchief which she flung away from her with a magnificent gesture of loathing, and all the time, unself-conscious, amused at herself,

"Look at this now—a bit of string to hang myself with: but my neck's too thick—he didn't think of that! And the pocket's— where's the pocket? Ouch! I can feel my knee—my knee's in the pocket. But who said anything about pockets? Look, just air— it's lined with air: but that's a swell style, the latest thing: there are more wearing pockets of air and linings of air at this minute than linings of silk. Who cares for the naval dears with their plackets and braid? The best part of mankind wears overcoats entirely of air. First a suit of skin, then a decoration of hair, then an overcoat of air!"

Then deciding that she was dissatisfied with her overcoat, air or no air, she would shuffle off a few steps, and Louie, who would have been standing, grinning but dissatisfied, sometimes rather stern, at the edge of the crowd, would take her arm and say, "Clare, Clare!"

"What, Louie?"

"Clare—" Louie knew that Clare only behaved like this when her poverty rankled worst; Clare's poverty was no secret to anyone—she came of a brilliant family that after the death of father and mother had come into the hands of a poor, stiffnecked maiden aunt. One eldest sister was even now at work, helping to keep the two younger sisters and small brother. As soon as Clare graduated, she would take up the burden. Half the weeks in the year it was a question whether Clare would have a roof over her head at all. What was there to say? Clare would smile at her ruefully and grip her hand.

"Ah, Louie, what do I care? When I get through I'll earn; but where will I be still? There's my sister and brother and two mortgages—the only thing that worries me is the boys: the brutes won't look at a poverty like me! What does it matter what I am?"

Louie was silent. Then stupidly she would say,

"Well, you're only fourteen, Clare—" Clare would open her arms wide, spreading the loose garments that fell about her, with a gesture that somehow recalled the surf beating on a coast, the surf of time or of sorrows,

"Look at me? Will I ever be any different?" Clare resolutely refused to visit Louie at her home and would never even cross the bridge to Eastport for fear of meeting Louie with her family; she would always refuse, hanging her head and smiling to herself, though at what, Louie could never make out.

"You don't want me, Louie: I'll see you at school."

One day, just before Christmas, she came, without galoshes, but dragging, on a stockinged foot, a completely ruined shoe. Her toes peeped through holes in the stockings. Some of the girls who were hanging about exclaimed, pointed, and others running up commenced to make a great hullabaloo. Clare stopped in her tracks and, laughing at the great fun, picked up the shoe out of the muddy snow and began swinging it round and round her head: suddenly it flew loose and seemed to fly into the sky, but it landed on the roof instead and while they all stood laughing hysterically, holding their bellies and going into shrieks of laughter, Clare rushed into the janitor's room, took a ladder, scrambled up to the roof, and began mounting it towards the shoe, making a fall of snow, but still going up carefully on hands and knees. Her patched and tired underwear could be seen all over the grounds. An old teacher (Clare was her protégée) came running and, in a stern high voice, cried out to Clare to come down quickly, while the janitor with a long pole began to poke after the shoe. Clare, looking round, and greeting her audience with a flustered laugh, began to back down again—the shoe slid towards her, she tweaked it off the roof and sent it flying down to the ground. She happened to be looking at her friend, the old teacher, and so the shoe struck the woman in the face. She started back but said nothing, only blushed and rubbed her face; and then she stooped and picked up the miserable object, and stood with it dangling in her hand until Clare had reached the ground again. The children, much struck, had fallen silent, and as Clare sheepishly came up to the woman and said, "I'm sorry, I'm sorry," and they looked from one to the other, they saw that Miss Harney (the mistress) was crying. She took Clare under the arm, upstairs and into her own room. Louie trailed after her, and because Miss Harney also liked her, she was allowed to remain there.

"Have you no other shoes?"

"No, ma'am," said Clare brightly.

"Why not?"

"No money, ma'am!"

"Don't call me 'ma'am,' Clare."

"No, ma'am—Miss—ma'am—Miss . . ."

Miss Harney shrugged, "I am going to send to get you a pair of shoes."

"No need, ma'am: no need at all, thankee kindly."

"Stop acting the fool, Clare."

"No'm, yes'm thankee'm."

Miss Harney, very tall, spare, spectacled, with iron-gray hair, struggled with a smile, "Clare, you don't have to go through this, surely? I'll write to your aunt. You have friends here: we'll gladly help you."

"Don't want any help: no'm," Clare said.

Soon the school was talking about it and saying the teachers had got together and bought Clare a blouse, skirt, and so forth, and that the very next day, out of pride, no doubt, Clare had come back in the former sordid outfit—but this protest did not last. She wore the better clothes, and during the winter Miss Harney looked after her constantly, for Clare had developed a bad cough. She parodied the cough too, of course: it was a great source of inspiration to her. Just before they broke up for Christmas, Clare tied the draw cord of the Venetian blind round her neck and accidentally fell out of the window.

When examination results were posted, Clare appeared in most lists at the top or as runner-up. Most often she would be "sick" the day before a test, or her aunt would be sick the week before a term examination. On the morning of the examination, Clare would turn up, ragged, but with a clean blouse and cheerful as ever. She would throw balls of paper about the room, write hard, begin early, and end late. Louie, meanwhile, spent so much time pouring out her energies for the love of Miss Aiden that though she worked like everyone else, her results were mediocre. But in Aiden's subjects, naturally, she was unequaled. The class went into examination on all literary subjects with great *sang-froid,* and it never entered anyone's head to try to compete with the great lover. The staff room made serious complaints: Louie worked only for one teacher, and her example set up little frenzies in the rest of the school amongst the younger girls: there were numerous cults now, and some of them had developed into secret societies. At first Louie had founded, with Leana, a secret society, wearing white ribbons with gold letters, SSAA (Secret Society for the Adoration of Aiden), but the inactive members eventually fell away. Parents complained about the plague of secrecy and suspected their children of dark schemes and evil thoughts. In a few weeks, all secret societies were suppressed, by the principal's order: one or two of them rebelliously stuck it out for a day or two, but these withered away under public ridicule and suspicion. When the story of Louie's Aiden Cycle became public, there then began a fashion in original poetry so that pathetic pallid serious-eyed girls would be seen sitting in classrooms and corners of the ground scribbling; and some would timidly send their efforts to Louie for criticism. Needless to say, the ferment round Miss Aiden irritated all the rest of the staff. Miss Aiden was admonished by all the older teachers and told that she must discourage her admirers. But who could? What teacher can discourage popularity? It was asking too much of her.

Sam (after the secret societies were beaten) displayed the greatest interest in Louie's friends and in Miss Aiden. In the noisy morning of some Sunday-Funday, he would always send one of the children flying inside to ask Louie,

"How are Aidoneus' bunions this morning?" or, "Daddy said to ask you does she Miss Aidin' Franco?" or, "Daddy said, Do you love him better than Miss Aiden?" and he begged Louie every day to bring home to Spa House, Claribella, or Clarior-e-tenebris, as he variously called her. Clare would meet Louie at the joining of Compromise and Duke of Gloucester Streets, and they would walk all round Annapolis; Clare would then cross the bridge with her again, even to the Eastport side, and from the middle of the bridge they would stand and look at Spa House while Louie pointed out its parts and named the Pollits who happened to be in sight. But beyond that, Clare would never go. Sam knew this was only a little girl's timidity, and sent loving messages to Clare, "Tell Clarigold from Little Sam-the-Bold that she gotta come the next Saturnday that is and paint the porch," and, "Tell Clarior-e-tenebris to come en wun woun [run round] the Wishing Tree." (Sam had planted a new Wishing Tree on the lawn in front of the house to attract the small fry of Eastport Village.)

All through the winter months, on any bright day after school, or after dinner, Sam and one of his children would be seen patrolling the dirt roads of Eastport, rowing up and down the creek, or taking long walks around Annapolis. On Saturday and Sunday afternoons, when the jobs round the house were done, they would sometimes take the train to Severnside, or even as far as Jones and beat around the hills, studying the birds, insects, and trees, if the roads and tracks were passable, getting up great roses in the children's cheeks and freezing their fingers and toes. Every Sunday, though, Sam and Louie alone walked out to free Louie from the house and to walk off her fat. She was by this time a mere barrel of lard, as everyone said; and nothing was more clownish on earth than Louisa with her "spiny gray eyes, long ass's face, lip of a motherless foal, mountainous body, sullen scowl, and silly smile" (as Henny remarked), going into ecstasies over Miss Aiden and forever scribbling about love.

[346]

"What is going on in your head, all this time, besides this foolishness?" Sam would often ask, in kind gravity. "You must be thinking about things too?" Louie would be silent, trying to recall anything she thought about besides Miss Aiden.

"You do think about things, as I have taught and shown you, Looloo-dirl?"

"Yes, of course," she would mutter, flustered.

"When you are ready, you will show me your thoughts," Sam would conclude, not wishing to annoy her. When he got away from the children where his weakness for playground leadership forced him to cavort and fool, he was as kind as he could possibly be; and he would explain this to Louisa,

"Naturally, I am thinking much about you, Looloo, but I am not saying anything; I know this is a phase and it will pass over; it belongs to your age and a little later on you will get out of it and you will laugh at yourself, I suppose—we all do." (How darkly the girl flushed! Certainly things passed in her mind that he was unaware of: he had himself well in hand, though, and left her to her own devices.) After a pause he would say, dubiously, "I can trust you, Looloo: I know I can trust my own girl; you will soon be a woman, and I know you will be very close to me; for although you tend to be mean now, you will improve—you have some of your dear mother's traits."

One Saturday in early April they went for a quiet walk along the back grass-grown streets and bays of rotting hulls, Sam hailing everyone they met (he knew most of Eastport by name), jollying the pickaninnies when they came to the daylight-pierced, damp-rotted shacks where the Negroes live—shells of verminous woods, with shrunken seams, afloat on the marsh and horrider than Coleridge's death ship, A. Gordon Pym's carrion hulk. These places, as all Eastport, are repugnant to the refined citizens of Annapolis, sure enough; but with the houses they condemn the population. Sam, burning with shame, had already sent in three memorials and was preparing a pamphlet, "Eastport Squalor: A Backwater of the Chesapeake," which his friend Saul Pilgrim would publish on his little press and sell. (If he was kicked feloniously out of the Department of Commerce, said Sam, it would be but one of Fate's little tricks, for the country at large would gain in other ways: his energies no longer being at the service of official business, he would seize the crying question of the moment, publicize it and regiment men's minds and the sympathies of the public-spirited. "I begin at home," said Sam, referring to his pamphlet.

Presently they came back from the mud-sunk cove, after interchanging a few words with the Ryatt boys, who were patching up and painting an old fore-and-aft coffin with a motor, which they had renamed "Our Dimes," and after saying hullo to the shopkeepers at the three corners and to "Coffin" (James) Lomasne, they turned to the Eastport Bridge, laughing at his scurrility. Jim Lomasne was a derelict of the Florida boom, native of Connecticut, who, working his way north after the collapse, had never got farther than Eastport. He had sold coffins and rowboats on all the dead-and-alive waterways and in all the bankrupt resorts of the coast. The coffins were for Negro and poor-white funerals; they were worth ten dollars at the outside, while Lomasne (as he shamelessly told all and sundry) sold them for seventy dollars and had laid up a nice piece of change for himself. His boat business was slow, and he was now offering to sell the land on which his rickety boat shed stood, as well as his coffin-*cum*-boat business to the first comer. He also tried to interest speculators in the lucrative or coffin side; but, as Sam peaceably observed, not even a Johns Hopkins fanatic collecting peculiarly loathsome antediluvian growths, or a syphilographer, would touch "Coffin" Lomasne with a forty-foot pole. He had two legs, but clearly he crawled on them; he had a backbone, but it was pliant as a willow wand; he had clothes and they were as clean as any boatbuilder's on the shore, but these clothes were looser than graveclothes, had a moral not a corporeal stench quite sensible to the nose, and though "Coffin" Lomasne did not lack flesh, through his long immersion in marshy places and abandoned, despised sumps, it clung to his bones like grave wax. You looked at Lomasne and saw an obsequious, fifty-year-old dead beat and, as soon as your back was turned, you felt certain that there stood a loathsome ghoul. But it amused Sam to chat with this mud turtle, and, still chanting and improvising on the immoral perfection of "Coffin," they crossed the bridge.

The afternoon had clouded after a still, warm blue day; the water was halfway down, and contained jellyfish. They paused and looked down to count them.

"They are early," said Sam. "What is it, Looloo? See if you know."

She hesitated and flushed, then said, *"Dactylometra?"*

"Dactylometra quinquecirrha, in the Chrysaora stage, thirty-two marginal lappets; you only get the forty-eight lappets and forty tentacles in the regions of greater salinity. You know, Looloo, I think we should begin to keep a salinity record of our poor little crick! Why shouldn't you turn out the Spa House Journal, or Natural History of Spa House, like Selborne, and you can put in the human beasts, too, what inhabit the area, or human ecology." He laughed into her face, with his sorcery: "Loo, you and me is going places, but good places. Now, take this: as far as I know, this yer form hasn't been recorded at this time of year: and in my humble opinion it presages an abnormal run in the bay. We will see. The daughter of a friend of mine has a job measuring the height of water in the Shenandoah—heow would you like a jeob like that, Lazybone?"

"All right!"

Sam laughed. The water was almost smooth, with long splinter-shaped ripples, and the long, delicate shells of rowboats stood obliquely along the near jetties, which were mere sticks and runways. Two handsome steam yachts were anchored in close, and a small two-master with a schooner prow. Over the low houses and bare trees rose the bell dome of Bancroft Hall. Everything was ships, shipping, and the sea. On the left hand were the shore houses (of which Spa House was one), grassy dead ends, and tree-topped bluffs around the little pooling creek.

"Lovely," said Sam sniffing, "lovely; came the northeast monsoon perhaps—but it blew this little Malay into a quiet harbor.

Despite the troubles that, you know so well, Looloo, have cast shadows on a life that was meant to be all sunshine, we will do well here."

They went along towards the Market Space and then Sam swerved left.

"Why are you going here?" asked Louie suddenly.

Sam smiled, "Hesk no kvastions en I tal no lies."

"You're going to Clare's place," she said in fright. Sam smiled, "I am a-follerin' my nose, and you is a-follerin' your poor little Sam."

Louie wrenched his hand, "No, Dad, don't go there: she doesn't want us to, they're too poor. She doesn't want us to go."

"Poverty isn't a disgrace," Sam remonstrated, "I'm surprised atcha, Looloo-dirl. I hope Clare isn't as stupid as that."

She dragged at his arm in a frenzy, "Dad, please don't go." She had gone scarlet, "Please don't."

He flew into a temper and grumbled, "Of all the stoopids I ever met; now her father can't see her best friend. I want to get to know your Claribella. I'm sure she's a good girl, and when you told me she was orphaned twice, and was such a good kid, she's the right girl for Looloo to know and git some foolish notions out of her head."

Louisa sulked. When they came to the weather-gray cabin, Sam went in the little picket gate and knocked at the side of the open door. Louie, waiting on the street, saw Clare's shape in the dark hallway and then Clare, standing oafishly in the doorway, taking in the scene. She was barefooted, and wore only a ragged sweater and skirt: her arms, bare to the shoulder, were covered with suds.

"I'm Louie's father," explained Sam, pleasantly, "and Louie talked my two ears flat about you, so I thought I'd come along and take you out for an ice-cream soda." Clare seemed pleased, stood considering, gave Louie a glance, and then with a bound, declared that she would come with them, but they must wait till she got into her bonnet and shawl. It was hideous, thought Louie. She did not wish to share Clare with her father. Sam, on the other hand, glowed with paternity; here he was, not only hands, ears, eyes, wisdom, and virtue for his little daughter (being buffeted too hard by the northeast monsoon), but he was friends and friendship too, ice-cream sodas and Saturday afternoons. There was nothing he would not do for Louie to bring their two worlds together.

"I like your Clare," said Sam. Louie perseveringly skinned her shoe on the curb.

They went up Main Street and into an Italian ice-cream parlor and restaurant. Sam was very jolly, calling the waiter "yon devious devil-may-care Dago," *sotto voce*, and saying all he could to make Clare giggle. When the ice creams came and they were sucking at them, he became serious and asked Clare what she would do for a living. "My living will be paying the rent," said Clare. Sam said that he did not know what Looloo (at this name Clare opened her eyes and then smiled secretly) would do, "because she was at time of writin' a heap of muddleheadedness, but it would parse over, no doubt." The two girls looked at each other over their sodas and giggled. Sam smiled, too, at their bent heads and was encouraged to say that "at the momuent Looloo thought of nothin' but eating of all the dickshunaries she could find and went around chock-full of big words aspewin' em out and destroyin' the peas of mind of the famerlee." Clare stuck to her soda but began to gulp dangerously. Sam approved of this enthusiasm and declared that Louie "went in for Christian martyrdom on a much larger scale than them aneshunt Dagos (by which I mean no more nor less than the Roman-arounds), and I really believe thet thet Jo Bunyan what made Uncle Dan wear shoes two sighs too big was the maggit what had got into Louie's brain." At this Louie left off laughing and looked thunder at the happy Sam. Clare went on tee-heeing to herself over the soda.

"I'm telling you, Clare," said Sam, genteelly, leaving off his Artemus Ward imitation for a moment, "because I know you're Looloo's best friend and maybe you can talk some reason into her skull: though I doubt it." He grinned and slewed his bright blue eyes towards Louisa, expecting her to be full of his fun. He was surprised to see she was not. He began a sprightly inquisition, looking quickly from one to the other, asking, How was Aidoneus, and, Did Clare adore old Aiden the way Looloo did, and, Did Clare think Old Aido was a good woman as well as an allfired beauty, "for beauty lives with kindness," and it was impossible to get anything out of the lyrical Loo but moonlight and roses.

"Do you like her, Clarior-e-tenebris?" he inquired, solicitously, "because I'll take your word for it: I can see you're as quick on the trigger as I am myself."

"She's a good scout," said Clare.

"She's a good scout, that's fine: that's wery satisfactory, wery with a wee: though who is she scoutin' for, that's the question?"

The conversation lapsed. Sam, after a hesitation, invited Clare to have another soda, which she eventually accepted and then Louie too had another. This uncommon blowout delighted Louie; she loved her father at present: and when he began to speak again, in that low, humming, cello voice and with that tender, loving face he had when beginning one of his paeans or dirges, she listened as well as Clare.

"If I had my way—if I were a Stalin or Hitler, Clarigold—I would abolish school altogether for children like you and Looloo, and would form them into communities with a leader, something like I am myself, a natural leader, for man only learns in communities, he is a social animal. I love children and what I should like best, what I should love, Claribella, would be to form the Eastport, or Annapolis, Junior Community and introduce a totally new curriculum. In it the children would wander by the forests and fields and get close to their denizens, the fauna and flora of stream, thicket, and plain—they would be nature lovers, bird lovers. (For don't think I don't understand this foolish little passion of Looloo's: it is good in itself, it needs only direction: I am not unsympathetic as she thinks in her poor big silly obstinate skull!) The system we have now is good at best for making ditchdiggers, clerks, and schoolmarms—not that I am one to laugh at schoolmarms—they are in the noblest profession in the world! But we must follow the curriculum of Nature herself.

They must be bird lovers, nature lovers, water lovers, fish lovers, those schoolmarms and dominies: they must not teach formally, but Nature herself must teach *them* to love her and to fossick in her treasury until they find out, slowly but oh, with how much wonder! the inexpressible beauties and glories of her secrets— though they are open secrets to who can see. We unconsciously understand many of her laws—the thing is to bring them to consciousness, to know her, to follow her. Then we should have a different generation, the free air for our arts and sciences, the free use of natural gifts, free speech, few laws, free government freely elected and changing frequently, and phalansteries here, and law in the heart of nature where naturalists and poets of nature develop. It will come. In the meantime I have thought much over Looloo and will put her among the aristocrats of the human mind. I can show her the light and many like her. What terrible losses do we endure in our foolish, cut-and-dried system, when upon natural genius they wish to put a government stamp with a number. I am only speaking of government schools —I am utterly indifferent to institutions run for class, greed, and snobbery. You and I and Looloo, Clarigold, could make the world over: it would be a glorious world then, the world of men and women of good will. We want it; others want it. Why cannot we have it? Yes, we will have it, perhaps in our own lifetime. Only we must get away from this dry-as-dust system which crushes the inspiration, the faith, dreams, hopes, aspirations of youth."

Gravely Clare burbled through her straw in the bottom of her empty soda glass.

"Looloo, for all her gloom and obstinacy," said Sam, in a yearning voice, "is beginning to understand me, whether she will or not—though why she fights against me, I can't make out— though I daresay she has told you a little since you are her best friend and playmate, Clare, about the little troubles we have both had—little troubles, scarcely worth mentioning, in a life-time, just a little stone Fate put in the path of both of us because we are one nature. But she thinks the way I do, or is beginning to: and that is all I ask. I want you to understand, Clare," he continued, pleading, "because I see Louie has not gone astray, she has chosen aright: you are the right friend for her, and I hope you and Looloo and I will have many intimate talks and walks together. For all education is outside, not inside, the schoolroom."

Clare sat very gravely tracing designs in the wet on the table. Once she raised her eyes and looked at Louie curiously, but Louie was not looking at her. Sam sighed with pleasure.

"Well," he said, stirring, "I suppose we better be stretching our legs, as well as our minds: what say, girls? Shall we walk a little?" He did not release them for a moment but walked them jollily round State Circle and through the retired green grounds of St. John's College, discoursing on everything that met his eye— a stray dog, and the inroads of worthless dogs on planted deer, bred bobwhites, and all wild life of their state and how all dogs should be abolished or at most held on a leash (dogs had many other vices: they carried hydatids, bred lice, bit men, howled at night, made the fair countryside hideous with their wolvish brigandage in the guise of house protection, were vilely lubricous in decent streets, fouled footways, ate their own vomit, smelled to high heaven, and fawned and crawled on man as no decent-spirited beast could!). Then he saw the great liberty oak and sang, in their ears, an ode to that; and so on, for an hour or two, during which Clare mumbled and sometimes grinned and Louie looked stonily ahead or desperately aside.

Soon Clare had to go home, but Sam took Louie's arm and they walked slowly home together, Louie in utmost silence, and Sam talking, pleading, holding her ear, trying to rouse her to sympathy and enthusiasm.

"You will soon understand many things, Looloo-girl."

She smiled sourly.

"You will be like me!"

She grinned, "How do you know I will be like you?" They had paused on the Eastport Bridge to look over to Spa House. Ernie and the twins were splashing about in the water, rushing out on the beach to shiver, flinging their arms about and rushing back into the warmish water again. At the same moment, Henny appeared running, and began beckoning with her arms and calling them out of the water.

"I don't want you to be like me," cried Sam, annoyed; "don't be such a dope. I only want you to think the way I do: and not even that if you have good reasons for your convictions."

Louie grinned sarcastically, "You say so: but you're always trying to make me think like you; I can't."

He became silent and walked along, dropping her hand, in a dignified stride. She felt terribly ashamed of herself: why couldn't she be civil, after the four ice-cream sodas for her and Clare? But as sure as he opened his mouth, she knew, she would begin to groan and writhe like any Prometheus; she smiled apologetically, "It's the nature of the beast."

Sam softened and looked down at her, "Why must you always be such an obstinate cuss?"

"I don't know."

"I have such dreams for you, Looloo. Don't always oppose me. I have enough opposition. Why aren't you frank with your dad? Why don't you tell me what you are always mooning about? You can come to me with everything. I thought at one moment that the demon had done her work, and that the forces of sin, crime, and evil had torn my daughter from me; and that even the onset of womanhood was making you more bitter. But the love you show for your teacher tells me that you are not like that: it is just a passing phase, a storm—let us say cat's-paw of the pubescent period. I know you have little troubles general to your age and sex, that no doubt upset you. And then there is the situation at home."

Louie's lip trembled, "When I begin to get near home, I begin to tremble all over—I don't know why. I never told any one what it is like at home."

"That is right, Looloo: a merry heart goes all the way; there is nothing we cannot forget if we have a high ideal fixed before us."

[355]

She said in a rebellious tone, "That is not the reason: I do not say it because no one would believe me!"

5 ✠ What will shut you up?

SPRING WAS COMING and Sam was very restless. For weeks he would love Gillian Roebuck; then he would go to see Saul Pilgrim's sister, Mrs. Virginia Prescott, a widow, in Francis Street, near Druid Hill Park. She sat amongst the rich and plentiful furniture left to her by the extinct Prescott and "planned" little meals for friends and let rooms. At times she gave music lessons. Sam thought her a wonderful little woman, and she obviously admired him, but in a respectable, respectful style. She was a round-faced, dark-eyed, dark-haired woman (like all Sam's women), with nice false teeth, a short thick neck, short, thick bosom and little waist, much corseted: she was of medium height and very light on her feet. Sam did not love her, but when his feeling for the nature-spelled girl, Gillian, became too strong, he went and talked to Virginia. He was unable to see Gillian because they both felt they were too conspicuous in either Baltimore or Washington, and Sam despised hole-in-the-corner meetings: it was not worthy of them.

But this spring Saturday that he walked out with the two young girls, the need for Gillian rushed back into his veins like a relapse into fever. Only by talking, diverting his own attention all the time, could he forget her, smile and save himself from despair; and so when he reached home, sure enough, he gathered all his little ones round him, stealing them from whatever occupation he found them in, setting them round the long table in the square dining room that looked up Spa Creek, and he began to tell them all that had happened that afternoon—the walk, the wicked dilapidation of the Negro houses, the charming little wooden village that a Negro woodworker had there (birds, dolls, Mary-quite-Contraries, houses, picket-fences all in miniature and painted, in a little Swiss village), the *Scyphomedusae,* and Clare, and all he had said to Clare and Louie, with new variations. Meanwhile Louie got supper, and Henny, nearly mad with toothache and neuralgia, was crying in her room, her head tied up in an old flannel nightgown that once belonged to Tommy. Filled with love, with his eye on Louie, who was running backwards and forwards with the supper dishes, and who was wearing the pretty flowered blue dress that she had got new for school, he said to the children,

"When Bluebeak [Louie] was very tiny and could hardly speak, she and I often communicated by human radio, telepathy: one day she was playing in a little blue dress, just the same blue as that blue dress she has now—it was made from the dress her mother, my dear Rachel, wore when she was married—we came out to Annapolis—isn't that queer, kids!—the day before and she wore it then, too (for we were very, very poor). Bluebeak (I called her 'Ducky' then), Ducky was playing with her blocks— and she was wonderful at building with them, so serious, stopping for nothing, nothing could disturb her, shrieks, the milkman coming, the streetcar, nothing—I was standing there, thinking about poor Uncle Ebby (he didn't look so old and worn then, though he had his troubles, he had bad troubles)—and my Ducky suddenly looked up and said, 'Wassamattr wi' Uncle Ebby, Daddy?' Later on, I tried experiments with Bluebeak and they always worked. I always knew when you were sick, Bluebeak" (he broke off, addressing Louie who had just come into the room with a glass of water in her hand), "and the strange thing, is, kids, I always know what Bluebeak is thinking."

The children giggled at the new name, Bluebeak.

"Her nose isn't blue," said Little-Sam thoughtfully.

Louie laughed. Sam thought she laughed at the new name, "Whop you tee-heein' at, Bluebeak?" he asked.

"You always know what I think!" she said and shouted with laughter.

"You think Sam-the-Bold can't fathom your great thoughts?"

[357]

"No."

"Then whop you larfin at poor Sam fower?"

"You don't always know what I think." She became even more hilarious.

"Don't be a goat, Bluebeak."

She kept on laughing.

"The way you think you're so clever," she managed to get out between explosions.

He frowned, "Stop that hysterical teeheeing, Looloo."

She began to calm down, only giving an occasional giggle; the children were all giggling, all their little bellies and shoulders shaking. He said solemnly, "I will always know what Bluebeak thinks all her life."

Ernie burst out, "I betcha you don't know what she's got written in her diary."

Sam's face cleared in a second. He looked at Ernie with surprise and delight, "A diary? Looloo, you bin keepin' a diary, after all. Why, I told you to, but I didn't know you did."

Louie protested that she did not but Ernie, only wishing to be of service, rushed into her bedroom and, though Louie rushed after him, he was back in a moment, ducking past her, evading her grabbing arm, and showing Sam the five-cent notebook which he had just taken from under her pillow. Sam began laughing like a jackass, and all the children began bobbing about, like targets in a shooting gallery, laughing and shouting. Ernie thrust it into Sam's hand, but he was serious: he did not laugh:

"You can't read it," he told his father.

Louie stood like a stone image at the door, looking stupidly at them all.

"What is it, Looloo?" asked Sam gently, pushing Ernest away from him.

"A notebook."

"I see that!" He had not opened it. "What's in it? Notes on nature?" He was very kind.

"No."

"What then?"

She flushed purple. "It's in code; in code—I make up my own code: so that no one can read."

"You can show your poor little dad," he cadged, and winked at the children who sat round simmering, waiting for the excitement. He insinuated, "It isn't something you're ashamed to show me, is it? You see, Looloo, though you think I'm too dopey to see through you, I know more'n you think."

It certainly was a pleasure to tease Louisa, for she fell into every trap.

"I never said you were a dope."

"Well, if I ain't a dope, I can see your own brilliant *aphorisms*," and he winked at the children, in a circle of winks—for the past few weeks Louie had been solemnly stuffing them with the aphorisms of La Rochefoucauld, results of French books she had got from the library. After a short struggle, she burst into tears and gave in, unexpectedly. He then opened the rolled, dog-eared little book (he was honorable, he had not looked at it without her permission!). On the first page were only a few lines.

(i) 8 2800 h3f34 5300 q 083

(ii) ejsy s dytsmhr yjomh yjsy ejrm s, omodyrt pt s v;rtl pt s kidyovr pg yjr I/2rsvr I/2tpmpimvrd s fre eptfd pbrt s ,sm smf ep,sm s vr;; nrhomd yp frbr;pI/2----

(iii) jdjayfvy jpcjatjqzj sntzn tl etljay fjhafjl ej----

(iv) Ii7i-7i5iii5iii-Ii7i-3i7ii-8iiIiii7i-4iii3iii3l3ii7ii 3i-6iiIi5ii-7ii5iii-4iii5iii5iii4ii-2iii-5iiiRiii-7ii3ii2ii-8ii2ii4iii4iii-Ii5ii2i-7ii3ii2ii-7i6i3iii2i2ii6iii-and the high barn, only yesterday found out they were dreams.

The code expert had apparently got tired of this slow way of writing, and the fifth entry was merely in her French: *"Dans les moyen âges les parents envoyaient les enfants à les etrangers."*

"What does this say?" asked Sam, after studying all these items and pointing to the fourth entry. The children crowded round in great curiosity, while Ernie, who worked codes in school with a friend of his, pretended to ignore it. But Louie could not read her own entries and had first to go into her bedroom whence she came again with several scraps of paper, which she held away from Sam. Then she slowly read, "As soon as it was light I ran to look for the well and the spider and the high barn, only yesterday found out they were dreams."

He was very puzzled, "What is it? What does it mean? Is it a dream?"

No: she explained that long ago before she could talk, she had dreamed about a well in the yard and never been able to understand why it was not there; she had tried to ask, but they had not understood her. So with other things. This treasure hunt fascinated Sam, who insisted on the translation of the other codes (the numbering referred to codes, one to four, not to the entries). After work that made her sweat, she finally read to him,

"*i*: I will never tell a lie."

"Well, that's a change, that's something good," said Sam, grinning and winking, his smiles reflected on all the little mirrors round him.

"*ii*: What a strange thing that when a minister or a clerk or a justice of the peace pronounces a few words over a man and a woman a cell begins to develop."

This caused Sam much consternation and merriment when he finally understood it, for though he had given Louie a book, and Henny had given her a talk about marriage, Louie now imagined that marriage was essential to conception and that, provided no powders were administered to the bride and groom (she had made cautious inquiries on this subject—did they eat anything special on their wedding day?), a miraculous or magical event took place during the marriage ceremony. This was confirmed by her reading of various sentimental stories in which, after a hasty wedding, the bridegroom departed leaving the bride at the altar, and yet some months later a baby appeared on the scene. She explained this, with embarrassment, but honestly enough, to Sam who guffawed into his hand, and worked himself up into a paroxysm of fun. But after the first few minutes, the children sat round sad and mystified, for in fact they saw nothing comical in Louie's theory. Heaving with laughter, Sam insisted on Louie's going on with the next item, even though she refused, with a very red face, and so she went on,

"*iii:* Everyday experience which is misery degrades me."

At this he pulled a long face; and then there was nothing more but the ungrammatical French sentence which meant, "In the Middle Ages parents sent (their) children to (into the care of) strangers."

However, this all struck Sam as very bizarre, and he thought over the whole thing during supper. When Louie wanted to go to her room "to do her homework," he made her come to work in the common room, as he called it, saying that he hoped she was not intending to do anything that she would be ashamed of in front of her little sister and brothers and himself; so that she stamped around the house in a great temper, and Henny opened her upstairs bedroom door and screamed out that she'd come down and strangle the great ox that thought it was funny to make so much noise.

When the children went to bed, Louie went up with them to tell them their story, leaving Sam sitting alone, down in the common room, and when she came back to gather up her books, he was still sitting there with misty eyes and a thoughtful expression. She said very sulkily, "Good night."

"Doin' beddybye so soon, Bluebeak?" Sam asked kindly.

"Yes."

"Sit down, Bluebeak, Sam-the-Bold wants to talk to you. What do you mean by saying misery degrades you? What can you know about misery?"

"The misery here at home." She knew it was cruel, and she would have said it a thousand times to make it sharper a thousand times. After a silence, he said sullenly, "Sit down!"

She sank into a chair, frowning at him. Presently he raised his eyes from the table where he was jumping a table knife,

"Well, Louie, since you're beginning to understand some

things and since you're occasionally getting a thought into that fat head of yours" (but after this insulting beginning, which she knew was only to cover timidity, he went on to tell her about his boyhood; and how in poverty and ignorant youth, with a gay, licentious father and a dying mother, he had begun his experiments in science and fought upwards, ever since).

"Your mother loved me dearly and short as was her life," said Sam in a weeping tone, "she sacrificed every deed, every thought to you and me: she was a most beautiful soul and I hope you will grow like her; in love we must sacrifice—love is sacrifice, and that is why for love of the people, I have sacrificed my whole life, and would again, had I a thousand lives. I love, all my life has been love, love to me is the whole world—love of nature, man and mankind's good, I mean. Man is naturally good, not wicked, though wicked men, more beasts than men, transformed by greed, have led him into evil. When the time for man comes, though, he will see and rise to the light—there is no need of revolution, but only of guidance, and through evolution and good laws by wise men administered, we will reach the good world, the new age of gold. I heard you speak the other day of the Augustan Age, Looloo: now, that was a wicked age. I wish they would not teach you history, for the pages of history are blotted with crime—only in the good around us, and in our own lives, can we do good. And even we are stained."

Louie had laid her sheets of paper down on the table and was idly scribbling on them. Sam paused for a moment, to attract her attention, but since she said nothing, he went on in a softer, more insinuating tone, "And you later on will lead others to understand: first you must come to understanding yourself. It is not study but the penetration of human motive, you see, Looloo. I think you can do that."

Outside was the plashing of the creeping tide, and the shrieks of young people on the little lighted houseboat, at the end of Shipwrights Street. They both listened to it, and to the breeze, still brittle, not fully leaved.

"The year is young, gawky," thought Sam to himself, "like poor Looloo, so ignorant of herself and me." He said in a low voice, "What are you thinking of, Looloo?"

She replied, with a rush, *It is night: now do all gushing fountains speak louder, and my heart also is a gushing fountain.*

"What is that?" She did not reply.

After a silence, he went on, "You know I call myself an agnostic; and perhaps you will be too, Looloo. But we both believe that good is paramount and will spread through the nations, perhaps through the help of the radio. I always said that a second Christ could arise with the radio, speaking to all mankind—though for that we need the universal tongue and not cranky Frongsay and guttural Deutsch: yes, I believe it will spread even to the mean-spirited Frogs and the savage Rossian Tartars, though they may be the cream of Tartars, since Lenin's little tricks——"

He waited for the laugh, but it did not come. Louie was scribbling at the other end of the table.

"I am not personally concerned in what anyone believes as long as he believes in those main principles which you have so often heard me set forth, so often that you know them by heart, Looloo, Looloo, Looloo!"

She raised a drained, martyred face.

"What are you writing, Looloo? Are you making notes of what your dad is telling you?"

She said nothing: her shoulders writhed slightly. He could see that all of two sheets were covered with her little scrawl.

He went on, "And in you I see sure signs of the love of man—Looloo, look at me: what are you writing?"

She sat with her head sunk between her shoulders. Amazed, he got up and came up to the other end of the table. She sat there without a movement. He bent over her shoulder and read,

Shut up, shut up, shut up, shut up, shut up, I can't stand your gassing, oh, what a windbag, what will shut you up, shut up, shut up. And so *ad infinitum.*

[363]

He was terribly hurt. He could hardly believe his eyes. He flung at her, thrusting her shoulder back so that he could look into her face, "What is the matter with you? You're mean and full of hate. You love hate. I think of love and you are all hate. Sitting there you look like some mean cur in the street, whining and sniveling; you look like a mean gutter rat: your devil of a stepmother has done for you. What can I do with a girl like you? You have no looks, and instead of trying to light up your sullen face with a smile, and beaming on people as I always do, you sit there scowling with a hangdog expression. Get out of my sight: go to bed. I don't understand you."

Half smiling, bursting with confusion, the hulking child rose, gathered together her papers, and went into her bedroom.

Sam flung himself into his armchair and then got up and went out. Louie heard the screen door close and felt a pain in her heart. She sat down on her bed when she had put her papers on the table. Then she rose mechanically and got out her pen and journal preparatory to writing her sonnet to Miss Aiden; but she sat staring at the blank page. She put her head in her hands and, not even crying, groaned, "What can I do? What will be the end of me?"

When Sam came back from a long pacing back and forth under the old maples and elms of the avenue, Louisa was sitting patiently at the common-room table waiting for him.

"Do you want some coffee, Dad?"

"Yiss, Looloo," he cast a pathetic look upon her.

When she set it before him, she sat down, folded her hands, and said, "I'm no good to you: why don't you let me go and live with the Bakens at Harpers Ferry? I could go to school there. What is the good of my staying here? You and mother are always fighting about me."

"Good heavens, I'm trying to bring you closer to me, and the first thing you think of is to go off to Harpers Ferry. It must never be, Louie—a woman must not leave her father's home till she goes to her husband: that is what I am here for, to look after you."

"But all these quarrels—we don't understand each other," Louie said sadly.

"Yes we do, Looloo girl," he answered gently, "yes we do: these are just little storms in a teacup that will pass over."

"No, I must go: you must let me be on my own," persisted Louie quietly. "What is the good—what is the good?"

Sam flushed, "If you were to go, Looloo-girl, I would blame your mother as I've never blamed her for anything. I would put all the blame on her shoulders for driving you from home. It has been her lifelong object to break up my home. I have always fought for the sanctity of my home. Do you want me to blame *her?*"

"No."

"Then there is nothing more to be said."

CHAPTER NINE

1 ❦ Sunday a Funday.

IT WAS MAY, fullest spring, and all the week Henny had been whimsical and cheerful: she was dressing a doll for the eighteenth birthday of Cathleen, Hassie's only child. Cathy had dark gold hair, a thick, creamy skin, and pretty, vacant, tender blue eyes under auburn brows. Her face was oval and empty of all but a little child's experience. By ill luck her squarish shoulders concealed her wide-set breasts, round as cups. Her frailty expressed itself in an eighteen-inch waist and thin legs and arms. She wound a bath towel round her waist before dressing and wore skirts as long as possible and long sleeves. The style of costume no longer favored eighteen-inch waists, and her powerful fat mother kept drumming in her ears that men no longer wished to embrace a matchstick middle. She was deeply ashamed of her figure, stooped to hide it, and clung fervently to her mother's side. Cathleen had been one of those rare children who love dolls passionately: her entire uncompanioned childhood had been spent nursing dolls and dreaming of them. An expensive doll had always come to her on every anniversary—birthday, Christmas, New Year's Day (which was the great Collyer re-union day at Monocacy), and at odd times during the year. Not only Hassie gave Cathleen dolls, but also all the relatives. Now that she was eighteen she had a doll collection and with factitious ardor still prattled about it, her only interest in life. Hassie, madly loving and maliciously depreciating her, accompanied her everywhere still. A *young girl,* brought up in tradi-

[366]

tions of the sweet-minded middle South, must go nowhere alone. (David Collyer had come first from Gloucester, Massachusetts, and his people from Biddeford, Maine, of old Devonshire people.) Henny and Hassie were great friends and for this eighteenth birthday had worked up a great surprise—Cathleen was to get six differently dressed dolls.

"I think it is so nice," said Hassie to all her friends, "it keeps Cathy's mind on the dolls and on looking after them, it gives her something to do: if she marries, the dolls will come in handy for her own nursery and if she doesn't—and you can never tell, men don't like wasp-waisted women any more, they think it means they have no stamina—if she doesn't marry, she always has the collection, hasn't she? It will be worth something. Every stitch in the dolls' clothing has been put in by hand. It's nice for girls, that's what I always say."

Henny sometimes said fretfully to Louie, "A lot of tomfoolery giving dolls to a great big woman who ought to be looking for a husband—does she think she'll keep her a child forever?"

But Henny got on well with Hassie, had a lot of fun with her, and collaborated with her. Of the three, Henny did the best sewing. Her long, strong, firm-tipped fingers gave her power and delicacy: she did beautiful Madeira embroidery, made darns fit for an old-fashioned ladies' workbook, and, when she could, sewed seams by hand with tiny stitches. She prided herself on it still and had even in the last few years taught Louie to sew and embroider. Every one in the immense double family praised "Henny's exquisite work." Now Henny had put out her best effort for the dressing of a dark-eyed, bisque-complexioned china doll (she still preferred the china dolls to the new composition and cloth ones, with their quaint upturned modern eyes). Henny and Hassie were full of wonderful lore and morality, all concerning dolls. Dolls should be expensive and daintily dressed; girls of eleven and so on should have baby dolls with real diapers; little children should have rag dolls (Henny had made a plenty of rag dolls for her family, running them up on

[367]

the machine); boys and girls alike should have dolls till about the age of eight; paper dolls taught them to do nice handwork, and so forth. They could discuss the doll question for hours and all most solemnly, laying down the law, and discussing the moral deformity that came from too-late or the wrong use of dolls. Henny's doll was dressed in the secrecy of her room. She said, a dozen times a week, "I have no home—they only allow me a room here, but it is my room." The little girls were allowed to come in after knocking, and would tiptoe forward, holding their breath, fascinated by Henny's magic. At other times she would be sniffing her smelling salts, or taking aspirin, or mending linen, or reading, always using her eyes which grew darker and more tired every day, always doing things that were private to herself. She was a charming, slatternly witch, their household witch; everything that she did was right, right, her right: she claimed this right to do what she wished because of all her sufferings, and all the children believed in her rights.

The entire house was a dark cavern of horrors and winds perpetually moving and howling. When Sam was in all day, now, Henny would send a message that she would be out all day: and, no more complaining of her untidy loose clothes and stray graying hairs and ugly old black hat, she would skip out of the house as soon as she could "to escape the damn hammering and whistling," and go up to town "to meet Hassie." She looked much older than she had in Washington; she was viler, she had lost even the seeming of respect for Sam, but she was merrier. For months she had not spoken to any one of the "mud rats" of Eastport, but after school opened and Tommy went to school, for the first time, she went over to "ladida" with his teacher, a nice little old maid called Miss Lake, and soon got to know "the parents." She had given up all pretensions to middle-class elegance. She was one of the Collyers of Baltimore, the bankrupt Collyers, she sneered and laughed at herself and, pointing to her old clothes, her grease spots, would say she was an old joke and life was an old joke.

The children were happier with this Henny than with the

other. She would always insult Sam when she mentioned him, but now with a laugh as if he was of no more consequence than the butcher or than dirty old "Coffin" Lomasne. Henny soon knew all the personalities of the place and as she used to jeer at the neighbors of Georgetown, now mocked at them instead. The children, too, became very friendly with the "mud rats," and Henny did not even try to keep them away from fishermen's and boatbuilders' children. "We're all mud rats," she would say to the children as they crowded about her bent shoulders, peering at her satin stitch or Madeira work, "my kids too: I'm not proud; well, I don't care what happens to you kids, I've done my best and if that's not satisfactory, you must try another shop." Then she would lift her head and laugh at them. She was turning into a dried-up, skinny, funny old woman, "I'm an old woman, your mother's an old woman, so I'll be an old woman, and I'll do what I please."

Sometimes Hassie would drive down to Annapolis, but it took her forty-five minutes and she could rarely leave the sea-food shop for the day: so, generally, Henny had to take the little rackety train which passed through hated woodland and straggly little suburbs (as Henny said) before at last teetering into Camden Station where Hassie would meet her. These days (the dividends coming much sooner and faster than anyone had expected, and Henny being able to get money irregularly from the not unkind Lessinum), Hassie and Henny went in for shopping sprees, following all the "opportunity" and "budget" sales and "throwouts below cost." Henny always came home exhausted but happy with bundles in her arms, or bundles to follow by express, while the children danced about or waited impatiently for the carrier and post. True, Sam had at last decided to ask for a job as biologist with the Maryland Conservation Commission, although he resolutely refused to work for "the prostituted press" or for "private greed," but their money had run out and now they were living entirely on credit, on Henny's promises, lies, and tricks, and on Henny's dividends. Sometimes when Henny was broke, Hassie would lend her money "until her check came in," and once more, then, Henny would come home, smiling, lovingly, to her brood, with her arms full and clothes for them all, and even something for Sam whose wardrobe was worn out, and even sometimes toys and rare delicacies that she craved for—crystallized violets, preserved ginger, pickled walnuts, and little lengths of cloth and little bits of confectioners' ingredients that she could use for school and church bazaars. For though Henny never went to parents' meetings and church services, she loved to donate things made by herself to their festivals, bazaars, and sales of work. A lot of the local women, especially the mothers, came to like her and respect her because (coming of such a fine family) she put on no airs, because the poor thing managed so well on nothing with so many dear, well-behaved children, and because she was so generous. She was a genius at making both ends meet indeed, for they managed to live and when she could, Henry disobeyed Sam's orders about substitute foods (margarine for butter, maize oil for olive oil, pork and beans for red meat), because, she said, her children should not live on trash, her children had to fight for their livings, having such a silly, puffed-up ignoramus of a father, her girls were not going to be underfed "mud rats." Sam ignored all her darts, and even pretended to ignore where the household money came from (he would find it lying on his desk, in this time of distress, with the usual note: "Samuel C. Pollit: Use this for your expenses,"), though he often spoke of their poverty and his sartorial misery, saying, "And I'm a good-looker too, the cheapest suits look like eighty dollar suits on me, and I can't even get twenty-five dollars for a suit because of the wickedness of men." About their money, as about everything, he was vague and sentimental. But in a few months he would be earning, and in the meantime, he said, "It was only right that the mother too should fend for her offspring." Henny, hearing this, would merely say, "Hrmph!" or, "The damn fool!" or, "Well, I'm doing it, aren't I?"

How thrilling were the days, for the children, when Henny was heard stirring early, before breakfast, and when they would see her already dressed for town, not in her wrapper! They would crowd round her shrilling, "Are you going to town, Mothering? Mothering, am I going to get my new suit today? Mothering, you ought to see the big hole in my shoe!" and Henny would push them away with her hands, laughing a bit, "Yes, yes, yes, now keep quiet and don't shout so loud or the Great I-Am will be asking questions and preaching about extravagance." At this the children would flush happily, giggle, and break up into atoms of humanity, but still ask softly, If they could have a belt, and, Whether Mothering was going to get Saul a baseball mitt or not. "Wait and see," Henny would say, "wait and see." Then off she would rush, leaving a sweet quiet in the house, the sun falling on unswept floors and undusted furniture. Charming was this slatternliness: this dirt was a heaven to the harassed children, and they loved Henny for leaving it so.

Meanwhile, Sam, whistling and singing operas and popular hits, would be leaving his trail of sawdust and brickdust, cement pellets and putty crumbs, and never an experiment in chemistry or physics did he perform nor ever work with them over a book, but only talked with tender abstraction of "great lives" and "great chemists" and of his own beautiful soul and sympathetic life story. He would reform the state, even the world, because through love he knew more than all the politicians, and yet the queer thing was that the children were always having to help him, tell him what Tommy and Evie and Louie were doing in the secrecy of their rooms or the nooks they had made their own. With what surprise and joy he would seize on all this information of his loving spies, showing them traits of character, drawing a moral conclusion from everything! Yes, he and the children were very close: they were leading an ideal life, and Sam felt very sorry, as he often told them, that he had to leave them soon and go back into the struggle, for his great fitness was to be leader of children. He hoped, he said, that all of his children would enter the service of the people and perhaps some of them would be schoolteachers, because to lead youth was beautiful, and then it was a safe job, and respected. Now, this appealed to the children who had been worrying about his job and their future jobs; especially to Ernie who studied the bills that came into the house and always asked his father how much money he earned every month, and tried to calculate, even, his mother's dividend earnings, a thing impossible because of the irregularity of her drawings.

This Sunday in mid-May, Henny was to go to town for Cathleen's birthday, and the house buzzed joyously from early morning, because a "new deal" was to be had by all members of the household—Henny was to have Sundays off, this being the first Sunday; Sam was to superintend the housework and show them all how easily it could be managed by "system" and "scientific management." The girls were to cook, the boys were to do the ordinary jobs of house upkeep such as hoeing, weeding, washing verandas, and moving heavy objects. Henny left early and as soon as she went, they all rushed in, clustered round their father, while he "started the machine going."

"Man must work and women must sweep," declared Sam, first of all. "Little-Womey, subbor cawf! Now, I'll show you all how to wash the dishes." Commanding from his honorable position behind the coffee cup, he made Little-Womey and Looloo scrape and stack the dishes in the wash-basin, get the dish towels, dishcloth, dish mop, and soap saver, while he entertained them with his philosophy and schemes for the world.

"The Philosopher at the Breakfast Table," he announced complacently, "we have risen superior to the raw struggle for supremacy, the tooth-and-nail stage; it is now a struggle of types, brains and philosophies. With a council of scientists running the world—" and so forth, and then, "If I were autocrat of all nations," with "supreme power, the lives of all, the life of the world in my hands," he told them what he would do. For example, he might arrange the killing off of nine tenths of mankind in order to make room for the fit. "This would be done by gas attacks on people living ignorant of their fate in selected areas, a type of eugenic concentration-camp; they would never know, but be hurled painlessly into eternity, or they would pass into the lethal chamber of time and never feel a pang."

"But you would keep yourself alive," said Louie unpleasantly.

"The great point in washing dishes," said Sam, "is to have the water bilin' and the dishes scraped and rinsed first under the tap: all extra grease should be removed and the plates can then be dipped and stacked without extra work. A little scientific method would eliminate all work from the household, so to speak: now, if me and not Henny was runnin' this institution, you would see: because all the improvements in household technique have been made by men, becaze women got no brains. Now, Looloo-Meany, is the water a-bilin'?"

"Yes."

"Then Sam-the-Bold es a-comin'," he sang, "quick's the word and smart's the action: watch me—we'll be through in two shakes of a dead lamb's tale. Ermy?" He gave all their whistles and marshaled them in order of age with the dish towels. "I hain't had time to make that there dish rack, but I got cheap labor well organized."

With a great deal of shouting and bumping they got through most of the dishes, and then Sam slid under the sink the oatmeal saucepan, coffeepot, and skillet, remarking that "the women could do the dirties next time." Sam then retired from scientific management and went out into the sun, "Can't miss great Sol's benefits," said he, "for a lot of women's messin'," and when they all hastened to jump on him and point out that he did no work, he only laughed and stretched himself on the grass. "I work with myed [my head], I got lieutenants to do the rest of the work," said he, and expatiated on the work he did with his head during the times he had his eyes closed. This foolery annoyed and amused the children; but while he rested, they scattered off to their innumerable occupations. Tommy had a gift for carving boats out of bits of wood: he imitated the skiffs, powerboats, and even the *Reina Mercedes*. The fish- and boatmen round the shore gave him bits of wood and showed him how to shape the hulls and prows and where to put the masts.

On one of his productions, a sort of marlin-bellied yacht, they had shown him how to fix a fin keel. He had a lifeboat round which Louie had looped a cord. Sam at once predicted great things for him as a boat designer: "Perhaps you can design special observation vessels for the Bureau of Fisheries, or the Government Chesapeake Fisheries which I envisage for the future"; then when Tommy had run out again to chat with his dearly beloved longshoremen and boat owners and Chesapeake sailors, Sam would shake his head at the others, "Tommy great lad, great lad, but no bean, no upperworks, a fine hull but no captain on the bridge: that's all, but no matter, no matter, we cain't all be philosophers and scientists: there be they what must hew water and draw wood."

It was jolly, though, with Henny away: the morning flowed away like a clear running tide. Sam schemed with them; they listened to the birds and wondered where the mourning dove was nesting. They had birdbaths and seedboxes in their grounds and the thick trees invited many birds. They had left a wilderness patch at the far end of the orchard where old ivy, clematis, and honeysuckle mantled the tottering fence; for the hedge dwellers and the low-flying, insect hunters who loved to dart and sway on the slender sappy masts, goldfinches and fly-catchers. Along the side porch, inside the beams, were five nests, two of house wrens and three untidy ones of sparrows: they had thrown out the sparrows' nests in order to leave the house wrens in peace. It was a thriving, thickly inhabited wilderness, and merely lazing and looking, amateur naturalists, they could have spent the day. No urgent calls for help—to beat eggs, string beans, peel potatoes, empty slops, came from the unwomaned house. "Peace, perfect peace," sighed Sam a dozen times in the morning.

When he felt cheerfully warm, they began to talk about the neighbors, about whom they had just as many comical legends as about the Georgetown neighbors; and the kingpin, of course, was the atrocious "Coffin" Lomasne. Fearful tales were told of him—he was a vile spider of usury spinning foolish, weak, necessitous flies into his web. Sam told them all about poor Lai Wan Hoe and his troubles with the usurers, how he had to embezzle and fly, all because of Usurious Greed; and how they should not say such a man was an octopus, because an octopus was a sweet, clean beast whose rose-pink flesh they had eaten, but who would want to eat ghoulish Lomasne? An octopus was swift as shadow, a subtle chameleon, brave, clever, a battler— who could say so of "Coffin" Lomasne? And then they invented wilder tales about "Coffin"—dead marines rose out of his cheap coffins at night; one night the sucking marsh would open underneath him and try to digest him into the black mud where his poor corpses, oozing from their cheap coffins, lay, but being too vile and indigestible, he would be spewed up again. He was so mean, said Sam (inventing freely), that he kept his own excrement in a pit and doled it out to his own vegetables. The children shrieked, gasped with laughter, and got red in the face; for in general such jokes were not allowed at Spa House. Sam averred that "Coffin" was slowly turning diarrhea color, his clothes were stolen "from the swaddling clothes they wraps corps [corpses] in," and his cap was a candle extinguisher stolen from a wake. He made his wife eat candles stolen from wakes, said Sam, and they ate dandelion salad. What were the rats and cats that hung round "Coffin" Lomasne's, asked Sam, especially at night? Where did "Coffin" put his money, Sam speculated. He pictured the money put away in one of the coffins, and then he pictured "Coffin's" end: one night at one o'clock when all slept and the mud bubbled round his place, the mud that could not digest him, three poor blacks, invisible in the black night, would come and take "Coffin," place him in one of his own coffin-rowboats and row him out and across the deeps of the Chesapeake; and when they came to the Happy Hunting Grounds of the dead Susquehannocks, the shady braves would skin him alive and skin him dead and burn him at the stake and chop him up to feed the ghosts of sharks upon, and those ghostly sharks expiring in a shady way would become devil sharks and feed upon the others, and so on to a great

Armageddon in the shadow world, all because no one could stand the poison of "Coffin's" shade.

The children breathed peacefully before this wonderful story of "Coffin" Lomasne and were half believing it; but at the end, to bring their father back and make him start another of his tales of marvels, they pricked him on a sore point—why was the local postal delivery at present being done by a relieving man, given into the hands of Popeye Banks? Popeye Banks was a revolting being of seventeen years old, with an exophthalmic goiter excruciating to see. Generally he wore eyeshades, but sometimes he did not. Sam declared he was feeble-minded as well, and gosh only knew what else he did and had! He probably stole and spied: he certainly leered and limped. Like many a handsome body, Sam was not only revolted by deformity and plainness but actually saw essential evil in it: and essential evil, most particularly, was what robbed him, Sam Pollit.

> *Join the Navee and see the world!*
> *And what'd we see? We saw the sea,*

sang Ernie.

The boys flew into an excited discussion of the Naval Academy's spring sports schedule, baseball and plebe baseball (here Sam stuck in his nose, and said on no account to use that British import, "plebe"), and crew and track—they despised "the sissies," but Naval Academy made up half their talk, and the boys all now had an interest in living: they did not miss the nation's capital for a moment, but felt that they were now living in the heart of the United States. Here they ("the sissies," that is) were visited by Dartmouth, Harvard, Princeton, Cornell, Columbia, University of Virginia, Pittsburgh, and, of course, their own Georgetown. Their life was full of passionate discussions. They blessed Sam for bringing them to this little creek which was a whirlwind of boy life, and Ermy had even begun to weaken—with his mathematical talents he might even go to the Academy: how the little boys would admire him then! Many of their schoolmates, and Louie's too, were children of

[376]

the Academy staff, and the boys brought home plenty of gossip: So-and-so was a stinker ("say a stench," emended Sam), and they were sissies, they had to arrange and sew their own clothes and sweep their own rooms like girls, and Navy could of course win this year—no Baltimore college had a ghost of a chance (for their patriotism was limited to Spa Creek, and the United States Naval Academy was a Spa Creek affair). Sam was very happy, for he saw his gang (he now called them "his plebes") very happy. The "little women" were discontented, but, after all, he was a man too: this was a man's world. All girls were discontented till they married and had men and babies.

Both Sam and Henny now speculated openly (though separately) about the sort of man Louisa would marry. Henny went to Hassie's fortune teller who told her her stepdaughter would marry an officer at the Annapolis Naval Academy. "It's wonderful," said Henny in great surprise, to all her friends and even to Louisa, "I am certain she never saw me before yesterday." She immediately began to believe that Louisa would marry a naval officer and she looked on Louisa with more respect, began at last to listen to Louie's pleas about getting a permanent and a dancing frock. "If you're going to begin going about," said Henny optimistically, "your father will simply have to give up his stupid ideas about dancing and all his insane puritanical ideas. A great big girl your age who has never had a dancing lesson!" and she went so far as to write a note to Sam on this subject: "Samuel C. Pollit: You must arrange for your daughter to get dancing lessons and a suitable dress." This note enraged Sam beyond belief; in it he saw only another vicious attempt of "women brought up in the Baltimore white-slave tradition," to debauch his daughter. He refused once for all to allow Louisa to take part in such orgies or even to think about them. Henny, with grim, bitten lip looking ugly as sin (for her lips were purplish now and her skin dry saffron), had gone out with Hassie on a shopping expedition and bought what she conceived to be a young girl's dress, a thing that might have suited her well enough in her young days, a peach-colored, silky, filmy cotton, made with three frills round the shoulders and a trail of roses hanging from the waist.

It ended in Louie's not going to any dances, however, and in "mooning and moping" over Miss Aiden till the entire family of Pollits thought the child was queer, while Hassie told Henny she must early look out for a husband for her, or else some accident would happen to the great overgrown child. Henny, though she felt old-fashioned now, began to look round Baltimore, surreptitiously, for a husband for her stepdaughter—there was time, of course; Louie was only fourteen, but she looked like seventeen at least, and, thought Henny, "I've got to save her before he makes her a bluestocking that no man will want!"

They lived in a strange world. Sam did not yet go to work (although now a job as biologist was assured); Henny picked money out of the wind; Louie had left this earth completely and was floating about somewhere between Elysium and Inferno; Ernie had become "a crank," and the little children were inextricable from some mazy world of birds, flowers, winds, and tides. Sam was as near happy as he could be, and his chief worry now was Ernie and his "miserliness." The greatest family joke now going was that Ernie was growing up to be a miser, both a reproach and a great joke. Sam, too, not long ago, deciding to take the bull by the horns and to be as scientific as possible, much perturbed because Louisa had an "unscientific" view of procreation, had come to her where she stood washing her long waterfall of hair in the bathroom, and after poking his nose this way and that round all the corners to be sure that "the childer" were not within earshot, had given her three books— Shelley's *Poems* (to help her poetry, said he), Frazer's *Golden Bough* (for the anthropological side of the question, said he), and James Bryce's book on Belgian atrocities (to explain our entry into the war and the need for America's policing the world, said he). Louie now read stern proofs of stranger fairy tales acted in reality, more gruesome than any Grimms have recorded, though the Grimms are fearful enough, with their tales of forest cannibalism and murders. From the two latter books Louie was

[378]

able to fill her daydreams and night thoughts with the mysteries of men's violence—women crucified (so it was set forth with judicial severity) and unborn children torn from their bellies, young girls sent into barns with detachments of soldiers and "the ripening grain," soldiers winding the hair of women round their sabers and thus dragging them to the floor to satisfy their bestial desires.

There was plenty of this, and during the warm advancing spring Louie became more and more thoughtful and round-eyed. Sam might rave at her woodenheadedness as he liked, she had too much to dream about. Now, "so that you can tell the good from the bad, and avoid what your own conscience tells you is the wrong thing," Sam had revealed to her in a few weeks, and without a word of his, the unspeakable madness of sensuality in past ages and concealed imaginations; nations had done this, armies, great names and glorious artists, and her father had told her to study the books carefully with the following strange words: "It is the father who should be the key to the adult world, for his daughters, for boys can find it out for themselves." After this, Sam turned shy and avoided saying one word more to her on all these subjects, even avoided her, and when she turned her darkened, staring eye on him by accident, he would glance away as if ashamed. But the more she read of these works, the more she felt guilty of power of her own, and she began suddenly to despise and loathe Sam with an adult passion.

A very unpleasant thing had been discovered in an outlying part of the district in recent weeks. A girl child having been found pregnant, her father, a jobless roustabout, had been accused of incest; the girl went to a state home, but the father, only accused by hearsay and on the confused testimony of the child, still remained at home. The papers contained accounts and mysterious charges which the children read eagerly but did not understand. Sam's hair rose on the first evening and, suddenly flaming with temper, shouting with rage, he seized a stick and declared that there and then he would head a posse of respectable fathers and citizens and go to chastise the editor of the paper. "I am a man of peace," cried Sam shouting with rage, "but this is a case where vigilante law comes into being and has its function. The miserable cowardly yellow devil who dares attack a father in his own home, on top of the sorrow he must be feeling at finding his daughter in trouble, a little girl with a baby to come—think of that, Looloo, a girl two years younger than you, poor baby!—has to suffer undefended an unspeakable charge like this. He is to be brought up on this charge," shouted Sam, grasping his walking stick, "and because he is poor, and has only one of those windblows of shacks to live in, they can attack him with impunity. Every decent-thinking man and decent-living man in this community will be roused by this: I am a man of peace but I would go myself and horsewhip the dirty cur," and a frightening typhoon raged for a long time, a storm with a high yellow glare and copper-colored waves hissing, licking, and rising round them.

But Sam did not go: he only cursed the editor and declaimed every day until the subject died down. The daughter had accused her own father, "poor miserable wretch," said Sam sternly, "baby taught to say something to help the cause of a wicked lawyer. No doubt, Loo and Ernie," he continued, "you will find behind this story some dreadful corruption: a landlord trying to evict the man—doubtless he is a good man who has tried, in the past, to show up the forces of evil, and this is their stenchful revenge. My boys and girls, mark this; and notice other things that I bring to your notice. Your father does not get angry about things for nothing. This world is full of corruption, and when the foul press, the sink of greed, the gutter of moneybags spewing its filth back to the gutter whence it came, the harlot of the world, begins to get its back up and get moral about something, be sure that things are not what they seem and that they are trying to cover up, not *expose*, a scandal. When a man is poor," said Sam solemnly, turning to Ernie and pouring his white heat into Ernie's serious, round eyes, "the world hates him: you must be prepared for that,

Ermo: you might fight it as I have. The entire gamut of scandal, hate, and lying is prepared for a poor man in this world who dares to work for the truth. That is why they got rid of me too: they feared me, for wickedness fears Truth."

Ernie stared at him for a moment longer and, getting slowly off the porch where they were all sitting now, looking at Sam's blond flame, walked off by himself. They saw his round brown head disappearing amongst the bushes, down towards the beach. Sam winked at them all, and, nudging Looloo, said *sotto voce,* "Thinking! A thoughtful head! Not a big head but a brain with many corrugations, I'll be bound!" He smiled and nodded at them all, "A good boy!"

It was a queer thing, that though Louie had been brought up on *The Origin of Species* and *The Animal Kingdom* (of Cuvier) and numerous works in biology and psychology, not to mention the works Sam had just given her, she scarcely comprehended at all the actions meant by "sexual commerce." But after this horrific happening which had taken place in one of these hideous far suburbs built on yellow sumps and dominated by the Gargantuan black pipes of Bethlehem Steel, with nothing but tracks over the mud and colorless dry grass, she got the idea that she had run up against one of the wickednesses of the universe, an infernal middle kingdom of horror that she alone could stand. For Sam could rave and the little children could look at her queerly when she blurted out the half-formed thoughts in her mind, but she felt sure that she only *felt* what was going on under the ribs of the visible world. Under the eternal belching black organ pipes of Bethlehem Steel was the vile lake that covered an agony of fire, a lake that hid something like Grendel, or the pained bowels of an Aetna, or the cancer of a Prometheus, and in this lake too was this hideous father with his lying child half smothered by the swelling fruit of her womb.

Louie's brain boiled by day and by night, and every joke of Sam's, every silly crack and harmless tease made her flame with a murderous revenge. Whenever she and he were at home, she would mutter at him (from a silent distance), "Vengeance is mine, I will repay." Against this went her terrible passion for Miss Aiden, childish in its ignorance, adult in its turbulency. At school she was in heaven, at home she was in a torture chamber. The children would often study her attentively and seem to know that she was now in a very strange world, but to Sam she only seemed "more muddleheaded than ever, instead of brighter as I had hoped." To escape Sam she would always run away from the house with her book, usually Shelley (she wanted to marry a man like Shelley, only Shelley), and read and learn. *The Cenci*, a famous piece, she had avoided for weeks because the subject seemed forbidding, but when she at last began to read it, she began marveling again, for it seemed that (eliminating the gloomy and gorgeous scene) Beatrice was in a case like hers. The Saturday afternoon before Henny went to town, then, with the doll for poor Cathleen, she had learned,

> . . . *I, alas!*
> *Have lived but on this earth a few sad years,*
> *And so my lot was ordered, that a father*
> *First turned the moments of awakening life*
> *To drops, each poisoning youth's sweet hope; . . . .*
> (Shelley: *The Cenci*, Act V, Scene 2)

It was mid-afternoon when they saw Louie coming up from the beach again: the blood-gold sun rimmed grass, leaves, and Louie's new-washed hair.

"See where Looloo walked by herself, thinking her thoughts," said Sam to the twins, who were stretched beside him on the grass at the western side of the house. "Always thinking, always mooning, it's a pity she didn't have her own mother for a few years, and she would have been better. You see, I think I made a mistake letting her talk to Bonniferous so much, when poor Bonniferous was here, for Bonniferous had silly ideas about going on the stage and now Looloo does nothing but talk to herself," and cheerily he hailed her, "Bluebeak? Is you talkin' to yousef or is you recitin' poetry?"

Louie stopped and looked at them and said very proudly, "Reciting poetry, if you must know."

"Come, recite it to us, Looloo," said Sam stretching himself. Louie did not wait a moment but stepped over to them and declaimed Cenci's speech,

> *God!*
> *Hear me! If this most specious mass of flesh,*
> *Which Thou hast made my daughter; this my blood . . .*
> > *this devil*
> *Which sprung from me as from a hell, was meant*
> *To aught good use . . .*

Sam stared and his eyes narrowed, but he was reassured by the book in her hand, the very one he had given her; Louie continued,

> *. . .   if her bright loveliness*
> *Was kindled to illumine this dark world . . .*

Sam repeated softly, "If her bright loveliness was kindled to illumine this dark world," and waited patiently for Louie to continue, always with the gentle smile playing on his long, well-formed lips. Louie stopped and said proudly again, "You're making fun of me!" She started to leave them.

"Stay, Looloo," begged Sam. "No, not to be made fun of." "Stupid Looloo," cried Sam, in surprise. "Looloo, afternoon tea in the common room."

When she brought in the jingling tray and set it down at the western end of the long table, Sam and the boys had a lighted candle before them, and Ernie, who was very keen on physics, was explaining to them that in the center of the flame was nothing but a cool spot: if you put a match there, said Ernie, it would not light. The children, giggling with excitement, began brushing their fingers through the flame, to feel the cool spot. Ernie held his finger there for a moment and pulled it away with a comical shriek, and then Sam put out his big yellow forefinger and put it into the flame and drew it away, blowing and making a great travesty of his sufferings. Looloo stood watching the candle's pale ear of light floating beside the dusty sunbeam streaming through the window.

"And Looloo try," said Ernie, appealing to her, "you try too, Looloo," for Ernest was always anxious that everyone should be convinced of his proofs. The children meanwhile were dashing their fingers back and forth in a silly way, giggling and licking their hands. Louie, with a slight smile, stuck out the little finger of her right hand and held it in the flame. The children's faces stilled with surprise, their eyes opened, and Sam, whose face had held as always a merry jeer, looked questioningly at her, and he suddenly cried, "Looloo, don't be a fool!" while Tommy said, "Ooh, Ooh, you'll hurt yourself," and Ernie said, "Looloo, don't." There was a nasty smell of frying flesh in the room. Louie withdrew her finger and showed it to them for an instant, charred, and then coolly walked out of the room to go and wrap it in oil. Evie and Little-Sam were bawling, and the others were pale with fright, while Sam repeated several times angrily, "Looloo is a cussed, mulish donkey: Looloo has not an ounce of sense in her bonnet." He even got up and came to the door of the kitchen and asked angrily, "Looloo, isn't it hurting you?"

"It is not hurting me," she said stiffly.

"It must be."

"Nothing hurts me if I don't want it to," she told him. He lumbered away, shrugging his shoulders and utterly at a loss. The child was beyond him. He made up his mind that he would never let Ernie get out of hand like that. As for Evie, she was not going to go to high school. He had made up his mind that it was the higher education that had "knocked spots off Looloo's common sense," as he now told his little family in a soft grumble, and he would eat his hat if they ever caught him making a cantankerous wretch out of Little-Womey.

But Ernie pussyfooted out to the kitchen and asked, "Doesn't it hurt, Louie?" to which Louie replied with a smile, "Yes, of course it hurts, but it doesn't matter." With the children she felt cool; all her passions flowed far above their unharmed heads. This evening Sam left her alone in the cool of her room upstairs; and it was this evening, looking at the sky bloom darkly and the pendent globe of Jupiter, that she had a splendid idea. In June would be Sam's birthday, and for it she would write a play which the children could act. She got out her pen and paper and, instead of writing for Miss Aiden, wrote for herself, not for the children, a strange little play. When it was written (there were scarcely twenty lines in it), she turned it into a secret language that she began to make up there on the spot. This was a good idea, she thought: so that she could write what she wished, she would invent an extensive language to express every shade of her ideas. "Everyone has a different sphere to express, and it goes without saying that language as it stands can never contain every private thought." But she was only a weakling and a mental dwarf now as before, and the new vocabulary did not ever exceed a few hundred words, nor was there ever more than one play written in it! She was called from this by a bump and Chappy's (Charles-Franklin's) scream, and as she plunged to the rescue, she heard again Sam's plaintive, bashful question to Little-Womey, "Why is Mothering out all day? Why is the Henny-penny always away from the chicken-lickens now? Don't she want to take her responsibilities any mower? Why, Little-Womey, soon you got to be my wife, I speck."

"Yes, Taddy," Evie answered, from the porch door, seeing that Chappy was already in Louie's arms. She rushed up, too, seeing that he still sobbed, "Wassamatter, Chappy? Hurt ooself?" Sam came running, snatched the little butter-blond boy away and started tossing him to the ceiling and at last ran off with him, hallooing and doing the round of the orchard. They heard Chappy's loud crowing laughs.

"Daddy said I could be his wife," Evie told Louie, looking up at her confidentially and not sure whether she would laugh and approve. Louie turned her back, and Evie's face fell.

2 ⚔ Miss Aiden to dinner.

Since May the little boys with real fishing tackle had been fishing the streams that feed the Severn, and the local coves, with Sam. Sam predicted a roaring summer. Saul Pilgrim, who did a fishing column for one of the Washington papers and who wrote fishing poetry which he syndicated, was to come down to Spa House, just about Sam's birthday, June twenty-third, on his way to Ocean City, for the big-game season. The boys had caught plenty of poor sport, gudgeons, minnows, even pike and sunfish, but they nagged Sam to be allowed to go with one or other of the fishermen and boatowners down to the Winter Quarter Shoals or the Tide Rips, for catching the game king, the marlin, who in midsummer here strikes his most northerly point. Sam refused, and the boys found to their sorrow that even the fishermen were joking; the marlin is no minnow, will fight from four to fifteen hours, and kills his fishers when he can. The season was now the talk of the bay, for many men idle during the year are in good work from May to November. About three hundred thousand persons go to the Chesapeake for the summer fishing, six hundred and thirty odd boats are employed at a rental of nearly three hundred thousand dollars yearly, a giant revenue for the tidewater section of Maryland; meantime, the bait for trout, spot, and croakers, chiefly peeler crabs in all stages, sold at from fifty cents to two dollars a dozen has increased the income of the crabber, and, in addition to the big boats, are all sorts of rowboats, sailing boats, canoes, and lighter craft. The boys looked forward to a raging summer. Sam and other fishermen predicted from certain signs (early swarming, strange electric weather) a great catch. The air was alive with fish stories, the points of a good fisherman, and Sam was full of indignations and moral points—depletion of the crab supply, use of beardless hooks, the democratization of game fishing, and the commercial utilization of the immense supply of big game fish taken in at this season and wasted. "The marlin is a singularly oily fish"; said Sam, "no doubt the flesh is inedible, though it may possibly be treated, but surely we ought to use this valuable supply of animal oil, thrashing about in the ocean under our noses. The fishing is done for us, at great expense by wealthy fishermen," and he proposed schemes for receiving the marlin as soon as it was caught after verification of size and poundage, and to try out the oil and use the offal for fertilizer perhaps. "We are now slowly awakening to the need for reforestation," said Sam, "and why should we lay waste the great treasuries of the sea?"

The house rang with all this great lore, for now Sam was in his fishy element; and, from long hearing and training, his sons and daughters were as expert with the hook, line, and sinker, as they were with the brace-and-bit and plumb-and-level. The boys were only at home half the day, being out with the men of the bay, getting information and swapping eagerness. Although friends had long since ceased to come to Sam's house, Saul Pilgrim, the author of the interminable serial, had patience and pity and, without false pride, he would sneak in and out of Spa House, without meeting its lady and without asking for a meal. He would come into the dark narrow hall (very different from the broad thoroughfare of Tohoga House) and, while Louie took his hat, would begin poems and conundrums,

> Oh, do not bring the catfish here,
> The catfish is a beast I fear,
> Don't bring him here at all!

and,

> If I were born a Pelican,
> I'd do my best to be a Man;
> If I were born a Man, I'd wish
> I might associate with Fish;
> If I were born a Fish—but then
> What use to wish? Men must be men.

[387]

and very solemnly to Louie he would ask, "Do you know Latin?
Well, translate this:

> *Isa belli haeres ago*
> *Fortibuses in aro*
> *An be sidem forte trux:*
> *Si voticinem! Pes an dux."*

When Henny would come gloomily downstairs, he would
murmur politely and make himself scarce till she had passed.
Then he and Sam would sit down over some tea or coffee and
biscuits, and it would be nothing but flannel bait, white-line
peelers, green bait, beach casting, mine bilge pollution, Conowingo Dam shad, rainbow trout, and *Tetrapturus albitus*. In
the days just gone Saul Pilgrim had got information for his
columns from Sam, and Sam still could put him right on the
technical and formal side, for Pilgrim had but a messy, literary
mind and scattered experience. The children would sit around
for a while, casting in questions and hearing strange things—
how, sure as the calendar, the blue tuna turned up in the
Bahamas on May fifteenth each year and then worked north,
arriving in Nova Scotia on July fifteenth, and then disappeared
entirely from view for nearly a year, though they were sighted
cruising round the Atlantic end of the Mediterranean, and
then, sure as the calendar, would turn up again in the Bahamas
on May fifteenth; how they were hunting him by boat and by
plane; of the great deeps off the Bahamas, when the sea, suddenly shelving from four hundred to four thousand fathoms,
looks like a low-lying island and fatefully attracts unwary planes
at nightfall; the mystery of what happens in those abysses, and
all the mysteries of the sea; what is bred in the Sargasso Sea?
They spun each other old true yarns, known to the children
from their cradles, but which they listened to again, about the
conger eel, born a thousand miles from shore in the Sargasso
Sea, transparent as glass, which, working slowly shoreward, turns
into the elver, and at last near the coast he begins to feed and
turn dark.

"Now," said Sam, turning to the wide-eyed children, "millions of those elvers are approaching our shores, entering our tidal basins and estuaries, here and all along the coast from Gulf to Gulf. In from five to twenty years, until they are older than you, much older than Looloo, they stay up streams and creeks and feed, and then the females begin to drop downstream again, sleeping in the daytime, traveling by night; then they change from that olive green to black, they meet the males, and males and females move out to sea. When they leave our shores they disappear, like so many migratory pelagic beings; no one knows how they go—whether in a great swarm like the great migrations of men in the Asiatic continent, or singly, on a tremendous love journey. Their offspring are found out over the watery abysses, beyond Florida and the Bahamas. Then it seems they die. Out there in mid-ocean, they meet the European eels, but they do not go back with the Frog eels and the Spik eels and the Arab eels—no sirree, their children all know where they come from, and they come back to America when they are born, ribboning transparently through the heavy, dark sea water."

The children grinned from ear to ear, and Saul (who only in fishing found peace from his termagant wife) would grin too, and then would earnestly turn to Sam again and ask, Did he think the migratory schools of tuna and marlin traveled all the year in the Gulf Stream, as they were always to be found in the Stream; but even so, how they knew the time of year was a mystery.

"Do they come on May fifteenth in leap year too?" asked Ernie with his mouth open, for the answer to pop in. Oh, they spent long hours together, and then the children saw a different sort of man, a thoroughly democratic sort of man who had no thought of grades and length of service, or of mortgages and of his sons' being great scientists—they saw the Fisherman Sam; and Sam would say that though crops and livestock were privately owned, and birds and freshwater fish might be claimed by the land-grabber, the sea was socialist, the fish of the sea was for all, and it was wrong and a shame that anyone should presume to get separate fishing licenses and go fishing for private interest in the free and democratic sea: the fish should belong to all, the whole nation, the entire world could live off the sea, if it were properly used. But look how rash we are! When Captain John Smith came to the Chesapeake, he could ladle fish out of the bay with a frying pan—to fish with a line was not necessary. In Hiawatha's time, the Great Lakes were stirring with fish, but we know so little that if the law did not arm inspectors and wardens, we would empty the whole giant Chesapeake system of fish, crustaceans, and bivalves, all that were edible, and kill what was left with the hideous effluvia of capitalism! "We are all the sons of old David Collyer," said Sam, not troubling to drop his voice, "cramming our mouths, satisfying every taste, and wrecking his fortune and even grubbing into the ground under the house he built for odd pieces of good fortune that might be left. We are nothing but the locust; and the Department of Agriculture should send out planes to destroy with gas bombs those locusts of our foreshores and fishing waters who decimate the commissariat of our great and good mother Nature." (Then, as a footnote, Sam mentioned his idea, that man himself should be decimated, and, with the good tithes left, a new race, especially interested in fish conservation, might be propagated.)

"Would you kill off everybody?" inquired Little-Sam thoughtfully. The children were much intrigued by this idea of universal destruction. But Saul Pilgrim was not interested in social ideas, and he would proceed with some idea of his in fish cookery. He wanted with Sam to work out a fish-cookery column "to interest the ordinary greedy and the housewife, who can be touched only through their stomachs," said Sam, "in the conservation of some of our wondrous wild life."

Then Tommy took him off secretly to the washhouse where, from behind the copper, he drew out the brace of boats he was making for Sam's birthday, June twenty-third, a whaleboat and a buckeye. The whaleboat was little different from his rowboats and dinghies, but Louie would put cord round it in loops and make it all right; and on the buckeye Louie would put three sails, and they would fill it with little shells to look like a heavy load of oysters. Little-Sam had been scouting round the district for weeks and now had a marble bag full of wire and flooring nails, brads, tacks, and staples that he had found—most of them new or only slightly weather-stained. Saul had been selling newspapers, running round with his pleasant rosy face and straw hair, in a pair of gaiters against the mud, to get money to buy his father a new brace-and-bit, but now he had only enough money for a putty knife or two hinges for the new gate they were making for the driveway from driftwood. Saul hoped that this tale would draw a nickel or two from Mr. Pilgrim's tender pocket, but it did not. Meanwhile, Ernie, with the same idea, was hanging impatiently in the background. Ernie was in the worst stew of the lot. (Ernie's morale had, as Sam frequently said, "disimproved," and he was showing a sad strain of Collyer sullenness and a tendency to weep when jeered at; so, to cure him of it, Sam had taken to calling him "Glossy-eyes.") Glossy-eyes had meant to buy for his father a new steel square, but money had been short for a long time. He would never empty his money box if he could; but Henny had been borrowing from him for her trips to town and other little things, and not only could not afford any interest any more, but hardly ever paid him back. Even when she got her checks, she usually spent nearly all the money in a day or two, and what was left had to be sent to butcher or grocer to keep him in a good temper. Henny would not allow her eldest son to do jobs round the neighborhood; but Ernie had collected a great store of empty bottles, old iron, old springs, and old lead which he cheerfully begged and collectedly "found" in every rotting corner of the creek and cove. When would he have money? Ernie wondered. When would they let him go and get a job? Old David was dead. Old Ellen lived in a tiny cottage with Barry, who was pressed for money to buy drink and had had to let his mistress go (everyone knew it, and Ernie had seen the cottage and been frightened to notice that Old Ellen sat in the kitchen calmly, with her plump parchment hands on her knees, and her old black dress stretched to her hanging throat, and her large old eyes clear of any determination). The estate was nearly all sold and the business loaded with debts. Uncle Norman Collyer had quarreled with the whole family, the whole family was in debt and mostly without jobs (for now Old David was dead, the business could not keep them), and Uncle Philip had shot himself.

Ernie thought about it all during long hours. He harried Henny many days with his questions and calculations. He alone knew, of all the children, that Daddy had realized on his life insurance, that there was no fire insurance, and that there was a second mortgage on the house. He knew there was some delay about Daddy's getting his new job, and he had already asked Sam to sell the strip of viny wilderness at Spa House alongside the dead end or at least build two garages there and rent them. With his money so low, Ernie found it next to impossible to sell his lead in dribs and drabs to get a few cents, but wanted to accumulate it, in order to get a fat sum at the end. If only his mother had allowed him to sell papers, he would have been happier. Meanwhile, Ernie's lead was a standing joke, and even Henny grumbled perpetually about his "damnfool lead collection collecting dust and making rust marks on the cement floor, under his bed." Sam wisely kept away from the washhouse while the children were showing their presents to Saul Pilgrim and, having nothing better to do, went into the boys' room to smile to himself and also to step off the dimensions of a darkroom for photography that he proposed to build in one corner of it, near the kitchen sink, until such time as he could build in a bench and sink for the darkroom. He moved Ernie's bed, and an astonishing sight met his eyes, five or six large lumps of lead, irregularly formed, and several small ones that seemed to have been hammered out of shape. He had not looked for several weeks and had no idea how Ernie had got so much. Beside the lead were the bottles and several pieces of iron. In moving the bed, he had upset a chamber pot, and the urine, with the sight of the lead and the rust marks on the floor, caused him to begin hallooing and howling for the children, in a great state of excitement, fun, and horror. Saul Pilgrim had to come in and see how his house was kept at eleven in the morning; and then Sam flung out of the room with him, until the mess was cleaned up, and then once outside he began to poh! and pooh! and fooey! and fwow! at the smells and sights, while the little boys stamped around giggling, and Ernie, the cause of all this, stood aside mournfully, until Sam called him "Glossy-eyes," when he turned the corner, even more mournfully, and went down to poke a stick in the sand and write his name, "Ernest Paine Pollit." On the beach their shouts still reached him, "Oh, fwow! What a pigsty!" and then commandment, "Goyls, clean up the stinking shop! It's a pigsty! It's a sump! It's a garbage tip! Chicago is a violet farm by comparison," then the boys giggling again, and a remark by Saul Pilgrim, and Henny shrieking out of a top window, "What's the matter?" and Sam, actually replying to her, "Tell the dirty girls to clean up this pigsty of a house for once," and Henny answering (all in the tops of the trees), "Ten maids couldn't clean up after the filth you slop over the house every minute," and Sam shouting, in a towering passion, "You look after my house and children, or I'll get a separation," and Henny yelling, "I couldn't look after your child if I had ten hands and twenty eyes. Why don't you stop her picking her nose?" (For Henny had had a row with Louie ten minutes ago.) After this came a calm, during which the girls, both bawling, cleaned up the room and stripped the beds to air, while Sam, in a low, sad voice, lectured the boys outside on female sluttishness, and told them the sort of wives they must pick. "When I saw my first baby was a girl," continued Sam, pathetically, "I gave a whoop of joy, I wanted a little girl——"

"Roll yourself into a hoop and roll away," cried Little-Sam boldly, and was immediately terrified. After months of silence and even savage mutism, he would come out with something queer and insolent, and could not stop it. Sam was used to him and merely gave him a mild kick in the pants. But Sam was quick enough to catch a little smile on his friend's face, so he led him round to look at the new aquaria, and then into the boys' room to ask his advice about the darkroom. Saul was an old hand and he knew better than to expect lunch; so about eleven-thirty he took himself off, after promising to send Sam a marlin for a birthday present, "the very next Tuesday as ever is," said he. The children saw him go without regret; they felt he was a silly man enough to be writing poems in newspapers about "Goin' Fishin'"; he had not handed out any nickels; he was in trouble with an old vixen (as Sam told them a thousand times), and his name, amongst his colleagues was "Baits" Pilgrim—even Sam often called him "Baits" or "Peelers."

When he had gone, "Now," said Sam, "tell Glossy-eyes to come and hump himself, too. I want to see that lead in the washhouse before lunch."

"Ernie's got lead, under his bed," sang Little-Sam, and danced. "And Ernie's got old iron; there's the ferry siren."

"It don't Mattapeake," said Sam.

Ernie rose slowly above the front rise (which Sam called the Butte) with a martyred expression.

"Lead out, Ermineus," shouted Sam.

Ernie smiled with constraint, "I'm collecting it."

"Collect it in the washus."

"I'm collecting it."

"It's gotta go to the washus, Ermineus," wheedled Sam; "lotsa room there; no one will run off with your coupla tonsa lead. Two centsa ton, oh, boy what fun, but when de war come, it will go into a gun—" He stopped and said gravely, "That's true: no Ermy, we cain't colleck lead. Ain't it enough to have the planes dropping bombs on ducks? We gotta get rid of it."

> *Ernie will knock them dead,*
> *With his lead,*

said Little-Sam.

"I'll get rid of it when I can sell it," said Ernie. "You kids leave me alone: you all suck round Pad."

"Now don't say that, Ermy," Sam reproached him: "they love

their father. Do you think the Gemini like a mountain of lead in their room?"

"You leave me alone," said Ernie.

"Now, Ermineus, now, now!"

"Well, you leave me alone," remarked Ernie sulkily.

Sam looked handsome, spiritual, when he reproved Ernie, "I don't want you to lose your temper, Erno; you're all right, you're a good sort, but sometimes you get that Collyer expression and then I want to kick your pants."

Ernie tried not to look like a Collyer. When lunch was finished, though, Sam felt intrigued by the lead, and he said nicely, to Ernie, patting his shoulder, "Well, kids, a little yob before readin' and writin' and 'rithmetic; we'll jes heft that lead out to the tool house." The twins gamboled ahead to their room, which was at the back, looking over the orchard, and when they got in, they began to shriek and tug. "There it is, there it is!" Little-Sam lugged forth a huge, misshapen gray lump. Ernie went for him, gave him a whack, and said, "You leave that lead alone or I'll murderya." Sam was bending over looking at the lead, and Ernie cried angrily, "You leave that lead alone, I collected it," and he gave Sam a push.

"What?" cried Sam, astonished. He pulled out the lead with assiduity after bestowing a bear cuff on Ernie. Ernie kicked him in the pants. Sam was so surprised as to be almost pleased. "Imagine doing that to your poor little Dad! Ermineus! Kids, Ermy akshooly went and kicked his poor little dad." Ernie grinned shamefacedly, "You leave my lead alone, and I won't."

"You won't anyhow," said Sam, giving him a good whack. Ernie turned angry. Sam had managed to drag all the heavy stuff out now and, bothered by the exertion, he said angrily to his eldest son, "Ernest, if you're going to sell it, why the juice don't you sell it?"

The children tattled, "And he went past on Thursday, and Ermy wouldn't."

"He's keeping it: he can't bear to part with it," the twins said.

"He's in love with it," said Evie, giggling and putting her fat brown hand over her mouth.

"He loves it," said Sam, smiling to himself.

"Oh, I love you, lead," said Saul falsetto. "Oh, I'm going to marry you, lead."

Ernie grinned faintly. Sam smiled, and commanded, "Now, ebblebody ep cawwy yout diss yer leadulead." (Everybody help carry out this lead.) The children buckled down and with much puffing and groaning heaved it all out, along the side porch across the lawn (which would some day be a tennis lawn), to the tool house which stood over near the dead-end street. Ernie stood by, not lifting a finger, disobeying Sam, grim until the last piece was stowed away. Sam surveyed him and then, with sundry comical kicks, told the children to start their homework. Ernie stood, self-contained, at the end of the porch. Sam went down the orchard, watching him from moment to moment, interested to see what he would do, ready to rush in and give a final nick, like a fisherman playing a game fish and ready for the plunge and tussle. As soon as they had dropped the last piece, grunting, and had made themselves scarce for fear of further jobs, Ernie rushed forward and began to drag and tug it all the way back. Sam let him take back two pieces before he fell upon him.

"Take that back!"

"It's my lead!" Ernie doggedly dragged out another lump.

"Do what you're told!" Sam dragged it from him and sent it loudly clopping across the yard towards the washhouse door. Ernie began to cry, at first, miserably and then bellowing, but obstinate, and rushed at his father like a bull calf,

"It's mine, don't touch it: it's mine, I collected it; it's mine!" He banged Sam with his two fists blindly. Sam caught him roughly by the arm and swung him round to look in his face. Ernie kept his face lowered and tried to punch Sam again.

Sam said sternly, giving him a mild kick, "Sam-the-Bold said, 'The washhouse'!"

"It's mine."

"Then you've got to sell it. What are you keeping it for?"

The family was again timidly collecting, in various stages of beach attire, at the far edge of the scene, peering through the trellis from the western porch. "What are you keeping it for?"

Saul shouted helpfully, "It's for your birthday, Pad!" Sam dropped Ernie's arm at once and said gently, "Is it for Sam-the-Bold that you're doing this?"

"I'm saving it!"

"Is it for me, Ermineus?"

"I'm saving it!"

Sam was beginning to smile to himself again, "It's nothing to be ashamed of."

"I'm saving it!"

Sam, suddenly tiring of the struggle, began to stretch his long legs across the grass. At the porch, Little-Sam whispered wonderingly, "Pad, he's taking it back again." Sam nodded, "Sure nuf! Sure's you're alive! Ermy's got some will power! Yessuh! And is it for me, really?"

"Yes," they all confirmed eagerly.

Sam was delighted. He wheeled the twins round cheerfully and began to march them. "Now then," he said, "To market, to market to buy a fat pig, home again, home again, jiggity-jig!"

When Louie started to bring out the lunch, she paused with a dish in her hand, and asked, smiling sillily, "Dad, can I ask Miss Aiden to lunch soon?"

"Old Aido," shouted Sam, in appreciation: "the bewchus dame shall grace our board. What say next Choosday, my burfday? Ask Old Aido to dinner next Choosday evo [evening]." Louie blushed and almost crumpled to the floor with pleasure. The children jeered a little, but they were anxious to see the famous and beloved beauty themselves. Henny, who was in the kitchen, grumbled a great deal, but gave in easily, only saying, "She must take potluck: I'm not making anything special for any hoity-toity schoolteacher."

"She's isn't hoity-toity, Mother: she's a wonderful woman, she's so kind and understanding, she's so nice, she's a wonderful woman."

"I don't doubt it," said Henny; "well, when she comes here she'll understand a few things too, if she's so wonderful." Louie never doubted for a moment that Henny would exert herself to make a good dinner for Miss Aiden, especially as it was Sam's birthday too; but Ernie worried like a major-domo, running five times on Sunday and twice daily on Monday and Tuesday to ask, "Mother, what will we give Miss Aiden? Mother, are we going to have roast meat? Mother, what are we going to have for dessert? Mother, will there be a clean napkin for Miss Aiden? Mother, will you have some of my snapdragons on the table or some of Saul's wallflowers? Mother, the oilcloth on each door-step is worn right out, you can't see the pattern."

At each excursion, Henny would grumble and mutter things like, "Let her see! Who is she, the wonderful woman? What do I care? Don't drive me crazy! Oh, you kids will have me in the bathouse! Stop bothering! I don't care if we eat off the floor!" Though Louie was too blind to see it (after ringing up Miss Aiden in Baltimore and getting her consent, being in a delirium of expectant love), Henny made no special preparations even for Sam's birthday. "Let his kids amuse him," said she, to Louie who, however, took no more notice of this ominous remark than of anything else. Henny secretly believed that Miss Aiden could not be such a bad creature "if she took an interest in such a slummicker as Louisa," and she made up her mind to let Miss Aiden see how the little girl really lived and how the grand Pollits really lived and how she, "the mother of so many children," really lived.

Sam's birthday began in a lovely morning, and everyone got up early. There was dew on everything, the cedar-waxwings were eating the mulberries, and there was the sound of a bombardment from the corrugated iron roof of the new shed, where the wasteful little wretches, in their hundreds, threw down scarcely tasted berries. There was haze over everything, dew on the ant-hills, and the determined, brilliant wasps were at work, scratching wood fiber off the old wooden bench with a light rasping sound, zooming dizzily and plastering with a do-or-die air. It was so steamy-soft that the birds were relatively silent, except the bobbing, stripping cedar-waxwings and the black "devils of the sky," far off with a soft cah-cah. The sky was gray with humidity, the sun could be looked at with the naked eye, a pan full of liquid, like a dish of snapdragon, and against this sky the leaves were sharp and austere as in a steel engraving. Henny, running about early to get the tea "so that the kids could prance around their father," declared that she felt nervous as a cat. Louie looked at the silky sulky reflections of sepia and dun in the creek and thought they were like the shades of a woman's unsunned breasts; there was a still, breeding, inward-looking moist atmosphere, so that it seemed beans would begin to push out of the earth suddenly; it was like a bride, heavy with child, dull and potent. Louie could hardly lift her heavy stumps, even when Henny called sharply, but she did arrive in the kitchen in time, and there Henny was kind to her, asked her if the children had all a present for their father, and what she had got for him; and furtively, and with a shamed face, Henny gave Louie a little parcel in tissue paper for him; it was a pair of hand-knitted socks (which he preferred and which were easier to reheel and retoe). "And your present?" whispered Henny. Louisa said, "I wrote a play." Henny looked at her curiously, wondering at her cheapness, but at length said, "Well, I suppose your father will like it, at any rate," and sent her off upstairs with the tea, where a great jamboree was in progress.

"Is this a present for Sambo-the-Great?" inquired Sam, lifting the tissue paper parcel off the tray.

"From Mother," said Louie.

Sam squinted comically at them all, opened it, and, after inspecting the knitting, said, "Well, I don't say no, boys and girls: socks is socks; but I love hinges and nayrers [nails] en doyleys, even ef the stitches which is there are a bit spidery, en doyleys Little-Womey, enwhaleboats en bugeyes what is on the way, en I will go fishin for eisters en whales disarvo [this afternoon], en I like the shavin' brush what Charles-Franklin guv me—" and he looked at Louie.

"And Louie wrote you a play," said Ernie, dancing with excitement. Louie marked time shamefacedly, "It's a tragedy, and it's only in one scene."

"Hit's doubtless a tragedy," remarked Sam, "en once seen, is seen pretty often: bit whar is hit?"

"In my room," Louie said unwillingly, "but the varmints" (she waved her hand towards Ernie and Evie, who for once dropped their squabble and glanced with meek conceit at each other), "the varmints know it; they are going to recite it."

"We learned it," burst out Evie, and looked all round the room, red with excitement. "And you can't understand it." Sam stared at them all, grinning and pleased as punch at the great secret, which he had known was simmering for the past week.

"We don't know what it means," said Ernie.

"Ernie is the father, and Evie is the little girl," Saul told them; "it is about a father and a little girl."

They were all mystified and excited. Sam said, "What's all this? Now, Little-Sam, you bring in the prog, en after prog we see the play."

The two actors scooped up the oatmeal with the greatest speed, but Sam insisted on everyone polishing his plate with his tongue, before the play. Then, when the coffee was put round, Louie came and put a piece of paper in front of Sam and herself recited the prologue, which was nothing but a quotation from Longfellow (*The Masque of Pandora*):

> *Every guilty deed*
> *Holds in itself the seed*
> *Of retribution and undying pain.*

Sam, with open mouth, meanwhile had been looking from her to the paper and from the paper to her, for on the top of the paper he read, in painful capitals: TRAGOS: HERPES ROM. JOST 1. When Louie had finished reciting, he asked in a most puzzled voice, "What is this, Louie?" Louie gravely pointed to the paper, "This means—TRAGEDY: THE SNAKE-MAN. ACT 1. There is only one act," she explained: "I thought we could do it too, this evening when Miss Aiden comes."

The two actors, meanwhile, were swollen with pride and agitation.

"Why isn't it in English?" asked Sam angrily. Louie was at a loss to explain this, so she scolded, "Don't put the children off. You follow on the paper." The others meanwhile left their places to crane at the sheet. "There are two actors," said Louie, "The man—*Rom*—whose name is Anteios; and the daughter—*Fill*—whose name is Megara. Evie is Megara, and Ernie is the *Rom*, Anteios."

"Why can't it be in English?" said Sam feebly. Louie smiled vacantly, like a little child, "I don't know—I thought—anyhow, go on, Anteios! Ia deven . . ."

The boy and Evie then proceeded to recite.

ANTEIOS: *Ia deven fecen sigur de ib. A men ocs ib esse crimened de innomen tach. Sid ia lass ib solen por solno or ib grantach.*

MEGARA: *Men grantach es solentum.* ("*Men juc aun,*" said Louie) *Men juc aun.* ("*Ben es bizar den ibid asoc solno ia pathen crimenid,*" said Louie, and Evie repeated it with several promptings.)

ANTEIOS: *Corso!* (shouted Ernie with enthusiasm). *Ib timer ibid rom.*

At this point, Evie, whose memory had failed completely, broke down and burst into tears, much to Louie's discomfiture. With a brusque gesture, she thrust Evie behind her into a seat against the wall (where she sobbed soundlessly for a minute and then looked up, her fat brown face pearled with two tears). Louie announced now, "I will do Megara: Evie forgot it."

MEGARA: *Timer este rom y este heinid pe ibid fill.*

"I don't understand," said Sam, with a floundering expression, "what is it?" Meanwhile Ernie rushed on,

ANTEIOS: *Ke aben ia fecend?*

MEGARA: *Tada jur vec tarquinid trucs ib rapen men solno juc men pacidud. Y hodo men solentum es du. Alienis dovo. Nomen de alienis es hein. Vad por ic vol fecen ibid ocs blog.*

ANTEIOS: *Ib esse asenen—asanen—men libid fill.*

MEGARA: *Sid ia pod ia vod chassen ib semba fills re Lear.*

ANTEIOS: *Roffendo!* (shouted Ernie and again shouted). *Ke tafelis!*

At this the children began to giggle and Ernie, repeating with a great shout, "*Roffendo! Ke tafelis!*" all the children cried, "*Roffendo! Ke tafelis!*"

"Do they know what it means?" asked Sam, rousing himself out of a perfect stupor of amazement. Louie explained reproach-fully, "Yes: that means, 'Horrible! What a she-devil!'" Sam's eyes popped, but further remarks were prevented by Ernie in-sisting with his cue "*Ke tafelis! Ke tafelis!*" Louie continued.

MEGARA: *Fill in crimen aco ib aben aunto plangid. Cumu mat dic ia cada: sol vec incriminenidud. Sid aten atem es grantach ke pos fecem. Ia ocen ib esse volid prin men aten men atem, men jur. Alienis vol mort ib.*

ANTEIOS: *Ke alienis? Esse ib imnen? Brass im, men fill.*

MEGARA: (Shrieking feebly) *No im! Suppo! Alienis garrots im! Herpes te!*

ANTEIOS: *Ke alienis? Esse im immen? Ke fecen ib? Brass, brass im!* (Aside) *Ma Herpes?* (At this point Ernie began to writhe and hiss, poking out his tongue instantly at all present, imitating a snake.)

MEGARA: (Shrieking feebly) *Ia mort. Ib esse alienis! Ib mort im! Occides! Occides! Mat!*

ANTEIOS: *Ia solno brass im. Men libid fill* (but in embracing Megara, Anteios hisses again like a snake).

MEGARA: (Shrieking hoarsely) *Mat, rom garrots im, Occides!* (And she dies.)

After this striking scene in double-dutch, Sam, looking with pale annoyance on Louie, asked what the Devil was the use of writing in Choctaw. What language was it? Why couldn't it be in English?

"Did Euripides write in English?" asked Louie with insolence, but at the same time she placed the translation in front of her father, and he was able to follow the *Tragedy of the Snake-Man, or Father.*

Father—Anteios and *Daughter—Megara.*

ANTEIOS: I must make sure of you. In my eyes you are guilty of a nameless smirch. If I leave you alone for only an hour you sin.

MEGARA: My sin is solitude. My joy too. Yet it is queer in your company only I feel guilty.

ANTEOIS: Naturally! You fear your father.

MEGARA: Fear to be a father and to be hated by your daughter.

ANTEIOS: What have I done?

MEGARA: Every day with rascally wiles you ravish my only joy, my peace of mind. And now my solitude is two. A stranger is there. The name of the stranger is hate. Go, for he would make your eyes bulge out.

ANTEIOS: You are sick, my beloved daughter.

MEGARA: If I could, I would hunt you out like the daughters of King Lear.

ANTEIOS: Horrible: what a she-devil!

MEGARA: (I am) an innocent girl that you have too much plagued. As mother says, I am rotten: but with innocence. If to breathe the sunlight is a sin, what can I do? I see you are determined to steal my breath, my sun, my daylight. The stranger will kill you.

ANTEIOS: What stranger? Are you mad? Kiss me, my daughter.

MEGARA: (Choking) Not me! Help! The stranger strangles me. Thou snake!

ANTEIOS: What stranger? Are you mad? What are you doing?

Embrace, kiss me. (Aside) The snake? (He tries to hiss to himself.)

MEGARA: (Shrieking) I am dying. You are the stranger. You are killing me. Murderer! Murderer! Mother!

ANTEIOS: I am only embracing you. My beloved daughter. (But he hisses.)

MEGARA: Mother, father is strangling me. Murderer! (She dies.)

As soon as Sam had read this, Louie also put beside his plate the vocabulary to prove that her translation and the words were quite correct; and with a cheek of burning pride, full of playwright's defiance, she waited for his verdict. Sam said slowly, "And where is Act II?" Louie was short. "It all happened in Act I." The children, oddly excited, shrieked with laughter, and Louie, after one glare, rushed out of the room. Sam fumbled with the papers, muttering, "I don't understand: is it a silly joke?" He asked the children, "Did Looloo tell you? What is her darnfool idea?"

Ernie explained,

"She said she would have written it in French, but she doesn't know enough grammer, she said. So she made up a language."

"Damn my eyes if I've ever seen anything so stupid and silly," complained Sam, looking at the vocabulary again. He shouted, "Looloo, you come back here: don't stay in there blubbering! Oh, for God's sake, it's my birthday: don't be an idiot." Louie trailed slowly out, while the children, chapfallen, considered her mournfully. Evie, extremely abashed at having forgotten her part, had squeezed herself into her mother's chair with Tommy and put her arm round his neck.

Sam said, "Sit down, Looloo: blow me down, if I know what's the matter with you. Instead of getting better, you are getting more and more silly." He suddenly burst into a shout, "If Euripides or any other Dago playwright makes you as crazy as that, you'd better shut up your books and come home and look after your brothers and sister. I can't understand it with a father like you have. I'm sorry I didn't insist on your learning science, and nothing but science. Whatever your stepmother's influence, you've had my training and love from the earliest days, and I did not expect you above all to be so silly: you were the child of a great love. However, I suppose you'll grow out of it." He sighed, "At least, I hope so: you're growing out of everything else. Well, let's say, some day you'll be better."

Louie began to squirm, and, unconsciously holding out one of her hands to him, she cried, "I am so miserable and poor and rotten and so vile and melodramatic, I don't know what to do. I don't know what to do. I can't bear the daily misery. I can't bear the horror of everyday life." She was bawling brokenly on the tablecloth, her shoulders heaving and her long hair, broken loose, plastered over her red face, "No wonder they all laugh at me," she bellowed. "When I walk along the street, everyone looks at me, and whispers about me, because I'm so messy. My elbows are out and I have no shoes and I'm so big and fat and it'll always be the same. I can't help it, I can't help it," and, still bellowing "I can't help it" with the manner and tone of a half-grown calf, Louie got up and staggered to her room. She stood at the door, halfway open, and beat on it with her soft half-open fists, crying brokenly, "I can't help it!" and weeping endlessly.

Sam said gravely, "Stop working yourself up into hysteria."

"They all laugh at me," cried Louie. "They all laugh at me: I can't stand it any more."

Unexpectedly, Ernie burst out crying, his brown, merry, escutcheon-shaped face bobbing up and down and his wide mouth gone into an oblong. Louie turned round towards them and advanced towards them, her eyes drowned with tears, her hair straying everywhere and darkened with water and her face slobbered over and, coming to the table, as to a jury, she asked in a firmer voice, but still crying, "What will become of me? Will life go on like this? Will I always be like this?" She appealed to Sam, "I have always been like this: I can't live and go on being like this?"

Sam testily cried, "Like what? Like what? What is all this about? I never heard so much idiotic drivel in my born days. Go and put your fat head under the shower. Is it because Miss Aiden is coming that you're making this—excruciating—stupid, oh, I can't find words to describe it. How can you be so stupid?"

Louie turned away again and trudged away, but she cried no more, and merely sat on her unmade bed in the room: while Henny could be heard muttering and cursing in the kitchen.

"A nice beginning to a beautiful day," said Henny. Well, to restore courage to the children, Sam began their invocation to the Free State, "With," said Sam,

"WITH Susquehanna, Pushmataha, Tuscarora, Octoraro, Co-
hongoroota,
AND   Assawoman, Mattawoman, Chesapeake, Matapeake,
Choptank, Tonytank, Tuckahoe, Piscataway,
AND   Nassawango, Conowingo, Annemessex, Honga,
AND   Wicomico, Rewastico, Chicamacomico, Chaptico,
AND—   Pohick!"

a barbarian chant with which they raised the roof and restored good humor. When this was done, they slid out of their places, and Sam pleasantly went to fit the hinges and watch the sailing of the quite-finished whaleboat and part-finished buckeye in the creek. The children were all excused from school for Sam's fortieth birthday.

"Fer," said Sam, "ef I cain't hev you all around me fer ter skelebrate my forty-years-young, what was the good of hevin you at all? Tell your teacher to put that up his pipe and smoke it. Ef I didn't want ter hev you, he wouldn't hev no job. Tell your teacher to put that up his pipe and smoke it." The children giggled.

Louie refused to stay at home for her father's birthday, but sped off to school as usual, much fretted to know what Clare would do. Yesterday she had avoided Clare, and Clare, with a grin, had kept away from her; and in class she had only sent Louie one note, saying, "Hollow groans from underneath the ground," one of her senseless scribblings which made Louie giggle, however, and relieved her. Today, Louie was sure to find Clare mooding round the gate waiting for her. The play, Tragos: Rom Herpes, which had been in rehearsal for a week, Louie now was impatient to show to Clare: before she had been as timid as a convent bride, and now she wanted to show it to the leg of the table itself if it showed signs of animation. Then, she had a bunch of wallflowers for Miss Aiden to keep up her spirits until the birthday dinner in the evening; and, instead of writing a sonnet for Miss Aiden, she had begun a play, called *Fortunatus*, in which a student, sitting alone in his room in the beaming moon, lifts his weary head from his book and begins by saying,

FORTUNATUS: *The unforgotten song, the solitary song,*
The song of the young heart in the age-old world,
Humming on new May's reeds transports me back
From the vague regions of celestial space——

(to Rosalind, his Marguerite, of course).

Louie's senses reeled with love: it was warm; and yesterday during a lesson out of doors, when Louie, with daring, had recited,

Spirit of Beauty, that dost consecrate
With thine own hues all thou dost shine upon;

(but did not continue this falsely appropriated "Hymn"), Miss Aiden, with a gentle smile remarked, "Love begets love they say!" For a moment, sensation ran through Louie like a sweet summer river, but afterwards she felt a little disappointed in Miss Aiden; it was improper in the goddess to respond. Miss Aiden, in fact, did not understand (having only just come from college) that all the best gods are made of stone and say nothing. At any rate, Louie now felt that the play of *Fortunatus* would celebrate Miss Aiden in a nobler and more austere way than the mere cycle of sonnets. On the way to school, in the bus, she stuffed in quickly the botany lesson. Fortunately, owing to Sam's eternal confidences, botany was second nature to her.

Back at home, Sam was happy as Aeneas in his happy moments, surrounded by his adoring companions and crew, and, occasionally offering up expressions of love and gratitude to his goddess, Nature, was circumambulating his estate. He had a happy idea and sent the twins round to all the houses in the neighborhood to ask their friends of junior school age and below school age to come to Spa House at three o'clock in that afternoon, to have ice cream and run round the new Wishing Tree, to celebrate Sam Pollit's birthday.

"And I wish," said Sam; "that dear little Mareta could come and Whitey and Borden, en evvlebody, en even the goat kid."

When Ernie and Louie got back from school, therefore, the Spa House wilderness was piebald with neighbors' children, venturing into desirous nooks and nests, paddling on the beach and climbing the gnarled, neglected fruit trees. By the morning mail, Sam had had a letter from Saul Pilgrim, "It looks like a catch, but I'll have to delay my present for a week or so, but keep your eyes skinned for a whopping big TETRAPTURUS" (marlin), and now he entertained some of the children with a tale of what he would do when he got the whopping big marlin that was promised to him: he would have a tent on the beach and charge one cent admission, but they could all come in free, by special admission, provided they ran round the Wishing Tree once each; and then he would boil that marlin down till it was nothing but oil, when they could each come with a little bottle and get two ounces to rub their arms for muscle strain, or oil their bikes, or give their mothers for dry skins, or even, perhaps, maybe, it might make automobiles go, though Sam could not swear to that yet. But at any rate he intended to oil the universe with the game, and make the luxurious sportsmanlike spearfish work for mankind.

At four o'clock sharp, the children were lined up for the ice cream that Sam had just sent for in pails, ranged from the biggest to smallest and the smallest first. What a pleasure that was for the toddling Doreen Monks, who lived in the cottage at the end of Second Street, and how irritated Red Lomasne was to come last! When they had been round once, Butch Brewer, looking in the pail, asked if he could take some home to his little brother, at which all the girls cried, "Ooh!" and shushed and giggled, themselves looking hungrily at the pails, while the Pollit children stood a little apart, somewhat grim, hoping there would be a bit left over for them after; but Sam at once made them all march round again and gave them all a lick-and-a-half, so that all was fair. . . .

Meanwhile Louie was inside, rubbing up the silver and peeling the vegetables, while Henny went upstairs to change her dress: and Ernie came inside, as soon as "the kids" began to straggle off (some of them disappointed that they hadn't received any presents, for they were confused about whose birthday party it was). Ernie hovered around Louie, much to her delight, asking a hundred questions: where was Miss Aiden now? (At the teashop with another teacher.) Louie began to set the table at sunset with her satellite Ernie. First came the threadbare damask cloth (Henny still thought all colored cloths vulgar and when she could, renewed her Irish damask). The cloth was much darned, yet in holes, and coffee-stained. Over the stains Louie adeptly fixed the cruets (they were not assorted, and one pair was a gift pair got with coupons), and the butter dish. There was one clean napkin for Miss Aiden. The water jug had been broken only the week before and so for water they used a large milk jug. Now Louie noticed, for the first time, that they had only one glass for water. She hunted high and low and found nothing but peanut-butter jars and the like. It dawned upon her that they had had no glasses for a long time; and then she called to mind a slow dwindling in goods, over years. She remembered that once they had had dozens of engraved water glasses, always of the same design, a Greek-key pattern, which had been with them for years, and then had come plain glasses got at the ten-cent stores (Henny despised the florid ones), and then gift glasses got with packets of tea, until now they had only one in the world. But she was enraptured by the dinner that was to come, too rapt to be ashamed, and went on with her work, now noticing that they were really poor, but not caring, for, she thought to herself, "Miss Aiden is above caring whether we have things or not" (but she thought Miss Aiden would observe that they had a wonderful water frontage and would probably think they were "temporarily distressed"). Like Henny, she had too much to do to be able to moon over details.

But Ernie was different. He went to look at the table and count the places, see that all was there, spoons, forks, knives, when he saw the glass, sitting solitary as a lighthouse on an atoll. He poked round, seeking the other glasses, and had to admit there were no more. This caused him to look at the vase, containing Little-Sam's wallflowers, which was an ugly thick tube from the ten-cent store; in a moment he was climbing the stairs, his rosy face most serious, and was in Henny's room (where she was taking an aspirin), asking, "Mother, where's the big silver vase; we had two big silver vases?" Henny cried, "Stop snooping, will you? It's put away." "But, Mother, can't we have it for dinner tonight?" "Oh, who is she, for the love of Mike," cried Henny, "is it Eleanor Roosevelt that's coming to dinner? I put all the silver away in Aunt Hassie's vault." "But why, Mother, why did you?" "You scoot; I've got a headache."

Ernie was dismayed. He sat down thoughtfully on Henny's old carpet hassock, and as his eye roved round the room, a fearful truth burst on him—there was nothing there, nothing that had been in the old house, nothing that had delighted his babyhood. He jumped up, "Mother, where are all your things from the dressing table?" "What's the matter with you tonight? Surely you're not in love with the wonderful woman, too. You're like a flea." "But, Mother, you had thirty-seven silver things—" He went, quite distracted, to the dressing table, where in the old days the three beveled mirrors had reflected brushes and combs in a silver tray, jewel case and pin trays, scent bottles and every conceivable tool and utensil for a lady's dressing table, all tooled silver. Now, here was a bakelite brush, comb, and mirror

[410]

and one pinbox. The cut-glass smelling bottles and even the beautiful little self-winding clock had disappeared. "Mother, why did you put them all in the vault?" he asked, coming to her chair. "Did you put your rings there, too?" "Yes," she replied sullenly; "everything."

He turned to the tallboy (which had once held his father's clothes), and searched on it too, for the things that had stood there, but it was bare except for a dusty linen cover and a neglected envelope. Henny watched him grimly, saying nothing. Ernie went impulsively to her wardrobe and pulled open the place where her hats usually were—where were the hats, the three black ostrich plumes got from her cousin, the silk opera cloak, ten years old, that she had once worn? Where was the collection of postcards, with stamps from all over the world, that had been there once—though he could not remember when he last played with them (it was a long time ago). He came back to her chair and looked down at her, while she looked up smiling grimly, into dark eyes like her own. "Mother, why did you put everything away? Did you put the hats and feathers and everything in the vault?" "No," Henny smirked, "they are at Uncle's." "At Uncle Barry's?" "Oh, leave me alone—" Henny broke off and got up. She went to the dressing table and brushed her hair, now almost entirely gray. "Mother, won't you get them back again? Why can't we have them?" She turned round desperately,

"Look, my son, don't pester Mother: I sold them! Now, don't you dare tell anyone, for if you do I'll break your neck. If you want your father howling after me, all you've got to do is to tell him, that's all: the Great I-Am is too damned full of himself to notice what's going on; that's why I don't listen to his raving about margarine and beans and such trash: I'm paying for the dinners, and I'll have what I like. If he knew—" She stopped, listened to the scattered, evening shouts of the children still playing round the place. "He can buy ice cream for all the dirty kids in the neighborhood!" She looked down at her tall twelve-year-old son, who was transfixed on the worn carpet, halfway to her, between the armchair and the table. "Ernie-boy," she continued sharply, "Mother has had to sell everything she ever owned that she could: I've sold the clothes off my back. I only can't sell this furniture and this carpet because they are too big, and he would notice that. Who knows?" she asked Ernie abruptly, "perhaps I'm a Goddamn fool! Perhaps he notices everything and is willing to let me bust my bones over his grocery bills, as long as he has swill to put in his belly; he's more of a child than you are, you poor little wretch. What luck have I? I don't suppose you'll be anything but a cheap little accountant yourself— you haven't any chance to make money with a father like that. And who is going to pay for your education? Listen, Ernie-boy, Mother would have committed suicide a thousand times before now, if it hadn't been for you, because I thought the Big-Mouth would get a job and give you a start and you'd be able to make money for Mother. When I saw you were a boy, I didn't care so much, although I went through hell before I ever saw your face, my boy: because, I thought, my baby boy will be growing up with me and when he's big enough I'll go off with him and perhaps—well, never mind: I don't want to start whining like the Man of Sorrows. Ernie-boy, don't you listen to anything you hear about your mother: you stick to me, baby-boy, or I'll just go and jump in the creek. I haven't any money for you or for anyone. He's taken everything, him and his eternal babies that he's got out of me. I don't know what to do, Ernie. Wait till she sees what I'm going to give her fine schoolmarm tonight. Irish stew and bread pudding. Perhaps she won't notice. She's going about foaming at the mouth with biggity ideas and snobbery such as I never heard, like her beautiful father; they're like as two peas in a pod: she probably won't notice what she's eating. (I wish her stupid crank of a father would notice what a silly stew she's getting into.) Do you hear? What I've got for dinner tonight, with a visitor coming, a fine lady who gets as much in a week as I get in a year, is Irish stew! You——"

"Mother, and there's only one glass."

"Don't I know it? Because we can't pay for a rotten little

maid, a kid that's going to trades school, or even Lomasne's little kid, I have to let that great big slummicker wash the dishes and smash every glass and plate in the house; and you kids are no better, with him jigging and singing and you all gaping with your mouths open when you're drying the dishes and dropping everything. Do you wonder I have to scream at you children? Every rag is in shreds, and every dish is smashed to smithereens. What does he care? As long as he can gas and gab and plume himself on his success in life."

Ernie looked at Henny, from his rounded eyes, with his face drooping. He trailed slowly off to the door and, as soon as he was clear, began to search the house from top to bottom; all, all things valuable had disappeared. Pottering dolefully to the room he shared with the twins, Ernie pried up the loose board (loosened by him) under which he kept his money box and sat down with it in his hand, wondering and occasionally shaking it a little. There were still in it two dollars and seventy-eight cents. Still thinking, he began to shake and poke at it to take out one of the coins, and presently one fell out into his hand. He stared. It was brassy; and then he wondered if it were a dream, for here was no American money, but the one-franc piece that he had often fingered in his mother's collection of foreign coins. In one of the open drawers of her dressing table, she had had, long ago, a heavy collection of old foreign coins. A silver groat, a giant old-fashioned English penny, heavy as four modern ones, a sixpence, some Roman and Chinese coins, a one-franc and a two-franc piece, in all worth very little. (It had been one of Ernie's dreams that here was a treasury worth much in exchange, but Sam had laughed and told him it was "Aunt Tabitha's weeping-willow brooch," which meant that it would bring nothing at all in the market.) Ernie shook again with agitation and this time succeeded in getting a rain of little coins, a few cents, the groat, a three-penny-bit; he shivered, thinking a horrible joke had been practiced on him by fairies or ghosts: and then came yawning into his head the picture of the empty drawer below, and he turned cold with fear—perhaps someone (Henny?) had changed his good money for this trash money. He shook and shook, in a frenzy, but with all the rattling, only the dream money came out, and as he shook out the last coin and heard that the light box made no sound but shook light as a feather, he became pale. He spread the money out before him and looked it over anxiously to see if there was any good money but the few cents, but there was not. He heard a sound, made a quick dart to cover the money, and looking up, with a blush, saw his mother. With great hollow eyes she stood looking at him. Her old red dressing gown, now tattered and dirty, was wrapped round her. Henny's eyes traveled, with a shocked expression, over the coins laid out on the floor. Ernie looked at them again and suddenly his eyes filled with tears; he began to choke, "Mother, someone—" and broke down into miserable sobs. Henny looked at him, with hollow cheeks and desperate eyes, and in a moment sank to her knees, plunged her face into her hands and began to utter cries, "Ugh-ugh." Ernie took no notice but sat amongst the ruin of his money box, scrabbling the coins with his finger, and crying accusingly. Henny took away her hands and, still sobbing windily, crawled over to him and began to collect the money that she put into the palm of her hand. Ernie held out his hand for it without looking, then feeling nothing but air in his hand, stopped in the middle of a hiccough and looked at her. "Ernie-boy," said Henny unctuously, "don't cry: Mother will put all the money back."

"Will you," he insisted, "will you?"

"Yes, dear; yes, dear."

"When?"

"When I get money: next week."

"What did you put that money in my box for, Mother?"

"I didn't want you to be disappointed, darling."

He got up and watched her stumble to her feet, tearing the gown again. She was carrying away the false coins with her. On the floor was the empty red money box. He could not understand what she meant: for to see the empty box there was like the end of his world: the difference between having his "bottom

[414]

dollar" there and having nothing was the same to him as waking in a dark hour of the night, hearing no clock and no cricket and no sigh, and not knowing whether it was the first or fifth hour of the night. At those times he would break into a sweat and wonder if the sun would rise again, at the appointed hour, ideas that he knew were silly but made him long for the ticking of the clock, which is the whole of life. Mother thought she would trick him with the worthless money, without knowing that she had smashed everything he had. He heard her trailing downstairs. He picked up the money box and put it back again under the board; and then he realized that Mother had found the board, pried it up, stolen his money, put in the bad money, and put the box back, all with the intention of fooling him. He felt sick, but as he did not know what had happened to him, he looked out the window to see the last of the neighbors' children chasing each other round the Wishing Tree and then went downstairs in a vacant mood and, hearing his father's whistle, answered at once, "Yes, Dad!" but all the evening, all through his father's chatter, he was thinking something strange: he did not know what it was.

At five o'clock Sam tied the Stars and Stripes to the Wishing Tree: this was the sign agreed upon, by which Miss Aiden was to know Spa House, when she looked from the end of Eastport Bridge. Louie, looking every minute from the front windows, saw her as soon as she came to the boathouse at the end of Duke of Gloucester Street, and shrieking, "Mother, she's coming," rushed madly round the house down the drive and along the street towards the bridge. At the gas station she slowed down, but too late, for her face was already scarlet. She had left behind her a pandemonium of brotherly laughs, fatherly witticisms, wondering children, staring neighbors and barking dogs, but when she reached the Eastport end of the bridge and looked towards Spa House, for one minute, to see the flag, she saw all her family, except Henny, lined up along the front grass, staring eagerly at the bridge. Very self-consciously she strutted along the bridge, looking everywhere, up, down, at Bancroft Hall, up the creek, at the boathouse, at the ferry, while the fat grin on her face swelled and swelled until she felt as if she must tumble into her own mouth. Miss Aiden was standing at the other end of the bridge, leaning graciously on the rail, taking in the scenery and waiting for her.

"Hello, dear Louie," she said, beaming on the flushed girl. This was the first time she had ever said "dear," and Louie was in ecstasy. She became very quiet and sedate in her great happiness; and then very talkative, pointing out the house, and the points of interest to the family. She even pointed out "Coffin" Lomasne, who was standing on his slipway and looking with interest at the banner attached to the Pollit Wishing Tree; and in long gabble told all about him, his coffins, and how he went, in the family, by the name of "Mud Turtle."

Louie had on the same soiled dress that she had worn to school, Miss Aiden observed, with hurt, for she had expected to be treated with more ceremony. However, she was flattered by the banner and by the family drawn up irregularly there under the trees, and all those eyes searching her from a distance. It was a dear old house, with wonderful old trees, and a sweet little bathing beach, as she told Louie, and they all must be very happy there, especially in summer. "Are there mosquitoes?" she asked. (Yes, there were: but they took measures against them: only Ernie and Tommy suffered badly from the bites.) "You don't need to go away for the holidays," said Miss Aiden. (Oh, but Louie would go, she hoped, to Harpers Ferry. She had a cousin there who had promised to take her down the river in a canoe, if it was not too dry.) "A boy cousin?" said Miss Aiden coquettishly. "Yes, a boy cousin, Dan." Miss Aiden had never been to Eastport before; it was an exceedingly poor part, run-down, with a few broken-down family houses, but splendid old run-to-seed patches that you could do something with, though the soil was poor. The entrance to Spa House was down a short muddy lane bordered with what appeared to be fishermen's cottages, with pails and clothes on the wooden porches. A broad new picket gate, however, with the words "Spa House" painted on it, showed her that she had arrived at Louie's home. The gate was ajar: they pushed it and came quickly up the curving rutty drive, under magnificent trees. The straggling bushes of the bank and somebody's rowboats came right up to the trees on the western side.

A reception committee awaited her, a tall, yellow-haired, red-faced man, with sparkling, self-satisfied eyes, rather heavy cheeks and nose and teeth well met in a kind of religious mouth, a man who would make a good, new-world dissenting minister, thought Miss Aiden. There was a bevy of children, none like Louie, with two blond and two dark boys and one very pretty little dark girl—Miss Aiden did not know if they were all Pollits or not. There was no sign of the mother. Miss Aiden was not experienced enough yet to enjoy meeting the girls' mothers, though she got on well with them afterwards, because of her cheerful good nature.

Louie was evidently very nervous. "Will you come inside and take off your hat?" she kept asking, at every break in the conversation. The conversation did not flag, because Mr. Pollit seemed to be a lively, agreeable, unassuming man with a lot of information that he was anxious to bestow upon her; he was very joky too, and Miss Aiden began to laugh with him in a way which, she noticed, did not seem to please Louie. At length, she went in with the girl. They entered by a wind-broken side porch, over a bit of coconut matting worn through to the boards, and came into a dark, dirty hall laid with defaced oilcloth. In the minute before coming into Louie's bedroom to take off her hat, Miss Aiden revised her visions of the Pollit homestead: they were a raggedy, rackety family, too big for their father's means, and living was hard with them, but no doubt they struggled to put a face on it. The reason Louie was untidy and even dirty was that they were poor and was not merely the slatternliness of adolescence. Miss Aiden was disappointed. She now imagined Mrs. Pollit to herself as a worn blonde slut with soft manners, Louie's predecessor (for she had no idea of the family history), and she was so startled that she hesitated for a moment when she saw come into the room a black-eyed, fever-ishly rouged hag with pepper-and-salt hair drawn back into a tight knot. Louie said hastily, "This is Miss Aiden. Miss Aiden, my mother."

"Louie," said the apparition, in a voice of sweet admonition, "take Miss Aiden into my room; it is more pleasant there." Mrs. Pollit had marks of gentility, but at present her graciousness seemed to pester her like an itch—she brought out the kindness irritably, struggling with her worse feelings apparently. Yet, Miss Aiden could tell that she bore her no grudge for coming. "Domestic rift," diagnosed Miss Aiden. She was astonished at the walnut suite in Mrs. Pollit's room: yet, on the bed was a worn and torn cover, and the table covers were not fresh. "De-cayed gentility," now thought Miss Aiden, "and in what a state of decay!"

But apart from a couple of pieces of furniture, the Pollits lived in a poverty that to her was actually incredible. They lacked everything. She was shown the bathroom, and found her-self in a shanty with wooden walls and a roughly cemented floor. One end of this was filled by a cement tub about five feet long by three deep; but the cement had a surface as rough as a coconut cake; Miss Aiden thought of submitting her soft, sleek, spoiled flesh to its gray rasping ridges and, thinking it impossible, looked about for a rubber sheet—they must use something to cover the cement when bathing. Everything was to match; home-made, rough and ready; instead of toilet paper, they used cut-up newspaper; there was no bathmat but a sodden crisscross of slats. "I had no idea," thought Miss Aiden, "that there was a place as primitive in the whole world"; and she began to wonder how they lived at all.

Greatly disappointed in her visit, she followed the excitable Louie out through the home-cemented back porch and into the orchard wilderness, which was a delightful playground and now in full leaf and dotted with little fruit. There was a stew cooking, and Miss Aiden saw the dark thin woman poking over the stove: she nodded gaily at them as they went past. Miss

Aiden could not keep back the question, "Does your mother like cooking?"

"Oh, no! she has too much to do," Louie said with unreflective candor.

Miss Aiden pursued, "You have a lot of brothers and sisters."

"Only one sister," said Louie: "that little fair girl is Mr. Lomasne's little girl. Yes, mother says she has too many," and she laughed.

"But she wanted them," pursued the teacher sentimentally.

"No, she didn't: the doctor said she should only have two— but they came"; Louie laughed.

The teacher looked down sharply, but saw only a fat, fair, laughing face: it's queer to know everything and know nothing at one and the same time, thought Miss Aiden.

Dinner was something Miss Aiden was never to forget; for she had passed what she considered a very rebellious, but what was really a very respectable life within the confines of the agreeably slick. Like Sam (though she was an honors student in English and Higher English), she saw truth, beauty, and progress in terms of the twenty-five-cent story magazines; in fact, she was but a handsome, gracious, and amiable young edition of Auntie Jo. First, from this house of misrule, came the sound of a beautiful gong, like the temple gongs in the movies; then the children came tearing up from all parts of the grassy waste, while two other children (which until this moment she had supposed Pollits) started to run down the avenue and away from Spa House. Mr. Pollit, who had neither washed his hands nor put on his coat, then started to whistle, and as he whistled shouts came from the scampering children, "Yes, Dad; yes, Taddy; yes, Dad, yippo": and so forth. Immediately, Louie, with a pleased confused face, came to fetch her in to the table, and they came into a long, boarded room, with dirty window curtains, a battered dresser, homemade wall shelves, and a long, oak table with fat Victorian legs, on which hung a dirty, worn tablecloth covered with the old silver and stained knives. A thin glass vase, dirty napkins in rings, and one water glass with a Greek-key pattern engraved graced this cloth. On the table besides were cruets, a slab of butter, and a loaf of bread. Miss Aiden found her place to be in front of the one water glass. Mr. Pollit then gave a whistle, and the team sat down, excepting Louie and the wife, who were juggling dishes in the kitchen, which was across the dark passage. Presently, without prelude, Louie began to hurry backwards and forwards with dishes of Irish stew, Miss Aiden getting the first, Mr. Pollit the second, and then in order of age.

"May I have a glass of water?" asked Miss Aiden sweetly, seeing none; but Louie at once seized the milk jug and poured out some for her. No one else got any. After they were all served, Louie and her mother came to sit down. As soon as Mrs. Pollit lifted her knife and fork, all followed suit and fell to in silence. Table talk was apparently considered improper in this family during the first course. As soon as Sam Pollit had finished, however, he began asking Miss Aiden if she liked fishing and if she knew that the Chesapeake was the finest little fishing hole in the world, he himself having fished there from the age of six; and that if she wanted to fish, the boys would take her out any day and not charge her fifteen dollars, the way the party boats did—or at least he didn't know. "Perhaps when Tommy grows up, he'll make us a party boat and then we'll all be rich—for three months a year." Laughter bubbled round the table at this happy prospect.

"Tommo's only six though," said Ernie, "and you have to have a boat, and the tackle costs about two hundred dollars, and there's the oil—"

"Oh, we'll run ours on marlin oil," declared Sam, "and ketch it for nothing! And won't the big boys swim after us when they smell their breruther's oily tang?"

Louie was very indignant at this stupid conversation, which she thought beneath Miss Aiden's level. Ernie did not raise even the ghost of a smile. Mrs. Pollit remained silent throughout, except to say to Tommy, "Tip your plate outwards, Tommy-boy!" and to Evie, under her breath, "Use *both* hands to wipe your mouth!"

Presently, during an awkward lull, while Louie was carrying out the dishes two at a time, Mr. Pollit said in a queer tone, distantly paternal, with a condescending expression, to his wife, "Have we salad, Henrietta?" The wife, flushing angrily, merely lowered her head over her plate and replied nothing. Miss Aiden flashed a look of astonishment from one to the other, then turned to Little-Sam, who sat at her side, "And are you the boatbuilder?" Sam, meanwhile, bit his lip; and in a moment repeated politely, "Have we a salad to come, Henrietta?" At this Henny coolly got up from her seat, smiling to Miss Aiden with an "Excuse me, please, I am the cook too," drew Evie after her, and, when she had stepped into the corridor, said gently to Evie, "Tell your father that the snails ate the lettuce, and I had no money to buy trimmings!" Evie turned back and demurely repeated this message to her father. The children gazed from their father to Miss Aiden, to see what she would make of this. The dessert was brought in by the mother and served by her: it was bread pudding, with some preserved berries from last year. Henny admitted that these were her preserves and carried off the trying situation (Miss Aiden could not help thinking) with aplomb. Yet, she was wondering, "Why did they invite me?" After dessert, Louie went to make the coffee, after asking her mother in a low tone, and her father in a high tone, and Miss Aiden in a languishing tone, what each would take. Mr. Pollit would have prolonged the meal, for he became spirited and garrulous after the coffee, but Mrs. Pollit, fixing her black eyes on his face with a meaningful glare of hate, and slightly rising, forced back the words on his lips, while Louie and Evie rose too slightly and so induced Miss Aiden to get up. The teacher offered to help with the dishes, seeing no help, but Sam said at once, "No, the girls will do it while I show you the lordly acres, Miss Aiden," and with a sort of rustic galloping gallantry, like a sheep dog, he got her out into the yard, and,

[421]

taking her elbow, began pointing out things to her and talking "nineteen to the dozen," as Henny declared.

"A fat chance you'll have to talk to your beautiful Miss Aiden," she cried. Louie was about to burst into tears. The most beautiful moment of her life had just passed: it had been when she walked with Miss Aiden up and down the aisles of the orchard. But all the time she was rushed, she could not collect her senses, for she knew the time was short: even when Miss Aiden stopped and, looking at her earnestly, begged her to work during the summer, for she would certainly be famous ("be famous," was what she said, though surely it was a hallucination), Louie was fretting that the time was so short; soon Miss Aiden would go away. Louie thus had no time to think about the house, nor how it looked; she was quite satisfied with it—they were poor, but it was spacious, and her expectations were infinite. There was a book called *Great Expectations,* which she had never read: she supposed, though, that it referred to something like her own great expectations, which were that at a certain moment, like a giant Fourth of July rocket, she would rise and obscure all other constellations with hers. She was likewise so used to hearing of her mother's rich family, and of her father's superiority in intellect and feelings to the rest of mankind, that she believed they all occupied an enviable position in the community. They had been brought up in Washington, and if the nation only knew of Sam's capacities, it would clamor for him—what more could be needed by a family? Enviously, she watched Sam, who grabbed everything, to his greater glory, grabbing Miss Aiden too: there he talked, endlessly, by the half hour. What could he be saying to her? Soon he would win her away entirely from Louie: Miss Aiden would think, What a clever, brilliant father Louie has—why Louie is not a patch on him! Louie was racked with disappointment. When she went out to empty the leavings into the garbage can, she went the long way round to overhear their words. Sam was saying, "And my little Looloo—I called her 'Ducky' then—at a very early age showed a most mulish disposition: that's why I'm speaking to

[422]

you, because she thinks so highly of you—" Looloo! Ducky! Oh, a hell of torment! Louie went back to the kitchen and burst into tears.

"What the dickens is the matter now?" asked Henny, without malice.

"He's talking to her—he's telling her everything——"

Henny shrugged her shoulders and went on cleaning the knives. "She's not a bad woman, and if she's not an absolute fool, she'll see the way I'm treated."

Louie flashed up with a smile of gratitude, "Oh, Mother, do you like her?"

"I like her, yes."

"Oh, Mother!"

"Don't faint," said Henny irritably, suppressing a smile. At last, Louie was able to get away, but Sam kept on talking cheerfully until the last moment, when he walked her to the gate. Louie was allowed to walk up to the station with Miss Aiden, a walk of about a mile. When they were on the Eastport Bridge, they heard a faint shout, and looking back, saw the Pollit clan lined up once more in front of the Wishing Tree, waving the flag at them.

"Your father is very amusing," said Miss Aiden, patronizingly. For the first time, Louie found the shadow of a ghost of a fault in Miss Aiden's manner.

3 ⚓ Delayed mail.

HAVING DELIVERED himself of his heartfelt sentiments once again, Sam was gay and went merrily footling round the place, looking for fresh worlds to conquer. "Tah yez wot I do," he declared, "I'll make Looloo-the-Zulu a new bookcase, now she's learned to read; feelin' fine! Old Aido's a nice old girl! I like Old Aido and if she'd ask me twice, I'd marry her." The children were nodding buttercups of giggles. Some of them departed to other occupations (to pore over the presents they had given Sam that day, for example), but the twins stayed with Sam, who now went into Louie's bedroom, to take down the old bookcase, which was about ten feet high, and measured the wall space for a new one. He began to dust off the top and there found all sorts of things—a forgotten pin box, a pill box with tacks in it, two knitting needles, and an out-of-date diary on which was written in capitals: THE AIDEN CYCLE.

"Sirprise after sirprise," announced Sam shaking his head; "well, blow me down ef it ain't poickry. Say, kids, Looloo's a dangblueblasted better poet then whut I am. Now, what do you know about that, Little-Sam? Say, quick, Sawbones, go get the kids: quick! When Looloo gits back frum a-walkin' out with her beloved, she'll find us all a-joying of her poickry. Quick, quick."

The call went out, and the children straggled back to the house. It was a lovely evening, and the grateful and fascinated children from the party were drifting back to the gate and the fences, poking their heads in and holding wistful conversations with the happy savages of Spa House.

"Oh, Jiminy Jee," sighed Ernie: "if we aren't always at his beck and call."

"You get along," cried Henny, hearing this, "or he'll be whistling and calling, and I can't stand any more today."

She rounded them up. Soon Louie's room was full of them, while Sam, standing on his small stepladder with the book in his hand, declaimed,

> All nature is in you, its monsters less;
> As nature monsters are, so less are you
> Than nature: nature lacks what you have more
> Than natural: unnatural, you bless
> Our lives too natural—yet world I'd rue
> Without this extra-nature I adore.

"Whut in the name of dingbingbusted commen sense," asked Sam, "is this? Hit's a crostword puzzle. Blow me darn, here's another!

> Pearlshell, pearl, and madrepore,
> Purple wampum, rich fish dyes,
> Of gold and silver a great store,
> In megaron, in mattamore;
> But, Rosalind, thou art much more.

Oh, Rosalind; oh, kiss me, Rosalind!"

At this moment, Tommy, who had watched in the falling night for Louie's return, bounded in shouting, "She's coming back now, she's on the bridge."

"Ooh," said Evie, "Daddy, she will be very angry with you."

"You ought to stop, Pad," said Ernie.

"She's in love with Miss Aiden, oh, Rosalind," chanted Sam, squirming. The children imitated him. "She worships Miss Aiden," said Little-Sam shrilly. "Oh, I love you, Miss Aiden."

"Shh!" said Sam leaning over mysteriously, as he was turning over a leaf, "Tommo! Go to the gate and tell me when Looloo is coming: tell Looloo I'm reading her poickry. See what she says! Eh?" There were varying tones of assent and dissent, but Tommy galloped off. Louie was coming home slowly, breathing in the soft-smelling, bayside, thickening air; bats flew, mosquitoes sang. She was glad no one was with her, for after all she had nothing to say to anyone, not even to Miss Aiden, since ravishment cannot be spoken.

"Louie, Louie!" It was Tommy calling her from the gate.

"What do you want?"

"Louie, Dad's reading all your poems!

Tommy saw the pale form pelting towards him, "Where?" she called, seizing him by the shoulder. He felt a tremor of fear and anticipation;

"In your room—he wanted to make—" but Tommy was alone, while a large dark shape rounded the corner of the drive. He ducked under the white railing to cut across the lawn, when he saw at his feet two oblong shapes, two letters left lying on the lawn. He picked them up and ran in. The light shone through the two windows of Louie's room, and he could see the mess of children in there, with Sam's laughing face and the book held out as he read; the children lounged round, uninterested. As he passed the open window Sam was saying, "Here's one (where's Looloo-dirl?)—

> *There is a sick one within these walls,*
> *She is mad I know by the songs she sings—*

Louie burst into the room. "Here's Louie, here's Louie," they sang out.

"Give to me," she shouted, "you give it to me!"

"No! Leave me read it," he wheedled. "You ain't got nuffin you don't want your Poor-Sam for to see, hev you?

> *I must confess I love you,*
> *I love you in my fashion,*
> *'Tis not from lack of passion*
> *I would not say I love——*

"Give it to me," shrieked the girl: "I'll make you." The children made way for her and she came up the first step after her father, grabbing for the book, which, of course, he waved away from her. He looked handsome, bewitching, never so handsome as when teasing, "'I love you.'"

She got off the step and stood underneath him, looking up and saying, "Give it to me, give it to me."

> *The Indian starling, flashing in the shade*
> *Is like your eye, all flecked with gold and blue——*

"Here," he said, throwing it to her, so that it fell on the floor, "take it away; and don't write such sickening tommyrot. Write if you want to, but not such silly nauseating stuff. I didn't think you'd be so silly as to fall for calf love for a teacher, I thought you had more in you.

"Looloo," he said turning away to the children, "is trying to practice poickry without a poick's license, and I think she ought to be fined or go to jail. Now, dear old Georgie the Fisherman says to me the other day, he says, with rather a shamefaced look, kids, because of his ignorance, becaze even fisherboys is rayther ashamed of their iggerance, not like Tommy here, and quite evidently with a automobile permit in mind—or whatever fat George Pudding-and-Pie thinks with—'Mr. Pollick,' sezee, 'wy do they give poicks licences to say things wrong?' In conversation that followed, I saw quite clearly that he thought poicks got licences like fishermen, maybe by the traffic department, so these dopey nuts who make schooldays so hard for poor fat boys could get their stuff printed with a licence. So I think we'll get Looloo a licence, maybe a dog licence."

Tommy, who had been listening with his mouth open, now pushed forward waving two letters in his hand, "Mothering says two letters for you, Pad: I found them in the wet grass."

"What," cried Sam, taking them: "that dopey Popeye Banks again! I'll write to the post office about having a nitwit for a letter carrier: I don't know why boys like him aren't sent to a lethal chamber, or just nipped in the bud at birth. The communication between men ought to be the most sacred of all things: and if we weren't so busy building warships," declared Sam, in a temper, "we would have money for better mail services; and if we weren't despised by people because we live in a mudhole. I'll make a complaint about this and get him removed."

He stopped, looking at what he had drawn out of the envelope. It was a triangle of newsprint dragged from yesterday's paper; round the borders in heavy penciling were insulting words, and part of the message was written across the print.

"What is it, Dad?"

He held it close to the ceiling light and made out words,

"You twofaced son of a bitch, would you like to know who was the dad of your last boy take a look in the internal revenue dept and you'll learn lots your wife certainly put one over on you you lowdown bastard while you were getting hot with the chink girlies you sap everyone knows it but you who was away ten months you sap Im glad they threw you out on your can even if your wife owes me an everybody in shoeleather pullenty."

"What is it, Dad?" (They could see enormity in his face.)

"It is one of the foulest things on this earth—" He was still puzzling it, hoping to read something different. His hand began to shake.

"Pad——"

"Get out!"

They ran away, looking back over their shoulders with startled eyes.

"Megalops!" cried Sam. (Megalops, infant crab, was his pet name for Charles-Franklin.) The children hid themselves, with receptive ears, round corners. But after this, Sam was silent. He had sat down on Louie's bed, doing nothing, apparently thinking, while the lights blazed away, running up the electricity bills.

It was a strange night: they were put to bed quickly, and Louie, with red eyes, leaned amongst them to tell them the story of Hawkins, the North Wind.

Evie said, "No, *The Spring House!* Ooh!"

Downstairs a great racket was going on, which was nothing but Henny and Sam going it hammer and tongs, with Henny saying, "You're a sneak and always were," and Sam shouting, "Indiscriminate sexual relations"; but the children paid no attention to it.

Tommy shouted, "No, the Indian ghosts!" while Little-Sam called for *The Invisible Snake.* But Louie, insisting that Hawkins was her new story, because she had just made it up, made it *Hawkins.*

"Chawkins?" queried Tommy with his invented foreign accent.

"One evening in October a black man was working in his potato patch at Jones, over by Rugby Hall; the sun was a flare burning up the trees and smoke and flames came from it. That was because it was cold. Now a withered and warty horse came up through the hill, with a man on its rumpbones; the sun was so low and red, it looked—I don't know what."

"My money box," said Ernie: "it's low and red."

"It looked like Ernie's money box. 'Peaslop,' said the man on the horse, 'I'm hungry and thirsty and I got to get down to the water tonight.' *Down by what water?* 'Down by Severnside.' *Then you better get going.* 'No, my horse's got his night eyes.' *Then stay to supper.* 'Now what you got?' *Got plenty.* The shack was all surrounded with garlic on strings and cobs of corn, beans in packets and black walnuts in bags, salt codfish in dozens and smoked shad in strings and black clove hams and black wild cherries. Then Ambrose, the man on the horse, wiped his hand across his mouth like this—whirrsh! (*Now, Mrs. Peaslop, you cook a dinner for a man with an empty stomach.*) The woman stuck her black head out of the window and yelled,

" 'I lack one thing for my fry, Peaslop.'

" 'And what's that?'

" 'That s my horse's mane, man.'

"The man came up quickly and cut off the horse's mane and threw it in the kitchen window. The frizzling went on and in a minute the woman looked out and sang out, 'I lack only one thing for my fry, Peaslop.'

" 'And what's that?'

" 'That's horse's tail, man.'

" 'I got horse's tail.'

"And the black man came and grabbed the horse's tail, cut off a handful, and threw it in the window. The man on the horse's rump meanwhile had gone right off to sleep, and he nodded, nid-nod, nid-nod, in the slight breeze that was coming up. Then the woman came to the window and yelled (though you couldn't see her, the night had got so black):

" 'There's one thing surely I need for my baking, Peaslop.'

" 'And what's that?'

" 'That's horse's warts.'

" 'Now, that's just what I got,' said Peaslop, and he cut them off and threw a handful through the window.

"But the woman yelled, though it was so dark you could see nothing but Peaslop's eyeballs rolling, 'There's one thing would make my stew better, Peaslop.'

" 'And what's that?'

" 'That's horse's hide; I do need that.'

"So Peaslop took a skinning knife, and he skinned that horse as quick as lightning just as it stood there with its head hanging, asleep in the black night and so quick and smart that the horse didn't know, but it shivered.

" 'My horse's catching cold,' said the man on the horse, Ambrose I mean. 'His teeth are chattering to themselves.'

" 'Horse's teeth,' said Peaslop, 'why that's just what would flavor my old woman's stew,' and he wrenched out the teeth to stop them from chattering.

" 'And my poor nag's knees are just knocking together,' complained Ambrose, 'and every one of his ribs are rattling.'

" 'Now horse's rib soup would make good stock for my old woman's stew,' said Peaslop. Without another word, so dark was it, he stole every horse's rib and every horse's shinbone without so much as tipping Ambrose a wink. But he left a hipbone for Ambrose to rest his weary bones upon.

" 'Now, friend Peaslop,' said the rider, 'my horse's flesh, it just quivers and quakes like a jelly without ice; and I'm very much afraid it's getting colder.'

" 'Then give me that flesh, it certainly will make a good roast for my old woman's table,' said Peaslop; and he snatched all the horse's fine roast from underneath Ambrose, but he still left him a hipbone to sit upon.

"Well, I don't know how fine that cooking must have been, that frying and baking and stewing and roasting and broiling and boiling and basting, nor the feasting and guzzling and gourmandizing that followed. Perhaps they would have put up

Ambrose for the night and given him his horse hale and whole again in the morning; only just at that moment was a low sighing moan.

"Ambrose, the horseman, sitting on his hipbone, looked around. He saw the stars and the heads of the woods, he saw the dim shine of water, he saw the track very pale snaking it into the woods, he saw the lamplight falling through the window, and he heard the frizzling and frying, but he didn't see Peaslop.

"'Is that you Peaslop? Is that you boy? Where you gone, boy?' he asked. 'Is that you crying and moaning, boy?'

"'No, sir, indeed, that isn't me,' said Peaslop. But it was so dark Ambrose couldn't see Peaslop, not even his rolling eyes. There came another moan, and it didn't stop. It went on softly, rising and falling, in the depth of the gully but rising more, till it had a high whine like a train under the hill.

"'Why, it's nothing but the train going down to Annapolis,' said Ambrose. Peaslop never said a word. He just breathed hard in the dark and flapped his hands and danced: but the bubbling of the stew in the kitchen went down.

"'I'm getting pretty cold, friend Peaslop,' said the man. All this time the moaning and sighing and wheezing went on. It got louder, and animals began to scuttle through the grass. It wasn't the wind, it was the animals, the groundhog, the weasel, the mouse, the skunk, and perhaps it was Peaslop dancing and flinging his arms. Now the crackling of the oven meat stopped, and it seemed the woman in the house was listening, too. But the moaning and crying went on and it rose always higher till suddenly it ended in a shriek.

"'Hawkins is calling,' cried the woman from the window.

"'Hawkins is calling,' cried the man from the potato patch. Then he took the hipbone in one hand and hurried to the porch and ran in the door and flung it shut, and the window went down with a bang, and the animals ran into the wood, and Ambrose sat there in the dark, in the new cold air that was beginning to blow. His horse was gone, and he had to get down to the river that night. He ran and knocked at the door and

[431]

listened. But there was no sound at all. Then a voice said, 'What is it?'

" 'It's Ambrose,' said he.

" 'What do you want?'

" 'My horse,' said he.

" 'Oh, call next summer,' cried Peaslop; 'we'll give you some pickings.'

"Just then Ambrose thought he heard his horse neighing in the potato patch, and he thought he heard him snorting in the woods, and he thought he heard him trampling on the track, and he thought he heard him galloping down the hill; and when he looked back and felt with his hands, the shack had disappeared.

" 'Peaslop,' he said.

" 'Hawkins,' cried a voice.

" 'Peaslop,' he cried, wringing his hands.

" 'Next summer,' said the voice.

"And the keen north wind came up over the sickly yellow woods, shrieking, *Hawkins!*"

Picturing the man on the horse's rump against the stars, the children lay loosely in the warm night; while things just as queer as *Hawkins* went on downstairs: Henny, of course, it was not Hawkins shrieking, and Daddy was trying to give away Charles-Franklin, "Megalops."

"He is not mine!"

"He is yours, I've told you a thousand times."

"How long was it going on?"

"Don't be a fool! I can't stand any more of it; I'll kill myself. You're going crazy. No wonder you're a laughingstock, believing every horrible bit of paper."

"There must be some basis for this; is Megalops mine? You haven't answered me direct."

Why was Daddy trying to get rid of Megalops? They couldn't understand it, but after listening for some time, they were too tired to puzzle over the whims of their fantastic father, and one after the other fell happily asleep. It had been a long and glorious day—Daddy's birthday, the neighborhood kids, the chasings round the Wishing Tree, their presents to Daddy for which they had saved up so long, and Miss Aiden coming to see them. Then, soon the holidays would be there, and they would have a glorious time, especially as Sam was still at home; and Sam had promised to take them down to Ocean City one day during the summer to see the people and the fishermen.

"You owe money still in Washington?—Megalops—he came early—who is the man?—" and they were all asleep but Ernie and Louie. Louie stood at her window, listening for a long time to the discussion downstairs (its tone had fallen now), and then she crawled into bed. After a while she lighted the candle she had sneaked upstairs and, pulling her diary out from under the pillow (for she resolved to carry it everywhere with her now), she wrote one line, "Married by misery, seeded by hate, bringing forth screams, feeding in insults." Tired and fully content, she put out the light, when she heard Evie stir in her corner. Evie's bed was hidden by the central chimney piece. Louie slipped out of bed, in the dark, and peered round the masonry. Evie was sitting up in bed. "Why aren't you asleep, Evie?"

Evie said nothing, but started to sniffle. Louie said sharply, "What's the matter?"

"I want to be sick," said Evie, beginning to cry.

"You mean in your stomach?"

"No-ho-ho!"

"Oh, stop it, you silly girl."

Evie began to sob inconsolably, lifting up her head like a little dog about to howl, "Ho-ho-ho!"

Louie got angry with her, "Tell me what's the matter? How can I do anything if you don't tell me?"

"I don't know-ho-ho!"

"I'm going back to bed!"

"I'm too tired! There's too much noise."

Louie instinctively took a quick step and put her arms round

[433]

Evie and kissed her on the head, "Shh-shh! Go to sleep. You had too much fun. Ssh!"

But Evie had opened the sluice gates, "I can't, I can't."

"Ssh! I'll tell you a story."

This had no effect. Louie continued quickly, "I'll tell you The Gunny-Wolf. 'And the little girl went pit-a-pat, pit-a-pat, pit-a-pat!'" Evie paused in her sobbing to listen, for this had always been her favorite ritual. "Ugh-huh!" she sobbed. "'And the wolf came galloping pickety-pack, pickety-pack. "Good evening, child!" "Good evening, wolf!"'"

Presently Evie consented to lie down, and though she listened half resentfully, she stopped crying. Louie got back into bed as soon as she could, for she had to think about Miss Aiden.

But the strange couple were still blackguarding each other below.

"I was a goodlooking girl before I met you!"

"Be quiet: perhaps the children are awake!"

"Is there anything they haven't heard? You tell them enough about your women: why can't they hear what you have to say?"

"Because I am an innocent father, and you are a guilty wife."

There was a cackling laugh, and Henny said, "It's a dirty lie; who but a dirty liar writes anonymous letters?"

Sam's voice said, "Henrietta, I admit I despise the anonymous letter and its author——"

"But this time it suits you because you're playing around with one of your childlike souls, one of those innocent girls who go out with other women's husbands."

"Henrietta, I forbid you to talk like that, with your dirty society-woman's mind!"

"You think I don't know about Gillian Roebuck and your secretaries? If you didn't go to bed with them, you're worse still, you see, according to the way I was brought up." Here came Henny's high chromatic artificial laugh.

Louie fell asleep. When she woke much later, there was a strange stillness in the house. She could see, through the open door, that the light was still on downstairs. Had they killed each other? She got up and stole to the head of the stairs; there was, in fact, a sort of scuffling, and Louie listened, in sacred terror, leaning on the stairhead: would they do for each other at last, would she come down and find them in pools of blood? She hoped so. She began to think busily—what would they do for food and shelter if both parents were gone? Aunt Hassie would take Evie and perhaps the little one, Chappy; everyone liked Ernie and he could find a home. Old Ellen would take one— there would be homes for all. (The twins were a problem— who wanted to be saddled with two boys at once?) She would, of course, go to the Bakens, live on the banks of the Jordan (the Shenandoah), and get a job watching the river rise and fall, and she would never have to think about the Pollits or Collyers again in her life.

Henny gave a fretful hysterical laugh, "Oh, leave me alone, you make me sick," and there was again a violent struggle, and then she heard Sam groan. That was it! She began to creep downstairs, expecting to see Henny kneeling in the lighted common room, with Sam's old-fashioned razor in her hand and Sam lying on the floor, with a gaping wound in his neck. But there was nobody in the common room. A broken cloisonné vase lay on the floor. Louie stood at the door of Henny's room for a while with her heart beating fast, and heard Henny weeping, but she did not dare go in and find out if and how murder had been done. She wandered out into the yard, while the breathing, warm, bloody house lay behind her. Presently she came back and crawled back into bed. In the morning she would look: she would be the first to find the bodies; now she was too tired to go through the melodrama of discovery and questions. She went to sleep with visions of herself comforting the children in the morning, running to the neighbors, sending telegrams. So sure was she of her role that when she woke in a sunny morning and heard her father's crisp, gay voice shouting to the boys, and smelled the customary smell of fire, she thought she was still dreaming. She listened while her heart began to throb again! The night before had been a dream then. She got out of bed and looked out the window: yes, there was Sam as large as life, like a great red and yellow apple bounding about.

When Louie came downstairs there was a letter for her from Clare (though she had seen Clare at school yesterday and would see her today) with writing all over the envelope, in her tiny eccentric scribble. In one corner was written, "Haste post haste!"; in the second, "Oh, Louie, the night is long!"; in a third, "Tooth-ache on the right side, knowing you are off at Spa House, that's on the left side!" and round the stamp was written in minute letters, "Oh, little stamp, I have writer's cramp, but I'll put one thing yet there; though they bar, mark and blur you, don't let it deter you, just stick till you get there!" On the stuck-down flap was written,

> *Pity poor Clare! Her summers are spent*
> *In thinking of mortgages, paying rent:*
> *Not so Louie! With curtain furled*
> *On a stage well set, Lou shook the world!*

The children began gathering round like crabs after a piece of bait, to laugh and peer at Clare's well-known comicalities. Sam came peering in, laughing, "She must be a nitwit to write to you in the evening when she'll see you in the morning—why can't it keep? And you must be a nitwit too: the Amorous Nit-wits!" At which everyone crowed with laughter, and Louie laughed till the tears ran down her blushing cheeks. She was laughing to prevent further questions and to avoid saying that she had written Clare a letter in school yesterday afternoon and delivered it herself on the way home. In this letter she had mildly said, "Everyone thinks I am sullen, surly, sulky, grim; but I am the two hemispheres of Ptolemaic marvels, I am lost Atlantis risen from the sea, the Western Isles of infinite promise, the apples of the Hesperides and daily make the voyage to Cytherea, island of snaky trees and abundant shade with leaves large and dripping juice, the fruit that is my heart, but I have a thousand hearts hung on every trees, yes, my heart drips along

[436]

every fence paling. I am mad with my heart which beats too much in the world and falls in love at every instant with every reflection that glimmers in it." And much more of this, which she was accustomed to write to Clare, stuff almost without meaning, but yet which seemed to have the entire meaning of life for her, and which made Clare exclaim a dozen times,

"Oh, Louie, I can't believe it, when I get your letters, you are the same person: when I meet you at school I keep looking at you in surprise!"

Louie would quietly reply, hanging her head, "Oh, I am afraid that I will go from the head down; I think I will go mad," to which Clare again replied, "I would give the top of my head to have the madness of your little finger."

These answers would fill Louie with melancholy, for she would suddenly see that she had done nothing, and she did not see how she could ever do anything. She would suddenly see a theater large as the world, in which herself, a great coconut shy, was the butt of a hundred thousand shrieks, hoots, and obscene jokes, a great vile blob of a fat girl covered with mud.

Very different from the political girls, the grinds, and the pretty boy-loving girls, Clare and Louie expended themselves in days of mad fervor about nothing at all.

4 ⚓ Summer morning scene.

LOUIE SPENT HALF AN HOUR grinning and moping and mowing over this letter of Clare's, forgot to put on the oatmeal, to take her bath, or do anything else. Even the tea had not been made. Henny remained incommunicable in her room, and when Louie at last came with the tea and knocked at the door, Henny shouted, "Whoever it is, go away!"

"It's your tea, Mother!"

"Put it down outside the door and go away!"

"Don't let it get cold!"

"I'll pour it all over your filthy face, if you don't go away."

Louie retreated, realizing Henny had one of her worst days before her. She made the oatmeal and got ready for school in a pensive mood. Evie sensed storm too, and when Ernie insulted her (as he always did, for there was a grudge from the womb, between them), she began crying quietly. Sam was meanwhile walking about outside, with his head in the air, and evidently cogitating over something very sad. His first hallooing had worn out. He came and stood beside Louie while she was making the oatmeal and, after a while, said in his finest violoncello tones, "You and I can readily understand, Looloo-dirl, the psychological storms and passions which poor Henny goes through, and we can have no feeling of reciprocated or retaliatory hate!"

"Why do we have to go through it?" asked Louie.

"We have a home—you have brothers and a sister! That is the only consideration for me," said Sam gently.

"Why did you have so many children?" Louie turned and faced him.

He shook his head gently, "Looloo, later on you will understand. A month before our marriage, I knew it would be a wellnigh hopeless union, yet so great is a young man's idea of what is honorable and sporting that I could not renege: and so I determined that the union would be fruitful and from misery would come much happiness and splendid men and women; the woman would not count, I thought: I would forget what I could not mend."

"I don't understand," muttered Louie, "why you married her at all, if you felt like that. Mother told me she didn't want to marry you."

Sam's face darkened; but after a moment he said, "And I was thinking of you, Looloo: you were a motherless little girl, and Henny seemed fond of you."

"I don't care, I don't care," suddenly cried Louie.

Sam stared at her, "What do you mean, you don't care? You

don't care for my thought for you? You don't care for my years of torture and what might well have been mental rot and spiritual death for me? You don't care for what I have been through—hell is a very temperate word!"

Louie began to snivel, "I heard it too much, I heard it too much!"

Sam said gravely, "I looked forward to your growing up; I was so happy when you were born—I thought a little girl would be easy to bring up and would have such belief in me."

"Oh, I heard it too often!"

He shrugged away angrily, "Control yourself: you are always so hysterical nowadays. If you didn't get yourself into such darnfool psychological excitements with silly Clare—I thought *she* had more sense!—and silly calf loves for teachers, and even thinking about boys, no better than any man's girl!—I can hardly bear to look at you! Get ready for school!"

"You don't understand, Dad: I am sympathetic, but I heard it too often; I can't stand it any more."

"You only want to think about yourself, that's the truth," Sam said morosely and went out again to walk up and down the grassy orchard. Presently, to show he bore the world no grudge, he began whistling the children round him, and they ran out complaining, in all stages of undress.

Henny suddenly issued out of her room, with her empty cup; and no sooner saw Louie than she pounced on her and scolded her for her appearance, her dirty dress, her cobbled stockings and down-at-heel shoes, her loose straggling hair ("like your disgusting Auntie Jo's") and puffed expression ("you look as if you spent the night in self-abuse, I'll make your father speak to you"). She rushed into the girl's room to look out a clean dress for her, hoping against hope to find something, and suddenly came out screaming that she'd kill that great stinking monster, that white-faced elephant with her green rotting teeth and green rotting clothes, and she'd tear out her dirty filthy hair by the roots rather than let her be seen at school in that state, as if she had never a comb or brush at home to care for her; that Samuel Pollit, who thought all the Pollit breed so fine, had better look at his own stinking daughter who wore the filthy rags that were all he gave her until they were too black to be thrown in "Coffin" Lomasne's black scum. She wanted to know whether Sam knew that his beautiful genius' clothes were smeared with filth and that most of the time the great big overgrown wretch with her great lolloping breasts looked as if she'd rolled in a pigsty or a slaughterhouse, and that she couldn't stand the streams of blood that poured from her fat belly and that he must get someone to look after such an unnatural big beast.

Sam had come into the house when Henny began her screams and stood there goggling, while Louie, going paler, stood petrified with horror and pride, looking reproachfully at her father and expecting him to scold Henny. But Sam goggled like some insignificant wretch crept in secretly on the Eleusinian mysteries, frightened but licking his lips. Henny went on to the worst outrages possible to her vivid imagination; though Louie went upstairs, blubbering so loudly that Sam at last had to go out and call up through the window that if she didn't stop he'd have to come and beat her, big girl as she was, for she could be heard across the bay. Suddenly Sam could stand no more, but went into the kitchen, took a dash of tea in a cup, and began striding off, up the avenue and into the streets, after going softly up to Louie's room and telling her that it would quiet down when he left, for Henny hated him so much that all this came from him. He had put his hand on Louie's shoulder to comfort her, but she shook him off and looked at him with such hate that he shrank back to the door and, with one solemn, reproachful look, went downstairs into the torment that was raging down there, and so away.

Meanwhile, Ernie had come into the common room ready for school, as he thought, in a dirty shirt, and Henny rushed at her son with a slap, which brought out a howl from him. No sooner did she hear the howl caused by herself than Henny felt she could not stand any of this life any longer, nor any of her children, and she rushed at Ernie again and began to beat him across the head, screaming at him, "Die, die, why don't you all die and leave me to die or to hang; fall down, die; what do I care? I beat my son to death: it's no worse than what I have to endure," and beat him still while her eyes started out of her head; her breathing became labored. She could hardly stand but had to clutch at the chair to support herself, screaming still, "I'll kill you children that make me go out of my mind, I'll beat you to death."

Ernie meanwhile, frightened by this and not thinking of defending himself, had fallen to his knees where he cried brokenly, in a warm, pleading voice, "Mother, don't, don't, Mother, Mother, Mother, Mother, Mother, don't, please, please, Mother, Mother!" but the noise of the belting went on until Louie, unable to bear it, rushed downstairs and caught her mother's arm, "Mother! Don't! What are you doing?" Then Henny, suddenly awaking from the horrible murderous delirium, looked at Louie, as if she were about to give an explanation, and fainted. Louie got a cushion and put it under her mother's head, and then pulled Ernie up, from where he lay on the floor sobbing, "Oh, Mother," and said to him, "Come on, get up, get up."

"My head hurts," said Ernie, refusing to get up; but at last Louie managed to drag him from the floor and to get him, still crying, into the boys' room to comb his hair and adjust his clothes. When Henny came to herself, she got up slowly, wiping her wrist across her face, her eyes black and hollow as they had never been, and she, strangely enough, went to the telephone and asked for the cost of a call to Washington, D. C. She telephoned Washington but got no reply, and came away, muttering that she would get him again in the evening—she must see someone who understood her. She then shooed the children off to school, saying that that day she could not bear them round the house, for she might do herself some mischief if she looked at them; and Louie was to give them all their lunches.

Louie at last dragged off to school one hour and a half late, her cheeks scarlet and the whites of her eyes red, and, blubbering still, she walked to school, getting there just before lunchtime, and had been crying to herself all the way, not noticing how everyone looked at her or so much as wondering what she looked like. She came into the silent playground and went straight to the class that was being held at this hour, which happened to be Miss Aiden's, not observing, still, how the few girls who passed her stared at her. She came slowly into the class, while Miss Aiden and all the pupils stared at her. Her dirty blouse, which lacked buttons, was open and showed a torn slip and foul underwear; her skirt, spotted with food, had a ripped hem at the bottom; she was slipshod, and her stockings had mud on them. Her long hair, usually plaited, hung all round her in wet streaks, and her face was twice its usual size, lobster-red and bloated with tears.

"What is the matter?" asked Miss Aiden faintly, after severely telling the girls to go back to their books.

"Nothing," said Louie.

"I think you have been crying, Louie."

"My mother is sick."

"Go to your place," said the teacher helplessly, with her clean, long fingers quickly fastening and tucking in the broken clothing. In the lunch interval she made the girl come to the empty classroom while with a borrowed needle and thread she sewed up the skirt.

5 ✠ Good-by, Bert Anderson.

SAM HAD STAYED OUT ALL DAY in Baltimore, and for once did not come home to supper. In the evening, about seven, Henny rang again to Washington, to Bert Anderson's flat where he usually was at this time of night, and made an appointment to see him the next day. To Louie, who happened to be cleaning knives in the kitchen, she came marching in, with her grimmest expression, and said,

"I'm going to Washington to see an old friend: I have to have some legal advice if I'm ever going to get out of this mess; and please don't tell your father, or you'll get me into some more trouble. Do you hear?"

"Yes, Mother."

She than rang Hassie and asked her if she could see her in town (in Baltimore), the next morning early, to talk over something very important. She still had the season ticket to Baltimore, and as for getting to the station, "I'll crawl there on my hands and feet, if necessary," said Henny angrily, "if I can't get the money for a taxi." She left a note on Sam's desk asking for money to go to Baltimore to see her lawyer, and after dining off a four-ounce-curry made for herself from cold meat and raisins, with chutney and tea, she shut herself into her room, determined not to come out again until it was time to leave for Baltimore. "I cannot go through such scenes and won't," said she.

Later, she made herself some tea, and then got into bed, to try and read the saga of upland Georgian gentility, which she had three times abandoned because she, Henny, had "no fancy big buck niggers to wait on her and lick her boots": but once more she threw it away. Where, indeed, was she to find heroes to succor her and how could she succeed in business with her spendthrift ways. "I'm a failure all right," said Henny; "and why don't they write about deadbeats like me—only it wouldn't sell!" Towards five, when the morning came, she fell asleep and when she woke up, Sam had again left the house to go to Washington and had left no money for her nor left her any word.

Thus, she had to set off in a great temper, to walk to the station by the poor cottages, the gas station, the wretched stores and whisky counters, by the boatsheds and over the bridge, by the Market Place, up the stony high street, round the State House and so to the low-set station, where some cars were stand-

[443]

ing without an engine, in an idle sort of way, apparently asleep and not dreaming of a timetable. But at the proper time they set off, just the same, and racketed through those stray houses, over the Severn and by those woody hills that Henny hated so much, in forty minutes or an hour arriving in Baltimore. As soon as she got outside the station, Henny saw the faithful green car and hobbled towards it. How her legs ached! Honest Hassie, more cushiony than ever, waited till her ant of a sister had got in and then asked,

"Well, my dear, what mess are you in this time? I suppose you want a drink? It's too early for me, but if you want to, we'll go to the Hi-Ho."

"I want money, and I want to go to Washington, and I want never to see that hypocritical gasbag again, if I can help it," Henny explained in her usual succinct way; "and I want you to lend me whatever money you can, Hassie, because I'm in one devil of a hole."

"When were you ever out of the hole?" asked Hassie comfortably. "What's the row?"

"Some son of a bitch wrote to that Forgotten Man that I married, an anonymous letter on a bit of newspaper and told him to wipe his whatyoumaycallit, with it, pardon me! and said Charlie was not Sam's child! I'd like to find the man and send him to Alcatraz; such people should be punished with the worst the law allows." Hassie was silent for a while as she maneuvered the car round a tricky corner and up a stony street, and then she said, mildly, "Well, old girl, not that I care, but what's the story?"

Henny said angrily, "Do you think I'd be such a fool as to let one of those professional bachelors——?"

"I don't know: I think you've been an awful donkey, Henny."

"What would you do in my place, may I ask? Compromise? With what? With the West Wind? Compromise with Mr. Here-There and Everywhere? Am I to spend the next twenty years in the high-minded company of a smug Philistine who doesn't so much as make me a decent husband? Have you any recipe for that? Don't be so tiresome! You don't know what you're talking about."

"Gosh," said Hassie, sighing, "I didn't say anything; don't get mad. You and Sam should never have married, that's all."

"Any marriage I made would have gone smash," cried Henny, scoffing and throwing back her head: "I was born for excitement."

Hassie brought the car to a stop, "Well, let's drown our sorrows in drink. I really ought to be at the store, old girl, but now you can tell me what happened. What did the beast say in the anonymous letter? Oh, it really is too foul just the same, isn't it?"

"I'd bet my bottom dollar that it's old Middenway, dirty old leering goat," said Henny, angrily staring at the bare table in the little booth. "I never could stand him, and I had to kowtow to him and ladida with his servant girl of a wife because I never could get enough to foot his dirty bills; and I left owing him ninety-four dollars if you want to know. I need that at once, but if I had a gun I'd go and shoot the rat. I wish I had a man and not a dishrag printed over with big words like 'constitutional rights' and 'progress'! Did you ever know me to do anything right in my life? I should have been drowned when a pup."

"You look so feverish," said Hassie. "What have you been doing? Have you been drinking? Your eyes are so bright! Are you well?"

Henny tossed her head, "Where the dickens would I get the money for drink? I'm just boiling mad, I'm going out of my mind: I may look cool and calm to you, but inside I'm one blaze, I'm insane."

"No, you're not, you're cool enough," said Hassie; "you're always pretty collected when you're not in a tantrum. Now, don't work yourself up."

Henny pointed to her cheeks, "I've been up all night, trying to think what to do. I realized where I was the other week, with June week—we used to flounce along and think we were the pick of the bunch; I should have married a mud rat or one of the boatmen then and there and saved myself a lot of hard work and worry and travel. I would have had the same kids and ended up in the same slops."

"Don't you think everyone has troubles?"

"A lot of people have a million dollars."

"How much do you owe?"

"Never mind; I want to have one friend left in the world."

"I don't like you going to see this man, Pet; it's disastrcus; I know it, I feel sure of it: I can see you're being terribly reckless. You might ruin yourself; you know how those things turn out. What good can he do you? I don't see it."

Henny laughed scornfully, "I've got to try everything. If he won't give me money, he'll put me up in his room for a night till I collect my senses!"

Hassie said tartly, "Of course, that's all Sam wants, to get the children forever. Have you gone mad?"

"He's my only friend," said Henny obstinately, wiping a tear from her eye. "Or was."

"There's a sale on at the Palais Royal," said Hassie at this; "I'll drive you over for it, you can see this fellow, and I'll meet you again wherever you like; but I won't leave you in Washington with him: that's beyond the limit. I'll wait for you. I still don't know what good it is, but I don't want you to go streeling off there making a spectacle of yourself, and I know you'd stop at nothing."

"All right," said Henny, "come along: don't let's sit here. I'll buy myself a new hat before I meet anyone: I look like a hundred-year-old hag in this. I'm a bag of bones, he probably won't know me. No one will recognize me now."

They got into Washington in about fifty minutes, but Henny spent a good deal of time feverishly turning over the remnant counters at the Palais Royal and other stores, Henny saying that a spot of shopping would pep her up and give her a bit of color in her cheeks, and "When I feel downright low, I can always get out of it by buying something." Hassie bought her a cheap new blouse and a hat, so that by lunchtime, when she was to meet Bert Anderson in Maynard's Ship Bar in Eye Street, she wore a new spotted veil to mask her thinness, and through this her large burning eyes glowed sickly.

Bert came prancing in exactly as in the old days, at one moment holding out his hands and looking for a place for his hat. "Henny, Henny, hullo! Where have you been?"

She said, "Hullo, Bert," thinkingly vaguely that he had the best of all bargains, being still young, strong, and fresh-colored and free.

They had the bar special, twice, but it did Henny little good. She could see Bert stealing glances at her both inquisitive and surmising.

"You didn't spend the winter in Florida at any rate, that's one good thing, not with the idle sons of riches," said Bert, rather low. "Are you eating? I got to snatch a quicky, Henny old girl. You're not staying in Washington with the Great Man? I say, I never sent you a word, it certainly was too bad about——"

"It must have been painful for you," she said.

He looked up quickly to catch her laugh. "Yes, yes, I had to go to the ILGWU to have my stitches taken out with laughin'. But you, poor thing; it came hard on you, eh? Been shopping?"

She muttered feverishly, "Someone sent him a dirty anonymous letter about me and you."

Bert's fork stopped halfway to his mouth, and his great brown eyes opened wide in his face, "Gee," he said, "Gee, Henny, that ain't so good! Who could ha' been the son of a bitch who—gee! You see, Henny, be sure your sin will find you out, as my old schoolteacher used to say when I wrote on the lavatory wall. What did he say?" He dropped his voice.

"I told him I had thought he prided himself on being above such things; he got hot and holy, and I got so mad I told him to blow his nose in it." She shrugged, "I'm through with him."

"Oh, you can't do that, you mustn't do that. The children, dear?"

"I thought I'd poison him myself, but I thought I might get

some money somehow and get away. Why couldn't I go to the Pryors at Frederick and stay? Why do I have to be chained to him?"

"Gosh," said Bert, "I didn't mean to get you into trouble, Henny. He wasn't mean to you, didn't beat you up?" He grinned palely and wiped the smile quickly off his face as he saw her black look. "Poor old Henny, no luck!"

"Listen," she said nervously, rushing ahead, "you remember one time, you said you wished I were free; I could use a little friendship now. If I see that man again tonight I'll go mad, I think: I'm sure to do something desperate."

He lifted his eyes slowly from his plate and gave her a long searching look, "Dearest, what do you want me to do?" he asked softly. He slapped his pockets, pretended to pull them inside out, "Money—I haven't it! A home—I haven't it! Someone to help you—how can I ask for you, Henny? Gosh, you used to be so rich!" He shook his head slowly, "And I really can't afford to let anything get about. It's not you, but it's my job and Mother —you know what old-fashioned old ladies are?" He nodded sympathetically. "Someone's got to get you out of this mess, though. I think you'd better go away to Frederick for a bit, don't you? And not see me—that's very important; never see me. Jesus, I hope no one—" he looked cautiously around. "Of course, I thought of this a long time ago, Henrietta, long before—" he nodded. "I was afraid, I told you I was afraid. We were too conspicuous. You see, if you were nobody and I wasn't a Government employee—but placed as we are, we can't hide under a doormat, can we?" He forced a laugh and looked up from his plate. "The principal thing is, don't lose your head. You shouldn't have come here, old girl. Jesus, it might be a trap. Perhaps he followed you."

"Oh!" She raised her eyes too from her cup, "Oh! What a life! What a man! Oh, you make me sick! Bert, you're big as an elephant with the soul of a mouse."

He frowned, "Look at it my way! Oh, gee, Henny darling,

don't go on that way; you know how I'm fixed. My mother's sick, and I've been going home straight from work for weeks. Really, I haven't been making whoopee; I've been a good boy, and if Sam started a suit, wouldn't it finish everything? What good would it do you? You see? You must go right away to Frederick, that's my advice to you, old girl: let it blow over. If he don't see you with me, he can't prove anything. It's just chitchat. He'll probably get over it. Have you got any dividends yet?"

"What about that?"

"If you do get them, old girl, you can still hold out on him."

She laughed, "Let's have a Scotch and soda, Bert! I haven't had a good time for so long; and I don't think you have, either: you're getting positively moldy."

He laughed, rounded his chest, "Well, I suppose I am that: I suppose being the good little boy does settle over me like a sort of mildew. Well, there are plenty of good times to come. I don't regret treading the straight and narrow for a change. It's amusing. I get new emotions!"

"You'll be whoring when I'm dead," Henny said bitterly, stirring her glass. "Do you want to take the afternoon off and give me a good time on what might be my last day on earth? Will you do that?" She begged him with her glowing eyes.

He was embarrassed, "Well, Henny, love, Jesus, I would, you know that—you and me have been really good friends; we got along all right. You understand things; you're the right cut. But I must go back to work; you don't want Bert to get demoted or promoted to the Civil Service Commission's carpet strip, or anything like that?"

"Bert," she begged.

"I wish there was a way out, I wish there was, believe me, Henny," he said uneasily.

"Will you meet me this evening then?" she asked, nervously.

"Well, I oughtn't to, you know the old girl expects me. No, I don't think I can, Henny old girl; sorry, really, I'm sorry."

She fastened a peculiar look on him, "You do take me for a two-dollar pickup, don't you? I always suspected there was no difference between me and the street trotters."

"Now, Henny," he said reproachfully.

"Because I've lost my money," she said to herself: "you know I half thought that this morning. Aren't you a bit ashamed!"

"Of what?" he cried.

"Of not coming with me on my last day on earth," she cried triumphantly.

"I don't understand you; what are you trying to fasten a scene on me for? Is this a setup?"

She began to light a cigarette, very carefully, with trembling hand, so that he leaned across the table and held it for her, "Poor Henny, poor old girl! Don't lose control, Henny."

"Advice is cheap. You are a bounder, aren't you?"

"Jesus, if you knew how I'd like to help you, Henny!"

"That's a wonderful end to my love affair," said Henny, her face blazing yellow; she turned her head aside and hid her eyes in her hand. He heard her whispering, "Oh, God, Oh, God, this is terrible!"

"Henny darling, you had me, and I had you, and this is no good, it's over. We can't go back. I can't help you. Why, I got you into this mess! See what good I am to you? Be sensible, old girl."

"That's smug."

He shrugged, "I am smug, I suppose: I come from the lower bourgeoisie, my dear."

Her breast was heaving with her painful breaths. He looked at her quizzically, "What exactly did you come for, Henrietta? Why did you do such a foolhardy thing? Are you really feeling desperate?"

"I'm being torn to pieces inside," she said in a rare contralto voice, looking sternly at him. "I don't know why I came, I knew you. You're not bad, but you're not good either. You're a loathsome thing! But I knew it. I don't blame you. At the beginning, that winter day—I nearly fainted when I saw you in your great jumbo BVD's and now I see you in your moral BVD's; it all hangs together. Don't think you're hurting me. You can't. I'm beyond all your yellow cowardly tricks. You never saw me again when you heard I was pregnant: when I rang up, even though we had a regular appointment, you threw it in my face that you had another girl to supper; not a letter all that time. You knew my money troubles—did I ask you for a cent?"

"Steady, there, steady: yes, you did, if the truth must be told. But we were going steady——"

She bit her lip. Then, after thinking a bit, looking down into her clasped hands, she said quietly, "I used to wait for the telephone to ring: the door wasn't a door but a living leather thing that might bang to and fro, to let you in. I used to dream at night I heard you coming to see me."

"Gee, old girl," he said collectedly.

"I wasn't in love with you, but I wasn't out of love with you, and I wanted your help. And you weren't there. I used to look down at all those lights and think, Somewhere under one of those lights Bert is singing some girl his old sweet song; why can't he take one night off to come and see me? That winter!"

"Jolly good thing I didn't! It's bad enough——"

She looked at him with hate, "I know where it came from: you were boasting round the place that you were sleeping with the wife of a departmental head and putting on his horns while he was away: everyone knew, I could tell by the way they looked at me."

"Why didn't you stop me—or stop yourself?"

"I can't go on, Bert; I'll scream."

"No, you won't," he said, alertly, getting up and picking up her wrap: "you're not hysterical. Now, will you go to the movies, and I'll see you again after work?"

"I wouldn't see anything in the movies, but what can I do? I'd rather go shopping, but I have no money."

"Well, I haven't any," he said rather sharply. Then, sweet again at once, he continued, "You ring me, old dear—or better, you wait for me in the old joint. 'Say baby, that ain't a joint, it's a dump.' Ha-ha-ha. Say, can you pay for a movie or are you flat, stony broke?"

She said sullenly, "You're not going to hand me a dollar on the sidewalk, are you? Go to hell, Bert! I'll be at the bar maybe."

"You'll be there, old girl, you'll be there," he said, apparently in high feather. He kissed her, "There, be a good girl."

She wandered round all the afternoon, sitting on public seats and looking in secondhand shops, wandering through the shops disconsolately. She met Hassie at last at the appointed hour and told her she was to meet "her friend" in a certain bar; but at last she told her which bar and Hassie gave her some more money, because she had bought a dress for Evie, enough to pay for a cocktail while she waited. She waited over an hour, with her one cocktail before her, but the door did not swing in that unique breezy way which was Bert. At last it did swing for her, though. In came Hassie, with a set expression, and after sitting beside her five minutes and talking vigorously, she persuaded her to come away. Henny had dark circles under her eyes.

"I rang too," she said. "I need another nickel to ring his home to see if an accident happened."

"Henny, don't be a fool."

"I can't believe he would do that, even so."

"Come and get a bite to eat at home with me: I'll ring up Sam and keep you overnight. Then you simply have to go back and face the music. And on Saturday I'll come down and talk to Sam. You ought to go away. You look done up."

She led her out. The broad, middle-aged lady leading the thin, wrecked, rakish one were studied by all the wildly gay Washington couples there, and a very audible ripple of laughter followed them, three girls near the door going into fits of laughter.

CHAPTER TEN

1 ❦ Baby's bedroom.

HENNY STAYED TWO DAYS at Hassie's, not paying much attention
to her troubles but reading and sitting round with Hassie or
Cathy or the servant, in the dark back room, furnished in oilcloth and dark-smeared pine, reading, tatting, and taking tea or
coffee. She sewed up some seams in Cathy's doll collection and
looked into the old trunk of silver from Monocacy which Hassie
had taken as her portion. There were two Dresden figures,
two shepherdesses, one in black lace and one in white, which
Louie had adored from babyhood; and Henny took these in a
duster to Hassie, asking if she could have them for the poor kid,
who always liked them so much.

"It is a rotten shame, when I think that the poor kid is
dragged into all our rotten messes," said Henny.

"I'm sure I don't want them," Hassie consented, bustling
about in a great blue-striped apron. The saline and slimy smell
of the wet cement floor of the fish store came through the back
screen door. Henny hated fish and complained about it good-
humoredly all the day. Fish was in the curtains, on the oilcloth, in the cooking, said Henny, while Cathy made a face.
There was practically nothing the wasp-waisted Cathy would
eat because of her delicacy; her father had made a living out of
foods made from entrails and offscourings, sausages and the like,
and loved tripes and stuffed neck and the parson's nose; her
mother was a sturdy fishwife, slapping down fish, stacking them
in salt, plunging her hand in barrels. Cathy had seen her mother

screw a chicken's neck and could eat no more; she could not eat a rabbit because she had seen it skinned; she could eat nothing but baby lamb chops and was doing her best to move into an esthetic vegetarianism, but the poor thing was too young to have any rights and still had to dive into the family messes. She sat round gratefully with her Auntie Henny who said "fwee" and "pooh" to everything, and listened owlishly to pungent tales of loathsome folk, scabby with leprosy, spineless with caries, both moral and medical, whom Henny and Hassie knew intimately, or met in the street.

Henny rang up every few hours to ask about Charles-Franklin and find out what the "children's father" was doing today, and what Louie was giving them for lunch, and whether they stayed up late singing and jigging with the children's father, or whether they went to bed, and how was Little-Sam's earache. At night she tossed, and would put on her bedside lamp at all hours of the night while she tried to read popular novels which she called, universally, silly rot, muck, and a lot of hooey. She was really waiting for Sam to come to get her, or for him to send a letter saying he had started divorce proceedings. She did not much care. Her life was such a ruin that she preferred not to think about it at all. But on the third day, she took the train back to Annapolis. It was Saturday. She saw the little ones on the lawn jumping up and down and for all she had to face, her heart beat faster: how odd that this tumble-down windy mansion in which she had to live with a despised man was home! But her heart sank as she came up the drive. The children, seeing that unusual sight, a taxi, serpentining into the drive, ran to it with screams and halloos and started tumbling all over her. She brushed them off, paid the taxi driver, and went in, saying, "Where's your father?"

"Oh, the marlin's coming: Mr. Pilgrim is sending Dad the marlin—they caught a marlin," Henny heard. "Why did you stay away, Moth? Why did you stay at Aunt Hassie's, Moth? It's coming by the ferry: they're sending it in a car to Matapeake, ooh, we're going to boil it!" Henny took no notice of this, but with a grim expression on her face went into her room. There she had a great shock: the little fairy daughter of "Coffin" Lomasne was standing at the dressing table prinking before the glass. Henny sank down on the bed, putting her hand over her heart. The little girl turned round guiltily and flushed.

"Who let you in?"

She said shyly that Mr. Pollit had let her come in to breakfast to play with Tommy. Henny sneered and laughed. For weeks, Tommy the boatbuilder had done little but think about Lomasne's baby girl, and could not understand why she could not come and live with them. Now, thought Henny, no sooner do I turn my back than even Tommy gets in another woman; what a pack men are! And of all little girls it has to be Sam's "Little-Fairy" Lomasne.

Sam came up from the tool shed where he had been arranging Ernie's bottles in a row, preparatory to washing them and stalking into the hall outside Henny's room said, "I see you've come back."

Henny was silent, but in a minute walked out of her room softly as a ghost, and passing him with a black look, but a distant pasty one not like her old recriminatory ones, went into the baby's room. Here she sat down, and Sam, having nothing to say, went outside again and began singing, "Dare to be a Daniel, dare to stand alone, dare to have a purpose true and dare to make it known."

Baby Chappy was on the front veranda, playing with his blocks without saying a word. Henny sat in the room he shared with Tommy in the front of the house and looked round. Louie had not yet made the beds: the twisted week-old sheets and battered pillows, the faded flannel pajama suits and ragged bedside mats with sand and loam ground into them, lay about in mild disorder, while the single finger of sun in the far corner sought for them and moved delicately towards the center of the oilcloth. Flies buzzed inside the wire screens on the windows. On Monday all that would have to go into the wash, and Henny had not paid Mrs. Lewis for the last Monday's wash. Louie came into her with a cup of tea. The room smelled of babies' dirt and babies' effluvia. Over Tommy's bed a great sun-tanned girl with wild curly hair grinned down from a grove of oranges—a poster that Tommy had fallen in love with at the age of one year. Over Charles-Franklin's bed was the picture that someone had given Henny on her wedding day, a brown man and a white-skinned girl kissing in a field of poppies at sunset, in a gilt rococo frame. Pollit art had never gone beyond this. On each side of the door was a sketch in water colors, one a sunken garden with trees by the Monocacy as it winds through Frederick, and one of the old Chesapeake and Ohio bridge which crosses the Monocacy River, with the low bushy landscape and the stones spouting water. Henny had only learned three things in her school life—water-color-painting, embroidery, and the playing of Chopin, and her children could not do one of these things. Instead, they were carving boats, painting outhouses, putting in rubble for cement floors. But she did not think about her futile, anemic youth now. Instead, she looked vaguely about, sniffing that familiar smell of fresh dirtiness which belongs to mankind's extreme youth, a pleasant smell to mothers. Henny had spent twelve years in that atmosphere.

"Poor Chappy," she thought mildly, "of course, he's just a Pollit like the rest: only Ernie is a Collyer, and he doesn't like me so much since the red money-box business—I don't blame him! Well, Tommy—but I don't want to see a son of mine to grow up getting women into messes; I'm not sorry for the stupid girls, but it's not sugarplum for either side. How tired I feel!" She was surprised to feel tired after a holiday. She thought, "I can't bear to get old, lose all my energy, not be able to sleep because I'm too weak to sleep, and snivel along after life. Oh, why shouldn't I live with Sam?—he's as good to me as any man would be: men are all the same. To beat them, you have to have so much energy—I haven't got it."

For a long time she thought of nothing but found it sweet to sit there and think of her boys' future: strange to say, Evie never entered her mind. She had never bothered about Evie, or tried to dress her well, or taught her household matters or manners, for she regarded such a nice, obedient, pretty girl as cursed from birth: "Some man will break her or bend her," she always said to Hassie bitterly; while about Louie she always said, "I'm sorry for the man *she* marries!" About the girls she only thought of marriage, and about marriage she thought as an ignorant, dissatisfied, but helpless slave did of slavery. She thought the boys would get on by the brutal methods of men, Pollit or Collyer. She fingered the little, dirty, glazed-chintz cover, the thin summer blanket with matted spots, the cotton sheet. Before she was married she had made up her mind never to have anything but linen sheets, but it was four years since she had had one, and the present sheets were of the shoddiest cotton, and Mrs. Lewis, who turned them yellow, with her conceit, kept saying, "I'm sure you never had whiter sheets, Miss!"

Henny thought, "I like a baby's room best: there are no books, no lead, no nonsense," and she thought of evenings when she had come in to see the usual sight, a baby's head lying sideways, the eyes closed, the fine dark hair growing thicker over the thin-skinned oval skull, the little nightgown frill, the eyes closed, and one fist clenched on the pillow. She pulled the edge of the blanket straight thoughtfully, "A mother! What are we worth really? They all grow up whether you look after them or not. That poor miserable brat of his is growing up, and I certainly licked the hide off her; and she's seen marriage at its worst, and now she's dreaming about 'supermen' and 'great men.' What is the good of doing anything for them? Anyhow, He always wins! Well, that girl has been cooking for them for three days: I suppose I'd better see about some lunch."

She looked out of the kitchen window and saw Louie lying on her back in the orchard, waving her arms in the air, with Sam and Saul sitting on her belly jigging up and down while she shrieked and laughed. The screen door swung, and Evie's pattering came down the hall, "Mother! Mother! You came home! Oh, Mother, we had such fun last night—we all had dinner in our bathing suits and after we had a water party; and the people over on the houseboat had a party too, in bathing suits, and Louie and Ernie swam over and looked in."

"Very nice. Did Louie tell you what she got for lunch?"

"Sausages and apple fritters; and last night we had 'cah-nah-pay.'" Evie giggled, "It was raw bacon and almonds out of your drawer, and Saul spat it out."

"I see you're living on Pollit distinction," said Henny. Sam's voice on the heavy, electric summer air sang out, "Megalops, Megalops! What are you donin?" Henny heard him going past the back veranda with the three boys, saying, "See what Mega-lops donin: he don't say nuffin, maybe he thinkin; wook [look], Little-Sam, Megalops drornin [drawing] designs in the dirt."

"He's eating dirt, Pad," shrieked Saul appreciatively. Louie, who had been trying to swing on a branch of a peach tree, de-sisted and looked soulfully after the three boys and their father.

"The baby's eating dirt, Looloo," shouted Ernie.

"Well, stop him," she shouted back, at the same time walking after them nonchalantly.

"Of course he's eating dirt," said Henny. "Who is looking after him? I'd give a lot to know what he's eaten the last three days."

There fell round the corner of the house a scatter of guffawing children, turning up the corners of their eyes and holding their hands over their mouths, "Moth! Oh-ho-ho! Mothering! The baby's eating—shh!—well he is!—shh!—Megalops is eating—she doesn't like you to call him that!—Daddy says to come and see, Mother: the baby's eating his own crap—shh!—excrement, Mother."

"Don't be silly, that's not a joke," Evie told Saul severely.

"He is, he is, go and see!"

"Didn't your silly fool of a father stop him?" cried Henny.

"Yes, Mother, but Daddy says its natural, it's no harm, only he stopped him too."

"And yesterday he ate a caterpillar," said Ernie gravely. The boys burst out laughing, again holding their sides and each other. "Ooh," cried Evie, "it's so dirty, it squidged out. . . ."

They shrieked with laughter. "And Louie ate a snail to show it wouldn't make you sick," Ernie said, "and Daddy said it didn't matter." Little-Sam dropped suddenly to the ground and began rolling about holding his belly, in a paroxysm of laughter. "We had a good time, Moth, we had such a good time," Saul said hopping about, trying to convince her she should have been there. "But Louie made some nasty things, and I got sick."

"I firmly believe that," Henny said grimly. "It is quite a pity I came home: Mr. Lomasne could have done a nice business in a few days. Evie, why haven't you emptied the slops? The little boys' room hasn't been touched. Has any work been done since I left? You'll all have cholera or typhoid yet."

"We have a schedule," Ernie cried, "and we're going to make a new bartenoom [bathroom], Moth: and I'm making the frun television." (The twins chanted, "Front elevation, frun television, from Tilly Buzzum!") "And next summer, Ermo is going away with his sissy Mervyn for a walking tour," cried Little-Sam. "Oh, Mervyn the Pervyn sat under a tree, and Ernie the Mernie said, 'What do I see?' "

"You shut up," said Henny, "before I go mad. I don't know why I came home. Why isn't someone doing the potatoes? So you have a schedule? Get out of here before I scream."

A great shout blew round the house, and they heard the sound of pelting footsteps. Sam was calling, "Kids! Kids and goats! Whistletime! Worktime! Gotta make da layout for da new bartenoom. Whar you got to, fellers?"

"Comin'! I'm a-comin'! O.K., Pad!" shouted the boys, running out and leaving Henny and Evie to get the dinner. Tommy burst in through the other door calling, "Molly! Molly!" looking wildly for the little blonde Lomasne girl; and at the same moment Ernie rushed in through the western door shouting, "I see Auntie Jo's car! She's coming to lunch! Auntie Jo's coming!"

"Go and stop her at the gate and ask her if she got any choc?" shouted Sam. The children rushed off to meet her. Henny worried, "I wonder what the silly old upholstered frump wants at this hour in the day? Does she expect lunch? Did you expect your Auntie Jo? What can she expect coming without notice?" Henny sliced away at the apples anxiously.

"I wish I could go and see her car," poor Evie pouted. "Look, Moth, I cut my finger."

"Oh, then go and don't drive me mad," cried Henny, more vexed than ever. "God knows what the Man of Sorrows has been up to! What the deuce is his big slummicking sister down here for before lunch?" She went impatiently to the baby's room to look out and saw Jo in great excitement walking about with Samuel, who seemed depressed; Jo expostulated, was bright with indignation; Sam put his hand to his eyes and brushed them. They turned and came towards the house.

"That's it," thought Henny, with indignation, "she pried and poked, and she found out—let the old maid go home, she knows nothing."

But when the yellow-haired couple came towards her, she saw they were both crying; and Sam said, "We found Bonnie, or rather—she came to Jo."

"I didn't recognize her," said Jo. "I opened the door and there was a terrible-looking woman, thin, with hair in a knot and looking——"

"She got a taxi to bring her to Jo's house because she knew she was going to be ill." Sam looked humbly at Henny, with a face tortured by shame and distress. "Bonniferous is there now, in Jo's flat: she had a baby there. I am going up to see the man."

"Where is the baby?" asked Henny.

"I don't know," Jo said.

"It's dead!"

"I don't know!"

"What are you talking about?"

"Someone came and took it away: I don't know. It wasn't I that arranged it. I won't keep her there, either. What am I to say? What can I tell them? She hasn't even a wedding ring."

"Where is the baby, Samuel?" Henny asked angrily. "What is it, a girl? A boy?"

"I didn't look and I didn't ask. Someone came last night and took it away and it may as well be dead: she will never see it again. I had to pay to have it taken away, and I don't wish to hear any more about it. I've never seen anything like it: she tried to kill herself, and she asked me to kill her. I didn't know what to do. She kept shrieking so loud you could have heard it a block away, and I tried to keep her quiet by putting a pillow over her mouth, but she was so strong I couldn't hold her down. They came at the door knocking, too. She got there at four and she kept it up till eleven-thirty, and there was I in jail with this horrible thing going on and people knocking at my door. At last the woman on the floor underneath got her husband to break in the door. She said she would go and get a woman, but I said, 'I would never allow my sister to be seen like that'; but she went anyhow. Think of my horrible position! She came back with a woman who did something—I don't know what; I never looked towards her. Then she asked me if she would send the baby away and told me what it would cost. I told her I would never pay for it, I knew nothing about it; but she insisted—I would have to pay for its keep, if there was no father, as it seemed—" Jo's voice broke in a sob.

She began to walk up and down the room, not looking at any of them, avoiding their glances, delivering a manifesto, "She isn't my sister: to come there at the last moment without giving me any warning, after being silent all that time and in that state— why didn't she die? I thought she was sure to. What am I to do? Everyone must know. She wouldn't be quiet; I kept trying to stop her. I had to give the woman ten dollars to take the horrible thing away, the baby, early this morning, and she's coming back on Monday. Don't you see it's blackmail? I'm ruined. I won't have her; I'm finished with her. Sam can do what he likes. She'll never see my face again. And this morning I had a telegram from Miss Atkinson—she was one of those who knocked at my door yesterday afternoon! What am I to say? I rang her up and told her someone was taken very ill with accidental poisoning, and we had to have the stomach-pump. But will she believe it? I've got to get that thing out of my rooms. What will I do, Henny?"

"Is she alive? What do you mean?"

"She's ill," said Jo solemnly.

"It would have been better if she'd died," said Henny.

"Will you come and get her, Henny? Down here no one comes: she could stay here until she can get up. Then she must go away. I'm sorry I have to talk about her."

Sam looked angry, "I'm going up at once to see the man."

"What can he do? He's married, isn't he? The rotten coward took a young girl, knowing he couldn't be stuck with her. Don't be wasting your valuable time."

"To think of the way I've lived and fought for every penny," said Jo, stopping and standing in front of Henny. "Now I must sell the house. I can't face the disgrace. I can't go back while she's there when I think of what she's done to me. A sister of mine!—oh, I don't know how I can bear it! How can this happen to me, when I've worked so hard. Miss Atkinson came with two of the teachers—we were going to have a cup of tea and go to the cinema. What can I say to them on Monday? I can't face it. I must get temporary leave. Oh, it's dreadful, it might ruin me, a thing like that."

"What about Bonnie, Jo?" Sam asked gently.

Jo shouted rudely, "Do you think I care about a thing like that, a prostitute trailing around with married men and having babies in the street? Oh, it's awful. It's awful, Henny. I don't know what to do. In our family—I didn't know such things happened."

"You big brass-mouthed old-maid cow," said Henny, "I hope a thousand worse things happen to you to teach you to be a bit human, instead of always prancing about with your head in the air."

"Henny! I thought that you at least—Henny! Don't, don't say that! You don't understand. You have your father's money and estate: I had to build up every cent of this with my own hands;

don't you see? It might ruin me. You don't know what it means to have to be your own father and mother the way I had to, and look out for your old age. You have a husband, little ones for your old age; but who is there for me? I'm darned if I'll stand such a thing," cried Jo, suddenly getting angry again. "I should have strangled her with my own hands, yesterday: I had the chance; I was too cursed weak. What difference would it make?"

"You ought to have had a man to make you wash floors and kick you in the belly when you didn't hurry up for him," said Henny with all the hate of a dozen years. "I'm as rotten as she is—I've had men too—I've gone trailing my draggletail in all sorts of low dives—I've taken money from a man to keep his children—I'm a cheat and a liar and a dupe and a weak idiot and there's nothing too low for me, but I'm still 'mountains high' above you and your sickly fawning brother who never grew up—I'm better than you who go to church and than him who is too good to go to church, because I've done everything. I've been dirty and low and done things you're both too stupid and too cowardly to do, but however low I am, I'm not so filthy crawling in the stench of the gutter, I haven't got a heart of stone, I don't sniff, sniff, sniff when I see a streetwalker with a ragged blouse, too good to know what she is: I hate her but I hate myself. I'm sick of the good ones; I'm sick of that stupid staring idiot standing goggling at me who's going to be as good as you are; nothing's too good for you, nothing's too bad for me; I'll go and walk the streets with that poor miserable brat sister of yours—we'll both get something to eat and some men to be decent to us, instead of loudmouthed husbands and sisters who want to strangle us—that's what you said, that's what you said, you can never go back on that, and in that your whole black cruel cold heart came out of you and you tried to strike her down with it, like a stone as he'd like to strike me down when he gets all he can out of me—and I know you both, I know you all —she's the only decent one and that's because she's like me—no good—good because she's no good—take your eyes off me, you staring idiot, get out of here, you filthy child—tell your daughter to get out of here—I can't stand it—" Henny could say no more but began to scream and then fell to the floor, bumping her head hard. Her eyes were closed; she seemed cold as stone.

Louie, with streaming eyes, went slowly to get her a cushion as so often before, while Jo said, "Well, in all my life!"

"Shut up, Jo: the trouble with you is you don't understand anything and you don't try to learn," Sam said, in a voice low and mortified. "Let us go outside and leave her alone. Louie, leave your mother to come to herself. Jo, I can't go on. You don't know what I have to put up with, so don't give me advice. I will go up with you, and you and I will get Bonnie out of your place. I'll bring her down here. Jo, you must try to be kinder. You are beyond human life."

"I've never done any wrong," said Jo, stony with pride and passion; "I've never done wrong to a single human being: no one can say that."

"Get your hat, Jo: we'll go and see Bonnie."

Henny groaned and stirred slowly. Louie, who had been watching, snuffling and sobbing in the corner of the room, came forward, "Will I help you up, Mother?"

"Yes, take me into the baby's room."

But when she got up she withdrew her hand quickly from the hated child's touch, and, going into the baby's room, slammed the door. Louie went round outside and peered in the window. Henny was lying on Tommy's bed, under the picture of the girl with oranges, and large tears were rolling from under her dry, tanned lids.

The boys, who had been playing down on the beach, now rushed up shrieking, "Auntie Jo; can we take your car to the ferry to get the marlin? It's coming now." So it happened that, as they couldn't let the marlin lie corrupting on the street end where the Matapeake ferry comes in, they went and brought home the marlin before Jo and Sam went to see Bonnie. The boys staggered down to the beach with the weighty spikefish. Its great eyes were sunken; it looked exhausted from its battle for life; there was a gaping wound in its deepest part. They attached it by a cord to a stake and immersed it in the creek, to keep it as fresh as possible till Sam came home. The children began to run towards Spa House from all over Eastport, and people started to look at them from the bridge and Shipwright's Street. The children were proud and happy and would not stir from the beach all the morning. The air was crisp, electric, nervous, but the children only flickered, leaped, and played like fish.

But Evie, up in the house, grunted under the tables and round the chairs, removing old dust and musing in a delirium of contentment: Louie had just told her that Auntie Bonnie had a little baby and that they were both coming to stay. Evie was already arranging in her mind that the baby should sleep in her room, so that she could mind it.

2 ✠ Gold mare's tail.

SAM DID NOT COME HOME till the sky was green and a cloud hung above Bancroft Hall and the lost horizon. He was alone. Bonnie had been neglected all day except for little visits of consolation from the neighbor from below and was ill, angry, and feverish when her brother got there. Where was the baby? The neighbor had told her that it was being looked after by a nurse, but she wanted to see it. Was it a boy or a girl? It was a boy with faint white hair. She must feed it. No, not for forty-eight hours. She whined, went to sleep, and woke up again, worrying about the baby, and said she must get up, and asked where the nurse was. The neighbor said, and believed, that Jo had gone to make arrangements for her to go to a nursing home with the baby. But Bonnie knew about Jo what no one else knew, having seen her in her agonized fury during the previous twenty-four hours. She would have stolen out if she could have moved, because she felt so weak that she was sure she was going to die. Very little had been done in the room: the flies buzzed, and it was sultry, thunderstorm weather. Bonnie cried and in her new helplessness and anxiety thought over the secrets of the past few months. She would never in her life admit her humiliations: she had been and would again be a gay, buzzing girl with the disease of optimism. When she woke once she found her loved brother Sam in her room and wept bitterly in his arms, saying how weak she felt and that she thought she was going to die.

Jo wanted to move Bonnie away at once, to avoid explanations, but Sam explained to her that Bonnie could not be moved ("Don't tell me—please tell me when you came from the maternity ward!—ridiculous!—I understand as well as you!—nonsense!" ejaculated Jo meanwhile); and he suggested that it would be better to keep Bonnie close and quiet till she could move, say a week or ten days, and then let her go out at nightfall. Bonnie could then go to him at Spa House, and he would come to fetch her.

Jo became very tormented at the idea that she would have to live in the same two-room apartment with Bonnie for a whole week or more, wrung her hands, and said she could not face the school—she must get sick leave, she could not face her tenants with rent day nearly due, and what would she do about the decorator who was coming to paint her walls Nile green? But Sam became stern and forbade her to move Bonnie; and as soon as she was so ordered the domineering, unruly Jo became meek at once, if not acquiescent. Sam told her to get food and clothing for Bonnie, saying bitterly that after such a few days the burden would fall on him, Jo need not fret. He was very thoughtful coming home, but the thickset woods and the broad, fish-silver Severn made his heart lighter. He had not been to see "the man, the card-trick horror," whom Jo asserted was the cause of Bonnie's downfall, because Bonnie had said so often and positively that the man was a bachelor, an actor now on tour (withholding his name), that Sam dared not interfere at present. He was grave and deeply ashamed, offended with Fate, not

[466]

with Bonnie; he muttered his favorite saying over and over as
the train racketed along,

Good name—in man—and woman—good my Lord,
Is—the Immediate—Jewel—of their—souls!
Who steals—my purse, steals trash—'tis something—nothing!
Good name—in man—and woman—good my Lord,
Steals trash—'tis something, nothing—good my Lord—
'Tis something, nothing, 'tis something, nothing—good name—

He stopped at the boat basin as always and chatted with the
captain of the *Mary III* and then walked to the bridge. Birds
were flying in funnels and purse seines in the steep air, dragging, trawling the air for insects, getting ready to settle in trees
and already in tree shapes. In the air was the strange cloud,
bright gold, in the shape of an ostrich feather or the tail of a
sculptured horse. It was late; the dark was closing globularly
round, and little was left but the green top and the strangely
lighted west. Many people stopped to look at the ominous cloud,
which, after remaining for some time with its pure, glittering,
fimbriate forms, began to dissolve; the light retired behind it
where it burned still. Gradually the texture of the rest of the
sky became apparent; the sky was covered with short mares' tails
of cloud which were now lengthening, anastomosing, knitting.
Sam heard a chattering on the other side and in the dusk saw
a small group of children, with "Coffin" Lomasne and old Bill
the fisherman, standing on his own beachlet, discussing the
marlin which lay in the water.

"Gee Whittaker!" said Sam, "she will pooh if I don't hurry,"
and he widened his stride.

The children had seen him though and came hallooing towards him. "Pad, you're so late; Pad, it's too late to cook the
spikefish; Dad, can we build the fire now under the copper?"
while Ernie came towards him chanting, while he pointed to the
flimsy sky, "Mares' tails and mackerel scales make heavy ships
carry light sails," the old saw.

As soon as dinner was finished, they went down with their own railway storm lantern (which was named "Old Man Hat") and with lamps borrowed from the boatmen, and with the ax saw and skinning knives, to dissect the fish. Soon Little-Sam came leaping down the dark earthy cliff to say the fire was hot and the water singing to the boil. They were going to boil the fish through the night. There were basins alongside, on boards on top of the washtubs, into which the oil was to be ladled as it floated to the top; and all the washed bottles, with some gallon jars, stood along the wall of the washhouse. Sam had made up his mind to show them an item of his economy and to provide for as many household oils as he could from this single fish. Henny sent a message out to ask how on earth she was to do the washing on Monday, but Sam sent back a message to say that the boys would get inside and scrub it out with sand and washing soda. They then cut the fish up fairly small into pieces six to nine inches in length and threw them into the copper in which was a little water (it should have been done in a double boiler, said Sam, but "necessity was the mother of invention"). They kept the head separate to boil in a caldron in the yard the next day, because Sam wanted to see how much oil was in the head alone, out of mere curiosity.

In about twenty minutes, at about nine-forty-five in the evening, a strong smell of fish stew arose, which increased as the boiling went on. They banked the fire, as the fish began to stick, and threw in more water. It was a to-and-fro all the time, with the children simmering and carrying messages to each other and to their father, and Henny coming out to find out what was that horrible smell and was it going on all night. The boiling water was now covered with large oil spots and scum, which they occasionally ladled off into the available enamel hand basins and the kitchen pail; long tubes of steam went off, and the air in the washhouse was palpable. Henny was walking through the house now, wringing her hands on her skirts and saying she would never get the smell out of the house.

"Hassie's place smells like fish, and I come home to this: my life has been one blessed fish chowder!"

Then when she had gone upstairs "away from the stink"—though, heavy as it was, almost leaden in the heavy air, it was rising slowly, and flowing round the house, to reach the second story and the roofs and chimney pots and float sluggishly away to other parts—the fun really began. It was a night of jamboree with Sam, the boys and girls, the fire on the lower part of their faces, taking turns at watching the fire under the boiler and telling long anecdotes, joking, reminiscing, Sam reciting, "Good name in man and woman, good my Lord," and Louie, "When Moloch in Jewry munched children with fury, 'twas thou Devil dining with pure intent." Presently the house was ready for the night, and they expostulated with Sam about the smell, one at a time, but ended by settling down with the others and dreamily taking it in.

"Superbus," cried Sam, *"superbus,* it is a good whiff; when you fellers snuff my mortal remains, it won't be half what this is!"

"Stop it!" cried Louie.

"They is stinx en stinx," Sam said, beginning to caper on his haunches; "they is good sniffs and bad whiffs; they is snot smells and pot smells; they is green-grown wells and hell's bells; they is dogs what prowls and cats what howls, and showers what lowers for hours and hours, and they's dead fish and dirty dish, en dead gulfweed what's dead indeed, en clams en corpses en barnacles en all of the salt sea's miracles; what is dead, what is dead en tho hit is dead, it floats en it bloats, en it gloats en—ef you stick a knife in it, whew!"

And he held his nose, while all around him they held their noses and said, "Phew!"

"Phew!" he continued, "say, kids, ain't you en me havin' a good time? Now, we got to take turns watchin' this yere fire all the livelong night; we cain't afford to let it get away from us: we live in a wooden house, though it don't look wooden. Now, who is game for a fishing expedish?"

[469]

"I think it's going to rain, Pad," said Little-Sam, wrinkling his nose; "it sure smells like rain."

As if in answer to him came a low growl, perhaps from the northwest, and the air trembled like a curtain.

"The fish will be there," said Sam, "but maybe we are too late. So we'll go to bed, and Little-Womey will take first watch till eight bells; then she will wake Looloo, who will take the dog watch becaze she is dogged, and then we will have two shifts, Little-Sam for two hours and Saul for two hours becaze they cain't do nothin' by halves."

"When will you watch, Pad?" asked Ernie.

"Now, I am doing the superintendin'," said Sam, "and I cain't watch, it stands to reason de boss cain't do everything." He grinned wickedly at them. However, when Henny heard the watches the children were to keep, she sent down an angry message from her room, and presently they drew up a new roster, in which each was to watch two hours, including Sam, to watch and keep the fire, skim the scum, stir the stew, and make a cup of tea for the watch to follow.

The night was with them. Mutterings ran through the sky, and the land began to moan, and the trees heaved as if the whole earth was a timbered ship trying to make headway on a threatening sea. The thundering increased, coming nearer, and brilliant lightning began, splitting the entire sky, in which balls of fire seemed to bounce in an instant from the close doorstep of heaven to earth; then the sky and earth began to shudder and dissolve into one another like one corrugated sheet along which the lightning spilled. The children ran about pallid and tremulous through all this, long trained to be afraid of none of the effects of nature, and yet surprised at this bizarre electric storm.

Upstairs, Henny could not sleep and went downstairs to get the baby, which she took back upstairs with her. She got into bed, holding the heavy body of the unconscious child as long as she could, and then placed it in the bed alongside her. Meanwhile, she could see what she was accustomed to see from her bedroom window—the ghastly tilted roofs, a bit of stony street, the clumsy wooden bridge, the colorless lashing water with shells of boats tossing. Somewhere beyond the world, an enormous voice shouted, whips cracked, and sheet-iron clanged through space, while every few minutes the flares of an open hearth, distant and beneath, lighted the entire sky. Sometimes it was as the seven candlesticks seized at the horizon and carried by a rushing wing flickering to the other verge. Surge after surge in spouts and cataracts roared the rain.

Henny once wrapped her dressing gown round her and rushed down the stairs furiously, to knock at Sam's door and ask if the children were not even to be allowed to have their night's sleep on account of the cursed great fish and if they were to be allowed to drown down there in the brimming yard.

"Go back to bed," called Sam's voice from behind the door.

"If the miserable fish has to be watched, I'll watch it, much as I hate it, rather than see the poor kids kept up all night for your idiot whims!"

"Go away," called Sam, "now you've wakened me, and I'll watch it."

Henny went upstairs grumbling and whimpering to herself, but when she saw him come out dressed, she went back to bed. She began to play cards, determined to take the next two-hour watch after Sam, instead of Saul, who had to be waked then according to the roster.

Darkness poured from the sky with the hissing as of falling ashes, trickles of fire, and sudden explosion. Henny got out her cards and started to play her famous double patience (with two packs of cards). The first layout was all hearts and diamonds, yet impossible to make a move, the second all clubs and spades and again impossible to make a move; the third time, the layout, mixed, looked unpromising, but the game started to come out with the greatest rapidity, and yet by accident not by bad shuffling, and Henny, used to cheating herself, this time was tempted to cheat the other way, blocking the solution. In five minutes the game was out! Henny forgot the storm and the fish in the copper and looked helplessly at the eight stacks of cards before her, each with a king on top. The game that she had played all her life was finished; she had no more to do: she had no game. She was angry and, picking up the cards again, shuffled them carefully and started to lay them out in the same old pattern, but she had only laid down nine cards when she was seized with such a violent nausea, such a feeling of the emptiness and aimlessness of the game—thinking that she might have to go through another fifteen or twenty years before it came out again! —that she gathered them quickly and threw them into her drawer loosely. She got up and looked out at the window and the surging, swelling, yellowed creek.

When Ernie, who was wakened by the storm, got up to see the change of watch, his mother said, "Tell your father to let Saul sleep: I will go and sort the clothes and do my knitting out there," and the message was delivered.

Sam, who merely regarded this as a feeble, shamefaced concession on Henny's part, an admission that she was interested in the marlin boiling and his planned economy, said mischievously, "All right, tell your mother that she can watch the fish from two to four A.M. if she wants to—but only if she wants to—and Saul can come at four."

Ernie said, "No, Tadpole, don't let her: you know Mother doesn't like the smell of fish."

Sam laughed, "There are more things in heaven and earth, Horatio, than are dreamed of in your philosophy. Never mind, son: what the eye doesn't see the mouth gapes at; the quickness of the intellect deceives the crooked; watch my patter, and I'll hear you picking my pocket: Mothering, my dear boy, has a sneaking interest in our little proceedings, and this is her queer, obstinate, mulish, womanish way of showing it—she pretends to sacrifice herself, when she really wants to be one of us!—don't you see that, Ermy? You must get to know women, Ermy! Women is trouble; women is cussed; you have got to learn to run women, boy, yes, sir. If Mother offers to watch the marlin, let her watch, says I."

Ernie, laughing uncertainly backed down. Louie, waked by

the commotion and the storm, came walking through the house and out to the washhouse too, and was most indignant when she heard that Henny was to watch, but Sam only laughed joyously, poked her in the ribs, and told her not to interfere, "Poor Old Mother Interference, someone ruined her appearance!"

Through the wet air, in the intervals of the storm, pockets of marlin fumes blew around them. Louie went storming upstairs, "Mother, I'm awake, I'll watch the boiling."

"You go to bed: you'll look like the usual boiled owl in the morning!"

"I'll watch!"

"I'll watch! I can't stand argument, go to bed. I hope I catch my death of cold!"

Louie, looking from their window, saw Sam and Ernie walking down to the bluff to look in the risen creek and plodding round the sodden grounds, squelching, laughing, dashing wet sprays in each other's face.

"Race you to the washus," cried Sam.

"All right," said Ernie.

Neither was a good runner, and the boy soon got a stitch in his side, so that Sam got there first.

"Beatcha," said Sam cheerfully, throwing down the stick he was carrying and darting into the washhouse to lift the lid and look into his stew. "My cooking," said Sam, "my cooking—worth something! What Sam-the-Bold cooks up ain't a angry stew like womenfolks. Sam-the-Bold cooks what air useful to man en horse en motorbike: the essential oil!"

Henny, with sunk angry eyes, got up and brushed past him suddenly. She said to the boy, "Ernie-dear, since your clever father is here, perhaps the stupid people can go and get something to eat: come, and I'll give you some milk and put you to bed."

Sam gave a comical jeering snarl, "Ermy-boy, you c'mere! Boy, you're on sentry-go: you're up, you may as well stick along o' Sam. Go tell your mother to make some corf for all hands."

"I'm so sleepy, Pad," said the boy.

[473]

"You do what the Old Man says," Sam smiled.

Henny said outside, to the white night, "I wish he'd stop play-ing his silly monkey tricks with the children and let them grow up," and she went into the house to make the fresh coffee. When it was made, she put it steaming on the table with fruit and sandwiches and, going to the door of the porch, called, "Ernie, tell your father his coffee's on the table."

"Is it on the table, is it on the table?" Sam shouted. "Can't come unless it's on the table."

"Oh, shut up," Henny said to herself. The boy looked at his father.

"Get me corf," said Sam; "then you get a drop of suthin good what slides down quick, and you go to bed. Meanwhile, you un-ravel them grapevines you got in the line, Ermy: you'll never make a proper fisherman with the instincts of a fisherman if you let grapevines stay in."

The boy took up the wet mess of tangled line and began to pick it over. As Sam continued to give him advice, Ernie sulkily moved across the yard to the kitchen to do his picking.

Sam felt lonely suddenly in the washhouse, with only the bubbling of the fish stew to keep him company. It was a glorious, rich smell certainly, and Sam counted on getting a gallon of oil at the least, probably nearer two gallons, but what was the pur-pose of it all? Wasn't his life empty, always amusing the kids, thinking up projects for them, teaching them to be good men and women when they ran off upon their own bents and a woman was always twisting them, snatching them away from him? I mustn't think that, thought Sam, shaking himself and beginning to hammer out bent nails that he had saved from old packing cases: waste not, want not, same applies to energy. Mustn't waste emotion, want it for a great job in the future, maybe: I may be called to a great position later on—never can tell, preparedness is everything: you work for years and the op-portunity comes—meanwhile, here I work with my little com-munity, leading it, creating a feeling in Eastport, a civic feeling, speaking to the Parents' Association about peace and progress, and soon I'll be helping to watch our waters and foreshores and increasing their fertility. Man is the symbol of fertility, and increase is his job. Yes, mustn't despair: everything comes to him who waits—waits with preparedness. Overcome all enemies, including spiritual enemies, weariness, disappointment. I carry the torch, I will pass it to one, two, three, of my spawn; in the meantime, I must watch, wait, pray—not pray, no, but learn to lead my fellow man, for the spirit was given to me. Where is Looloo? These are thoughts which she should understand. Poor, lost, worrying Looloo! I bet she's awake now; because my spirit is awake and between her and me is immediate communication, mental radio. . . .

Sam walked round the house. As he reached the front lawn, Henny's light went out. The effluvia of the fish, all that could be conveyed by air, were seeping again round the house, for the storm was passing away at last, and all that remained of it was the flickering of the sky, fringes of rainy cloud, and the pools of water underfoot. The water in the creek was lapping high too. It seemed to Sam that nature was licking at his feet like a slave, like a woman, that he had read of somewhere, that washed the feet of the man she loved and dried them with her hair.

The light went on in Louie's room. "Just as I thought," said Sam to himself, "I knew it." He saw Louie come to the veranda and look out, look down on him, and then go back. He thought, "It's early, nearly light, and she's awake: we'll go for a little walk since she's awake." He went back into the house and crept up the stairs, thinking about Jenny Maxim, the little girl in Baltimore, that he met at Mrs. Pilgrim's house and who was so in love with Nature. Henny's door was shut. Louie was muttering in her room, but the door stood open. The light was on, and through the crack of the door Sam perceived Louie lying on her bed with her hands crossed behind her head (she was twisting her hair round and round on her fingers), and he heard her say, " 'Bear me out in this, thou great democratic God! who didst not refuse to the swart convict Bunyan the pale poetic pearl: Thou who didst clothe with doubly hammered leaves of finest gold, the stumped and paupered arm of old Cervantes. . . .'" (Melville: *Moby Dick*.) Sam, who was ignorant of all literature and thought Louie had invented this herself (but said to himself that it was no more than might be expected of a child of Samuel Clemens Pollit), leaned against the crack, peering still and smiling to himself.

After a silence, during which he breathed quietly, he heard her begin to mutter again, "'Enmity calls for death and I am longing for life'" (Nijinsky's letter to Diaghilev), but at this Sam merely smiled again, thinking with joy, yes, she loves love and hates hate even as I do. Nothing could be better for a lead-in to his heart-to-heart talk with her that he planned in this dawn (it could be her watch with the fish, for example, and they could let Little-Sam sleep).

"There is love in the city, lust in the country," said Louie to herself; "the storm suffocates the land, the creek ravishes the beach, the hilltop violates the sky——"

At this, Sam came into the room and said sternly, "I hear a lot of darn nonsense, but I don't hear much sense: what sort of an author are you quoting, Looloo-girl?"

Louie frowned menacingly, "Nobody: I made it up."

"A nice sort of thing to make up," said Sam. "You are too much alone: I hear so much stupidity, I can't understand it. Get up and get dressed, I want to talk to you."

"It isn't morning," said Louie, burning red and angry.

"It is your watch at the marlin boiling, and anyhow, I am up and I see I have to say many things to you."

Louie curled her lip, "You don't know anything."

"Get dressed, you dogged wretch."

"Well, you go out."

Sam withdrew, pulling the door violently after him and shouting through it, "Now hurry, hurry: Samulam want to talk," being pleasant again so that she would be friendly when she came downstairs. The fire was now low, and Sam said, "Let us watch the dawn rise, we will just walk about over to the cove and back, and peek in at the fire all the time," and after they had looked in at the stew on which the oil was now in some spots two inches thick, they began their walk down the heavy-headed avenue, dark with rain. Banks of loose cloud covered the sky, floating higher and away. The east seemed distant, a glum blue, but the waves and trees seemed still of one element.

"Looloo," said Sam solemnly, "I perhaps should have spoken to you as a woman before. We should like relations between men and women to be ideal, but, as you are apparently coming to realize, they are not. Your own bringing-up, whatever its apparent defects, has helped you to realize that we must not blame either side: it is all a question of adjustment and patience. I hope you will be happy, Looloo. The great question is self-control, Looloo, and to fix the mind on the many many problems of science, both solved and unsolved. In the arcanum of the unsolved of nature is much for busy brains to do: I hope you will be of the number of the searchers and finders. What do you want to do, Looloo?" She was silent. "You can tell your father."

"I don't know."

"Now, for women there is a greater freedom. I am hoping that you will choose to remain with me and work with me for the greater freedom of all men; but you must understand in your own life that liberty isn't libertinism, not that that is yet a problem for you, though men and women alike today, as they go out in the world, face temptations. Now, you must know without my telling you, Looloo-girl, that temptation in sex, which comes to some early and some late and to some happy ones not at all, can betray us into being not ourselves. I heard you mention something which, I might say, had a venereal implication—symbols, examples, words, which—of the meaning of which you are doubtless not quite cognizant as yet—whatever you feel like, Looloo, and I leave that all to you. Remember that self-control is our only safeguard and that the abuses of the instinct lead to—either waste of energy and emotion and the finer feelings, or indiscriminate recourse to members of the other sex, upon which follows venereal disease, a thing too dreadful to contemplate or to talk about and which I would not have to speak about if you

[477]

had a decent mother—but you have not: this duty is left in the hands of a father. I feel as embarrassed about it as you. Promise me, Looloo (this is a strange thing to be talking about in such a wild, pure dawn, between night and day, between sea and sky), that if you are thinking of a man or boy, you will not think seriously of him without marriage; or if you must, if you must ever go with man or boy, Looloo—I leave it to you, it seems inadvisable to me, understanding these things so much better than you—that you will first demand a medical certificate from him."

Louie laughed, "I will never do that."

"Never promise?"

"Never do it. It's so silly."

"You know not whereof you speak," said Sam huskily.

"I love, I love, I only know about love," cried Louie madly, bursting into tears. "What has that to do with it? You keep out of it."

"Hush, Looloo: I was speaking to Ernie too tonight, and I told him when he begins to think about girls he must tell me."

Louie said bitterly, "There is one thing I am quite sure of: he never will. Not one of the children will ever confide in you."

He looked at her, shocked, "Looloo! But I confide in you! I tell you all I can, suited to your understanding of life and human nature! My dear girl, naturally, you look upon me as a father, someone above ordinary temptations, but that is not so: I have been tempted. The worst thing about temptation is," he smiled coaxingly at her, "Looloo, is that you want to yield to it. You even like it!" He smiled to himself and looked at the ground. "There is a wonderful young woman, Looloo, who seems to me to be—is—my perfect mate: it would be for me one of those marriages made in heaven. I cannot think of it because of your mother. Naturally. But she too feels this way about me, and she would sacrifice everything for me, if it were possible. I said to her, 'I know you, my girl, I know you would give up everything for me: all I would ask out of life now—for my pride has fallen—is to have you be my constant companion, to be by my side, in my utmost need to go by my side. I know' (I told her only yesterday, Looloo) 'that life means little to you either, without me. I know you are prepared to live in a little flat waiting for me when I can come, that you will live in the back street of life, without children, but the two of us facing the future wide-eyed and full of its promise, that is even better than children, perhaps—and besides I have children'—and she said, 'Yes,' Looloo," his voice broke: "she said, 'Yes,' she would do so.

"But I cannot ask her to do it! It is dishonorable in the eyes of the world. And the little old world is not always wrong. Good name is something too. Without good name, Looloo, what good could I do? Most people are simple good folk: they believe in the plain, honest ways of living, the old-fashioned ways that my mother believed in. No, we cannot contravene the ways of the honest, humble poor, the ways of innocence and the integrity of family life. The home, the hearth, the family and fatherhood, the only ideals the old Romans ever had that were any good, little as they lived up to them."

Louie burst out crying.

Sam said tenderly, "Always blubbering, Looloo, what a big mass of blubber yet!"

"You must let me leave you," said Louie, "you must give me some freedom."

He became stern, "Looloo, you will never leave me, you must never leave me: you and I must cleave together through the storms to come. The house is cold and full of bitter hate. I told my darling girl that, too. I want you, Looloo, as a bulwark between me and her hate, a bulwark of living love. I cannot live in such an atmosphere of hate. It is not for me. And I know it is hard on you, too, Looloo—now don't tell me that again; but if you could know what you meant to me when I first saw you come from your mother's womb. Women have meant so much in my life, believing in me (as they believe in men, for they are born to do that, Looloo, and that's why I don't want you cynical), listening to me, loving me too, I verily believe, though I was always too modest and bashful perhaps, to rightly see love when it came, and always helping me and wanting to love

[479]

Nature, as I loved it. Women are the blessing of men. Oh, Loo-loo, if I could have had the right wife, what a great man I would have been! Certainly a good one, better than I am now. And our children, happy in the love of father and mother, play-ing round my feet, growing from innocent, lusty, laughing baby-hood to strong forthright boyhood and to wide-eyed, idealistic youth, and to vigorous loving manhood! But I am satisfied with what I have: do not think I am criticizing your brothers and dear Little-Womey. They may not be all exactly as I would have wished, but they are dear to me: they will go the right path and follow the light; they will come through, Looloo. I want you to know I am optimistic for you all."

He waited for a response, then added, "What have you to say to me about your own little affairs, Looloo?"

"I want to leave home."

"After all I have said to you?"

"I must leave home. You must give me some money to go to Harpers Ferry."

"I must, I must! I won't! You're still in tutelage, thank God, and I hope still to make you more amenable! I won't have this cussed obstinacy. I'll break that miserable dogged spirit of yours: it will get you nowhere. What man will look at you with your piggish, sulky, thick face always gloomy? Do you think any man is going after a face like that? Thank God, now women can get jobs anyhow, if they have sufficient education; when I was a boy some looks were necessary: you had to charm men. You can get your living, but I want to see you happy. You have got to cheer up; you have got to smile. Don't you notice when we walk down the street together that the women and men too look after me with a smile; and that they look at you surprised at your glum, stupid, sullen air?"

"I notice," said Louie. "You must let me go. I will have to go, anyhow."

"What can a girl do by herself?"

"Clare and I are going on a walking trip this summer by our-selves."

"With boys, I suppose."

"Oh, no!—we are going to walk."

"What fools, what stupid puppies!" He flung himself off to the distance of two yards in advance. "Stupid little spoiled conceited puppies. What can two girls do on the road? Don't you know that you are helpless? What will you do at night? Where will you sleep? In the fields?"

"At Auntie Jo's and at Harpers Ferry and at Hazel's in Charlestown, West Virginia," said Louie. "We thought it all out, and Clare has friends too, and there are the Pryors, Mother's relatives in Frederick. It is not stupid at all."

"Where will you get the money? To live, to eat?"

"Why—" she faltered, "I suppose, they will give us something to eat."

He said savagely, "If you want to know, your aunt at Harpers Ferry has just refused to take you for the summer; she cannot afford it any more—no sooner does the Collyer money fade than all my resources go: the servility of men is humiliating. That's something you don't happen to know about. You are going to stay here, and be a good daughter to me, and look after your brothers and sister; and I am going to send Henny away, if you are so obstinate as to force me to tell you. Your stepmother has deceived me often—" he ceased speaking and held his hands before his face, squeezing them together, "with another, with another man. I never thought such a thing would come into my family life. I have been the best of husbands, never deceived her, whatever the temptations, and they are many. And now I know what has been going on for years. Why, in the very first years— my own very best friend—a man called Mark Colefax, hard as it is for me to pronounce his name—after him I never thought I could believe in friendship again—your stepmother went out with him: I trust, she said it was no more. But all men lie in those situations through a mistaken idea of gallantry, and I never found out the truth. Now, however, thanks, I regret to say, to a horrible anonymous letter, filthy but true, I know that your mother was going out with a man when I was away in the

[481]

Pacific, and I hardly know—Looloo, Looloo!—" he began to sob, and Looloo stood still, frightened, "Looloo!—I hardly know whether Chappy, my little big-eyed Megalops, is mine or not. A human life—and perhaps it were better he had never been born. Outside the pale, perhaps; perhaps it will come to light. What will I do then?"

"What will Mother do?"

"She has made her bed: let her lie on it. I cannot worry about a woman who never worried for a moment about my name. Yet," he said, with regret, "I have to, Looloo: we have had children together—that is the infernal tie, the bond of carnality. I don't know what to do."

After a silence, during which they turned towards the fateful Spa House, he said, in a low voice, "You see, you see, Looloo? You see why you must stay by me forever? I have had too many burdens."

She was silent until they reached the house. The dawn broke clear, with light yellow wisps of cloud scattered over a wide, wind-swept sky. Sam took her silence as submission and, brushing away his sorrows, went cheerfully back to poke the fire under the copper.

3 ✵ The offal heap.

AT BREAKFAST TIME, the children, tired and excited, beat time on tin plates and chanted, while porridge was being brought in, "Am marlin, is marlin, was marlin, be marlin, marlin along of me!"

Sam shouted, "Who for the washus, kids! Who wants to take up the stand?"

"No one," said Little-Sam: "we wanna rest, Big Chief."

Sam told them that "arter brekker" (after breakfast) he was going to photograph the marlin's head, and then put it on to boil in the yard, for "serpently bad weather was a-blowin' up." He told them that during the night he had had a good idea—he would take down the chimneys before the gale came, because he reckoned that gale was going to be a humdinger. He was afraid of falling from roofs, with his vertigo (which fear the twins and Ernie shared), and yet he loved the altitude and great sweep of landscape. He told them that as soon as he got into the Conservation Department he was going to agitate for a plane for his own use in observation, and that they would soon see their own beloved Dad circling over Spa House, and that they must arrange bags of coffee (in a thermos) and bananas and choc, so that he could come over with a big hook and pick them up while he was on his job. He could also get letters that way and telephone messages, and Mothering could send up her fifty-foot bills.

Sam had now rigged up the developing room in one corner of the boys' bedroom and after breakfast, while the girls fixed up the house, with many yawns and flagging, stumbling steps, the boys rushed between the washhouse, the photographic room, and the caldron in the yard, which had just been put on a tripod, over a bricked-in fire, all put up for the occasion. Presently they had a picture of the twins holding the marlin's head and Tommy holding his nose, in a group, Sam all the time expatiating on light and sun's angle, lenses and how he could get a better photograph with an old kodak than most people could with a Zeiss-Tessar, papers, chemicals. "Scenes that are brightest, te-te-te-te-TE!" sang Sam; "All chime in! Ain't home nice? Te-te-te-te-te! Da-da-da-da! Fathead, you're tipping the bottle of KCN," he continued to Little-Sam, "Da-da-da. KCN kills customers neatly, kindly, cunningly noxious; kids, cyanide nullifies! One bit of that, my lads, in a glass of water and you ain't, maybe twa draps for Little-Sam because he's mean. What is KCN, my boyos?"

They told him.

"Ah-ha," said Sam, going on with his work, "it looks like salt or sugar to you, but you know what it am? It am death, complete—to-tal annihilation: yes, rabbits take a whiff of that, and they don't even wait for the Angel of Death. Light doesn't go as fast as KCN. In that little bottle, see, is death for one and death for all, you take that, kids, for your alevena, and—

> *Looloo doesn't want to leave home,*
> *Ermy doesn't collect lead,*
> *Evie doesn't pipe her eye,*
> *Gemini don't insult their poor little **dad**,*
> *Tommy doesn't run after Fairy,*
> *Megalops doesn't eat crap!*

You all just get awful tired and you lie down and you don't get up no mo'; so be careful, oh, be keerful, for the results of that are fearful! See, kids, quick, quick! It's coming and it's not so bad, but it ain't good either, bad light today. And now, who's for the washus watch?"

Little-Sam hastened to claim the washhouse watch; then it was Ernie and Saul for the taking down of the chimney, Tommy to watch the marlin head, Evie to cover up the furniture in the house with cloths to keep off the dust, Louie to get alevena, and Mother to get the lunch.

Sam, on the roof, began to sing. The cries came, "Under below!" and the bricks came flying down into the grass. The sun began to heat the roof, and Sam called out that his head was swimming, but he was staying up just the same: "where there's a will there's a way." In the house, dust crept down the chimney, or shot down in handfuls, with soot and bits of brick. Henny grumbled; the "three women," in fact, were crabby and saw no beauty or generosity in Sam's liveliness. Sam had taken the bricks out of the south chimney as far as he could reach and now went cautiously over the roof to the north. The sky was getting cottony again. Suddenly Louie shouted, "Alevena," and Sam and Saul came off the roof, sliding hastily down the ladder, hungry, red-faced, inclined to squabble. They crowded into the common room and sat round the table like a crowd of parrots.

Sam sent for the raccoon, Procyon, and Procyon paraded up and down the table, nosing at them, shaking hands with them, sniffing at things. While Louie was pouring out the tea in the kitchen, Sam started hallooing for bananas, his favorite "alevena food." On the table were the bread and margarine but no bananas. Sam beat on his plate with his knife, shouting,

"Mothering, Mothering, bananas, bananas! Go and tell Mothering bananas," he told Evie, who slid off her seat. Tommy, apple-cheeked, gay and square-set, rushed to the kitchen and shouted, "Mothering, bananas!"

They all shouted this. Henny muttered. Louie, with cups of tea, stalked in, saying severely, "There are no bananas. Don't make such a noise."

"Mothering, bananas," cried Sam.

"Tell the children's father, there are none," Henny said bitterly. "Have we a banana tree? Have we a money tree?"

"Our father, we have none. Have we a bamoney tree?" inquired Tommy, meanwhile imitating an express train.

"Dad, Mother says there aren't any," Evie said.

Sam flushed with anger. "Why aren't there any bananas? I don't ask for much. I work to make the Home Beautiful for one and all, and I don't even get bananas. Everyone knows I like bananas. If your mother won't get them, why don't some of you? Why doesn't anyone think of poor little Dad?" He continued, looking in a most pathetic way round the table, at the abashed children, "It isn't much. I give you kids a house and a wonderful playground of nature and fish and marlin and everything, and I can't even get a little banana. And bananas are very healthy. Who here likes bananas?"

"We all do, Pad," said Saul cheerfully.

"Then we should all think of them. Now, I'll detail someone each week who must get the bananas."

"With what?" said a voice from the kitchen. "Bananas don't grow in the sea. Tell your father I had no money for them."

"It's all I ask for," Sam lowered his voice and with a plaintive voice continued his banana song. "All I esks for is a pore wittoo [little] bandana: I works a-takin' deown de chimbleys so that the heouse won't be knocked to smithereens in the next gale en yore little mushheads with it, en so that Mothering kin sleep peaceful like—though why she should with what she's been a-doin' to your poor dad, I don't know—en all I esks is a pore wittoo bandana sangwidge en I don't get whut I esks. You cain't blame me for a-grumblin', I ain't a grumblin' man; I'm a goldurn cheerful man considerin' whut I hev to put up with——"

"Oh, dry up," said Henny's voice.

"Shh," said Louie.

"Don't shush me," complained Sam, "I got a right to utter a few improving words in my own home, I hope." He went on droning dolefully, "All I wants is a pore little bandana en I don't get nuffin I esk fower: who's a-goin' deown to the cornder to get their pore wittoo dad a coupla bandanas."

The twins said they would go.

"Orright," Sam whined. "The Gemini kin go en get their pore little dad the bandanas wot ought to hev bin here afore, en the heouse weren't full to bustin' of lazy womenfolk which some of them is traipsin' eout and spendin' money in bargin basements not to say wuss and which some of them is got their heads full of boys and which some of them don't come to their pore little dad's bedroom no mo' in da fornin," he said, fixing a watery eye on Evie, who squirmed and dropped her eyes. "Womenfolk ain't no good, en yore pore little Dad wot was brought up to worship women as sweet pure beings. He's hed to learn a lot these last few days."

"I could wring his neck with pleasure," said Henny in the kitchen, to Louie.

"En I mout fall off de roof," said Sam to the children, "en whut would you do, Ermy? Whut would you do ef your father broke his neck?"

"Nothing," Ernie said coolly.

"Nuffin!" Sam shook his head, looked round the table tragically. "Ermy wouldn't do nuffin?"

"What could I do?" inquired Ernie. "You would be dead."

"Too logical," said Sam, laughing into his hand, meanwhile, "Well, here are the bananas. Hooray! Now get busy. Now, why did we have to wait? You see, no foresight, no order, no preparation! Everyone thinking of their own mean business. A woman who eats away the foundations of the house like a mean little termite, it's soft, it's little, it doesn't seem to count, but it's got uncles, aunts, cousins, children that it teaches to eat away at the house, and soon, down comes the house. Now, did you notice, kids, that the termites have got into the piano? Now, I want you to take a lesson from that. Dad is carpentering away, while the white ant eats at the house: but we will carpenter faster than Mothering eats away. Some day I will tell you kids what is the termite that's trying to eat away your father's loving heart and his peace of mind, but not now, but she—it's your own mother, kids—but she can hear me, and she knows what I'm talking about. Now, kids, some day you'll know what I'm doing for you. And whut I mean is, that this yere bandana business is only another example of whut I mean."

Suddenly Henny appeared between the drapes and said loudly, "You and the children ate all the bananas last night, and I've had too much to do cleaning up after your filth to think of bananas. Another thing is, I want some money. And I'm damned if I'll put up with your insults day and night. I'll take poison. Do you think I'm going to hang round here and let the children hear their mother insulted?"

Sam did not even look at her, but said, looking down at the table,

" 'The one thet fust gits mad's most ollers wrong,' es Mr. Lowell up and said. De fack is, kids, there warn't no bandanas: a hegskuze is a hegskuze; a bandana is a bandana; I cain't eat no hegskuzes en I got a nawful big hole in my stumjack."

The children laughed; Henny muttered. Louie came in, red as a turkey cock, "You should be ashamed, Dad!"

"When she walks she wobbles," said Sam.

"I despise you," said Louie.

"Now, Louie, now Looloo! Looloo always sich a hothead:

[487]

Louie a pighead cause she got a bighead! I always had a lot of trouble with my head, kiddos—nedakes [headaches] en sich, becaze I got a bighead. Now Sausam, they have big heads and they was meant to do a lot wiv em; en Louie would do a lot wiv her big head if she wasn't sich a lame duck en sich a goose en sich a turkey cock, now—With a gobble-gobble here and a gobble-gobble there!" (The children repeated this.) Sam continued, "With a hwonk-hwonk here and hwonk-hwonk there, and where are you going my pretty maid? For to mind my father's barnyard! For to mind my father's barnyard. En if Looloo weren't sich a wet hen, she'd do all right."

"I'm the ugly duckling, you'll see," shrieked Louie.

"You're ugly all right and when you walk you wobble, and you're all wet, I swan, en you've got a long neck and a big beak so maybe you're a swan—" Little-Sam said. "And she has a sweet voice like a swan," and Evie said, "And Louie does a dance, *The Dying Swan.*"

They shrieked with laughter. Louie burst out into loud, raucous sobs and rushed from the house, while Sam said, in some surprise, "The great big galoot: why, girls are no better than boys at that age," and he laughed heartily.

Tommy ran after Louie to see where she had gone and found her crouching by the copper fire and poking it into a bright flame.

"What are you crying for, Louie?" he said patting her on the arm. "Don't cry, Louie, don't cry! He's only fooling."

" 'What is fun to you is death to me,' " said Louie. "That is what the frog said to the boys, you know?"

"Yes, I know that story."

"Well, go and tell him that."

Tommy ran back to the common room where alevena was in progress and, grinning somewhat, planted himself on his two legs while he recited, "Pad, I have a message for you from Looloo. 'What is fun to you is death to me.' "

"Did she tell you to tell me that?"

"Yes."

Sam shook his head, "Looloo always was very tragic."

"Ooh," shouted Little-Sam, "ooh, Pad! Ooh, whew! It's getting me, Pad."

"Whappills?" inquired Sam, in delight.

"Ow, wow," said Saul instantly, holding his belly, and writhing, "It's got me, chilluns. Farewell, my bluebell, farewell to you. I'm dying, Pad."

"Whippills?" inquired Sam again, enchanted.

"It's nawful," cried Ernie and let out a shout of joy.

"The marlin," explained Evie, with disgust. "They're fooling. They're doing it all the morning. Mother is angry with them."

"Go on," said Sam, "go on? What is it?"

"Oh, it's a-follerin' of me," cried Little-Sam, looking behind, craning his neck over both shoulders. He slid off the homemade wooden bench, "I can smell it here—look, there it is, oh, look out the window, oh, the crick is yaller, oh, the oil."

"Tell Mother I died bravely," said Sam, pleased with their skit.

"Why don't you take it off now, Deddy?" asked Tommy.

Sam began to chant, "We're a-goin' to rav marlin erl, marlin erl, marlin erl; we're gona rav marlin balm, marlin salve, marlin butter, marlin oingming; we're gona eat marlin, be marlin, think marlin, sleep marlin; it's marlin for our bikes and marlin for kikes. Say, let's go, while we're having a bit of a rest and put the oil into bottles."

"No sooner said than done," said Saul.

The stuff had been boiling for over twelve hours, and Sam now told them to rake the fire out. The cleaning-up was a great satisfaction to him. The entire crew of children (except Louie) was around him, grunting as they carted the gluey soup out in all the large household utensils, buckets, basins, watering cans, and pots. The liquid they dumped on the children's gardens, along the fences, near the dead end near Lomasne's shed and in front along the lawn, round the Wishing Tree. The tatters of fish, mostly jellied skin and bones, they were to take and put in a heap at the bottom of the orchard. Over these remains they sprinkled loam to keep off the flies. Sam said that at "one fell swoop" they had two sorts of manures—fish offal and ashes, and if this was not a wonderful example of planned economy, they had only to tell him what might be. Meanwhile, in the washhouse now stood nine large and five small bottles of unrefined marlin oil, which would be refined at an early date, said Sam. Sam at first had meant to boil the marlin down to glue, but too many exclamations by Henny had let him know that she expected the copper to be ready for the weekly wash bright before tomorrow morning, and Sam's work gang was pretty tired already. He knew he would have to clean up before nightfall. Little-Sam, who hadn't much stomach, was just staggering out with a bucketful of marlin remains, when he dropped it at his feet and looked frightened.

"Little feels sick," declared Saul.

"What, with marlin? Not with marlin!" said Sam, laughing, and ordered the boy to take it to the offal heap, which, after a moment, he did.

"Triumph of mind over matter," said Sam, nodding to the others, and when Little-Sam came back, to illustrate this, ordered Little-Sam to take out another shovelful. Little-Sam sulkily did so, but in a minute dropped it and looked mutinously up at his father.

"Take dat offal marlin to dat offal heap, Little-Sam," said Sam gently.

The boy bent down, then gave his father an appalled look, turned from the family, and disgraced himself.

"Little-Sam frowin' up da marlin," said Sam.

Suddenly Henny was before them, black and angry as a witch, her loose hair flying out, "You ought to be ashamed, a man your size tormenting the children," she cried. "If I were to tell the neighbors what you do, you wouldn't be so high and mighty."

Sam ignored her but addressed himself to Tommy, her favorite,

"Tommy, my boy, one of my great handicaps in life was my weak stomach; now, many a great man has had a weak stomach:

Julius Caesar had one, though I don't want any of you to go round with an army. Now, you kids have got to have strong stomachs. Little-Sam here is the dead spit of his old man, and he got to have a strong stomach: he got to stomach anything. I made myself stronger, when a lad, because I recognized my weakness, by boiling the flesh off carcasses for their skeletons and articulating the skeletons—also taught myself anatomy. And I had no father interested in me. Now, Little-Sam, and you have. Now, Little-Sam," he continued very gravely, "you get some more," and he picked up the shovel and handed it to Little-Sam.

"Are you insane?" cried Henny.

"Get out of my way," Sam growled. "You get to the kitchen and mind your business—don't you put your spoke in here, or I'll get rid of you, mind that; I'll have no more interfering with my children and putting them against me; now, get out of here."

Little-Sam, expecting his mother to intervene, sullenly stooped and picked up another shovelful of the mess. He took two steps away, bent over it, but when he passed Sam suddenly threw it down and put both hands on his belly.

"Sam," cried his father, "stop that belching. No hysteria, come along! Look," he said, turning angrily to his wife, "this is your doing! He would have been on his way in perfect calm but for you: don't I know there's no kindness in this, but sabotage? Do you think I don't see through your miserable tricks? You pretend to defend them in order to make me seem harsh and cruel. I'll have no more of it. Get back to the kitchen, you miserable wretch. Little-Sam, you come back here before I whale you: look sharp."

"Ai, ai," cried Henny, beginning to cry like a little girl, and putting the fold of her dressing gown to her face, "ai, ai!"

"Daddy," said Evie. "Little is sick, what do you do it for?"

"You stop imitating your mother and looking at me with that sneaking Collyer grimace, ready to burst into tears," said Sam. Evie turned pale but dared not cry.

[491]

"Little-Sam is sick," said Saul severely to his father. Sam gave him an admonitory kick in the shins, shaking his head meaningly.

"No," Little-Sam bellowed surprisingly, "no, it makes me sick."

"There," said Sam, throwing out his hands and getting up, "there, she's done it—and you've done it, Pollux [to Saul], stirring up rebellion! There's one thing you don't understand about Little-Sam: I understand him because he is myself. Now, I suffered in life from a certain diffidence, which in Little-Sam is sullenness and morbidity: I'll conquer it. Castor [Little-Sam], you come here!"

The eight-year-old boy suspiciously and slowly drew near, eying his father with all the hate of his wide blue eyes.

"I'll finish this," Sam said.

He picked up the dipper that Henny used for the washing, sunk it in the bottom of the copper, and drew it out half full. He took Little-Sam by the neck, drew him out of the washhouse, and, when he stood on the newly cemented yard outside the door, suddenly flung the liquid over him, drenching him. Little-Sam and the children were petrified with surprise. Sam did not even laugh but considered his son triumphantly. Not a tremor passed over the boy's face. He stood dripping with the juice, fish tatters on his head, one long shred of skin hanging down over one eye, making him look like the offspring of a mermaid and a beachcomber. He looked funny. Suddenly, Ernie began to grin, his face widened, and he began to laugh; the laugh spread, and the children stood round the queer little Neptune laughing, Sam joining in, and only Saul, the twin, standing by as quiet as Little-Sam himself. Henny, standing with evil face inside the glassed-in porch, gabbled furiously to Louie, and in a minute, it was Louie dashing forth, crying to her father not to be "so horrible, so disgusting," that broke up the circle. It was cooler than the season that day, and Little-Sam had begun to pick the wet shirt off his arms, saying, "Ooh, it's nasty!"

"Good," said Sam, "good! Now Little-Sam, you take another shovelful down to the manure heap, and you can go and get washed. Kids, read, mark, learn, and inwardly digest! Little-Sam could and did get over his abhorrence, you see! And if I didn't have a lot of interfering, miserable beasts," he gave a kind of malicious smile at the two little girls, "I'd have you all right in no time. I'm sorry," he continued to Evie, "I'm sorry I didn't take a dipperful of that and sling it at your Motherings: it would have taught her a thing or two; it would have given her something to think about, instead of always filling that empty, worthless head with the wrongs done to her. I'm the one that's suffered, I'm the one that's had things to think about, but do you see me go about sniveling and calling names? Women is the devil! The tyranny of tears, Little-Womey, and don't you never make no man suffer that." He began to laugh, as he saw Little-Sam trotting off with the fish offal to the manure heap. "Yes, Ermy," he said confidentially, putting his arm round his eldest son's neck and drawing him closer, "you know I should have done the same to Looloo too: I'll bet she would have kicked up a riot, oh, boy! Why didn't I think of that? Will I do it, eh, will I do it?"

"Not now, it's all over," Ernie said.

Sam laughed, "All right: whatever you say."

Now the twins came back and Saul said, "Pad, can Little go and have a shower now?"

Louie came to the back door and shouted indignantly, "Now Mother fainted! It's your fault."

"Good heavens, you mean wretch!" said Sam. "You'd think she enjoyed it! Can't Little-Sam use his own tongue to ask his little father for a shower?"

Little-Sam said nothing.

"Eh?" inquired Sam, "did he cough up his tongue, too?"

"He's got fish in his mouth," said Saul.

At this the children burst out laughing excitedly again, and Sam had the sense to send Little-Sam away, for he saw that he was working up to a roar of misery. The old shower room opened on to the new cement yard. They could see the two butter-yellow boys standing under the shower, both scrubbing away at Little-Sam's body and hair. Meanwhile Sam sat down to wait for lunch.

"Too much trubsy, love," he said to Little-Womey, "do myed, love." While she stroked his head, he watched the twins with pleasure and directed their operations.

"Drop your clobber [clothes] in the cornder, it's washday tomorrow: rub yourself down. Twins is queer cattle," he continued in a low tone to Evie, "there's no hegsplaining twins. (Little-Sam, don't make yourself too clean, you can get inside the copper and clean it after lunch: it's very convenient.) Twins are not two children, but one, you see, love: one egg that has split and become two of the same. Twins have always known each other from the same moment, from the day they were jellies: yiss, love, Castor and Pollux were jellies and sardines and lizards and funny monsters all the time together; they had to fight for their life at the same time and came into the world at the same time, only twenty minutes' difference."

Ernie came up inquisitively, "And if one twin has a pain in his leg, the other feels it too: a boy at school got hit in the leg with a ball, and his brother had a pain," he laughed.

"Wery inconwenient," said Sam, "but wery mysterioso. But they mustn't be sissies, just the same, neither one nor the other."

Although they scrubbed the copper out with soft sand and kitchen powder, they could not get out the fish smell. It was in all the cracks of the old cement floor, in the hairy timbers of the walls and shelves, in the chimney, the washtubs, the mangle, wringer, clothes boxes, and the dirty clothes. The fourteen bottles were greasy with it; and Sam, at last giving up the job of cleaning, decided to try a few experiments with the oil first drawn off, from which a sediment was now drifting down. He oiled the bike with it, wiping off the excess on various bits of rag, oiled his old brown tramping shoes, cracked and stiff with spring mud, rubbed down a few bits of old iron going rusty, massaged Tommy's legs to see if it would keep off the blains he usually got in spring, and sent in a bottle of the best to Henny to tell her to try cooking with it. After this, he suddenly felt very tired and said he must have a snooze before he went up on the roof again.

The sun had come out hot again; and the house settled down to a needed siesta, by which time the heavy reek of fish oil rose up, swirled quietly round, and invaded the timbers of the house. One marlin had been enough, with their kneading, manuring, trotting about, plastering, oiling, and dripping, to give Spa House a scent of its own for many years to come. When they were all resting, prior to the four o'clock snack, Henny came downstairs in one of her silk dressing gowns, to look round. At least they had cleaned the copper, and perhaps it was imagination when she thought she smelled it in everything. On the shelf in the washhouse were bottles neatly labeled in Sam's capitals: FISH-FRY, BIKE-OIL, MARLIN-BALM, MACHINE-OIL, HAIR-OIL, LEATHER-GREASE; OIL, OIL, OIL on the rest. When she went back upstairs, she was conscious of the rich rotten smell and the softness of it in her hair; there was a faint mark already on the pillow where she had lain and a greasy finger mark on the library book. She lifted her old slippers and smelled it on their sodden soles; there was a dark mark on the light gray silk hem. Just when she had reached this point in her examination, Evie came panting up the stairs, holding a little medicine bottle in her hand.

"Daddy says, you can use this instead of cold cream: he says please try it, because whale oil is very good for the skin."

Henny took it without a word and stood in the doorway while Evie deprecatingly climbed downstairs again. Then she marched into Louie's room to show the girl how impossible her father was. Louie was stretched out on her unmade bed, dead asleep, with her legs resting high up on the back of the bed, and a book open on her chest.

4 ⚡ A headache.

HENNY FROWNED AT THE STREAKY CREEK through the window and turned back to her room, pulling the door after her. She began going through bundles of papers and old letters that she pulled out from long-closed drawers.

A telephone ringing without answer presently woke the house. Ernie came panting upstairs, excited, "Moth, it's Miss Wilson, Tommy's teacher."

"Tell her I'm out."

"She says to say can she see you for a minute if she comes over?"

"Tell her I'm out."

"O.K."

At the same time she heard Sam shouting outside, "Hey, Tommo! Your teacher is coming to pay us a visit."

"Oh, keep your sticky beak out," muttered Henny miserably. Louie, who had awakened, wanted to know if Miss Wilson was coming: "No, no, no, no," Henny said.

Then there was Sam questioning Ernie in the hall and, "Your mother told you to tell a lie and you told it, despite what I've told you?"

Then some muttering. "More trouble," said Henny to Louie. "Why doesn't he drop down dead? Was he sent by God to worry women?"

Then Ernie coming upstairs and saying, "Mother, Daddy says you are not to make us tell lies," with a very frightened face; and Henny screaming at Sam over the balustrade, and Sam shouting, "Shut up."

Ernie was stuck on the stairs between them but Louie withdrew backwards into her room.

"You wanted to see the old maid so you could pour your woes into her ears," Henny cried; while Sam, pushing Ernie aside, started to come upstairs, saying in a deep voice that she must close her trap.

But Henny went on laughing, "You can't shut me up now. You want the truth, let it be the truth: he only wants the truth, but he wants my mouth shut. Why don't you leave me alone? This is my house. Go and sit on the beach with your clothes. I'm sick and tired of washing the fish out and your dirty papers full of big talk."

"Henny," said Sam sullenly, "you be quiet or leave my house. I have the whiphand now, owing to your own deed; if you do not get out, I will put you out by the force of law."

She screamed hoarsely, "You get out of here, get out, I'll kill you, I'll kill you; you've only been waiting for this like a great foul monster waiting, sneaking, lying in wait to take my children away. If you touch them I'll kill you: if you try to put me out, I'll kill you."

She turned quickly to Louie, who was standing thoughtfully in the doorway, and shouted, panting, "Louie, don't you ever let a man do that; don't you ever do what his women are doing —a woman's children are all she has of her body and breath, don't let him do that, Louie, don't let him do that. He has been waiting for years to snatch them from me; now the dirty wretch has been watching me and thinks he has an excuse. Don't let him."

She picked up a slipper which had stood on the washstand since she had smelled the fish oil on the sole and rushed at him to strike him in the eyes with the heel. He seized her arm and tried to bend it down. "Put that down, you fool, you madwoman," he bellowed. "You'll push me downstairs, Henny—look out!"

"I'll kill you," she panted, "I'll push you downstairs, I don't care if I go too. I'll break your neck."

She suffocated, struggled as he put his large hand over her mouth, bit it.

"Henny, Henny," he cried in desperation himself, "shut up. Don't let our children hear."

She tore the hand away in a violent spasm. "You rotten flesh," she screamed, insane, "you rotten, rotten thing, you dirty sweaty pig, pig, pig."

She vomited insults in which the word "rotten" rose and fell, beating time with it.

"Henny, shut your foul mouth." He let go of her and flung away to the doorway of Louie's room, himself revolted by her and the terrible struggle.

The children who had crept into the hall below stood rooted to the floor, listening to this tempest, trembling. Louie sank down on her bed in a stupor, her heart beating hard. It was not the quarrel, nor even the threats of murder, but the intensity of the passions this time that stifled them all. And why, out of a clear sky? They never asked any reasons for their parents' fights, thinking all adults unreasonable, violent beings, the toys of their own monstrous tempers and egotisms, but this time it seemed different.

Henny was shrieking, "Ernest, Ernest, Louie, your father's struck me; come and save me, Ernest, your father's killing me, he's trying to kill me, help——"

Louie started up and rushed out into the hall, "Leave her alone."

"Henny, Henny, be quiet, or I'll knock you down," shouted the desperate man.

She rushed to her window, which was at the back nearest a neighbor (though that was still a hundred and fifty yards distant), and cried, "I'll call Mrs. Paine: I'll tell everyone in the street, and you won't get away with this, you rotten foul murderer. You think you're so fine with your bragging and science and human understanding—oh, I've heard all about it till I could scream myself insane with the words; and you can run everything, and world problems, when all the time it's other women, you hypocrite, you dirty, bloodless hypocrite, too good, other women, scientific women, young girls, and your own wife— I'll write to all your scientific societies, I'll write to the Conservation Department, I'll tell them what my life has been—beat me, knock me down, I can't stand it. You threaten but do nothing,

[498]

nothing to give me a chance, to get out, not till you've got something on me to steal my children: you won't—you won't—I'm going to kill them all, I'll kill them all tonight, I'll pour that stinking oil on fire down your throat and kill my children, you won't get them—there'll be a sight tomorrow for the people to see: try to explain that away, try to explain it to God or in hell, wherever you go——"

"Louie," said Sam sternly, "go and throw cold water over your mother; go and force her to be quiet. If she sees you—" But Louie had only entered the room, in her confused, embarrassed way, when Henny turned to her and began to vociferate abominable insults, and pushed her out of the room after which she locked the door, and shouted through the door, "I'm going to kill myself; tell your dirty father to go downstairs. I'll kill myself, I'll do it: I can't stand it any longer."

"Mother, Mother," called Louie.

Ernie had come upstairs and now rushed to the door and beat on it, crying out, "Mother, don't, don't, please."

Henny was silent. Louie sobbed brokenheartedly against the door, and Ernie seemed to have lost his wits. He sank to her feet and blubbered there.

"She won't do it," said Sam nervously.

They heard the children whimpering downstairs, and Sam with a gesture sent Louie down to them, but she clung to the door, "No, no, Mother, don't!"

Suddenly, they heard the bolt being drawn: Henny stood there with chalk-white face, her great eyeholes, coal-black, "Get out of here, you lot of howlers, leave me alone."

"Henny," said Sam; but at that she screamed in such a fury, "If you speak another word to me in your life, I'll slit my throat the same minute," that they all retreated, leaving her again behind the bolted door.

There she stayed for hours. Louie, creeping breathlessly up the stairs, avoiding the creaking boards as well as she could, heard the tearing of papers stop and Henny call out, "Who's that spying on me now?" and then would ask feebly, "Can I get you a cup of tea, Mother?" until Henny at last answered, "Yes, I'll take a phenacetin: this headache is killing me."

Louie saw her mother at last. Henny was dressed, as if to go to town, but only snarled when Louie showed her surprise. There was a smell of fire at which Sam bolted upstairs to thunder on the door and ask (without response) what Henny was doing; and at last, Henny came downstairs with her hat on, an old red hat, left over from the previous summer. At once Sam barred her way, asked her where she was going, if she was coming back to her home again, and particularly ordered her not to show herself in the streets, looking like a hag of eighty in that skittish little hat. Then he snatched it from her head. At once Louie ran up, full of indignation, calling upon Ernie to defend his mother, but Ernie was too overwhelmed to know how or when to defend her. As she at last ran jerkily down the avenue, in a black hat, sobbing and trying to fix the collar of her blouse, Ernie ran after her with a very pale, working face, to ask if she was going to come home again.

"I don't know," she replied stonily.

"Won't I ever see you again?"

"I don't know."

"Where are you going?"

"I don't know."

"Mother," he burst out crying, buried his face in her waist, "are you going to kill the children?"

"Don't be a fool; I'll leave that to your father."

"You won't give me my money back, Mother?"

"Do you think I have any money, you poor wretch? I don't know if I have any. Perhaps I'll have to beg on the streets to get my train fare; perhaps I'll have to go on my knees to Jim Lomasne to get a dollar; perhaps I'll have to scrub a floor first for his wife. Where do you think money comes from? I'll never be able to pay you any money in your life, Ernie, and you may as well get used to the idea now. I'm broke, so dead broke that I don't know where to turn; I'm out of my mind, Ernie, and don't pay any attention to what Mother says."

"You won't pay me," he said, hanging on to the stuff of her dress, "Mother, you owe me so much, five dollars and eighty-nine cents. I can't save it up any more, we're so poor."

"You poor wretch," she said, bursting into tears, "you poor sniveling little kid: why do you have to get into my messes? Well, it makes me feel so rotten—go on, go away, go back."

"Are you going to beg for money, Mother?"

"Yes," she cried impatiently, "yes, yes, I am: I'm going down in the dirt. Now, leave me alone. Go back and tell Louie to give you something to eat."

She forced him away at last and in great trembling herself made her way along the street. Ernie and Louie watched for a long time but did not see her cross the bridge. Louie was afraid she had gone to drown herself.

However, late that night, Henny did return, and no sooner was she in the house than Sam, fresh and angry, began a great scene asking where she had been; but to this he got no response. The children were asleep, but not so Louie. She was afraid that the man and woman would kill each other: yet the quarrel dragged on, with its long tedious conversations and spurts of drama, all through the night. She would hear Henny drinking tea, or Sam drinking coffee; each would retire to a separate room, but would come out again, to rage again, first one, then the second, as if they could never have enough of this rage.

"I look awful," thought Louie, "and it is because I have no decent home; and the children are all getting sulky-looking too, except Evie, and she's going to be browbeaten for life. They're too cowardly to separate. If I killed them both we would be free. The only thing is, I don't want to go to jail, I must get through school and go on the stage, so I have to go to dramatic school. All this quarreling and crying is just ruining my face for the stage too. I'm pretty stupid though, clumsy that is, and I'd be sure to make a mess of things, if I killed them with a knife. There would be the fingerprints and blood marks; I know myself, I'd never get rid of them, and I'd be sure to give myself away after. The thing to do is to do something that is sure but looks like an accident. Poison! Permanganate, the thing that girl killed herself with when Uncle Barry left her with a baby, that's no good; carbolic acid neither, because of the pain and the length of time. There is that cyanide, but it's so quick——"

She paused for a while to wonder about the cyanide, frightened of it because it seemed too simple and quick. She went on to think that if the cyanide worked she would then have a houseful of children on her hands, have to explain things: "How did it happen?" "I don't know; I wasn't there!" "Where were you?" "In bed: Mother was making the morning tea." (Absurd! How could she slip down unobserved, and slip upstairs into bed again, and yet be sure that none of the children got the cyanide?) No, "How did it happen?" "I was making the tea, and saw Mother slip something into the cup but thought it was for her headache." (Absurd! The children would recognize the cyanide bottle, and she certainly would.) No.

Louie puzzled about this until her head ached. Then she began to worry about the children. First: Ernie would go to the grandmother, Evie and the twins, for a short time to Aunt Hassie, Tommy to Aunt Eleanor, and Hazel Grey in Charlestown would take the baby. She would go to Harpers Ferry, or Auntie Jo's, or Miss Aiden's, preferably the last, to finish her education. She must be very careful about her attitude—let it be sullen, stupid, she had better say she had been badly beaten the night before and did not remember much: "They were always quarreling." Louie saw herself in court and began to sweat, for surely the lawyers smart as foxes would see through her transparent lies, her miserable devices. "But then," thought Louie, "I am still a schoolgirl—my confusion will be put down to trouble: who will suspect me?" Then she thought that perhaps a lot of people thought she was a very wicked, lying child, believing Henny's tales (what she believed to be Henny's tales), and that the finger of suspicion would veer to her in no time. She could not sleep but, after tossing for a long time in her bed, got up and sat by the window, thinking this thing over. Only one thing was certain: it must be done, to save the children. "Who cares for them but me?" she thought coldly. "Those two selfish, passionate people, terrible as gods in their eternal married hate, do not care for them; Mother herself threatened to kill them. Perhaps she would: at any rate, their life will be a ruin even if they are allowed to go on living. There is no question of it: I have the will, I must have the firmness to get rid of the two parents." She no longer thought of Sam as her father: she had not thought of him as anything but a mouthy jailer for months; as for Henny, she did not see how her fate would be better if she went on living. Louie had doubts of herself that made her sweat cold again. She had brought so little to fruit in her life: she sometimes thought she had dementia praecox, and at other times thought she was a terrifying genius, and at other times again thought she was one of those pitiful sham-talents which glitter in youth and dance in maturity and are malicious apes, sometimes suicides later on in the dread arctic of age, around forty.

Now she thought of these three possibilities and turned from one to the other like a weathercock; but it was only because she doubted her ability to do the deed and fool people afterwards. She never once doubted that the right thing to do was to use cyanide tomorrow morning, or that she must liberate the children: it fell to her, no one else would do it or understand the causes as she did. Then she would at once be free herself. She made up her mind to do it at last. She planned the few simple motions necessary to get the cyanide, take out a little (with gloves on), put it in a small pillbox that she had in her drawer (no, false move—in a pillbox she would take from Henny's drawer tomorrow morning or next time Henny went down in this infernal night), and so on. Let the rest take care of itself, thought Louie: "I am sure to cry, that will help me out a lot: they won't question a child deprived of its parents in a morning, and there will be the children to get breakfast for." She saw, with free lungs and a regularly beating heart, that this was the right thing to do: she should have done it before but had not had the insight nor the will. Everything was will: "The world stands aside to let the man pass who knows whither he is going!"

Louie fell into a light refreshing sleep but woke up soon after, and was able to steal into Henny's room to get the pillbox, during one of Henny's trips downstairs. The quarrel raged again. This she did with perfect ease, and even pushed her self-assurance so far as to go downstairs where the unhappy pair were and noticed that her mother was eating one of her nervous meals—tea, almost black, with toast and mustard pickles.

"What are you wandering about for, looking like a boiled owl?" Henny demanded harshly. Louie looked at her for a while calmly, thinking, "Perhaps I won't see her alive again"; and then she turned, humping her shoulders as she passed her father, not even looking at him, her flesh revolting at his nearness. He said nothing to her, but when she was on the stairs, she heard Henny snarl, "Why don't you go to bed: you see the children can't sleep? Are you going to stay up all night to pick on me?" Louie heard her father creak heavily into a chair. "Yes," thought Louie, "I won't have any peace with their squabbles."

5 ⚓ Monday morning.

HENNY SLEPT VERY LITTLE, in a restless rage, and got up at five to sort the washing. The fish smell had by this time seeped into everything in the lower house, it seemed: and Henny hung over the basket, cursing like a fishwife indeed. An electric storm threatened again. Henny always hated them and felt ready for a fight before them; but this was the sort of weather that suited Louie best—she always felt lithe, vigorous, and calm before a storm. The weather had been electric for some time, the skies unusual, and the winds various. They all felt certain by their own animal symptoms of the approach of big weather. The sky was barred with cloud, and the trees were uneasy. Sam felt qualmish, with a slight fever this morning, and lay late in bed, calling to the children to get up, and to Evie to come and stroke his head. It reminded him of Singapore. He kept the Venetian blind down and in a weak, sick voice kept making his little jokes, calling his syce, wishing, with all its faults, that for a moment he were back in dear old Singapura. "A man should travel," he told Evie suddenly: "home deadens a man's wits: I'm a better man away from home"—but scarcely were these words out of his mouth than he regretted them, dark treachery to his home, his native land, and his loved ones!

"Looloo," he called, feebly. "Dotta det up, Loogoobrious: maka da tea."

She woke up and thought at once, "This is the morning, and I slept late!" She put on her dressing gown, took the little box, and with a stern strut went downstairs, not replying to the few remarks addressed to her on the way. She thought, "This is the hour: soon it will be all over." She put on the kettle, began to arrange the cups fussily, making a noise about it, when there were yet some cups to get down, slipped into the boys' room, which opened on to the kitchen, and into the darkroom. The boys were both up. Ernie had left a pile of clothes, his pajamas, perhaps, ready for the wash, through the bars of the bottom of his bed, but there was no one in the room. But her hand trembled, and she was only just putting some grains of cyanide into the box when she heard a noise and saw Henny in the kitchen.

"What are you messing in there for at this time of the morning when we're all so late?" called Henny. "Give me a cup of tea before I pass out. Every rotten thing in the place is alive with his fish oil; I'm nearly going mad with headache."

With a scarlet blush that covered her entire body, Louie came out of the darkroom, but Henny did not see her—she was already bustling back to the washhouse with a pile of kitchen towels. "God," thought Louie (the first time she ever used that word), "Oh, God, I nearly was caught." Her heart began to beat so heavily that she could hardly stand. She was now afraid that she would never have the strength to do it, with her blood beating so madly. She made the tea in a convulsion of trembling, and when it was made, a nausea of fear and doubt came over her

—was she doing the right thing? To settle it, she slid the grains of cyanide all into one large breakfast cup, holding the box through her apron meanwhile, blew the grains off her apron into the cup, and threw the box into the garbage pail. At this moment she heard her father thumping cheerfully downstairs and talking to Evie. "I can never do it," thought Louie and turned round, to back up against the table on which the cup stood. There stood Henny.

"My womb is tearing," said Henny, holding her body, "with the weight of the great lolloping sheets. I am in such agonies that I don't know how to bear it. How can this go on another week? He takes no notice; I know my insides are torn to pieces—" She stopped and examined Louie, "What are you staring at me like that for? What is the matter with me? Don't stare at me!" Louie had lost all power of speech. Henny now recollected something, "What did you do? I saw you doing something!" Louie opened her mouth but only like a fish taking in air: she was struck dumb. She pointed to her mouth, the cup, shook her head. At this moment, Sam came into the kitchen, bringing with him the little carved wooden chest in which were the six tiny cups made from carved wood and lined with soft silver.

"Daforno," said Sam, gently ignoring Henny, "daforno, we is going to hev our tea in poor Lai Wan Hoe's beautiful little gift to his god-master—no, he had too much brains to think I was a god." He planted the little chest tenderly on the pine table and, pointing to the big cups, said "Frow dat out, Looloo, we goin to hev Chinese tea daforno: it's so hot I reckon we ought always to have it, anyhow."

Louie looked from one to the other, waiting for what she could not imagine to open before her; but she was unable to speak a word: she just shook her head to them, to herself. Henny, with blazing black eyes, was looking wildly at the child; she raised her hand and pointed at her but said nothing. Then she said slowly, "You beast, you pair of beasts, my womb is torn to pieces with you—the oil is everywhere and your dirty sheets falling on to me to suffocate me with the sweat, I can't stand it any

[506]

more—she's not to blame, she's got guts, she was going to do it—she's not to blame, if she were to go stark staring mad—your daughter is out of her mind—" Sam looked at Henny with hatred. "All right," said Henny, "damn you all!"

She snatched the cup and drank it off quickly, a look of horror filling her as if she would have stopped herself but could not arrest the motion. She made a few steps with the cup, while Sam said, very puzzled, "What is this? What is going on?" Louie tried to explain but could only shake her head: even in her mind she could not think of any words. At the outer door of the kitchen leading to the glassed-in porch, Henny stopped, turned round, and then fell straight towards them, to her full length along the new cement floor.

This time Sam was shocked, for Henny had fallen face forwards and met the pavement with a heavy crack. The cup smashed. Louie still stood staring, with rather an amiable expression (for she was trying to say something), at her father, mother, and Evie. Evie had already run for the cushions and was trying to stick them under her mother's head; and, for once, Sam helped her. He said anxiously, "I think Mothering is rather badly hurt, we must get her to bed."

Louie came forward, and Sam, taking her quietness for disobedience, frowned at her but said nothing. He called Ernie but couldn't get any of the boys. They staggered with her to the boys' room and laid her on Ernie's bed. Sam kept whistling for the boys, and now they heard the cries coming running, "Yippo! Yippills! Yes, Pad!"

Henny's forehead and nose were bruised and cut. "Get some water and peroxide," said Sam irritably, "you ought to know what to do."

Louie gave a deep sigh and said slowly, with a clogged tongue, "Whatever is this?" She tried to pull the bundle of Ernie's clothes off the bottom of the bedstead. He had stuffed two dirty pillowcases inside his pajamas; two corners of one protruded from the top like ears. The funny little shawl that Louie had knitted for Tommy, yellow wool with a face in red wool, and that Tommy took to bed for a comforter, had been fixed over this end of the pillow slips to make a face. A piece of string round "the neck" attached this manikin to the bed. She pulled at the knot.

"Get the water and a sponge," said Sam irritably.

Louie left the manikin and started to the door, but there she stopped and said, "I think she's dead."

"Don't be a goat."

"I think she's dead, Dad."

" 'Dead, Dad, Dead Dad,' " he said: "go and do what you're told."

Louie turned round, saying in a deep rebellious tone, "What's the use? You'd better call a doctor, or you'll be in trouble."

Sam was astonished at this, and, pulling Henny's sleeve, said gently, "Henny? Henny? Pet?" He said to Evie, who looked worried, "I think Mothering's got concussion."

Louie returned with the little basin of water, which she put down beside the bed on a chair littered with boys' clothes. The children, who had stayed outside, to hear from her about their mother's accident, now came peeping, tiptoeing round the door, like birds creeping back to spy on a motionless man in a clearing. Tommy laughed suddenly, a laugh clear as summer river babble, "Look, there's Ermy!" Ernie frowned. Tommy giggled, "Ermy hanged himself: he jacked himself up." He pointed to the thing hanging on the bottom of the bed. "Look, he-he, he took my shawl for his face." Sam's face browned with its flush, "What are you talking about, you dope?" Tommy suppressed his laugh, "That's Ermy. He said he hanged himself!" Sam's eyes wandered back anxiously to Henny. Louie was bending over her listening; she got up, with unmoving face, "You see, you listen! Her heart isn't beating." Sam started with an expression of terror, and bent over. He jumped back, "First aid, kids, clear out! Get the doctor, Louie." Louie half smiled, "I told you she was dead."

Ernie rushed past the knot of children and threw himself on his mother, pulling at the bosom of her dressing gown, disarranging it wildly, screaming, "Mother, Mother, you aren't dead?

Is she dead? Is she dead? She isn't dead!" He began to moan, saying, "Mother" and a moan. The children stood stricken in the doorway. Sam, after a queer movement of his chin, looking round as it were for help on all sides, strode through and over the huddled children and rushed to the telephone. Louie patiently came up and began sponging the forehead. "Let me do it," said Ernie excitedly, and he began pasting away at the forehead, thinking that was a way to cure her. The children began to break down, each in his own way, and Chappy, sitting on the porch, who had just been bitten by an ant, began to yell for assistance. They heard Sam talking into the telephone, and then his quick tread. He began to question them, "What was Mother doing?" And the scene he had witnessed came to his mind: "What were you and Mother quarreling about?"

"Nothing," said Louie, "only the dirty clothes; then Mother said she would take poison, and she drank a cup of tea full of cyanide."

Sam thundered, "What?"

"She had it in a little pillbox," faltered Louie; "she threw it in the garbage can!"

Sam rushed to the photographic chamber. They heard him running out verifying, saying aloud, "This is terrible! Oh, God, what a terrible thing! I never thought she meant it. God above, Louie, Louie!"

Tommy came out with great round black eyes, Henny's eyes, and, tiptoeing up to his raging father, whispered, "Pad, will we go to school today?"

At this moment, the front-door bell rang. Louie, thinking it was the doctor, ran to open the door and saw standing there a middle-aged woman, with streaky black hair, a puffy, good-natured face, and brown eyes, in a go-to-meeting straw hat and a speckled silk dress. She looked at her for a minute without recognition and then saw it was Tommy's teacher, Miss Wilson. Miss Wilson seemed embarrassed but said stiffly, "Is your mother in?"

"No," said Louie, "that is—she's sick."

"I'm sorry," said the woman stiffly, "I tried to get her yesterday on the phone and Saturday too, but either she wasn't in all the week end, or she wouldn't answer me. It's very important."

"What is it? What is it?" cried Sam testily, "What is it? You must go away. There has been a dreadful accident."

"I'm Miss Wilson, Tommy's teacher," said the woman. "I'm at the school; I wanted to see Mrs. Pollit about the money."

Sam looked confused, and the woman had to keep on explaining to him how important it was, that it was urgent about the money.

"Money, what money?" Sam asked confusedly again.

"It's the money: the piano's no good to me," said the woman, anxiously. "What can I do with a grand piano? I let her give me that security. I'm sorry if she's sick. I really am. I know she's a good woman. I like Mrs. Pollit. I respect her. But it's just now, I've got to pay some things, my taxes were so high——"

Sam said, "Mrs. Wilson, will you come back? Mrs. Pollit has had a bad accident. I don't know if she will live," and he sobbed.

"Oh," cried the woman, "Oh! Oh, no! Oh, I didn't mean—oh, about the money. I'll manage somehow—but when can I come to see you? I wouldn't trouble her for the world, only—" Suddenly she began to cry too and asked for a glass of water, so that they had to take her into the common room while the children began to gather slowly round her; and, between crying and drinking her water, and wiping her eyes, she gabbled some story about lending Henny one hundred dollars at six per cent. against the grand piano, though she knew you could hardly sell such things nowadays when the rage was for little pianos: but that as Henny was the sister-in-law of Miss Josephine Pollit, such a splendid woman, and Mr. Pollit too, everyone knew him, but now she found out that Mrs. Pollit had borrowed too from the teacher of the twins and from Ernie's teacher, and she had been to the high school and taken fifteen dollars for clothing from Louie's teacher, and now she heard that Mr. Lomasne, that horrible man, a dreadful usurer who lent fifty dollars and then you owed him money for the rest of your life, and she didn't know

[510]

what else, and she was afraid she would never see her money again. She was a poor woman. She didn't grudge Mrs. Pollit the money—she was a good woman, a wife and mother, but she had to have it: she had a mother to keep herself and an old father— she sobbed and sobbed till she became inarticulate.

At this moment, the doctor arrived. Miss Wilson waited passionately to hear what was the matter with Mrs. Pollit and when she heard that she was dead, she let out a dreadful cry and threw her arms round Tommy, calling him her "poor dear little darling, how dreadful for the baby!" At last she went, but at the door she stopped and asked Louie, very low and ashamed, if she thought she would get her money. "I'm so ashamed, dear, but I'm a poor woman myself, and I'm getting on," she said. Then she nodded and walked away with a tottering gait, till she got to the avenue and was lost to view.

Louie turned back to give the children some breakfast.

6 ⚹ Truth never believed.

IT WAS THREE WEEKS since what remained of Henrietta Pollit, after the disgrace of a coroner's inquest, had gone into the earth; that earth was the Collyer plot in Greenmount Cemetery. A strange company of jackals, smelling each other, had slunk, or strutted before the coroner—Jim Lomasne and a busy, neat little downtown usurer, the manager of an auto loan company, and good-looking, respectable little Archie Lessinum, and even Henny's sisters, Auntie Jo, Louie, Sam, Miss Wilson, and Miss Aiden, and it had come out that the meek, sweet-smiling, unassertive Henrietta had been a bundle of sordid secrets, from life's end to life's end, had not only stripped herself naked to pay the household bills and the usurious interests which had mounted and mounted from the time she had had Ernie, but had begged and cadged from every member of her family, from domestic

[511]

suppliers, the children's teachers, and all sorts of strangers, to all telling her story of the children's needs.

Where had it all gone? people asked: but Archie Lessinum found that no mystery—where had the Collyer estate gone? he asked. With twelve children to rear and of those, some to marry and many incapacitated sons (incapacitated by temperament) to keep, and their families after them, the good-natured, self-made merchant David Collyer had had no difficulty in dissipating a great estate. What was left was held in spendthrift trust for his sons and daughters, all but Hassie (a trustee) financial ne'er-do-weels. The estate needed repairs, had second mortgages to pay off; old Ellen Collyer had to be kept; and only after her death, and at the time when the estate became self-supporting again, would it begin to pay out dividends to the many sons and daughters or their heirs. Now, each of them had numerous heirs, Henny being no different from any other Collyer in this, Hassie and Eleanor alone being exceptions. The money due to Ernie and the other children of Henrietta, when the dividends began to come in, would be very little: but as they were young minors, this money, for the time being, would be applied to paying off Henny's large debts. But Henny had begun owing money from the time she was married. She had contracted debts before many times, but these had always been paid by her indulgent father. These debts had been kept secret from her husband, whose puritan wrath she feared, though not from her money-wise family; and, lacking his firm hand, she had run on and on, until at the last she had come into the hands of despicable, predatory usurers like James Lomasne, who lent without papers and collected through blackmail.

All one could say of Lomasne was that he had a peculiar reputation for an honest man: Lomasne, on the other hand, said, with great assurance and an appearance of charitable respectability, that he had lent money indeed to his neighbor Mrs. Pollit, but only because he liked the children and he knew she was in need —and he ventured to make some remarks upon the character of Samuel C. Pollit which revolted everyone. His honesty was

[512]

shown by his having signed no papers with Mrs. Pollit and having never demanded any interest. She paid him back when she could—but so little had she paid him back that there was still owing to him a sum of five hundred fifty dollars. He had lent this money, too, he said, because Mr. Pollit had told him he would go into his boat-and-coffin business: and he regarded this money lent to Mrs. Pollit more in the light of an investment, and then, they were friends and neighbors, and Mr. Pollit took an exceeding interest in his little girl, "Fairy," as in all other little girls of the neighborhood.

True, the world was all ears and eyes for Sam's misfortune, but Sam bore it with noble dignity, for now at least people knew what he had borne all these years. But as to where the money had gone, he was as innocent as a babe, he told the creditors later on: it was like lightning opening the ground at his feet, and now, to a certain extent, he could understand some of the rages of the unfortunate, guilty, but miserable woman. She had been harassed by the bloodhounds of debt; their tongues had been belling in her brain, their maws opening at her shins, their hell-breath mixing with her breath all these years. Yes, if she had only confided in him, he would have been able to deny publicly his responsibility and so take possibility of credit away from her, or he would have been able to rein her in, save her from this criminal recklessness. For she knew, he said sadly, to Jo, alas! she knew only too well what money waste was: it was in the blood. She knew better than he, but she was a foolish, weak, silly woman with a taste for extravagance and no means of gratifying it. Where did the money go? They must not ask him. His salary would have been ample for a sensible woman, and he should have known better than to marry a rich girl with no idea of a planned economy.

Now, he proposed a five-year-plan for his creditors: he refused to let one borrowed cent go round the world in ragged trousers with his name to it—he would pay back everything. He had no money. They saw in him a penniless man, whose good name had been torn from his back by the wickedness of the world, but he

[513]

would win his way back, make a new world for his children, and pay back all the money that the wretched creature had borrowed. There was not even any sense to all this waste: it was mere pointless ruin, for the money had gone to buy clothes and food that would have been paid for out of his salary if his salary had not been eaten up secretly by the loan sharks and bloodsucking usurers against whom he had no recourse, since their procedures were illegal. He walked back to Spa House a beaten man, with his pockets out and his name mud-spattered, true, said he; but what did he care for slander and name-slinging? In five years he would have paid off all, and his children would be prouder than ever of their father's honor; his truth crushed to earth would rise again, fresher from her mud bath.

For a few weeks they remembered Henny. They would hear her footsteps in the hall, in her bedroom upstairs; Louie would hear her in the kitchen making tea or poking the fire on a few Mondays, out in the washhouse. Streams of visitors came, mostly women, to look after the motherless children, so horribly orphaned, and to help out the fourteen-year-old girl who now would be "a little mother to them all" (as no one failed to remark): they helped with the cooking, put the children to bed, even scrubbed and washed, neighbors, aunts, cousins alike, and Sam's men friends, who had secreted themselves for years in their dugouts in Baltimore and Washington, began to roll down in cars or on shanks' ponies and hold long commiserating confabs with him. The world had changed entirely. Aunt Hassie had a quarrel with Aunt Eleanor about who should take Chappy for a few weeks, until Sam got a housekeeper. Aunt Hassie won, and the anemic Cathy, who up till now had played with her platoon of dolls, now had a human doll to take care of. She got some color in her cheeks and even put on a little flesh round the waist, and Hassie began to think that it would be a good idea if she, Hassie, adopted Chappy and let Cathy get married to some good man who could bring her up firmly.

The friendly folk who came down gave the children small pieces of money and one day, after quite a party of them had gone, Ernie found a five-dollar bill in the grass. He could hardly believe his good luck, but went round in silence for several hours, at the end of which he took the money to his father and said glumly, that he supposed one of the visitors had dropped it. Sam, however, who had in the meantime inquired into Ernie's finances (needing money himself), told Ernie rather gruffly that he could keep it until its claimant turned up. Its claimant never turned up, and this led Ernie into several heartening thoughts about the possibility of money's dropping from heaven upon the place beneath. He made up his mind to leave school as soon as possible and go out into that world in which five-dollar bills nested in double-lined pockets, and yet where so little care was taken of such charming nestlings that no one noticed them when they flapped off clumsily on their own account.

When the guests went each day, then was the time that the image of Henny started to roam, and also in the early mornings, before Sam started to whistle them up and also just after. The window curtains flapped, the boards creaked, a mouse ran, and Henny was there, muttering softly to herself, tapping a saucepan, turning on the gas. The children were not frightened. They would say, laughing, somewhat curious, "I thought I heard Mothering," and only Evie or Tommy ("that little kissing-bug who is always mugging me," as Henny had said) would look a bit downcast; and perhaps Chappy missed her, that queer, gypsy-like, thin, tanned, pointed face with big black eyes rolling above him which, with its regular white teeth, had looked for, begged for his smiles, had tickled him into smiles, and hugged him just under its chin, when he smiled. But Chappy was away learning to punch playfully the large bosom of Hassie, and already his ideas of faces were confused.

For days Louie would not think of her, having too much to do. It was the summer vacation, and the entire work of the house, outside washing day, fell on Louie and Evie, with occasional help from the boys. Sometimes women came and helped, sometimes Sam would do the dishes; and not only was there so much to do, but the boys and Sam grumbled bitterly about the food, their beds, and so on. Not all would grumble at once. Ernie would come sweetly to them with that touching dependence on them that women laugh at but cultivate in their husbands, and ask, with melancholy, about his buttons or his socks; or Tommy would come, rather timidly, to show a large hole just "come somehow" in his shirt, or bathing trunks would have to be mended before they were "arrested by the society for indecency." This period was hard for them, but it was in many ways sweet, too. Sam told them that soon they would have someone to help them. He thought that someone might be Bonniferous.

Yes, Bonniferous had run away from Auntie Jo's in rebellion, hate, and anger, saying dreadful things, saying she was going to get her baby somehow, find it wherever they had stuck it, even if it was underground, and bury it herself, or if it was living, make a living for it herself, "any way, any way at all" (and when they repeated this, the women would lower their voices and look at each other). But Sam had already been several times to the police to ask them to look for Bonnie and to look for her baby too, for perhaps one was with the other. He liked the police: they were good, decent fellows, helping people in misery, keeping order, punishing only crime, and friendly enough if one approached them in the right spirit as man to man, not calling them names (for they were only workers like him and his friends), but jollying them, being kind to them. And these kind men liked him, too. The Commissioner himself had put himself out to help Sam; so that now Sam had every hope of soon seeing his favorite sister again. He had spoken very severely, in the midst of his sorrow, to the frightened and contrite Jo. Jo showed her contrition in the usual way, by gobbling, quarreling, and blaming everyone but herself; but she was contrite, said Sam, and she would show it: she would be kind to Bonnie, she had promised it. She would make clothes for the lost little baby born beyond the pale.

So the little girl struggled on from day to day, hoping to hear about Bonniferous and, in the meantime, getting the house into a mess much worse than ever poor Henny had got it in. Sam was puzzled by all this, and was heard, at least once a day, to wonder how on earth he had got into "sich a passel of uncompetent shemailes": when Bonniferous came back to them, with her little baby, he would have to "organize them shemailes, and all would run like clockwork under scientific management." Life was noisy, busy, and full of speculations, and so Louie had little time to think about the strange day when Henny died.

But sometimes, when she least expected it, she would think about it: the terror of it, and her secret complicity would seem so naked to the sky that she would break out into an icy sweat and wonder that no one could hear what was going on in her brain. She would never tell anyone, and this was as a corpse sealed up in the house which she alone knew of and which would eventually molder and leave little trace, until the mindless years, with the vague gesture of an idiot, brought it unaccusingly to light. This was a terror she could live with. But she lived a queer life, and the noises, cries, philosophies of others seemed like silly games that kindergarten children play. She was on the other side of a fence; there was a garden through the chinks that she had once been in, but could never be in again. Yet she did not care. She still believed that she had done the only right thing, the only firm thing, and that Fate itself had not only justified her but saved her from consequences. It annoyed her only to hear Sam talking about Henny's rash act, dreadful deed, and shameful self-ruin, folly next to wickedness and mindless self-destruction, and the long, long talks he had with one and another about the whole thing. "What do you know?" she would think. She soon reached a point when she could not sit at the table with him and listen to his misbegotten notions and morality with its mistaken examples. When they were served, she would take her own plate and go with it to sit on the front lawn, or down the orchard, and no matter how many messages were sent to her to come in and join the family, she would obstinately and even mutely sit there, self-righteous, proud, and contemptuous.

The tempests of July and the swamped earth and flooded

rivers had come to wash away the sorrows of Henny: headstones sank in the graveyard, and the new earth piled over her fell in. Towards the end of July it was as if Henny too had stormed, but in another room in the universe, which was now under lock and key.

On Monday the twenty-fifth, the heavy rain having at last stopped, Sam went into Baltimore to talk about a favorite project of his. Many friends had urged him to try to get on to a radio program, and they thought either foreign affairs or the children's hour would suit him, but he himself thought of himself as "Uncle Sam," and for some time had discussed his "Uncle Sam" with friends, journalists (whom he highly respected as a communicating medium between recondite truth and the truth-hungry mob), and "responsible" people with whom he was intimate. Sam was no bootlicker of people in high place: he so honestly admired them, and so wholeheartedly believed that capacity is always rewarded by "the people" in the shape of high place that his love for them was a pure thing. Sam had been doing the rounds of the elect of the people, for some time, and saw "Uncle Sam" as "an eventuality of the immediate future." On his Uncle Sam Hour, he would tell not only folk tales that had been handed down from our forefathers, things devised in their frontier nights after hand-to-hand battles with hardship, and distorted stories brought over from crooked old Europe, but also tales of our revolutionary past, high deeds of stern men and brave women whereby we won the freedom we have, such freedom that, thank Heaven, there is no need to go through again the turmoil that now confronts poor bonded Europe. He would lead them by the hand down the highways of the world and the bypaths of Nature and teach them all her secrets, even as Hiawatha learned them.

Sam had no difficulty in interesting advertisers, and these were days of great hope for him: at last he had found his function. He had told his children and friends for many years that the radio was the great new medium of spreading enlightenment—radio and the movies. He wished that he knew the directors of M.G.M. and Warner Brothers, for they must be good men, since they catered to the people, and he had the same dear wish about Franklin D. Roosevelt and Stephen S. Wise. They made mistakes, he felt, but after a short talk with them, they would become his friends, and he could give them ideas, put them more intimately in touch with the people, a thing for which they lived. He had always said that though, no doubt, Jesus Christ never existed, the idea of "the second coming" was a touching illustration of mankind's wish for uplift and regeneration; and that if a real savior ever came, he would come over the radio. Perhaps, he, Samuel Clemens Pollit, was a forerunner of the truly great man. At any rate he would begin by touching the heart of the little world, the Lilliputians. Far from despising the advertisers of radio programs, he liked them, he thought them wonderfully humane people because, instead of merely broadcasting crude publicity, they wished to entertain and educate the people.

After a most satisfactory talk with a sponsor, Sam took a walk this Monday down South Eutaw Street, between Lexington and Mulberry Streets, to look in the pet shops, and then turned up Mulberry Street to go to the library. Coming towards him was a touching young mother, with long silver-gilt hair, and a baby in her arms. Sam's heart jumped, his eyes misgave him, and then he saw that it really was Bonnie. He rushed to her and took her into his arms.

"Oh, Bonniferous! Bonniferous! Why didn't you come to your poor brother? Bonniferous! Where are you? Everyone has been looking for you. Did you know Henny died? I am all alone, Bonniferous."

Sam wept openly, and Bonnie wept openly, and then the baby (which was a boy and which Bonnie was quite sure was her baby) wept openly, and as he had the great lust for weeping in him, he outdid them, and insisted upon attention to himself alone. Sam was for taking Bonnie home at once, but Bonnie had to get her things and give notice at the place where she worked and——

"And see the man?" inquired Sam, in a sad voice.

"Oh!" cried Bonnie, "I'll never look at him again if I live to be a hundred."

Then Sam wanted to know if the boy was to be without a father, and Bonnie said better no father than such a wretch; and Sam said, in that case, he would be its father—what difference would another little fellow make in his great phalanstery of sons down at Spa House? He was getting two jobs, both in the public service (later on he would be a biologist)—his own children were growing up, and Bonnie could look after the house for him and save him the expense of a housekeeper: and he would protect her. Perhaps later on, she would find a good man—Mr. Right, this time, not Mr. Wrong. He saw Bonnie to her room, kissed his new nephew (whom she had called "Samuel-Charles"), and went galloping home, singing to himself. He could hardly wait to get home, burst into the house, and tell them all the wonderful news: they had a new brother, Samuel-Charles (yes, another Sam, Little-Sam), and he would soon be Uncle Sam on his own Hour, he thought. "All things work together for the good of him that loves the Truth," said the train to him as it rattled down towards the Severn, "all things—work—together—for the good—of him—that loves—the TRUTH!" Even Henny's death had worked for him: even Henny's debts, for now he had got a new sphere of influence, and friends had rallied round him in an altogether unexpected way. "It is—lovely—to be loved!" said the train to him. "It is splendid—to be—loved! If we only—can—live up—to the thoughts—of us—by them—that love us!"

When he got home, there were jobs to do. The house could never run without him. The icebox had broken down; and he rejoiced in his handyman's skill as he showed them the wherefore and how easy it was to fix it with a little *knowledge*. At dinnertime, he showed them how to fry the fish in a new oil he had brought from town—it made an exceeding stench, but who cared?—now that querulous poor Mothering was not here to smell it. Then gently he chid the girls for this and that, a floor not washed, a dirty window, and over the dinner table (he insisted on Louie's being present this time and ignored the sullen, brutish face she put on, as she sat there mute in Henny's place) he told them the details of his new home economy. There would be three shemailes for the interior—Bonnie, Louie, and Evie, and all the horsework, the donkeywork, would be done by his great tribe of men. Charles-Franklin, Chappy (little Megalops was coming home, he said, with a faint droop of the eyes that they did not comprehend), and the new Charles, Samuel-Charles, a wonderful little boy with a great blond head full of brains and bright salty eyes, very observant, although only five weeks old, sure to be something exceptional; and he told them there was a superstition about boys born like Samuel-Charles, though he could not tell it to them till they grew up. Now, he said, nothing lacked, nothing at all: it only remained for Louie to cheer up, bear a hand, and stand there as his lieutenant when he piped all hands on deck.

After dinner, he took Louie for a long walk, round by the great house in its seedy grounds, by the unspeakable ruin of the Negro village, which had suffered so much in these storms, and by the slimy, rotting cove where the carcasses of old boats were, and spoke out all his heart to her—what the future would mean for him and her, if only she would stick to him and be happy.

"The same old story," muttered Louie at last.

Sam shot her a troubled glance. "Looloo, now that poor Henny has left us, so awfully, so mistakenly, but gone, I thought a weight would be lifted off your shoulders. A young girl should bloom like a peach tree, but you are sullen, like a tree that will not bloom."

They were both silent for a while. At last, out of her terrible gloom, Louie said quietly, "One night you were quarreling all night: I was standing up there next to the box I had from my mother, that redwood box full of pieces and patches."

"I know," said Sam, sympathetically, "with the little bit of blue dress she wore the day I proposed, and the little blue dress you wore when she died, and your baby shawl."

"It was a very oppressive night," said Louie, "and I saw a tree

[521]

wave, like a shoal of fish that suddenly darts aside after they have been drifting in the water. Then I thought I saw an eagle dash itself against my window. Then I thought I would kill both of you."

"Looloo!"

She took no notice of him, except that a very tiny smile crept round her mouth, the first, in his company, in many weeks. "I am telling the truth: I never lie. Why should I lie? Those who lie are afraid of something."

"Pull yourself together: what is the matter with you? I don't understand you."

She smiled more, "You never will." She chuckled, "You never will either. Thank goodness. But it is true—I got some cyanide out of your darkroom and put it in a pillbox, you know that pillbox—I got it out of Mother's room the night before, and I meant to put it in both cups, but I lost my nerve, I suppose; I didn't quite know what I was doing, I only put it in one cup. I got frightened." She became sober, depressed.

"Looloo! Be quiet! I won't allow this incredible absurdity to go on."

"Then you came in with the cups—but before that, Mother came in, and I think she saw me. Anyhow, she seemed to know: then she didn't say anything except what she said then, 'I don't blame her, you can't blame her, she's not to blame if she were to go stark staring mad'—she meant, it was just the same, that anyone would have. Then she took it: she couldn't stand it any more."

"Looloo! 'Couldn't stand it any more!' You don't know that I had to stand everything. The tyranny of tears: one person bears, and the other person cries and shrieks, and everyone—even you, even you—sympathize with her. And you make up this incredible, insane, neurotic story. For it is neurotic. I thought you had self-control. And you make up the damnedest, stupidest, most melodramatic lie I ever heard in all my born days. You talk about the truth. You don't know what truth is. The truth isn't in you, only some horrible stupid mess of fantasies mixed up

[522]

with things I can't even think about. What happened to you? Henny ruined you. I have got to take you away from school and keep you at home with me until you recover. You are not yourself."

"You don't notice anything. Everything has to be what you say," said Louie. "For instance, Ernie was so unhappy at that time, right on that morning, that he tried to hang himself."

"What do you mean?"

"You remember—we took mother in, to his bed?"

"I know."

"On the bottom of the bed was that doll he had rigged up. It was himself. The children told us, don't you remember: it was Ernie. Ernie hung himself. He made a doll. How do you know he mightn't have done it really?"

"Child's play, horseplay," he said roughly. "That only goes to show how far out of your senses you are, Looloo, that in a little joke like that you see melodrama. I am going to take you away from all this foolery, this drama and poetry and nonsense they are putting into your head. You haven't a good brain at all—you are just crammed with the most idiotic nonsense I ever heard of in my life. It has got to end. You are coming home to me, and I am going to watch every book you read, every thought you have."

"All right! All right! You remember when you used to take me to see the Lincoln Memorial, walking along the Reflecting Pool from your office on Saturdays. I learned from him, not from you. You used to say your heart always beat when you were going towards it; my heart used to beat, but you always thought about yourself. When I was at Harpers Ferry, I only thought about John Brown. I always thought Israel Baken was just like him—my grandfather. Not a Pollit, thank goodness, not one of you."

"That mean old vicious superstitious man!" Sam ejaculated. "Yes, you are like him, I am sorry to say. Your mother had none of that."

"What do you know about my mother? She was a woman. I

[523]

found a letter from her in the old redwood box. Someone who died sent it back to her when they knew they were dying. It was just after you were married. She said, 'Samuel is a very young man. I am very sick or I would not be writing such foolish things, I am sure. But he does not understand women or children. He is such a good young man, he is too good to understand people at all.'"

Sam said dreamily, "Yes, I was a very good young man. I never allowed a breath of scandal or of foolish small talk to be spoken in my presence; and your mother understood me. She was ready to sacrifice everything for me. Perhaps she loved me even better than I loved her. But I was very young: I did not see things as I see them now. She loved you too dearly, 'little Ducky,' as she called you. It is a pity you never had a mother."

"Well, I'm my own mother," Louie said, without emotion. "And I can look after myself. I want you to let me go away. You can't want me to live in the house with you after what I was going to do."

"If you think I believe that cock-and-bull nonsense you made up out of your soft, addled melodramatic bean," he said with rough good humor, "you have another thunk coming, my girl. You are going to stay here with me until you get out of this stupid adolescent crisis, and that's all there is to it."

"Then you don't believe me?"

"Of course not. Do you think I'm going to be taken in by a silly girl's fancies? You must think me a nitwit, Looloo, after all." He laughed and put his arm on her shoulder, "Foolish, poor little Looloo."

She shook him off and said nothing. Sam went on talking to her gently, chidingly, lovingly. When they reached home, she made him another cup of coffee and went upstairs. Out of the old redwood box she took an old-fashioned bag made of grass and raffia, and embroidered in beads by her mother, at one time. Into this she put a few clothes and a dollar bill that one of the visitors had given her after Henny's death. She hardly slept at all, but when she heard Sam begin his whistling early the next

[524]

morning, she got up and dressed quickly and quietly. She heard the warm, old, jolly, pulsating home life beginning its round: "Little-Womey, *Philohela minor!* Git up, git up!" It was only six o'clock, and the boys were still drowsily groaning and rubbing their heads on their pillows. She heard Evie grumbling in her bed and dragging herself out of it and Sam thumping on the wall: "You, Gemini, hey, you Navel Academy, what's about your early-morning swim?" She expertly got downstairs and to the kitchen with her satchel. Once there, she banged the kettle about to sound as if she were making the tea, and heard Evie's grumble, "Looloo's making it," and, taking some food out of the icebox (she was always hungry), she ran out of the house and in no time was screened by the trees and bushes of the avenue. She smiled, felt light as a dolphin undulating through the waves, one of those beautiful, large, sleek marine mammals that plunged and wallowed, with their clever eyes. As she crossed the bridge (looking back and seeing none of the Navel Academy as yet on their little beach, or scrambling down the sodden bluff), she heaved a great breath. How different everything looked, like the morning of the world, that hour before all other hours which Thoreau speaks of, that most matinal hour. "Why didn't I run away before?" she wondered. She wondered why everyone didn't run away. Things certainly looked different: they were no longer part of herself but objects that she could freely consider without prejudice.

In a few minutes, she reached Clare's little cottage and saw Clare walking about in her nightdress, down the passage. Clare came to the door, seeing her, with big eyes, and half whispered, "I say, where are you going?"

"I'm going to Harpers Ferry. I'm going to my Auntie Jo's to get some money, and then I'm going out there; won't you come along?" Clare stared at her longingly, but Louie could tell from her hesitation that she was going to refuse. "You won't come, too?"

"Oh, Louie! Oh, Louie! Oh, Louie!"

"You won't come?"

"I can't."

"Why not?"

"I just can't. I don't know why not. I have my little sister."

"I suppose, if I had any decency," said Louie slowly, "I'd think of my little sister and brothers, but there's Auntie Bonnie. No, there are plenty of them. Well—good-by."

"Are you really going?"

"Yes, of course."

"You're all right," said Clare.

"Why don't you come, Clare? What is the good of staying here?"

"I can't, Louie, I can't."

"All right." Louie turned about and went down the path till she got to the gate, then she looked back. Clare had come to the front door. A milkman was coming down the street. Louie lingered, "I'll write you a letter when I get there."

"You send me your address, and I'll write to you."

It was this that was final: Louie's last hope went then. "Well," said Louie, going out of the gate, "I won't see Miss Aiden any more, will I?"

"What will she say?" asked Clare. "Well, anyhow, I suppose, you'll come back for school."

"Will I?" cried Louie, awaking from a doleful mood, "will I? No, I won't. I'll never come back."

Clare sniffed, and Louie saw that she was crying. Louie looked at her stupidly and, humping one shoulder, began to walk away.

"Good-by, Louie!"

"Good-by!" She walked away without looking back, feeling cheated and dull. Clare did not really think she should go. She walked across the market space and into Main Street, looking into a little coffee shop and wondering if she would have a cup of coffee. She had never been in there, because it was like a fishermen's hangout, dingy and dubious. But no, she walked on. Everyone looked strange. Everyone had an outline, and brilliant, solid colors. Louie was surprised and realized that when you run away, everything is at once very different. Perhaps she would get on well enough. She imagined the hubbub now at Spa House, as they discovered that she was not bursting up the stairs with their morning tea. They would look everywhere and conclude that she had gone for a walk. "So I have," she thought, smiling secretly, "I have gone for a walk round the world." She pictured Ernie, Evie, the twins, darling Tommy, who loved the girls already and loved her, too; but as for going back towards Spa House, she never even thought of it. Spa House was on the other side of the bridge.

SECOND EDITION

Statistics: The Exploration and Analysis of Data

SECOND EDITION

Statistics: The Exploration and Analysis of Data

Jay Devore
California Polytechnic State University, San Luis Obispo

Roxy Peck
California Polytechnic State University, San Luis Obispo

Duxbury Press
An imprint of Wadsworth Publishing Company
Belmont, California

Statistics Editor: *Michael J. Sugarman*
Editorial Assistant: *Carol Ann Benedict*
Production Editor: *Marjorie Z. Sanders*
Interior and Cover Designer: *Sharon L. Kinghan, Susan Haberkorn*
Print Buyer: *Vena M. Dyer*
Art Editor: *Lisa Torri*
Permissions Editor: *Carline Haga*
Copy Editor: *Linda L. Thompson*
Technical Illustrator: *J.A.K. Graphics*
Cover Photograph: © *Herb Charles Ohlmeyer/Fran Heyl Associates*
Compositor: *Weimer Incorporated*
Cover Printing: *Lehigh Press Lithographers/Autoscreen*
Printing and Binding: *R. R. Donnelley & Sons Company/Crawfordsville*

1   2   3   4   5   6   7   8   9   10—97   96   95   94   93

Library of Congress Cataloging-in-Publication Data
Devore, Jay L.
   Statistics, the exploration and analysis of data / Jay Devore and
   Roxy Peck. — 2nd ed.
      p.   cm.
   Includes bibliographical references and index.
   ISBN 0-534-19614-4
   1. Mathematical statistics.   I. Peck, Roxy.   II. Title.
QA276.D48   1993
001.4′22—dc20   92-18203
                                                                    CIP

To Sidney Devore and Lucelle Peck ★ ★ ★

Preface

Statistics: The Exploration and Analysis of Data is intended for use as a textbook in introductory statistics courses at two- and four-year colleges and universities. We believe that the following special features of our book distinguish it from other texts.

Features

A Traditional Structure with a Modern Flavor

The topics included in almost all introductory texts are here also. However, we have interwoven some new strands that reflect current and important developments in statistical analysis. These include stem-and-leaf displays, box plots, transformations, residual analysis, normal probability plots, and distribution-free confidence intervals. The organization gives instructors considerable flexibility in deciding which of these topics to include in a course.

The Use of Real Data

Many students are skeptical of the relevance and importance of statistics both to their own interests and goals and to the greater concerns of our society. Contrived problem situations often reinforce this skepticism. A strategy that we have employed successfully to motivate students is to present examples and exercises that involve data extracted from journal articles, newspapers, and other published sources. Most examples and exercises in the book are of this nature. They cover a very wide range of disciplines and subject areas, but addressing the statistical questions posed does not require familiarity with the various problem settings.

Mathematical Level and Notational Simplicity

A good background in high school algebra constitutes sufficient mathematical preparation for reading and understanding the material presented herein. However, students at this level often have much difficulty mastering the mathematical notation and arguments used in many introductory texts. We want students to focus on concepts without having to grapple with formula and symbol manipulation. To achieve this, we have sometimes used words and phrases in place of symbols. We hope that this makes the exposition more accessible to those who are apprehensive about their mathematical skills.

The Use of Computer Output

The ability of the computer to perform many computations and operations (such as ordering, grouping, and drawing pictures) very quickly has stimulated the development of much new statistical methodology. The wide availability of statistical computer packages such as MINITAB, BMDP, SAS, and SPSS has made it much easier for investigators to analyze their own data using old or new methods. Statistical software for microcomputers has also proliferated. To highlight the role of the computer in contemporary statistics, we have included sample output from the aforementioned packages throughout the book. In addition, numerous exercises contain data that could be analyzed by a statistical package, though use of the book does not presuppose access to any such package.

The Role of Probability

All too often students find probability difficult, remain unconvinced of its relevance to inference, and let their difficulties color their attitude to the remainder of the course. Our treatment of probability is informal and intuitive. The presentation here has been somewhat expanded from that of the first edition, but we have organized the material so that the few topics not needed for inference can easily be skipped (see the detailed suggestions that follow).

Pedagogical Aids

Each chapter begins with a Preview describing a real-world problem situation. The Encore at the end of the chapter shows how the methods just presented can be applied to the situation. There are a great many worked examples. An exercise set appears at the end of each section, and a supplementary set concludes each chapter. Boxes are used to call out important definitions, concepts, and procedures. A key concepts list summarizes the contents of each chapter. In addition, a student's solutions manual, instructor's manual, transparency masters, and a test bank are available from the publisher.

Topic Coverage

Our book can be used in courses as short as one quarter or as long as one year in duration. Particularly in shorter courses, an instructor will need to be selective in deciding which topics to include and which to set aside. The book divides naturally into four major sections: descriptive methods (Chapters 2–4), probability material (Chapters 5–8), the basic one- and two-sample inferential techniques (Chapters 9–12), and more advanced inferential methodology (Chapters 13–16). We have joined a growing number of books in including an early chapter (Chapter 4) on descriptive methods for bivariate numerical data. This early exposure raises questions and issues that should stimulate student interest in the subject, and is also advantageous for those teaching courses in which time constraints preclude covering advanced inferential material. However, this chapter can easily be postponed until the basics of inference have been covered, and then combined with Chapter 13 for a unified treatment of regression and correlation.

With the possible exception of Chapter 4, Chapters 1–10 should be covered in order. We anticipate that most will then continue with the two-sample and paired data material of Chapters 11 and 12, though regression could be covered before either of these. Analysis of variance (Chapter 15) and/or categorical data analysis (Chapter 16) can be discussed prior to the regression material of Chapters 13–14. In addition to flexibility in the order in which chapters are covered, material in some sections can be skipped entirely, just in part, or postponed. The following commentary identifies these sections.

CHAPTER 1:   The basic terminology in Section 2 is essential; students should be required to read "Three Good Reasons" (Section 1) on their own.

CHAPTER 2:   The first four sections should be covered, but data transformations (Section 5) is an optional topic.

CHAPTER 3:   Sections 1 and 2 contain core material, but Section 3, and in particular the discussion of box plots, can easily be skipped.

CHAPTER 4:   As discussed earlier, this material can be covered to any desired extent at this point. Whenever regression and correlation are presented, residual plots (Section 4) and transformations (Section 5) are optional.

CHAPTER 5:   In response to user feedback and comments from reviewers, we have expanded coverage of probability somewhat in this edition. However, the material has been organized so that those who want to spend a minimal amount of time in this area can easily do so. Only the first three sections need be covered (even conditional probability in Section 3 can be skipped if the defining condition for independence is taken as $(P(A \ and \ B) = P(A) \cdot P(B))$. The general addition and multiplication rules in Section 4 are not used in the sequel, and the counting rules developed in Section 5 can be mentioned in passing if and when the binomial distribution is introduced.

CHAPTER 6:   The first three sections on general concepts of random variables and discrete distributions are important. Section 4, on the binomial distribution, is optional in that this material is not a prerequisite for discussing properties of a sample proportion and inferences about a population proportion.

CHAPTER 7:   General concepts related to continuous random variables and basic properties of the normal distribution are, of course, essential. Those pressed for time can easily omit the normal approximation and normal probability plots from Section 3.

CHAPTER 8:   The material here on sampling distributions of statistics is absolutely fundamental. We have emphasized the simulation approach, as opposed to calculations based on probability rules, and have included computer output from several extensive simulation experiments.

CHAPTER 9:   Once the first section on point estimation and second on large-sample confidence intervals for a population mean have been covered, the other two sections can be presented in either order or postponed until after hypothesis testing has been introduced.

CHAPTER 10:   Sections 1 and 2 present the basic concepts of hypothesis testing, and Sections 3, 5, and 6 describe the standard one-sample test procedures for a population mean and proportion. Section 4 discusses P-values, which have appeared with increasing frequency in recent years in summaries of statistical analyses. Although it is possible to omit this material, we do not recommend doing so. For those who believe that the determination of type II error probabilities is slighted in introductory texts, the optional Section 7 includes a discussion of how β can be obtained for several important tests.

CHAPTER 11:   The usual two-sample z and t tests and confidence intervals based on independent samples appear in Sections 1–3. The distribution-free (nonparametric) Wilcoxin rank-sum test and associated confidence interval are introduced in Section 4. This material can be covered at this point, deleted entirely, or discussed in conjunction with other distribution-free methods from the last sections of Chapters 12 and 15.

CHAPTER 12:   Section 1 discusses the advantages of a paired experiment, after which the paired t test and confidence interval are presented in Section 2. Wilcoxin's signed-rank test and the associated confidence interval are given in Section 3; as with the rank-sum procedures, this material can be omitted or postponed.

CHAPTER 13:   The first three sections present the simple linear regression model and related inferential procedures. If Chapter 4 has not already been covered, appropriate material from that chapter should be integrated into the present chapter. Section 4 presents inferences concerning the population correlation coefficient; prerequisite material appears in Section 4.2. A major focus of exploratory data analysis has been the study of residuals from a fitted model. Section 5 discusses the use of residuals to check the adequacy of the simple linear regression model; this material is mentioned only briefly in the next chapter.

CHAPTER 14:   Multiple regression analysis is frequently not part of an introductory course. For those who have the time and inclination, our focus on concepts and the use of computer output should make this material accessible and useful. Section 1 discusses various models, including the use of interaction and dummy predictors. It is not necessary to cover all these models before moving on to the methods of analysis in Sections 2 and 3. Various aspects of model building, including variable selection and multicollinearity, are considered in the last section.

CHAPTER 15:   Section 1 presents the fundamental ideas of single-factor ANOVA. This is supplemented by a discussion of sums of squares, computations, and ANOVA tables in Section 2. Once past these sections, the remaining sections can be covered in almost any order. For example, one might choose to skip Section 3 on multiple comparisons, discuss randomized block experiments (Section 4), and omit the last two sections on two-factor and distribution-free ANOVA.

CHAPTER 16:   The usual test procedures based on the chi-squared distribution are presented here.

Acknowledgments

Many people have made valuable contributions to the preparation of this book. We have derived great benefit from many discussions with our colleague John Groves, who also prepared several of the supplements. Debbie Rossi, Jim Daly, and Joyce Curry-Daly were invaluable in reviewing examples and checking calculations. Numerous constructive criticisms and suggestions came from the manuscript reviewers. Typing chores were admirably handled by Pat Fleischauer. Mike Sugarman, Marjorie Sanders, Linda Thompson, Alex Kugushev, and many others at Brooks/ Cole and Wadsworth were very helpful in bringing this project to fruition.

Finally, the support of our families, friends, and colleagues made our task much easier.

Jay Devore
Roxy Peck

A Note to the Student

In all likelihood, you have started reading this book because it is the text for an introductory statistics course required of all students in your major. You may well be thinking to yourself that if it weren't for this requirement, you wouldn't be enrolled in a statistics course and could then spend your time in more interesting and productive ways. Perhaps you are even somewhat apprehensive about your ability to do well in the course, since you've probably heard through the grapevine that mastering statistics requires some facility for mathematical reasoning and manipulation. If you are indeed ambivalent about studying statistics and a bit fearful of what lies ahead, please realize that these feelings are shared by many other students. We hope to lay these fears to rest in short order by convincing you that statistics is important for gaining a better understanding of the world around you, relevant to your particular interests and field of study, and accessible even if you have a very modest mathematical background. To this end, the book emphasizes concepts and an intuitive presentation of the core methodology used in a wide variety of applications. Statistics does rest on a mathematical foundation, but we have tried to keep the notation and mathematical development simple. We hope the result is a friendly and informal survey that will help you in various ways long after the course is finished.

The key to success in your statistics course, as in so many endeavors, is to start with a positive attitude and resolve to invest a reasonable amount of time and effort. It won't always be easy and may occasionally be frustrating. (We ourselves sometimes get quite frustrated when attempting to learn new material.) But with the right attitude and commitment of your resources, we think that understanding, enjoyment, and a sense of accomplishment will quickly follow.

Contents

4

5

6

Random Variables and Discrete Probability Distributions   252

7

Continuous Probability Distributions   289

*After Chapter 10, coverage and ordering will depend on the individual instructor's taste, so no
sections have been marked as optional.

11

Inferences Using Two
Independent Samples   486

15   The Analysis of Variance   731

16   The Analysis of Categorical Data and Goodness-of-Fit Methods   803

APPENDIX   Statistical Tables   849

Statistics: The Exploration and Analysis of Data

1

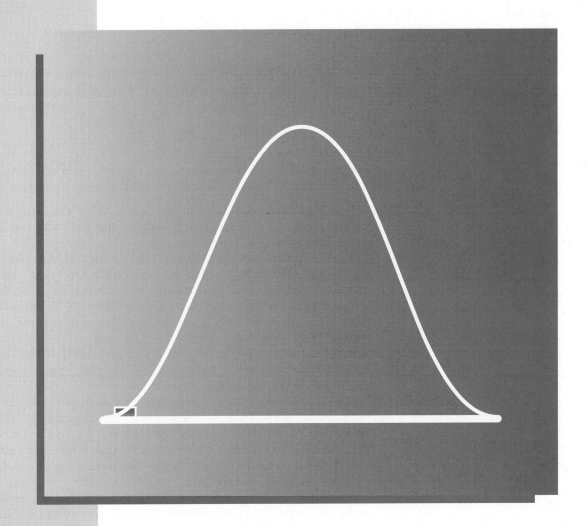

Introduction

1.1 Three Good Reasons

Do you wish someone would give you three good reasons why you should take statistics as part of your college curriculum? Well, we're prepared to do just that.

First Good Reason

Numerical information is everywhere. In one day's newspapers (*Los Angeles Times* and *San Francisco Chronicle,* February 8, 1992) alone, we found the following:

- Data from a survey of California employers, which was used to estimate the jobless rate for the state and also to estimate that California lost 239,100 jobs during January of 1992.
- The results of a study by researchers at the University of Maryland on the sleeping habits of Americans. Based on data collected in a survey of Californians, the researchers concluded that more than half of adults that live in the San Francisco Bay Area go to bed before 11 P.M. As a result CBS and NBC affiliates in the Bay Area plan a change to "early prime time," beginning their prime-time programming at 7 P.M. rather than 8 P.M.
- A report on the controversy over drug testing at the 1992 Winter Olympics. The report included a numerical analysis of the risk of false positive and false negative results for the proposed testing technique.
- Data on the number of animals impounded by Los Angeles city-run and county-run animal shelters. Each animal was classified according to whether it was claimed by its owner, sold, or destroyed. Figures for the two types of shelters were compared and the data was used to attempt to refute claims made by a city council member that the city-run shelters destroyed a higher proportion of animals than did county-run shelters.
- The results of two different election polls focusing on the Democratic candidates in the 1992 New Hampshire primary. One poll reported that Bill Clinton had a 13-point lead over Paul Tsongas (and stated that the poll had a margin of error of 4 percentage points). The second poll, conducted on the same day, reported 19% for Clinton and 28% for Tsongas, based on a survey of 284 Democrats (no margin of error reported). This seeming inconsistency can be attributed to both statistical and nonstatistical factors.
- The results of a University of California research study of 589 women who had delivered a child by Caesarean section. The data collected was used to describe in quantitative terms the risk associated with attempting natural delivery of a second child when the first child had been delivered by Caesarean section.
- An analysis of ozone, nitrogen dioxide, and carbon monoxide levels over time and by location for the Los Angeles metropolitan area, along with forecasts for future levels.

How can you decide whether what is being reported is reasonable and whether the conclusions drawn are justified? To be an educated consumer of reports of this sort, you need to be able to extract information from graphs and charts and to follow numerical arguments. Familiarity with statistical data analysis techniques and methods of reasoning can be a big help.

Second Good Reason

Statistical techniques are being used to make decisions that affect your life and welfare:

- Insurance companies use statistical techniques to set automobile insurance rates.
- Medical researchers use statistical methods to make recommendations regarding the choice between surgical and nonsurgical treatment of various diseases.
- The Environmental Protection Agency takes samples from water sources and performs various statistical analyses on the resulting data to determine whether there is evidence of contamination.
- The financial aid offices of many universities survey students in order to obtain estimates of the cost of going to school. These estimates are then used to set criteria for financial aid eligibility.

An understanding of the underlying statistical techniques will allow you to decide whether decisions that affect your well-being are made in a reasonable way.

Third Good Reason

No matter what line of work you pursue, you will probably find yourself in situations where informed decisions are required. In order to make an informed decision you must be able to do the following:

1. Decide whether existing information is adequate or whether additional information is required.
2. If necessary, collect further information. Data gathering must be conducted in a thoughtful and reasonable way in order to ensure that the resulting information is not misleading.
3. Summarize the available data in a useful and informative manner.
4. Analyze the available information.
5. Draw conclusions, make decisions, and assess the risk of an incorrect decision.

Statistical methods introduced in this text provide a framework for these steps.

Numerical information and inferences based on such information are encountered both in the pursuit of professional goals and in daily life. **Statistics** is the scientific discipline that provides methods that help us make sense of such data. Statistical methodology is being employed with increasing frequency in the social sciences, natural sciences, and agriculture to aid in organizing, summarizing, and drawing conclusions from data. The pervasiveness of statistical analysis in reports and studies done by investigators in many different subject areas has led educators in these areas to recognize the importance of statistical literacy. An exposure to statistical reasoning and the most widely used methods for analyzing data is now viewed as an integral part of a college education.

Some individuals regard conclusions based on statistical analyses with a great deal of suspicion. Extreme skeptics, usually speaking out of ignorance, characterize the discipline as a subcategory of lying—something used for deception rather than for positive ends. However, we believe that statistical methods, used intelligently, constitute a set of powerful tools for gaining insight into the world around us. We hope that this text will help you to understand the logic behind statistical reasoning, prepare you to apply statistical methods appropriately, and enable you to recognize when others are not doing so.

1.2   Populations, Samples, and Statistics

For hundreds of years, individuals have been using statistical tools to organize and summarize data. Many of these tools—bar charts, tabular displays, various plots of economic data, averages and percentages—appear regularly in newspapers, magazines, and technical journals. Methods that organize and summarize data aid in effective presentation and increased understanding; such methods constitute a branch of the discipline called **descriptive statistics.**

Often the individuals or objects studied by an investigator come from a much larger collection, and the researcher's interest goes beyond just data summarization. It is frequently the larger collection about which the investigator wishes to draw conclusions. The entire collection of individuals or objects about which information is desired is called the **population** of interest. A **sample** is a subset of the population selected in some prescribed manner for study. The second major branch of statistics, **inferential statistics,** involves generalizing from a sample to the population from which it was selected. This type of generalization involves some risk, since a conclusion about the population will be reached on the basis of available, but incomplete, information. It may happen that the sample is, in some sense, unrepresentative of the population from which it came. An important aspect in the development of inference involves quantifying the associated risks.

Considering some examples will help you to develop a preliminary appreciation for the scope and power of statistical methodology. We describe here three problems that can be handled using techniques to be presented in this text. First, suppose that a university has just implemented a new phone registration system. Students interact with the computer by entering information from a Touch-Tone® phone to select classes for the term. In order to assess student opinion regarding the effectiveness of the system, a survey of students is to be undertaken. Each student in a sample of 400 will be asked a variety of questions (such as the number of units received, and the number of attempts required to get a phone connection). The result of such a survey will be a rather large and unwieldy data set. In order to make sense out of the raw data and to describe student responses, it is desirable to summarize the data. This would also make the results more accessible to others.

Descriptive techniques to be presented in Chapters 2 and 3 could be used to accomplish this task. In addition, inferential methods from Chapters 9 and 10 could be employed in order to use the sample information to draw various conclusions about the experiences of all students at the university who used the registration system.

As a second example, consider a business application. Suppose that a publisher of college textbooks has two different machines that are used to bind the printed pages. One characteristic that affects the overall quality of the finished book is the strength of the binding. The publisher would like to determine if there is a significant difference between the two machines with respect to average binding strength. Strength could be measured for one sample of books bound by the first machine and for a second sample of books bound by the second machine. Hypothesis-testing techniques (to be introduced in Chapters 10, 11, and 12) could then be used to analyze the resulting data and provide the publisher with an answer to the question posed.

A final example comes from the discipline of forestry. When a fire occurs in a forested area, decisions must be made as to the best way to combat the fire. One possibility is to try to contain the fire by building a fire line. If building a fire line requires four hours, the decision as to where the line should be built involves making a prediction of how far the fire will spread during this period. Many factors must be taken into account, including wind speed, temperature, humidity, and time elapsed since the last rainfall. Regression techniques (Chapters 13 and 14) will enable us to develop a model for the prediction of fire spread using information available from past fires.

EXERCISES 1.1–1.7 SECTION 1.2

1.1 Give a brief definition of the terms *descriptive statistics* and *inferential statistics*.

1.2 Give a brief definition of the terms *population* and *sample.*

1.3 The student senate at a university with 15,000 students is interested in the proportion of students who favor a change in the grading system to allow for $+$ and $-$ grades (that is, $B-$, B, $B+$, rather than just B). Two hundred students are interviewed to determine their attitude toward this proposed change. What is the population of interest? What group of students constitutes the sample in this problem?

1.4 The supervisors of a rural county are interested in the proportion of property owners who support the construction of a sewer system. Because it is too costly to contact all 7000 property owners, a survey of 500 (selected at random) is undertaken. Describe the population and sample for this problem.

1.5 Representatives of the insurance industry wished to investigate the monetary loss due to damage to single-family dwellings in Pasadena, California, resulting from an earthquake that occurred on December 3, 1988. One hundred homes were selected for inspection from the set of all single-family homes in Pasadena. Describe the population and sample for this problem.

1.6 A consumer group conducts crash tests of new model cars. To determine the severity of damage to 1993 Mazda 626s resulting from a 10-mph crash into a concrete wall, six cars of this type are tested and the amount of damage is assessed. Describe the population and sample for this problem.

1.7 A building contractor has a chance to buy an odd lot of 5000 used bricks at an auction. She is interested in determining the proportion of bricks in the lot that are cracked and therefore unusable for her current project, but she does not have enough time to inspect all 5000 bricks. Instead, she checks 100 bricks to determine whether each is cracked. Describe the population and sample for this problem.

CHAPTER ONE SUMMARY OF KEY CONCEPTS AND FORMULAS

Term or Formula	Comment
Descriptive statistics	Numerical, graphical, and tabular methods for organizing and summarizing data.
Population	The entire collection of individuals or measurements about which information is desired.
Sample	A part of the population selected for study.
Inferential statistics	Methods for generalizing from a sample to the population from which the sample was selected.

References

Tanur, Judith, ed. *Statistics: A Guide to the Unknown.* Belmont, Calif.: Wadsworth, 1989. (Short articles by a number of well-known statisticians and users of statistics, all very nontechnical, on the application of statistics in various disciplines and subject areas.)

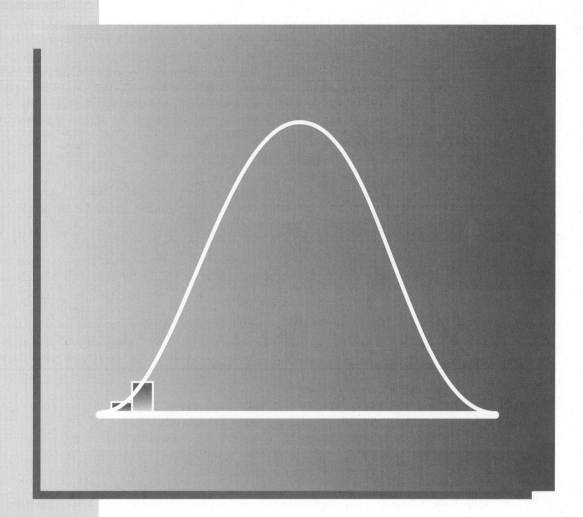

Tabular and Pictorial Methods for Describing Data

Ecologists have devoted much effort to studying range boundaries for various plant and animal populations. In particular, attempts have been made to identify factors that might explain how far north or south particular species are found. As part of one such study, the paper "Temperature and the Northern Distributions of Wintering Birds" (*Ecology* (1991):2274–2285) gave the accompanying body masses (in grams) for 50 different bird species that had previously been thought to have northern boundaries corresponding to a particular isotherm.

7.7	10.1	21.6	8.6	12.0	11.4	16.6	9.4	9.8	10.2
15.9	11.5	9.0	8.2	20.2	48.5	21.6	26.1	6.2	93.9
31.0	12.5	19.1	21.0	28.1	10.6	31.6	6.7	5.0	68.8
10.9	21.5	14.5	23.9	19.8	20.1	6.0	99.6	19.8	16.5
9.0	19.6	11.9	32.5	448.0	21.3	17.4	36.9	34.0	41.0

What are the most interesting features of this data set? In particular, can we identify a typical or representative mass? Are the data values highly concentrated about that typical value or do they spread out a great deal? Are there any unusually small or large masses relative to the remaining observations? What percentage of the masses exceed 50 gm, what percentage are between 10 and 20 gm, and so on? In this chapter we show how such data can be summarized in a table or picture so that questions of the sort just posed can be addressed and directions for further analysis suggested. These summary techniques are applied to the bird mass data in the Chapter Encore.

Introduction

When we make observations on or record characteristics of individuals or objects in some collection, the result is a body of data. Sometimes data is gathered in order to address specific issues and questions; on other occasions, the nature of the information contained in a set of data may not be obvious to those who requested or gathered the data. In either case, an important first step in extracting information and gaining insight is to organize the data and perhaps summarize it so that its salient features are more clearly revealed. Methods for organization and summarization depend on the nature of the data in hand, so we will first distinguish between several different types of data. The remainder of the chapter introduces some useful tabular and pictorial methods for describing and exploring data.

2.1 Types of Data

The individuals or objects in any particular group typically possess many attributes that might be studied. Consider as an example a group of students currently enrolled in a statistics course. One attribute is the brand of calculator owned by each student (Sharp, Hewlett-Packard, Casio, and so on). Another attribute of potential interest is the number of courses for which each student is registered (1, 2, 3, . . .), and yet another is the distance from the university to each student's permanent residence. In this example *calculator brand* is a categorical attribute, since each student's response to the query "What brand of calculator do you own?" is a category. The collection of responses from all these students forms a **categorical data set.** The other two attributes, *number of units* and *distance,* are both numerical in nature. Determining the value of such a numerical attribute (by counting or measuring) for each student results in a **numerical data set.**

EXAMPLE 2.1

A sample of 15 people who belong to a certain tennis club is selected. Each one is then asked which brand of racket he or she uses. The resulting set of responses is

{Head,   Prince,   Prince,   Wilson,   Yonex,   Head,
    Yamaha,   Head,   Head,   Prince,   Yamaha,   Kennex,
    Prince,   Wilson,   Yonex}[1]

This is a categorical data set.

EXAMPLE 2.2

A sample of 20 automobiles of a certain type is selected and the fuel efficiency (miles per gallon, or mi/gal) is determined for each one. The resulting numerical data set is

{29.8,   27.6,   28.3,   28.7,   27.9,   29.9,   30.1,   28.0,   28.7,   27.9,
   28.5,   29.5,   27.2,   26.9,   28.4,   27.9,   28.0,   30.0,   29.6,   29.1}

In both of the preceding examples, the data sets consisted of observations (categorical responses or numbers) on a single attribute. Such data sets are called *univariate.*

[1] We will often use braces to enclose the members of a set.

> **DEFINITION**
>
> A data set consisting of observations on a single attribute is a **univariate data set.** A univariate data set is **categorical** (or **qualitative**) if the individual observations are categorical responses; it is **numerical** (or **quantitative**) if the observations are numbers.

In some studies, attention focuses simultaneously on two different attributes. For example, both the height (in.) and weight (lb) might be recorded for each individual in a group. The resulting data set consists of pairs of numbers, such as (68, 146). This is called a **bivariate data set. Multivariate data** results from obtaining a category or value for each of two or more attributes (so bivariate data is a special case of multivariate data): for example, multivariate data would result from determining height, weight, pulse rate, and systolic blood pressure for each individual in a group. Much of this book will focus on methods for analyzing univariate data. In the last several chapters we consider briefly the analysis of some bivariate and multivariate data.

Two Types of Numerical Data

With numerical data, it is useful to make a further distinction. Visualize a number line (Figure 2.1) for locating values of the numerical attribute being studied. To every possible number (2, 3.125, -8.12976, etc.) there corresponds exactly one point on the number line. Now suppose that the attribute of interest is the number of cylinders of an automobile engine. The possible values of 4, 6, and 8 are identified in Figure 2.2(a) by the dots at the points marked 4, 6, and 8. These possible values are isolated from one another on the line; around any possible value we can place an interval that is small enough so that no other possible value is included in the interval. On the other hand, the line segment in Figure 2.2(b) identifies a plausible set of possible values for quarter-mile time. Here the possible values comprise an entire interval on the number line, and no possible value is isolated from the other possible values.

FIGURE 2.1
A number line

FIGURE 2.2
Possible values of a variable
(a) Number of cylinders
(b) Quarter-mile time

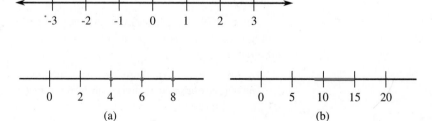

> **DEFINITION**
>
> Numerical data is **discrete** if the possible values are isolated points on the number line. Numerical data is **continuous** if the set of possible values forms an entire interval on the number line.

Discrete data usually arises when each observation is determined by counting (the number of classes for which a student is registered, the number of petals on a certain type of flower, and so on).

EXAMPLE 2.3

The number of telephone calls per day to a drug hotline is recorded for 12 days. The resulting data set is

$$3 \quad 0 \quad 4 \quad 3 \quad 1 \quad 0 \quad 6 \quad 2 \quad 0 \quad 0 \quad 1 \quad 2$$

Possible values for the *number of calls* are 0, 1, 2, 3, . . .; these are isolated points on the number line, so we have a sample consisting of discrete numerical data.

The sample of fuel efficiencies in Example 2.2 is an example of continuous data. A car's fuel efficiency could be 27.0, 27.13, 27.12796, or any other value in an entire interval. Other examples of continuous data arise when task completion times are observed, body temperatures are recorded, or packages are weighed. In general, data is continuous when observations involve making measurements, as opposed to counting.

In practice, measuring instruments do not have infinite accuracy. Thus possible measured values do not form a continuum on the number line. The distinction between discrete and continuous data will nevertheless be important in our discussion of probability models.

EXERCISES 2.1–2.4   SECTION 2.1

2.1   Classify each of the following attributes as either categorical or numerical. For those that are numerical, determine whether they are discrete or continuous.
  a. Number of students in a class of 35 who turn in a term paper before the due date
  b. Sex of the next baby born at a particular hospital
  c. Amount of fluid (oz) dispensed by a machine used to fill bottles with soda pop
  d. Thickness of the gelatin coating of a vitamin E capsule
  e. Birth classification (only child, first born, middle child, last born) of a math major

2.2   Classify each of the following attributes as either categorical or numerical. For those that are numerical, determine whether they are discrete or continuous.
   a. Brand of personal computer purchased by a customer
   b. State of birth for someone born in the United States
   c. Price of a textbook
   d. Concentration of a contaminant (micrograms/cm^3, or μg/cm^3) in a water sample
   e. Zip code (Think carefully about this one.)
   f. Actual weight of coffee in a 1-lb can

2.3   For the following numerical attributes, state whether each is discrete or continuous.
   a. The number of checks received by a grocery store during a given month that bounce
   b. The amount by which a 1-lb package of ground beef decreases in weight (because of moisture loss) before purchase
   c. The number of New York Yankees during a given year who will not play for the Yankees the following year
   d. The number of students in a class of 35 who have purchased a used copy of the textbook
   e. The length of a 1-year-old rattlesnake
   f. The altitude of a location in California selected randomly by throwing a dart at a map of the state
   g. The distance from the left edge at which a 12-in. plastic ruler snaps when bent sufficiently to cause a break
   h. The price per gallon paid by the next customer to buy gas at a particular station

2.4   For each of the following situations, give some possible data values that might arise from making the observations described.
   a. The country of manufacture for each of the next ten automobiles to pass through a given intersection is noted.
   b. The grade point average for each of the 15 seniors in a statistics class is determined.
   c. The number of gas pumps in use at each of 20 gas stations at a particular time is determined.
   d. The actual net weight of each of 12 bags of fertilizer having a labeled weight of 50 lb is determined.
   e. Fifteen different radio stations are monitored during a 1-hr period and the amount of time devoted to commercials is determined for each one.
   f. The brand of breakfast cereal purchased by each of 16 customers is noted.
   g. The number of defective tires is determined for each of the next 20 automobiles stopped for speeding on a certain highway.

2.2   Stem-and-Leaf Displays

Some preliminary organization of a data set will often reveal useful information and open up paths of inquiry. A **stem-and-leaf display** is an effective way to organize numerical data without expending much effort. Each observation is regarded as consisting of two pieces. One or more of the leading digits make up the **stem,** and the trailing digit or digits constitute the **leaf.** For example, the data set might consist of verbal SAT scores (whole numbers between 200 and 800). One choice of stems is the set of leading digits: 2, 3, 4, 5, 6, 7, 8. Then 641 has stem 6 (so the stem unit is hundreds) and leaf 41 (the leaf unit is ones, the place value of the digit on the far right). If all scores in the data set were between 500 and 599 (a very homogeneous group), a more sensible choice for stem is the first two digits. Thus 538 would have stem 53 (unit = tens, since the far right digit, 3, occupies the tens place) and leaf 8 (unit = ones).

STEPS FOR CONSTRUCTING A STEM-AND-LEAF DISPLAY

1. Select one or more leading digits for the stem values. The trailing digit or digits become the leaves.
2. List possible stem values in a vertical column.
3. Record the leaf for every observation beside the corresponding stem value.
4. Indicate the units for stems and leaves someplace in the display.

EXAMPLE 2.4

Americans are becoming increasingly concerned with the incidence of crime, and voluminous data is being collected to document the magnitude of the problem. Table 2.1 displays data on number of rapes per 100,000 residents for the 50 states and the District of Columbia (*The World Almanac,* 1992).

TABLE 2.1 Rapes per 100,000 residents

AL	32.9	IL	39.4	MT	24.4	RI	24.7
AK	72.9	IN	37.9	NB	30.0	SC	53.7
AZ	40.9	IA	18.4	NV	62.2	SD	34.3
AR	43.3	KS	40.4	NH	31.3	TN	49.5
CA	42.6	KY	29.0	NJ	29.8	TX	51.5
CO	46.2	LA	42.2	NM	49.7	UT	37.8
CT	27.9	ME	19.7	NY	29.8	VT	25.9
DE	88.1	MD	45.7	NC	34.3	VA	31.0
DC	49.9	MA	33.7	ND	17.8	WA	64.0
FL	52.4	MI	77.6	OH	46.8	WV	23.6
GA	53.6	MN	34.0	OK	47.0	WI	20.7
HI	32.5	MS	44.1	OR	46.9	WY	29.5
ID	27.3	MO	32.5	PA	25.8		

A good choice for stem is the leading (tens) digit. The leaf of an observation then consists of both the ones and tenths digits. For example,

Alabama: 32.9 → stem = 3, leaf = 29

Delaware: 88.1 → stem = 8, leaf = 81

The leaves are entered in the display of Figure 2.3 in the order given in Table 2.1: first 29 beside the stem value 3, then 29 beside the stem 7, and so on (commas are needed to separate successive leaves when each leaf consists of more than one digit).

FIGURE 2.3
Stem-and-leaf display of
crime rates for rape

1	84, 97, 78
2	79, 73, 90, 44, 98, 98, 58, 47, 59, 36, 07, 95
3	29, 25, 94, 79, 37, 40, 25, 00, 13, 43, 43, 78, 10
4	09, 33, 26, 62, 99, 04, 22, 57, 41, 97, 68, 70, 69, 95
5	24, 36, 37, 15
6	22, 40
7	29, 76
8	81

Stem: Tens
Leaf: Ones and tenths

The display shows that the smallest and largest values are 17.8 and 88.1, respectively. This latter value seems especially large relative to the other 50 rates. (Why is Delaware so unusual?) Most values are between 20 and 65, and a "typical," or "representative," value is in the high 30s.

A stem-and-leaf display is useful for locating a central (typical) value and for assessing the extent to which observations spread out about the center. **Outliers** (unusually small or large values) are easy to spot, and regions of high concentration become apparent.

Repeated Stems

Sometimes a natural choice of stems gives a display in which too many observations are concentrated in just a few stems. A more informative picture may be obtained by writing each stem value twice, once for low leaves and once for high leaves.

EXAMPLE 2.5

The paper "The Acid Rain Controversy: The Limits of Confidence" (*Amer. Statistician* (1983):385–394) presented data on average sulfur dioxide emission rates (lb/million Btu) for industrial and utility boilers in 47 states (data from Alaska, Hawaii, and Idaho was not given). A stem-and-leaf display of the data appears in Figure 2.4. There are only five stems, and each leaf is a single digit (tenths).

FIGURE 2.4
Stem-and-leaf display of
emission rates

0	3 6 4 5 2 7 2 7 7 5 1 6 9 6
1	5 5 3 2 2 0 4 0 7 5 5 4 9 0 7 8 7 8 4
2	3 7 2 5 7 9 1 9
3	8 6 4 7
4	2 5

Stem: Ones
Leaf: Tenths

Figure 2.5 displays the same data using stems 0L, 0H, 1L, 1H, . . . , 4L, and 4H. Any observation whose leaf was 0, 1, 2, 3, or 4 (low) in the original display goes in the corresponding L row, and observations with leaves 5, 6, 7, 8, or 9 are in H rows. This second display shows quite nicely how the 47 observations are distributed along the measurement scale.

FIGURE 2.5
Display of emission rates using repeated stems

Stem		Leaves									
0L	3	4	2	2	1						
0H	6	5	7	7	7	5	6	9	6		
1L	3	2	2	0	4	0	4	0	4		
1H	5	5	7	5	5	9	7	8	7	8	
2L	3	2	1								
2H	7	5	7	9	9						
3L	4										
3H	8	6	7								
4L	2										
4H	5										

Stem: Ones
Leaf: Tenths

Computer-Generated Stem-and-Leaf Displays

The computer is a very powerful tool for doing statistical analysis, because it can perform routine data organization and arithmetic calculations many times as fast as these tasks can be done by hand. Most such analysis is done using prepared packages of statistical computer programs. With a package of this sort, the user takes advantage of a program that has already been written. It is necessary only to enter the data properly and then give the computer a command that causes the desired operation to be performed. The most frequently used packages are MINITAB, BMDP (Biomedical Computer Programs), SAS (Statistical Analysis System), and SPSS (Statistical Package for the Social Sciences). Almost all the methods of analysis we discuss in this book can be carried out using any one of these four as well as many other packages.

Figure 2.6 pictures a MINITAB stem-and-leaf display for the emissions data of Example 2.5. Repeated stems were used, and within each stem the leaves were automatically ordered from smallest to largest.

Comparative Displays

Frequently an analyst has two groups of data and wishes to see if they differ in some fundamental way. A comparative stem-and-leaf display, in which the leaves from one group extend to the right of the stem values and those from the other group to the left, can give preliminary visual impressions and insights.

FIGURE 2.6
A computer-generated display using MINITAB

```
Stem-and-leaf of EMISS     N = 47
Leaf unit = 0.10
0      12234
0      556667779
1      000223444
1      5555777889
2      123
2      57799
3      4
3      678
4      2
4      5
```

EXAMPLE 2.6

The Institute of Nutrition of Central America and Panama (INCAP) has carried out extensive dietary studies in various parts of Central America. One such study reported on in the paper "The Blood Viscosity of Various Socioeconomic Groups in Guatemala" (*Amer. J. of Clinical Nutrition* (Nov. 1964):303–307) determined

FIGURE 2.7
Comparative stem-and-leaf display of serum total cholesterol values
(I) Urban Guatemalans
(II) Low-income rural Indian Guatemalans

```
I                                            9 ‖ 5
                                            10 ‖ 8 8
                                            11 ‖ 5 4                         II
                                            12 ‖ 9 9 4
                                  3   4     13 ‖ 5 1 6 6 1 9
                                            14 ‖ 0 6 4 5 2 3 8 3 4 2
                                      5     15 ‖ 2 8 7 2 5 8
                                            16 ‖ 6 5 2
                            9  5  0     17 ‖ 5 4 3 2 1
                         1  4  8  9     18 ‖ 0 9 1
                         9  7  0  6     19 ‖ 2 4 7
             1  5  4  5  5  0  1  0  6  20 ‖ 4
                               4  7     21 ‖
                      2  7  8  7  2     22 ‖ 3 6 0
                         4  6  4  9     23 ‖ 1
                         2  9  4  1     24 ‖
                                  2     25 ‖
                                        26 ‖
                               9  3     27 ‖
      HI: 330            4  4  4  28 ‖
```

Stem: Hundreds and tens
Leaf: Ones

values of various physiological characteristics for several groups of Guatemalans. The stem-and-leaf display pictured in Figure 2.7 gives serum total cholesterol values (mg/L) both for a sample of high-income urban individuals and for a sample of low-income rural Indians. The first sample contains one value, 330, that is far above the rest of the data. Rather than extend the stems to capture this value at the bottom of the display, it is marked at the bottom with the symbol "HI." This is routinely done in computer-generated displays for unusually high or low values.

A first impression is one of great variability in cholesterol values when each sample is considered separately. For low-income rural Indians (group II), values run from 95 to 231, a range of $231 - 95 = 136$. Disregarding for the moment the one outlying value on the high end of the display, the range for high-income urban individuals is $284 - 133 = 151$, not greatly different from the range for group II. A reasonable central value for group I is one in the low 200s (a stem of 20), and for group II a central value would be in the high 140s or low 150s. Notice that the shapes of the two sides of the display are rather similar, each rising to a peak near a central value and then declining. Roughly speaking, the main difference between the two groups is in location. If we were to push the display for group II down five or six stem values (50 or 60 cholesterol units), the two halves would be quite similar. The suggested explanation for this difference in location is the presence of more fats in group I diets. A formal statistical analysis would yield more precise information on the size of the shift in location.

EXERCISES 2.5–2.11 SECTION 2.2

2.5 The Bureau of Justice's *Statistics Bulletin* on jail inmates for 1982 reported the following inmate population sizes for 40 of the smaller federal prisons:

644	512	448	730	401	450	419	647	792	885
501	458	755	569	417	405	509	440	402	624
603	599	791	407	433	559	777	856	492	400
484	554	634	553	723	565	424	417	524	468

Using stems 4, 5, 6, 7, and 8, construct a stem-and-leaf display for this data.

2.6 Consider the accompanying batch of exam scores. First construct a stem-and-leaf display in which each stem occurs just once. Then construct a display that repeats each stem. What feature of the data is highlighted by this second display?

74	89	80	93	64	67	72	70	66	85	89	81	81	71
74	82	85	63	72	81	81	95	84	81	80	70	69	66
60	83	85	98	84	68	90	82	69	72	87	88		

2.7   The accompanying observations are yardages for a sample of golf courses recently listed by *Golf Magazine* as being among the most challenging in the United States. Construct a stem-and-leaf display, and explain why your choice of stems seems preferable to any of the other possible choices.

6526	6770	6936	6770	6583	6464	7005	6927
6790	7209	7040	6850	6700	6614	7022	6506
6527	6470	6900	6605	6873	6798	6745	7280
7131	6435	6694	6433	6870	7169	7011	7168
6713	7051	6904	7105	7165	7050	7113	6890

2.8   Soil pH, a measure of the extent to which soil is acidic or basic, is one characteristic that plays an important role in the suitability of soil to support vegetation at mine reclamation sites. The article "A Dual-Buffer Titration Method for Lime Requirement of Acid Minesoils" (*J. Environ. Qual.* (1988):452–456) reported the following data on pH for 26 minesoil specimens.

3.59	4.36	3.86	4.25	4.46	4.53	2.62	6.79	6.49
4.27	3.84	4.78	4.65	2.91	3.90	6.00	2.83	3.58
4.43	4.58	4.75	3.49	4.11	3.58	5.21	4.41	

Construct a stem-and-leaf display. Based on your display, does the data set appear to contain any outliers (observations far removed from the bulk of the data)?

2.9   The accompanying values are rental rates per foot for boat storage at the 19 marinas in Marina del Rey (Calif.) and the 17 marinas at the Los Angeles–Long Beach Harbor (Source: *Los Angeles Times*, June 5, 1983).

Marina Del Rey				Los Angeles–Long Beach			
$6.37	$6.60	$6.27	$6.49	$4.60	$4.75	$4.70	$8.75
$6.64	$6.82	$7.16	$6.45	$4.50	$5.40	$6.00	$6.00
$5.60	$5.95	$4.50	$6.60	$6.50	$6.00	$5.00	$5.00
$6.00	$6.82	$7.04	$5.30	$5.50	$4.35	$4.50	$5.20
$7.05	$7.05	$6.96		$4.95			

Construct a comparative stem-and-leaf display for rent per foot for the two areas. What conclusions can you draw from the stem-and-leaf display concerning differences between the two locations?

2.10 The accompanying data on elementary school student–teacher ratios for the 50 states and the District of Columbia appeared in the September 1987 issue of *NEA Today*.

Student-teacher ratios								
AL	19.84	IL	17.95	MT	15.70	RI	15.35
AK	20.83	IN	18.63	NB	15.18	SC	17.75
AZ	20.49	IA	15.83	NV	20.46	SD	15.57
AR	18.15	KS	15.46	NH	15.89	TN	19.85
CA	22.88	KY	18.66	NJ	14.86	TX	17.52
CO	18.19	LA	18.24	NM	18.01	UT	24.04
CT	13.96	ME	16.27	NY	14.66	VT	14.07
DE	16.05	MD	17.69	NC	18.87	VA	16.39
DC	15.34	MA	14.80	ND	15.02	WA	20.72
FL	17.17	MI	20.90	OH	18.65	WV	15.34
GA	18.57	MN	17.31	OK	16.47	WI	16.62
HI	19.68	MS	18.57	OR	17.41	WY	13.45
ID	20.69	MO	16.38	PA	16.40		

a. Construct a stem-and-leaf display. What is a "representative" student-teacher ratio? Does the data set contain any outliers?

b. What percentage of the states have a ratio exceeding 20?

2.11 The Los Angeles Board of Education has enacted a policy that prohibits students who do not have at least a C average from participating in extracurricular activities. The *Los Angeles Times* (May 17, 1983) reported the percentages of ineligible students for 47 Los Angeles high schools. Figures were reported separately for athletes and nonathletes.

Percent ineligible									
Athletes	27	12	15	15	21	15	17	14	21	27
Nonathletes	24	25	48	17	3	3	14	18	52	22
Athletes	15	10	36	19	29	35	16	13	17	18
Nonathletes	4	14	29	18	13	17	14	23	25	15
Athletes	13	28	24	40	35	10	16	37	26	18
Nonathletes	15	6	34	48	45	12	38	28	29	34
Athletes	8	21	17	21	20	15	39	37	10	23
Nonathletes	14	18	17	7	24	34	44	13	16	14
Athletes	14	12	16	8	29	17	9			
Nonathletes	15	20	18	9	30	25	8			

Construct a comparative stem-and-leaf display of the percent of ineligible students for athletes and nonathletes. Based on your stem-and-leaf display, do you think there is evidence that the percentage of disqualified students tends to be smaller for nonathletes than for athletes? Justify your answer.

2.3   Frequency Distributions

A stem-and-leaf display is not always an effective summary technique. It cannot be used for categorical data. In addition, a stem-and-leaf display is unwieldy when the data set contains a great many observations. A frequency distribution is useful for summarizing even a very large data set in a compact fashion.

Frequency Distributions for Categorical Data

A **frequency distribution** is a table that displays the categories, frequencies, and relative frequencies. The **frequency** for a particular category is the number of observed responses that fall into that category. The corresponding **relative frequency** is the fraction or proportion of observed responses in the category. Suppose, for example, that 26 of the 80 tennis players in a sample use a Wilson racket. Then the frequency for the category *Wilson* is 26, and the relative frequency is $26/80 = .325$. (Thus 32.5% of the observed responses are Wilson.)

EXAMPLE 2.7

The increasing emphasis on exercise has resulted in a near-avalanche of sports-related injuries. Consider the accompanying data set in which the type of injury for each of 82 incidents was recorded (the resulting percentages agree closely with those given for a larger sample in the paper "Profile of Sport/Leisure Injuries Treated at Emergency Rooms of Urban Hospitals" (*Canadian J. of Sports Sciences* (1991):99–102)). The following coding is used:

Sp = sprain	Co = contusion	F = fracture
St = strain	L = laceration	Ch = chronic
Di = dislocation	Cn = concussion	De = dental

F	Sp	Sp	Co	F	L	F	Co	Co	Ch	Sp	Sp	F	Sp	St	Di	F
Co	Co	Cn	Sp	F	Sp	Co	St	L	Sp	Co	Co	St	F	F	Sp	Co
F	Ch	F	De	L	Sp	Sp	Sp	St	Co	Co	Di	St	F	Cn	F	Co
Sp	Sp	Co	Co	F	Sp	L	Sp	Sp	F	Ch	Co	Sp	St	St	Co	L
Sp	St	Ch	Di	F	Co	F	St	L	Sp	Sp	Co	Sp	F			

The frequency distribution appears as Table 2.2. A tally column has been included so that only one pass through the data is necessary (the first tally mark in the fracture row, the second and third in the sprain row, and so on). Most of the injuries (almost 70%) are of the first three types.

TABLE 2.2   Frequency distribution for type of injury

Category	Tally	Frequency	Relative frequency
1. Sprain	~~卌 卌 卌 卌~~ 卌 卌 卌 卌 ‖	22	.268
2. Contusion	卌 卌 卌 ‖‖	18	.220
3. Fracture	卌 卌 卌 ‖	17	.207
4. Strain	卌 ‖‖‖	9	.110
5. Laceration	卌 ‖	6	.073
6. Chronic	‖‖‖	4	.049
7. Dislocation	‖‖	3	.037
8. Concussion	‖	2	.024
9. Dental	‖	1	.012
		82	1.000

The sum of relative frequencies should be 1, but there may be a slight discrepancy due to rounding.

Frequency Distributions for Discrete Numerical Data

Discrete numerical data almost always results from counting. In such cases, each observation is a whole number. If, for example, possible values are 0, 1, 2, 3, . . . , then these are listed in a column. A running tally is kept as a single pass is made through the data. The number of tally marks beside each value gives the frequency of that value. Dividing each frequency by the total number of observations gives the corresponding relative frequency.

EXAMPLE 2.8

A sample of 708 bus drivers employed by public corporations was selected and the number of traffic accidents in which each was involved during a 4-year period was determined ("Application of Discrete Distribution Theory to the Study of Noncommunicable Events in Medical Epidemiology," *Random Counts in Biomedical and Social Sciences,* G. P. Patil, ed. University Park, PA: Penn. State Univ. Press, 1970). A listing of the 708 sample observations would look something like this:

3,   0,   6,   0,   0,   2,   1,   4,   1, . . . , 6,   0,   2

The frequency distribution (Table 2.3) shows that 117 of the 708 drivers had no accidents, a relative frequency of 117/708 = .165 (or 16.5%). Similarly, the proportion of sampled drivers with one accident is .222 (or 22.2%). The largest sample observation was 11 (presumably this driver was not at fault for most of these).

TABLE 2.3   Frequency distribution for number of accidents by bus drivers

Number of accidents	Frequency	Relative frequency
0	117	.165
1	157	.222
2	158	.223
3	115	.162
4	78	.110
5	44	.062
6	21	.030
7	7	.010
8	6	.008
9	1	.001
10	3	.004
11	1	.001
	708	.998

We can easily calculate other quantities of interest from the relative frequencies.

$$\text{(i)} \left(\begin{array}{c} \text{proportion with at} \\ \text{most 1 accident} \end{array} \right) = \left(\begin{array}{c} \text{proportion} \\ \text{with 0} \end{array} \right) + \left(\begin{array}{c} \text{proportion} \\ \text{with 1} \end{array} \right)$$

$$= .165 + .222$$

$$= .387 \quad \text{(or 38.7\%)}$$

$$\text{(ii)} \left(\begin{array}{c} \text{proportion with at} \\ \text{least 6 accidents} \end{array} \right) = \left(\begin{array}{c} \text{proportion} \\ \text{with 6} \end{array} \right) + \left(\begin{array}{c} \text{proportion} \\ \text{with 7} \end{array} \right) + \cdots + \left(\begin{array}{c} \text{proportion} \\ \text{with 11} \end{array} \right)$$

$$= .030 + .010 + \cdots + .001$$

$$= .054 \quad \text{(or 5.4\%)}$$

$$\text{(iii)} \left(\begin{array}{c} \text{proportion with} \\ \text{between 4 and 7} \\ \text{(inclusive)} \end{array} \right) = \left(\begin{array}{c} \text{proportion} \\ \text{with 4} \end{array} \right) + \cdots + \left(\begin{array}{c} \text{proportion} \\ \text{with 7} \end{array} \right)$$

$$= .110 + .062 + .030 + .010$$

$$= .212$$

Frequently a data set contains a few large values that are significantly separated from the bulk of the observations. For example, consider adding two more drivers, one with 16 accidents and one with 21 accidents, to the 708 drivers of Example 2.8. Rather than list individual count values all the way to 21, we might stop listing at 10 and add one further category, *at least 11* (often written ≥ 11). Then 3 of the 710 observations (the 11, the 16, and the 21) would belong in this category. Table 2.4 presents the resulting computer-generated frequency distribution.

TABLE 2.4 Computer-generated frequency distribution for number of accidents (using SPSS)

Category label	Code	Absolute freq.	Relative freq. (PCT)
0	0	117	16.5
1	1	157	22.1
2	2	158	22.3
3	3	115	16.2
4	4	78	11.0
5	5	44	6.2
6	6	21	3.0
7	7	7	1.0
8	8	6	.8
9	9	1	.1
10	10	3	.4
AT LEAST 11	11	3	.4
	TOTAL	710	100.0

Frequency Distributions for Continuous Data

The difficulty with continuous data, such as observations on reaction time (seconds) or fuel efficiency (miles per gallon), is that there are no natural categories. The way out of this dilemma is to define our own categories. For fuel efficiency data, suppose that we mark off some intervals on a horizontal miles-per-gallon measurement axis, as pictured in Figure 2.8. Each data value should fall in exactly one of these intervals. If the smallest observation were 25.3 and the largest were 29.8, we might use intervals of width .5, with the first one starting at 25.0 and the last one ending at 30.0. The resulting intervals are called **class intervals,** or just *classes.* The classes play the same role that the categories played earlier, with frequencies and relative frequencies tabulated as before.

FIGURE 2.8
Suitable class intervals for miles-per-gallon data

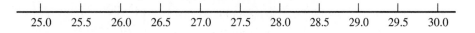

There is one further difficulty: where should we place an observation such as 27.0, which falls on a boundary between classes? Our convention will be to define intervals so that such an observation is placed in the upper rather than the lower class interval. Thus, in our frequency distribution, a typical class will be 26.5–<27.0, where the symbol < is a substitute for the phrase *less than.* The observation 27.0 would then fall in the class 27.0–<27.5.

EXAMPLE 2.9

The trace element zinc is an important dietary constituent partly because it aids in the maintenance of proper immune response. The accompanying data on zinc intake (mg/MJ) for a sample of 40 patients with rheumatoid arthritis was read from a graph in the paper "Plasma Zinc and Copper Concentrations in Rheumatoid Arthritis: Influence of Dietary Factors and Disease Activity" (*American J. Clinical Nutrition* (1991):1082–1086).

8.0	12.9	13.0	8.9	10.1	7.3	11.1	10.9	6.2	8.1	8.8	10.4	15.7	13.6
19.3	9.9	8.5	11.1	10.7	8.8	10.7	6.8	7.4	4.8	11.8	13.0	9.5	8.1
6.9	11.5	11.2	13.6	4.9	18.8	15.7	10.8	10.7	11.5	16.1	9.9		

The smallest observation is 4.8 and the largest is 19.3. It seems reasonable to start the first class interval at 3.0 and let each interval have a width of 3.0. This gives as class intervals

$$3–<6 \qquad 6–<9 \qquad 9–<12 \qquad 12–<15 \qquad 15–<18 \qquad 18–<21$$

Table 2.5 displays the resulting frequency distribution (the tally column is usually omitted).

TABLE 2.5 Frequency distribution for zinc intake (mg/MJ)

Class interval	Tally	Frequency	Relative frequency
1. 3–<6	II	2	.050
2. 6–<9	⊮ ⊮ II	12	.300
3. 9–<12	⊮ ⊮ ⊮ I	16	.400
4. 12–<15	⊮	5	.125
5. 15–<18	III	3	.075
6. 18–<21	II	2	.050
		40	1.000

Various relative frequencies can again be added together to yield other interesting information. For example,

$$\begin{pmatrix} \text{proportion of} \\ \text{individuals with} \\ \text{intake} < 12 \end{pmatrix} = \begin{pmatrix} \text{proportion in} \\ \text{first class} \end{pmatrix} + \begin{pmatrix} \text{proportion in} \\ \text{second class} \end{pmatrix} + \begin{pmatrix} \text{proportion in} \\ \text{third class} \end{pmatrix}$$

$$= .050 + .300 + .400$$
$$= .750 \quad (75\%)$$

and

$$\begin{pmatrix} \text{proportion of} \\ \text{individuals with} \\ \text{intake between} \\ 6 \text{ and } 15 \end{pmatrix} = \begin{pmatrix} \text{proportion in} \\ \text{second class} \end{pmatrix} + \begin{pmatrix} \text{proportion in} \\ \text{third class} \end{pmatrix} + \begin{pmatrix} \text{proportion in} \\ \text{fourth class} \end{pmatrix}$$

$$= .300 + .400 + .125$$
$$= .825 \quad (82.5\%)$$

There are no strict guidelines for selecting either the number of class intervals or the interval lengths. Using a few relatively wide intervals will bunch the data, whereas using a great many relatively narrow intervals may spread the data over too many intervals, so that no interval contains more than a few observations. Neither type of distribution will give an informative picture of how values are distributed over the range of measurement. Generally speaking, with a small amount of data there should be relatively few intervals, perhaps between five and ten, whereas with a large amount of data, a distribution based on 15 to 20 (or even more) intervals is often recommended. Two people making reasonable and similar choices for the number of intervals, their width, and the starting point of the first interval should obtain very similar summaries of the data.

Class Intervals of Unequal Width

Figure 2.9 pictures a data set in which there are a great many observations concentrated near one another at the center of the set and just a few outlying, or stray, values both below and above the main body of data. If a frequency distribution is based on short intervals of equal width, a great many intervals will be required to capture all observations, and many of them will contain no observations (zero frequency). On the other hand, only a few wide intervals will capture all values, but then most of the observations will be grouped into a very few intervals. Neither choice will yield an informative distribution. In such a situation it is best to use a few relatively wide class intervals at the ends of the distribution and some shorter intervals in the middle.

FIGURE 2.9
Three different choices of
class intervals for a
data set with outliers
(a) Many short intervals
of equal width
(b) A few wide intervals
of equal width
(c) Intervals of unequal width

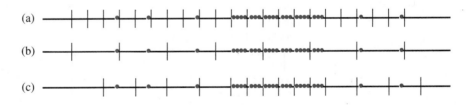

Cumulative Relative Frequencies

Suppose that the first four class intervals in a frequency distribution are 0–<25, 25–<50, 50–<75, 75–<100, with corresponding relative frequencies .05, .10, .12, and .18. Consider the cumulative sums of these relative frequencies.

$$.05 = \text{proportion of observations less than } 25$$
$$.05 + .10 = .15 = \text{proportion of observations less than } 50$$
$$.05 + .10 + .12 = .27 = \text{proportion of observations less than } 75$$
$$.05 + .10 + .12 + .18 = .45 = \text{proportion of observations less than } 100$$

Each such cumulative sum is the proportion of observations less than the upper limit of the corresponding class interval. These cumulative sums are called **cumulative relative frequencies**; they are often displayed in a column next to the relative frequencies. Notice that each cumulative relative frequency is the sum of the previous one and the current relative frequency. For example,

$$\begin{pmatrix} \text{fourth cumulative} \\ \text{relative frequency} \end{pmatrix} = \begin{pmatrix} \text{third cumulative} \\ \text{relative frequency} \end{pmatrix} + \begin{pmatrix} \text{fourth relative} \\ \text{frequency} \end{pmatrix}$$

$$= .27 + .18$$

$$= .45$$

EXAMPLE 2.10

The strength of welds used in aircraft construction has been of great concern to aeronautical engineers in recent years. Table 2.6 gives a frequency distribution for shear strengths (lb) of ultrasonic spot welds made on a certain type of alclad sheet ("Comparison of Properties of Joints Prepared by Ultrasonic Welding and Other Means," *J. Aircraft* (1983):552–556). The cumulative relative frequencies are .01, .01 + .02 = .03, .03 + .09 = .12, .12 + .14 = .26, and so on.

TABLE 2.6   Frequency distribution with cumulative relative frequencies

Class interval	Frequency	Relative frequency	Cumulative relative frequency
4000–<4200	1	.01	.01
4200–<4400	2	.02	.03
4400–<4600	9	.09	.12
4600–<4800	14	.14	.26
4800–<5000	17	.17	.43
5000–<5200	22	.22	.65
5200–<5400	20	.20	.85
5400–<5600	7	.07	.92
5600–<5800	7	.07	.99
5800–<6000	1	.01	1.00
	100	1.00	

Thus the proportion of welds with strength values less than 5400 is .85 (that is, 85% of the observations are below 5400). Notice also that any particular relative frequency is the difference between two consecutive cumulative relative frequencies. For example,

$$\begin{pmatrix} \text{relative frequency} \\ \text{for 5000–<5200} \end{pmatrix} = \begin{pmatrix} \text{cum. rel. freq.} \\ \text{for 5000–<5200} \end{pmatrix} - \begin{pmatrix} \text{cum. rel. freq.} \\ \text{for 4800–<5000} \end{pmatrix}$$

$$= .65 - .43$$

$$= .22$$

Sometimes a published article will contain only cumulative relative frequencies, from which the relative frequencies themselves are easily calculated.

Cumulative relative frequencies can also be computed and displayed in a frequency distribution for discrete data.

EXERCISES 2.12–2.24   SECTION 2.3

2.12   Each of 25 students was asked to identify the dictionary he or she uses. The resulting responses were as follows (with A = American Heritage, F = Funk and Wagnalls, M = Macmillan, R = Random House, W = Webster's).

A	R	A	W	W	M	W	R	R	F	A	W	R
R	R	M	W	A	W	R	R	F	W	W	A	

a. Construct a relative frequency distribution for the type of dictionary used.
b. Suppose that the 25 students polled constitute a sample selected from all students at a certain state university. Use the frequency distribution to estimate the proportion of all students at the university who use a Webster's dictionary.

2.13   The *Journal of Marketing Research* (February 1975) published the results of a study in which 22 consumers reported the number of times that they had purchased a particular brand of a product during the previous 48-week period. The results were as follows.

0	2	5	0	3	1	8	0	3	1	1
9	2	4	0	2	9	3	0	1	9	8

a. Construct a relative frequency distribution for the number of purchases.
b. What proportion of the shoppers in this study never bought the brand under investigation?
c. Suppose that each of the 22 shoppers in this study had made exactly nine purchases of the product during the previous 48 weeks. What proportion of the shoppers purchased the particular brand of the product under investigation more than half of the time? All the time?

2.14   In the paper "Reproduction in Laboratory Colonies of Bank Vole" (*Oikos* (1983):184), the authors presented the results of a study on litter size. (According to Webster's, a vole is a small rodent with a stout body, blunt nose, and short ears!) As each new litter was born, the number of babies was recorded, and the following results were obtained.

Size of litter										
3	6	5	6	5	7	5	7	6	6	6
4	6	5	6	4	3	5	6	4	5	9
6	5	6	1	9	7	8	3	7	4	5
5	6	7	3	6	6	9	4	5	7	5
6	8	6	4	7	5	7	4	5	8	6
7	2	7	7	3	3	5	4	6	4	6
3	7	8	5	7	7	7	7	9	8	7
6	7	6	4	7	10	5	2	3	6	6
4	7	6	7	5	5	5	7	5	8	8
4	9	7	5	4	6	5	8	4	5	6
6	3	6	8	6	8	6	5	8	6	11
4	7	6	8	9	7	3	8	3	4	6
4	5	7	5	6	5	7	6	9	3	5
9	7	5	6	7	5	8	6	8	8	6
5	7	4	8	7	7	7	5	3	8	6
10	4	5	5	5						

    a. Construct a relative frequency distribution for this data.

    b. What proportion of the litters had more than 6 babies? Between 3 and 8 (inclusive)?

    c. Is it easier to answer questions like those posed in (b) using the relative frequency distribution than it would be using the raw data given in the table? Explain.

2.15   Compute the cumulative relative frequencies for the data of Exercise 2.14 and use them to answer the following questions.

    a. What proportion of observations are at most 8? At least 8?

    b. What proportion of litters contain between 5 and 10 (inclusive) offspring?

2.16   Is it really the case, as it might seem to an unsuccessful and frustrated angler, that 10% of those fishing reel in 90% of the fish caught? More generally, how is the number of fish caught distributed among those who are trying to catch them? The

Number of fish caught	Number of anglers (frequency)
0	515
1	65
2	60
3	66
4	53
5	55
6	27
7	25
8	25
9	20
	911

accompanying table presents data from a survey of 911 anglers done during a particular time period on the lower Current River in Canada ("Fisherman's Luck," *Biometrics* (1976):265–271).

a. Calculate the relative frequencies. (Express each one using four digits of decimal accuracy.)

b. What proportion of those in the sample caught no fish? One fish? At most one fish?

c. What proportion of the 911 anglers caught at least five fish? More than five fish?

d. Calculate the cumulative relative frequencies for the sample of 911 fishermen. Then use them to answer the questions posed in part (c).

e. Suppose the sample had included an additional four anglers, with numbers of fish caught being 12, 14, 19, and 25 for these four. Construct a frequency distribution that has exactly one more row than the one just displayed.

2.17 The concentration of suspended solids in river water is an important environmental characteristic. The paper "Water Quality in Agricultural Watershed: Impact of Riparian Vegetation during Base Flow" (*Water Resources Bull.* (1981):233–239) reported on concentration (in parts per million, or ppm) for several different rivers. Suppose that the following 50 observations had been obtained for a particular river:

55.8	60.9	37.0	91.3	65.8	42.3	33.8	60.6	76.0	69.0
45.9	39.1	35.5	56.0	44.6	71.7	61.2	61.5	47.2	74.5
83.2	40.0	31.7	36.7	62.3	47.3	94.6	56.3	30.0	68.2
75.3	71.4	65.2	52.6	58.2	48.0	61.8	78.8	39.8	65.0
60.7	77.1	59.1	49.5	69.3	69.8	64.9	27.1	87.1	66.3

a. Why can't you base a frequency distribution on the class intervals 0–10, 10–20, 20–30, 30–40, ... , 90–100?

b. Construct a frequency distribution using class intervals 20–<30, 30–<40, ... , 90–<100. (The resulting distribution agrees with that for one of the rivers discussed in the paper.)

c. What proportion of the concentration observations were less than 50? At least 60?

d. Just from the frequency distribution, can you determine the proportion of sample observations less than 65? Explain. Can you *estimate* this proportion from the distribution? How does your estimate compare with the actual value of the proportion?

2.18 Refer to the concentration data given in Exercise 2.17.

a. Obtain the cumulative relative frequencies for the class intervals specified in part (b) of that problem.

b. Use the cumulative relative frequencies to calculate the proportions described in part (c) of Exercise 2.17.

c. Use the cumulative relative frequencies to calculate the proportion of observations in the interval 40–<70.

d. Just from the frequency distribution, can you determine the proportion of observations that are at most 40? Explain.

2.19   In a study of warp breakage during the weaving of fabric (*Technometrics* (1982):63), 100 pieces of yarn were tested. The number of cycles of strain to breakage was recorded for each yarn sample. The resulting data is given here.

86	146	251	653	98	249	400	292	131	169
175	176	76	264	15	364	195	262	88	264
157	220	42	321	180	198	38	20	61	121
282	224	149	180	325	250	196	90	229	166
38	337	65	151	341	40	40	135	597	246
211	180	93	315	353	571	124	279	81	186
497	182	423	185	229	400	338	290	398	71
246	185	188	568	55	55	61	244	20	284
393	396	203	829	239	236	286	194	277	143
198	264	105	203	124	137	135	350	193	188

a. Using class intervals 0–<100, 100–<200, and so on, construct a relative frequency distribution for breaking strength.

b. If weaving specifications require a breaking strength of at least 110 cycles, approximately what proportion of the yarn samples would be considered unsatisfactory? Answer using your relative frequency distribution.

2.20   The results of the 1990 census included a state-by-state listing of population density. The following values are the number of people per square mile for each of the 50 states.

AL	79.6	IN	154.6	NB	20.5	SC	115.8
AK	1.0	IA	49.7	NV	10.9	SD	9.2
AZ	32.3	KS	30.3	NH	123.7	TN	118.3
AR	45.1	KY	92.8	NJ	1042.0	TX	64.9
CA	190.8	LA	96.9	NM	12.5	UT	21.0
CO	31.8	ME	39.8	NY	381.0	VT	60.8
CT	678.4	MD	489.2	NC	136.1	VA	156.3
DE	340.8	MA	767.6	ND	9.3	WA	73.1
FL	239.6	MI	163.6	OH	264.9	WV	74.5
GA	111.9	MN	55.0	OK	45.8	WI	90.1
HI	172.5	MS	54.9	OR	29.6	WY	4.7
ID	12.2	MO	74.3	PA	265.1		
IL	205.6	MT	5.5	RI	960.3		

a. Construct a relative frequency distribution for state population density.

b. In your relative frequency distribution of part (a), did you use class intervals of equal widths? Why or why not?

c. Use the relative frequency distribution to give an approximate value for the proportion of states that have a population density of more than 100 people per square mile. Is the approximate value close to the actual value?

2.21   The paper "Lessons from Pacemaker Implantations" (*J. Amer. Med. Assoc.* (1965):231–232) gave the results of a study that followed 89 heart patients who had received electronic pacemakers. The time (in months) to the first electrical malfunction of the pacemaker was recorded.

24	20	16	32	14	22	2	12	24	6
10	20	8	16	12	24	14	20	18	14
16	18	20	22	24	26	28	18	14	10
12	24	6	12	18	16	34	18	20	22
24	26	18	2	18	12	12	8	24	10
14	16	22	24	22	20	24	28	20	22
26	20	6	14	16	18	24	18	16	6
16	10	14	18	24	22	28	24	30	34
26	24	22	28	30	22	24	22	32	

a. Summarize this data in the form of a frequency distribution using class intervals of 0–<6, 6–<12, and so on.

b. Compute the relative frequencies and cumulative relative frequencies for each class interval of the frequency distribution of part (a).

c. Show how the relative frequency for the class interval 12–<18 could be obtained from the cumulative relative frequencies.

Use the cumulative relative frequencies to give approximate answers to the following questions.

d. What proportion of those who participated in the study had pacemakers that did not malfunction within the first year?

e. If the pacemaker must be replaced as soon as the first electrical malfunction occurs, approximately what proportion required replacement between 1 and 2 years after implantation?

f. Estimate the time at which about 50% of the pacemakers had failed.

g. Estimate the time at which only about 10% of the pacemakers initially implanted were still functioning.

2.22 Birth weights for 302 eighth-born Chinese males born in Singapore are summarized in the accompanying frequency distribution (*Ann. Human Genetics* (1954):58–73).

Weight (in ounces)	Frequency
72–<80	4
80–<88	5
88–<96	19
96–<104	52
104–<112	55
112–<120	61
120–<128	48
128–<136	39
136–<144	19

a. Construct the cumulative relative frequency distribution for this data.

b. What proportion of observed birth weights are less than 96? At least 96? Can you use the given information to determine what proportion of birth weights are at most 96? Explain.

c. Roughly what proportion of birth weights are less than 100? In answering this question, what assumption are you making about the 52 observations in the 96–<104 class interval?

d. Approximately what birth weight is such that 50% of the observed weights are less than that weight value?

2.23   A student obtained data on fuel efficiency (mi/gal) and constructed a frequency distribution using the eight class intervals 27.0–<27.5, 27.5–<28.0, . . . , 30.5–<31.0. He then calculated and reported the following cumulative relative frequencies: .09, .23, .38, .35, .72, .80, .93, 1.00. Comment.

2.24   Referring to Exercise 2.12, would it make sense to calculate cumulative relative frequencies? Explain.

2.4 Histograms

A **histogram** is a pictorial representation of the information in a frequency distribution. Pictures often have more impact and stay with us longer than tabulated numerical information. The general idea is to represent each relative frequency by a rectangle.

> **CONSTRUCTING A HISTOGRAM (BAR CHART) FOR CATEGORICAL DATA**
>
> 1. Draw a horizontal line and write the category names at regularly spaced intervals.
> 2. Draw a vertical line and scale it using relative frequency values (frequencies themselves can also be used).
> 3. Above each category label, draw a rectangle whose height is the corresponding relative frequency (alternatively, frequency). All rectangles should have the same base width.

The *area* of each rectangle is proportional to the corresponding relative frequency. To see what this means, consider the following partial listing of frequencies and relative frequencies.

class:	1	2	3	. . .
frequency:	30	60	75	. . .
relative frequency:	.06	.12	.15	. . .

The relative frequency for the second class is twice that for the first class, and the same relationship holds for the frequencies. Therefore, the area of the rectangle for the second class must be twice the area of the rectangle for the first class. Similarly, $.15/.06 = 2.5$, so

$$\left(\begin{array}{c}\text{area of rectangle}\\\text{for class 3}\end{array}\right) = 2.5\left(\begin{array}{c}\text{area of rectangle}\\\text{for class 1}\end{array}\right)$$

EXAMPLE 2.11

In many surveys, a group of individuals is selected, and then one or more attempts are made to contact each individual. The paper "I Hear You Knocking but You Can't Come In: The Effects of Reluctant Respondents and Refusers on Sample Survey Estimates" (*Soc. Methods and Research* (Aug. 1982):3–32) reported on a study of how group composition changed as the number of attempts to contact increased. Table 2.7 gives relative frequencies for labor force categories.

TABLE 2.7 Relative frequencies for labor force categories

Category	After one attempt to contact (234 responses)	After ten attempts to contact (1049 responses)
Full-time	.286	.524
Part-time	.103	.108
Looking	.051	.048
Retired	.226	.132
Not working	.333	.189
	.999	1.001

FIGURE 2.10
Histograms for the labor force
frequency distribution
(a) After one attempt
(b) After ten attempts

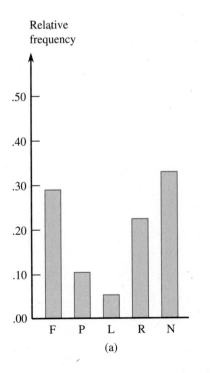

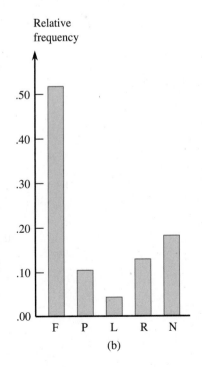

Figure 2.10 presents the corresponding histograms. They are obviously quite different. Making only a single attempt to contact might yield sample information that is quite misleading.

Numerical Data

As we did for frequency distributions, we distinguish here between discrete and continuous data.

CONSTRUCTING A HISTOGRAM FOR DISCRETE DATA

1. Draw a vertical scale marked with either relative frequencies or frequencies. The height of each rectangle will then match the corresponding relative frequency or frequency.
2. Mark possible values on a horizontal scale. Each rectangle should be centered at the value to which it refers, and the widths should be identical. If possible values are whole numbers, each base width should be 1 (so the rectangle will extend .5 to either side of the value).

EXAMPLE 2.12

Figure 2.11 shows a histogram corresponding to the frequency distribution for the number of accidents given in Table 2.3. There is a peak at the values 1 and 2, and then a smooth decline in relative frequencies as we move to the right. A computer-

FIGURE 2.11
Histogram for number of accidents by bus drivers

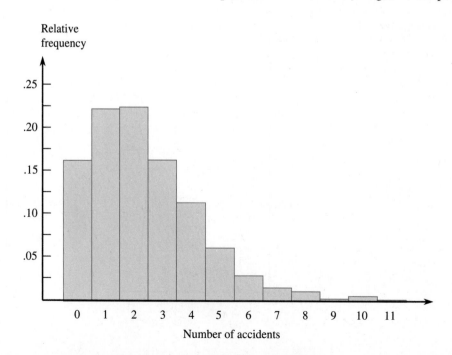

generated histogram (using SPSS) appears in Figure 2.12. Such histograms are typically not as attractive as hand-drawn versions.

FIGURE 2.12
Histogram from SPSS for number of accidents by bus drivers

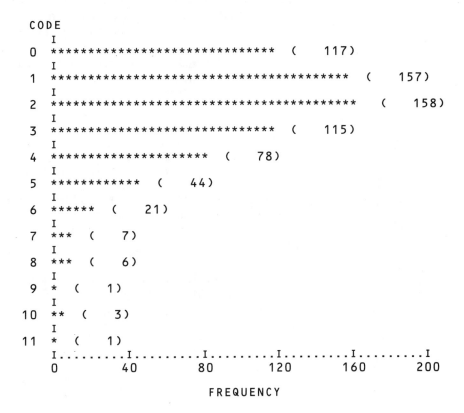

```
CODE
    I
 0  *****************************  (    117)
    I
 1  ****************************************  (    157)
    I
 2  *****************************************  (    158)
    I
 3  ****************************  (    115)
    I
 4  ********************  (    78)
    I
 5  ************  (    44)
    I
 6  ******  (    21)
    I
 7  ***  (    7)
    I
 8  ***  (    6)
    I
 9  *  (    1)
    I
10  **  (    3)
    I
11  *  (    1)
    I.........I.........I.........I.........I.........I
    0        40        80       120       160       200
                      FREQUENCY
```

For continuous data, each rectangle in a histogram sits above the corresponding class interval on a horizontal measurement axis.

CONSTRUCTING A HISTOGRAM FOR CONTINUOUS DATA

1. Mark boundaries of the class intervals on a horizontal axis. The rectangle corresponding to a particular interval is drawn directly above that interval.
2. If the class intervals have identical widths, either relative frequencies or frequencies can be used on the vertical scale.
3. When class widths are different, the vertical scale *should not* be marked with frequencies or relative frequencies. Instead, a correct picture (one for which area is proportional to relative frequency) results if the height of each rectangle is calculated according to the following formula:

$$\text{height} = \frac{\text{relative frequency}}{\text{interval width}}$$

EXAMPLE 2.13

Mercury contamination is a serious environmental concern. Mercury levels are particularly high in certain types of fish. Citizens of the Republic of Seychelles, a group of islands in the Indian Ocean, are among those who consume the most fish in the world. The paper "Mercury Content of Commercially Important Fish of the Seychelles, and Hair Mercury Levels of a Selected Part of the Population" (*Environ. Research* (1983):305–312) reported the following observations on mercury content (ppm) in the hair of 40 fishermen.

13.26	32.43	18.10	58.23	64.00	68.20	35.35
33.92	23.94	18.28	22.05	39.14	31.43	18.51
21.03	5.50	6.96	5.19	28.66	26.29	13.89
25.87	9.84	26.88	16.81	37.65	19.63	21.82
31.58	30.13	42.42	16.51	21.16	32.97	9.84
10.64	29.56	40.69	12.86	13.80		

A reasonable choice for class intervals is to start the first interval at zero and let each one have width 10. The resulting frequency distribution is displayed in Table 2.8, and the corresponding histogram appears in Figure 2.13.

TABLE 2.8   Frequency distribution for hair mercury content of Seychelles fishermen (ppm)

Class interval	Frequency	Relative frequency
0–<10	5	.125
10–<20	11	.275
20–<30	10	.250
30–<40	9	.225
40–<50	2	.050
50–<60	1	.025
60–<70	2	.050
	40	1.000

FIGURE 2.13
Histogram for hair mercury
content of Seychelles
fishermen

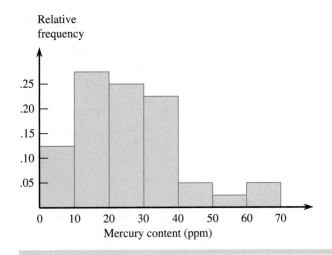

EXAMPLE 2.14

Individuals asked for the values of characteristics such as age or weight sometimes shade the truth in their responses. The paper "Self-Reports of Academic Performance" (*Soc. Methods and Research* (Nov. 1981):165–185) focused on such characteristics as SAT scores and grade point average. For each student in a sample, the difference in GPA (reported − actual) was determined. Positive differences resulted from individuals reporting grade point averages larger than the correct values. Most differences were close to zero, but there were some rather gross errors. Because of this, a frequency distribution based on unequal class widths gives an informative yet concise summary. Table 2.9 displays such a distribution based on classes with boundaries at −2.0, −.4, −.2, −.1, 0, .1, .2, .4, and 2.0.

TABLE 2.9   Frequency distribution for errors in
reported GPA

Class interval	Relative frequency	Width	Height
−2.0–<−.4	.023 2.3%	1.6	.014 1.4
−.4–<−.2	.055	.2	.275
−.2–<−.1	.097	.1	.970
−.1–<0	.210	.1	2.100
0–<.1	.189	.1	1.890
.1–<.2	.139	.1	1.390
.2–<.4	.116	.2	.580
.4–<2.0	.171	1.6	.107

Figure 2.14 displays two histograms based on this frequency distribution. The histogram of part (a) is correctly drawn, in that height = relative frequency/ interval width. The histogram of part (b) has height = relative frequency and is therefore not correct. In particular, this second histogram considerably exaggerates the incidence of grossly overreported and underreported values—the areas of the two most extreme rectangles are much too large.

FIGURE 2.14
Histograms for errors in reporting GPA
(a) A correct picture (height = relative frequency/width)
(b) An incorrect picture (height = relative frequency)

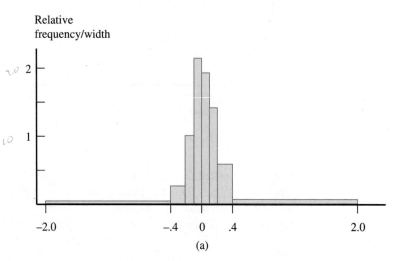

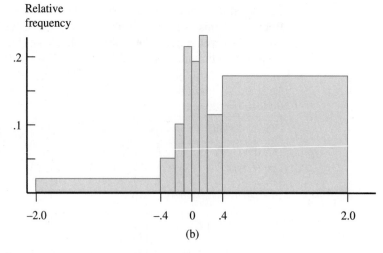

Histogram Shapes

It is often desirable to describe the general shape of a histogram. For this purpose, it suffices to consider a *smoothed histogram* obtained by approximating the histogram itself with a smooth curve. This is illustrated in Figure 2.15.

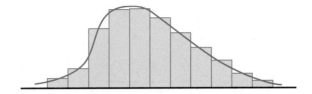

FIGURE 2.15
Approximating a histogram
by a smooth curve

One characterization of general shape relates to the number of peaks, or **modes.** A histogram is said to be **unimodal** if it has a single peak, **bimodal** if it has two peaks, and **multimodal** if it has more than two peaks. These shapes are illustrated in Figure 2.16. Many numerical data sets give rise to a unimodal histogram. Occasionally we encounter a bimodal histogram—an example would be a histogram of adult heights, with one peak at roughly 5 ft 6 in. for women and another peak at roughly 5 ft 9 in. for men—but rarely does a histogram with more than two peaks occur.

FIGURE 2.16
Smoothed histograms with
various numbers of modes
(a) Unimodal
(b) Bimodal
(c) Multimodal

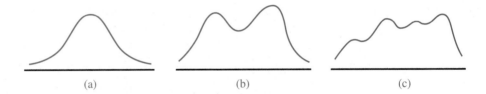

Within the class of unimodal histograms, there are still several important distinctive shapes. A unimodal histogram is **symmetric** if there is a vertical *line of symmetry* such that the part of the histogram to the left of the line is a mirror image of the part to the right (bimodal and multimodal histograms can also be symmetric in this way). Several different symmetric smoothed histograms are pictured in Figure 2.17.

FIGURE 2.17
Several symmetric unimodal
smoothed histograms

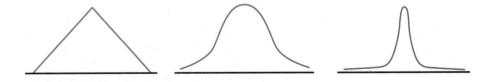

Proceeding to the right from the peak of a unimodal histogram, we move into what is called the **upper tail** of the histogram. Going in the opposite direction moves us into the **lower tail.**

A unimodal histogram that is not symmetric is said to be **skewed.** If the upper tail of the histogram stretches out farther than the lower tail, then the distribution of values is **positively skewed.** If, on the other hand, the lower tail is longer than the upper tail, the histogram is **negatively skewed.** These two types of skewness are illustrated in Figure 2.18.

FIGURE 2.18
Two examples of skewed
smoothed histograms
(a) Positive skew
(b) Negative skew

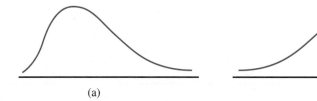

(a)   (b)

Positive skewness is much more frequently encountered than is negative skewness. An example giving rise to positive skewness is the distribution of single-
family home prices in Los Angeles County, where most homes are moderately
priced (at least for California), whereas the relatively few homes in Beverly Hills
and Malibu have much higher price tags.

One rather specific shape, a **normal curve,** arises more frequently than any
other in statistical applications. Many histograms can be well approximated by a
normal curve (for example, characteristics such as blood pressure, brain weight,
adult male heights, adult female heights, and I.Q. scores). Here we mention briefly
several of the most important qualitative properties of such a curve, postponing a
more detailed discussion until Chapter 7. A normal curve is not only symmetric but
also bell-shaped; it looks like the curve in Figure 2.19(a). However, not all bell-
shaped curves are normal. Starting from the top of the bell, the height of the curve
decreases at a well-defined rate when moving out into either tail. (This rate of
decrease is specified by a certain mathematical function.)

FIGURE 2.19
Three examples of
bell-shaped histograms
(a) Normal
(b) Heavy-tailed
(c) Light-tailed

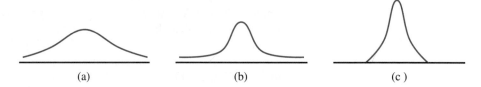

(a)   (b)   (c)

A curve with tails that do not decline as rapidly as the tails of a normal curve
is said to specify a **heavy-tailed** distribution (compared to the normal curve).
Similarly, a curve with tails that decrease more rapidly than the normal tails is
called **light-tailed.** Figure 2.19(b) and (c) illustrates these possibilities. Many inferential procedures that work well (result in accurate conclusions) when the population distribution is approximately normal tend to break down when the population
distribution is heavy-tailed, prompting much recent interest in alternative methods
of analysis that are not so sensitive to the nature of the tails.

Do Sample Histograms Resemble the Population Histogram?

Statistical inference involves using information contained in a sample to draw conclusions about a population. The extent to which this endeavor will be successful
depends on how closely various characteristics of the sample resemble the analo-

gous population characteristics. When we form a sample histogram, is it centered at roughly the same place as is the population histogram? Does it spread out to the same extent? Do the two histograms have the same number of peaks? Do the peaks occur at roughly the same place or places?

An issue intimately related to the one just raised is the extent to which histograms based on different samples from the same population resemble one another. If two different sample histograms can be expected to differ from one another in obvious ways, then at least one of them will differ substantially from the population histogram, resulting in unreliable inferences. **Sampling variability**—the extent to which samples differ from one another and from the population—is a central idea in statistics. In later chapters we develop quantitative measures for assessing sampling variability, and these play a key role in our inferential methods. Here we present a small example to suggest how sample histograms resemble one another and the population histogram.

EXAMPLE 2.15

Example 2.8 gives data on the number of accidents in which each of 708 bus drivers was involved over a certain time period. The corresponding histogram is given in Figure 2.11. Although the 708 observations actually constituted a sample from the population of all bus drivers, here we will regard the 708 observations as constituting the entire population. Figure 2.11, which is the first histogram in Figure 2.20, then represents the population histogram. The other four histograms in Figure 2.20 are based on four different samples of 50 observations each from this population.

The five histograms certainly resemble one another in a general way, but there are also some obvious dissimilarities. The population histogram rises to a peak and then declines smoothly, whereas the sample histograms tend to have more peaks, valleys, and gaps. Although the population data set contained an observation of 11, none of the four samples did. In fact, in the first two samples the largest observations were 7 and 8, respectively. Fortunately, when we study numerical characteristics of samples and populations—most important, measures of center and spread—we will see that sample characteristics tend to resemble population characteristics more closely than the pictures in Figure 2.20 might suggest.

FIGURE 2.20
A comparison of population
and sample histograms for
number of accidents

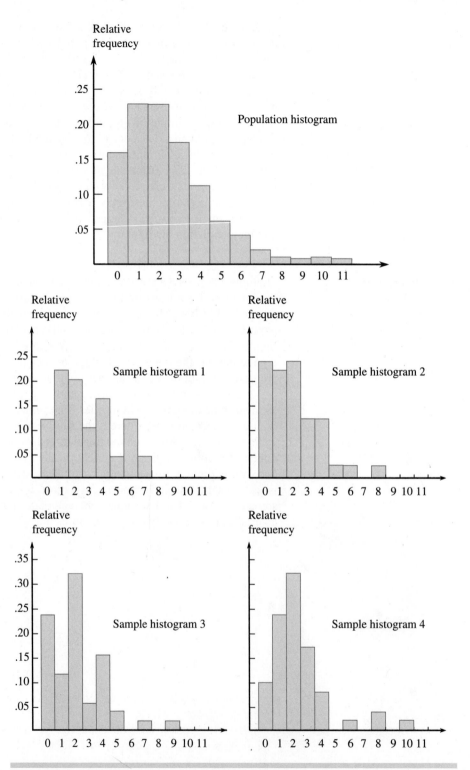

2.25 A common problem facing researchers who rely on mail questionnaires is that of nonresponse. In the paper "Reasons for Nonresponse on the Physicians' Practice Survey" (*Proc. Social Statistics Amer. Stat. Assoc.* (1980):202), 811 doctors who did not respond to the A.M.A. Survey of Physicians were contacted about the reason for their nonparticipation. The results are summarized in the relative frequency distribution given below.

Reason	Relative frequency
No time to participate	.264
Not interested	.300
Don't like surveys in general	.145
Don't like this particular survey	.025
Hostility toward the government	.054
Desire to protect privacy	.056
Other reason for refusal	.053
No reason given	.103

Draw the histogram corresponding to the frequency distribution.

2.26 Many researchers have speculated that a relationship exists between birth order and vocational preferences. This theory is investigated in the paper "Birth Order and Vocational Preference" (*J. of Experimental Educ.* (1980):15–18). In this study, 244 New York City high school students were given the Self-Directed Search Test. This test is designed to identify occupational preferences by classifying the student into one of six categories: realistic, investigative, artistic, social, enterprising, and conventional. The results are summarized in the two accompanying frequency distributions.

Vocational class	Firstborn	Later born
Conventional	38	9
Realistic	26	19
Enterprising	24	15
Social	12	15
Artistic	12	21
Investigative	10	43

a. Construct two histograms to represent occupational preference—one for firstborns and one for those born later.
b. What inferences would you make based on a comparison of the two histograms?

2.27 The article on sports injuries cited in Example 2.7 reported the following data on injuries in noncontact sports.

Sport	No. of injuries	Sport	No. of injuries
Touch football	38	Jogging/running	11
Soccer	24	Bicycling	11
Basketball	19	Volleyball	7
Baseball/softball	11	Others	47

Calculate relative frequencies and draw the corresponding histogram.

2.28 The article "Associations between Violent and Nonviolent Criminality" (*Multivariate Behavioral Research* (1981):237–242) reported the number of previous convictions for 283 adult males arrested for felony offenses. The following frequency distribution is a summary of the data given in the paper.

Number of previous convictions	Frequency
0	0
1	16
2	27
3	37
4	46
5	36
6	40
7	31
8	27
9	13
10	8
11	2

Draw the histogram corresponding to this frequency distribution.

2.29 In a study of author productivity ("Lotka's Test," *Collection Mgmt.* (1982): 111–118) a large number of authors were classified according to the number of papers they had written and the results were presented in the following frequency distribution.

Number of papers	Number of authors (frequency)
1	784
2	204
3	127
4	50
5	33
6	28
7	19
8	19
9	6
10	7
11	6

(continued)

| | *(continued)* |
Number of papers	Number of authors (frequency)
12	7
13	4
14	4
15	5
16	3
17	3

a. Construct a histogram for this frequency distribution.

b. Suppose the five 15s, three 16s, and three 17s had been lumped into a single row labeled "≥15". Would you be able to draw a histogram? Explain.

c. Suppose that instead of the last three rows, there had been a single row, labeled 15–17, with frequency 11. Would you be able to draw a histogram? Explain.

2.30 The accompanying histogram, based on data in the paper "Service Frequency, Schedule Reliability, and Passenger Wait Times at Transit Stops" (*J. of Trans. Research* (1981):465–471) shows the time (in minutes) that people had to wait for the next scheduled bus when buses were running on a 20-min schedule. Suppose that the histogram is based on a sample of 300 waiting times. Construct the corresponding frequency distribution.

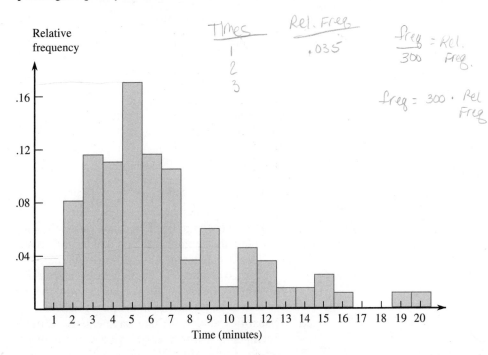

2.31 The mileage traveled before the first major motor failure for each of 191 buses was reported in an article that appeared in *Technometrics* ((November 1980):588). The frequency distribution appearing in that paper is given here.

Distance traveled (thousands of miles)	Frequency
0–<20	6
20–<40	11
40–<60	16
60–<80	25
80–<100	34
100–<120	46
120–<140	33
140–<160	16
160–<180	2
180–<200	2

a. Draw the histogram corresponding to this frequency distribution.

b. Use the histogram to estimate the proportion of all buses of this type that operate for more than 100,000 mi before the first major motor failure.

c. Use the histogram to estimate the proportion of all buses that have the first major motor failure after operating for between 50,000 and 125,000 mi.

 2.32 Suppose the information in Exercise 2.31 had been summarized in the following table.

Distance	Frequency
0–<40	17
40–<60	16
60–<80	25
80–<100	34
100–<120	46
120–<140	33
140–<180	18
180–<220	2

a. What are the widths of the eight class intervals? What are the corresponding relative frequencies?

b. Divide each relative frequency calculated in (a) by the corresponding width to obtain the heights of the rectangles for a histogram.

c. The tallest rectangle has a height of about .012. Mark 0, .002, .004, .006, .008, .010, .012, and .014 on the vertical axis, and then draw the histogram.

d. What is the area of the rectangle above the fifth class interval? What is the total area of all rectangles in the histogram?

2.33 Disparities among welfare payments by different states has been the source of much political controversy. The accompanying table reports average payment per person in the Aid to Families with Dependent Children Program for the 1990 fiscal year.

Alaska	244.90	Washington	160.41	Oregon	135.99
California	218.31	Idaho	97.93	Nevada	100.25
Arizona	93.57	Utah	118.36	Wyoming	113.84
Montana	114.95	Colorado	111.20	New Mexico	81.87
Texas	56.79	Oklahoma	96.98	Kansas	113.88
Nebraska	115.15	South Dakota	95.52	North Dakota	130.49
Minnesota	171.75	Iowa	129.58	Missouri	91.93
Arkansas	65.96	Louisiana	55.81	Mississippi	40.22
Alabama	39.62	Tennessee	65.93	Kentucky	85.21
Illinois	112.28	Wisconsin	155.04	Michigan	154.75
Indiana	92.43	Ohio	115.26	Maine	150.12
New Hampshire	164.20	Vermont	183.36	Massachusetts	200.99
Rhode Island	179.37	Connecticut	205.86	New York	193.48
New Jersey	121.99	Pennsylvania	127.70	West Virginia	82.94
Delaware	113.66	Maryland	132.86	Virginia	97.98
North Carolina	91.95	South Carolina	71.91	Georgia	91.31
Florida	95.43	Hawaii	187.71		

Construct a relative frequency distribution for this data using equal interval widths. Draw the histogram corresponding to your frequency distribution.

2.34 The behavior of children watching television has been a much-studied phenomenon. Now the same attention is being given to children engaged in playing with toys. The paper "A Temporal Analysis of Free Toy Play and Distractibility in Young Children" (*J. of Exp. Child Psychology* (1991):41–69) reported the following data on play-episode lengths (s) for a particular 5-year-old boy.

Class	Frequency
0–<5	54
5–<10	44
10–<15	28
15–<20	21
20–<40	31
40–<60	15
60–<90	16
90–<120	5
120–<180	8

a. Display this information in a histogram.
b. What proportion of episodes lasted at least 20 s?
c. Roughly what proportion of episodes lasted between 40 and 75 s?

2.35 An exam is given to students in an introductory statistics course. What is likely to be true of the shape of the histogram of scores if
a. The exam is quite easy?
b. The exam is quite difficult?

c. Half the students in the class have had calculus, the other half have had no prior college math courses, and the exam emphasizes mathematical manipulation? Explain your reasoning in each case.

2.36   Construct a histogram corresponding to each of the five frequency distributions given in the following table, and state whether each histogram is symmetric, bimodal, positively skewed, or negatively skewed.

Class interval	Frequency				
	I	II	III	IV	V
0–<10	5	40	30	5	6
10–<20	10	25	10	25	5
20–<30	20	10	8	8	6
30–<40	30	8	7	7	9
40–<50	20	7	7	20	9
50–<60	10	5	8	25	23
60–<70	5	5	30	10	42

2.37   Using the following class intervals, devise a frequency distribution based on 70 observations whose histogram could be described as follows.
   a. Symmetric   **b.** Bimodal
   c. Positively skewed   **d.** Negatively skewed

Class interval
100–<120
120–<140
140–<160
160–<180
180–<200

2.5   Transforming Data for Ease of Description (Optional)

A primary objective of data analysis is to find ways of describing and summarizing data that are both simple and insightful. A stem-and-leaf display or histogram of a data set may initially suggest a rather complicated distribution. In such cases, a transformation or reexpression of the data values may help to simplify the description process and increase understanding of the variable under investigation. By transforming data, we mean using some specified mathematical operation (for example, square root, logarithm, or reciprocal) on each data value to produce a set of **transformed data**. We can then study and summarize the distribution of these transformed values. With a single data set, a transformation is usually chosen to yield a distribution of transformed values which is more symmetric (or, even better, more closely approximated by a normal curve) than was the original distribution. In later chapters we consider applying transformations to achieve other objectives.

EXAMPLE 2.16

A data set that has been used by several authors to introduce the concept of transformation (see "Exploratory Methods for Choosing Power Transformations," *J. Amer. Stat. Assoc.* (1982):103–108, for example) consists of values of March precipitation for Minneapolis–St. Paul over a period of 30 years. These values are displayed in Table 2.10, along with the square root of each value, and histograms of both the original and transformed data appear in Figure 2.21. The distribution of the original data is clearly skewed, with a long upper tail. The square-root transformation has resulted in a substantially more symmetric distribution, with a typical (that is, central) value near the 1.25 boundary between the third and fourth class intervals. In Exercise 2.38 you are asked to consider the cube-root transformation (transformed value = (original value)$^{1/3}$), which is favored by some meteorologists.

TABLE 2.10   Original and square-root transformed values of March precipitation in Minneapolis–St. Paul over a 30-year period

Year	Precipitation	$\sqrt{\text{Precipitation}}$	Year	Precipitation	$\sqrt{\text{Precipitation}}$
1	.77	.88	16	1.62	1.27
2	1.74	1.32	17	1.31	1.14
3	.81	.90	18	.32	.57
4	1.20	1.10	19	.59	.77
5	1.95	1.40	20	.81	.90
6	1.20	1.10	21	2.81	1.68
7	.47	.69	22	1.87	1.37
8	1.43	1.20	23	1.18	1.09
9	3.37	1.84	24	1.35	1.16
10	2.20	1.48	25	4.75	2.18
11	3.00	1.73	26	2.48	1.57
12	3.09	1.76	27	.96	.98
13	1.51	1.23	28	1.89	1.37
14	2.10	1.45	29	.90	.95
15	.52	.72	30	2.05	1.43

FIGURE 2.21
Histograms of precipitation data
(a) Untransformed data
(b) Square-root transformed data

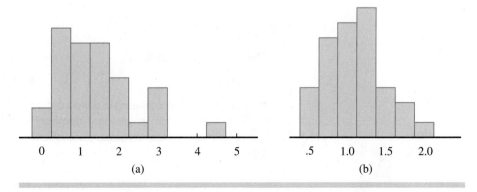

Square-root and reciprocal transformations are particular cases of a more general type of transformation.

DEFINITION

A **power transformation** is defined by first specifying an exponent or power, p, which could be either a positive or negative number, and then computing transformed values according to

transformed value $= $ (original value)^p

The value $p = \frac{1}{2}$ gives the square-root transformation and $p = -1$ gives the reciprocal transformation (reciprocal $= 1/\text{value}$).

The book *Applications, Basics, and Computing of Exploratory Data Analysis*, listed in the chapter references, gives a good elementary discussion of power transformations, along with suggested quantitative methods for assessing the extent to which a transformation achieves symmetry.

Taking $p = 0$ results in every transformed value equaling 1, which is not at all informative. Instead, it is customary to think of $p = 0$ as corresponding to a logarithmic transformation—taking the logarithm of each data value. This is the most frequently encountered transformation in statistics, so it is worth considering in some detail. We begin with a brief discussion of logarithms.

Logarithmic Transformations

The number 100 can be expressed as $(10)^2$, so the base 10 logarithm of 100 is 2. Similarly, $1000 = (10)^3$, so the base 10 logarithm of 1000 is 3, and $3.1623 = (10)^{.5}$, so .5 is the base 10 logarithm of 3.1623. In general, any positive number can be expressed as 10 raised to some power, and the power is called the base 10 logarithm of the number.

DEFINITION

Given a particular number, if

number $= (10)^n$

for a specified value n, then n is called the **base 10 logarithm** of that number. This is usually written as $\log_{10} (\text{number}) = n$.

For most numbers, computing $\log_{10}$ requires substantial calculation, so many statistics books used to include a table of such logarithms. Now many relatively inexpensive calculators have a $\log_{10}$ key; entering a number and pressing this key immediately yields the desired logarithm. We have not included a table of logarithms, so we'll give you $\log_{10}$ values whenever we want you to work with them.

Base 10 is not the only useful base for logarithms. Because of the way in which computers work, base 2 is important in computer science. In scientific work the base $2.718281828 \ldots$, denoted by the letter e, is very useful; logarithms to this base are called **natural logarithms** and are denoted by ln. Many calculators have both $\log_{10}$ and ln keys. For simplicity, let's concern ourselves for the moment only with $\log_{10}$.

A log transformation is usually applied to data that is positively skewed (a long upper tail). This affects values in the upper tail substantially more than values in the lower tail, yielding a more symmetric—and often more normal—distribution.

EXAMPLE 2.17

Exposure to beryllium is known to produce adverse effects on lungs as well as on other tissues and organs in both laboratory animals and humans. The paper "Time Lapse Cinematographic Analysis of Beryllium—Lung Fibroblast Interactions" (*Envir. Research* (1983):34–43) reported the results of experiments designed to study the behavior of certain individual cells that had been exposed to beryllium. An important characteristic of such an individual cell is its interdivision time (IDT). IDT's were determined for a large number of cells both in exposed (treatment) and unexposed (control) conditions. The authors of the paper state that "The IDT distributions are seen to be skewed, but the natural logs do have an approximate normal distribution." The same property holds for $\log_{10}$ transformed data. We give representative IDT data and the resulting histograms in Figure 2.22, which are in agreement with the authors' statement.

	IDT	$\log_{10}(IDT)$		IDT	$\log_{10}(IDT)$		IDT	$\log_{10}(IDT)$
1.	28.1	1.45	15.	60.1	1.78	29.	21.0	1.32
2.	31.2	1.49	16.	23.7	1.37	30.	22.3	1.35
3.	13.7	1.14	17.	18.6	1.27	31.	15.5	1.19
4.	46.0	1.66	18.	21.4	1.33	32.	36.3	1.56
5.	25.8	1.41	19.	26.6	1.42	33.	19.1	1.28
6.	16.8	1.23	20.	26.2	1.42	34.	38.4	1.58
7.	34.8	1.54	21.	32.0	1.51	35.	72.8	1.86
8.	62.3	1.79	22.	43.5	1.64	36.	48.9	1.69
9.	28.0	1.45	23.	17.4	1.24	37.	21.4	1.33
10.	17.9	1.25	24.	38.8	1.59	38.	20.7	1.32
11.	19.5	1.29	25.	30.6	1.49	39.	57.3	1.76
12.	21.1	1.32	26.	55.6	1.75	40.	40.9	1.61
13.	31.9	1.50	27.	25.5	1.41			
14.	28.9	1.46	28.	52.1	1.72			

FIGURE 2.22
Histograms of IDT data
(a) Untransformed data
(b) Log$_{10}$ transformed data

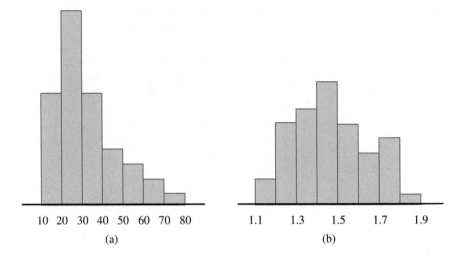

(a)   (b)

Selecting a Transformation

A particular transformation may on occasion be dictated by some theoretical argument, but often this is not the case. Then one may wish to try several different transformations in order to find one that is satisfactory. Figure 2.23, taken from the paper "Distribution of Sperm Counts in Suspected Infertile Men" (*J. of Reproduction and Fertility* (1983):91–96), illustrates what can result from such a search. Other workers in this field had previously used all three of the transformations illustrated, but these investigators strongly favored the square-root transformation for their data. Information about other graphical techniques and quantitative methods for selecting a transformation can be found in several of the chapter references.

FIGURE 2.23
Histograms of sperm concentrations for 1711 suspected infertile men
(a) Untransformed
(b) Log transformed

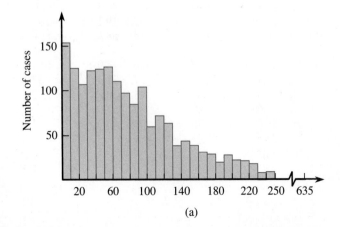
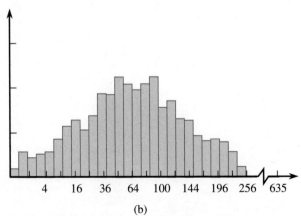

(a)   (b)

FIGURE 2.23 (*continued*)
(c) Square-root transformed
(d) Cube-root transformed
(Source: Mortimer and Lenton (1983). Reproduced by permission.)

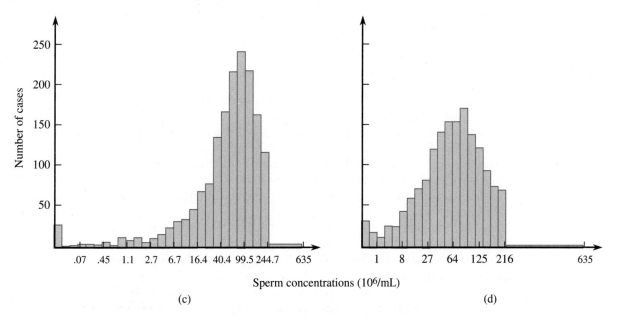

Sperm concentrations (10^6/mL)

(c)   (d)

EXERCISES 2.38–2.41   SECTION 2.5

2.38 The first example in this section examined rainfall data for Minneapolis–St. Paul. The square-root transformation was used to obtain a distribution of values that was more symmetric than the distribution of the original data. Another power transformation that has been suggested by meteorologists is the cube root: Transformed value = (original value)$^{1/3}$. The original values and their cube roots (the transformed values) are given. Construct a histogram of the transformed data. Compare your histogram to those given in Figure 2.21. Which of the cube-root and the square-root transformations appears to result in the most symmetric histogram?

Original	.32	.47	.52	.59	.77	.81	.81	.90
Transformed	.68	.78	.80	.84	.92	.93	.93	.97
Original	.96	1.18	1.20	1.20	1.31	1.35	1.43	1.51
Transformed	.99	1.06	1.06	1.06	1.09	1.11	1.13	1.15
Original	1.62	1.74	1.87	1.89	1.95	2.05	2.10	2.20
Transformed	1.17	1.20	1.23	1.24	1.25	1.27	1.28	1.30
Original	2.48	2.81	3.00	3.09	3.37	4.75		
Transformed	1.35	1.41	1.44	1.46	1.50	1.68		

2.39 The given values represent age at onset of Parkinson's disease for 40 males suffering from the disease.

64	68	60	60	64	63	64	59	64	54	58
63	59	62	64	63	59	59	58	61	63	67
63	63	61	63	64	60	64	62	61	63	64
63	66	66	68	61	61	63				

a. Construct a relative frequency distribution for this data set and draw the corresponding histogram.

b. Would you describe this histogram as having a positive or negative skew?

c. Would you recommend transforming the data? Explain.

2.40 One hundred observations on the breaking strength of yarn were given in Exercise 2.19. Use the data given there to complete the following.

a. Construct a frequency distribution using the class intervals 0–<100, 100–<200, and so on.

b. Draw the histogram corresponding to the frequency distribution in part (a). How would you describe the shape of this histogram?

c. Find a transformation for this data that yields a histogram that is more symmetric than the original data.

2.41 The article "The Distribution of Buying Frequency Rates" (*J. of Marketing Research* (1980):210–216) reported the results of a 3½-year study of dentifrice purchases. The authors conducted their research using a national sample of 2071 households and recorded the number of toothpaste purchases for each household participating in the study. The results are given in the accompanying frequency distribution.

Number of purchases	Number of households (frequency)
10–<20	904
20–<30	500
30–<40	258
40–<50	167
50–<60	94
60–<70	56
70–<80	26
80–<90	20
90–<100	13
100–<110	9
110–<120	7
120–<130	6
130–<140	6
140–<150	3
150–<160	0
160–<170	2

a. Draw a histogram for this frequency distribution. Would you describe the histogram as positively or negatively skewed?

b. Does the square-root transformation result in a histogram which is more symmetric than that of the original data? (Be careful—this one is a bit tricky, since you don't have the raw data; transforming the endpoints of the class intervals will result in class intervals that are not necessarily of equal widths, so the histogram of the transformed values will have to be drawn with this in mind.)

ENCORE

The chapter preview presented data on body mass for each of 50 different bird species. Observations were reported to the nearest tenth of a gram (one digit to the right of the decimal point), and all except one were less than 100. A natural choice for stem values is the tens digit, 0, 1, 2, . . . , but there are two problems. First, the largest observation is 448.0, so it cannot reasonably be included on the main part of the display. Second, so many observations fall in the 1 row (between 10.0 and 19.9, inclusive) that if the tenths digit is included in each leaf, the display runs off the page. So one possibility is to truncate the tenths digit (so that, for example, 10.6 becomes just 10), resulting in the following display.

```
0 ‖ 7 8 9 9 9 8 6 6 5 6 9
1 ‖ 0 2 1 6 0 5 1 2 9 0 0 4 9 9 6 9 1 7
2 ‖ 1 0 1 6 1 8 1 3 0 1
3 ‖ 1 1 2 6 4
4 ‖ 8 1
5 ‖
6 ‖ 8
7 ‖
8 ‖                                   Stem:  Tens digit
9 ‖ 3 9                               Leaf:  Ones digit
HI: 448
```

It is not necessary to truncate data if repeated stems are used. The following display incorporates two repeats, one for low leaves and another for high leaves. The most prominent feature of either display is the positive skewness (toward large values). This makes it more difficult to select a representative value than in the case of a symmetric display; a reasonable choice is a value in the high teens or low 20s (1H or 2L rows in the second display). There is a rather substantial spread about any typical value, the largest observation is clearly an extreme outlier, and 68.8, 93.9, and 99.6 appear to be at least mild outliers.

0H	7.7, 8.6, 9.4, 9.8, 9.0, 8.2, 6.2, 6.7, 5.0, 6.0, 9.0
1L	0.1, 2.0, 1.4, 0.2, 1.5, 2.5, 0.6, 0.9, 4.5, 1.9
1H	6.6, 5.9, 9.1, 9.8, 9.8, 6.5, 9.6, 7.4
2L	1.6, 0.2, 1.6, 1.0, 1.5, 3.9, 0.1, 1.3
2H	6.1, 8.1
3L	1.0, 1.6, 2.5, 4.0
3H	6.9
4L	1.0
4H	8.5
5L	
5H	
6L	
6H	8.8

Stem: Tens digit
Leaf: Ones and tenths digits

HI: 93.9, 99.6, 448.0

A MINITAB STEM command gave the following display.

```
Stem-and-leaf of mass   N = 50
Leaf Unit = 10
(46)   0  0000000000011111111111111111111222222222233333344
   4   0  699
   1   1
   1   1
   1   2
   1   2
   1   3
   1   3
   1   4 4
```

Repeated stems are used, but the extreme outlier appears directly on the display, so virtually all the observations are crowded into a single row of the display—clearly we could all do better than the computer here!

Construction of a frequency distribution requires that class intervals be chosen. Without the largest observation, a reasonable choice would be 0–<10, 10–< 20, . . . , 90–<100, with equal class widths. But since 448.0 is so much larger than the other observations, using narrow equal-width intervals would give a very unwieldy table (most intervals would contain no observations), whereas using wide intervals would compress all values into just one or two classes. The accompanying frequency distribution and histogram are based on classes of varying widths. (Recall that for each class, height = (relative frequency)/(class width).) The histogram is neither easy to draw nor very attractive. Inclusion of the outlier 448.0 causes a problem for any specification of class intervals.

Class	Frequency	Relative frequency	Height = (relative frequency) / width
5–<10	11	.22	.044
10–<15	10	.20	.040
15–<20	8	.16	.032
20–<25	8	.16	.032
25–<30	2	.04	.008
30–<40	5	.10	.010
40–<50	2	.04	.004
50–<100	3	.06	.0012
100–<500	1	.02	.00005

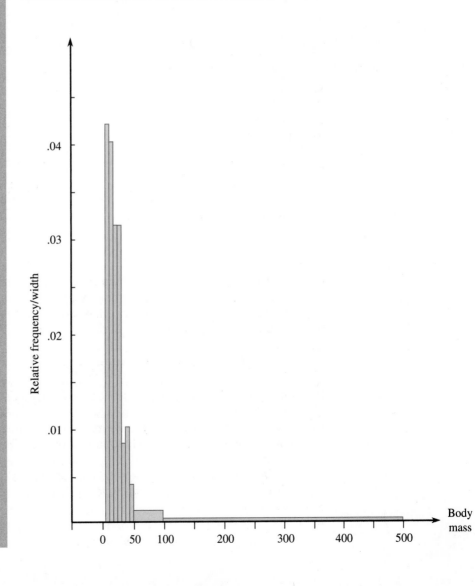

The substantial skewness of the data suggests the desirability of finding a transformation for which the distribution of transformed values is reasonably symmetric or, even better, well approximated by a normal curve. Here we show both a stem-and-leaf display and a histogram of the logarithms of the original observations. (The histogram appears on the next page.)

```
07 ‖ 9  0  8
08 ‖ 9  3
09 ‖ 3  7  9  5  1  7  5
10 ‖ 0  8  6  1  6  3  4  8
11 ‖ 0  6
12 ‖ 2  0  8  2  9  4
13 ‖ 3  1  3  2  3  8  0  0  3
14 ‖ 2  9  5
15 ‖ 0  1  7  3
16 ‖ 9  1
17 ‖
18 ‖ 4
19 ‖ 7                              Stem:   Ones and tenths digits
20 ‖ 0                              Leaf:   Hundredths digit
HI: 2.65
```

The distribution of transformed values is better behaved than was the original distribution, but our goal of symmetry has clearly not been achieved. We tried several other transformations, and the one that produced the best results was the reciprocal of the square root of body mass:

$$\text{transformed value} = \frac{1}{\sqrt{\text{original value}}}$$

(for example, transforming the first observation gives $1/\sqrt{7.7} = .360$). A histogram of the transformed values from MINITAB is shown on page 59. There is a rather substantial resemblance to a normal curve. A more sophisticated assessment involving the use of a normal probability plot (see Section 7.3) indicates that the transformed data is very well fit by a normal curve. Perhaps there is some biological basis for this transformation. (A colleague gratuitously commented that our own weights would certainly look more "normal" when transformed in this manner!)

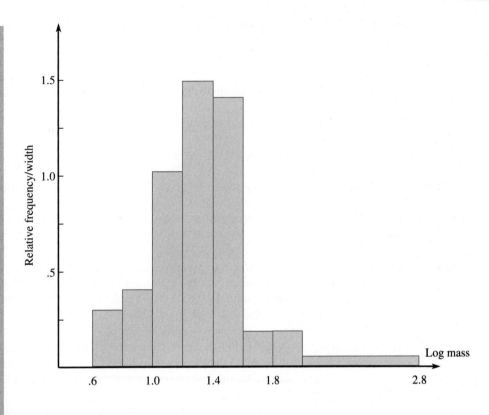

```
Histogram  N = 50
Midpoint   Count
    50       1    *
   100       3    ***
   150       4    ****
   200      13    *************
   250       9    *********
   300      10    **********
   350       6    ******
   400       3    ***
   450       1    *
```

CHAPTER TWO SUMMARY OF KEY CONCEPTS AND FORMULAS

Term or Formula	Comment
Categorical data	Individual observations are categorical responses (nonnumerical).
Numerical data	Individual observations are numerical in nature.
Discrete numerical data	Possible values are isolated points along the number line.
Continuous numerical data	Possible values form an entire interval along the number line.
Bivariate and multivariate data	Each observation consists of two (bivariate) or more responses or values.
Stem-and-leaf display	A method of organizing quantitative data in which the stem values (leading digit(s) of the observations) are listed in a column, and the leaf (trailing digit(s)) for each observation is then listed beside the corresponding stem. Sometimes stems are repeated to stretch the display.
Frequency distribution	A table that displays frequencies and relative frequencies (proportions) for the different categories (when data is categorical), values of a counting variable, or class intervals (when observations are on a continuous variable).
Histogram	A picture of the information in a frequency distribution. A rectangle is drawn above each category label, value of a counting variable, or class interval. The rectangle's area is proportional to the corresponding relative frequency (or, equivalently, frequency).
Histogram shapes	A (smoothed) histogram may be unimodal (a single peak), bimodal (two peaks), or multimodal. A unimodal histogram may be symmetric, positively skewed (a long right or upper tail), or negatively skewed. A frequently occurring shape is that of a normal curve.
Transformed data	The result of applying a specified mathematical operation (for example, square root or logarithm) to each observation in the original data set. A transformation is applied in order to make description and summarization easier.

SUPPLEMENTARY EXERCISES 2.42–2.57

2.42 The accompanying frequency distribution of the number of years of continuous service at the time of resignation from a job with an oil company appeared in the paper "The Role of Performance in the Turnover Process" (*Academy of Management J.* (1982):137–147). Construct the histogram corresponding to this frequency distribution. Which terms introduced in this chapter (symmetric, skewed, and so on) would you use to describe the histogram?

Years of service	Frequency
0–<1	4
1–<2	41
2–<3	67
3–<4	82
4–<5	28
5–<6	43
6–<7	14
7–<8	17
8–<9	11
9–<10	7
10–<11	14
11–<12	6
12–<13	14
13–<14	5
14–<15	2

2.43 A sample of 50 individuals who recently joined a certain travel club yielded the following responses on occupation (C = clerical, M = manager/executive, P = professional, R = retired, S = sales, T = skilled tradesperson, O = other):

P R R M S R P R C P M R T O R S R S P M
R P C R R S T P P C M S R R P R S R R P
M P R R S C P R S M

Describe this data set.

2.44 A random sample of 60 preschool-age children who were participating in a day-care program was used to obtain information about parental work status.

The two given frequency distributions appeared in the paper "Nutritional Understanding of Preschool Children Taught in the Home of a Child Development Laboratory" (*Home Econ. Research J.* (1984):52–60).

Work status of mother	Frequency
Unemployed	41
Employed part time	13
Employed full time	6

Father's occupation	Frequency
Professional	21
Craftsperson	19
Manager	6
Proprietor	7
Other	7

a. Construct a relative frequency distribution for the mothers' work statuses. What proportion of the mothers work outside the home?

b. Draw the histogram corresponding to the frequency distribution for the fathers' occupations.

2.45 The paper "Paraquat and Marijuana Risk Assessment" (*Amer. J. of Public Health* (1983):784–788) reported the results of a 1978 telephone survey on marijuana usage. The accompanying frequency distribution gives the amount of marijuana (in grams) smoked per week for those respondents who indicated that they did use the drug.

Grams smoked per week	Frequency
0–<3	94
3–<11	269
11–<18	70
18–<25	48
25–<32	31
32–<39	10

(continued)

(continued)

Grams smoked per week	Frequency
39–<46	5
46–<53	0
53–<60	1
60–<67	0
67–<74	1

a. Display the information given in the frequency distribution in the form of a histogram.

b. What proportion of respondents smoked 25 or more grams per week?

c. Use the histogram to estimate the proportion of respondents who smoked more than 15 g per week.

2.46 Data on engine emissions for 46 vehicles is given here (*Technometrics* (November 1980):487).

Vehicle	HC	CO	Vehicle	HC	CO
1	.50	5.01	2	.65	14.67
3	.46	8.60	4	.41	4.42
5	.41	4.95	6	.39	7.24
7	.44	7.51	8	.55	12.30
9	.72	14.59	10	.64	7.98
11	.83	11.53	12	.38	4.10
13	.38	5.21	14	.50	12.10
15	.60	9.62	16	.73	14.97
17	.83	15.13	18	.57	5.04
19	.34	3.95	20	.41	3.38
21	.37	4.12	22	1.02	23.53
23	.87	19.00	24	1.10	22.92
25	.65	11.20	26	.43	3.81
27	.48	3.45	28	.41	1.85
29	.51	4.10	30	.41	2.26
31	.47	4.74	32	.52	4.29
33	.56	5.36	34	.70	14.83
35	.51	5.69	36	.52	6.35
37	.57	6.02	38	.51	5.79
39	.36	2.03	40	.49	4.62
41	.52	6.78	42	.61	8.43
43	.58	6.02	44	.46	3.99
45	.47	5.22	46	.55	7.47

a. Construct a frequency distribution and histogram for the hydrocarbon (HC) emissions data.

b. Construct a frequency distribution and histogram for the carbon monoxide (CO) data.

c. Are the HC and CO histograms symmetric or skewed? If they are both skewed, is the direction of the skew the same?

2.47 The following data refers to active repair times (hours) for an airborne communication receiver.

1.1	4.0	0.5	5.4	2.0	0.5	0.8	9.0	5.0	3.3
0.3	0.7	2.2	22.0	4.0	2.7	1.0	3.0	1.0	1.5
24.5	1.5	3.3	2.5	1.0	0.8	1.5	0.6	10.3	1.3
0.7	2.0	4.7	3.0	0.8	1.0	8.8	0.6	4.5	7.0
0.7	5.4	1.5	1.5	0.2	7.5	0.5			

a. Construct a stem-and-leaf display in which the two largest values are displayed separately in a row labeled HI.

b. Construct a histogram based on six class intervals with zero as the lower limit of the first interval and interval lengths of 2, 2, 2, 4, 10, and 10, respectively.

2.48 Suppose that the accompanying observations are heating costs for a sample of two-bedroom apartments in Southern California for the month of November.

Heated with gas					
25.42	26.12	25.22	23.60	27.77	28.52
21.60	29.49	26.22	25.52	20.19	23.99
26.32	23.38	26.77	31.56	25.54	22.72
27.58	29.96	26.20	23.97	28.17	18.01
22.98					

Heated with electricity					
33.52	51.01	41.99	33.80	25.93	30.32
32.06	39.86	24.62	31.80	48.58	44.65
31.30	35.04	19.24	40.78	43.39	34.78
25.43	33.82	26.47	34.62	32.02	27.98
30.92					

Use several methods from this chapter to compare costs for the two types of heating.

2.49 The two accompanying frequency distributions appeared in the paper "Aqueous Humour Glucose Concentration in Cataract Patients and its Effect on the Lens" (*Exp. Eye Research* (1984):605–609). The first is a frequency distribution of lens sodium concentration (in mM) for nondiabetic cataract patients, while the second is for diabetic cataract patients. Draw the histogram corresponding to each frequency distribution. Do you think that the distributions for the population of all diabetic patients and for the population of nondiabetic cataract patients are similar? Explain.

Sodium concentration (mM)	Nondiabetic frequency	Diabetic frequency
0–<20	7	0
20–<40	12	0
40–<60	5	1
60–<80	1	2
80–<100	0	3
100–<120	1	2
120–<140	1	1
140–<160	4	0
160–<180	8	1
180–<200	3	0
200–<220	2	0
220–<240	1	0

2.50 Referring to Exercise 2.49, construct the cumulative relative frequencies corresponding to the frequency distribution of lens sodium concentration (in mM) of nondiabetic cataract patients. Use them to answer the following questions.
   a. What proportion of the nondiabetic cataract patients had a lens sodium concentration below 100 mM?
   b. What proportion of the nondiabetic cataract patients had a lens sodium concentration between 100 and 200 mM?
   c. What proportion of the nondiabetic cataract patients had a lens sodium concentration of at least 140 mM?
   d. Find a sodium concentration value for which approximately half of the observed sodium concentrations are smaller than this value.

2.51 The two given frequency distributions of storm duration (in minutes) are based on data appearing in the article "Lightning Phenomenology in the Tampa Bay Area" (*J. of Geophysical Research* (1984):11,789–805). Construct a histogram for each of the frequency distributions and discuss the similarities and differences between the two with respect to shape.

Storm duration	Single-peak storms: frequency	Multiple-peak storms: frequency
0–<25	1	0
25–<50	17	1
50–<75	14	1
75–<100	11	3
100–<125	8	2
125–<150	8	2
150–<175	5	1
175–<200	4	3
200–<225	3	1
225–<250	2	6
250–<275	0	4
275–<300	1	2

2.52 The paper "The Acid Rain Controversy: The Limits of Confidence" (*Amer. Statistician* (1983):385–394) gave the accompanying data on average SO_2 (sulfur dioxide) emission rates from utility and industrial boilers (lb/million Btu) for 47 states. (Data from Idaho, Alaska, and Hawaii was not given.)

2.3	2.7	1.5	1.5	0.3	0.6	4.2	1.3	1.2	0.4
0.5	2.2	4.5	3.8	1.2	0.2	1.0	0.7	0.2	1.4
0.7	3.6	1.0	0.7	1.7	0.5	0.1	0.6	2.5	2.7
1.5	1.4	2.9	1.0	3.4	2.1	0.9	1.9	1.0	1.7
1.8	0.6	1.7	2.9	1.8	1.4	3.7			

   a. Summarize this set of data by constructing a relative frequency distribution.
   b. Draw the histogram corresponding to the frequency distribution in part (a). Would you describe the histogram as symmetric or skewed?

c. Use the relative frequency distribution of part (a) to compute the cumulative relative frequencies.

d. Use the cumulative relative frequencies to give the approximate proportion of states with SO_2 emission rates that
   i. were below 1.0 lb/million Btu;
   ii. were between 1.0 and 2.0 lb/million Btu;
   iii. were at least 2.0 lb/million Btu.

2.53 The Los Angeles Unified School District includes 49 public high schools. The *Los Angeles Times* (January 20, 1985) published the average math SAT exam score for each of the 49 schools. Use several of the methods described in this chapter to summarize this data.

Average SAT math score for 49 public high schools						
341	477	461	456	349	481	499
328	471	436	440	414	448	503
399	335	332	422	356	375	488
406	375	458	341	468	404	482
464	475	398	317	466	470	463
409	478	469	404	487	439	459
464	502	472	480	481	402	339

2.54 The soil stability index (SSI) of eroded topsoil was recorded for 41 randomly selected sites under dry conditions and for 39 randomly selected sites under green conditions ("Use of Landsat Radiance Parameters to Distinguish Soil Erosion, Stability, and Deposition in Arid Central Australia," *Remote Sensing of Environment* (1984):195–209). Construct and interpret a comparative stem-and-leaf display.

Soil stability index											
Dry conditions						**Green conditions**					
31	44	44	44	36	36	20	20	20	20	21	21
36	45	37	45	45	38	21	24	24	24	24	25
39	39	39	39	39	39	25	25	25	25	27	27
39	39	39	39	40	40	27	27	27	28	28	28
40	40	40	40	40	40	30	30	30	41	41	41
41	41	41	41	42	42	42	42	50	50	50	50
42	42	43	43	43		50	50	59			

2.55 Americium 241 (^{241}Am) is a radioactive material used in the manufacture of smoke detectors. The article "Retention and Dosimetry of Injected ^{241}Am in Beagles" (*Radiation Research* (1984): 564–575) described a study in which 55 beagles were injected with a dose of ^{241}Am (proportional to the animals' weights). Skeletal retention of ^{241}Am (μCi/kg) was recorded for each beagle, resulting in the given data.

.196	.451	.498	.411	.324	.190	.489	.300
.346	.448	.188	.399	.305	.304	.287	.243
.334	.299	.292	.419	.236	.315	.447	.585
.291	.186	.393	.419	.335	.332	.292	.375
.349	.324	.301	.333	.408	.399	.303	.318
.468	.441	.306	.367	.345	.428	.345	.412
.337	.353	.357	.320	.354	.361	.329	

a. Construct a frequency distribution for this data and draw the corresponding histogram.

b. Write a short description of the important features of the shape of the histogram.

2.56 The clearness index was determined for the skies over Baghdad for each of the 365 days during a particular year ("Contribution to the Study of the Solar Radiation Climate of the Baghdad Environment," *Solar Energy* (1990):7–12). The accompanying table gives the results.

Class	Frequency
.15–<.25	8
.25–<.35	14
.35–<.45	28
.45–<.50	24
.50–<.55	39
.55–<.60	51
.60–<.65	106
.65–<.70	84
.70–<.75	11

a. Determine relative frequencies and draw the corresponding histogram.

b. Cloudy days are those with a clearness index smaller than .35. What percentage of the days were cloudy?

c. Clear days are those for which the index is at least .65. What percentage of the days were clear?

2.57 The accompanying figure appeared in the paper "EDTA-Extractable Copper, Zinc and Manganese in Soils of the Canterbury Plains" (*New Zealand J. of Ag. Res.* (1984):207–217, reprinted with permission). A large number of topsoil samples were analyzed for manganese (Mn), zinc (Zn), and copper (Cu), and the resulting data was summarized using histograms. The authors transformed each data set using logarithms in an effort to obtain more symmetric distributions of values. Do you think the transformations were successful? Explain.

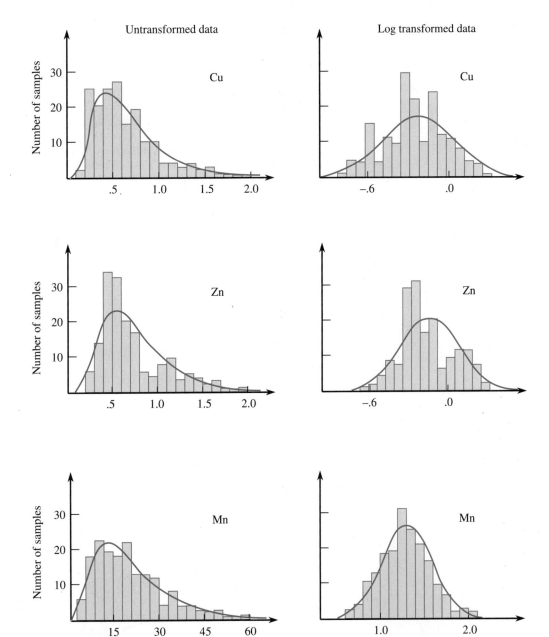

References

Chambers, John, William Cleveland, Beat Kleiner, and Paul Tukey. *Graphical Methods for Data Analysis.* Belmont, Calif.: Wadsworth, 1983. (This is an excellent survey of methods, illustrated with numerous interesting examples.)

Cleveland, William. *The Elements of Graphing Data.* Belmont, Calif.: Wadsworth, 1985. (An informal and informative introduction to various aspects of graphical analysis.)

Freedman, David, Robert Pisani, Roger Purves, and Ani Adhikari. *Statistics.* New York: W. W. Norton, 1991. (An excellent, very informal introduction to concepts, with some insightful cautionary examples concerning misuses of statistical methods.)

Koopmans, Lambert H. *An Introduction to Contemporary Statistics.* Boston: Duxbury, 1986. (The first part of this book contains an interesting presentation of both traditional descriptive methods and the more recently developed exploratory techniques.)

Moore, David. *Statistics: Concepts and Controversies.* New York: W. H. Freeman, 1991. (A nonmathematical yet highly entertaining introduction to our discipline—two thumbs up!)

Velleman, Paul, and David Hoaglin. *Applications, Basics, and Computing of Exploratory Data Analysis.* Boston: Duxbury, 1981. (Subtitled "ABC's of EDA," this book contains a good treatment of exploratory methods.)

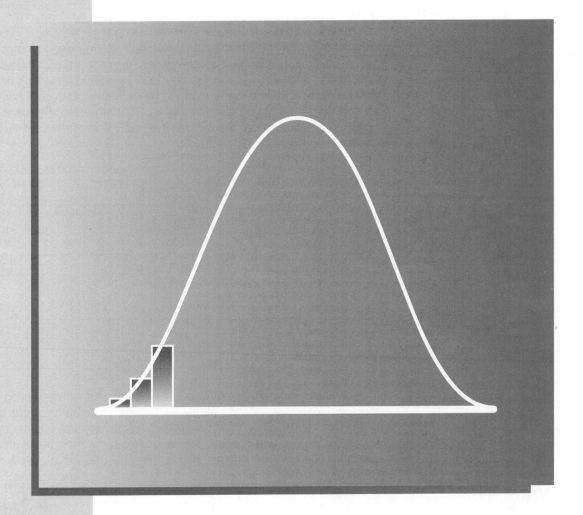

Numerical Summary Measures

PREVIEW

In recent years there has been some evidence to suggest that high indoor radon concentration may be linked to the development of childhood cancers, but many health professionals remain unconvinced. A recent article ("Indoor Radon and Childhood Cancer," *The Lancet* (1991):1537–1538) presented the accompanying data on radon concentration (Bq/m^3) in two different samples of houses. The first sample consisted of houses in which a child diagnosed with cancer had been residing. Houses in the second sample had no recorded cases of childhood cancer.

						Cancer						
10	21	5	23	15	11	9	13	27	13	39	22	7	20
45	12	15	3	8	11	18	16	23	16	34	10	15	11
18	210	22	11	6	17	33	10	9	57	16	21	18	38

						No Cancer						
9	38	11	12	29	5	7	6	8	29	24	12	17	11
3	9	33	17	55	11	29	13	24	7	11	21	6	39
29	7	8	55	9	21	9	3	85	11	14			

We could compare and contrast these samples by constructing comparative stem-and-leaf displays and histograms, but such a comparison can be somewhat subjective. Alternatively, it is desirable to summarize each sample by calculating several quantities that convey information about the most interesting features of the data. The resulting summaries can then be used to identify similarities and differences in the two samples.

Introduction

Stem-and-leaf displays, frequency distributions, and histograms are effective in conveying general impressions about the distribution of values in a data set. To gain deeper insights and develop methods for further analysis, however, we need compact and precise ways of describing and characterizing data. Here we will see how we can summarize and convey some important features of a data set by using just a few numerical summary quantities computed from the data. In Section 3.1 we introduce the mean and median as measures of the center of a numerical data set. The variance and standard deviation are presented in Section 3.2 as measures of the extent to which data spreads out about the center. The last section illustrates how these and other summarizing quantities and techniques convey information about prominent features of a data set.

3.1   Describing the Center of a Data Set

An informative way to describe the location of a numerical data set is to report a central value, one that is representative of the observations in the set. The two most popular measures of center are the *mean* and the *median*.

The Mean

The **mean** of a set of numerical observations is just the familiar arithmetic average, the sum of observations divided by the number of observations. Values in such a data set are observations on a numerical variable. The variable might be the number of traffic accidents, the number of pages in a book, reaction time, yield from a chemical reaction, etc. For the case of sample data, it is helpful to have concise notation for the variable, sample size, and individual observations. Let

x = the variable for which we have sample data

n = the number of sample observations (sample size)

x_1 = the first sample observation

x_2 = the second observation

$\vdots$

x_n = the nth (last) sample observation

As an example, we might have a sample consisting of $n = 4$ observations on $x = $ battery lifetime (h): $x_1 = 5.9$, $x_2 = 7.3$, $x_3 = 6.6$, $x_4 = 5.7$. Notice that the value of the subscript on x has no relationship to the magnitude of the observation. In this example, x_1 is not the smallest observation, only the first one obtained by an investigator, and x_4 is not the largest observation.

The sum of $x_1, x_2, \ldots, x_n$ can be denoted by $x_1 + x_2 + \cdots + x_n$, but this is cumbersome. The Greek letter Σ is traditionally used in mathematics to denote summation. In particular, Σx will denote the sum of the x values in the data set under consideration.

DEFINITION

The **sample mean** of a numerical sample $x_1, x_2, \ldots, x_n$, denoted by $\bar{x}$, is

$$\bar{x} = \frac{\text{sum of all observations in the sample}}{\text{number of observations in the sample}}$$

$$= \frac{x_1 + x_2 + \cdots + x_n}{n} = \frac{\Sigma x}{n}$$

EXAMPLE 3.1

Physical anthropologists frequently use fossil measurements to provide evidence for various anthropological theories. The paper "A Reconsideration of the Fontech-evade Fossils" (*J. of Phys. Anthropology* (1973):25–36) reported the following data on height of the left frontal sinus (in mm) for a sample of $n = 14$ fossils known to be Neanderthals.

$$x_1 = 42 \quad x_2 = 27 \quad x_3 = 25 \quad x_4 = 40 \quad x_5 = 33 \quad x_6 = 31 \quad x_7 = 42$$
$$x_8 = 34 \quad x_9 = 35 \quad x_{10} = 25 \quad x_{11} = 29 \quad x_{12} = 30 \quad x_{13} = 29 \quad x_{14} = 35$$

The sum of these sample values is $42 + 27 + \cdots + 35 = 457$, so the sample mean height is

$$\bar{x} = \frac{\Sigma x}{n} = \frac{457}{14} = 32.6$$

Thus we could report 32.6 mm as a representative sinus height value for this sample (even though there is no skull in the sample with this value).

The data values in Example 3.1 were all integers, yet the mean was given as 32.6. It is common practice to report one extra digit of decimal accuracy for the mean.[1] This allows the value of the mean to fall between possible observable values (for example, the average number of children per family could be 1.8, whereas no single family will have 1.8 children). It could also be argued that the mean carries with it more precision than does any single observation.

The sample mean $\bar{x}$ is computed from sample observations, so it is a characteristic of the particular sample in hand. It is customary to use a Roman letter to denote such a *sample* characteristic, as we have done with $\bar{x}$. Characteristics of the entire population are usually denoted by Greek letters. One of the most important such characteristics is the population mean.

> **DEFINITION**
>
> The **population mean,** denoted by μ, is the average of all x values in the entire population.

For example, the true average fuel efficiency for all 600,000 cars of a certain type under specified conditions might be $\mu = 27.5$ mi/gal. A sample of $n = 5$ cars might yield efficiencies

27.3, 26.2, 28.4, 27.9, 26.5

from which we obtain $\bar{x} = 27.26$ (somewhat smaller than μ). However a second sample might give $\bar{x} = 28.52$, a third $\bar{x} = 26.85$, and so on. The value of $\bar{x}$ varies

---

[1] Often $\bar{x}$ is used in the calculation of other quantities. More digits may then be necessary to ensure accurate results. A first instance of this will appear in the next section.

from sample to sample, whereas there is just one value for μ. Later on we shall see how the value of $\bar{x}$ from a particular sample can be used to draw various conclusions about the value of μ.

EXAMPLE 3.2

The 50 states plus the District of Columbia contain a total of 3137 counties. Let x denote the number of residents of a county. Then there are 3137 x values in the population. The sum of these 3137 values is 248,709,873 (1990 census), so the population average value of x is

$$\mu = \frac{248,709,873}{3137} = 79,282.7 \text{ residents per county}$$

We used *The World Almanac and Book of Facts* to select three different samples at random from this population of counties, each sample consisting of five counties. The results appear in Table 3.1, along with the sample mean for each sample.

TABLE 3.1   Three samples from the population of all U.S. counties
(x = number of residents)

Sample 1		Sample 2		Sample 3	
County	x Value	County	x Value	County	x Value
Fayette, TX	20,095	Stoddard, MO	28,895	Chattahoochee, GA	16,934
Monroe, IN	108,978	Johnston, OK	10,032	Petroleum, MT	519
Greene, NC	15,384	Sumter, AL	16,174	Armstrong, PA	73,478
Shoshone, ID	13,931	Milwaukee, WI	959,275	Smith, MI	14,798
Jasper, IN	24,960	Albany, WY	30,797	Benton, MO	13,859
Σx =	183,348	Σx =	1,045,173	Σx =	119,588
$\bar{x}$ =	36,669.6	$\bar{x}$ =	209,034.6	$\bar{x}$ =	23,917.6

Not only are the three $\bar{x}$ values different from one another—because they are based on three different samples and the value of $\bar{x}$ depends on the x values in the sample—but none of the three comes close to the value of the population mean, μ. If we did not know the value of μ but had only sample 1 available, we might use $^- =$ 36,669.6 as an *estimate* of μ, but our estimate would be far off the mark. Alternatively, we could combine the three samples into a single sample with $n = 15$ observations:

$$x_1 = 20,095, \ldots, x_5 = 24,960, \ldots, x_{15} = 13,859$$

$$\Sigma x = 1,348,109$$

$$\bar{x} = \frac{1,348,109}{15} = 89,873.9$$

This is closer to the true value of μ but still not very satisfactory as an estimate. The problem here is that there is so much variability in the population of x values (the largest is $x = 8,863,164$ for Los Angeles County and the smallest is $x = 107$ for Loving County, Texas, which few people evidently love) that it is difficult for a sample of 15 observations, let alone just 5, to be reasonably representative of the population. But don't lose hope! Once we learn how to measure variability, we'll also see how to take it into account in making accurate inferences.

A potential drawback to the mean is that its value can be greatly affected by the presence of even a single outlier (an unusually large or small observation) in the data set.

EXAMPLE 3.3

A sample of $n = 8$ fiction books is selected from a library's collection, and page length of each one is determined, resulting in the following data.

$$x_1 = 247 \quad x_2 = 312 \quad x_3 = 198 \quad x_4 = 780$$
$$x_5 = 175 \quad x_6 = 286 \quad x_7 = 293 \quad x_8 = 258$$

The sample mean is

$$\bar{x} = \frac{\Sigma x}{n} = \frac{2549}{8} = 318.6$$

The data is displayed in Figure 3.1. Many would argue that 318.6 is not a very representative value for this sample, since it is larger than all but one of the observations. (Without the outlier, $\bar{x} = 252.7$!)

FIGURE 3.1
The data from Example 3.3

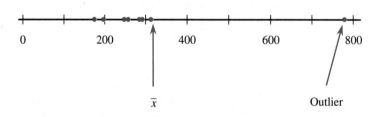

We now turn our attention to a measure of center that is quite insensitive to outliers.

The Median

The median strip of a highway divides the highway in half, and the median of a numerical data set performs an analogous function. Once the numbers in the set have been listed in order from smallest to largest, the **median** is the middle value in the list and divides the list into two equal parts. Let us first consider the case of a sample containing n observations. When n is an odd number (say, 5), the sample median is the single middle value. But when n is even (say, 6), there are two middle values in the ordered list, so we average them to obtain the sample median.

> **DEFINITION**
>
> The **sample median** is obtained by first ordering the n observations from smallest to largest (with any repeated values included, so that every sample observation appears in the ordered list). Then
>
> $$\text{sample median} = \begin{cases} \text{the single middle value if } n \text{ is odd} \\ \text{the average of the two middle values if } n \text{ is even} \end{cases}$$

EXAMPLE 3.4

The risk of developing iron deficiency is especially high during pregnancy. The problem with detecting such deficiency is that some methods for determining iron status can be affected by the state of pregnancy itself. Consider the following data on transferrin receptor concentration for a sample of women with laboratory evidence of overt iron-deficiency anemia ("Serum Transferrin Receptor for the Detection of Iron Deficiency in Pregnancy," *Amer. J. of Clinical Nutrition* (1991): 1077–1081).

$$x_1 = 15.2 \qquad x_2 = 9.3 \qquad x_3 = 7.6 \qquad x_4 = 11.9$$
$$x_5 = 10.4 \qquad x_6 = 9.7 \qquad x_7 = 20.4 \qquad x_8 = 9.4$$
$$x_9 = 11.5 \qquad x_{10} = 16.2 \qquad x_{11} = 9.4 \qquad x_{12} = 8.3$$

The list of ordered values is

7.6   8.3   9.3   9.4   9.4   9.7   10.4   11.5   11.9   15.2   16.2   20.4

2 middle values

Thus

$$\text{sample median} = \frac{9.7 + 10.4}{2} = 10.05$$

The sample mean is

$$\bar{x} = \frac{\Sigma x}{n} = \frac{139.3}{12} = 11.61$$

somewhat larger than the median because of the outliers 15.2, 16.2, and 20.4.

The **population median** plays the same role for the population that the sample median plays for the sample. It is the middle value in the ordered list consisting of all population observations.

We previously noted that the mean—population or sample—is very sensitive to even a single value that lies far above or below the rest of the data. The value of the mean is pulled out toward such an outlying value or values. The median, on the other hand, is quite insensitive to outliers. For example, the largest sample observation (20.4) in Example 3.4 can be increased by an arbitrarily large amount without changing the value of the median. Similarly, an increase in the second or third largest observations does not affect the median, nor would a decrease in several of the smallest observations.

This stability of the median is what sometimes justifies its use as a measure of center. Income distributions are commonly summarized by reporting the median rather than the mean, since otherwise a few very high salaries would distort the resulting typical salary.

Comparing the Mean and the Median

Figure 3.2 presents several smoothed histograms that might represent either a distribution of sample values or a population distribution. Pictorially, the median is the value on the measurement axis that separates the histogram into two parts with .5 (50%) of the area under each part of the curve. The mean is a bit harder to visualize. If the histogram were placed on a fulcrum with a sharp point, it would tilt unless the fulcrum were positioned exactly at the mean. The mean is the balance point for the distribution.

FIGURE 3.2
Picturing the mean
and the median

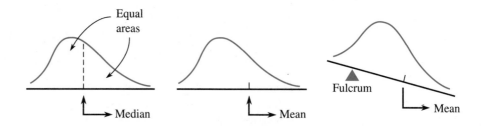

When the histogram is symmetric, the point of symmetry is both the dividing point for equal areas and the balance point, so the mean and median are identical. However, when the histogram is unimodal (single-peaked) with a longer upper tail, the relatively few outlying values in the upper tail pull the mean up, so that it lies above the median. For example, an unusually high exam score raises the mean but does not affect the median. Similarly, when a unimodal histogram is negatively skewed, the mean is smaller than the median (see Figure 3.3).

FIGURE 3.3
Relationship between the
mean and the median

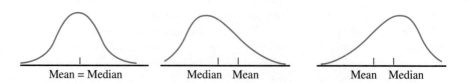

Categorical Data

The natural numerical summary quantities for a categorical data set are the relative frequencies for the various categories. Each relative frequency is the proportion (fraction) of responses that are in the corresponding category. Often there are only two possible responses (a *dichotomy*)—male or female, does or does not have a driver's license, did or did not vote in the last election, and so on. It is convenient in such situations to label one of the two possible responses S (for success) and the other F (for failure). As long as further analysis is consistent with the labeling, it is immaterial which category is assigned the S label. When the data set comprises a sample, the fraction of S's in the sample is called the *sample proportion of successes.*

DEFINITION

The **sample proportion of successes,** denoted by p, is

$$p = \left(\begin{array}{c} \text{sample proportion} \\ \text{of successes} \end{array} \right) = \frac{\text{number of } S\text{'s in the sample}}{n}$$

EXAMPLE 3.5

The use of antipollution equipment on automobiles has substantially improved air quality in certain areas. Unfortunately, many car owners have tampered with smog control devices to improve performance. A sample of $n = 15$ cars was selected, and each was classified as S or F, according to whether or not tampering had taken place. The resulting data was

$S, F, S, S, S, F, F, S, S, F, S, S, S, F, F$

This sample contains nine S's, so

$$p = \frac{9}{15} = .60$$

That is, 60% of the sample responses are S's, so in 60% of the cars sampled, there has been tampering with the air pollution control devices.

The Greek letter π will be used to denote the **population proportion of S's.** We shall see later how the value of p from a particular sample can be used to make inferences about π.

Trimmed Means

The extreme sensitivity of the mean to even a single outlier and the extreme insensitivity of the median to a substantial proportion of outliers can make both suspect as a measure of center. Statisticians have proposed a *trimmed mean* as a compromise between these two extremes.

> **DEFINITION**
>
> A **trimmed mean** is computed by first ordering the data values from smallest to largest, deleting a selected number of values from each end of the ordered list, and finally averaging the remaining values. The **trimming percentage** is the percentage of values deleted from each end of the ordered list.

EXAMPLE 3.6

The paper "Snow Cover and Temperature Relationships in North America and Eurasia" (*J. of Climate and Appl. Meteorology* (1983):460–469) used statistical techniques to relate amount of snow cover on each continent to average continental temperature. Data presented there included the following ten observations on October snow cover for Eurasia during the years 1970–1979 (in million km^2):

6.5   12.0   14.9   10.0   10.7   7.9   21.9   12.5   14.5   9.2

The ordered values are

6.5   7.9   9.2   10.0   10.7   12.0   12.5   14.5   14.9   21.9

Since 20% of 10 is 2, the 20% trimmed mean results from deleting the two observations at each end of the ordered list and averaging the remaining six values:

$$20\% \text{ trimmed mean} = \frac{9.2 + 10.0 + 10.7 + 12.0 + 12.5 + 14.5}{6} = 11.48$$

The mean, 12.01, is a 0% trimmed mean—no deletion before averaging. In this example, the median, 11.35, is a 40% trimmed mean, the largest possible trimming percentage when $n = 10$. The 20% trimmed mean is a good choice here for a representative October snow cover value.

A trimmed mean with a small-to-moderate trimming percentage—between 5% and 25%—is less affected by outliers than the mean, yet is is not as insensitive as the median. Trimmed means are therefore being used with increasing frequency.

EXERCISES 3.1–3.15   SECTION 3.1

3.1   The accompanying data on concentration of lead (ppm) in core samples taken at 17 Texaco drilling sites appeared in the paper "Statistical Comparison of Heavy Metal Concentrations in Various Louisiana Sediments" (*Environ. Monitoring and Assessment* (1984):163–170).

55   53   55   59   58   50   63   50   50
48   56   63   54   53   56   50   55

a. Compute the sample mean.
b. Compute the sample median. How do the values of the sample mean and median compare?
c. The paper also gave the accompanying data on zinc concentration (ppm). Compute and interpret the value of the sample mean.

86   77   91   86   81   87   94   90   70
92   90   108   112   101   88   99   98

3.2   The paper "The Pedaling Technique of Elite Endurance Cyclists" (*Int. J. of Sport Biomechanics* (1991):29–53) reported the accompanying data on single-leg power at a high workload.

244   191   160   187   180   176   174
205   211   183   211   180   194   200

a. Calculate and interpret the sample mean and median.
b. Suppose that the first observation had been 204 rather than 244. How would the mean and median change?

3.3   The paper cited in Exercise 3.2 also reported values of single-leg power for a low workload. The sample mean for $n = 13$ observations was $\bar{x} = 119.8$ (actually 119.7692), and the 14th observation, somewhat of an outlier, was 159. What is the value of $\bar{x}$ for the entire sample?

3.4   The paper "Penicillin in the Treatment of Meningitis" (*J. Amer. Med. Assoc.* (1984):1870–1873) reported the body temperatures (°F) of patients hospitalized with meningitis. Ten of the observations were as follows.

104.0   104.8   101.6   108.0   103.8   100.8   104.2   100.2   102.4   101.4

a. Compute the sample mean.
b. Do you think the 10% trimmed mean would differ much from the sample mean computed in part (a)? Why? Answer without actually computing the trimmed mean.

3.5   In anticipation of the 1984 Olympics, the *Los Angeles Times* (August 15, 1983) reported the ozone levels at several sites that were to be used for Olympic events the following summer. Listed next are the ozone readings (in ppm) taken at noon from July 28 to August 12 at East Los Angeles College.

10	14	13	18	12	22	14	19
22	13	14	16	3	6	7	19

a. Compute the sample mean.

b. Compute the sample median.

c. Compute the 6.25% trimmed mean (by deleting the smallest and largest values before averaging). Is this a more representative measure than the sample mean or median? Explain.

d. Consider now the ozone levels for a second Olympic site, the Coliseum.

8	13	10	9	16	12	13	14
17	13	9	16	5	9	8	12

Describe the center of this data set using the mean and the median. How do the values of the mean and median for the Coliseum compare to those for East Los Angeles College?

3.6 One of the problems with which health service administrators must deal is patient dissatisfaction. One common complaint focuses on the amount of time that a patient must wait in order to see a doctor. In a survey to investigate waiting times, medical-clinic secretaries were asked to record the waiting times (measured from arrival at the clinic until doctors are seen) for a sample of patients. The data (from *Statistics and Public Policy,* Fairley, William and Frederick Mosteller, eds. Reading, Mass.: Addison-Wesley, 1977) for one day is given in the accompanying table.

Waiting time (min)

40	30	40	55	30	60	35	55	40
35	5	10	65	35	35	30	30	60
35	25	65	30	30	45	85	25	25
10	10	15						

a. Describe a typical waiting time by using both the mean and the median. Which do you think is the most representative measure of the center of the data set? Why?

b. Compute a 10% trimmed mean. How does the trimmed mean compare in value to the mean and median calculated in part (a)?

3.7 Consider the following statement: Over 65% of the residents of Los Angeles earn less than the average wage for that city. Could this statement be correct? If so, how? If not, why not?

3.8 Five experimental animals were put on a certain diet for several weeks, and another five animals were put on a second diet. The resulting weight gains (in pounds) at the end of the period were as follows:

Diet 1:	12	13	7	5	15
Diet 2:	11	14	3	13	4

Without doing any calculation, decide which group of animals achieved the larger average weight gain. (Hint: Base your reasoning on the ordered values from each sample.)

3.9   Reconsider the situation described in Exercise 3.8, but suppose now that the weight gains for the second diet are 5, 13, 11, 10, and 3 lbs. Without doing any calculation, say how the average gain for the first diet compares to that for the second diet. (Hint: Again order the observations from smallest to largest within each sample.)

3.10   A sample consisting of four pieces of luggage was selected from among those checked at an airline counter, yielding the following data on x = weight (lb):

$$x_1 = 33.5, \qquad x_2 = 27.3, \qquad x_3 = 36.7, \qquad x_4 = 30.5$$

Suppose one more piece is selected; denote its weight by x_5. Find a value of x_5 so that $\bar{x}$ = sample median.

3.11   Refer to Exercise 3.10, and suppose that the weights for the first four pieces of luggage are

$$x_1 = 30, \qquad x_2 = 49, \qquad x_3 = 29, \qquad x_4 = 31$$

If x_5 is between 31 and 49, can it be the case that $\bar{x}$ = sample median? Explain your reasoning. (Hint: Let $x_5 = 31 + k$, where $k \geq 0$; now what can be said about $\bar{x}$?)

3.12   Suppose that the ten patients whose temperatures were given in Exercise 3.4 received treatment with large doses of penicillin. Three days later, temperatures were again recorded, and the treatment was considered successful if there had been a reduction in a patient's temperature. Denoting success by S and failure by F, the ten observations are

S   S   F   S   S   S   F   F   S   S

a. What is the value of the sample proportion of successes?
b. Replace each S with a 1 and each F with a 0. Then calculate $\bar{x}$ for this numerically coded sample. How does $\bar{x}$ compare to p?
c. Suppose that it is decided to include 15 more patients in the experiment. How many of these would have to be S's to give p = .80 for the entire sample of 25 patients?

3.13   An experiment to study the lifetime (in hours) for a certain type of component involved putting ten components into operation and observing them for 100 h. Eight of the components failed during that period, and those lifetimes were recorded. Denote the lifetimes of the two components still functioning after 100 h by 100+. The resulting sample observations were

48   79   100+   35   92   86   57   100+   17   29

Which of the measures of center discussed in this section can be calculated, and what are the values of those measures? (Note: The data from this experiment is said to be "censored on the right.")

3.14   An instructor has graded 19 exam papers submitted by students in a certain class of 20 students, and the average so far is 70 (the maximum possible score is 100). How high would the score on the last paper have to be to raise the class average by one point? By two points?

3.15   A certain college has two sections of introductory statistics during a particular semester. One section has 20 students and the other has 100 students.
   a. What is the mean number of students per section (the average over sections)?
   b. Let x_1 denote the number of students in the first student's class, let x_2 be the number of students in the second student's class, and so on (up through x_{120}). What is the average of these x values? (This is the mean class size when averaged over students rather than classes.)
   c. From a student perspective, which of the two averages, the one calculated in part (a) or the one in part (b), is more pertinent?

3.2   Describing Variability in a Data Set

Reporting a measure of center gives only partial information about a data set. It is also important to describe the spread of values about the center. The three different samples displayed in Figure 3.4 all have mean = median = 45. There is much variability in the first sample compared to the extent of spread in the third sample. The second sample shows less variability than the first and more than the third; most of the variability in the second sample is due to the two extreme values being so far from the center.

FIGURE 3.4
Three samples with the same center and different amounts of variability

Sample

1.   20, 40, 50, 30, 60, 70

2.   47, 43, 44, 46, 20, 70

3.   44, 43, 40, 50, 47, 46

Mean = Median

The simplest measure of variability is the **range,** which is the difference between the largest and smallest values. Generally speaking, more variability will be reflected in a larger range. However, variability depends on more than just the distance between the two most extreme values. The first two samples of Figure 3.4 both have a range of 50, but there is substantially less dispersion in the second sample.

Deviations from the Mean

Let us focus on sample data. Our primary measures of variability will depend on the extent to which each sample observation deviates from the sample mean $\bar{x}$. Subtracting $\bar{x}$ from each observation gives us the set of deviations from the mean.

DEFINITION

The n **deviations from the sample mean** are the differences

$$x_1 - \bar{x}, \ x_2 - \bar{x}, \ldots, \ x_n - \bar{x}$$

A particular deviation is positive if the x value exceeds $\bar{x}$ and negative if the x value is less than $\bar{x}$.

EXAMPLE 3.7

Durability of materials is a major concern of engineers. The accompanying observations are on $x =$ lifetime of power apparatus insulation (h) under specified experimental conditions ("On the Estimation of Life of Power Apparatus Insulation under Combined Electrical and Thermal Stress," *I.E.E.E. Trans. on Elec. Insulation* (1985):70–78):

$$
\begin{array}{lllll}
x_1 = 501 & x_2 = 1072 & x_3 = 1905 & x_4 = 282 & x_5 = 1122 \\
x_6 = 2138 & x_7 = 1202 & x_8 = 851 & x_9 = 741 & x_{10} = 1585
\end{array}
$$

The sample mean is $\bar{x} = 11{,}399/10 = 1139.9$.

The observations and corresponding deviations are displayed in Table 3.2.

TABLE 3.2 Deviations of insulation lifetimes from the mean

Observation number	Observation (x)	Deviation ($x - \bar{x}$)
1	501	−638.9
2	1072	−67.9
3	1905	765.1
4	282	−857.9
5	1122	−17.9
6	2138	998.1
7	1202	62.1
8	851	−288.9
9	741	−398.9
10	1585	445.1

The sixth deviation, $x_6 - \bar{x} = 2138 - 1139.9 = 998.1$, is positive and quite large because $x_6 = 2138$ greatly exceeds the mean. The fifth observation, $x_5 =$

1122, is just a bit below $\bar{x}$ on the measurement scale, yielding a negative deviation, -17.9, that is small in magnitude.

Generally speaking, the larger the magnitudes of the deviations, the greater the amount of variability in the sample. Thus the magnitudes of the deviations for the first sample in Figure 3.4 substantially exceed those for the third sample, implying more dispersion in sample 1.

We now consider how to combine the deviations into a single numerical measure. A first thought is to calculate the average deviation; that is, add the deviations together—this sum can be denoted compactly by $\Sigma(x - \bar{x})$—and divide by n. This does not work, though, because negative and positive deviations counteract one another in the summation.

Except for the effects of rounding in computing the deviations, it is always true that $\Sigma(x - \bar{x}) = 0.$[2] Thus the average deviation is always zero and so cannot be used as a measure of variability.

EXAMPLE 3.8

It is easily verified that the sum of the $n = 10$ deviations in Example 3.7 is exactly zero. The sample mean for the $n = 14$ Neanderthal sinus heights given in Example 3.1 is (to one decimal place) 32.6. The corresponding deviations are

9.4	-5.6	-7.6	7.4	0.4	-1.6	9.4
1.4	2.4	-7.6	-3.6	-2.6	-3.6	2.4

The sum of these deviations is .60. The discrepancy between this and zero is due entirely to rounding. Using $\bar{x} = 32.64$ gives $\Sigma(x - \bar{x}) = .04$. Carrying more digits of decimal accuracy in $\bar{x}$ gives a sum even closer to zero.

The Variance and Standard Deviation

The standard way to prevent negative and positive deviations from counteracting one another is to square them before combining. Then deviations with opposite signs but the same magnitude, such as $+20$ and -20, will make identical contributions to variability. The squared deviations are $(x_1 - \bar{x})^2$, $(x_2 - \bar{x})^2$, . . . , $(x_n - \bar{x})^2$, and their sum is

$$(x_1 - \bar{x})^2 + \cdots + (x_n - \bar{x})^2 = \Sigma(x - \bar{x})^2$$

---

[2] $\Sigma(x - \bar{x}) = (x_1 - \bar{x}) + (x_2 - \bar{x}) + \cdots + (x_n - \bar{x})$
$\qquad = \Sigma x - n\bar{x} = \Sigma x - n(\Sigma x/n) = \Sigma x - \Sigma x = 0$

Dividing this sum by the sample size n gives the average squared deviation. However, for a reason to be explained shortly, a divisor slightly smaller than n will be used.

DEFINITION

The **sample variance,** denoted by s^2, is the sum of squared deviations from the mean divided by $n - 1$. That is,

$$s^2 = \frac{\Sigma(x - \bar{x})^2}{n - 1}$$

The **sample standard deviation** is the square root of the variance and is denoted by s.

A large amount of variability in the sample is indicated by a relatively large value of s^2 or of s, while a small value of s^2 or s goes along with a small amount of variability. For most statistical purposes, s is the desired quantity, but s^2 must be computed first. Notice that whatever unit is used for x (such as lb or sec), the squared deviations and therefore s^2 are in squared units. Taking the square root gives a measure expressed in the same units as x.

EXAMPLE 3.9

(*Example 3.1 continued*) Table 3.3 presents squared deviations for the Neanderthal sinus height data using $\bar{x} = 32.64$.

TABLE 3.3   Deviations and squared deviations for the Neanderthal sinus height data

Observation	$(x - \bar{x})$	$(x - \bar{x})^2$
42	9.36	87.6096
27	-5.64	31.8096
25	-7.64	58.3696
40	7.36	54.1696
33	.36	.1296
31	-1.64	2.6896
42	9.36	87.6096
34	1.36	1.8496
35	2.36	5.5696
25	-7.64	58.3696
29	-3.64	13.2496
30	-2.64	6.9696
29	-3.64	13.2496
35	2.36	5.5696

Sum: $427.2144 = \Sigma(x - \bar{x})^2$

Thus,

$$s^2 = \frac{\Sigma(x - \bar{x})^2}{n - 1} = \frac{427.2144}{13} = 32.8626 \text{ cm}^2$$

$$s = \sqrt{32.8626} = 5.73 \text{ cm}$$

A Note Concerning Computation

The computation of s^2 using the defining formula can be a bit tedious. An alternative expression for the numerator of s^2 simplifies the arithmetic by eliminating the need to calculate the deviations. This alternative necessitates distinguishing between two different quantities that involve squaring and summation of the data:

1. First sum x values; then square the sum to obtain $(\Sigma x)^2$.
2. First square each x value; then sum the squares to obtain Σx^2.

If, for example, $x_1 = 3$ and $x_2 = 5$, then

$$(\Sigma x)^2 = (3 + 5)^2 = 8^2 = 64$$
$$\Sigma x^2 = x_1{}^2 + x_2{}^2 = 3^2 + 5^2 = 9 + 25 = 34$$

So the order in which the two operations, squaring and summation, are carried out makes a difference!

A computational formula for the sum of squared deviations is

$$\Sigma(x - \bar{x})^2 = \Sigma x^2 - \frac{(\Sigma x)^2}{n}$$

Thus a **computational formula for the sample variance** is

$$s^2 = \frac{\Sigma x^2 - \dfrac{(\Sigma x)^2}{n}}{n - 1}$$

According to this formula, after squaring each x value and adding these to obtain Σx^2, the single quantity $(\Sigma x)^2/n$ is subtracted from the result. Instead of the n subtractions required to obtain the deviations, just one subtraction now suffices.

The computed value of s^2, whether obtained from the defining formula or the computational formula, can sometimes be greatly affected by rounding in $\bar{x}$ or $(\Sigma x)^2/n$. Protection against adverse rounding effects can virtually always be achieved by using four or five digits of decimal accuracy beyond the decimal accuracy of the data values themselves.

EXAMPLE 3.10

(*Example 3.9 continued*) For efficient computation, it is convenient to place the x values in a single column (or row) and the x^2 values just beside (or below) them. Adding the numbers in these two columns (or rows) then gives Σx and Σx^2, respectively.

Observation number	x	x^2
1	42	1,764
2	27	729
3	25	625
4	40	1,600
5	33	1,089
6	31	961
7	42	1,764
8	34	1,156
9	35	1,225
10	25	625
11	29	841
12	30	900
13	29	841
14	35	1,225
	Sums: $\Sigma x = 457$	$\Sigma x^2 = 15,345$

Thus

$$\frac{(\Sigma x)^2}{n} = \frac{(457)^2}{14} = \frac{208,849}{14} = 14,917.7857$$

so

$$s^2 = \frac{15,345 - 14,917.7857}{14 - 1} = \frac{427.2143}{13} = 32.863$$

$$s = \sqrt{32.863} = 5.73 \text{ mm}$$

All statistical computer packages will calculate a variety of descriptive measures. Output resulting from use of the MINITAB Describe command with the sinus height data follows. Note that MINITAB gives the mean, median, and standard deviation as well as several other sample quantities.

	N	MEAN	MEDIAN	TRMEAN	STDEV	SEMEAN
SINUS HEIGHT	14	32.64	32.00	32.50	5.73	1.53

	MIN	MAX	Q1	Q3
SINUS HEIGHT	25.00	42.00	28.50	36.25

Interpretation and Properties

A standard deviation may be informally interpreted as the size of a "typical" deviation from the mean. Thus, in Example 3.10, a typical deviation from $\bar{x} = 32.6$ is about 5.73.

We computed $s = 5.73$ in Example 3.10 without saying whether this value indicated a large or small amount of variability. At this point it is better to use s for comparative purposes than for an absolute assessment of variability. If we obtained a sample of skulls of a second type and computed $s = 2.1$ for those skulls, then we would conclude that there is more variability in our original sample than in this second sample. A particular value of s can be judged large or small only in comparison to something else.

There are measures of variability for the entire population that are analogous to s^2 and s for a sample. These measures are called the **population variance** and **population standard deviation** and are denoted by σ^2 and σ, respectively. (We again use a lowercase Greek letter for a population characteristic.) The population standard deviation σ is expressed in the same units of measurement as are the values in the population. As with s, the value of σ can be used for comparative purposes.

In many statistical procedures we would like to use the value of σ, but unfortunately it is not usually available. We therefore have to use in its place a value computed from the sample that we hope is close to σ (that is, a good *estimate* of σ). This is why the divisor $n - 1$ is used in s^2: the value of s^2 as we defined it tends to be a bit closer to σ^2 than if s^2 were defined using a divisor of n. We will say more about this in Chapter 9.

The Interquartile Range (Optional)

As with $\bar{x}$, the value of s can be greatly affected by the presence of even a single unusually small or large observation. The *interquartile range* is a measure of variability that is resistant to the effects of outliers. It is based on quantities called *quartiles*. The *lower quartile* separates the bottom 25% of the data set from the upper 75%, and the *upper quartile* separates the top 25% from the bottom 75%. The *middle quartile* is the median. Figure 3.5 illustrates the locations of these quartiles for a smoothed histogram.

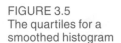
FIGURE 3.5
The quartiles for a
smoothed histogram

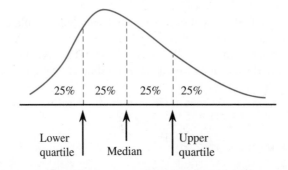

The quartiles for sample data are obtained by dividing the n ordered observations into a lower half and an upper half; if n is odd, the median is included in both halves. The two extreme quartiles are then the medians of the two halves.

DEFINITION

lower quartile = median of the lower half of the sample

upper quartile = median of the upper half of the sample

(If n is odd, the median of the entire sample is included in both halves.)

The **interquartile range (iqr),** a resistant measure of variability, is given by

iqr = upper quartile − lower quartile

EXAMPLE 3.11

Cardiac output and maximal oxygen uptake typically decrease with age in sedentary individuals, but these decreases are at least partially arrested in middle-aged individuals who engage in a substantial amount of physical exercise. To understand better the effects of exercise and aging on various circulatory functions, the paper "Cardiac Output in Male Middle-Aged Runners" (*J. of Sports Medicine* (1982): 17–22) presented data from a study of 21 middle-aged male runners. Figure 3.6 is a stem-and-leaf display of oxygen uptake values (mL/kg·min) while pedaling at 100W on a bicycle ergometer.

FIGURE 3.6
Stem-and-leaf display of
oxygen uptake (mL/kg·min)

12	81
13	
14	95
15	97, 83
16	
17	90
18	34, 27
19	94, 82
20	99, 93, 98, 62, 88
21	15
22	16, 24
23	16, 56

HI: 35.78, 36.73

Stem: Ones
Leaf: Hundredths

The sample size $n = 21$ is an odd number, so the median, 20.88, is included in both halves of the sample.

Lower half:	12.81	14.95	15.83	15.97	17.90	18.27
	18.34	19.82	19.94	20.62	20.88	
Upper half:	20.88	20.93	20.98	20.99	21.15	22.16
	22.24	23.16	23.56	35.78	36.73	

Each half of the sample contains 11 observations, so each quartile is the sixth value in from either end of the corresponding half. This gives us

lower quartile $= 18.27$

upper quartile $= 22.16$

and

$$iqr = 22.16 - 18.27 = 3.89$$

The sample mean and standard deviation are 21.10 and 5.75, respectively. If we were to change the two largest values from 35.78 and 36.73 to 25.78 and 26.73 (so that they are still the two largest values), the median and the interquartile range would not be affected, whereas the mean and standard deviation would change to 20.14 and 3.44, respectively.

The resistant nature of the iqr follows from the fact that up to 25% of the smallest sample observations and up to 25% of the largest can be made more extreme without affecting its value.

The **population interquartile range** is the difference between the upper and lower population quartiles. If a histogram of the data set under consideration (whether a population or a sample) can be reasonably well approximated by a normal curve, then the relationship between the standard deviation (sd) and inter-quartile range is roughly sd $=$ iqr/1.35. A value of the standard deviation much larger than iqr/1.35 suggests a histogram with heavier (or longer) tails than a normal curve. For the oxygen uptake data of Example 3.11, we had $s = 5.75$, while iqr/1.35 $= 3.89/1.35 = 2.88$. This suggests that the distribution of sample values is indeed heavy-tailed compared to a normal curve.

EXERCISES 3.16–3.27   SECTION 3.2

3.16   The paper "Improving Fermentation Productivity with Reverse Osmosis" (*Food Technology* (1984):92–96) summarized the results of an investigation into glucose concentration (g/l) for a particular blend of malt liquor. Eight batches were ana-lyzed, resulting in the given glucose concentrations.

74   54   52   51   52   53   58   71

a. Using $\bar{x} = 58.125$, calculate the deviations from the mean and verify that their sum is zero.

b. Use the deviations in part (a) to calculate s^2 and s.

3.17 Iron status in athletes is important because of the central role of this mineral in the synthesis of hemoglobin and enzymes fundamental to energy production. An investigation of such matters was reported in the paper "Iron Status in Winter Olympic Sports" (*J. of Sports Sciences* (1987):261–271). Consider the following sample observations on hemoglobin level (g/dl) for female alpine skiers.

    14.6   14.3   15.1   12.7   11.8   13.4   13.8

Use the computational formula to calculate s^2 and then obtain the sample standard deviation.

3.18 A study of the relationship between age and various visual functions (such as acuity and depth perception) reported the following observations on area of scleral lamina (mm^2) from human optic nerve heads ("Morphometry of Nerve Fiber Bundle Pores in the Optic Nerve Head of the Human," *Experimental Eye Research* (1988):559–568).

2.75	2.62	2.74	3.85	2.34	2.74	3.93	4.21	3.88
4.33	3.46	4.52	2.43	3.65	2.78	3.56	3.01	

a. Calculate Σx and Σx^2.

b. Use the values calculated in part (a) to compute the sample variance s^2 and then the sample standard deviation s. How can the value of s be interpreted?

3.19 **a.** Give two sets of five numbers that have the same mean but different standard deviations.

b. Give two sets of five numbers that have the same standard deviation but different means.

3.20 Although bats are not known for their eyesight, they are able to locate prey (mainly insects) by emitting high-pitched sounds and listening for echoes. A paper appearing in *Animal Behavior* ("The Echolocation of Flying Insects by Bats" (1960):141–154) gave the following distances (in cm) at which a bat first detected a nearby insect.

    62   23   27   56   52   34   42   40   68   45   83

a. Compute the sample mean distance at which a bat first detects an insect.

b. Compute the sample variance and standard deviation for this data set. How would you interpret these values?

3.21 The paper "Evaluating Variability of Filling Operations" (*Food Technology* (1984):51–55) gave data on the actual amount of fluid dispersed by a machine designed to disperse 10 oz. Ten observed values were used to compute $\Sigma x = 100.2$ and $\Sigma x^2 = 1004.4$. Compute the sample variance and standard deviation.

3.22   For the data in Exercise 3.20, add -10 to each sample observation. (This is the same as subtracting 10.) For the new set of values, compute the mean and the deviations from the mean. How do these deviations compare to the deviations from the mean for the original sample? How does s^2 for the new values compare to s^2 for the old values? In general, what effect does adding the same number to each observation have on s^2 and s? Explain.

3.23   For the data of Exercise 3.20, multiply each data value by 10. How does s for the new values compare to s for the original values?

✓ 3.24   The first four deviations from the mean in a sample of $n = 5$ reaction times were .3, .9, 1.0, and 1.3. What is the fifth deviation from the mean? Give a sample for which these are the five deviations from the mean.

3.25   Refer to the data in Exercise 3.18 on scleral lamina areas.
   a. Determine the lower and upper quartiles.
   b. Calculate the value of the interquartile range.
   c. If the two largest sample values, 4.33 and 4.52, had instead been 5.33 and 5.52, how would this affect the iqr? Explain.
   d. By how much could the observation 2.34 be increased without affecting the iqr? Explain.
   e. If an eighteenth observation, $x_{18} = 4.60$, is added to the sample, what is the iqr?

3.26   The following numbers are salinity values for water specimens taken from North Carolina's Pamlico Sound.

7.6	7.7	4.3	5.9	5.0	10.5	7.7	9.5	12.0	12.6
6.5	8.3	8.2	13.2	12.6	13.6	14.1	13.5	11.5	12.0
10.4	10.8	13.1	12.3	10.4	13.0	14.1	15.1		

   a. Calculate the value of s.
   b. Calculate iqr/1.35. How does this compare to s, and what does it suggest about the shape of the histogram of this data?

3.27   The standard deviation alone does not measure relative variation. For example, a standard deviation of $1 would be considered large if it is describing the variability from store to store in the price of an ice cube tray. On the other hand, a standard deviation of $1 would be considered small if it is describing store-to-store variability in the price of a particular brand of freezer. A quantity designed to give a relative measure of variability is the *coefficient of variation*. Denoted by CV, the coefficient of variation expresses the standard deviation as a percent of the mean. It is defined by the formula

$$CV = 100 \cdot \frac{s}{\bar{x}}$$

Consider the two given samples. Sample 1 gives the actual weight (in ounces) of the contents of cans of pet food labeled as having a net weight of 8 oz. Sample 2 gives the actual weight (in pounds) of the contents of bags of dry pet food labeled as having a net weight of 50 lb.

Sample 1:	8.3	7.1	7.6	8.1	7.6	8.3	8.2	7.7	7.7	7.5
Sample 2:	52.3	50.6	52.1	48.4	48.8	47.0	50.4	50.3	48.7	48.2

a. For each of the given samples, calculate the mean and the standard deviation.
b. Compute the coefficient of variation for each sample. Do the results surprise you? Why or why not?

3.3 Summarizing a Data Set (Optional)

A measure of center can be combined with a measure of variability to obtain informative statements about how values in a data set are distributed along the measurement scale. Often statements of interest refer to observations that are a specified number of standard deviations from the mean.

EXAMPLE 3.12

Consider a data set of IQ scores with mean and standard deviation 100 and 15, respectively. We can make the following statements:

a. Because $100 - 85 = 15$, we say that a score of 85 is "one standard deviation *below* the mean." Similarly, 115 is "one standard deviation *above* the mean."

b. Since $(2)(15) = 30$ and $100 + 30 = 130$, $100 - 30 = 70$, the scores 70, 71, 72, ..., 129, 130 are those *within* two standard deviations of the mean.

c. Because $100 + (3)(15) = 145$, the scores 146, 147, 148, ... exceed the mean by more than three standard deviations.

Chebyshev's Rule

Without knowing anything more about the data set than just the mean and standard deviation, **Chebyshev's Rule** gives information about the proportion of observations that fall within a specified number of standard deviations of the mean. The rule applies to both a sample and a population.

CHEBYSHEV'S RULE

Consider any number k which is at least 1. Then *the proportion of observations that are within k standard deviations of the mean is at least* $1 - (1/k^2)$.

Substituting selected values of k gives the following table.

Number of standard deviations, k	Proportion within k standard deviations
2	At least $1 - \frac{1}{4} = .75$
3	At least $1 - \frac{1}{9} = .89$
4	At least $1 - \frac{1}{16} = .94$
4.472	At least $1 - \frac{1}{20} = .95$
5	At least $1 - \frac{1}{25} = .96$
10	At least $1 - \frac{1}{100} = .99$

EXAMPLE 3.13

Tensile strength is one of the most important properties of various wire products used for industrial purposes. The article "Fluidized Bed Patenting of Wire Rods" (*Wire J.* (June 1977):56–61) reported on a sample of tensile strength observations (in kg/mm^2) for specimens of a certain type of wire. Summary quantities were

$$n = 129 \qquad \bar{x} = 123.6 \text{ kg/mm}^2 \qquad s = 2.0 \text{ kg/mm}^2$$

Figure 3.7 displays values that are 1, 2, and 3 standard deviations from the mean.

FIGURE 3.7
Measurement scale for the tensile strength data

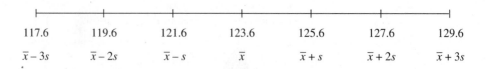

117.6	119.6	121.6	123.6	125.6	127.6	129.6
$\bar{x} - 3s$	$\bar{x} - 2s$	$\bar{x} - s$	$\bar{x}$	$\bar{x} + s$	$\bar{x} + 2s$	$\bar{x} + 3s$

Chebyshev's Rule allows us to assert the following:

a. The proportion of observations between 119.6 and 127.6 is at least .75. Since 75% of the sample size, 129, is 96, at least 96 of the values are in the interval from 119.6 to 127.6.

b. The interval from 117.6 to 129.6 includes all values within three standard deviations of the mean. Because at least 89% of the observations are in this interval, at most 11% of the observations are either less than 117.6 or exceed 129.6.

c. The values 116.6 and 130.6 are 7 kg/mm^2 from the mean, so they are $7/2 = 3.5$ standard deviations from $\bar{x}$. Substituting $k = 3.5$ into the expression in Chebyshev's Rule gives

$$1 - 1/k^2 = 1 - 1/(3.5)^2$$
$$= 1 - .082$$
$$= .918$$

Therefore at least 91.8% (or 118) of the observations are in this interval.

d. From part (b), at most 11% of the observations are outside the interval from 117.6 to 129.6, but they are *not* necessarily equally divided between the two ends of the sample. Thus we *cannot* say that at most 5.5% exceed 129.6. The distribution of values may be quite skewed. The best we can say is that at most 11% exceed 129.6.

Because Chebyshev's Rule is applicable to any data set (distribution), whether symmetric or skewed, we must be careful when making statements about the proportion above a particular value, below a particular value, or inside or outside an interval that is not centered at the mean. The rule must be used in a conservative fashion. There is another side to this conservatism. Whereas the rule states that at least 75% of the observations are within two standard deviations of the mean, in many data sets substantially more than 75% of the values satisfy this condition. The same sort of understatement is frequently encountered for other values of k (numbers of standard deviations).

EXAMPLE 3.14

Figure 3.8 gives a stem-and-leaf display of IQ scores of 112 children in one of the early studies that used the Stanford revision of the Binet–Simon intelligence scale. (See the well-known book *The Intelligence of School Children* by L. M. Terman (Boston: Houghton Mifflin Company, 1919).)

FIGURE 3.8
Stem-and-leaf display
of IQ scores

```
 6 ‖ 1
 7 ‖ 2 5 6 7 9
 8 ‖ 0 0 0 0 1 2 4 5 5 5 6 6 8
 9 ‖ 0 0 0 0 1 1 2 3 3 3 4 4 6 6 6 6 7 7 8 8 8 9
10 ‖ 0 0 0 1 1 2 2 2 2 2 3 3 3 5 6 6 6 7 7 7 7 8 8 9 9 9 9 9
11 ‖ 0 0 0 0 1 1 2 2 3 3 3 3 4 4 4 4 4 7 7 8 9 9
12 ‖ 0 1 1 1 1 1 2 3 4 4 5 6 6 9
13 ‖ 0 0 6
14 ‖ 2 6
15 ‖ 2
```

Stem: Tens
Leaf: Ones

Summary quantities include

$$\bar{x} = 104.5 \qquad s = 16.3 \qquad 2s = 32.6 \qquad 3s = 48.9$$

Table 3.4 shows how Chebyshev's Rule considerably understates actual percentages.

TABLE 3.4 Summarizing the distribution of IQ scores

k = no. of sd's	$\bar{x} \pm ks$	Chebyshev	Actual
2	71.9 to 137.1	at least 75%	96% (108)
2.5	63.7 to 145.3	at least 84%	97% (109)
3	55.6 to 153.4	at least 89%	100% (112)

The Empirical Rule

The fact that statements deriving from Chebyshev's Rule are frequently very conservative suggests that we should look for rules that are less conservative and more precise. The most useful such rule is the **Empirical Rule,** which can be applied whenever the distribution of data values can be reasonably well described by a normal curve. The word *empirical* means deriving from practical experience, and practical experience has shown that a normal curve gives a reasonable fit to many data sets.

EMPIRICAL RULE

If the histogram of values in a data set can be reasonably well approximated by a normal curve, then

Roughly 68% of the observations are within one standard deviation of the mean.

Roughly 95% of the observations are within two standard deviations of the mean.

Roughly 99.7% of the observations are within three standard deviations of the mean.

The Empirical Rule makes "approximately" instead of "at least" statements, and the percentages for $k = 1, 2$, and 3 standard deviations are much higher than those allowed by Chebyshev's Rule.

EXAMPLE 3.15

One of the earliest papers to argue for the wide applicability of the normal distribution was "On the Laws of Inheritance in Man. I. Inheritance of Physical Characters" (*Biometrika* (1903):375–462). Among the data sets discussed in the paper was one consisting of 1052 measurements of mothers' statures. The mean and standard deviation were

$$\bar{x} = 62.484 \text{ in.}, \qquad s = 2.390 \text{ in.}$$

A normal curve did provide a good fit to the data. Table 3.5 contrasts actual percentages with those from Chebyshev's Rule and the Empirical Rule. Clearly the Empirical Rule here is much more successful and informative than Chebyshev's Rule would have been.

TABLE 3.5   Summarizing the distribution of mothers' statures

No. of sd's	Interval	Actual	Empirical	Chebyshev
1	60.094 to 64.874	72.1%	68%	$\geq 0\%$
2	57.704 to 67.264	96.2%	95%	$\geq 75\%$
3	55.314 to 69.654	99.2%	99.7%	$\geq 89\%$

Our detailed study of the normal distribution and areas under normal curves in Chapter 7 will enable us to make statements analogous to those of the Empirical Rule for values other than $k = 1, 2,$ or 3 standard deviations. For now, note that it is rather rare to see an observation from a normally distributed population that is further than two standard deviations from the mean (only 5%), and it is very surprising to see one that is more than three standard deviations away. If you encountered a mother whose stature was 72 in., you would probably conclude that she was not part of the population described by the data set in Example 3.15.

Measures of Relative Standing

When you obtain your score after taking an achievement test, you probably want to know how it compares to scores of others who have taken the test. Is your score above or below the mean and by how much? Does your score place you in the top 5% of those who took the test, or only among the top 25%? Questions of this sort are answered by finding ways to measure the position of a particular value in a data set relative to all values in the set. One such measure involves calculating a *z score* (sometimes called a *standard score*).

DEFINITION

The *z* **score** corresponding to a particular observation in a data set is

$$z \text{ score} = \frac{\text{observation} - \text{mean}}{\text{standard deviation}}$$

> The z score tells us how many standard deviations the observation is from the mean. It is positive or negative according to whether the observation lies above or below the mean.

EXAMPLE 3.16

Suppose that two graduating seniors, one a marketing major and the other an accounting major, are comparing job offers. The accounting major has an offer for $25,000 per year, and the marketing student has one for $23,000 per year. Summary information about the distributions of offers are as follows:

accounting: mean $= 26,000$ standard deviation $= 1500$

marketing: mean $= 22,500$ standard deviation $= 1000$

Thus

$$\text{accounting } z \text{ score} = \frac{25,000 - 26,000}{1500} = -.67$$

(so $25,000 is .67 standard deviations below the mean), whereas

$$\text{marketing } z \text{ score} = \frac{23,000 - 22,500}{1000} = .5$$

Relative to the appropriate data sets, the marketing offer is actually more attractive than the accounting offer (though this may not offer much solace to the marketing major).

The z score is particularly useful when the distribution of observations is approximately normal. In this case, by the Empirical Rule, a z score outside the interval from -2 to $+2$ will occur in about 5% of all cases, whereas a z score outside the interval from -3 to $+3$ will occur only about .3% of the time.

A particular observation can be located even more precisely by giving the percent of observations that fall at or below that observation. If, for example, 95% of all test scores are at or below 650, whereas only 5% are above 650, then 650 is called the *95th percentile* of the data set (or of the distribution of scores). Similarly, if 10% of all scores are at or below 400 and 90% are above 400, then the value 400 is the 10th percentile.

> **DEFINITION**
>
> For any particular number r between 0 and 100, the **rth percentile** is the value such that r percent of the observations in the data set fall at or below that value.

Figure 3.9 illustrates the 90th percentile of a data set. We have already met several percentiles in disguise. The median is the 50th percentile, and the lower and upper quartiles are the 25th and 75th percentiles, respectively.

FIGURE 3.9
90th percentile from a
smoothed histogram

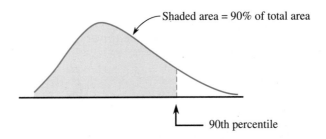

Shaded area = 90% of total area

90th percentile

EXAMPLE 3.17

The frequency distribution in Table 3.6 was constructed from information in the paper "An Alternative Procedure for Estimating Speed Distribution Parameters on Motorways and Similar Roads" (*Transportation Research* (1976):25–29). The data values are speeds (mi/h) of randomly selected vehicles traveling on a major British highway.

TABLE 3.6 Relative and cumulative relative frequencies for vehicle speed data

Class	Relative frequency	Cumulative relative frequency
30–<35	.003	.003
35–<40	.017	.020
40–<45	.055	.075
45–<50	.105	.180
50–<55	.124	.304
55–<60	.206	.510
60–<65	.185	.695
65–<70	.129	.824
70–<75	.096	.920
75–<80	.047	.967
80–<85	.015	.982
85–<90	.013	.995
90–<95	.004	.999
95–<100	.001	1.000

$$\frac{.9 - .824}{.920 - .824} = \frac{x}{5}$$

Because 51% of the observations are at most 60, the 51st percentile for this data set is 60. Similarly, since the cumulative relative frequency for the 70–75 class interval is .920, the 92nd percentile is 75.

There is no class for which the cumulative relative frequency is .90. We shall therefore approximate the 90th percentile. Table 3.6 shows that the desired percentile is between 70 and 75. The cumulative relative frequency up to the value 70 is .824, so the additional relative frequency needed is .900 − .824 = .076. The relative frequency of the entire 70–75 class is .096. This suggests starting at 70 and moving the fraction .076/.096 of the way to the next class boundary:

$$90\text{th percentile} \approx 70 + \frac{.076}{.096}(5) = 73.958 \approx 74$$

Thus roughly 90% of the area under the corresponding histogram lies to the left of 74. That is, about 90% of the drivers on this particular highway drive at speeds below 74 mi/h.

Box Plots (Optional)

It would be nice to have a method of summarizing data that gives more detail than just a measure of center and spread and yet less detail than a stem-and-leaf display or histogram. A *box plot* is one such technique. It is compact, yet it provides information about center, spread, symmetry versus skewness of the data, and the presence of outlying values. To make the plot resistant to the presence of outliers, it is based on the median and interquartile range rather than the mean and standard deviation.

CONSTRUCTION OF A BOX PLOT

1. Draw a rectangular box whose left edge is at the lower quartile and whose right edge is at the upper quartile. (So the box width is iqr.) Draw a vertical line segment inside the box at the median.
2. Place marks at distances 1.5 iqr from either end of the box—these are the **inner fences.** Similarly, place marks for the **outer fences** at distances 3 iqr from either end.
3. Extend horizontal line segments ("whiskers") from each end of the box out to the most extreme observations that are still within the inner fences.
4. **Mild outliers** are observations between the inner and outer fences. Show them as shaded circles. **Extreme outliers,** those observations beyond the outer fences, are shown as open circles.

The regions associated with mild and extreme outliers are illustrated in Figure 3.10. The presence of such outliers, especially the extreme ones, can cause trouble for many standard inferential procedures. Such observations should be investigated to see if they resulted from errors or exceptional behavior of some sort. In a large data set whose histogram is well approximated by a normal curve, only about .7% of the observations (7 out of every 1,000) will be outliers, and only about .0002% (2 out of every 1,000,000) will be extreme outliers. So, if a small sample from some population contains an extreme outlier, it is likely that a normal curve will not give a good approximation to the population histogram.

FIGURE 3.10
Regions for mild and extreme
outliers in a box plot

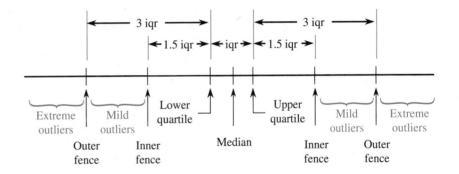

EXAMPLE 3.18

The accompanying data came from an anthropological study of rectangular shapes (*Lowie's Selected Papers in Anthropology,* Cora Dubois, ed. Berkeley, Calif.: Univ. of Calif. Press, 1960, pp. 137–142). Observations were made on the variable $x =$ width/length for a sample of $n = 20$ beaded rectangles used in Shoshoni Indian leather handicrafts.

| .553 | .570 | .576 | .601 | .606 | .606 | .609 | .611 | .615 | .628 |
| .654 | .662 | .668 | .670 | .672 | .690 | .693 | .749 | .844 | .933 |

The quantities needed for constructing a box plot are:

median = .641

lower quartile = .606   upper quartile = .681   iqr = .681 − .606 = .075

1.5 iqr = .1125   3 iqr = .225

inner fences: .606 − .1125 = .4935,   .681 + .1125 = .7935

outer fences: .606 − .225   = .381,   .681 + .225   = .906

The most extreme observations on either side of the median that are within the inner fences are .553 and .749. Thus the whiskers extend out to these two values. There are no outliers of either type on the lower end of the sample. The second largest sample observation, .844, is a mild outlier (it falls between the inner and outer fences), and the largest, .933, is an extreme outlier. The box plot appears as Figure 3.11. The median line is not at the center of the box, so there is a slight

FIGURE 3.11
Box plot for rectangle data

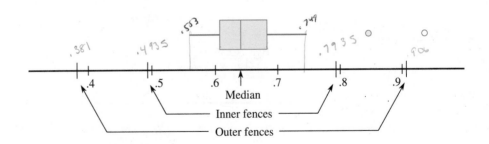

asymmetry in the middle half of the data. However, the most striking feature is the presence of the two outliers. These two x values considerably exceed the "golden ratio" .618, used since antiquity as an aesthetic standard for rectangles.

With two or more data sets consisting of observations on the same variable (for example, miles per gallon for two types of car, weight gains for a control group and a treatment group, and so on), side-by-side box plots convey initial impressions concerning similarities and differences.

EXAMPLE 3.19

Two biological disturbances that are closely associated in adults suffering from endogenous depression (depression with no obvious external cause) are cortisol hypersecretion and shortened REM period latency (the elapsed time from sleep onset to the first rapid eye movement period). The paper "Plasma Cortisol Secretion and REM Period Latency in Adult Endogenous Depression" (*Amer. J. of Psychiatry* (1983):750–753) reported on a comparison of REM period latency for patients with hypersecretion and patients with normal secretion. The data values (as read from graphs) appear next:

hypersecretion sample ($n = 8$): .5, 1, 2.4, 5, 15, 19, 48, 83
   median $= 10$
      lower quartile $= 1.7$ upper quartile $= 33.5$
         iqr $= 31.8$ 1.5 (iqr) $= 47.7$

normal secretion sample ($n = 17$): 5, 5.5, 6.7, 13.5, 31, 40,
   47, 47, 59, 62, 68, 72, 78, 84, 89, 105, 180
   median $= 59$
      lower quartile $= 31$ upper quartile $= 78$
         iqr $= 47$ 1.5 (iqr) $= 70.5$

Figure 3.12 displays a comparative box plot based on this data. Each sample has a mild outlier and an upper tail rather longer than the corresponding lower tail. This skewness led the investigators to transform the data by logarithms prior to a formal comparison. The impression from the box plot that normal secretion REM period latency values are substantially above those for hypersecretion was then confirmed by a formal analysis.

FIGURE 3.12
Comparative box plot for REM period latency data

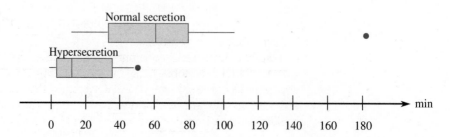

Figure 3.13 shows a computer-generated comparative box plot using MINI-TAB. Notice how computer keyboard characters replace hand-drawn characters—the median location is identified by the $+$ symbol and a mild outlier by an asterisk. The first mark (tick) on the measurement axis is at zero. The symbol .3E $+$ 1 represents $(.3)(10^1)$, or 3, so successive dashes are 3 units long. There is no lower whisker emanating from the bottom box because the whisker is so short relative to the scaling that even a single dash would be too long.

FIGURE 3.13
Computer-generated comparative box plot using MINITAB

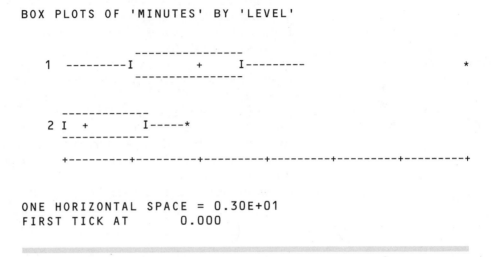

```
BOX PLOTS OF 'MINUTES' BY 'LEVEL'


                        ----------------
    1   ---------I              +         I---------                        *
                        ----------------


          -------------
    2  I  +          I-----*
          -------------

       +---------+---------+---------+---------+---------+---------+
```

```
ONE HORIZONTAL SPACE = 0.30E+01
FIRST TICK AT       0.000
```

EXERCISES 3.28–3.45   SECTION 3.3

3.28 The average playing time of records in a large collection is 35 min, and the standard deviation is 5 min.

    a. Without assuming anything about the distribution of times, at least what percentage of the times are between 25 and 45 min?

    b. Without assuming anything about the distribution of times, what can be said about the percentage of times that are either less than 20 min or greater than 50 min?

    c. Assuming that the distribution of times is normal, approximately what percentage of times are between 25 and 45 min? Less than 20 min or greater than 50 min? Less than 20 min?

3.29 In a study to investigate the effect of car speed on accident severity, 5000 accident reports of fatal automobile accidents were examined and the vehicle speed at impact was recorded for each one. It was determined that the average speed was 42 mi/h and that the standard deviation was 15 mi/h. In addition, a histogram revealed that vehicle speed at impact could be described by a normal curve.

a. Roughly what proportion of vehicle speeds were between 27 mi/h and 57 mi/h?

b. Roughly what proportion of vehicle speeds exceeded 57 mi/h?

3.30 Mobile homes are very tightly constructed for energy conservation. This may lead to a buildup of pollutants generated indoors. The paper "A Survey of Nitrogen Dioxide Levels Inside Mobile Homes" (*J. Air Pollut. Control Assoc.* (1988): 647–651) discussed various aspects of NO_2 concentration in these structures.

a. In one sample of homes in the Los Angeles area, the mean NO_2 concentration in kitchens during the summer was 36.92 ppb and the standard deviation was 11.34. Making no assumptions about the shape of the histogram, what can be said about the percentage of observations between 14.24 and 59.60?

b. Inside what interval is it guaranteed that at least 89% of the concentration observations will lie?

c. In a sample of non–Los Angeles homes, the average kitchen concentration during the winter was 24.76 ppb and the standard deviation was 17.20. Do these values suggest that the histogram of sample observations did not closely resemble a normal curve? (Hint: What is $\bar{x} - 2s$?)

3.31 A sample of concrete specimens of a certain type is selected and the compressive strength of each one is determined. The mean and standard deviation are calculated as $\bar{x} = 3000$ and $s = 500$, and the sample histogram is found to be very well approximated by a normal curve.

a. Approximately what percentage of the sample observations are between 2500 and 3500, and what result justifies your assertion?

b. Approximately what percentage of sample observations are outside the interval from 2000 to 4000?

c. What can be said about the approximate percentage of observations between 2000 and 2500?

d. Why would you not use Chebyshev's Rule to answer the questions posed in parts (a) through (c)?

3.32 The *Los Angeles Times* (Oct. 30, 1983) reported that a typical customer of the 7-Eleven convenience stores spends $3.24. Suppose that the average amount spent by customers of 7-Eleven stores is the reported value of $3.24 and that the standard deviation for amount of sale is $8.88.

a. Based on the given mean and standard deviation, do you think that the distribution of the variable *amount of sale* could have been normal in shape? Why or why not?

b. What can be said about the proportion of all customers that spend more than $20 on a purchase at a 7-Eleven store?

3.33 Exercise 2.8 gave the accompanying 26 observations on pH for specimens of minesoil.

3.59	4.36	3.86	4.25	4.46	4.53	2.62	6.79	6.49
4.27	3.84	4.78	4.65	2.91	3.90	6.00	2.83	3.58
4.43	4.58	4.75	3.49	4.11	3.58	5.21	4.41	

a. Compute the upper and lower quartiles and then the interquartile range.

b. How large or small does an observation have to be in order to be considered an outlier? An extreme outlier? Are there any mild outliers or extreme outliers in the sample?

c. Construct a box plot for this data and comment on any interesting features.

3.34 The percentages of juice lost after thawing for 19 different strawberry varieties appeared in the paper "Evaluation of Strawberry Cultivars with Different Degrees of Resistance to Red Stele" (*Fruit Varieties J.* (1991):12–17).

46	51	44	50	33	46	60	41	55	46
53	53	42	44	50	54	46	41	48	

a. Compute the upper quartile, lower quartile, and interquartile range.

b. Are there any observations that are mild outliers? Extreme outliers?

c. Construct a box plot and comment.

3.35 A student took two national aptitude tests in the course of applying for admission to colleges. The national average and standard deviation for the first test were 475 and 100, respectively, whereas for the second test the average and standard deviation were 30 and 8, respectively. The student scored 625 on the first test and 45 on the second. Use z scores to determine on which exam the student performed better.

3.36 Suppose that your younger sister is applying for entrance to college and she has taken the SAT exams. She scored at the 83rd percentile on the verbal section of the test and at the 94th percentile on the math section of the test. Since you have been studying statistics, she asks you for an interpretation of these values. What would you tell her?

3.37 The paper "Modeling and Measurements of Bus Service Reliability" (*Trans. Research* (1978):253–256) studied various aspects of bus service and presented data on travel times from several different routes. We give here a frequency distribution for bus travel times from origin to destination on one particular route in Chicago during peak morning traffic periods.

Class	Frequency	Relative frequency
15–<16	4	.02
16–<17	0	.00
17–<18	26	.13
18–<19	99	.49
19–<20	36	.18
20–<21	8	.04
21–<22	12	.06
22–<23	0	.00
23–<24	0	.00
24–<25	0	.00
25–<26	16	.08

a. Construct the corresponding histogram.

b. Compute the following (approximate) percentiles.

    i. 86th **ii.** 15th **iii.** 90th **iv.** 95th **v.** 10th

3.38   Exercise 3.6 has data on waiting times for patients at a medical clinic. Construct a box plot of the data. Does it indicate that there are any extreme or unusual observations in the sample?

3.39   An advertisement for the "30-in. wonder" that appeared in the September 1983 issue of the journal *Packaging* claimed that the 30-in. wonder weighs cases and bags up to 110 lb and provides accuracy down to ¼ oz. Suppose that a 50-oz weight was repeatedly weighed on this scale and the weight readings recorded. The mean value was 49.5 oz and the standard deviation was .1. What can be said about the proportion of the time that the scale actually showed a weight that was within ¼ oz of the true value of 50 oz? (Hint: Try to make use of Chebyshev's Rule.)

3.40   Suppose your statistics professor returned your first midterm exam with only a z score written on it. She also tells you that a histogram of the scores was closely described by a normal curve. How would you interpret each of the following z scores?

    a. 2.2   **b.** $-.4$ **c.** -1.8 **d.** 1.0   **e.** 0

3.41   The paper "Answer Changing on Multiple-Choice Tests" (*J. of Experimental Education* (1980):18–21) reported that for a group of 162 college students, the average number of responses changed from the correct answer to an incorrect answer on a test containing 80 multiple choice items was 1.4. The corresponding standard deviation was reported to be 1.5. Based on this mean and standard deviation, what can you tell about the shape of the distribution of the variable, *number of answers changed from right to wrong*? What can you say about the number of students who changed at least six answers from correct to incorrect?

3.42   The article "Does Air Pollution Shorten Lives?" (from the book *Statistics and Public Policy*) states that when the sulfate level for 117 standard metropolitan statistical areas was recorded, the resulting mean and standard deviation were 47.2 mg/m³ and 31.3 mg/m³, respectively. Use this information to make a statement about the proportion of metropolitan areas that have sulfate levels below 109.8 mg/m³.

3.43   The average reading speed of students completing a speed reading course is 450 words per minute (wpm). If the standard deviation is 70 wpm, find the z score associated with each reading speed.

    a. 320 wpm   **b.** 475 wpm   **c.** 420 wpm   **d.** 610 wpm

3.44   The accompanying data values are 1989 per capita expenditures on public libraries for each of the 50 states (New York is the highest and Arkansas is the lowest).

29.48	24.45	23.64	23.34	22.10	21.16	19.83	19.81	19.25
19.18	18.62	18.01	17.95	17.23	16.53	16.29	15.89	15.85
14.74	14.53	14.46	13.83	13.64	13.37	13.16	13.09	12.66
12.37	11.93	11.85	11.71	11.53	11.34	10.99	10.55	10.24
10.06	9.84	9.65	8.94	8.72	8.22	8.13	8.01	7.70
7.56	7.46	7.04	6.58	5.98				

a. Summarize this data set with a frequency distribution. Construct the corresponding histogram.

b. Use the histogram in part (a) to find approximate values of the following percentiles:

   i. 50th   **ii.** 70th   **iii.** 10th   **iv.** 90th   **v.** 40th

3.45 The accompanying table gives the mean and standard deviation of reaction times (sec) for each of two different stimuli.

	Stimulus 1	Stimulus 2
Mean	6.0	3.6
Standard deviation	1.2	.8

If your reaction time for the first stimulus is 4.2 s and for the second stimulus is 1.8 s, to which stimulus are you reacting (when compared to all others) relatively more quickly?

CHAPTER THREE SUMMARY OF KEY CONCEPTS AND FORMULAS

Term or Formula	Comment
$x_1, x_2, \ldots, x_n$	Notation for sample data consisting of observations on a variable x, where n is the sample size.
Sample mean, $\bar{x} = \dfrac{\Sigma x}{n}$	The most frequently used measure of center of a sample. It can be very sensitive to the presence of even a single outlier (unusually large or small observation).
Population mean, μ	The average x value in the entire population.
Sample median	The middle value in the ordered list of sample observations. (For n even, the median is the average of the two middle values.) It is very insensitive to outliers.
Trimmed mean	A measure of center in which the observations are first ordered from smallest to largest, one or more observations are deleted from each end, and the remaining ones are averaged. In terms of sensitivity to outliers, it is a compromise between the mean and median.

Term or Formula	Comment
Deviations from the mean: $x_1 - \bar{x}, x_2 - \bar{x}, \ldots,$ $x_n - \bar{x}$	Quantities used to assess variability in a sample. Except for rounding effects, $\Sigma(x - \bar{x}) = 0$.
The sample variance, $s^2 = \dfrac{\Sigma(x - \bar{x})^2}{n - 1}$ **and standard deviation,** $s = \sqrt{s^2}$	The most frequently used measures of variability for sample data.
$\Sigma x^2 - \dfrac{(\Sigma x)^2}{n}$	The computing formula for the numerator of s^2.
The population variance σ^2 **and standard deviation** σ	Measures of variability for the entire population.
Quartiles and the interquartile range	The lower quartile separates the smallest 25% of the data from the remaining 75%, and the upper quartile separates the largest 25% from the smallest 75%. The interquartile range (iqr), a measure of variability less sensitive to outliers than s, is the difference between the upper and lower quartiles.
Chebyshev's Rule	This rule states that for any number $k \geq 1$, *at least* $100[1 - (1/k^2)]\%$ of the observations in *any* data set are within k standard deviations of the mean. It is typically conservative in that the actual percentages often considerably exceed $100[1 - (1/k^2)]$.
Empirical Rule	This rule gives the approximate percentage of observations within one standard deviation (68%), two standard deviations (95%), or three standard deviations (99.7%) of the mean when the histogram is well-approximated by a normal curve.
z score	This quantity gives the distance between an observation and the mean expressed as a certain number of standard deviations. It is positive (negative) if the observation lies above (below) the mean.
rth percentile	The value such that r percent of the observations in the data set fall at or below that value.
Box plot	A picture that conveys information about the most important features of a data set: center, spread, extent of skewness, and presence of outliers.

ENCORE

D

ata on radon concentration for two different samples of houses was introduced in the Chapter Preview. Here we first organize the data by means of a comparative stem-and-leaf display.

1. Cancer			2. No Cancer
9 6 8 3 7 9 5	‖	0 ‖	9 5 7 6 8 3 9 7 6 7 8 9 9 3
8 6 0 7 1 8 1 5 0 6 6 8 1 5 2 3 3 1 5 0	‖	1 ‖	1 2 2 7 1 7 1 3 1 1 4
1 2 3 0 2 7 3 1	‖	2 ‖	9 9 4 9 4 1 9 1
8 3 4 9	‖	3 ‖	8 3 9
5	‖	4 ‖	
7	‖	5 ‖	5 5
	‖	6 ‖	
	‖	7 ‖	
HI: 210	‖	8 ‖	5

Stem: Tens digit
Leaf: Ones digit

Calculation of numerical summaries proceeds as follows:

cancer: $n = 42$, $\Sigma x = 958$, $\Sigma x^2 = 62{,}936$

$$\bar{x} = \frac{958}{42} = 22.8$$

$$s^2 = \frac{62{,}936 - (958)^2/42}{41} = 1002.06$$

$$s = \sqrt{1002.06} = 31.7$$

$$\text{median} = \frac{16 + 16}{2} = 16.0$$

no cancer: $n = 39$, $\Sigma x = 747$, $\Sigma x^2 = 25{,}277$

$$\bar{x} = \frac{747}{39} = 19.2$$

$$s^2 = \frac{25{,}277 - (747)^2/39}{38} = 288.66$$

$$s = \sqrt{288.66} = 17.0$$

$$\text{median} = 12.0$$

The values of both the mean and median suggest that the cancer sample is centered somewhat to the right of the no-cancer sample on the measurement scale. The mean, however, exaggerates the magnitude of this shift. If we eliminate the obvious outlier from each sample, then

$$\text{cancer } \bar{x} = \frac{958 - 210}{41} = 18.2$$

$$\text{no-cancer } \bar{x} = \frac{747 - 85}{38} = 17.4$$

In Chapter 11 we develop methodology for deciding whether the two population mean radon concentrations, μ_1 and μ_2, are different.

The values of s^2 and s initially suggest more variability in the cancer sample, but this distorted view is attributable entirely to the outlier 210. Eliminating it from the cancer sample and 85 from the no-cancer sample gives

cancer $s = 11.4$ (down from 31.7!)

no-cancer $s = 13.3$ (down from 17.0)

This is confirmed by comparing the two interquartile ranges, which are insensitive to outliers:

$$\text{cancer iqr} = \text{upper quartile} - \text{lower quartile}$$
$$= 22 - 11$$
$$= 11$$
$$\text{no-cancer iqr} = \frac{29 + 24}{2} - \frac{8 + 9}{2}$$
$$= 18.0$$

There is definitely somewhat less dispersion in the cancer sample. This is because of the 27 observations less than 20 in that sample, only 7 are less than 10, whereas 14 of the 25 observations less than 20 in the other sample are less than 10 (look at the first two rows of the stem-and-leaf display).

To construct box plots we need quartiles $\pm$ 1.5 iqr and quartiles $\pm$ 3 iqr:

cancer:	lower quartile $-$ 1.5 iqr	$= 11 - 1.5(11)$	$= -5.5$
	upper quartile $+$ 1.5 iqr	$= 22 + 1.5(11)$	$= 38.5$
	lower quartile $-$ 3 iqr	$= 11 - 3(11)$	$= -22$
	upper quartile $+$ 3 iqr	$= 22 + 3(11)$	$= 55$
no-cancer:	lower quartile $-$ 1.5 iqr	$= 8.5 - 1.5(18)$	$= -18.5$
	upper quartile $+$ 1.5 iqr	$= 26.5 + 1.5(18)$	$= 53.5$
	lower quartile $-$ 3 iqr	$= 8.5 - 3(18)$	$= -45.5$
	upper quartile $+$ 3 iqr	$= 26.5 + 3(18)$	$= 80.5$

The observations 39 and 45 in the cancer sample are mild outliers, and both 57 and 210 are extreme outliers. The mild outliers in the no-cancer sample are the two 55's; only 85 is an extreme outlier. The accompanying box plots give an appealing summary of the two samples.

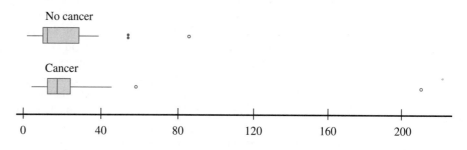

No cancer

Cancer

0   40   80   120   160   200

SUPPLEMENTARY EXERCISES 3.46–3.63

3.46 Five randomly selected normal rats were treated with an injection of HRP (horseradish peroxidase). The total number of injured neurons in the fourth nerve nucleus was recorded. The resulting data was: 209, 187, 123, 184, and 194. (Source: "The Injury Response of Nerve Fibers in the Anterior Medullary Velum of the Adult Rat," *Brain Research* (1984):257–268). Compute and interpret the values of the sample mean and standard deviation.

3.47 Strength is an important characteristic of materials used in prefabricated housing. Each of 11 prefabricated plate elements was subjected to a severe stress test and the maximum width (in millimeters) of the resulting cracks was recorded. The given data appeared in the paper "Prefabricated Ferrocement Ribbed Elements for Low-Cost Housing" (*J. of Ferrocement* (1984):347–364). Compute the sample mean, median, and standard deviation for this data set.

| .684 | .598 | .924 | .483 | 3.520 | 3.130 |
| 2.650 | 2.540 | 1.497 | 1.285 | 1.038 | |

3.48 Eleven sediment samples from Gannoway Lake in Texas were analyzed for concentration of iron (μg/g) and zinc (μg/g). The given data appeared in the paper "The Analysis of Aqueous Sediments for Heavy Metals" (*J. Environ. Science and Health* (1984):911–924).

| iron | 2.5 | 4.5 | 1.5 | 3.2 | 3.3 | 1.8 | 3.4 | 3.4 | 4.0 | 3.9 | 2.9 |
| zinc | 62 | 66 | 39 | 67 | 50 | 220 | 89 | 110 | 68 | 66 | 69 |

a. Calculate the sample mean and median for the iron concentration data. Are the numerical values of the mean and median roughly equal?

b. Calculate the sample mean and median for the zinc concentration data. Which of the two would you recommend as a measure of location? Explain.

c. Which of the samples (iron or zinc) has a larger variance? Answer without actually computing the two sample variances. Explain the reason for your selection.

3.49 Age at death (in days) for each of 12 infants who died of sudden infant death syndrome was given in the paper "Post-Mortem Analysis of Neuropeptides in Brains from Sudden Infant Death Victims" (*Brain Research* (1984):277–285). The resulting observations were 54, 55, 56, 60, 60, 60, 105, 120, 135, 140, 154, and 247.

a. Compute and interpret the values of the sample mean, median, variance, and standard deviation.

b. Calculate the upper and lower quartiles and the interquartile range. Is the value 247 a mild or extreme outlier?

c. Construct a box plot for this data set.

3.50 The air quality in major cities is monitored on a regular basis. The *Los Angeles Times* (October 25,

1984) reported that a first-stage smog alert occurs when the index of pollutants in the air is between 200 and 275. A second-stage smog alert occurs when the index exceeds 275. Suppose that the index of pollutants has a distribution with mean 125 and standard deviation 75. Without assuming anything about the shape of the distribution, what can be said about the proportion of days on which a first-stage smog alert is declared? What can be said about the proportion of days on which a second-stage alert is declared?

3.51 The paper "Sodium–Calcium Exchange Equilibria in Soils as Affected by Calcium Carbonate and Organic Matter" (*Soil Science* (1984):109) gave ten observations on soil pH. The data resulted from analysis of ten samples of soil from the Central Soil Salinity Research Institute experimental farm.

Soil pH	8.53	8.52	8.01	7.99	7.93
	7.89	7.85	7.82	7.80	7.72

a. Calculate and interpret the values of the sample mean, variance, and standard deviation.
b. Compute the 10% trimmed mean and the sample median. Do either of these values differ much from the value of the sample mean?
c. Find the upper quartile, the lower quartile, and the interquartile range.
d. Illustrate the location and spread of this sample using a box plot.

3.52 The *New York Times* News Service reported that the average price of a home in the United States in 1984 was $101,000, whereas the median price was $80,900. What do the relative sizes of the mean and median imply about the shape of the distribution of home prices?

3.53 Age at diagnosis for each of 20 patients under treatment for meningitis was given in the paper "Penicillin in the Treatment of Meningitis" (*J. Amer. Med. Assoc.* (1984):1870–1874). The ages (in years) were as follows:

18	18	25	19	23	20	69	18	21	18
18	20	18	18	20	18	19	28	17	18

a. Calculate the values of the sample mean and the standard deviation.
b. Calculate the 10% trimmed mean. How does the value of the trimmed mean compare to that of the sample mean? Which would you recommend as a measure of location? Explain.
c. Compute the upper quartile, the lower quartile, and the interquartile range.
d. Are there any mild or extreme outliers present in this data set?
e. Construct the box plot for this data set.

3.54 Although blood pressure is a continuous variable, its value is often reported to the nearest 5 mm Hg (for example, 100, 105, 110, and so on). Suppose that the actual blood pressure values for nine randomly selected individuals are

118.6	127.4	138.4	130.0	113.7
122.0	108.3	131.5	133.2	

a. If values are reported as suggested (rounded to the nearest 5 mm Hg), what is the sample of the *reported* values and what is the median of this sample?
b. Suppose that the second individual's blood pressure is 127.6 rather than 127.4 (a small change in a single value). How does this change the median of reported values? What does this say about the median's sensitivity to rounding or grouping of the data?

3.55 The accompanying observations are carbon monoxide levels (ppm) in air samples obtained from a certain region.

9.3	10.7	8.5	9.6	12.2	16.6	9.2	10.5
7.9	13.2	11.0	8.8	13.7	12.1	9.8	

a. If a trimmed mean is calculated by first deleting the smallest and largest observations, what is the corresponding trimming percentage? Answer this question if the two smallest and two largest observations are deleted.
b. Calculate the two trimmed means referred to in part (a).

c. Using the results of part (b), how might you calculate a measure of center for this sample that could be regarded as a 10% trimmed mean?

3.56 In recent years, many teachers have been subject to increased levels of stress that have contributed to disenchantment with teaching as a profession. The paper "Professional Burnout Among Public School Teachers" (*Public Personnel Mgmt.* (1988):167–189) looked at various aspects of this problem. Consider the following information on total psychological effects scores for a sample of 937 teachers.

Burnout level	Range of scores	Frequency
Low	0–21	554
Moderate	22–43	342
High	44–65	41
	$\bar{x} = 19.93$ $s = 12.89$	

a. Draw a histogram.
b. Mark the value of $\bar{x}$ on the measurement scale, and use the histogram to locate the approximate value of the median. Why are the two measures of center not identical?
c. In what interval of values are we guaranteed to find at least 75% of the scores, irrespective of the histogram shape? From the histogram, roughly what percentage of the scores actually fall in this interval?

3.57 The amount of radiation received at a greenhouse plays an important role in determining the rate of photosynthesis. The accompanying observations on incoming solar radiation were read from a graph in the paper "Radiation Components over Bare and Planted Soils in a Greenhouse" (*Solar Energy* (1990):1–6).

6.3	6.4	7.1	7.7	8.4	8.5	8.8	8.9	9.0
9.1	10.0	10.1	10.2	10.6	10.6	10.7	10.7	10.8
10.9	11.1	11.2	11.2	11.4	11.9	11.9	12.2	13.1

Use some of the methods discussed in this chapter and the previous one to describe this data.

3.58 The accompanying data on milk volume (g/day) was taken from the paper "Smoking during Pregnancy and Lactation and Its Effects on Breast Milk Volume" (*American J. of Clinical Nutrition* (1991):1011–1016):

Smoking mothers	621	793	593	545	753	655
	895	767	714	598	693	
Nonsmoking mothers	947	945	1086	1202	973	981
	930	745	903	899	961	

Compare and contrast the two samples.

3.59 a. Suppose that n, the number of sample observations, is an odd number. Under what conditions on the sample will $\bar{x}$ and the sample median be identical?
b. If $n = 10$, when will $\bar{x}$ and the 10% trimmed mean be identical?

3.60 a. A statistics instructor informed her class that the median exam score was 78 and the mean was 70. Sketch a picture of what the smoothed histogram of scores might look like.
b. Suppose that the majority of students in the class studied for the exam, but a few students had not. How might this be reflected in a smoothed histogram of exam scores?

3.61 The *Los Angeles Times* (December 22, 1983) reported that the average costs per day of a semiprivate hospital room for California, Oregon, and Washington were $268, $210, and $220, respectively. Suppose that you were interested in the average cost per day of a semiprivate hospital room in these three West Coast states combined. If each state contained the same number of hospital rooms, we could average the three values given. However, this is not the case, so the three averages must be weighted in proportion to the respective number of hospital rooms in each state. In general, if $\bar{x}_1, \bar{x}_2, \bar{x}_3, \ldots, \bar{x}_n$ are n group means and $w_1, w_2, \ldots, w_n$ are the respective weights, the **weighted mean** $\bar{x}_w$ is defined to be

$$\bar{x}_w = \frac{w_1\bar{x}_1 + w_2\bar{x}_2 + \cdots + w_n\bar{x}_n}{w_1 + w_2 + \cdots + w_n}$$

The number of hospital rooms in California, Oregon, and Washington are 120,000, 30,000, and 45,000, respectively. Use the given formula with $w_1 = 120,000$, $w_2 = 30,000$, and $w_3 = 45,000$ to find the average cost of a hospital room on the West Coast.

3.62 Suppose that an auto dealership employs clerical workers, salespeople, and mechanics. The average monthly salaries of the clerical employees, salespeople, and mechanics are $1100, $1800, and $1900, respectively. If the dealership has three clerical employees, ten salespeople, and eight mechanics, find the average monthly wage for all employees of the dealership. (Hint: Refer to Exercise 3.61.)

3.63 Suppose that the distribution of scores on an exam is closely described by a normal curve with mean 100. The 16th percentile of this distribution is 80.
  a. What is the 84th percentile?
  b. What is the approximate value of the standard deviation of exam scores?
  c. What z score is associated with an exam score of 90?
  d. What percentile corresponds to an exam score of 140?
  e. Do you think there were many scores below 40? Explain.

References

See the References at the end of Chapter 2.

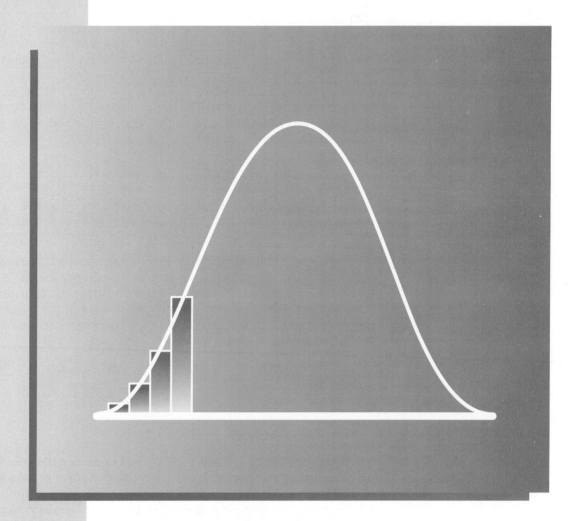

Summarizing
Bivariate Data

PREVIEW

An accurate assessment of oxygen consumption provides important information for determining energy-expenditure requirements for physically demanding tasks. The paper "Oxygen Consumption During Fire Suppression: Error of Heart Rate Estimation" (*Ergonomics* (1991):1469–1474) reported on a study in which oxygen consumption (mL/kg/min) during a treadmill test was determined for a sample of ten firefighters. Then oxygen consumption at a comparable heart rate was measured for each of the ten individuals while performing a fire-suppression simulation. This resulted in the accompanying data.

Firefighter	1	2	3	4	5	6	7	8	9	10
Treadmill consumption	51.3	34.1	41.1	36.3	36.5	35.4	35.4	38.6	40.6	39.5
Fire-simulation consumption	49.3	29.5	30.6	28.2	28.0	26.3	33.9	29.4	23.5	31.6

The investigators noticed that in every case consumption during the fire simulation was lower than while on a treadmill. They then developed a technique for predicting consumption while performing the task from the value of treadmill consumption and also gave a quantitative assessment of the effectiveness of the prediction method. In this chapter we show how linear regression analysis can accomplish these objectives.

Introduction

The methods of Chapters 2 and 3 are appropriate for describing and summarizing univariate data. Frequently an investigator is interested not in just a single attribute of individuals or objects in a population but in two or more attributes and their relationship to one another. A forester might study the growth characteristics of a certain type of tree with special attention to the relationship between age and height. An environmental researcher might wish to know how lead content of soil varies with distance from a major highway. The extent to which attitude regarding corporal punishment of school children is affected by parent's age and social class may be the subject of an investigation by sociologists. A model relating first-year college grade-point average to high school grades, SAT or ACT scores, and various family characteristics would be useful to admissions officers trying to predict whether or not an applicant would be a successful student. Many other similar examples should occur to you.

A **multivariate** data set is one that consists of measurements or observations on each of two or more variables. The most important special case involves just two variables, x and y, and the resulting data is usually called **bivariate.** Examples include x = age of a tree and y = height of the tree; x = distance from a highway and y = lead content of soil at that distance; and x = religious preference and y =

political party affiliation. Each observation in a bivariate data set consists of a pair of values. The first element in the pair is the value of x and the second is the value of y.

The focus in this chapter is on <u>bivariate numerical data</u>, that is, data for which both x and y are numerical variables. This type of data arises very frequently in applied work. In addition, a thorough grasp of this case is an important stepping stone to multivariate data analysis. As in Chapters 2 and 3, our concern here is with data description and summarization. Inferential methods for bivariate numerical data as well as for data sets where x and y are categorical variables are presented in later chapters.

4.1   Scatter Plots

When data is bivariate with both x and y numerical variables, each observation consists of a pair of numbers, such as (14, 5.2) or (27.63, 18.9), where the x value is the first number in the pair and the y value is the second number. An unorganized list of observed pairs yields little information about the distribution of x values and y values separately and even less information about how strongly and in what manner the two variables are related to one another. In Chapter 2 we saw how pictures could help make sense of univariate data. The most informative picture based on bivariate numerical data is called a scatter plot.

A **scatter plot** is a picture of bivariate numerical data in which each pair of values (each observation) is represented by a point located on a rectangular coordinate system, as pictured in Figure 4.1(a). The horizontal axis is identified with values of x and is marked so that any x value can be easily located. Similarly, the vertical axis—the y axis—is also marked for easy location of y values. Figure 4.1(b) pictures the point corresponding to (4.5, 15). This point is located above the value $x = 4.5$ on the horizontal axis and to the right of the value $y = 15$ on the vertical axis.

FIGURE 4.1
Constructing a scatter plot
(a) Rectangular coordinate system for a scatter plot of bivariate data
(b) The point in the plot corresponding to the observation (4.5, 15)

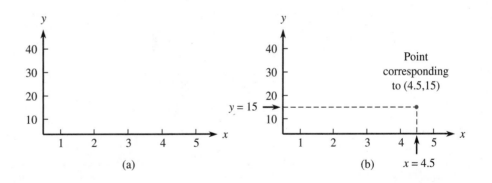

EXAMPLE 4.1

The production of legumes, an important food crop in many parts of the world, is greatly affected by the presence of pests and diseases that they carry. The paper "Influence of Wind Speed on Residence Time of *Uroleucon ambrosiae* Alatae on Bean Plants" (*Environ. Entom.* (1991):1375–1380) reported on a study in which groups of transient alate aphids were placed on bean plants and the elapsed time until half the aphids had departed was observed. The two variables studied were

x = wind speed (m/s)

y = residence half-time (h)

Selected data is as follows (the order in which observations were obtained was not given in the paper, so for convenience they are listed here in increasing order of x values).

				Observation			
	1	2	3	4	5	6	7
x	0.00	0.06	0.50	0.55	0.75	0.75	0.79
y	0.2	1.8	1.3	0.6	0.5	0.6	3.9

			Observation			
	8	9	10	11	12	13
x	1.00	1.04	1.22	1.64	1.73	1.73
y	3.3	5.3	5.7	7.0	3.5	6.8

Thus $(x_1, y_1) = (0.00, 0.2)$, $(x_4, y_4) = (0.55, 0.6)$, and so on. A scatter plot appears in Figure 4.2.

FIGURE 4.2
Scatter plot of data from
Example 4.1

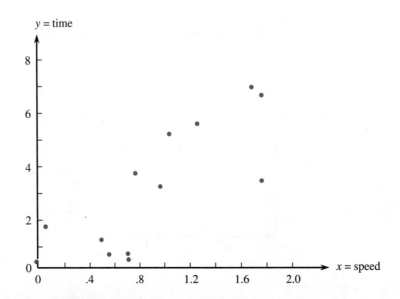

Here are some things to notice about the data and plot.

1. There are several observations that have identical x values yet different y values (for example, $x_5 = x_6 = .75$, but $y_5 = .5$ and $y_6 = .6$). Thus the value of y is *not* determined solely by x but also by various other factors.
2. There is a tendency for y to increase as x does. That is, larger values of residence time tend to be associated with larger values of wind speed (a positive relationship between the variables).
3. It appears that the value of y could be predicted from x by finding a line that is reasonably close to the points in the plot. (The authors of the paper superimposed such a line on their plot.)

The horizontal and vertical axes in the scatter plot of Figure 4.2 intersect at the point $(0, 0)$. In many data sets either the values of x or of y or of both variables differ considerably from zero relative to the ranges of the values. For example, a study of how air conditioner efficiency is related to maximum daily outdoor temperature might involve observations for temperatures $80°, 82°, \ldots, 98°, 100°$. When this is the case, a more informative plot may result from intersecting the axes at some point other than $(0,0)$ and marking the axes accordingly.

EXAMPLE 4.2

Bicyclists are well aware that, even when a street has a bike lane, riding may pose considerable risks if the street and lane are poorly designed. The paper "Effects of Bike Lanes on Driver and Bicyclist Behavior" (*ASCE Trans. Eng. J.* (1977): 243–256) reported the accompanying data on

$\quad x =$ available travel space (distance between a cyclist and the roadway center line)

and

$\quad y =$ separation distance between a bike and a passing car (determined by photography)

x	12.8	12.9	12.9	13.6	14.5	14.6	15.1	17.5	19.5	20.8
y	5.5	6.2	6.3	7.0	7.8	8.3	7.1	10.0	10.8	11.0

Figure 4.3 displays two scatter plots of the data, one with the axes intersecting at $(0, 0)$ and the other with the axes intersecting at $(12, 5)$. The points in the first plot are crowded together in the upper right-hand corner, making it difficult to see any patterns. At first glance there appears to be no strong evidence of curvature in this plot. The second plot is less crowded and, consequently, more revealing. In particular, except for the point $(15.1, 7.1)$, the plot exhibits some curvature. If the objective were to develop a model for predicting y from x, Figure 4.3(b) suggests that some curve fit to the data might yield better predictions than would result from fitting a straight line to the data.

FIGURE 4.3
Scatter plots for the data
of Example 4.2
(a) Axes intersecting at (0, 0)
(b) Axes intersecting at (12, 5)

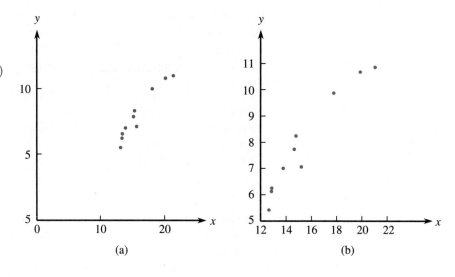

(a)   (b)

Computer-Generated Scatter Plots

FIGURE 4.4
MINITAB scatter plot of
y = bills passed versus
x = bills introduced

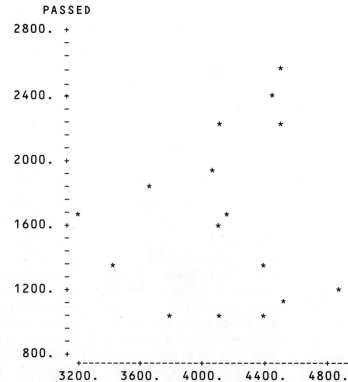

One of the most attractive features of the standard statistical computer program packages is their ability to produce scatter plots and various other plots. Figure 4.4 (on the previous page) shows a MINITAB scatter plot of data for which

x = number of bills introduced in Congress

y = number of bills passed by Congress

The 16 observations are for the 80th Congress (1947–1948), 81st Congress, . . . , and 95th Congress (1977–1978). Notice that the axes do not intersect at (0, 0). We let the computer choose the point of intersection and markings on the axes for this plot, although there is an option that allows the user to make his or her own specifications. The most interesting thing about this plot is that there is no pattern. There appears to be no strong relationship between the number of bills introduced and the number passed. This would provide support for those who have proposed a limitation on the number of bills that a senator or representative could introduce.

Sometimes two or more points are located so closely to one another that the computer cannot print a separate asterisk for each point. The appearance of the

FIGURE 4.5
Scatter plots in which the symbol 2 represents two points at the same location (total of 35 observations)
(a) MINITAB
(b) SPSS

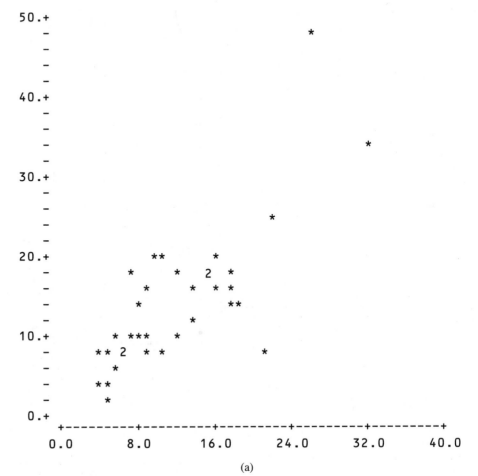

(a)

FIGURE 4.5
(b) SPSS

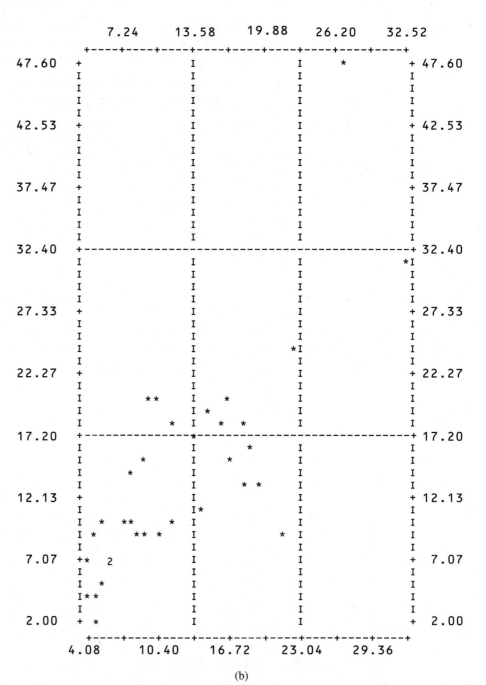

(b)

number 2 on a scatter plot indicates that there are 2 points at or near that location; 3, 4, and other numbers are also used to indicate multiple observations at the same location. An illustration appears in Figure 4.5 (on pages 119 and 120), where

x = mercury content of a newborn child's hair

y = mercury content of the child's mother's hair

The data was taken from the article mentioned in Example 2.13.

EXERCISES 4.1–4.6   SECTION 4.1

4.1 Manganese (Mn) is thought to be critical to the health of newborn human infants. The paper "Manganese Intake and Serum Manganese Concentration of Human Milk-fed and Formula-fed Infants" (*Amer. J. of Clinical Nutrition* (1984):872–878) gave the following data on Mn intake and serum Mn level for eight milk-fed infants. Use these data to construct a scatter plot. Does the plot suggest that there is a relationship between Mn intake and serum Mn level?

Intake (μg/kg/day)	.34	.35	.39	.39	.41	.41	.49	.68
Serum Mn (μg/L)	2.8	1.9	3.3	5.6	4.2	5.6	4.2	7.9

4.2 The decline of water supplies in certain areas of the United States has created the need for increased understanding of relationships between economic factors such as crop yield and hydrologic and soil factors. The paper "Variability of Soil Water Properties and Crop Yield in a Sloped Watershed" (*Water Resources Bull.* (1988): 281–288) gave data on grain sorghum yield (y, in g/m-row) and distance upslope (x, in m) on a sloping watershed. Selected observations appear in the accompanying table.

x	0	10	20	30	45	50	70	80	100	120	140	160	170	190
y	500	590	410	470	450	480	510	450	360	400	300	410	280	350

a. Construct a scatter plot.
b. As distance upslope increases, how does crop yield tend to behave?

4.3 Many of us are all too familiar with the effects of stress on humans. In recent years researchers have focused increasing attention on how stress affects nonhuman behavior. The accompanying data on x = plasma cortisol concentration (ng cortisol/mL plasma) and y = oxygen consumption rate (mg/kg/h) for juvenile steelhead after three 2-min disturbances was read from a graph in the paper "Metabolic Cost of Acute Physical Stress in Juvenile Steelhead" (*Trans. of Amer. Fish. Soc.* (1987): 257–263); the paper also included data for unstressed fish.

x	25	36	48	59	62	72	80	100	100	137
y	155	184	180	220	280	163	230	222	241	350

a. Is the value of y determined solely by the value of x? Explain your reasoning.
b. Construct a scatter plot of the data.
c. Does an increase in plasma cortisol concentration appear to be accompanied by a change in oxygen consumption rate? Comment.

4.4   The metabolic effect of cross-country skiing was the subject of the research study described in the paper "Metabolic Modifications Caused by Sport Activity: Effect in Leisure-Time Cross-Country Skiers" (*J. of Sports Med.* (1983):385–392). Subjects were participants in a 24-h cross-country relay. Age and blood CPK concentration were recorded 12 h into the relay. Use the given data to construct a scatter plot. Would you describe the pattern in this plot as approximately linear?

Skier	1	2	3	4	5	6	7	8	9
Age (x)	33	21	19	24	25	32	36	35	36
CPK (y)	180	300	520	480	580	440	380	480	520

Skier	10	11	12	13	14	15	16	17	18
Age (x)	24	25	44	51	50	52	55	62	57
CPK (y)	1040	1360	640	260	360	400	280	300	400

4.5   The accompanying data on x = food consumption (g/kg/day) and y = ^{22}Na (sodium 22) turnover (mEq/kg/day) for captive gray wolves appeared in the paper "Validation of Estimating Food Intake in Gray Wolves by ^{22}Na Turnover" (*J. Wildlife Mgmt.* (1991):59–71).

x	38.9	39.3	42.3	45.9	46.2	46.7 food consumption
y	1.19	1.12	1.26	1.48	1.41	1.54 Na turnover

a. Construct a scatter plot in which the axes intersect at (0, 0).
b. Construct a scatter plot in which the axes intersect at (38, 1.1) (as did the authors of the paper). Is this plot more appealing than the one of (a)? Explain.
c. How would you describe the pattern in the plot of (b)?

4.6   A number of research studies have looked at the relationship between water stress and plant productivity. The paper "Water Stress Affecting Nitrate Reduction and Leaf Diffusive Resistance in Coffea Arabica L. Cultivars" (*J. of Horticultural Sci.* (1983):147–152) examined water availability and nitrate activity in five different types of coffee plants. Data on water potential (x) and nitrate activity (y) for the Angustifolia and Nacional varieties are given.

	Angustifolia										
x	−10	−11	−11	−14	−15	−15	−16	−16	−16	−17	−18
y	3.2	3.0	5.4	3.5	3.0	3.6	4.8	3.2	2.4	4.6	1.6
x	−19	−20	−21	−22	−23	−23	−23	−24			
y	3.4	4.0	1.4	.4	.8	1.8	2.0	.2			

	Nacional										
x	−10	−12	−12	−13	−14	−14	−14	−14	−14	−15	−15	−15
y	9.8	8.0	13.0	6.0	5.0	6.0	7.2	10.4	10.8	7.8	9.0	11.0
x	−15	−16	−16	−17	−18	−18	−18	−18	−18	−18	−19	−20
y	14.0	6.6	14.2	3.4	8.0	8.2	8.6	9.2	11.6	12.0	5.2	9.4

a. Draw a scatter plot for the Angustifolia data. Does the plot look linear?

b. Construct a scatter plot for the Nacional data. Would you describe the relationship between nitrate activity and water potential exhibited by this data set as linear?

c. Discuss the similarities and differences between the scatter plots of nitrate activity versus water potential for Angustifolia and Nacional coffee plants.

4.2 Correlation

A scatter plot of bivariate numerical data gives a visual impression of how strongly the values of x are related to the values of y with which they are paired. But to make precise statements and draw conclusions from data, we need to go beyond pictures. Our objective now is to develop a numerical measure of how strongly the x and y values in such a sample are related. It is customary to call such a measure a **correlation coefficient** (from co-relation).

Figure 4.6 displays several scatter plots that indicate different types of relationships between the x and y values. The plot in Figure 4.6(a) suggests a very strong *positive relationship* between x and y; for every pair of points in the plot, the one with the larger x value also has the larger y value. That is, an increase in x is inevitably paired with an increase in y. The plot in Figure 4.6(b) shows a strong *tendency* for y to increase as x does, but there are a few exceptions. For example, the x and y values of the two points in the extreme upper right-hand corner of the plot go in opposite directions (x increases but y decreases). Nevertheless, a plot such as this would again indicate a rather strong positive relationship. Figure 4.6(c) suggests that x and y are *negatively related*—as x increases, there is a tendency for y to decrease. Obviously the negative relationship in this plot is not as strong as the positive relationship in Figure 4.6(b), although both plots show a well-defined linear pattern. The plot of Figure 4.6(d) is indicative of no strong relationship between x and $y;$ there is no tendency for y either to increase or decrease as x increases. Finally, as illustrated in Figure 4.6(e), a scatter plot can show evidence of a strong positive (or negative) relationship through a pattern that is curved rather than linear in character.

FIGURE 4.6
Scatter plots illustrating various types of relationships
(a) and (b) Positive relationship, linear pattern
(c) Negative relationship, linear pattern
(d) No relationship or pattern
(e) Positive relationship, curved pattern

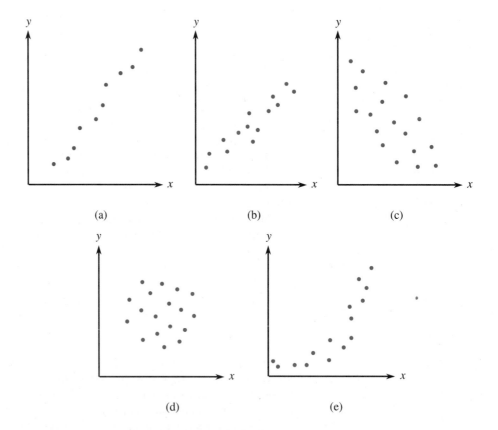

Pearson's Sample Correlation Coefficient

Let (x_1, y_1), (x_2, y_2), . . . , (x_n, y_n) denote a sample of (x, y) pairs. Figure 4.7(a) shows a scatter plot of such data indicating a substantial positive relationship: points on the right part of the plot, which have large x values, tend to be higher (have larger y values) than those on the left. A vertical line through $\bar{x}$ and a horizontal line through $\bar{y}$ divide the plot into four regions. In region I, both x and y are larger than their mean values, so the deviations $x - \bar{x}$ and $y - \bar{y}$ are both positive and so is the product $(x - \bar{x})(y - \bar{y})$. The product of deviations is also positive for any point in region III, because there both deviations are negative and multiplying two negative numbers gives a positive number. Any point in the other two regions gives rise to a negative value for $(x - \bar{x})(y - \bar{y})$, since one term in the product is negative and the other is positive. But because almost all points lie in regions I or III, almost all products are positive, so the *sum* of products $\Sigma(x - \bar{x})(y - \bar{y})$ will be a large positive number.

Similar reasoning for the data displayed in Figure 4.7(b), which exhibits a strong negative relationship, implies that $\Sigma(x - \bar{x})(y - \bar{y})$ will be a large nega-

FIGURE 4.7
Breaking up a scatter plot according to the signs of $x - \bar{x}$ and $y - \bar{y}$
(a) A positive relation
(b) A negative relation
(c) No strong relation

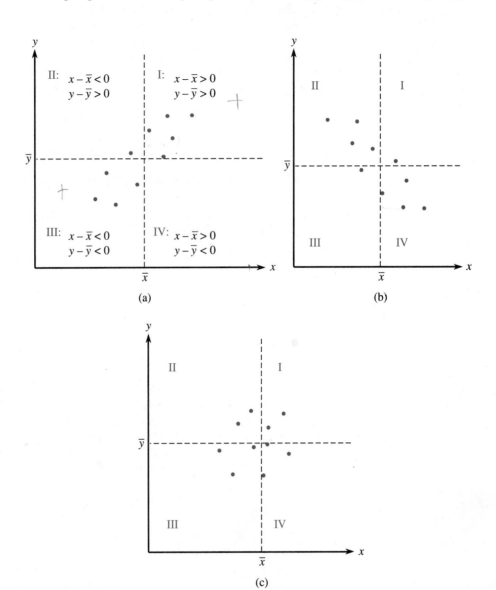

tive number. When there is no strong relationship, as in Figure 4.7(c), positive and negative products tend to counteract one another, producing a value of $\Sigma(x - \bar{x})(y - \bar{y})$ that is close to zero. In summary, $\Sigma(x - \bar{x})(y - \bar{y})$ seems to be a reasonable measure of the degree of association between x and y; it will be a large positive number, a large negative number, or a number close to zero according to whether there is a strong positive, a strong negative, or no strong relationship.

Unfortunately our proposed measure has a serious deficiency: its value depends on the choice of unit for measuring either x or y. Suppose, for example, that x is height. Each height expressed in inches is 12 times the corresponding height expressed in feet. It follows that when the unit for x is inches, the value of $\Sigma(x - \bar{x})(y - \bar{y})$ will be 12 times what it is for x given in feet. A measure of the inherent strength of the relationship between x and y should give the same value whatever the units for the variables; otherwise our impressions can be distorted by the choice of units.

A straightforward modification of $\Sigma(x - \bar{x})(y - \bar{y})$ leads to the most popular measure of association, one that is free of the defect just alluded to and has other attractive properties.

DEFINITION

Let $\bar{x}$ and s_x denote the sample mean and standard deviation for the x values in the pairs (x_1, y_1), (x_2, y_2), . . . , (x_n, y_n) and let $\bar{y}$ and s_y denote the sample mean and standard deviation of the y values. Then **Pearson's sample correlation coefficient** r is given by

$$r = \frac{\Sigma(x - \bar{x})(y - \bar{y})}{(n - 1)s_x s_y}$$

Before discussing various properties of r, let's look at a computational example.

EXAMPLE 4.3

An accurate assessment of soil productivity is an essential input to rational land-use planning. Unfortunately, as the author of the article "Productivity Ratings Based on Soil Series" (*Prof. Geographer* (1980):158–163) argues, an acceptable soil productivity index is not so easy to come by. One difficulty is that productivity is determined partly by which crop is planted, and the relationship between yield of two different crops planted in the same soil may not be very strong. To illustrate, the paper presents the accompanying data on corn yield x and peanut yield y (mT/Ha) for eight different types of soil:

Observation	1	2	3	4	5	6	7	8
x	2.4	3.4	4.6	3.7	2.2	3.3	4.0	2.1
y	1.33	2.12	1.80	1.65	2.00	1.76	2.11	1.63

corn
peanut

It is easily verified that

$$\Sigma x = 25.7 \qquad \Sigma x^2 = 88.31 \qquad s_x^2 = .821250 \qquad s_x = .906228$$
$$\Sigma y = 14.40 \qquad \Sigma y^2 = 26.4324 \qquad s_y^2 = .073200 \qquad s_y = .270555$$

Using $\bar{x} = 25.7/8 = 3.2125$ and $\bar{y} = 14.40/8 = 1.8000$,

$$\Sigma(x - \bar{x})(y - \bar{y}) = (x_1 - \bar{x})(y_1 - \bar{y}) + \cdots + (x_8 - \bar{x})(y_8 - \bar{y})$$
$$= (2.4 - 3.2125)(1.33 - 1.8000) + \cdots + (2.1 - 3.2125)(1.63 - 1.8000)$$
$$= .3819 + \cdots + .1891$$
$$= .5960$$

Thus

$$r = \frac{\Sigma(x - \bar{x})(y - \bar{y})}{(n - 1)s_x s_y} = \frac{.5960}{7(.9062)(.2706)} = .347$$

The accompanying scatter plot (Figure 4.8) suggests that $r = .347$ is indicative of only a weak positive relationship.

FIGURE 4.8
Scatter plot of y = peanut yield versus x = corn yield

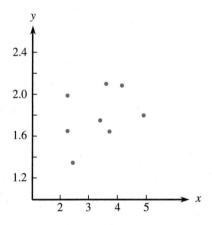

A computational formula for r, similar to the one for the sample variance, circumvents the need to compute the x and y deviations.

> A computational formula for r is
>
> $$r = \frac{\Sigma xy - [(\Sigma x)(\Sigma y)/n]}{\sqrt{\Sigma x^2 - [(\Sigma x)^2/n]} \sqrt{\Sigma y^2 - [(\Sigma y)^2/n]}}$$

In addition to n, this formula requires the five sums Σx, Σy, Σx^2, Σy^2, and Σxy. A tabular format containing five columns for the x, y, x^2, y^2, and xy values helps in organizing the computations, with each derived sum recorded below the corresponding column.

EXAMPLE 4.4

(*Example 4.3 continued*) Here again are the $n = 8$ observations on corn yield (x) and peanut yield (y) presented earlier.

x	y	x^2	y^2	xy
2.4	1.33	5.76	1.7689	3.192
3.4	2.12	11.56	4.4944	7.208
4.6	1.80	21.16	3.2400	8.280
3.7	1.65	13.69	2.7225	6.105
2.2	2.00	4.84	4.0000	4.400
3.3	1.76	10.89	3.0976	5.808
4.0	2.11	16.00	4.4521	8.440
2.1	1.63	4.41	2.6569	3.423
25.7	14.40	88.31	26.4324	46.856
↑	↑	↑	↑	↑
Σx	Σy	Σx^2	Σy^2	Σxy

Then

$$r = \frac{46.856 - [(25.7)(14.40)/8]}{\sqrt{88.31 - [(25.7)^2/8]}\ \sqrt{26.4324 - [(14.40)^2/8]}}$$

$$= \frac{.5960}{(2.3977)(.7158)}$$

$$= .347, \quad \text{as before}$$

Properties of r

1. *The value of r does not depend on the unit of measurement for either variable.* If, for example, x is height, the factor of 12 that appears in the numerator when changing from feet to inches will also appear in the denominator, so the two will cancel and leave r unchanged. The same value of r results from height expressed in inches, meters, or miles. If y is temperature, expressing values in °F, °C, or °K will give the same value of r. The correlation coefficient measures the inherent strength of relationship between two numerical variables.

2. *The value of r does not depend on which of the two variables is labeled x.* Thus if we had let x = peanut yield and y = corn yield in Example 4.3, the same value, r = .347, would have resulted.
3. *The value of r is between* -1 *and* $+1$. A value near the upper limit, $+1$, is indicative of a substantial positive relationship, whereas an r close to the lower limit, -1, suggests a prominent negative relationship. A useful informal rule for characterizing the nature of the relationship in everyday language is as follows: We say the relationship is

    strong if either $r \geq .8$ or $r \leq -.8$;

    moderate if either $.5 < r < .8$ or $-.8 < r < -.5$;

    weak if $-.5 \leq r \leq .5$.

    It may seem surprising that a value of r as extreme as $-.5$ or $.5$ should be in the "weak" category; an explanation for this is given later in the chapter.
4. $r = 1$ *only when all the points in a scatter plot of the data lie exactly on a straight line that slopes upward. Similarly,* $r = -1$ *only when all the points lie exactly on a downward-sloping line.* Only when there is a perfect linear relationship between x and y in the sample will r take on one of its two possible extreme values. If there is any deviation from a straight line, then r will be strictly between -1 and $+1$ (that is, $-1 < r < 1$).
5. *The value of r is a measure of the extent to which x and y are* **linearly** *related*— that is, the extent to which the points in the scatter plot fall close to a straight line. A value of r close to zero does not rule out any strong relationship between x and y; there could still be a strong relationship but one that is not linear.

EXAMPLE 4.5

In recent years much effort has been expended by environmental scientists in tracing the sources of acid rain. Nitrates are a major constituent of acid rain, and arsenic has been proposed as a tracer element. The accompanying data on x = nitrate concentration (μM) of a precipitation sample and y = arsenic concentration (nM) is a subset of that contained in the paper "The Atmospheric Deposition of Arsenic and Association with Acid Precipitation" (*Atmospheric Environ.* (1988):937–943).

Obs.	1	2	3	4	5	6	7	8	9	10	11	12
x	11	13	18	30	36	40	50	58	67	82	91	102
y	1.1	.5	2.4	1.2	2.1	1.2	4.0	2.3	1.7	3.7	3.0	3.9

The scatter plot displayed in Figure 4.9 shows a clear positive relationship. The summary quantities needed for the calculation of r are

$$\Sigma x = 598 \qquad \Sigma y = 27.1 \qquad \Sigma x^2 = 40{,}172$$
$$\Sigma y^2 = 76.59 \qquad \Sigma xy = 1642.9$$

FIGURE 4.9
Scatter plot of the data from
Example 4.5

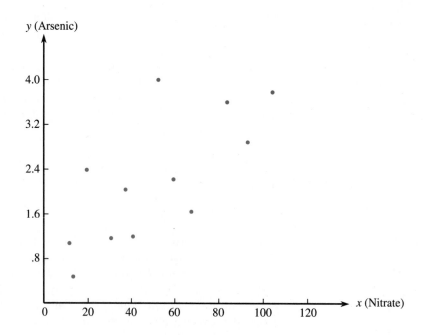

from which we get

$$r = \frac{292.4167}{\sqrt{10,371.6667}\,\sqrt{15.3892}}$$

$$= .732$$

This is evidence of a moderate positive relationship.

EXAMPLE 4.6

The accompanying data on y = glucose concentration (g/L) and x = fermentation time (days) for a particular brand of malt liquor was read from a scatter plot appearing in the paper "Improving Fermentation Productivity with Reverse Osmosis" (*Food Tech.* (1984):92–96).

x	1	2	3	4	5	6	7	8	fermentation time
y	74	54	52	51	52	53	58	71	glucose conc

Figure 4.10 shows a scatter plot, from which we see that there appears to be a strong relationship, but *not* a linear one, between x and y. With

$$\Sigma x = 36 \qquad \Sigma x^2 = 204 \qquad \Sigma y = 465 \qquad \Sigma y^2 = 27{,}615 \qquad \Sigma xy = 2094$$

we have

FIGURE 4.10
Scatter plot of the data
from Example 4.6

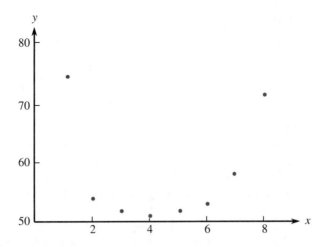

$$r = \frac{2094 - [(36)(465)/8]}{\sqrt{204 - [(36)^2/8]}\ \sqrt{27{,}615 - [(465)^2/8]}}$$

$$= \frac{1.5000}{(6.4807)(24.2255)}$$

$$= .0096 \approx .01$$

This shows the importance of interpreting r as measuring the extent of any *linear* relationship. We should not conclude that there is no relation whatsoever just because $r \approx 0$.

The Population Correlation Coefficient

The sample correlation coefficient r measures how strongly the x and y values in a *sample* of pairs are related to one another. There is an analogous measure of how strongly x and y are related in the entire population of pairs from which the sample $(x_1, y_1), \ldots, (x_n, y_n)$ was obtained. It is called the **population correlation coefficient** and is denoted by ρ (notice again the use of a Greek letter for a population characteristic and Roman letter for a sample characteristic). We'll never have to calculate ρ from the entire population of pairs, but it is important to know that ρ satisfies properties paralleling those of r:

1. ρ is a number between -1 and $+1$ that does not depend on the unit of measurement for either x or y or on which variable is labeled x and which is labeled y.
2. $\rho = +1$ or -1 if and only if all (x, y) pairs in the population lie exactly on a straight line, so ρ measures the extent to which there is a linear relationship in the population.

Later on we show how the sample characteristic r can be used to make an inference concerning the population characteristic ρ. In particular, r can be used to decide whether or not $\rho = 0$ (no linear relationship in the population).

Correlation and Causation

A value of r close to 1 indicates that relatively large values of one variable tend to be associated with relatively large values of the other variable. This is far from saying that a large value of one variable *causes* the value of the other variable to be large. Correlation (Pearson's or any other) measures the extent of association, but **association does not imply causation.** It frequently happens that two variables are highly correlated not because one is causally related to the other but because they are both strongly related to a third variable. Among all elementary-school children, there is a strong positive relationship between the number of cavities in a child's teeth and the size of his or her vocabulary. Yet no one advocates eating foods that result in more cavities in order to increase vocabulary size (or working to decrease vocabulary size in order to protect against cavities). Number of cavities and vocabulary size are both strongly related to age, so older children tend to have higher values of both variables than do younger ones. Among children of any fixed age, there would undoubtedly be little relationship between number of cavities and vocabulary size.

Scientific experiments can frequently make a strong case for causality by carefully controlling the values of all variables that might be related to the ones under study. Then, if y is observed to change in a "smooth" way as the experimenter changes the value of x, the most plausible explanation would be a causal relationship between x and y. In the absence of such control and ability to manipulate values of one variable, we must admit the possibility that an unidentified underlying third variable is influencing both the variables under investigation. A high correlation in many uncontrolled studies carried out in different settings can marshal support for causality—as in the case of cigarette smoking and cancer—but proving causality is often a very elusive task.

Spearman's Rank Correlation Coefficient (Optional)

Pearson's correlation coefficient r identifies a strong linear relationship between x and y but may miss a strong relationship that is not linear. In addition, the value of r can be greatly affected by the presence of even one or two outlying (x, y) pairs that are far from the main part of the scatter plot. Spearman's correlation coefficient r_s is a measure that is not as sensitive as r to outlying points and identifies both linear and nonlinear relationships. It does so by using the *ranks* of the x and y observations rather than the observations themselves.

To compute r_s, first replace the smallest x value by its rank, 1, the second-smallest x value by its rank, 2, and so on. Similarly, the smallest y value is replaced by its rank, 1, the second smallest by its rank, 2, and so on. Suppose, for example, that $n = 4$ and the data pairs are

(110, 24.7)   (125, 24.2)   (116, 22.6)   (95, 23.5)

Then we have

x value	110	125	116	95
Rank	2	4	3	1

and

y value	24.7	24.2	22.6	23.5
Rank	4	3	1	2

The resulting rank pairs are

(2, 4)   (4, 3)   (3, 1)   (1, 2)

If there is a strong positive relationship between x and y, the x observations with small ranks tend to be paired with y observations having small ranks. An extreme case of this, the rank pairs (1, 1), (2, 2), (3, 3), (4, 4), occurs whenever a larger x value is always associated with a larger y value. Alternatively, large x ranks paired with small y ranks indicate a negative relationship, the most extreme case being (1, 4), (2, 3), (3, 2), and (4, 1) for $n = 4$ observations.

Once the rank pairs have been determined, Spearman's r_s is just Pearson's coefficient r applied to these rank pairs. To simplify the formula for r_s, note that the ranks for n observations (x values or y values) are the n integers 1, 2, 3, ..., n. The average and standard deviation of this set of integers are $(n + 1)/2$ and $\sqrt{n(n + 1)/12}$, respectively. Since the denominator of r is $(n - 1)s_x s_y$, the denominator of r_s becomes

$$(n - 1) \sqrt{\frac{n(n + 1)}{12}} \sqrt{\frac{n(n + 1)}{12}} = \frac{n(n - 1)(n + 1)}{12}$$

DEFINITION

Spearman's rank correlation coefficient r_s is Pearson's correlation coefficient applied to the rank pairs obtained by replacing each x value by its rank and each y value by its rank:

$$r_s = \frac{\sum\left[x\,\text{rank} - \left(\frac{n + 1}{2}\right)\right]\left[y\,\text{rank} - \left(\frac{n + 1}{2}\right)\right]}{\dfrac{n(n - 1)(n + 1)}{12}}$$

As with r, the value of r_s is between -1 and 1. A value close to 1 or -1 indicates a strong relationship, whereas a value close to zero indicates a weak relationship.

EXAMPLE 4.7

The paper "The Relation Between Freely Chosen Meals and Body Habits" (*Amer. J. Clinical Nutrition* (1983):32–40) reported results of an investigation into the relationship between body build and energy intake of an individual's diet. A measure of body build is the Quetelet index (x), with a high value of x indicating a thickset individual. The variable reflecting energy intake is y = dietary energy density. There were nine subjects in the investigation, and the resulting (x, y) pairs are given in Table 4.1. With $n = 9$,

$$\frac{n + 1}{2} = \frac{10}{2} = 5$$

$$\frac{n(n - 1)(n + 1)}{12} = \frac{(9)(8)(10)}{12} = 60$$

From Table 4.1, the numerator of r_s is 57, so

$$r_s = \frac{57}{60} = .95$$

This indicates a very strong positive relationship between the x and y values in the sample.

TABLE 4.1   Data and calculations for Example 4.7

Subject	x	y	x rank	y rank	$\left(x\,\text{rank} - \dfrac{n + 1}{2}\right)\left(y\,\text{rank} - \dfrac{n + 1}{2}\right)$
1	221	.67	3	3	$(-2)(-2) = 4$
2	228	.86	6	5	$(1)(0) = 0$
3	223	.78	4	4	$(-1)(-1) = 1$
4	211	.54	1	2	$(-4)(-3) = 12$
5	231	.91	7	7	$(2)(2) = 4$
6	215	.44	2	1	$(-3)(-4) = 12$
7	224	.90	5	6	$(0)(1) = 0$
8	233	.94	8	9	$(3)(4) = 12$
9	268	.93	9	8	$(4)(3) = 12$
					Sum = 57

Figure 4.11 displays a scatter plot of the data. The point (268, .93) is a clear outlier and considerably distorts the linear pattern in the plot. The value of Pearson's r is only .658.

Consider the effect on r and r_s of changing x_9. If 268 is replaced by 234, then (234, .93) is no longer an outlier. The value of r_s remains at .95, since 234 has the same x rank as 268, but the value of r for the altered data set rises dramatically to .92.

FIGURE 4.11
A MINITAB scatter plot for the
data of Example 4.7

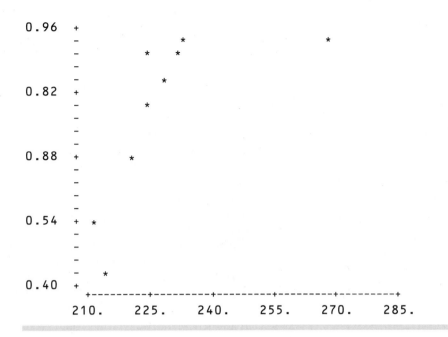

```
0.96  +
      -                                          *                           *
      -                          *        *
      -
      -                    *
0.82  +
      -              *
      -
      -
      -
0.88  +              *
      -
      -
      -
0.54  +  *
      -
      -
      -
      -  *
0.40  +
      +---------+---------+---------+---------+---------+
      210.     225.     240.     255.     270.     285.
```

The objective of some experiments is to make comparisons by having individuals rank the objects or entities in a specified group. Thus some television viewers might be asked to rank a group of programs in order of decreasing preference, or some wine connoisseurs might convene for the purpose of ranking a group of wines in order of descending quality. In such cases the data values consist of sets of rankings rather than observations on numerical variables. Spearman's r_s can be applied directly to two sets of such rankings to measure the extent to which those doing the rating agree in their judgments. The calculations are exactly like those done in Example 4.7 once the x and y ranks have been determined. Several examples of this type are given in the exercises.

The procedure for calculating r_s must be modified somewhat if there are ties in either the x values or the y values (for example, three pairs with $x = 27.5$). One of the chapter references can be consulted to find out how this is done.

EXERCISES 4.7–4.26   SECTION 4.2

4.7   For each of the following pairs of variables, indicate whether you would expect a positive correlation, a negative correlation, or no correlation. Explain your choice.
a. Maximum daily temperature and cooling costs

b. Interest rate and number of loan applications

c. Incomes of husbands and wives when both have full-time jobs

d. Height and IQ

e. Height and shoe size

f. Score on the math section of the SAT exam and score on the verbal section of the same test

g. Time spent on homework and time spent watching television during the same day by elementary-school children

h. Amount of fertilizer used per acre and crop yield (Hint: As the amount of fertilizer is increased, yield tends to increase for awhile but then tends to start decreasing.)

4.8   Is the following statement correct? Explain why or why not.
A correlation coefficient of zero implies that no relationship exists between the two variables under study.

4.9   Draw two scatter plots, one for which $r = 1$ and a second for which $r = -1$.

4.10   A number of different methods for measuring growth rate in lobsters are discussed in the paper "A Comparison of Techniques for the Measurement of Growth in Adult Lobsters" (*Aquaculture* (1984):195–199). Twenty-three adult female lobsters were included in the study and both dry weight and volume were recorded for each one. Letting x denote dry weight (in g) and y volume (in mL), summary quantities for the data given in the paper are

$$n = 23 \qquad\qquad \Sigma(x - \bar{x})^2 = 557{,}582.1$$
$$\Sigma(y - \bar{y})^2 = 6{,}347{,}190.0 \qquad \Sigma(x - \bar{x})(y - \bar{y}) = 1{,}410{,}933.1$$

Use this information to calculate the correlation coefficient. Would you describe the correlation between dry weight and volume as positive or negative? As weak, moderate, or strong?

4.11   Sixteen different air samples were obtained at Herald Square in New York City, and both the carbon monoxide concentration x (ppm) and benzo(a) pyrene concentration y ($\mu g/10^3 m^3$) were measured for each sample ("Carcinogenic Air Pollutants in Relation to Automobile Traffic in New York City," *Environ. Science and Tech.* (1971):145–150).

x	2.8	15.5	19.0	6.8	5.5	5.6	9.6	13.3
y	.5	.1	.8	.9	1.0	1.1	3.9	4.0

x	5.5	12.0	5.6	19.5	11.0	12.8	5.5	10.5
y	1.3	5.7	1.5	6.0	7.3	8.1	2.2	9.5

Compute the sample correlation coefficient for this data. What does the value of r suggest about the nature of the relationship between x and y?

4.12   The accompanying data on diesel oil consumption rate measured by the drain-weight method (x) and measured by the Cl-trace method (y), both in grams per hour, was read from a graph in the paper "A New Measurement Method of Diesel Engine Oil Consumption Rate" (*J. of Soc. Auto Engr.* (1985):28–33).

x	4	5	8	11	12	16	17	20	22	28	30	31	39
y	5	7	10	10	14	15	13	25	20	24	31	28	39

$$\Sigma x = 243 \quad \Sigma y = 241 \quad \Sigma x^2 = 5965 \quad \Sigma y^2 = 5731 \quad \Sigma xy = 5805$$

Determine the value of the sample correlation coefficient. Does there appear to be good agreement between the two methods?

4.13 Toughness and fibrousness of asparagus are major determinants of quality. This was the focus of a study reported in "Post-Harvest Glyphosate Application Reduces Toughening, Fiber Content, and Lignification of Stored Asparagus Spears" (*J. of Amer. Soc. Horticultural Science* (1988):569–572). The paper reported the following data (read from a graph) on x = shear force (kg) and y = percent fiber dry weight.

x	46	48	55	57	60	72	81	85	94
y	2.18	2.10	2.13	2.28	2.34	2.53	2.28	2.62	2.63

x	109	121	132	137	148	149	184	185	187
y	2.50	2.66	2.79	2.80	3.01	2.98	3.34	3.49	3.26

$$n = 18 \quad \Sigma x = 1950 \quad \Sigma x^2 = 251{,}970$$
$$\Sigma y = 47.92 \quad \Sigma y^2 = 130.6074 \quad \Sigma xy = 5530.92$$

a. Calculate the value of the sample correlation coefficient.
b. How would you describe the nature of the relationship between the two variables?
c. If shear force increases, what happens to percent fiber dry weight?

4.14 The article "Reduction in Soluble Protein and Chlorophyll Contents in a Few Plants as Indicators of Automobile Exhaust Pollution" (*Int. J. of Environ. Studies* (1983):239–244) reported the accompanying data on x = distance from a highway (m) and y = lead content of soil at that distance (ppm).

x	.3	1	5	10	15	20
y	62.75	37.51	29.70	20.71	17.65	15.41

x	25	30	40	50	75	100
y	14.15	13.50	12.11	11.40	10.85	10.85

a. Calculate the value of the sample correlation coefficient r.
b. Construct a scatter plot. Is the value of r an effective summary quantity for describing the relationship between the two variables?

4.15 An employee of an auction house has a list of 25 recently sold paintings. Eight artists were represented in these sales. The sale price of each painting appears on the list. Would the correlation coefficient be an appropriate way to summarize the relationship between artist (x) and sale price (y)? Why or why not?

4.16   A sample of automobiles traversing a certain stretch of highway is selected. Each one travels at roughly a constant rate of speed, though speed does vary from auto to auto. Let x = speed and y = time needed to traverse this segment of highway. Would the sample correlation coefficient be closest to .9, .3, −.3, or −.9? Explain.

4.17   Suppose that sample x and y values are first expressed in standard units by means of

$$x' = \frac{(x - \bar{x})}{s_x} \quad \text{and} \quad y' = \frac{(y - \bar{y})}{s_y}$$

How does the value of $\Sigma x'y'$, the sum of the products of these standardized values, relate to r? (Hint: The denominator of r is $(n - 1)\, s_x s_y$.)

4.18   Suppose that x and y are positive variables and that a sample of n pairs results in $r \approx 1$. If the sample correlation coefficient is computed for the n pairs (x_1, y_1^2), $(x_2, y_2^2), \ldots, (x_n, y_n^2)$—that is, for the (x, y^2) pairs—will the resulting value also be approximately 1? Explain.

4.19   A sample of $n = 5$ (x, y) pairs gives (1, 1), (2, 2), (3, 3), (4, 4), and (5, y_5). It must be the case that both $x \geq 0$ and $y \geq 0$. Could r be negative?

4.20   Nine students currently taking introductory statistics are randomly selected, and both the first midterm exam score (x) and the second midterm exam score (y) are determined. Three of the students have the class at 8 A.M., another three have it at noon, and the remaining three have a night class. The resulting (x, y) pairs are as follows.

				x_1 78.7	76.0
8 A.M.:	(70, 60)	(72, 83)	(94, 85)		
Noon:	(80, 72)	(60, 74)	(55, 58)	x_2 65.0	68.0
Night:	(45, 63)	(50, 40)	(35, 54)	x_3 43.3	52.3

a.   Calculate the sample correlation coefficient for the nine (x, y) pairs.

b.   Let $\bar{x}_1$ = the average score on the first midterm for the 8 A.M. students and $\bar{y}_1$ = the average score on the second midterm for these students. Let $\bar{x}_2$ and $\bar{y}_2$ be these averages for the noon students, and $\bar{x}_3$ and $\bar{y}_3$ be these averages for the evening students. Calculate r for these three $(\bar{x}, \bar{y})$ pairs.

c.   Construct a scatter plot of the nine (x, y) pairs and construct another one of the three $(\bar{x}, \bar{y})$ pairs. Can you see why r in part (a) is smaller than r in part (b)? Does this suggest that a correlation coefficient based on averages (an "ecological" correlation) might be misleading? Explain.

4.21   Doctors have always cautioned against extreme low-calorie weight-loss diets (under 500 calories per day). The paper "Cardiac Dysfunction in Obese Dieters: A Potentially Lethal Complication of Rapid Massive Weight Loss" (*Amer. J. Clinical Nutrition* (1984):695–702) summarized the findings of a study of healthy adults who died suddenly either during or shortly after having been on a very low-calorie diet. The data in the paper was used to rank the 16 female subjects on the basis of initial body mass (kg/m^2) and length of time (months) on a low-calorie diet, and these ranks are given. Use this data to compute Spearman's rank correlation coefficient.

How does the value of r_s compare to the value of Pearson's correlation coefficient, $r = .824$, given in the paper?

			Ranks					
Body mass	1	2	3	4	5	6	7	8
Time on diet	1	3	4	11	8	2	7	9

			Ranks					
Body mass	9	10	11	12	13	14	15	16
Time on diet	5	12	6	15	10	16	13	14

4.22 The fuel price index (FPI) and consumer price index (CPI) in the United States for the years 1970–1981 are given (*Transportation Quarterly* (1983):28).

Year	1970	1971	1972	1973	1974	1975
FPI	51.7	53.7	53.8	55.7	79.2	89.6
CPI	64.0	66.8	69.0	73.3	81.4	88.8

Year	1976	1977	1978	1979	1980	1981
FPI	97.6	100.0	106.6	153.3	206.2	229.9
CPI	93.9	100.0	107.7	119.8	136.0	150.1

a. Draw a scatter plot with x denoting FPI and y denoting CPI. Does the plot exhibit a weak, moderate, strong, or perfect linear relationship?
b. Calculate the value of r for this data set.
c. Compute Spearman's rank correlation coefficient, r_s.
d. How do the values of r and r_s compare? Does it surprise you that $r_s = 1$ but $r \neq 1$? Explain why or why not.

4.23 In a study of variables thought to be related to urban gang activity, seven Chicago-area communities were ranked according to prevalence of ganging, percent of residents who are African-American, median family income, and percent of families below poverty level ("Youth Gangs," *Pacific Sociol. Rev.* (1981):366). The authors of this paper analyzed this data using Spearman's rank correlation coefficient.

Community	Prevalence of ganging	Percent African-American	Median income	Percent below poverty level
A	2	3	7	1
B	4	6	6	4
C	7	7	1	7
D	5	5	2	5
E	6	4	3	6
F	3	2	5	3
G	1	1	4	2

a. Calculate r_s for the following pairs of variables.

   i. Ganging prevalence and percent African-American

   ii. Ganging prevalence and median income

   iii. Ganging prevalence and percent below poverty level

b. Based on the coefficients in (a), which of the variables seems to exhibit the strongest relationship with ganging prevalence?

4.24 The accompanying data (taken from "Rating the Risks" (*Environment* (1979):19)) shows how three groups of people ranked the relative riskiness of 30 activities and technologies. A rank of 1 represents the most risky activity.

a. Use Spearman's rank correlation coefficient to assess the extent to which the following pairs of groups agree in their rankings of relative risks.

   i. Students and nonstudents

   ii. Students and experts

   iii. Nonstudents and experts

b. Which two groups exhibit the most agreement in ranking?

c. Where in the ranking would you put taking a statistics course?

	Ranks		
	Group 1	Group 2	Group 3
Activity	Nonstudents	College students	Experts
Nuclear power	1	1	20
Motor vehicles	2	5	1
Handguns	3	2	4
Smoking	4	3	2
Motorcycles	5	6	6
Alcoholic beverages	6	7	3
Private aviation	7	15	12
Police work	8	8	17
Pesticides	9	4	8
Surgery	10	11	5
Fire fighting	11	10	18
Large construction	12	14	13
Hunting	13	18	23
Spray cans	14	13	26
Mountain climbing	15	22	29
Bicycles	16	24	15
Commercial aviation	17	16	16
Electric power	18	19	9
Swimming	19	30	10
Contraceptives	20	9	11
Skiing	21	25	30
X rays	22	17	7
High school/college football	23	26	27
Railroads	24	23	19
Food preservatives	25	12	14
Food coloring	26	20	21
Power mowers	27	28	28

(continued)

	Ranks		
	Group 1	Group 2	Group 3
Activity	Nonstudents	College students	Experts
Prescription antibiotics	28	21	24
Home appliances	29	27	22
Vaccinations	30	29	25

4.25 Ranking wines is a common practice at wine tastings. Suppose that after tasting nine wines, two judges rank the wines as follows:

Wine	A	B	C	D	E	F	G	H	I
Judge 1	7	1	3	2	8	5	9	6	4
Judge 2	9	4	1	3	7	5	6	8	2

Compute r_s as a measure of agreement between the two judges.

4.26 Let d_1 denote the difference (x rank $-$ y rank) for the first (x, y) pair, d_2 denote this difference for the second (x, y) pair, and so on. It can be shown that

$$r_s = 1 - \frac{6\Sigma d^2}{n(n^2 - 1)}$$

a. Use this formula to compute r_s for the data of Example 4.7.
b. What does this formula imply about the value of r_s when there is a perfect positive relationship? Explain.

4.3 Fitting a Line to Bivariate Data

Given two variables x and y, the general objective of *regression analysis* is to use information about x to draw some type of conclusion concerning y. Often an investigator will want a prediction of the y value that would result from making a single observation at a specified x value—for example, predict product sales y during a given period when shelf space for displaying the product is $x = 6$ ft^2. The different roles played by the two variables are reflected in standard terminology: y is called the **dependent** or **response variable** and x is referred to as the **independent** or **predictor variable.**

A scatter plot of y versus x (that is, of the (x, y) pairs in a sample) will frequently exhibit a linear pattern. It is natural in such cases to summarize the relationship between the variables by finding a line that is as close as possible to the points in the plot. Before doing so, let's review some elementary facts about lines and linear relationships.

Suppose that a car dealership advertises that a particular model of car can be rented for a flat fee of \$25 plus an additional \$.20 per mile. If this type of car is rented and driven for 100 miles, the dealer's revenue y is

$$y = 25 + (.20)(100) = 25 + 20 = 45$$

More generally, if x denotes distance driven (miles), then

$$y = 25 + .20x$$

That is, x and y are linearly related.

The general form of a linear relation between x and y is $y = a + bx$. A particular relation is specified by choosing values of a and b. Thus one such relationship is $y = 10 + 2x$, while another is $y = 100 - 5x$. If we choose some x values and compute $y = a + bx$ for each value, the points in the scatter plot of the resulting (x, y) pairs fall exactly on a straight line.

DEFINITION

The relationship

$$y = a + bx$$

is the equation of a straight line. The value of b, called the **slope** of the line, is the amount by which y increases when x increases by 1 unit. The value of a, called the **y, or vertical, intercept** of the line, is the height of the line above the value $x = 0$.

The equation $y = 10 + 2x$ has slope $b = 2$, so each 1-unit increase in x results in an increase of 2 in y. When $x = 0$, $y = 10$, and the height at which the line crosses the vertical axis (where $x = 0$) is 10. This is illustrated in Figure 4.12(a).

FIGURE 4.12
The graphs of two straight lines
(a) A line with slope $b = 2$ and y intercept $a = 10$
(b) A line with slope $b = -5$ and y intercept $a = 100$

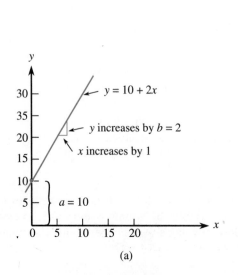

(a)

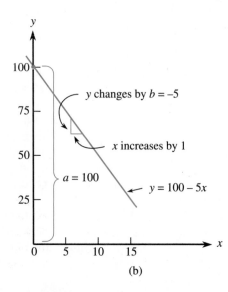

(b)

The slope of the line determined by $y = 100 - 5x$ is -5, so y increases by -5 (that is, decreases by 5) when x increases by 1. The height of the line above $x = 0$ is $a = 100$. The resulting line is pictured in Figure 4.12(b).

It is easy to draw the line corresponding to any particular linear equation. First choose any two x values and substitute them into the equation to obtain the corresponding y values. Then plot the resulting two (x, y) pairs as two points. The desired line is the one passing through these points. For the equation $y = 10 + 2x$, substituting $x = 5$ yields $y = 20$, whereas using $x = 10$ gives $y = 30$. The two points are then $(5, 20)$ and $(10, 30)$. The line in Figure 4.12(a) does indeed pass through these points.

Fitting a Straight Line: The Principle of Least Squares

Figure 4.13 shows a scatter plot with two lines superimposed on the plot. Line II clearly gives a better fit to the data than does Line I. The line that gives the most effective summary of the approximate linear relation is the one that in some sense is the best-fitting line, the one closest to the sample data. To measure the extent to

FIGURE 4.13
Lines I and II give poor and
good fits, respectively,
to the data

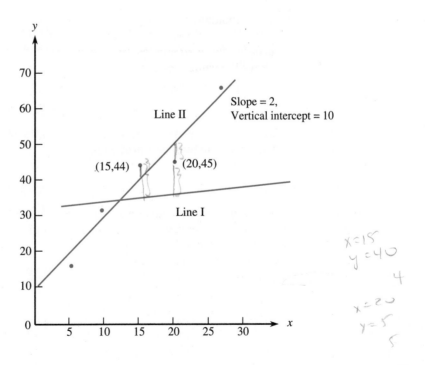

which a particular line provides a good fit, let's focus on the vertical deviations from the line. For example, Line II in Figure 4.13 has equation $y = 10 + 2x$ and the third and fourth points from the left are (15, 44) and (20, 45), respectively. The vertical deviations are then

$$3\text{rd deviation} = y_3 - \text{height of the line above } x_3$$
$$= 44 - [10 + 2(15)]$$
$$= 4$$

and

$$4\text{th deviation} = 45 - [10 + 2(20)]$$
$$= -5$$

A positive deviation results from a point that lies above the chosen line, and a negative deviation from a point that lies below this line. A particular line gives a good fit if the deviations from the line are small in magnitude. Line I in Figure 4.13 fits poorly, because all deviations from that line are larger in magnitude (some are much larger) than the corresponding deviations from Line II.

We now need a way to combine the n deviations into a single measure of fit. The standard approach is to square the deviations (to obtain nonnegative numbers) and sum these squared deviations.

DEFINITION

The most widely used criterion for measuring the goodness-of-fit of a line $y = a + bx$ to bivariate data $(x_1, y_1), \ldots, (x_n, y_n)$ is the sum of the squared deviations about the line:

$$\Sigma[y - (a + bx)]^2 = [y_1 - (a + bx_1)]^2$$
$$+ [y_2 - (a + bx_2)]^2 + \cdots + [y_n - (a + bx_n)]^2$$

The line that gives the best fit to the data is the one that minimizes this sum; it is called the **least squares line.**[1]

Fortunately the equation of the least squares line can be obtained without having to calculate deviations from any particular line. This is because mathematical techniques can be applied to obtain relatively simple formulas for the slope and vertical intercept of the least squares line.

$\hat{y}$ = least squares line

---

[1]The least squares line is frequently referred to as the *sample regression line.*

> The slope of the least squares line is
>
> $$b = \frac{\Sigma xy - [(\Sigma x)(\Sigma y)/n]}{\Sigma x^2 - [(\Sigma x)^2/n]}$$
>
> and the y intercept is
>
> $$a = \bar{y} - b\bar{x}$$
>
> We shall write the equation of the least squares line as
>
> $$\hat{y} = a + bx$$
>
> where the ˆ above y emphasizes that $\hat{y}$ is a prediction of y resulting from the substitution of a particular x value into the equation.

Obtaining the least squares line requires first calculating Σx, Σy, Σx^2, and Σxy. In addition, we will shortly need Σy^2 and, of course, n. These six quantities are called *summary statistics*. As illustrated in the next example, computations are expedited by using a tabular format with columns for x, y, x^2, xy, and y^2. After placing the appropriate entries in each column, the column sums are the summary statistics (this same format was suggested for correlation calculations).

EXAMPLE 4.8

Landslides are common events in tree-growing regions of the Pacific Northwest, so their effect on timber growth is of special concern to foresters. The paper "Effects of Landslide Erosion on Subsequent Douglas Fir Growth and Stocking Levels in the Western Cascades, Oregon" (*Soil Science Soc. of Amer. J.* (1984):667–671) reported on the results of a study in which growth in a landslide area was compared with growth in a previously clear-cut area. Here we present data on clear-cut growth, with x = tree age (years) and y = 5-year height growth (cm).

	Observation							
	1	2	3	4	5	6	7	8
x	5	9	9	10	10	11	11	12
y	70	150	260	230	255	165	225	340

	Observation							
	9	10	11	12	13	14	15	16
x	13	13	14	14	15	15	18	18
y	305	335	290	340	225	300	380	400

A scatter plot of this data appears in Figure 4.14. Notice that for each of the x values 9, 10, 11, 13, 14, 15, and 18, there are two y observations. In each case the two y values are different. For example, $x_2 = x_3 = 9$ whereas $y_2 = 150$ and $y_3 = 260$. We immediately conclude that y is not completely determined by x, for if it were, repeated observations at the same x value would have to yield identical y values. Yet the plot shows evidence of a rather strong relationship—a tendency for y to increase as x does. Furthermore, the general pattern in the plot can reasonably be described as linear: the points in the plot appear to be distributed about some straight line that slopes upward.

FIGURE 4.14
Scatter plot for the data
of Example 4.8

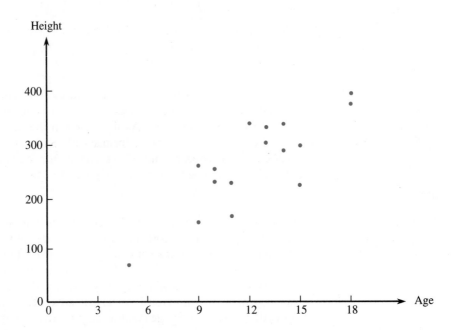

The values of the summary statistics come from the accompanying tabular format.

Obs.	x	y	x^2	xy	y^2
1	5	70	25	350	4,900
2	9	150	81	1,350	22,500
3	9	260	81	2,340	67,600
4	10	230	100	2,300	52,900
5	10	255	100	2,550	65,025
6	11	165	121	1,815	27,225
7	11	225	121	2,475	50,625
8	12	340	144	4,080	115,600
9	13	305	169	3,965	93,025
10	13	335	169	4,355	112,225

(continued)

Obs.	x	y	x^2	xy	y^2
11	14	290	196	4,060	84,100
12	14	340	196	4,760	115,600
13	15	225	225	3,375	50,625
14	15	300	225	4,500	90,000
15	18	380	324	6,840	144,400
16	18	400	324	7,200	160,000
Sum:	197	4,270	2,601	56,315	1,256,350
	↑	↑	↑	↑	↑
	Σx	Σy	Σx^2	Σxy	Σy^2

Thus,

$$\bar{x} = \frac{\Sigma x}{n} = \frac{197}{16} = 12.3125$$

$$\bar{y} = \frac{\Sigma y}{n} = \frac{4270}{16} = 266.8750$$

The slope of the least squares line is

$$b = \frac{\Sigma xy - [(\Sigma x)(\Sigma y)/n]}{\Sigma x^2 - [(\Sigma x)^2/n]}$$

$$= \frac{56,315 - [(197)(4270)/16]}{2601 - [(197)^2/16]}$$

$$= \frac{56,315 - 52,574.3750}{2601 - 2425.5625}$$

$$= \frac{3740.6250}{175.4375}$$

$$= 21.321696$$

and the vertical intercept is

$$a = \bar{y} - b\bar{x} = 266.8750 - (21.321696)(12.3125)$$
$$= 4.351618$$

This gives us

$$\hat{y} = 4.351618 + 21.321696x$$
$$\approx 4.352 + 21.322x$$

as the equation of the least squares line. The reason for giving so many digits of decimal accuracy in a and b will become apparent in the next section. The interpretation of b is that for trees that differ in age by 1 year, the increase in growth associated with the older trees is roughly 21.322 cm. To predict a 5-year height growth when the tree age is 12.5 years, simply substitute 12.5 into the equation:

$$\hat{y} = 4.352 + (21.322)(12.5) \approx 270.9 \text{ cm}$$

Similarly, the predicted height growth when $x = 10$ years is

$$\hat{y} = 4.352 + (21.322)(10) \approx 217.6 \text{ cm}$$

Notice that there are two sample observations for which $x = 10$ years, and the y values in both cases are larger than 217.6. So in the scatter plot, both of these points lie above the least squares line (see Figure 4.15).

FIGURE 4.15
Scatter plot and least squares line for the data of Example 4.8

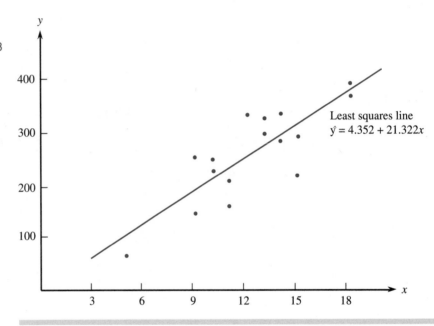

EXAMPLE 4.9

Millions of Muslims all over the world participate in controlled or partial fasting during the month of Ramadan. The paper "Body Weight Loss and Changes in Blood Lipid Levels in Normal Men on Hypo-caloric Diets during Ramadan Fasting" (*Amer. J. of Clinical Nutrition* (1988):1197–1210) reported on a study carried out to assess the physiological effects of such fasting. The accompanying table gives selected data (read from a graph) on x = percent change in body weight during phase two of the fasting period (in this phase experimental subjects received a high-fat, low-carbohydrate diet) and y = high-density lipo-protein cholesterol level (mg/dL).

x	−5	−3.2	−2.2	−1.7	−1.6	−1.5	−.9	0	0	1.2	1.6	1.7	2.8
y	43	50	61	63	47	57	51	60	67	76	70	51	74

A scatter plot is displayed in Figure 4.16. The predominant pattern is linear, though the points in the plot spread out rather substantially about *any* line (even the least squares line). Nevertheless, we shall follow the paper's authors in using the principle of least squares to obtain a summarizing line.

FIGURE 4.16
Scatter plot and least squares line for the data of Example 4.9

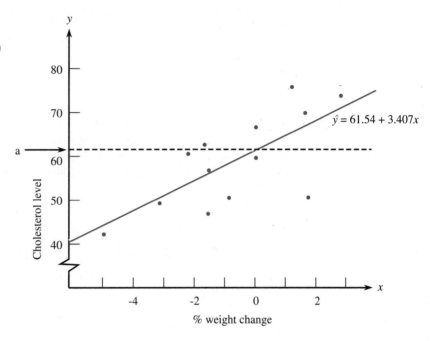

The summary statistics are as follows:

$$n = 13 \qquad \Sigma x = -8.8 \qquad \Sigma x^2 = 63.32$$
$$\Sigma y = 770 \qquad \Sigma y^2 = 46{,}940 \qquad \Sigma xy = -325.80$$
$$\bar{x} = -.676923 \qquad \bar{y} = 59.230769$$

The slope of the least squares line is

$$b = \frac{-325.80 - [(-8.8)(770)/13]}{63.32 - [(-8.8)^2/13]}$$
$$= \frac{195.430769}{57.363077}$$
$$= 3.406909$$

and the vertical intercept is

$$a = 59.230769 - (3.406909)(-.676923)$$
$$= 61.536984$$

This gives us (after rounding)

$$\hat{y} = 61.54 + 3.407x$$

as the equation of the least squares line. For an experimental subject whose weight decreases by one percent during phase two, the predicted HDL–cholesterol level is

$$\hat{y} = 61.54 + 3.407(-1) \approx 58.1$$

The least squares line should not be used here to predict cholesterol level for a value of percent change in body weight such as $x = -10$ or $x = 8$. These x values are well outside the range of the data, so there is no evidence to support extrapolation of an approximate linear relationship.

Calculations involving the least squares line can obviously be quite tedious, and fitting a function to multivariate data is even worse. This is where the computer comes to our rescue. All the standard statistical packages fit a straight line to bivariate data when asked to do so. To accomplish this, a regression command or option is used. (This terminology is explained shortly.)

EXAMPLE 4.10

The decline of visual acuity and sensitivity in adults as age increases is a well-known phenomenon. The paper "Neuron Loss in the Aging Visual Cortex of Man" (*J. of Gerontology* (1980):836–841) presented the following data on neurons per gram of tissue (y) for $n = 16$ males of various ages (x, in years). A scatter plot of the data in Figure 4.17 shows a linear pattern.

FIGURE 4.17
Scatter plot of the data in Example 4.10 with the least squares line superimposed

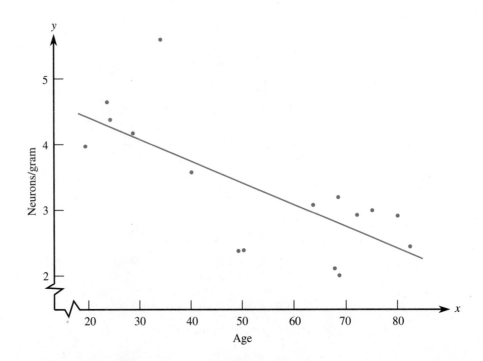

x	20	24	25	29	35	41	50	51
y	4.0	4.7	4.4	4.2	5.6	3.6	2.9	2.3

x	64	68	69	69	73	76	81	83
y	3.1	2.1	2.0	3.2	2.9	3.0	2.9	2.4

Figure 4.18 displays a small portion of the MINITAB output resulting from a regression command. Instead of x and y, the variable labels *age* and *neurons* are used. The equation at the top is exactly the rounded equation whose use was suggested earlier. In the rectangular table just below the equation, the first row gives information about the y intercept, a, and the second row gives information concerning the slope, b. In particular, the "coefficient" column contains the values of a and b using more significant figures than appear in the rounded equation. (We explain the contents of the last columns in Chapter 13.)

FIGURE 4.18
MINITAB output for the data
of Example 4.10

```
THE REGRESSION EQUATION IS
NEURONS = 5.21 − 0.0351 AGE
       Y =      a  + (bx)
PREDICTOR        COEF   ST. DEV.  T-RATIO      P
CONSTANT       5.2130    0.4615    11.29  0.000
AGE          −0.035091  0.008001   −4.39  0.001
```

Regression

The least squares line is often called the **sample regression line.** This terminology comes from the relationship between the least squares line and Pearson's correlation coefficient. To understand this relationship, we first need alternative expressions for the slope b and equation of the line itself. A bit of algebraic manipulation yields the results

$$b = r \cdot \frac{s_y}{s_x}$$

$$\hat{y} = \bar{y} + r \cdot \frac{s_y}{s_x}(x - \bar{x})$$

You do not need to use these formulas in any computations, but several of their implications are important for appreciating what the least squares line does.

1. When $x = \bar{x}$ is substituted in the equation of the line, $y = \bar{y}$ results. That is, the least squares line passes through the *point of averages* $(\bar{x}, \bar{y})$.

2. Suppose for the moment that $r = 1$, so that all points lie exactly on the line whose equation is

$$\hat{y} = \bar{y} + \frac{s_y}{s_x}(x - \bar{x})$$

Consider an x value that is one standard deviation above $\bar{x}$:

$$x = \bar{x} + s_x \Rightarrow \hat{y} = \bar{y} + \frac{s_y}{s_x}(\bar{x} + s_x - \bar{x})$$

$$= \bar{y} + s_y$$

That is, with $r = 1$, when x is one standard deviation above its mean, we predict that the associated y value will be one standard deviation above its mean. Similarly, if $x = \bar{x} - 2s_x$ (two standard deviations below its mean), then

$$\hat{y} = \bar{y} + \frac{s_y}{s_x}(\bar{x} - 2s_x - \bar{x})$$

$$= \bar{y} - 2s_y$$

also two standard deviations below the mean. If $r = -1$, then $x = \bar{x} + s_x$ results in $\hat{y} = \bar{y} - s_y$, so the predicted y is also one standard deviation from its mean but on the opposite side of $\bar{y}$ from where x is relative to $\bar{x}$. In general, if x and y are perfectly correlated, the predicted y value associated with a given x value will be the same number of standard deviations (of y) from its mean, $\bar{y}$, as x is from its mean, $\bar{x}$.

3. Suppose that x and y are not perfectly correlated. To be specific, take $r = .5$, so the least squares line has the equation

$$\hat{y} = \bar{y} + .5\left(\frac{s_y}{s_x}\right)(x - \bar{x})$$

Then

$$x = \bar{x} + s_x \Rightarrow \hat{y} = \bar{y} + .5\left(\frac{s_y}{s_x}\right)(\bar{x} + s_x - \bar{x})$$

$$= \bar{y} + .5s_y$$

That is, for $r = .5$, when x lies one standard deviation above its mean, we predict that y will be only one-half standard deviation above its mean.

There is similar behavior in predicting y when r is negative. If $r = -.5$, then the predicted y value will be only half the number of standard deviations from $\bar{y}$ that x is from $\bar{x}$, but x and the predicted y will now be on opposite sides of their respective means.

> Consider using the least squares line to predict the value of y associated with an x value some specified number of standard deviations away from $\bar{x}$. Then the predicted y value will be only r times this number of standard deviations from $\bar{y}$. In terms of standard deviations, except when $r = 1$ or -1, the predicted y will always be closer to $\bar{y}$ than x is to $\bar{x}$.

Using the least squares line for prediction results in a predicted y which is pulled back in, or regressed, toward its mean compared to where x is relative to its mean. This regression effect was first noticed by Sir Francis Galton (1822–1911), a famous biologist, while studying the relationship between the heights of fathers and their sons. He found that the predicted height of a son whose father was above average in height would also be above average (because r is positive here) but not by as much as the father; he found a similar relationship for a father whose height was below average. This regression effect has led to the term **regression analysis** for the collection of methods involving the fitting of lines, curves, and more complicated functions to bivariate and multivariate data.

The alternate form of the regression (least squares) line emphasizes that predicting y from knowledge of x is not the same problem as predicting x from knowledge of y. The slope of the least squares line for predicting x is $r \cdot (s_x/s_y)$ rather than $r \cdot (s_y/s_x)$, and the intercepts of the lines are also usually different. It makes a difference whether y is regressed on x, as we have done, or whether x is regressed on y. The regression line of y on x should not be used to predict x, since it is not the line which minimizes the sum of squared x deviations.

EXERCISES 4.27–4.38 SECTION 4.3

4.27 It has been observed that Andean high-altitude natives have larger chest dimensions and lung volumes than do sea-level residents. Is this also true of lifelong Himalayan residents? The paper "Increased Vital and Total Lung Capacities in Tibetan Compared to Han Residents of Lhasa" (*Amer. J. Phys. Anthro.* (1991):341–351) reported on the results of an investigation into this question. Included in the paper was a plot of vital capacity (y) versus chest circumference (x) for a sample of 16 Tibetan natives, from which the following data was read.

x	79.4	81.8	81.8	82.3	83.7	84.3	84.3	85.2
y	4.3	4.6	4.8	4.7	5.0	4.9	4.4	5.0

x	87.0	87.3	87.7	88.1	88.1	88.6	89.0	89.5
y	6.1	4.7	5.7	5.7	5.2	5.5	5.0	5.3

a. Construct a scatter plot. What does it suggest about the nature of the relationship between x and y?

b. The summary statistics are

$$\Sigma x = 1368.1 \qquad \Sigma y = 80.9 \qquad \Sigma x^2 = 117{,}123.85$$
$$\Sigma y^2 = 412.81 \qquad \Sigma xy = 6933.48$$

Verify that the equation of the least squares line is $\hat{y} = -4.54 + .1123x$, and draw this line on your scatter plot.

c. Roughly what change in vital capacity is associated with a 1-cm increase in chest circumference? With a 10-cm increase?

d. What vital capacity would you predict for a Tibetan native whose chest circumference is 85 cm?

e. Is vital capacity completely determined by chest circumference? Explain.

4.28   The accompanying data on the percent of red pine scale nymphs (a forest insect) in early and middle stages (x) and overwintering mortality rate (y) appeared in the paper "Population Dynamics of a Pernicious Parasite: Density-Dependent Vitality of Red Pine Scale" (*Ecology* (1983):710–718).

x	20	32	36	42	43	46	48	51	60
y	81	81.5	83	87	84	84.5	86.5	89	86.5

a. Construct a scatter plot for this data set.

b. The least squares line relating x and y given in the paper was $\hat{y} = 76.2 + .2x$. Draw this line on your scatter plot.

c. What would you predict for the overwintering mortality rate if 50% of the scale nymphs were in early or middle substages?

d. Would it be reasonable to use this line to predict mortality rate associated with 80% of the nymphs being in early or middle substages? Explain.

4.29   Milk samples were obtained from 14 Holstein–Friesian cows, and each was analyzed to determine uric acid concentration (μ mol/L). In addition to acid concentration, the total milk production (kg/day) was recorded for each cow, as shown in the accompanying table ("Metabolites of Nucleic Acids in Bovine Milk," *J. of Dairy Science* (1983):723–728).

Cow	1	2	3	4	5	6	7
Milk production	42.7	40.2	38.2	37.6	32.2	32.2	28.0
Acid concentration	92	120	128	110	153	162	202

Cow	8	9	10	11	12	13	14
Milk production	27.2	26.6	23.0	22.7	21.8	21.3	20.2
Acid concentration	140	218	195	180	193	238	213

Let x denote milk production and y denote uric acid concentration.

a. Draw a scatter plot for this data.

b. Using the following summary quantities, compute the least squares line.

$$n = 14, \ \Sigma x^2 - [(\Sigma x)^2/n] = 762.012, \ \Sigma xy - [(\Sigma x)(\Sigma y)/n] = -3964.486$$

c. Draw the least squares line on your scatter plot. (Hint: Substitute $x = 25$ into the equation of the least squares line to find one point (x, y) on the line. Repeat with $x = 40$. Then draw a line through these two points.)

d. What uric acid concentration would you predict for a cow whose total milk production was 30 kg/day?

e. Would you feel comfortable using the least squares line to make a prediction for a cow whose total milk production was 10 kg/day? Explain your answer.

4.30 Infestation of crops by insects has long been of great concern to farmers and agricultural scientists. The paper "Cotton Square Damage by the Plant Bug, *Lygus hesperus,* and Abscission Rates" (*J. of Econ. Entom.* (1988):1328–1337) reported data on $x = $ age of a cotton plant (days) and $y = $ percent damaged squares. Consider the accompanying $n = 12$ observations (read from a scatter plot in the paper).

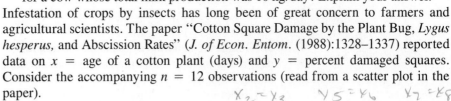

x	9	12	12	15	18	18	21	21	27	30	30	33
y	11	12	23	30	29	52	41	65	60	72	84	93

a. Why is it obvious that the value of y is not determined solely by x?

b. Does a scatter plot suggest that the least squares line will effectively summarize the relationship between the two variables?

c. The summary statistics are

$$\Sigma x = 246 \quad \Sigma x^2 = 5742 \quad \Sigma y = 572 \quad \Sigma y^2 = 35{,}634 \quad \Sigma xy = 14{,}022$$

Determine the equation of the least squares line.

d. Predict the percent of damaged squares when the age is 20 days.

4.31 Exercise 4.3 gave the accompanying data on $x = $ plasma cortisol concentration and $y = $ oxygen consumption rate for juvenile steelhead.

x	25	36	48	59	62	72	80	100	100	137
y	155	184	180	220	280	163	230	222	241	350

a. Establish a tabular format with columns headed x, y, x^2, xy, and y^2. Place the given data in the first two columns, fill in the entries for the remaining three columns, and add the numbers in each column to obtain summary statistics. Then determine the slope and vertical intercept of the least squares line, and give the equation of the line.

b. Interpret b in the context of this problem situation.

c. Predict the value of the oxygen consumption rate that would be observed for a single fish having plasma cortisol concentration 50 ng/mL.

4.32   The paper "Ion Beam–Assisted Etching of Aluminum with Chlorine" (*J. of Elec-trochem. Soc.* (1985):2010–2012) gave the accompanying data (read from a graph) on chlorine flow (x, in SCCM) through a nozzle used in a plasma etching process and etch rate (y, in 100 A/min).

x	1.5	1.5	2.0	2.5	2.5	3.0	3.5	3.5	4.0
y	23.0	24.5	25.0	30.0	33.5	40.0	40.5	47.0	49.0

a. Why is it obvious that the value of y is not completely determined by the value of x?

b. Verify that the values of the summary statistics are

$$\Sigma x = 24.0 \quad \Sigma y = 312.5 \quad \Sigma x^2 = 70.50 \quad \Sigma xy = 902.25 \quad \Sigma y^2 = 11{,}626.75$$

c. Obtain the equation of the least squares line.

d. Predict the etch rate for an observation made when chlorine flow is 2.5 A/min.

4.33   Athletes competing in a triathlon participated in a study described in the paper "Myoglobinemia and Endurance Exercise" (*Amer. J. of Sports Med.* (1984):113–118). The following data on finishing time x (h) and myoglobin level y (ng/mL) was read from a scatter plot in the paper.

x	4.90	4.70	5.35	5.22	5.20	5.40	5.70	6.00
y	1590	1550	1360	895	865	905	895	910

x	6.20	6.10	5.60	5.35	5.75	5.35	6.00
y	700	675	540	540	440	380	300

a. Obtain the equation of the least squares line.

b. Interpret the value of b.

c. What happens if the line in part (a) is used to predict the myoglobin level for a finishing time of 8 h? Is this reasonable? Explain.

4.34   The paper "Increased Oxygen Consumption during the Uptake of Water by the Eversible Vesicles of Petrobius Brevistylis" (*J. of Insect Phys.* (1977):1285–1294) presented the results of a regression involving variables x = weight increase (mg) when a dehydrated insect was allowed access to water and y = increased oxygen uptake (μL) above the mean resting rate. Data read from a graph gave the following summary statistics.

$$n = 20 \qquad \Sigma x = 63.5 \qquad \Sigma y = 17.26$$
$$\Sigma x^2 = 311.74 \qquad \Sigma xy = 71.51 \qquad \Sigma y^2 = 19.9625$$

a. Obtain the equation of the least squares line.

b. The only observation with an x value larger than 7 was $(x_{20}, y_{20}) = (9.8, 1.9)$. It is of interest to know whether this point has greatly influenced the equation of the least squares line. Compute the least squares line based on just the remaining 19 observations, and comment on the difference between this line and the line of part (a). (Hint: Simply adjust the summary statistics; for example, new Σx = old Σx − 9.8, and so on.)

4.35 Explain why it can be dangerous to use the least squares line to obtain predictions for x values that are either substantially larger or smaller than those contained in the sample.

4.36 The sales manager of a large company selected a random sample of n = 10 salespeople and determined for each one the values of x = years of sales experience and y = annual sales (in thousands of dollars). A scatter plot of the resulting (x, y) pairs showed a marked linear pattern.

   a. Suppose that the sample correlation coefficient is r = .75 and average annual sales is $\bar{y}$ = 100. If a particular salesperson is 2 standard deviations above the mean in terms of experience, what would you predict for that person's annual sales?

   b. If a particular person whose sales experience is 1.5 standard deviations below average experience is predicted to have an annual sales value that is 1 standard deviation below average annual sales, what is the value of r?

4.37 Explain why the slope b of the least squares line always has the same sign (positive or negative) as does the sample correlation coefficient r.

4.38 The accompanying data resulted from an experiment in which weld diameter, x, and shear strength, y (lb), were determined for five different spot welds on steel. A scatter plot shows a pronounced linear pattern. With $\Sigma(x - \bar{x})^2$ = 1000 and $\Sigma(x - \bar{x})(y - \bar{y})$ = 8577, the least squares line is $\hat{y}$ = −936.22 + 8.577x.

x	200	210	220	230	240
y	813.7	785.3	960.4	1118.0	1076.2

   a. Since 1 lb = .4536 kg, strength observations can be reexpressed in kilograms through multiplication by this conversion factor: new y = .4536(old y). What is the equation of the least squares line when y is expressed in kilograms?

   b. More generally, suppose that each y value in a data set consisting of n (x, y) pairs is multiplied by a conversion factor c (which changes the units of measurement for y). What effect does this have on the slope b (that is, how does the new value of b compare to the value before conversion), on the y intercept a, and on the equation of the least squares line? Verify your conjectures by using the given formulas for b and a. (Hint: Replace y by cy and see what happens—and remember, this conversion will affect $\bar{y}$.)

4.4   Assessing the Fit of a Line

Once the best-fit (least squares) line has been obtained, it is natural to ask how effectively the line summarizes the relationship between x and y; that is, we would like a quantitative indicator of the extent to which y variation can be attributed to the approximate linear relationship between the two variables. Such an assessment is based on the vertical deviations from the least squares line.

Predicted Values and Residuals

If the x value for the first observation is substituted in the equation for the least squares line, the result is $a + bx_1$, the height of the line above x_1. The point (x_1, y_1) in the scatter plot also lies above x_1, so the difference

$$y_1 - (a + bx_1)$$

is the vertical deviation (residual) from this point to the line (see Figure 4.19). A point lying above the line gives a positive deviation, and a point below the line results in a negative deviation. The remaining vertical deviations come from repeating this process for $x = x_2$, then $x = x_3$, and so on.

FIGURE 4.19
Positive and negative deviations (residuals) from the least squares line

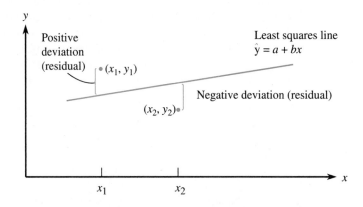

DEFINITION

The **predicted** or **fitted values** result from substituting each sample x value in turn into the equation for the least squares line. This gives

$$\hat{y}_1 = \text{1st predicted value} = a + bx_1$$
$$\hat{y}_2 = \text{2nd predicted value} = a + bx_2$$
$$\vdots$$
$$\hat{y}_n = n\text{th predicted value} = a + bx_n$$

The **residuals** from the least squares line are the n quantities

$$y_1 - \hat{y}_1, \quad y_2 - \hat{y}_2, \ldots, \quad y_n - \hat{y}_n$$

Each residual is a difference between an observed y value and the corresponding predicted y value.

EXAMPLE 4.11

The ability of proteins to bind fat is important in improving the flavor and texture of meat. The paper "A Simple Turbidimetric Method for Determining the Fat-Binding Capacity of Proteins" (*J. of Agric. and Food Chem.* (1983):58–63) proposed the use of regression methods for predicting fat-binding capacity (FBC) y from other protein characteristics. The first predictor used in the study was $x =$ surface hydrophobicity (HBCTY), a measure of the extent to which water is not attracted to the protein's surface. The $n = 8$ observations appear in the accompanying tabular format. A scatter plot is displayed in Figure 4.20.

Obs.	x HBCTY	y FBC	Predicted y value	Residual
1	6.0	37.70	28.77	8.93
2	28.0	10.10	50.71	−40.61
3	95.0	105.90	117.54	−11.64
4	39.0	85.30	61.68	23.62
5	66.0	92.30	88.62	3.68
6	5.0	19.10	27.77	−8.67
7	47.0	105.80	69.66	36.14
8	55.0	66.20	77.64	−11.44

FIGURE 4.20
Scatter plot of the data
from Example 4.11

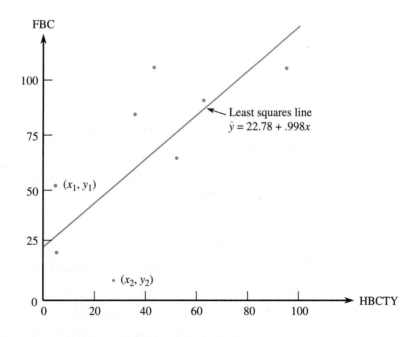

The summary statistics are

$$n = 8 \qquad \Sigma x = 341 \qquad \Sigma y = 522.4$$
$$\Sigma x^2 = 20{,}981 \qquad \Sigma xy = 28{,}697.1 \qquad \Sigma y^2 = 44{,}474.38$$

from which we get

$$b = .99750616 \approx .9975$$

and

$$a = 22.78129993 \approx 22.78$$

The first predicted value is

$$\hat{y}_1 = a + bx_1 = 22.78 + (.9975)(6.0) = 28.77$$

and the corresponding residual is

$$y_1 - \hat{y}_1 = 37.70 - 28.77 = 8.93$$

The second predicted value and residual are

$$\hat{y}_2 = a + bx_2 = 22.78 + (.9975)(28.0) = 50.71$$

and

$$y_2 - \hat{y}_2 = 10.10 - 50.71 = -40.61$$

As Figure 4.20 shows, this extreme negative residual is a consequence of (x_2, y_2) being far below the least squares line. The remaining predicted values and residuals are displayed in the table with the data.

The Coefficient of Determination

Variation in y can effectively be explained by an approximate straight-line relationship when the points in the scatter plot fall close to the least squares line—that is, when the residuals are small in magnitude. A natural measure of variation about the least squares line is the sum of the squared residuals. (Squaring before combining prevents negative and positive residuals from counteracting one another.) A second sum of squares is needed to assess the total amount of variation in observed y values without reference to x.

DEFINITION

The **residual sum of squares,**[2] denoted by **SSResid**, is given by

$$SSResid = \Sigma(y - \hat{y})^2$$
$$= (y_1 - \hat{y}_1)^2 + (y_2 - \hat{y}_2)^2 + \cdots + (y_n - \hat{y}_n)^2$$

The **total sum of squares,** denoted by **SSTo,** is defined as

$$SSTo = \Sigma(y - \bar{y})^2$$
$$= (y_1 - \bar{y})^2 + (y_2 - \bar{y})^2 + \cdots + (y_n - \bar{y})^2$$

> These sums of squares can be obtained using just the summary statistics via the following computational formulas:
>
> $$SSResid = \Sigma y^2 - a\,\Sigma y - b\,\Sigma xy$$
>
> $$SSTo = \Sigma y^2 - \frac{(\Sigma y)^2}{n}$$

don't need a + b

As with any sum of squares in statistics, SSResid and SSTo cannot be negative. The computing formula for SSResid is quite sensitive to rounding. Using as many digits of decimal accuracy as possible in the values of a and b will ensure an accurate result.

EXAMPLE 4.12

(*Example 4.11 continued*) The summary statistics and values of a and b for the hydrophobicity–fat-binding capacity data were given earlier. Substitution yields

$$
\begin{aligned}
SSResid &= \Sigma y^2 - a\,\Sigma y - b\,\Sigma xy \\
&= 44{,}474.38 - (22.78129993)(522.4) - (.99750616)(28{,}697.1) \\
&= 44{,}474.38 - 11{,}900.95 - 28{,}625.53 \\
&= 3947.90
\end{aligned}
$$

$$
\begin{aligned}
SSTo &= \Sigma y^2 - \frac{(\Sigma y)^2}{n} \\
&= 44{,}474.38 - \frac{(522.4)^2}{8} \\
&= 44{,}474.38 - 34{,}112.72 \\
&= 10{,}361.66
\end{aligned}
$$

Although SSResid is rather sizable (because several residuals are large in magnitude), it is relatively small when compared to SSTo.

The residual sum of squares is the sum of squared deviations from the least-squares line. As Figure 4.21 illustrates, SSTo is also a sum of squared deviations from a line—the horizontal line at height $\bar{y}$. Since the least squares line is by definition the one having the smallest sum of squared deviations, it follows that SSResid $\leq$ SSTo. The two sums of squares will be equal only when the least squares line *is* the horizontal line.

---

[2]Some sources refer to this as the **error sum of squares** and denote it by **SSE.**

FIGURE 4.21
Geometric interpretations of
SSResid and SSTo
(a) SSResid = sum of
squared deviations from
least-squares line
(b) SSTo = Sum of squared
deviations from horizontal line
at height $\bar{y}$

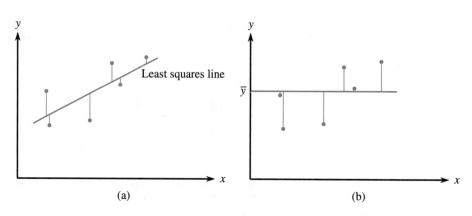

(a)   (b)

The residual sum of squares is often referred to as a measure of "unexplained" variation. It is the amount of variation in y that cannot be attributed to the linear relationship between x and y. When SSResid = 0, all points in the scatter plot fall exactly on the least squares line; all y variation can be attributed to the linear relationship; and no y variation is left unexplained. The larger the value of SSResid, the greater the amount of y variation that cannot be explained by the approximate linear relationship. Similarly, SSTo is interpreted as a measure of total variation. The larger the value of SSTo, the greater the amount of variability in $y_1, y_2, \ldots, y_n$. The ratio SSResid/SSTo is the fraction or proportion of total variation that is unexplained by a straight-line relation. Subtracting this ratio from 1 gives the proportion of total variation that *is* explained.

DEFINITION

The **coefficient of determination,** denoted by r^2, is given by

$$r^2 = \frac{SSTo - SSResid}{SSTo} = 1 - \frac{SSResid}{SSTo}$$

It is the proportion of variation in y that can be attributed to a linear relationship between x and y in the sample.

Multiplying r^2 by 100 gives the percentage of y variation attributable to the approximate linear relationship. The closer this percentage is to 100%, the more successful is the relationship in explaining variation in y.

EXAMPLE 4.13

We found that for the hydrophobicity–fat-binding capacity data of Examples 4.11 and 4.12,

SSResid = 3947.90   SSTo = 10,361.66

Thus,

$$r^2 = 1 - \frac{\text{SSResid}}{\text{SSTo}}$$

$$= 1 - \frac{3947.90}{10,361.66}$$

$$= 1 - .381$$

$$= .619$$

so 61.9% of the sample variation in FBC is explained by the approximate linear relationship with hydrophobicity. In many situations, to have 61.9% of the variation explained would be quite respectable, but in this particular instance the investigators were not satisfied, so they proceeded to an analysis involving more than a single predictor variable.

EXAMPLE 4.14

The Arabian Sea suffers from oxygen depletion to a greater extent than almost any other part of an open ocean. Dentrification, the process by which nitrates and nitrites are reduced to other forms of nitrogen, is one step in the oxidation of organic matter to carbon dioxide and the consequent reduction of oxygen. The paper "Evidence for and Rate of Dentrification in the Arabian Sea" (*Deep Sea Research* (1978):431–435) reported on a study in which water samples were selected and x = salinity (%) and y = nitrate level (μM/L) were determined. A regression analysis was then carried out. The accompanying data is a subset of that contained in the article. A scatter plot is shown in Figure 4.22.

FIGURE 4.22
Scatter plot for the data
from Example 4.14

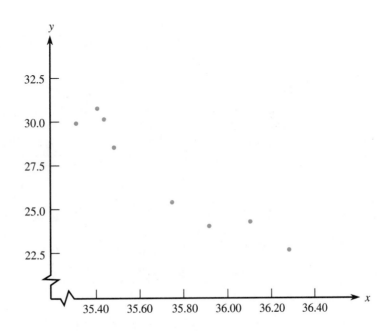

x	35.43	36.10	35.74	35.30	35.40	35.91	35.48	36.28
y	30.0	24.2	25.4	29.8	30.7	24.0	28.5	22.7

$$n = 8 \qquad \Sigma x = 285.64 \qquad \Sigma y = 215.3$$
$$\Sigma x^2 = 10{,}199.6894 \qquad \Sigma xy = 7679.612 \qquad \Sigma y^2 = 5864.87$$

$$b = \frac{\Sigma xy - (\Sigma x)(\Sigma y)/n}{\Sigma x^2 - (\Sigma x)^2/n} = \frac{-7.6745}{.9132} = -8.403964$$

$$a = \bar{y} - b\bar{x} = 26.9125 - (-8.403964)(35.7050)$$
$$= 26.9125 + 300.063535$$
$$= 326.976035$$

$$\hat{y} = a + bx = 326.976 - 8.404x$$

$$\text{SSResid} = \Sigma y^2 - a\,\Sigma y - b\,\Sigma xy$$
$$= 5864.87 - (326.976035)(215.3) - (-8.403964)(7679.612)$$
$$= 5864.87 - 70{,}397.940 + 64{,}539.183$$
$$= 6.113$$

$$\text{SSTo} = \Sigma y^2 - \frac{(\Sigma y)^2}{n}$$
$$= 5864.87 - 5794.26125 = 70.60875$$

$$r^2 = 1 - \frac{\text{SSResid}}{\text{SSTo}} = 1 - \frac{6.113}{70.60875} = .913$$

Thus 91.3% of the observed variation in nitrate level can be attributed to an approximate linear relationship between the nitrate level and salinity. Use of the least squares line appears to provide an effective method for predicting nitrate level at any specified value of salinity (within the range of the given data).

The symbol r was used in Section 4.2 to denote Pearson's sample correlation coefficient. It is not coincidental that r^2 is used to represent the coefficient of determination. The notation suggests how these two quantities are related:

(correlation coefficient)^2 = *coefficient of determination*

Thus, if $r = .8$ or $r = -.8$ then $r^2 = .64$, so that 64% of the observed variation in the dependent variable can be attributed to the linear relationship. Notice that because the value of r does not depend on which variable is labeled x, the same is true of r^2. The coefficient of determination is one of the very few quantities calculated in the course of a regression analysis whose value remains the same when the role of dependent and independent variables are interchanged. When $r = .5$, we get $r^2 = .25$, so only 25% of the observed variation is explained by a linear relation. This is why values of r between $-.5$ and $.5$ can fairly be described as evidence of a weak relationship.

Standard Deviation about the Least Squares Line

The coefficient of determination measures the extent of variation about the best fit line *relative* to overall variation in y. A high value of r^2 does not by itself promise that the deviations from the line are small in an absolute sense. A typical observation could deviate from the line by quite a bit, yet these deviations might still be small relative to overall y variation. Recall that in Chapter 3 the sample standard deviation $s = \sqrt{\Sigma(x - \bar{x})^2/(n - 1)}$ was used as a measure of variability in a single sample; roughly speaking, s is the typical amount by which a sample observation deviates from the mean. There is an analogous measure of variability when a line is fit by least squares.

> **DEFINITION**
>
> The **standard deviation about the least squares line** is given by
>
> $$s_e = \sqrt{\frac{\text{SSResid}}{n - 2}}$$

Roughly speaking, s_e is the typical amount by which an observation deviates from the least squares line. The subscript e serves to distinguish s_e from our earlier s based on a sample of x observations. Notice that SSResid $= \Sigma(y - \hat{y})^2$ plays the same role here that the sum of the squared deviations $\Sigma(x - \bar{x})^2$ played in defining s. Justification for division by $n - 2$ and the use of the subscript e are given in Chapter 13.

EXAMPLE 4.15

The values of $x =$ commuting distance and $y =$ commuting time were determined for workers in samples from three different regions. Data and the results of calculations appear in Table 4.2; the three scatter plots are displayed in Figure 4.23.

TABLE 4.2 Data and summary quantities for Example 4.15

Region	1		2		3	
	x	y	x	y	x	y
	15	42	5	16	5	8
	16	35	10	32	10	16
	17	45	15	44	15	22
	18	42	20	45	20	23
	19	49	25	63	25	31
	20	46	50	115	50	60

	1	2	3
b	1.685714	2.142295	1.126557
a	13.666672	7.868852	3.196729
SSTo $= \Sigma(y - \bar{y})^2$	114.83	5897.5	1627.33
SSResid	65.10	65.10	14.48
r^2	.433	.989	.991
s_e	4.03	4.03	1.90

FIGURE 4.23
Scatter plots for Example 4.15
(a) Region 1
(b) Region 2
(c) Region 3

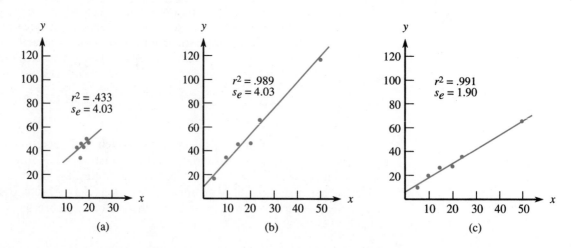

For sample 1, a rather small proportion of variation in y can be attributed to an approximate linear relationship, and a typical deviation from the least squares line is roughly 4. The amount of variability about the line for sample 2 is the same as for sample 1 but the value of r^2 is much much higher because y variation is much greater overall in sample 2 than in sample 1. Sample 3 yields roughly the same high value of r^2 as does sample 2, but the typical deviation from the line for sample 3 is only half that for sample 2. A complete picture of variation requires that both r^2 and s_e be computed.

Plotting the Residuals (Optional)

It is important to have methods for identifying unusual or highly influential observations and revealing patterns in the data that may suggest how an improved fit can be achieved. A plot based on the residuals is very useful in this regard.

DEFINITION

A **residual plot** is a plot of the (x, residual) pairs—that is, of the points $(x_1, y_1 - \hat{y}_1), (x_2, y_2 - \hat{y}_2), \ldots, (x_n, y_n - \hat{y}_n)$.

A desirable plot is one that exhibits no particular pattern (such as curvature or much greater spread in one part of the plot than in another part) and has no point that is far removed from all others. A point falling far above or below the horizontal line at height zero corresponds to a large residual, which may indicate some type of unusual behavior, such as a recording error, nonstandard experimental condition, or atypical experimental subject. A point whose x value differs greatly from others in the data set may have exerted excessive influence in determining the fitted line. One method for assessing the impact of such an isolated point on the fit is to delete it from the data set and then recompute the best-fit line and various other quantities. Substantial changes in the equation, predicted values, r^2, and s_e warn of instability in the data. More information may then be needed before reliable conclusions can be drawn.

EXAMPLE 4.16

In Example 4.7 we presented $n = 9$ observations on x = Quetelet index (a measure of body build) and y = dietary energy density. The data appears again in Table 4.3, from which the least squares line is

$$\hat{y} = -.898457 + .00733014x$$

and

$$r^2 = .433 \qquad s_e = .148$$

The corresponding predicted values, residuals, and points in the residual plot are also given in Table 4.3, and the plot itself appears as Figure 4.24 (on page 169).

TABLE 4.3   Data for Example 4.16

x	y	$\hat{y} = -.898 + .00733x$	Residual $= y - \hat{y}$	Points in the residual plot
221	.67	.722	−.052	(221, −.052)
228	.86	.773	.087	(228, .087)
223	.78	.736	.044	(223, .044)
211	.54	.648	−.108	(211, −.108)
231	.91	.795	.115	(231, .115)
215	.44	.678	−.238	(215, −.238)
224	.90	.744	.157	(224, .157)
233	.94	.810	.131	(233, .131)
268	.93	1.066	−.136	(268, −.136)

There is an obvious pattern in the residual plot—the points on the extremes lie below the zero line, whereas the points in the middle are above this line. The primary reason for this is the presence of the observation (268, .93). Deleting it and using the remaining eight observations results in

$$\hat{y} = -4.226 + .02249x$$

as the new equation of the least squares line. In addition,

$$r^2 = .834 \qquad s_e = .0822$$

Clearly, a, b, r^2, and s_e all change substantially as a result of this deletion. Notice, though, that the residual $-.136$ corresponding to this influential observation is not the largest residual in the data set. In trying to make the squared deviations small, the least squares line is pulled very far toward the discrepant point. Either this point represents a very unusual departure from a strong approximate linear relationship, or else it suggests the possibility that y may begin to decrease as x continues to increase (a curved relationship). More data is required before a judgment can be made.

Deletion of the observation corresponding to the largest residual ($-.238$) also changes the value of the important summary quantities, but these changes are not profound. For example, the new equation is $\hat{y} = -.460 + .00555x$, and the predicted values do not change dramatically. This observation does not appear to be all that unusual.

Looking at a residual plot after fitting a line amounts to examining y after removing any linear dependence on x. This can sometimes more clearly bring out the existence of a nonlinear relationship.

EXAMPLE 4.17

Consider the accompanying data on $x =$ height (in.) and $y =$ average weight (lb) for American females aged 30–39 (taken from *The World Almanac and Book of Facts*). The scatter plot displayed in Figure 4.25(a) appears rather straight.

FIGURE 4.24
Plots from MINITAB for data
in Example 4.16
(a) Scatter plot
(b) Residual plot from line
based on full sample

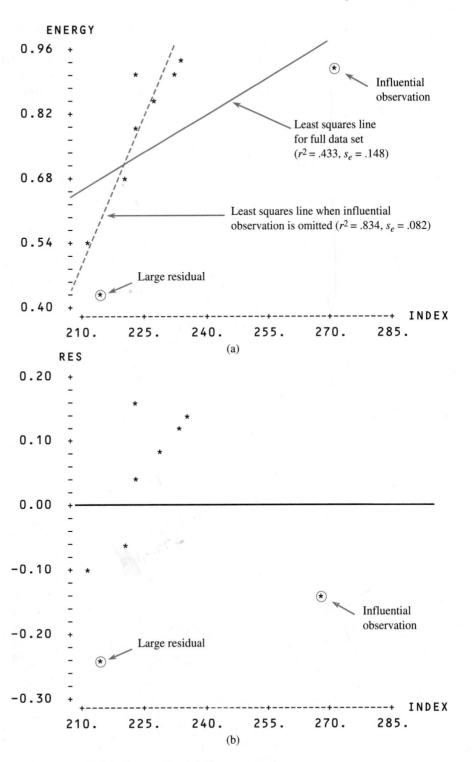

However, when the residuals from the least squares line ($\hat{y} = -98.23 + 3.596x$) are plotted, substantial curvature is apparent (even though $r^2 \approx .99$). It is not accurate to say that weight increases in direct proportion to height (linearly with height). Instead, average weight increases somewhat more rapidly in the range of relatively large heights than it does for relatively small heights.

x	58	59	60	61	62	63	64	65
y	113	115	118	121	124	128	131	134

x	66	67	68	69	70	71	72
y	137	141	145	150	153	159	164

FIGURE 4.25
Plots for data from
Example 4.17
(a) Scatter plot
(b) Residual plot

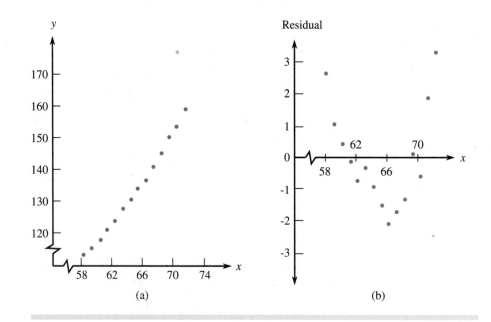

(a)   (b)

Resistant Lines

The least squares line can be greatly affected by the presence of even a single observation that shows large discrepancy in the x or y direction from the rest of the data. When the data set contains such unusual observations, it is desirable to have a method for obtaining a summarizing line that is resistant to the influence of these stray values. In recent years many methods for obtaining a resistant (or robust) line have been proposed. You should consult a statistician or a book on exploratory data analysis to obtain information about such methods.

EXERCISES 4.39–4.52   SECTION 4.4

4.39   The paper "Root Dentine Transparency: Age Determination of Human Teeth Using Computerized Densitometric Analysis" (*Amer. J. Phys. Anthro.* (1991):25–30) reported on an investigation of methods for age determination based on tooth characteristics. With y = age (years) and x = percentage of root with transparent dentine, a regression analysis for premolars using an image-analyser method to determine x gave $n = 36$, SSResid = 5987.16, and SSTo = 17,409.60. Calculate and interpret the values of r^2 and s_e.

4.40   The paper cited in Exercise 4.39 gave a scatter plot in which x values were for anterior teeth. Consider the accompanying representative subset of the data.

x	15	19	31	39	41	44	47	48	55	65
y	23	52	65	55	32	60	78	59	61	60

$\Sigma x = 404$ $\Sigma x^2 = 18,448$ $\Sigma y = 545$ $\Sigma y^2 = 31,993$ $\Sigma xy = 23,198$
$a = 32.080888$ $b = .554929$

a. Calculate the predicted values and residuals.
b. Use the results of (a) to obtain SSResid and r^2.
c. Does the least squares line appear to give very accurate predictions? Explain your reasoning.

4.41   The decline of salmon fisheries along the Columbia River in Oregon has caused great concern among commercial and recreational fishermen. The paper "Feeding of Predaceous Fishes on Out-Migrating Juvenile Salmonids in John Day Reservoir, Columbia River" (*Trans. Amer. Fisheries Soc.* (1991):405–420) gave the accompanying data on y = maximum size of salmonids consumed by a northern squaw fish (the most abundant salmonid predator) and x = squawfish length (both in mm).

x	218	246	270	287	318	344	375	386	414	450	468
y	82	85	94	127	141	157	165	216	219	238	249

$n = 11$ $\Sigma x = 3776$ $\Sigma x^2 = 1,365,310$
$\Sigma y = 1773$ $\Sigma y^2 = 323,931$ $\Sigma xy = 659,010$

a. What value of maximum size would you predict for a squawfish whose length is 375 mm, and what is the residual corresponding to the observation (375, 165)?
b. What proportion of observed variation in y can be attributed to the approximate linear relationship between the two variables?

4.42   There have been numerous studies on the effects of radiation. Data on the relationship between degree of exposure to ^{242}Cm alpha particles (x) and the percentage of exposed cells without aberrations (y) appeared in the paper "Chromosome Aberrations Induced in Human Lymphocytes by D-T Neutrons" (*Radiation Research* (1984):561–573).

x	.106	.193	.511	.527	1.08	1.62	1.73	2.36	2.72	3.12	3.88	4.18
y	98	95	87	85	75	72	64	55	44	41	37	40

Summary statistics are

$$n = 12 \qquad \Sigma x = 22.027 \qquad \Sigma y = 793$$
$$\Sigma x^2 = 62.600235 \qquad \Sigma xy = 1114.5 \qquad \Sigma y^2 = 57{,}939$$

a. Obtain the equation of the least squares line.
b. Calculate SSResid and SSTo.
c. What percentage of observed variation in y can be explained by the approximate linear relationship between the two variables?
d. Calculate and interpret the value of s_e.
e. Using just the results of (a) and (c), what is the value of Pearson's sample correlation coefficient?

4.43 The paper "Crop Improvement for Tropical and Subtropical Australia: Designing Plants for Difficult Climates" (*Field Crops Research* (1991):113–139) gave the accompanying data on x = crop duration (days) for soybeans and y = crop yield (tons/ha).

x	92	92	96	100	102	102	106	106	121	143
y	1.7	2.3	1.9	2.0	1.5	1.7	1.6	1.8	1.0	.3

$$\Sigma x = 1060 \qquad \Sigma x^2 = 114{,}514 \qquad \Sigma y = 15.8 \qquad \Sigma y^2 = 27.82$$
$$\Sigma xy = 1601.1 \qquad a = 5.20683380 \qquad b = -0.3421541$$

a. Construct a scatter plot of the data. Do you think the least squares line will give accurate predictions?
b. The largest x value in the sample greatly exceeds the remaining ones. Delete the corresponding observation from the sample and recalculate the equation of the least squares line. Does this observation greatly affect the equation of the line?
c. What effect does the deletion suggested in (b) have on the value of r^2? Can you explain why this is so?

4.44 A study was carried out to investigate the relationship between the hardness of molded plastic (y, in Brinell units) and the amount of time elapsed since termination of the molding process (x, in hours). Summary quantities include

$$n = 15 \qquad \text{SSResid} = 1235.470 \qquad \text{SSTo} = 25{,}321.368$$

Calculate and interpret the coefficient of determination.

4.45 Data on x = age of a cotton plant and y = percent damaged squares was presented in Exercise 4.30. In addition to the summary statistics given there, $a = -19.669528$ and $b = 3.284692$.
a. Compute the value of residual sum of squares.
b. What percentage of observed variation in y can be attributed to an approximate linear relationship between the two variables?

c. Repeat part (a) using the rounded values $a = -19.67$ and $b = 3.28$. Does rounding make a difference?

4.46   Exercise 4.2 gave data on x = distance upslope and y = grain sorghum yield. Summary quantities include

$$n = 14 \quad \Sigma x = 1185 \quad \Sigma x^2 = 151,825 \quad \Sigma xy = 449,850 \quad \Sigma y = 5960$$
$$\Sigma y^2 = 2,631,200 \quad b = -1.060132.$$

a. Calculate SSResid and SSTo.
b. Calculate r^2, the proportion of observed variation in yield explained by an approximate linear relationship between distance and yield. Based on this value, do you feel comfortable in describing the relationship as approximately linear? Explain.

4.47   Refer to Example 4.9, in which we carried out a regression of y = cholesterol level on x = percent weight change.
a. Use the equation of the least squares line given there to calculate the residuals.
b. Use the residuals from part (a) to calculate SSResid.
c. Compute SSResid using the computational formula given in this section along with the values of a and b calculated in Example 4.9.
d. Repeat part (c) using the rounded values $a = 61.5$ and $b = 3.4$. Does rounding make a substantial difference?
e. Is "approximately linear" an accurate description of the relationship between the variables? Explain.

4.48   Anthropologists often study soil composition for clues as to how the land was used during different time periods. The accompanying data on x = soil depth (cm) and y = percent montmorillonite in the soil was taken from a scatter plot in the paper "Ancient Maya Drained Field Agriculture: Its Possible Application Today in the New River Floodplain, Belize, C.A." (*Ag. Ecosystems and Environ.* (1984): 67–84).

x	40	50	60	70	80	90	100
y	58	34	32	30	28	27	22

a. Draw a scatter plot of y versus x.
b. The equation of the least squares line is $\hat{y} = 64.50 - .45x$. Draw this line on your scatter plot. Do there appear to be any large residuals?
c. Compute the residuals and construct a residual plot. Are there any unusual features in the plot?

4.49   a. Is it possible that both r^2 and s_e could be large for a bivariate data set? Explain. (A picture might be helpful.)
b. Is it possible that a bivariate data set could yield values of r^2 and s_e that are both small? Explain. (Again, a picture might be helpful.)
c. Explain why it is desirable to have r^2 large and s_e small if the relationship between two variables x and y is to be described using a straight line.

4.50   A scatter plot appearing in the article "Thermal Conductivity of Polyethylene: The Effects of Crystal Size, Density, and Orientation on the Thermal Conductivity"

(*Polymer Eng. and Sci.* (1972):204–208) suggests the existence of a relationship between y = thermal conductivity and x = a measure of lamellar thickness. In the accompanying data, there is an x value that is much larger than the other x values.

x	240	410	460	490	520	590	745	8300
y	12.0	14.7	14.7	15.2	15.2	15.6	16.0	18.1

a. The least squares line for the given data set is $\hat{y} = 14.5 + .0004x$ and the computed values of r^2 and s_e are .533 and 1.246, respectively. Construct a residual plot.

b. The (x, y) pair (8300, 18.1) looks like it might be an influential observation. Try omitting it from the data set and computing the least squares line for the remaining data. Do the values of the intercept and slope differ much from those computed using the full data set?

c. Construct a residual plot using the least squares line in (b) and the data set that does not include (8300, 18.1). How does its appearance compare with the residual plot in (a)?

d. Again using the data set and line resulting from omission of (8300, 18.1), compute r^2 and s_e and compare these to the values reported in (a) for the full data set.

4.51 **a.** Show that the sum of the residuals $\Sigma[y - (a + bx)]$, is zero. (Hint: Substitute $a = \bar{y} - b\bar{x}$ and then use facts about $\Sigma(x - \bar{x})$ and $\Sigma(y - \bar{y})$.)

b. Let the residuals be denoted by $e_1, e_2, \ldots, e_n$ and consider fitting a line to the (x, e) pairs—that is, to the points in the residual plot—using the method of least squares. Then

$$\text{slope of the least squares line} = \frac{\Sigma(x - \bar{x})(e - \bar{e})}{\Sigma(x - \bar{x})^2}$$

From (a), $\bar{e} = 0$, so $e - \bar{e} = e = y - (a + bx) = y - \bar{y} - b(x - \bar{x})$. Use this to show that the slope in the given expression is zero, so that the residual plot has no tilt (though it may still have a nonlinear pattern if a straight-line fit is not appropriate).

4.52 Some straightforward but slightly tedious algebra shows that SSResid $= (1 - r^2)\Sigma(y - \bar{y})^2$, from which it follows that

$$s_e = \sqrt{\frac{(n - 1)}{(n - 2)}}\sqrt{1 - r^2}\, s_y$$

Unless n is quite small, $(n - 1)/(n - 2) \approx 1$, so $s_e \approx \sqrt{1 - r^2}\, s_y$.

a. For what value of r is s_e as large as s_y? What is the least squares line in this case?

b. For what values of r will s_e be much smaller than s_y?

c. A study by the Berkeley Institute of Human Development (see the book *Statistics* by Freedman et al. listed in the Chapter 2 references) reported the following summary data for a sample of $n = 66$ California boys:

$r \approx .80$

At age 6, average height $\approx$ 46 in., standard deviation $\approx$ 1.7 in.
At age 18, average height $\approx$ 70 in., standard deviation $\approx$ 2.5 in.

What would s_e be for the least squares line used to predict 18-year-old height from 6-year-old height?

d. Referring to (c), suppose you wanted to predict the past value of 6-year-old height from knowledge of 18-year-old height. What is the equation for the appropriate least squares line, and what is the corresponding value of s_e?

4.5 Transforming Data to Straighten a Plot and Fit a Curve (Optional)

When the points in a scatter plot exhibit a linear pattern, it is relatively easy to find a line that gives a good fit to the points in the plot. Such a line then describes an approximate relationship between x and y. A linear relationship is easy to interpret (for example, the impact on y of a specified change in x is easily assessed), departures from the line are easily detected, and using the line to predict y from knowledge of x is straightforward. Often, though, a scatter plot shows a strong curved pattern rather than a straight-line pattern. In this case, finding a "nice" curve that fits the observed data well may not be very easy, and departures from the selected curve may not be as apparent as departures from a straight line would be.

An alternative to fitting a curve is to find a way to transform x values and/or y values so that a scatter plot of the transformed data has a linear appearance. Sometimes a transformation is suggested by a theoretical model that relates y to x, but frequently the investigator would like the data to suggest an appropriate transformation. In this latter case, several transformations may have to be tried to find one which works. A type of transformation that statisticians have found useful for straightening a plot is a **power transformation.** A power (exponent) is first selected, and each original value is raised to that power to obtain the corresponding transformed value. Table 4.4 displays a ladder of the most frequently used power

TABLE 4.4   Power transformation ladder:
Transformed value = (original value)^{POWER}

Power	Transformed value	Name
3	(Original value)^3	Cube
2	(Original value)^2	Square
1	Original value	No transformation
$\frac{1}{2}$	$\sqrt{\text{Original value}}$	Square root
$\frac{1}{3}$	$\sqrt[3]{\text{Original value}}$	Cube root
0	Log (original value)	Logarithm
-1	1/(original value)	Reciprocal

transformations. The power 1 corresponds to no transformation at all. Using the power 0 would transform every value to 1, which is certainly not informative, so statisticians use the logarithmic transformation in its place. Other powers intermediate to or more extreme than those listed can be used, of course, but they are less frequently needed than those on the ladder. Notice that these are the same transformations suggested in Chapter 2 for transforming a single data set to obtain a more symmetric distribution.

Figure 4.26 is designed to suggest where on the ladder we should go to find an appropriate transformation. The four curved segments labeled 1, 2, 3, and 4 represent shapes of curved scatter plots that are commonly encountered. Suppose that a scatter plot looks like the curve labeled 1. Then to straighten the plot, we should use a power on x that is up the ladder from the no-transformation row (x^2 or x^3) and/or a power on y that is also up the ladder from the power 1. Thus we might be led to squaring each x value, cubing each y, and plotting the transformed pairs. If the curvature looks like curved segment 2, a power up the ladder from no transformation for x and/or a power down the ladder for y (for example, $\sqrt{y}$ or log (y)) should be used.

FIGURE 4.26
Scatter plot shapes and where to go on the transformation ladder to straighten the plot

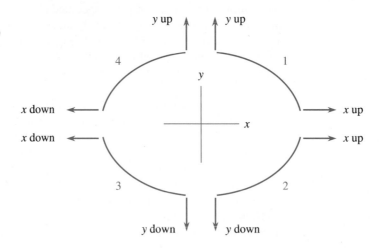

In many parts of the world a typical diet consists mainly of cereals and grains, and many individuals suffer from a substantial iron deficiency. The paper "The Effects of Organic Acids, Phytates, and Polyphenols on the Absorption of Iron from Vegetables" (*British J. Nutrition* (1983):331–342) reported the accompanying data on

x = proportion of iron absorbed

and

y = polyphenol content (mg/g)

when a particular vegetable is consumed. The scatter plot of the data in Figure 4.27(a) shows a clear curved pattern, which resembles the curved segment 3 in Figure 4.26. This suggests that x and/or y should be transformed by a power down the ladder from 1. The authors of the paper applied a square-root transformation to each variable. The resulting scatter plot in Figure 4.27(b) is reasonably straight.

Vegetable	x	y	$\sqrt{x}$	$\sqrt{y}$
Wheat germ	.007	6.4	.084	2.53
Aubergine	.007	3.0	.084	1.73
Butter beans	.012	2.9	.110	1.70
Spinach	.014	5.8	.118	2.41
Brown lentils	.024	5.0	.155	2.24
Beetroot greens	.024	4.3	.155	2.07
Green lentils	.032	3.4	.179	1.84
Carrot	.096	.7	.310	.84
Potato	.115	.2	.339	.45
Beetroot	.185	1.5	.430	1.22
Pumpkin	.206	.1	.454	.32
Tomato	.224	.3	.473	.55
Broccoli	.260	.4	.510	.63
Cauliflower	.263	.7	.513	.84
Cabbage	.320	.1	.566	.32
Turnip	.327	.3	.572	.55
Sauerkraut	.327	.2	.572	.45

FIGURE 4.27
Scatter plot of data
from Example 4.18
(a) Original data
(b) Square-root
transformed data

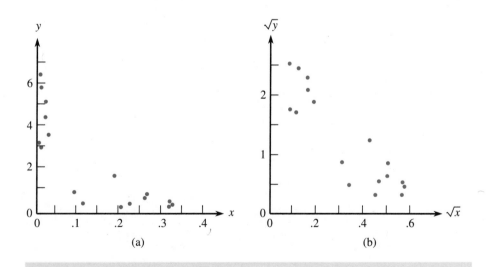

(a)   (b)

EXAMPLE 4.19

The article "Reduction in Soluble Protein and Chlorophyll Contents in a Few Plants as Indicators of Automobile Exhaust Pollution" (*Int. J. of Environ. Studies* (1983):239–244) reported the accompanying data on x = distance from a highway (m) and y = lead content of soil at that distance (ppm).

x	.3	1	5	10	15	20
y	62.75	37.51	29.70	20.71	17.65	15.41

x	25	30	40	50	75	100
y	14.15	13.50	12.11	11.40	10.85	10.85

Figure 4.28(a) displays a scatter plot of the data. The curvature in the plot is very pronounced. The authors of the paper did not suggest a transformation for straightening the plot. Since the curvature is like that of the curved segment labeled 3 in Figure 4.26, we tried a number of transformations down the ladder for both x and y. The plot in Figure 4.28(b) is the result of transforming x by logarithms and leaving y untransformed. Figure 4.28(c) displays the plot resulting from a log transformation of both x and y. These latter two plots are reasonably straight, and there is little reason for preferring one to the other.

We also went further down the ladder and tried a reciprocal transformation for both x and y ($1/y$ versus $1/x$). The resulting plot, shown in Figure 4.28(d), is quite curved, indicating that we have gone too far down the ladder. You might think that going too far would produce the curvature of segment 1 in Figure 4.26, which is opposite what we started with (segment 3). However, the plot of $1/y$ versus $1/x$ actually looks like segment 3 because taking reciprocals reverses the ordering of numbers: $2 < 4$, but $\frac{1}{2} > \frac{1}{4}$. Some authors have suggested using $-1/x$ and $-1/y$, which preserves order, and a plot of $-1/y$ versus $-1/x$ does indeed look like segment 1.

FIGURE 4.28
MINITAB scatter plots for original and transformed data from Example 4.19
(a) y versus x
(b) y versus $\log(x)$
(c) $\log(y)$ versus $\log(x)$
(d) $1/y$ versus $1/x$

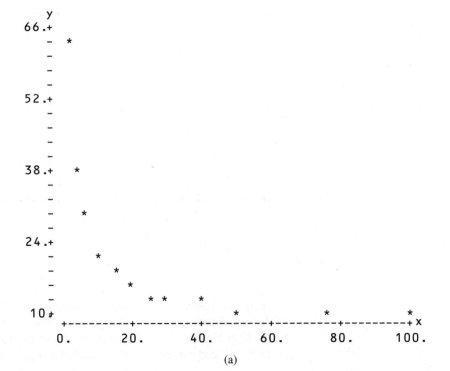

(a)

FIGURE 4.28
(continued)

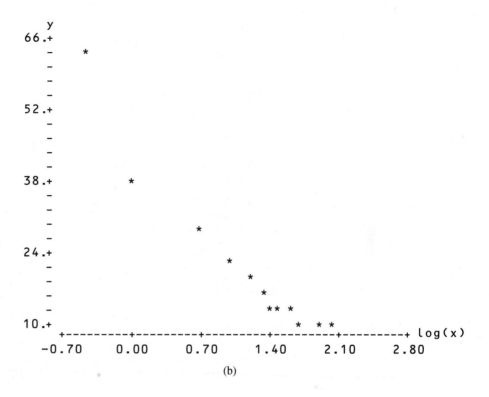

(b)

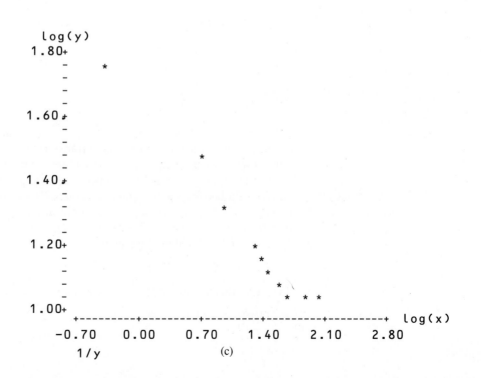

(c)

FIGURE 4.28
(continued)

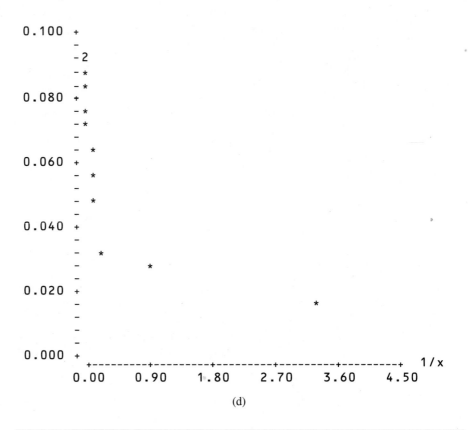

(d)

Fitting a Curve

When the scatter plot shows a curved pattern, a transformation of x and/or y can often straighten the plot. Once such a transformation has been identified, the principle of least squares can be used to fit a line to the transformed data. After obtaining the least squares line, the transformation can be reversed to yield a curved relationship between the original variables. For example, suppose that a plot of $\log(y)$ versus $\log(x)$ is reasonably straight and that the least squares line for the transformed data has vertical intercept 2 and slope -3. Then $\log(y)$ and $\log(x)$ are approximately related by the equation

$$\log(y) = 2 - 3 \log(x)$$

To reverse this transformation, we now take the antilog of each side of the equation:

$$(10)^{\log(y)} = (10)^{2-3[\log(x)]}$$

Using the properties
$$(10)^{\log(y)} = y$$
$$(10)^{2-3[\log(x)]} = (10)^2 (10)^{-3[\log(x)]}$$
$$(10)^{-3[\log(x)]} = x^{-3}$$

the resulting equation is $y = 100x^{-3}$ (that is, $y = 100/x^3$). The graph of this equation is a curve shaped like the arc labeled 3 in Figure 4.26.

EXAMPLE 4.20

The problem of soil erosion is faced by farmers all over the world. The paper "Soil Erosion by Wind from Bare Sandy Plains in Western Rajasthan, India" (*J. Arid Environ.* (1981):15–20) reported on a study of the relationship between wind velocity x (km/h) and soil erosion y (kg/day) in a very dry environment, where erosion control is especially important. We present selected data extracted from the paper. Figure 4.29(a) displays a scatter plot of the data. Comparison of the plot with the arcs of Figure 4.26 suggests moving down the ladder in y and/or up the ladder in x. Figure 4.29(b) displays a plot of $y' = \log(y)$ versus x, which is quite straight (so transformation of x is not necessary).

Observation	x	y	$y' = \log(y)$	Observation	x	y	$y' = \log(y)$
1	13.5	5	.6990	8	21	140	2.1461
2	13.5	15	1.1761	9	22	75	1.8751
3	14	35	1.5441	10	23	125	2.0969
4	15	25	1.3979	11	25	190	2.2788
5	17.5	25	1.3979	12	25	300	2.4771
6	19	70	1.8451	13	26	240	2.3802
7	20	80	1.9031	14	27	315	2.4983

Finding the least squares line for the 14 (x, y') pairs requires that we first calculate the usual summary statistics:

$$\Sigma x = 281.5 \qquad \Sigma x^2 = 5961.75 \qquad \Sigma y' = 25.7157$$
$$\Sigma(y')^2 = 50.945033 \qquad \Sigma xy' = 548.2677$$

from which

$$a = -.243184 \qquad b = .103447$$

The least squares line that summarizes the relationship between x and $y' = \log(y)$ has equation

$$\log(y) = -.243184 + .103447x$$

FIGURE 4.29
MINITAB plots for the data
of Example 4.20
(a) *y* versus *x*
(b) log(*y*) versus *x*

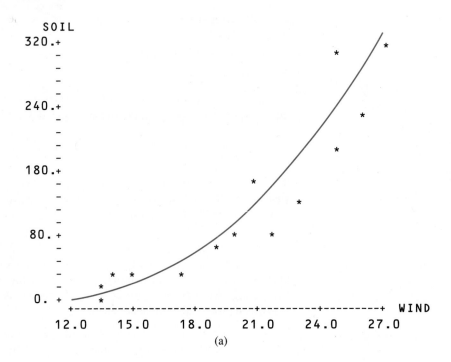

(a)

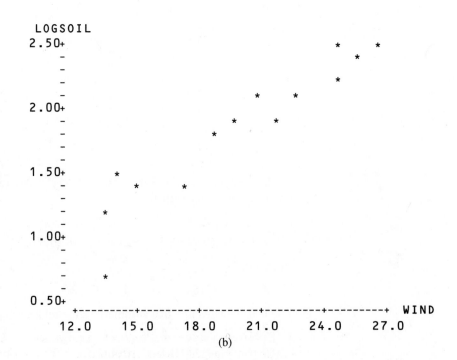

(b)

The antilog of $\log(y)$ is y itself; equating this to the antilog of the right-hand side of the equation gives

$$y = 10^{-.243184+.103447x} = (10^{-.243184})(10^{.103447})^x$$
$$= .5712(1.2690)^x$$

The resulting equation $y = .5712(1.2690)^x$ is called an **exponential function** (of x), since x appears as an exponent on the right-hand side. By substituting various x values and using a calculator that can raise a number to any desired power (for example, $(1.2690)^{15}$, $(1.2690)^{17.5}$, $(1.2690)^{20}$), points on the graph of this function can be identified. They can then be connected in a smooth fashion to obtain a prediction curve, which we have superimposed on the scatter plot of Figure 4.29(a). For any x, the corresponding predicted y value is the height of the curve above that x value. The predicted y value when $x = 15$ is

$$\hat{y} = .5712(1.2690)^{15} = 20.357$$

(The observed y for this value of x is 25.)

For $x = 16$,

$$\hat{y} = .5712(1.2690)^{16} = 25.83$$

It would be dangerous to make a prediction for x much larger than 27, the largest x value in the sample, since the amount of soil erosion presumably levels off at some point rather than continuing to increase explosively.

EXERCISES 4.53–4.62 SECTION 4.5

4.53 The accompanying data on leaf diffusive resistance (y) and water potential (x) for one variety of coffee plant has been read from a scatter plot that appeared in the paper mentioned in Exercise 4.6.

x	−10	−10	−11	−11	−12	−12	−13	−13	−14	−16	−17
y	14	16	13	15	10	14	8	11	13	10	11

x	−17	−18	−22	−22	−23	−24	−24	−24	−25	−25	−26
y	18	12	17	32	20	24	26	44	36	54	52

a. Construct a scatter plot for the given data set.
b. Can you suggest a transformation from Table 4.4 that might help straighten this plot? Explain the rationale for your suggestion (you need not actually construct the plot).

4.54   The scatter plot of the data given in Exercise 4.53 shows quite a bit of curvature. Examination of Figure 4.26 suggests that two possible transformations for straightening this plot are log y and $1/y$. Use the given transformed values to construct a scatter plot using log y and x and a scatter plot using $1/y$ and x. Which plot appears to be the straightest?

y	14	16	13	15	10	14	8	11	13	10	11
log y	1.15	1.20	1.11	1.18	1.00	1.15	.90	1.04	1.11	1.00	1.04
$1/y$	.071	.063	.077	.067	.100	.071	.125	.091	.077	.100	.091

y	18	12	17	32	20	24	26	44	36	54	52
log y	1.26	1.08	1.23	1.51	1.30	1.38	1.41	1.64	1.56	1.73	1.72
$1/y$	.056	.083	.059	.031	.050	.042	.038	.023	.028	.019	.019

4.55   The accompanying data on x = viscera mass (kg) and y = body gross energy (mcal) was read from a graph in the paper "Body Composition and Condition Evaluation of White-Tailed Deer Fawns" (*J. Wildlife Mgmt.* (1991):39–51).

x	y	$x' = \log(x)$	$y' = \log(y)$
1.9	16	.2788	1.2041
2.2	23	.3424	1.3617
2.5	26	.3979	1.4150
2.6	24	.4150	1.3802
3.0	34	.4771	1.5315
3.3	29	.5185	1.4624
3.4	40	.5315	1.6021
3.5	45	.5441	1.6532
5.0	77	.6990	1.8865
5.1	65	.7076	1.8129
5.4	90	.7324	1.9542
5.9	104	.7709	2.0170
6.1	97	.7853	1.9868
6.1	113	.7853	2.0531

a. Construct a scatter plot of y versus x. What does it suggest about the nature of the relationship between x and y?

b. The least squares line has equation $\hat{y} = -31.074 + 21.751x$, SSTo = 15,114.93, and SSResid = 657.27. How effective is a straight line in summarizing the relation between x and y?

c. The residuals are 5.7, 6.2, 2.7, -1.5, $-.2$, -11.7, -2.9, $-.1$, $-.7$, -14.9, 3.6, 6.7, -4.6, and 11.4. What does a residual plot suggest about the relationship?

d. Find the equation of the least squares line for the x', y' data (as did the authors of the paper). Does a linear relation between transformed variables seem more reasonable than one between the original variables? Explain.

e. Use the results of (d) to predict y when $x = 5.0$.

4.56 The paper "Aspects of Food Finding by Wintering Bald Eagles" (*The Auk* (1983): 477–484) examined the relationship between the time that eagles spend aerially searching for food (indicated by the percentage of eagles soaring) and relative food availability. The data below is taken from a scatter plot that appeared in this paper. Let x denote salmon availability and y denote the percent of eagles in the air.

x	0.0	0.0	0.2	0.5	0.5	1.0
y	28.2	69.0	27.0	38.5	48.4	31.1

x	1.2	1.9	2.6	3.3	4.7	6.5
y	26.9	8.2	4.6	7.4	7.0	6.8

a. Draw a scatter plot for this data set. Would you describe the plot as linear or curvilinear?

b. One possible transformation that might lead to a straighter plot involves taking the square root of both the x and y values. Use Figure 4.26 to explain why this might be a reasonable choice of a transformation.

c. Construct a scatter plot using the variables $\sqrt{x}$ and $\sqrt{y}$. Is this scatter plot straighter than the plot in (a)?

d. Using Table 4.4, can you suggest another transformation that might be used to straighten the original plot?

4.57 Data on salmon availability (x) and the percent of eagles in the air (y) is given in the previous exercise.

a. Calculate the correlation coefficient for this data.

b. Since the scatter plot of the original data appeared curved, transforming both the x and y values by taking square roots was suggested. Calculate the correlation coefficient for the variables $\sqrt{x}$ and $\sqrt{y}$. How does this value compare with that of (a)? Does this indicate that the transformation was successful in straightening the plot?

4.58 Penicillin was administered orally to five horses and the concentration of penicillin in the blood was determined after five different lengths of time (a different horse was used each time). The accompanying data appeared in the paper "Absorption and Distribution Patterns of Oral Phenoxymethyl Penicillin in the Horse" (*Cornell Veterinarian* (1983):314–323).

(x) Time elapsed (h)	1	2	3	6	8
(y) Penicillin concentration (mg/mL)	1.8	1.0	.5	.1	.1

Construct scatter plots using the following variables. Which transformation, if any, would you recommend?

a. x and y

b. $\sqrt{x}$ and y

c. x and $\sqrt{y}$

d. $\sqrt{x}$ and $\sqrt{y}$

e. x and $\log(y)$ (the values of $\log(y)$ are .26, 0, $-.30$, -1, -1)

4.59   The paper "Population Pressure and Agricultural Intensity" (*Annals of the Assoc. of Amer. Geog.* (1977):384–396) reported a positive association between population density and agricultural intensity. The given data consists of measures of population density (x) and agricultural intensity (y) for 18 different subtropical locations.

x	1.0	26.0	1.1	101.0	14.9	134.7	3.0	5.7	7.6
y	9	7	6	50	5	100	7	14	14

x	25.0	143.0	27.5	103.0	180.0	49.6	140.6	140.0	233.0
y	10	50	14	50	150	10	67	100	100

a. Construct a scatter plot of agricultural intensity versus population density. Is the scatter plot compatible with the statement of positive association made in the paper?

b. The scatter plot in (a) is curved upward like segment 2 in Figure 4.26, suggesting a transformation that is up the ladder for x or down the ladder for y. Try a scatter plot that uses y and x^2. Does this transformation straighten the plot?

c. Try drawing a scatter plot that uses $\log y$ and x. The $\log y$ values, given in order corresponding to the y values, are .95, .85, .78, 1.70, .70, 2.00, .85, 1.15, 1.15, 1.00, 1.70, 1.15, 1.70, 2.18, 1.00, 1.83, 2.00, and 2.00. How does this scatter plot compare with that of (b)?

d. Next consider a scatter plot that uses both a transformation on x and a transformation on y: $\log y$ and x^2. Is this effective in straightening the plot? Explain.

4.60   The growth rate of lichen was the subject of a study reported in the paper "Lichen Growth Responses to Stress Induced by Automobile Exhaust Pollution" (*Science* (1979):423–424). The accompanying data is taken from a scatter plot illustrating the relationship between initial population size (area in mm^2) and percent area increase over a 6-month period. Construct a scatter plot for this data. If the scatter plot exhibits curvature, try to find a transformation that straightens the plot.

Population size (x)	.02	.02	.03	.05	.06	.06	.08	.09	.14
Percent increase (y)	200	190	150	155	150	130	90	140	50
Population size (x)	.14	.15	.22	.22	.55	.61	1.49	1.65	
Percent increase (y)	80	40	40	30	30	35	50	55	

4.61   Determining the age of an animal can sometimes be a difficult task. One method of estimating the age of harp seals is based on the width of the pulp canal in the seal's canine teeth. To investigate the relationship between age and the width of the pulp canal, age and canal width were measured for seals of known age. The accompanying data is a portion of a larger data set that appeared in the paper "Validation of Age Estimation in the Harp Seal Using Dentinal Annuli" (*Canadian J. of*

Fisheries and Aquatic Sci. (1983):1430–1441). Let x denote age (years) and y denote canal length (mm).

x	.25	.25	.50	.50	.50	.75	.75	1.00	1.00	1.00
y	700	675	525	500	400	350	300	300	250	230

x	1.00	1.00	1.25	1.25	1.50	1.50	2.00	2.00	2.50	2.75
y	150	100	200	100	100	125	60	140	60	50

x	3.00	4.00	4.00	5.00	5.00	5.00	5.00	6.00	6.00
y	10	10	10	10	15	10	10	15	10

Construct a scatter plot for this data set. Would you describe the relationship between age and canal length as linear? If not, suggest a transformation that might straighten the plot.

4.62   A frequently encountered problem in crop planting situations involves deciding when to harvest in order to maximize yield. The accompanying data on $x =$ date of harvesting (number of days after flowering) and $y =$ yield (kg/ha) of paddy, a grain farmed in India, appeared in the paper "Determination of Biological Maturity and Effect of Harvesting and Drying Conditions on Milling Quality of Paddy" (*J. of Ag. Eng.* (1975):353–361). Construct a scatter plot of this data. Can the methodology discussed in this section be used to select a straightening transformation? Why or why not? What kind of a curve might provide a reasonable fit to the plot?

x	16	18	20	22	24	26	28	30
y	2508	2518	3304	3423	3057	3190	3500	3883

x	32	34	36	38	40	42	44	46
y	3823	3646	3708	3333	3517	3241	3103	2776

CHAPTER FOUR SUMMARY OF KEY CONCEPTS AND FORMULAS

Term or Formula	Comment
Scatter plot	A picture of bivariate numerical data in which each observation (x, y) is represented as a point located with respect to a horizontal x axis and a vertical y axis.
Pearson's sample correlation coefficient $$r = \frac{\Sigma xy - [(\Sigma x)(\Sigma y)/n]}{\sqrt{\Sigma x^2 - [(\Sigma x)^2/n]} \sqrt{\Sigma y^2 - [(\Sigma y)^2/n]}}$$	A measure of the extent to which sample x and y values are linearly related.

Term or Formula	Comment
Spearman's correlation coefficient r_s	Pearson's r applied to the *ranks* of the x and y values. It will detect both linear and nonlinear relationships and is not as sensitive to outliers as is r.
Principle of least squares	The method used to select a line that summarizes an approximate linear relationship between x and y. The least squares line is the line that minimizes the sum of the squared vertical deviations from the points in the scatter plot.
$$b = \frac{\Sigma xy - [(\Sigma x)(\Sigma y)/n]}{\Sigma x^2 - [(\Sigma x)^2/n]}$$ $$a = \bar{y} - b\bar{x}$$	The slope and vertical (y) intercept of the least squares line.
Predicted (fitted) values $\hat{y}_1, \ldots, \hat{y}_n$	Obtained by substituting the x value for each observation into the least squares line: $\hat{y}_1 = a + bx_1, \ldots, \hat{y}_n = a + bx_n$
Residuals	Obtained by subtracting each predicted value from the corresponding observed y value: $y_1 - \hat{y}_1, \ldots, y_n - \hat{y}_n$. These are the vertical deviations from the least squares line.
Residual (error) sum of squares $\text{SSResid} = \Sigma(y - \bar{y})^2$	The sum of the squared residuals is a measure of y variation that cannot be attributed to an approximate linear relationship (unexplained variation).
Total sum of squares $\text{SSTo} = \Sigma(y - \bar{y})^2$	The sum of squared deviations from the sample mean $\bar{y}$ is a measure of total variation in the observed y values.
Coefficient of determination $$r^2 = 1 - \frac{\text{SSResid}}{\text{SSTo}}$$	The proportion of variation in observed y's that can be attributed to an approximate linear relationship.
Standard deviation about the least squares line $$s_e = \sqrt{\frac{\text{SSResid}}{n - 2}}$$	The size of a "typical" deviation from the least squares line.
Power transformation	An exponent, or power, p is first specified, and then new (transformed) data values are calculated as *transformed value* = (original value)^p. A logarithmic transformation is identified with $p = 0$. When the scatter plot of original data exhibits curvature, the power transformation of x and/or y will often result in a scatter plot that has a linear appearance.

ENCORE T he data on *x* = oxygen consumption (mL/kg/min) while on a treadmill and *y* = consumption during a fire-suppression simulation, first given in the Chapter Preview, is displayed here along with a scatter plot.

Observation	1	2	3	4	5	6	7	8	9	10
x	51.3	34.1	41.1	36.3	36.5	35.4	35.4	38.6	40.6	39.5
y	49.3	29.5	30.6	28.2	28.0	26.3	33.9	29.4	23.5	31.6

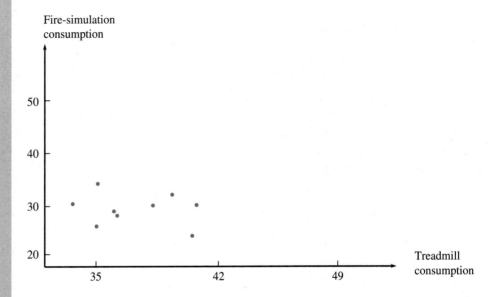

After examining the scatter plot, the investigators decided to fit a line to the data using the principle of least squares. The resulting line can then be used to predict fire-simulation oxygen consumption for a firefighter whose treadmill consumption was known. We used the statistical package MINITAB to do this, and the following output resulted. (Whatever is unfamiliar to you at this point is discussed in Chapter 13.)

```
The regression equation is
firecon = -11.4 + 1.09 treadcon

Predictor          Coef          Stdev        t-ratio           p
Constant         -11.37          12.46         -0.91       0.388
treadcon         1.0906          0.3181          3.43       0.009

s = 4.740   R-sq = 59.5%   R-sq (adj) = 54.4%
```

Analysis of Variance

SOURCE	DF	SS	MS	F	p
Regression	1	264.06	264.06	11.75	0.009
Error	8	179.74	22.47		
Total	9	443.80			

Obs.	treadcon	firecon	Fit	Stdev. Fit	Residual	St. Resid
1	51.3	49.30	44.58	4.23	4.72	2.20RX
9	40.6	23.50	32.91	1.60	-9.41	-2.11R

R denotes an obs. with a large st. resid.
X denotes an obs. whose X value gives it large influence.

The equation of the least squares line is

$$\hat{y} = -11.37 + 1.0906x$$

and 59.5% of observed variation in *y* can be attributed to the approximate linear relation between the two variables.

The output indicates something else that is pretty obvious from the scatter plot but was evidently missed by the investigators: the *x* value for the first observation is so much larger than the other nine *x* values that this observation may be very influential in the regression calculations (see the X flag on the output). A scatter plot from MINITAB of the remaining nine observations after eliminating (51.3, 49.3) is given here. There is very little evidence of a linear relationship in this plot. In confirmation of this, the value of r^2 after fitting the least squares line to these nine data points is only .027; only 2.7% of observed variation in fire-simulation oxygen consumption can now be explained by the linear relation between this variable and treadmill consumption. Clearly more data needs to be collected before a firm conclusion can be drawn about the nature of the relationship.

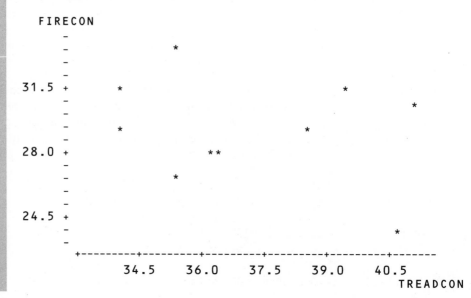

SUPPLEMENTARY EXERCISES

4.63 Silane coupling agents have been used in the rubber industry to improve the performance of fillers in rubber compounds. The accompanying data on y = tensile modulus (in MPa, a measure of silane coupling effectiveness) and x = bound rubber content (%) appeared in the paper "The Effect of the Structure of Sulfur-Containing Silane Coupling Agents on Their Activity in Silica-Filled SBR" (*Rubber Chem. and Tech.* (1984):675–685).

x	16.1	31.5	21.5	22.4	20.5	28.4
y	4.41	6.81	5.26	5.99	5.92	6.14

x	30.3	25.6	32.7	29.2	34.7
y	6.84	5.87	7.03	6.89	7.87

$n = 11$ $\quad$ $\Sigma x = 292.9$ $\quad$ $\Sigma x^2 = 8141.75$
$\Sigma y = 69.03$ $\quad$ $\Sigma y^2 = 442.1903$ $\quad$ $\Sigma xy = 1890.200$

a. Construct a scatter plot for this data. Does the plot look linear?
b. Find the equation of the least squares line.
c. Compute and interpret the value of r^2.

4.64 The relationship between depth of flooding and the amount of flood damage was examined in the paper "Significance of Location in Computing Flood Damage" (*J. of Water Resources Planning and Mgmt.* (1985):65–81). The data on x = depth of flooding (feet above first-floor level) and y = flood damage (as a percent of structure value) was obtained using a sample of flood insurance claims.

x	1	2	3	4	5	6	7	8	9	10	11	12	13
y	10	14	26	28	29	41	43	44	45	46	47	48	49

a. Obtain the equation of the least squares line.
b. Construct a scatter plot and draw the least squares line on the plot. Does it look as though a straight line provides an adequate description of the relationship between y and x? Explain.
c. Predict flood damage for a structure subjected to 6.5 ft of flooding.
d. Would you use the least squares line to predict flood damage when depth of flooding is 18 ft? Explain.

4.65 An investigation was carried out to study the relationship between speed (ft/s) and stride rate (number of steps taken/s) among female marathon runners. Resulting summary quantities included

$n = 11$ $\qquad$ $\Sigma(\text{speed}) = 205.4$
$\Sigma(\text{speed})^2 = 3880.08$ $\qquad$ $\Sigma(\text{rate}) = 35.16$
$\Sigma(\text{rate})^2 = 112.681$ $\quad$ $\Sigma(\text{speed})(\text{rate}) = 660.130$

a. Calculate the equation of the least squares line that you would use to predict stride rate from speed.
b. Calculate the equation of the least squares line that you would use to predict speed from stride rate.
c. Calculate the coefficient of determination for the "stride rate on speed" regression of part (a) and for the "speed on stride rate" regression of part (b). How are these related?

4.66 Consider the four (x, y) pairs $(0, 0)$, $(1, 1)$, $(1, -1)$, and $(2, 0)$.
a. What is the value of the sample correlation coefficient r?
b. If a fifth observation is made at the value $x = 6$, find a value of y for which $r > .5$.
c. If a fifth observation is made at the value $x = 6$, find a value of y for which $r < -.5$.

4.67 It is certainly plausible that workers are less likely to quit their jobs when wages are high than when they are low. The paper "Investigating the Causal Relationship between Quits and Wages: An Exercise in Comparative Dynamics" (*Economic Inquiry* (1986):61–83) presented the accompanying data on x = average hourly wage and y = quit rate (number of employees per 100 who left jobs during 1986). Each observation is for a different industry.

x	8.20	10.35	6.18	5.37	9.94	9.11	10.59	13.29
y	1.4	0.7	2.6	3.4	1.7	1.7	1.0	0.5

x	7.99	5.54	7.50	6.43	8.83	10.93	8.80
y	2.0	3.8	2.3	1.9	1.4	1.8	2.0

a. Does the data demonstrate unequivocally that quit rate is determined at least in part by factors other than wages? What does your intuition suggest?

b. Construct a scatter plot of the data. What does the plot suggest about the nature of the relationship?

c. Use the summary statistics $\Sigma x = 129.05$, $\Sigma x^2 = 1178.9601$, $\Sigma y = 28.2$, $\Sigma y^2 = 64.34$, and $\Sigma xy = 218.806$ to obtain the equation of the least squares line.

d. Predict the quit rate for an industry with an average hourly wage of $7.50, and calculate the corresponding residual.

e. What proportion of observed variation in quit rate can be attributed to an approximate linear relationship?

4.68 The paper "Biomechanical Characteristics of the Final Approach Step, Hurdle, and Take-Off of Elite American Springboard Divers" (*J. Human Movement Studies* (1984):189–212) gave the following data on y = judge's score and x = length of final step (m) for a sample of seven divers performing a forward pike with a single somersault.

y	7.40	9.10	7.20	7.00	7.30	7.30	7.90
x	1.17	1.17	.93	.89	.68	.74	.95

a. Construct a scatter plot.

b. Calculate the slope and intercept of the least squares line. Draw this line on your scatter plot.

c. Calculate and interpret the value of Pearson's sample correlation coefficient.

d. Compute the value of Spearman's rank correlation coefficient, r_s. (For tied scores, assign the average of the ranks that would have been assigned had they differed slightly; for example, if the values of 7.3 in the score row were slightly different, they would be ranked 4 and 5, so each is assigned rank $(4 + 5)/2 = 4.5$). How does the value of r_s compare to that of r from (c)?

4.69 The paper cited in Exercise 4.68 also gave the accompanying data on score and flight time for seven divers completing a reverse half-somersault. Compute the value of the correlation coefficient. Would you characterize the relationship between these two variables as a strong positive linear relationship? Explain.

Score	7.5	8.3	7.6	6.8	7.4	7.5	6.5
Time(s)	.45	.45	.45	.40	.41	.40	.46

4.70 The accompanying data on movie production costs, promotion costs, and worldwide ticket sales (all in millions of dollars) appeared in an article on "Dumb Movies" in the *Los Angeles Times* (January 20, 1985).

Movie	Production costs	Promotion costs	Ticket sales
Animal House	$ 2.9	$3	$150
Meatballs	1.4	2	70
Caddyshack	4.8	4	60
Stripes	10.5	4.5	85
Spring Break	4.5	5	24
Porky's	4.8	9	160
Fast Times at Ridgemont High	5.0	4.9	50
Porky's II	7.0	7.5	55
Hot Dog—The Movie	2.0	4	22
Bachelor Party	7.0	7.5	38
Revenge of the Nerds	7.0	7.5	42
Police Academy	4.5	4	150

a. Compute and interpret the value of the correlation coefficient for production costs and ticket sales.

b. Compute and interpret the value of the correlation coefficient for promotion costs and ticket sales.

4.71 The accompanying data on y = concentration of penicillin-G in pig's blood plasma (units/mL) and x = time (min) from administration of a dose of penicillin (22 mg/kg body weight) appeared in the paper "Calculation of Dosage Regimens of Antimicrobial Drugs for Surgical Prophylaxis" (*J. Amer. Vet. Med. Assoc.* (1984):1083–1087).

x	5	15	45	90	180	240	360	480	1440
y	32.6	43.3	23.1	16.7	5.7	6.4	9.2	.4	.2

a. Construct a scatter plot for this data.

b. Using the ladder of transformations of Section 4.5, suggest a transformation that might straighten the plot. Give reasons for your choice of transformation.

4.72 The accompanying data resulted from an experiment in which x was the amount of catalyst added to accelerate a chemical reaction and y was the resulting reaction time.

x	1	2	3	4	5
y	49	46	41	34	25

a. Calculate r. Does the value of r suggest a strong linear relationship?

b. Construct a scatter plot. On the basis of this plot, does the word *linear* really provide the most effective description of the relationship between x and y? Explain.

4.73 The least squares intercept a and slope b come from solving a system of two linear equations called the **normal equations**:

$$na + (\Sigma x)b = \Sigma y$$
$$(\Sigma x)a + (\Sigma x^2)b = \Sigma xy$$

a. Verify by direct substitution that

$$a = \bar{y} - b\bar{x} = \frac{\Sigma y}{n} - b\frac{\Sigma x}{n},$$

$$b = \frac{\Sigma xy - [(\Sigma x)(\Sigma y)/n]}{\Sigma x^2 - [(\Sigma x)^2/n]}$$

is the solution to this system of equations.

b. Show that the first normal equation implies that the sum of the residuals from the least squares line is zero—that is, that $\Sigma(y - \hat{y}) = 0$. (Hint: Recall that $\hat{y} = a + bx$.)

4.74 a. Show that

$$\text{SSResid} = \text{SSTo} - b \cdot (\text{numerator of } b)$$

(Hint: Use the computational formula for SSResid and the fact that $a = \bar{y} - b\bar{x}$.)

b. Argue that the expression for SSResid in part (a) implies that SSResid ≤ SSTo. (Hint: Both b and the numerator of b have the same sign.)

References

Neter, John, William Wasserman, and Michael Kutner. *Applied Linear Statistical Models.* Homewood, Ill. Richard D. Irwin, Inc., 1985. (The first half of this book gives a comprehensive, up-to-date treatment of regression analysis without overindulging in mathematical development; a highly recommended reference.)

Younger, Mary Sue. *A Handbook for Linear Regression.* Boston, Mass.: Duxbury Press, 1985. (A good, thorough introduction to many aspects of regression; particularly recommended for its discussion of various statistical computer packages.)

5

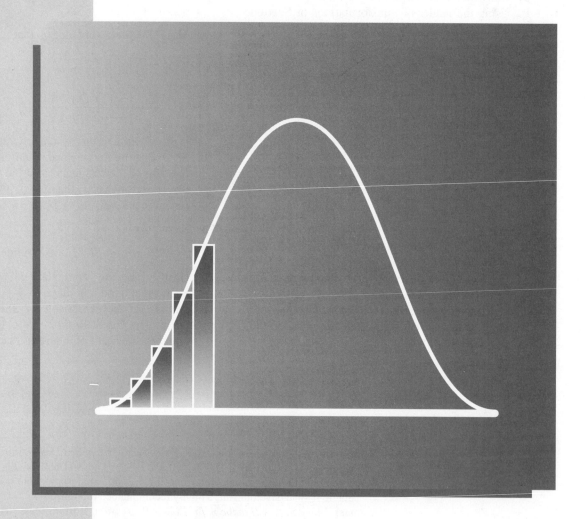

Probability

PREVIEW   Methods for jury selection have become much more sophisticated in recent years as both the defense and prosecution worry about identifying jurors that are favorable to their side. In a criminal trial, every juror is questioned by a lawyer from each side, but the responses may not reveal a bias that actually exists. Furthermore, because the legal definition of bias is quite narrow, what many of us would consider bias might not be cause for a juror to be excused by the judge. Given that a juror has survived the questioning process (not been excused for cause), how likely is it that the individual has no bias? Is biased against the prosecution? Is biased against the defense? In this chapter we show how probability methods can be used to formulate such questions precisely and answer them once underlying assumptions have been carefully stated.

Introduction

Almost all our everyday activities involve some aspects of uncertainty. There is uncertainty concerning the number of cars in line at a bank's drive-up window, concerning whether or not an appliance will need repair while still under warranty, concerning the amount of weight one might lose on a particular diet, and so on. **Probability** is the scientific discipline devoted to studying uncertainty in a systematic fashion.

The first growth spurt of probability occurred during the 17th century in attempts to answer questions concerning games of chance. Even today games of chance suggest many interesting questions that can be answered using methods from probability. For example, it used to be thought that the odds in blackjack virtually always favored the house (the dealer's employer), but in the 1960s probability methods were used to discover many situations (involving cards not yet dealt) in which the advantage lay with the individual bettor. In the 20th century the scope of probability has enlarged considerably as investigators have attempted to deal with uncertainty in both scientific contexts and in everyday life. Probability methods have recently been used to increase understanding of such diverse phenomena as the spread of an epidemic through a population, the mechanism of memory recall, the operating characteristics of various computer time-sharing systems, the diffusion of particles through a membrane, changes in consumers' brand preferences over time, social class mobility through succeeding generations, and (of course) what tomorrow's weather might be like. Here we introduce just a few of the most important concepts and methods of probability, focusing on those most frequently used in statistical contexts. In later chapters, probability will be used to specify the degree of reliability for various inferential procedures.

5.1   Chance Experiments and Events

The basic ideas and terminology of probability are most easily introduced in situations that are both familiar and reasonably simple. Thus, some of our initial examples will involve such mundane activities as tossing a coin once or several times, selecting one or more cards from a deck, and rolling a single die or several dice. Once the basics are in place, we shall move to more interesting and realistic situations.

Chance Experiments

When a single coin is tossed, it can land head up or tail up. The selection of a single card from a well-mixed deck could result in the ace of spades, the five of diamonds, the jack of hearts, or any one of the other 49 possibilities. Consider rolling both a red die and a green die. One possible outcome is (4, 1)—that is, the red die lands with four dots facing up and the green die shows one dot on its upturned face. Another outcome is (3, 3), and yet another is (1, 4). There are 36 possibilities (6 in which the red die shows 1, another 6 in which it shows 2, and so on). Prior to carrying out one of these activities, there is uncertainty as to which outcome will result.

> **DEFINITION**
>
> A **chance experiment** is any activity or situation in which there is uncertainty concerning which of two or more possible outcomes will result.

Rolling a die might not seem like much of an experiment in the usual sense of the word, but our usage is broader than what is typically implied. A chance experiment could also refer to determining whether or not each person in a sample supports the death penalty (an opinion poll or survey) or to an investigation carried out in a laboratory to study how varying the amount of a certain chemical input affects the yield of a product.

EXAMPLE 5.1

Consider the experiment in which two people are randomly selected from a list of all new homeowners in a certain area. The type of mortgage—fixed rate (F) or adjustable rate (A)—is then noted for each one. The first person can be in either the F or A category, and for each of these there are two further possibilities for the second person. Thus there are four possible experimental outcomes:

FF, FA, AF, AA

The four outcomes of Example 5.1 can be displayed in a picture called a **tree diagram,** as illustrated in Figure 5.1. The two line segments (branches) leading out from the initial point on the left side of the diagram correspond to the two possibilities for the first individual selected; these are sometimes referred to as *first-generation branches.* There are two further *second-generation branches* emanating from the tip of each first-generation branch, corresponding to the possibilities for the second individual selected. Starting from the initial point, a particular outcome results from selecting a first-generation branch followed by a second-generation branch. The four possible outcomes are shown on the right side of the diagram.

FIGURE 5.1
A tree diagram for Example 5.1

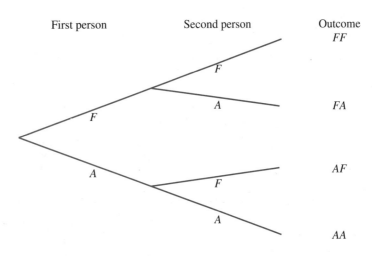

If three people rather than two are selected, there are eight possible outcomes (four from adding an additional *F* to each outcome just considered and an additional four from adding an *A*). Figure 5.2 shows the corresponding tree diagram, which contains three generations of branches.

FIGURE 5.2
A tree diagram for Example 5.1 when three people are selected

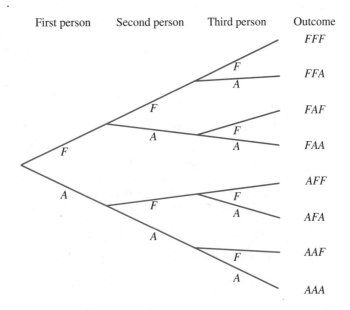

197

EXAMPLE 5.2

All but one of the jurors for a trial have been selected. There are four potential jurors—individuals, *a, b, c,* and *d*—left to question. All four are acceptable to the prosecution, but two of the four, *a* and *b,* are unacceptable to the defense and so will be excused if questioned. Suppose that the potential jurors are selected for questioning in random order (by drawing slips of paper from a box), with the process terminating when an acceptable juror (*c* or *d*) is questioned. There are three different types of possible outcomes.

Type of outcome	Outcomes
One potential juror is questioned	*c, d*
Two potential jurors are questioned	*ac, ad, bc, bd*
Three potential jurors are questioned	*abc, abd, bac, bad*

Figure 5.3 shows the corresponding tree diagram. This diagram lacks the symmetry exhibited by the diagrams in Figures 5.1 and 5.2, because here some outcomes result in earlier termination of the experiment than do others.

FIGURE 5.3
A tree diagram for Example 5.2

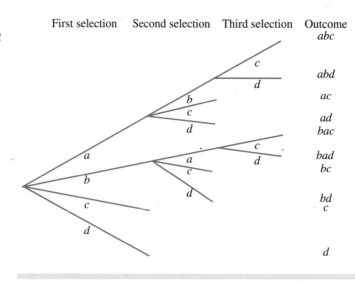

First selection   Second selection   Third selection   Outcome
abc
abd
ac
ad
bac
bad
bc
bd
c
d

The collection (or set) of all possible experimental outcomes is frequently referred to as the **sample space** of the experiment. When listing elements of a set, it is customary to enclose them in braces. Thus the sample space for the two-person experiment of Example 5.1 is

sample space $= \{FF, FA, AF, AA\}$

and for Example 5.2 it is

sample space $= \{c, d, ac, ad, bc, bd, abc, abd, bac, bad\}$

Events

An individual who tosses a pair of dice may be interested in which particular one of the 36 possible outcomes will result. Alternatively, interest may focus on whether the outcome will be in the group consisting of (1, 4), (2, 3), (3, 2), (4, 1), those outcomes having a sum value of five. In the situation summarized in Figure 5.2, the number of homeowners having adjustable-rate mortgages may be of primary concern. Outcomes in the group *AAF, AFA, FAA* are those for which exactly two homeowners have adjustable-rate mortgages. More generally, an investigator will often wish to know whether the resulting outcome belongs to some specified collection.

DEFINITION

An **event** is any collection of possible outcomes from a chance experiment. A **simple event** is an event consisting of exactly one outcome.

We usually represent an event by an uppercase letter such as A. Sometimes different letters are used to denote different events—A, B, C, and so on—but on other occasions the same letter with different numerical subscripts, such as E_1, E_2, E_3, ..., may be used for this purpose.

EXAMPLE 5.3

Reconsider the situation of Example 5.1, in which each of two homeowners was categorized as having either an adjustable-rate mortgage (A) or a fixed-rate mortgage (F). We had

    sample space $= \{FF, FA, AF, AA\}$

Because there are four outcomes, there are four simple events:

    $O_1 = \{FF\}, \qquad O_2 = \{FA\}, \qquad O_3 = \{AF\}, \qquad O_4 = \{AA\}$

One event of interest is

    $B = \{FF, FA, AF\}$

A word description of B is that it consists of all outcomes for which at least one person had a fixed-rate loan. Another event is

    $C = \{AF, AA\}$

In words, C is the event that the first person selected has an adjustable-rate loan.

EXAMPLE 5.4

The sample space for the jury selection situation in Example 5.2 was

    $\{c, d, ac, ad, bc, bd, abc, abd, bac, bad\}$

Some events of potential interest are

$A = \{c, d\}$

$\qquad$ = the event that exactly one potential juror is questioned

$B = \{c, ac, bc, abc, bac\}$

$\qquad$ = the event that individual c is selected

$O_1 = \{c\}, \qquad$ a simple event

$O_2 = \{ad\}, \qquad$ another simple event

Because there are ten possible outcomes, there are ten simple events; the number of nonsimple events is quite large.

In general, only one outcome, and thus one simple event, will occur when an experiment is performed. However, the resulting outcome will often be contained in many nonsimple events. We shall say that a given event has occurred whenever the resulting outcome is contained in the event. If the outcome in Example 5.3 is AF, then the (simple) event O_3 has occurred, as has $B = \{FF, FA, AF\}$ (at least one of the two individuals selected did have a fixed-rate loan) and $C = \{AF, AA\}$, but $D = \{FF, FA\}$ did not occur—the first person selected did not have a fixed-rate loan. Typically, many events occur simultaneously when an experiment is performed, though most will not be of interest.

Forming New Events

Once some events have been specified, there are several useful ways of manipulating them to create new events.

> **DEFINITION**
>
> Let A and B denote two events.
>
> 1. The event **not A** consists of all experimental outcomes that are not in A.[1]
> 2. The event **A or B** consists of all experimental outcomes that are in at least one of the two events, that is, in A or in B or in both of these.[2]
> 3. The event **A and B** consists of all experimental outcomes that are in both A and B, that is, the outcomes common to the two events.[3]

---

[1]*Not A* is sometimes called the *complement* of A and is denoted by A' or $\overline{A}$.
[2]*A or B* is sometimes called the *union* of the two events and is denoted by $A \cup B$.
[3]*A and B* is sometimes called the *intersection* of the two events and is denoted by $A \cap B$.

EXAMPLE 5.5

An observer stands at the bottom of a freeway offramp and records the turning direction (L or R) of each of three successive vehicles. The sample space contains eight outcomes:

$$\{LLL, RLL, LRL, LLR, RRL, RLR, LRR, RRR\}$$

These outcomes could also be displayed in a tree diagram containing three generations of branches. Each of these outcomes determines a simple event. For example,

$$O_1 = \{LLL\}, \qquad O_2 = \{RLL\}, \qquad \text{and so on}$$

Other events include

$$A = \{RLL, LRL, LLR\}$$
$$= \text{the event that exactly one of the cars turns right}$$
$$B = \{LLL, RLL, LRL, LLR\}$$
$$= \text{the event that at most one of the cars turns right}$$
$$C = \{LLL, RRR\}$$
$$= \text{the event that all cars turn in the same direction}$$

Here are some events that can be formed from those just defined:

$$not\ C = \{RLL, LRL, LLR, RRL, RLR, LRR\}$$
$$= \text{the event that not all cars turn in the same direction}$$
$$A\ or\ C = \{RLL, LRL, LLR, LLL, RRR\}$$
$$B\ and\ C = \{LLL\} = O_1$$

Notice also that event A and event C have no outcomes in common.

It frequently happens, as was the case for events A and C in Example 5.5, that two events have no common outcomes. There is special terminology for such situations.

DEFINITION

Two events A and B that have no common outcomes are said to be **disjoint, or mutually exclusive.**

In particular, any two different simple events are disjoint, since each contains a single outcome and they are different.

It is sometimes useful to draw an informal picture of events in order to visualize relationships. In a **Venn diagram,** the collection of all possible outcomes, that is, the sample space (itself an event), is shown as the interior of a rectangle. Other events are then identified with specified regions inside this rectangle. Figure 5.4 illustrates several Venn diagrams.

FIGURE 5.4
Venn diagrams

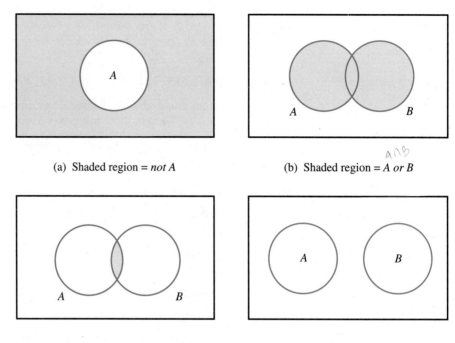

(a) Shaded region = *not A*   (b) Shaded region = *A or B*

(c) Shaded region = *A and B*   (d) Two disjoint events

The use of the *or* and *and* operations can be extended to form new events from more than two initially specified events.

DEFINITION

Let $A_1, A_2, \ldots, A_k$ denote k events.

1. The event **A_1 or A_2 or ... or A_k** consists of all outcomes in at least one of the individual events $A_1, A_2, \ldots, A_k$.
2. The event **A_1 and A_2 and ... and A_k** consists of all outcomes that are simultaneously in every one of the individual events $A_1, A_2, \ldots, A_k$.

These k events are **disjoint** if no two of them have any common outcomes.

Venn diagrams illustrating these concepts appear in Figure 5.5.

FIGURE 5.5
Venn diagrams

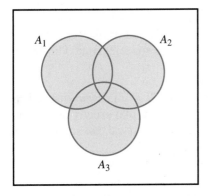

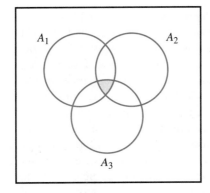

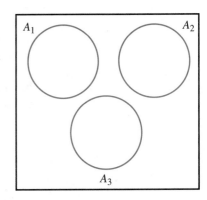

(a) A_1 *or* A_2 *or* A_3 (b) A_1 *and* A_2 *and* A_3 (c) Three disjoint events

EXAMPLE 5.6

The instructor in a seminar class consisting of four students has an unusual way of asking questions. Four slips of paper numbered 1, 2, 3, and 4, respectively, are placed in a box. The student to whom any particular question is to be addressed is then determined by selecting one of these four slips. Suppose that one question is to be posed during each of the next two class meetings. One possible outcome is (3, 1)—the first question is addressed to student 3 and the second to student 1; there are 15 other possibilities. Now consider the events

$A = \{(1, 1), (2, 2), (3, 3), (4, 4)\}$
$B = \{(1, 1), (1, 2), (1, 3), (1, 4), (2, 1), (3, 1), (4, 1)\}$
$C = \{(3, 1), (2, 2), (1, 3)\}$
$D = \{(3, 3), (3, 4), (4, 3)\}$
$E = \{(1,1), (1, 3), (2, 2), (3, 1), (4, 2), (3,3), (2, 4), (4, 4)\}$
$F = \{(1, 1), (1, 2), (2, 1)\}$

Then

A *or* C *or* $D = \{(1, 1), (2, 2), (3, 3), (4, 4), (3, 1), (1, 3), (3, 4), (4, 3)\}$

The outcome (3, 1) is contained in each of the events B, C, and E, as is the outcome (1, 3), and these are the only two common outcomes, so

B *and* C *and* $E = \{(3, 1), (1, 3)\}$

The events C, D, and F are disjoint because no outcome in any one of these events is contained in either of the other two events.

EXERCISES 5.1–5.9   SECTION 5.1

5.1   Consider the experiment in which the type of transmission—automatic (A) or man-
       ual (M)—is recorded for each of the next two cars purchased from a certain dealer.
       a. What is the set of all possible outcomes (the sample space)? (Hint: The experi-
       ment is similar to that of Example 5.1.)
       b. Display the possible outcomes in a tree diagram.
       c. List the outcomes in each of the following events: B = the event that at least
       one car has an automatic transmission; C = the event that exactly one car has
       an automatic transmission; D = the event that neither car has an automatic
       transmission. Which of these events are simple events?
       d. What outcomes are in the event B *and* C? In the event B *or* C?

5.2   Suppose that a (six-sided) die is rolled and then a coin is tossed.
       a. Display the possible outcomes in a rectangular table with a row for each of the
       six sides of the die and a column for each side of the coin.
       b. Display the possible outcomes on a tree diagram.
       c. Let D_1 denote the event that the upturned face on the die shows a 1, let E denote
       the event that an even number results from the die toss, and let F be the event
       that the head side of the coin lands up. List the outcomes in these three events.
       d. Referring to part (c), list the outcomes in the event *not E* and the outcomes in
       the event *not F.*
       e. Referring to part (c), what outcomes are in the event *E or F*? In *E and F*?
       f. Is any pair of the events defined in part (c) disjoint? Which one(s)?

5.3   A college library has four copies of a certain book; the copies are numbered 1, 2,
       3, and 4. Two of these are randomly selected (using four slips of paper). The first
       book selected will be placed on two-hour reserve, and the second one may be
       checked out on an overnight basis.
       a. Construct a tree diagram to display the 12 outcomes in the sample space.
       b. Let A denote the event that at least one of the books selected is an even-
       numbered copy. What outcomes are in A?
       c. Suppose copies 1 and 2 are first printings, whereas copies 3 and 4 are second
       printings. Let B denote the event that exactly one of the copies selected is a first
       printing. What outcomes are contained in B?

5.4   A library has five copies of a certain text on reserve, of which two copies (1 and 2)
       are first printings and the other three (3, 4, and 5) are second printings. A student
       examines these books in random order, stopping only when a second printing has
       been selected.
       a. Display the possible outcomes in a tree diagram.
       b. What outcomes are contained in the event A, that exactly one book is examined
       before the experiment terminates?
       c. What outcomes are contained in the event C, that the experiment terminates
       with the examination of book 5?

5.5   Suppose that starting at a certain time, batteries coming off an assembly line are
       examined one-by-one to see whether they are defective (let D = defective and
       N = not defective). The experiment terminates as soon as a nondefective battery
       is obtained.

a. Give five possible experimental outcomes.
b. What can be said about the number of outcomes in the sample space?
c. What outcomes are in the event E, that the number of batteries examined is an even number?

5.6 Refer to Exercise 5.5, and now suppose that the experiment terminates only when *two* nondefective batteries are obtained.

a. Let A denote the event that at most three batteries must be examined in order to terminate the experiment. What outcomes are contained in A?
b. Let B be the event that exactly four batteries must be examined before the experiment terminates. What outcomes are in B?
c. What can be said about the number of possible outcomes?

5.7 A family consisting of three people—P_1, P_2, and P_3—belongs to a medical clinic that always has a physician at each of stations 1, 2, and 3. During a certain week, each member of the family visits the clinic exactly once and is randomly assigned to a station. One experimental outcome is (1, 2, 1), which means that P_1 is assigned to station 1, P_2 to station 2, and P_3 to station 1.

a. There are 27 possible outcomes; list them. (Hint: First list the nine outcomes in which P_1 goes to station 1, then the nine in which P_1 goes to station 2, and finally the nine in which P_1 goes to station 3. A tree diagram might help.)
b. List all outcomes in the event A, that all three people go to the same station.
c. List all outcomes in the event B, that all people go to different stations.
d. List all outcomes in the event C, that no one goes to station 2.
e. Identify outcomes in the following events: *not B, not C, A or B, A and B, A and C.*

5.8 An engineering construction firm is currently working on power plants at three different sites. Define events E_1, E_2, and E_3 as follows:

$$E_1 = \text{the plant at site 1 is completed by the contract date}$$
$$E_2 = \text{the plant at site 2 is completed by the contract date}$$
$$E_3 = \text{the plant at site 3 is completed by the contract date}$$

The accompanying Venn diagram pictures the relationships among these events.

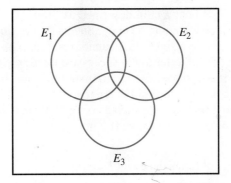

Shade the region in the Venn diagram corresponding to each of the following events (redraw the Venn diagram for each part of the problem).

a. At least one plant is completed by the contract date.

b. All plants are completed by the contract date.

c. None of the plants is completed by the contract date.

d. Only the plant at site 1 is completed by the contract date.

e. Exactly one of the three plants is completed by the contract date.

f. Either the plant at site 1 or both of the other two plants are completed by the contract date.

5.9 Consider a Venn diagram picturing two events *A* and *B* that are not disjoint.

a. Shade the event *not (A or B)*. On a separate Venn diagram, shade the event (*not A*) *and* (*not B*). How are these two events related?

b. Shade the event *not (A and B)*. On a separate Venn diagram, shade (*not A*) *or* (*not B*). How are these two events related?

(Note: These two relationships together are called **DeMorgan's laws.**)

5.2   The Definition of Probability and Basic Properties

When any given chance experiment is performed, some events are relatively likely to occur, whereas others are not so likely to occur. For a specified event *E*, we want to assign a number to this event that gives a precise indication of how likely it is that *E* will occur. This number is called *the probability of the event E* and is denoted by *P(E)*. The value of *P(E)* will depend on how frequently *E* occurs when the experiment is performed repeatedly.

EXAMPLE 5.7

One of the simplest chance experiments involves tossing a coin just once. Let's define an event *H* for this chance experiment by

H = the event that the coin lands with its head side facing up

Frequently we hear a coin described as "fair," or we are told that there is a 50% chance of a coin landing head up. Such a description cannot refer to the result of a single toss, since a single toss cannot result in both a head and a tail. Might "fairness" and "50%" refer to ten successive tosses yielding exactly five heads and five tails? Not really, since it is easy to imagine a coin characterized as fair landing head up on only three or four of the ten tosses.

Suppose that we take such a coin and begin to toss it over and over. After each toss, we compute the relative frequency of heads observed so far, that is, the value of the ratio

$$\frac{\text{number of times the event } H \text{ occurs}}{\text{number of tosses}}$$

Suppose the results of the first ten tosses are as follows.

Toss number	1	2	3	4	5	6	7	8	9	10
Outcome	T	H	H	H	T	T	H	H	T	T
Cumulative no. of H's	0	1	2	3	3	3	4	5	5	5
Relative freq. of H	0	.5	.667	.75	.6	.5	.571	.625	.556	.5

Figure 5.6 illustrates how the relative frequency of heads fluctuates during a sample sequence of 50 tosses. Much empirical evidence suggests that *as the number of tosses increases, the relative frequency of heads does not continue to fluctuate wildly but instead stabilizes and approaches some fixed number (limiting value).* This stabilization is illustrated for a sequence of 1000 tosses in Figure 5.7.

FIGURE 5.6
Relative frequency of heads in the first 50 of a long series of tosses

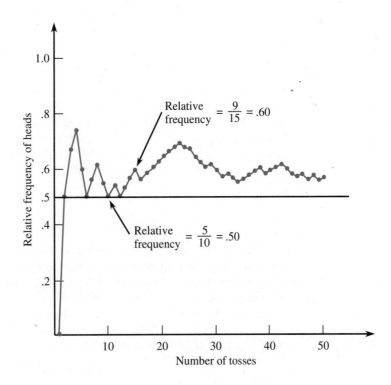

FIGURE 5.7
Stabilization of the
relative frequency of
heads in coin tossing

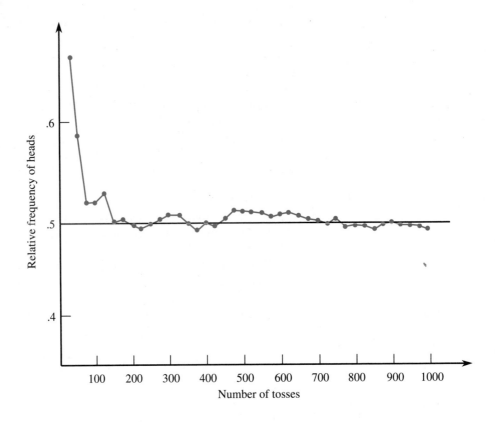

Because each relative frequency is between 0 and 1, the limiting value is also. It is then natural to call the coin "fair" if the limiting value is .5. The 50% chance doesn't refer to exact results in some fixed number of tosses, such as 10 or 100, but to what happens to the relative frequency of heads as we repeat the chance experiment over and over and over again. In terms of probability, we say that the probability that the event H will occur is .5, and we write $P(H) = .5$.

EXAMPLE 5.8

Consider selecting a single card from a well-mixed deck of 52 cards. Card players would surely say that there is a 25% chance of selecting a card whose suit is clubs (as opposed to spades, diamonds, or hearts). In other words, if the event C consists of all cards (outcomes) whose suit is clubs, there is a 25% chance that the event C will occur. To interpret this, think of performing this chance experiment over and over again: Select a first card, replace and shuffle, select a second card, replace and shuffle, and so on. If we examine the ratio

$$\text{relative frequency of } C = \frac{\text{number of times } C \text{ occurs}}{\text{number of replications}}$$

as the number of replications increases, the relative frequency stabilizes at the value .25; that is, $P(C) = .25$. One implication of this is that the limiting relative frequency of the event *not C* is .75; that is,

$$P(not\ C) = .75 = 1 - P(C)$$

Let's complicate matters by considering the experiment in which five cards are dealt from the deck (some people call this a poker hand). One interesting event is

$F =$ the event that all five cards are from the same suit

(called a flush in poker). Consider performing this experiment repeatedly—deal five cards, replace and shuffle, again deal five cards, replace and shuffle, and so on—and tracking the quantity

$$\text{relative frequency of } F = \frac{\text{number of times } F \text{ occurs}}{\text{number of replications}}$$

This relative frequency also stabilizes as the number of replications increases, but the limiting value is not obvious even to poker players. Probability methods can be used to show that it is .00198, so the chance of such a hand occurring is much less than 1%.

These examples motivate the following general definition of probability.

DEFINITION

The **probability of an event E,** denoted by $P(E)$, is the value approached by the relative frequency of occurrence of E in a very long series of replications of a chance experiment.

Because $P(E)$ is the limiting value of E's relative frequency of occurrence, it is a number between 0 and 1. Thus E can be judged relatively unlikely or likely according to where the value of $P(E)$ lies, compared to the extremes of 0 and 1.

For a single toss of a *fair* coin, $P(\text{head up side}) = .5$. When a single card is selected from a well-mixed deck, $P(\text{selected card is a heart}) = .25$. When we informally speak of a 10% chance of occurrence, we mean a probability of .10.

Our definition of probability depends on being able to perform a chance experiment repeatedly under identical conditions. However, probability language and concepts are often used in situations in which replication is not feasible. For example, when a new product is introduced, the marketing manager might state that the probability of its being successful is .3. Or, a public utility executive may testify that the probability of a nuclear plant meltdown during the next decade is .00000001. The most common alternative to the definition of probability based on relative frequency is a subjective, or personal, interpretation. Here probability is a measure of how strongly a person believes that an event will occur. This interpretation permits two people with different opinions to assign different probabilities to the same event (reflecting differing strengths of belief). However, both subjective probabilities and those based on limiting relative frequencies do satisfy the same general rules of probability, so probabilities of complex events can be calculated once probabilities of simple events have been specified. We will not pursue subjective probabilities any further. The relative frequency definition is intuitive, very widely used, and most relevant for the inferential procedures that we present.

Properties of Probability

There would seem to be a practical difficulty at this point: how can we find $P(E)$ without performing a long series of chance experiments? Consider, for example, the experiment in which a fair die is rolled once. Fairness implies a limiting relative frequency (probability) of $\frac{1}{6}$ for each of the six outcomes (simple events). Also, if E is the event consisting of the even outcomes 2, 4, 6, then

$$\begin{pmatrix} \text{relative freq.} \\ \text{of } E \end{pmatrix} = \begin{pmatrix} \text{relative freq.} \\ \text{of 2} \end{pmatrix} + \begin{pmatrix} \text{relative freq.} \\ \text{of 4} \end{pmatrix} + \begin{pmatrix} \text{relative freq.} \\ \text{of 6} \end{pmatrix}$$

This implies that

$$P(E) = \frac{1}{6} + \frac{1}{6} + \frac{1}{6} = \frac{3}{6} = .5$$

More generally, prior experience with or careful thought about an experiment will often suggest appropriate probabilities for the simple events. Then some general rules can be used to calculate the probabilities of more complex events.

PROPERTIES OF PROBABILITY

1. For any event E, $0 \le P(E) \le 1$.
2. The sum of probabilities of all simple events must be 1.
3. For any event E, the probability $P(E)$ is the sum of the probabilities of all simple events corresponding to outcomes contained in E.
4. For any event E,

$$P(E) + P(not\ E) = 1$$

so $P(not\ E) = 1 - P(E)$ and $P(E) = 1 - P(not\ E)$.

Figure 5.8 shows a situation in which Property 3 applies. There are six outcomes and, therefore, six simple events, three of which are contained in E.

FIGURE 5.8
$P(E) = P(O_2) + P(O_3) + P(O_5)$

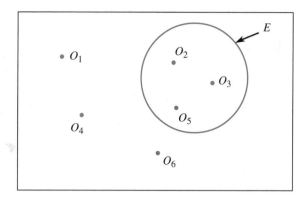

EXAMPLE 5.9

Customers at a certain department store pay for purchases either with cash or with one of four types of credit card. Store records indicate that 30% of all purchases involve cash, 25% are made with the store's own credit card, 18% with Mastercard, 15% with Visa, and the remaining 12% of purchases with an American Express card. The accompanying table displays the probabilities of the simple events for the experiment in which the mode of payment for the next transaction is observed.

Mode of payment	Cash	Store card	MC	V	AE
Simple event	O_1	O_2	O_3	O_4	O_5
Probability	.30	.25	.18	.15	.12

Let E be the event that the next purchase is made with a nationally distributed credit card. This event consists of outcomes MC, V, and AE, so

$$P(E) = P(O_3) + P(O_4) + P(O_5)$$
$$= .18 + .15 + .12$$
$$= .45$$

That is, in the long run, 45% of all purchases are made using one of the three national cards. Additionally,

$$P(not\ E) = 1 - P(E)$$
$$= 1 - .45$$
$$= .55$$

which could also have been obtained by noting that *not E* consists of outcomes corresponding to simple events O_1 and O_2.

The property $P(E) = 1 - P(not\ E)$ is surprisingly useful. This is because there are many situations in which calculation of $P(not\ E)$ is much easier than direct determination of $P(E)$.

Equally Likely Outcomes

Experiments involving tossing fair coins, rolling fair dice, or selecting cards from a well-mixed deck have equally likely outcomes. For example, if a fair die is rolled once, each outcome (simple event) has probability $\frac{1}{6}$. With E denoting the event that the outcome is an even number, we saw earlier than $P(E) = \frac{3}{6}$. This is just the ratio of the number of outcomes in E to the total number of possible outcomes. The following box presents the generalization of this result.

CALCULATING PROBABILITIES WHEN OUTCOMES ARE EQUALLY LIKELY

Consider an experiment that can result in any one of N possible outcomes. Denote the corresponding simple events by $O_1, O_2, \ldots, O_N$. If these simple events are equally likely to occur, then

1. $P(O_1) = 1/N, \quad P(O_2) = 1/N, \quad \ldots, \quad P(O_N) = 1/N$
2. For *any* event E

$$P(E) = \frac{\text{number of outcomes in } E}{N}$$

EXAMPLE 5.10

A video store has received four copies of a foreign movie. Two copies, 1 and 2, are subtitled and the other two, 3 and 4, are dubbed. A clerk randomly selects two copies to send to a branch store. Possible outcomes are

$$\{(1, 2), (1, 3), (1, 4), (2, 3), (2, 4), (3, 4)\}$$

By virtue of the selection method, the six outcomes are equally likely, so

$$P(O_1) = P(O_2) = \cdots = P(O_6) = \frac{1}{6}$$

Let E be the event that both selected videos are of the same type: $E = \{(1, 2), (3, 4)\}$. Since E contains two outcomes,

$$P(E) = \frac{2}{6} \doteq .333$$

If F denotes the event that at least one of the selected copies is dubbed, F consists of all outcomes except $(1, 2)$, so

$$P(F) = \text{\%} = .833$$

When the number of outcomes is large, it can be quite tedious to determine N and the number of outcomes in a specified event E by listing outcomes. In such cases these numbers can often be obtained by using counting methods developed by mathematicians. The last section of this chapter introduces several techniques of this type.

An Addition Rule

We have seen how the probability of an event can be calculated by adding together simple event probabilities. Simple events are by definition disjoint. This addition process is also legitimate when calculating certain probabilities involving events that are disjoint but not necessarily simple.

THE ADDITION RULE FOR DISJOINT EVENTS

Let E and F be two disjoint events. Then

$$P(E \text{ or } F) = P(E) + P(F)$$

More generally, if events $E_1, E_2, \ldots, E_k$ are disjoint, then

$$P(E_1 \text{ or } E_2 \text{ or} \ldots \text{ or } E_k) = P(E_1) + P(E_2) + \cdots + P(E_k)$$

In words, the probability that any of these k events occurs is the sum of the probabilities of the individual events.

EXAMPLE 5.11

A large auto center has dealers that sell cars made by a number of different manufacturers. Three of these are Japanese: Honda, Nissan, and Toyota. Consider the manufacturer and model of the next car purchased, and define events E_1, E_2, and E_3 by

$$E_1 = \text{Honda}, \qquad E_2 = \text{Nissan}, \qquad E_3 = \text{Toyota}$$

Notice that E_1 is not a simple event, since there are Honda Civics, Honda Accords, and Honda Preludes.

Supposing that $P(E_1) = .25$, $P(E_2) = .18$, and $P(E_3) = .14$, the addition rule gives

$$P(\text{Honda } or \text{ Nissan } or \text{ Toyota}) = P(E_1) + P(E_2) + P(E_3)$$
$$= .25 + .18 + .14$$
$$= .57$$

The probability that the next car purchased is *not* one of these three types is

$$P(not\ (E_1\ or\ E_2\ or\ E_3)) = 1 - .57 = .43$$

In Section 5.4, we show how $P(E\ or\ F)$ can be calculated when the two events are not disjoint.

EXERCISES 5.10–5.22   SECTION 5.2

5.10   Insurance status—covered (C) or not covered (N)—is determined for each individual arriving for treatment at a hospital's emergency room. Consider the experiment in which this determination is made for two randomly selected patients. The simple events are $O_1 = \{CC\}$, $O_2 = \{CN\}$, $O_3 = \{NC\}$, and $O_4 = \{NN\}$. Suppose that probabilities are $P(O_1) = .81$, $P(O_2) = .09$, $P(O_3) = .09$, and $P(O_4) = .01$.
   a. What outcomes are contained in the event A, that at most one patient is covered, and what is $P(A)$?
   b. What outcomes are contained in the event B, that the two patients have the same status with respect to coverage, and what is $P(B)$?

5.11   Suppose the accompanying information on births in the United States over a given period of time is available to you.

Type of birth	Number of births
Single birth	41,500,000
Twins	500,000
Triplets	5,000
Quadruplets	100

Use this information to approximate the probability that a randomly selected pregnant woman who reaches full term:
   a. Delivers twins
   b. Delivers quadruplets
   c. Gives birth to more than a single child

5.12   A mutual fund company offers its customers several different funds: a money-market fund, three different bond funds (short, intermediate, and long-term), two stock funds (moderate and high-risk), and a balanced fund. Among customers who own shares in just one fund, the percentages of customers in the different funds are as follows.

Money-market	20%	High-risk stock	18%
Short bond	15%	Moderate-risk stock	25%
Intermediate bond	10%	Balanced	7%
Long bond	5%		

A customer who owns shares in just one fund is randomly selected.

a. What is the probability that the selected individual owns shares in the balanced fund?

b. What is the probability that the individual owns shares in a bond fund?

c. What is the probability that the selected individual does not own shares in a stock fund?

5.13 A radio station that plays classical music has a "by request" program each Saturday evening. The percentages of requests for composers on a particular night are as follows.

Bach	5%	Mozart	21%
Beethoven	26%	Schubert	12%
Brahms	9%	Schumann	7%
Dvorak	2%	Tchaikovsky	14%
Mendelssohn	3%	Wagner	1%

Suppose that one of these requests is randomly selected.

a. What is the probability that the request is for one of the three B's?

b. What is the probability that the request is not for one of the two S's?

c. Neither Bach nor Wagner wrote any symphonies. What is the probability that the request is for a composer who wrote at least one symphony?

d. What is the probability that the request is for a piece by one of the main characters in the movie *Amadeus*? (If you don't know who this is, see the movie!)

5.14 The accompanying table gives the type of program and the percentage of households watching each program at 6 P.M. among subscribers to a certain television cable service.

Channel	Program	% Watching	Channel	Program	% Watching
2	National news	14	9	Comedy	12
3	Local news	7	10	National news	4
4	National news	10	11	Drama	10
5	Local news	8	12	Game show	8
7	Game show	15	13	Movie	12

(The percentages are for those who are watching at this time, not for all subscribers.) A household is randomly selected from among those watching at this time.

a. What is the probability that the household is watching the local news? Is watching any news?

b. What is the probability that the household is watching either a game show or a comedy?

c. What is the probability that the household is not watching a game show?

P(A)+P(B) -P(A∩B) [handwritten in left margin]

5.15   A single card is randomly selected from a well-mixed deck. (A deck has 52 cards, with four suits—spades, hearts, diamonds, and clubs—and 13 denominations—aces, twos, . . . , queens, and kings.)

    a. How many simple events are there?

    b. What is the probability of each simple event?

    c. What is the probability that the selected card is a heart? A face card (jack, queen, or king)?

    d. What is the probability that the selected card is both a heart and a face card?

    e. Let A = the event that the selected card is a face card and B = the event that the selected card is a heart. What is $P(A \ or \ B)$?

5.16   After mixing a deck of 52 cards very well, 5 cards are dealt out.

    a. It can be shown that (disregarding the order in which the cards are dealt) there are 2,598,960 possible hands, of which only 1287 are hands consisting entirely of spades. What is the probability that a hand will consist entirely of spades? What is the probability that a hand will consist entirely of a single suit?

    b. It can be shown that exactly 63,206 hands contain only spades and clubs, with both suits represented. What is the probability that a hand consists entirely of spades and clubs with both suits represented?

    c. Using the result of part (b), what is the probability that a hand contains cards from exactly two suits?

5.17   After all students have left the classroom, a statistics professor notices that four copies of the text were left under desks. At the beginning of the next lecture, the professor distributes the four books in a completely random fashion to each of the four students (1, 2, 3, and 4) who claim to have left books. One possible outcome is that 1 receives 2's book, 2 receives 4's book, 3 receives his or her own book, and 4 receives 1's book. This outcome can be abbreviated (2, 4, 3, 1). *book* [handwritten]   *1 2 3 4 student* [handwritten]

    a. List the other 23 possible outcomes.

    b. Which outcomes are contained in the event that exactly two of the books are returned to their correct owners? Assuming equally likely outcomes, what is the probability of this event?

    c. What is the probability that exactly one of the four students receives his or her own book?

    d. What is the probability that exactly three receive their own books?

    e. What is the probability that at least two of the four students receive their own books?

5.18   An individual is presented with three different glasses of cola, labeled *C, D,* and *P.* He is asked to taste all three and then list them in order of preference. Suppose that the same cola has actually been put into all three glasses.

    a. What are the simple events in this ranking experiment, and what probability would you assign to each one?

    b. What is the probability that *C* is ranked first?

    c. What is the probability that *C* is ranked first and *D* is ranked last?

5.19   The student council for a School of Science and Math has one representative from each of the five academic departments: biology (B), chemistry (C), mathematics (M), physics (P), and statistics (S). Two of these students are to be randomly selected for inclusion on a university-wide student committee (by placing five slips of paper in a box, mixing, and drawing out two of them).

    a. What are the ten possible outcomes (simple events)?

    b. From the description of the selection process, all outcomes are equally likely; what is the probability of each simple event?

    c. What is the probability that one of the committee members is the statistics department representative?

    d. What is the probability that both committee members come from "laboratory science" departments?

5.20 A video store sells two different brands of VCR, each of which comes with either two heads or four heads. The accompanying table gives the percentages of recent purchasers buying each type of VCR.

Brand	Number of heads	
	2	4
M	25%	16%
Q	32%	27%

Suppose that a recent purchaser is randomly selected and both the brand and the number of heads are determined.

    a. What are the four simple events?

    b. What is the probability that the selected purchaser bought brand Q, with two heads?

    c. What is the probability that the selected purchaser bought brand M?

5.21 A library has five copies of a certain text, of which copies 1 and 2 are first printings, and copies 3, 4, and 5 are second printings. Two copies are to be randomly selected to be placed on 2-hour reserve.

    a. What is the probability that both selected copies are first printings?

    b. What is the probability that both copies selected are second printings?

    c. What is the probability that at least one copy selected is a first printing?

    d. What is the probability that the selected copies are different printings?

5.22 Suppose that a six-sided die is "loaded" so that any particular even-numbered face is twice as likely to be observed as any particular odd-numbered face.

    a. What are the probabilities of the six simple events? (Hint: Denote these events by $O_1, \ldots, O_6$. Then $P(O_1) = p$, $P(O_2) = 2p$, $P(O_3) = p, \ldots, P(O_6) = 2p$. Now use a condition on the sum of these probabilities to determine p.)

    b. What is the probability that the number showing is an odd number? Is at most 3?

    c. Now suppose the die is loaded so that the probability of any particular simple event is proportional to the number showing on the corresponding upturned face; that is, $P(O_1) = c$, $P(O_2) = 2c, \ldots, P(O_6) = 6c$. What are the probabilities of the six simple events? Calculate the probabilities of part (b) for this die.

5.3   Conditional Probability and Independence

Sometimes the knowledge that one event has occurred changes the likelihood that another event will occur. One example involves a population in which .1% of all individuals have a certain disease. The presence of the disease cannot be discerned from outward appearances, but there is a diagnostic test available. Unfortunately, the test is not infallible: 80% of those with positive test results actually have the disease; the other 20% showing positive test results are false positives. To cast this in probability terms, consider the experiment in which an individual is randomly selected from the population. Define events by

E = the event that the individual has the disease

F = the event that the individual's diagnostic test is positive

Let $P(E|F)$ denote the probability of the event E *given that* the event F has occurred. The preceding information then implies that

$$P(E) = .001, \qquad P(E|F) = .8$$

That is, prior to diagnostic test information, the occurrence of E is unlikely, whereas once it is known that the test result is positive, the likelihood of the disease increases dramatically. (If this were not so, the diagnostic test would not be very useful.)

The next example suggests how a *conditional* probability $P(E|F)$ can be calculated from other previously specified probabilities.

EXAMPLE 5.12

A GFI (ground fault interrupt) switch will turn off power to a system in the event of an electrical malfunction. A spa manufacturer currently has 25 spas in stock, each equipped with a single GFI switch. The switches are supplied by two different sources, and some of them are defective, as summarized in the accompanying table.

	Nondefective	Defective	
Source 1	10	5	15
Source 2	8	2	10
	18	7	25

A spa is randomly selected for testing. Let

E = the event that the GFI switch in the chosen spa is from source 1

F = the event that the GFI switch in the chosen spa is defective

The tabulated information implies that

$$P(E) = \frac{15}{25} = .60,$$

$$P(F) = \frac{7}{25} = .28$$

$$P(E \text{ and } F) = \frac{5}{25} = .20$$

event F occured

Now suppose that testing reveals a defective switch. (Thus the chosen spa is one of the seven in the *Defective* column.) How likely is it that the switch came from the first source? Since five of the seven defectives are from source 1, intuition suggests that

$$P(E|F) = P(\text{source 1}|\text{defective}) = \frac{5}{7} \approx .714$$

Notice that this is larger than the "original" probability $P(E)$. This is because source 1 has a much higher defective rate than does source 2.

An alternative expression for the conditional probability is

$$P(E|F) = \frac{5}{7} = \frac{5/25}{7/25} = \frac{P(E \text{ and } F)}{P(F)}$$

That is, $P(E|F)$ is a ratio of two previously specified probabilities: the probability that both events occur divided by the probability of the "conditioning event" F. Additional insight comes from the Venn diagram of Figure 5.9. Once it is known that the outcome lies in F, the likelihood of E (also) occurring is the "size" of ($E \text{ and } F$) relative to that of F.

FIGURE 5.9
Venn diagram for
Example 5.12 (each
dot represents one switch)

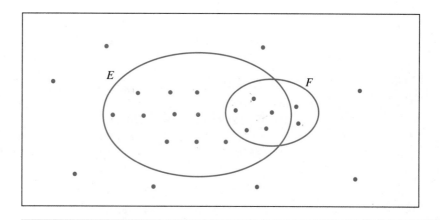

The results of the previous example help motivate a general definition of conditional probability.

> **DEFINITION**
>
> Let E and F be two events with $P(F) > 0$. The **conditional probability of the event E given that the event F has occurred,** denoted by $P(E|F)$, is
>
> $$P(E|F) = \frac{P(E \text{ and } F)}{P(F)}$$

EXAMPLE 5.13

A large lending institution gives both adjustable-rate mortgages and fixed-rate mortgages on residential property. It breaks residential property into three categories: single-family houses, condominiums, and multifamily dwellings. The accompanying table, sometimes called a *joint probability table,* displays probabilities appropriate to this situation.

	Single-family	Condo	Multi-family	
Adjustable	.40	.21	.09	.70
Fixed	.10	.09	.11	.30
	.50	.30	.20	

Thus 70% of all mortgages are adjustable rate, 50% of all mortgages are for single-family properties, 40% of all mortgages are adjustable-rate for single-family properties (both adjustable-rate *and* single-family), and so on. Define events E and F by

E = the event that a mortgage is adjustable-rate

F = the event that a mortgage is for a single-family property

Then

$$P(E|F) = \frac{P(E \text{ and } F)}{P(F)} = \frac{.40}{.50} = .80$$

That is, if we focus only on loans made for single-family properties, 80% of them are adjustable-rate loans. Notice that $P(E|F)$ is larger than the original (unconditional) probability $P(E) = .70$. Also,

$$P(F|E) = \frac{P(E \text{ and } F)}{P(E)} = \frac{.40}{.70} = .571 > .5 = P(F)$$

Defining another event C by

C = the event that a mortgage is for a condominium

we have

$$P(E|C) = \frac{P(E \text{ and } C)}{P(C)} = \frac{.21}{.30} = .70$$

Notice that $P(E|C) = P(E)$, so if we are told that a mortgage is for a condominium, the likelihood that it is adjustable remains unchanged.

Independence

When two events E and F are such that $P(E|F) = P(E)$, the likelihood that event E has occurred is the same after learning that F has occurred as it was prior to information about F's occurrence. That is, the chance of E having occurred is unaffected by the knowledge that F has occurred. We then say that E and F are independent of one another.

DEFINITION

Two events E and F are said to be **independent** if

$P(E|F) = P(E)$

If E and F are not independent, they are said to be **dependent** events.

The defining relationship for independence could just as well have been stated $P(F|E) = P(F)$, since either equality implies the other one. In words, two events are independent if the chance that one of them has occurred is unchanged once it is known that the other has occurred. Moreover, independence of events E and F implies the following additional three relationships:

$$P(not\ E|F) = P(not\ E)$$
$$P(E|not\ F) = P(E)$$
$$P(not\ E|not\ F) = P(not\ E)$$

A very useful relationship equivalent to the independence of E and F is the multiplication rule given in the following box.

THE MULTIPLICATION RULE FOR TWO INDEPENDENT EVENTS

The events E and F are independent if and only if

$P(E\ and\ F) = P(E) \cdot P(F)$

That is, independence implies the relation $P(E\ and\ F) = P(E) \cdot P(F)$, and this relation implies independence.

Thus if E occurs 50% of the time when an experiment is repeatedly performed, F occurs 20% of the time, and E and F are independent, then E and F will occur together 10% of the time in the long run (since $(.5)(.2) = .1$).

EXAMPLE 5.14

Let E be the event that your statistics professor begins class on time and let F be the event that your philosophy professor does likewise. Suppose that E and F are independent (intuitively, a very reasonable assumption, since behavior of one professor should be unaffected by behavior of the other), with $P(E) = .9$ and $P(F) = .6$. Then

$$P(E \text{ and } F) = P(\text{both professors begin class on time})$$

$$= P(E) \cdot P(F) = (.9)(.6) = .54$$

Also

$$P(\text{not } E \text{ and not } F) = P(\text{neither professor begins on time})$$

$$= P(\text{not } E) \cdot P(\text{not } F) = (.1)(.4) = .04$$

The probability that exactly one of the two begins on time is

$$1 - (.54 + .04) = .42$$

The concept of independence extends to more than two events. Consider three events E_1, E_2, and E_3. Then independence means not only that

$$P(E_1|E_2) = P(E_1)$$

$$P(E_3|E_2) = P(E_3)$$

and so on, but also that

$$P(E_1|E_2 \text{ and } E_3) = P(E_1)$$

$$P(E_1 \text{ and } E_3|E_2) = P(E_1 \text{ and } E_3)$$

and so on. Furthermore, independence again implies the validity of a multiplication rule.

> Events $E_1, E_2, \ldots, E_k$ are **independent** if knowledge that some of the events have occurred does not change the probabilities that any particular one or more of the other events has occurred. Independence implies that
>
> $$P(E_1 \text{ and } E_2 \text{ and } \ldots \text{ and } E_k) = P(E_1) \cdot P(E_2) \cdots P(E_k).$$
>
> Thus when events are independent, the probability that all occur together is the product of the individual probabilities. Furthermore, this relationship remains valid if one or more E_i's is replaced by the event *not E_i*.

EXAMPLE 5.15

A microcomputer system consists of a monitor, a disk drive, and the computer itself. Let

E_1 = the event that the newly purchased monitor operates properly

E_2 = the event that the newly purchased disk drive operates properly

E_3 = the event that the newly purchased computer operates properly

Suppose that these three events are independent, with

$$P(E_1) = .99, \qquad P(E_2) = .90, \qquad P(E_3) = .95$$

The probability that all three components operate properly (that is, that the system functions) is

$$\begin{aligned}
P(E_1 \text{ and } E_2 \text{ and } E_3) &= P(E_1) \cdot P(E_2) \cdot P(E_3) \\
&= (.99)(.90)(.95) \\
&\approx .85
\end{aligned}$$

In the long run, roughly 85% of such systems will operate properly. The probability that only the monitor operates properly is

$$\begin{aligned}
P(E_1 \text{ and not } E_2 \text{ and not } E_3) &= P(E_1) \cdot P(\text{not } E_2) \cdot P(\text{not } E_3) \\
&= (.99)(.10)(.05) \\
&= .00495
\end{aligned}$$

Sampling with and without Replacement

Many applications of probability rules involve sampling from a single population. Here is a simple example that introduces an important distinction.

EXAMPLE 5.16

Consider selecting three cards from a deck. This selection can be made either **without replacement** (dealing three cards off the top) or **with replacement** (replacing each card and shuffling before selecting the next card). You can probably already guess that one of these selection methods gives independence of successive selections, whereas the other does not. To see this more clearly, define these events:

E_1 = the event that the first card is a spade

E_2 = the event that the second card is a spade

E_3 = the event that the third card is a spade

For sampling with replacement, the probability of E_3 is .25, regardless of whether either E_1 or E_2 occurs, since replacing selected cards gives the same deck for the third selection as for the first two. Whether either of the first two cards is a spade has no bearing on the third card selected, so the three events E_1, E_2, and E_3 are independent.

When sampling is without replacement, the chance of a spade on the third draw very definitely depends on the results of the first two draws. If both E_1 and E_2

occur, only 11 of the 50 remaining cards are spades. Since any one of these 50 has the same chance of being selected, the probability of E_3 in this case is

$$P(E_3|E_1 \text{ and } E_2) = \frac{11}{50} = .22$$

Alternatively, if neither of the first two cards is a spade, then all 13 spades remain in the deck for the third draw, so

$$P(E_3|\text{not } E_1 \text{ and not } E_2) = \frac{13}{50} = .26$$

Information about the occurrence of E_1 and E_2 affects the chance that E_3 has occurred, so for sampling without replacement, the events are not independent.

In opinion polls and other types of surveys, sampling is virtually always done without replacement. For this method of sampling, the results of successive selections are not independent of one another. This is unfortunate, because many results from probability and statistics are much easier to state and use when independence can be assumed. The next example suggests that under certain circumstances, the selections in sampling without replacement are approximately independent.

EXAMPLE 5.17

A lot of 10,000 industrial components consists of 2500 manufactured by one firm and 7500 manufactured by a second firm, all mixed together. Three components are to be randomly selected without replacement. Let

E_1 = the event that the first component selected came from firm 1

E_2 = the event that the second component selected came from firm 1

E_3 = the event that the third component selected came from firm 1

Reasoning as in the card-selection example,

$$P(E_3|E_1 \text{ and } E_2) = \frac{2498}{9998} = .24985$$

$$P(E_3|\text{not } E_1 \text{ and not } E_2) = \frac{2500}{9998} = .25005$$

Although these two probabilities differ slightly, to three decimal places they are both .250. We conclude that the occurrence or nonoccurrence of E_1 or E_2 has virtually no effect on the chance that E_3 will occur. For practical purposes, the three events can be considered independent.

The essential difference between the situations of Example 5.16 and Example 5.17 is the size of the sample relative to the size of the population. In the former example, a relatively large proportion of the population was sampled (3 out of 52), whereas in the latter example, the proportion of the population sampled was quite small (only 3 out of 10,000).

> If the individuals or objects in a sample are selected without replacement from a population and the sample size is small relative to the population size, the successive selections are approximately independent. As a reasonable rule of thumb, independence can be assumed if at most 5% of the population is sampled.

This result justifies the assumption of (approximate) independence in many statistical problems.

EXERCISES 5.23–5.36 SECTION 5.3

5.23 Two different airlines have a flight from Los Angeles to New York that departs each weekday morning at a certain time. Let E denote the event that the first airline's flight is fully booked on a particular day, and let F denote the event that the second airline's flight is fully booked on that same day. Suppose that $P(E) = .7$, $P(F) = .6$, and $P(E \text{ and } F) = .54$.
  a. Calculate $P(E|F)$, the probability that the first airline's flight is fully booked given that the second airline's flight is fully booked.
  b. Calculate $P(F|E)$.
  c. Are E and F independent events? Explain.

5.24 A card is selected from a well-mixed deck. Let E be the event that the card is a heart, and let F be the event that the card is a face card.
  a. Determine $P(E)$ and $P(F)$.
  b. Determine $P(E|F)$ and $P(F|E)$.
  c. Are E and F independent events? Explain intuitively why this is so.

5.25 The probability that a randomly selected customer at a certain gas station checks the oil level is .10. The probability that a randomly selected customer checks tire pressure is .04. The probability that a randomly selected customer checks both oil level and tire pressure is .008.
  a. Given that a customer checks the oil level, what is the probability that the customer checks tire pressure?
  b. If a randomly selected customer checks tire pressure, what is the probability that the oil level is checked also?
  c. Are the events "checks oil level" and "checks tire pressure" independent? Explain.

5.26 In Example 5.13 we showed that $P(E|C) = P(E)$.
  a. Verify that $P(C|E) = P(C)$.
  b. Verify that $P(not\ C | not\ E) = P(not\ C)$.

5.27   A certain model of car comes in a two-door version, a four-door version, and a hatchback version. Each version can be equipped with either an automatic transmission or a manual transmission. The accompanying table gives the relevant proportions.

	Version		
Transmission type	TD	FD	HB
A	.32	.27	.18
M	.08	.04	.11

A customer who has purchased one of these cars is randomly selected.
a. What is the probability that this customer purchased a car with an automatic transmission? A four-door car?
b. Given that the customer purchased a four-door car, what is the probability that it has an automatic transmission?
c. Given that the customer did not purchase a hatchback, what is the probability that the car has a manual transmission? How does this conditional probability compare to the (unconditional) probability that the car has a manual transmission?

5.28   An insurance company offers four different deductible levels—none, low, medium, and high—for its homeowner's policyholders, and three different levels—low, medium, and high—for its automobile policyholders. The accompanying table gives proportions for the various categories of policyholders who have both types of insurance. For example, the proportion of individuals with both low homeowner's deductible and low auto deductible is .06 (6% of all such individuals).

	Homeowner's			
Auto	N	L	M	H
L	.04	.06	.05	.03
M	.07	.10	.20	.10
H	.02	.03	.15	.15

Suppose an insured individual is randomly selected.
a. What is P(low auto deductible | low homeowner's deductible)?
b. Given that the selected individual does not have a high auto deductible, what is the probability that he or she does not have a high homeowner's deductible?

5.29   A certain university has ten cars available for use by faculty and staff upon request. Six of these are Chevrolets and four are Plymouths. On a particular day, only two requests for cars have been made. Suppose that the two cars to be assigned are chosen in a completely random fashion from among the ten.
a. Let E denote the event that the first car assigned is a Chevrolet. What is $P(E)$?

b. Let F denote the probability that the second car assigned is a Chevrolet. What is $P(F|E)$?

c. Use the results of (a) and (b) to calculate $P(E\text{ and }F)$.

5.30   A construction firm has bid on two different contracts. Let E_1 be the event that the bid on the first contract is successful, and define E_2 analogously for the second contract. Suppose that $P(E_1) = .4$, $P(E_2) = .3$, and that E_1 and E_2 are independent events.

a. Calculate the probability that both bids are successful (the probability of the event E_1 and E_2).

b. Calculate the probability that neither bid is successful (the probability of the event (*not* E_1) *and* (*not* E_2)).

c. What is the probability that the firm is successful in at least one of the two bids?

5.31   Consider the system of four components connected as illustrated in the accompanying diagram. Let E_1 denote the event that component 1 functions properly, and define events E_2, E_3, and E_4 analogously for the other three components. Suppose that $P(E_1) = P(E_2) = P(E_3) = P(E_4) = .9$ and that E_1, E_2, E_3, and E_4 are independent events.

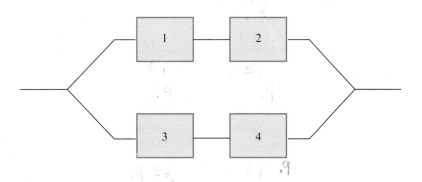

a. Because the two components in the 1–2 subsystem are connected in series, this subsystem will function if and only if the two components both function. What is the probability that this subsystem functions? What is the probability that the 3–4 subsystem functions?

b. What is the probability that both subsystems function?

c. Because the subsystems are connected in parallel, the system will function if at least one of the two subsystems (1–2 or 3–4) functions. What is the probability that the system functions?

5.32   This case study is reported in the article "Parking Tickets and Missing Women," which appears in the book *Statistics: A Guide to the Unknown* (see the Chapter 1 references). In a Swedish trial on a charge of overtime parking, a police officer testified that he had noted the position of the two air valves on the tires of a parked car: to the closest hour, one was at the one o'clock position and the other was at the six o'clock position. After the allowable time for parking in that zone had passed, the policeman returned, noted that the valves were in the same position, and ticketed the car. The owner of the car claimed that he had left the parking place in time and had returned later. The valves just happened by chance to be in the same positions. An "expert" witness computed the probability of this occurring as $(\frac{1}{12})(\frac{1}{12}) = \frac{1}{144}$.

a. What reasoning did the expert use to arrive at the probability of $\frac{1}{144}$?

b. Can you spot the error in the reasoning that leads to the stated probability of $\frac{1}{144}$? What effect does this error have on the probability of occurrence? Do you think that $\frac{1}{144}$ is larger or smaller than the correct probability of occurrence?

5.33   A particular airline has 10 A.M. flights from Chicago to New York, Atlanta, and Los Angeles. Let A denote the event that the New York flight is full, and define events B and C analogously for the Atlanta and Los Angeles flights. Suppose that $P(A) = .6$, $P(B) = .5$, $P(C) = .4$, and the three events are independent.

a. What is the probability that all three flights are full? That at least one flight is not full?

b. What is the probability that only the New York flight is full? That exactly one of the three flights is full?

5.34   A shipment of 5000 printed circuit boards contains 40 that are defective. Two boards are chosen at random, without replacement. Consider the two events

E_1 = the event that the first board selected is defective

E_2 = the event that the second board selected is defective

a. Are E_1 and E_2 dependent events? Explain in words.

b. Let *not* E_1 be the event that the first board selected is not defective (the event that E_1 does not occur). What is $P(not\ E_1)$?

c. How do the two probabilities $P(E_2|E_1)$ and $P(E_2|not\ E_1)$ compare?

d. Based on your answer to part (c), would it be reasonable to view E_1 and E_2 as approximately independent? Explain your answer.

5.35   A store sells two different brands of dishwasher soap, B_1 and B_2. Each brand comes in three different sizes: small (S), medium (M), and large (L). The proportions of the two brands and of the three sizes purchased are displayed as marginal totals in the accompanying table.

		Size			
		S	M	L	
Brand	B_1				.40
	B_2				.60
		.30	.50	.20	

Suppose that any event involving brand is independent of any event involving size. What is the probability of the event that a randomly selected purchaser buys the small size of brand B_1 (the event B_1 *and* S)? What are the probabilities of the other brand-size combinations?

5.36   Let E_1 denote the event that the next fire to occur in a certain city is a single-alarm blaze. Similarly, let E_2 be the event that the next fire is in the two-alarm category.

Suppose that $P(E_1) = .4$ and $P(E_2) = .3$. What is $P(E_1|E_2)$? What is $P(E_2|E_1)$? Are disjoint events independent? Explain.

5.4 General Addition and Multiplication Rules (Optional)

In Section 5.2 we saw how $P(E\ or\ F)$ or, more generally, $P(E_1\ or\ \ldots\ or\ E_k)$ could be calculated by adding individual event probabilities together when the events were disjoint. The previous section discussed computation of $P(E\ and\ F)$ or, more generally, $P(E_1\ and\ \ldots\ and\ E_k)$ by multiplying individual event probabilities when the events were independent. Here we consider addition rules for events that are not disjoint and multiplication rules for events that are not independent.

The computation of $P(E\ or\ F)$ when the two events are not disjoint requires more care than in the case of disjoint events. Consider Figure 5.10, in which E and F overlap. The area of the shaded region $(E\ or\ F)$ is not the sum of E's area and F's area. This is because when the two individual areas are added, the area of the intersection $(E\ and\ F)$ is counted twice. Similarly, $P(E) + P(F)$ includes $P(E\ and\ F)$ twice, so this intersection probability must then be subtracted to obtain $P(E\ or\ F)$.

FIGURE 5.10
Shaded region equals $(E\ or\ F)$, and $P(E\ or\ F) \neq P(E) + P(F)$

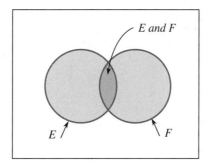

General Addition Rule

GENERAL ADDITION RULE FOR TWO EVENTS
For any two events E and F,

$$P(E\ or\ F) = P(E) + P(F) - P(E\ and\ F)$$

In words, to calculate the probability that at least one of the two events occurs, we add the two individual probabilities together and then subtract the probability that both events occur. When E and F are disjoint, the event $E\ and\ F$ contains no outcomes. Then $P(E \text{ and } F) = 0$ and this addition rule reduces to the earlier one for disjoint events. This general rule can be used to determine any one of the four probabilities $P(E)$, $P(F)$, $P(E \text{ or } F)$, or $P(E \text{ and } F)$, provided that the other three are known.

EXAMPLE 5.18

Suppose that 60% of all customers of a large insurance agency have automobile policies with the agency, 40% have homeowner's policies, and 25% have both types of policies. If a customer is randomly selected, what is the probability that he or she has at least one of these two types of policies with the agency? Let

E = the event that the selected customer has auto insurance

F = the event that the selected customer has homeowner's insurance

The given information implies that

$$P(E) = .60, \qquad P(F) = .40,$$

and

$$P(E \text{ and } F) = .25,$$

from which we obtain

$$P(\text{customer has at least one of the two types}) = P(E \text{ or } F)$$
$$= P(E) + P(F) - P(E \text{ and } F)$$
$$= .60 + .40 - .25$$
$$= .75$$

The event that the customer has neither type of policy is *not* $(E \text{ or } F)$, so

$$P(\text{customer has neither type}) = 1 - P(E \text{ or } F) = .25$$

Now let us determine the probability that the selected customer has exactly one type of policy. The Venn diagram of Figure 5.11 shows that the event "at least one," that is, $E \text{ or } F$, consists of two disjoint parts: "exactly one" and "both." Thus

$$P(\text{at least one}) = P(E \text{ or } F)$$
$$= P(\text{exactly one}) + P(\text{both})$$
$$= P(\text{exactly one}) + P(E \text{ and } F)$$

so

$$P(\text{exactly one}) = P(E \text{ or } F) - P(E \text{ and } F)$$
$$= .75 - .25$$
$$= .50$$

FIGURE 5.11
Venn diagram for Example 5.18

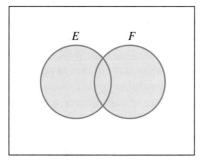

(a) At least one (*E or F*)

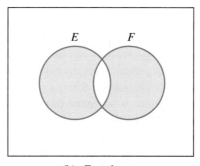

(b) Exactly one

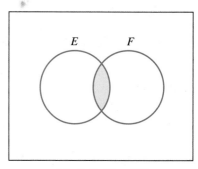

(c) Both (*E and F*)

The addition rule for more than two nondisjoint events is rather complicated. For example, in the case of three events,

$$P(E \text{ or } F \text{ or } G) = P(E) + P(F) + P(G) - P(E \text{ and } F)$$
$$- P(E \text{ and } G) - P(F \text{ and } G) + P(E \text{ and } F \text{ and } G)$$

A more advanced treatment of probability can be consulted for examples and extensions of these methods.

General Multiplication Rule

The definition of conditional probability states that

$$P(E|F) = \frac{P(E \text{ and } F)}{P(F)}$$

Multiplying both sides by $P(F)$ gives a useful expression for the probability that both events will occur.

GENERAL MULTIPLICATION RULE FOR TWO EVENTS

$$P(E \text{ and } F) = P(E|F) \cdot P(F)$$

The right-hand side of this equation is the product of two probabilities, the first conditional and the second unconditional. In the case of independence, $P(E|F) = P(E)$ and this multiplication rule reduces to the earlier one: $P(E \text{ and } F) = P(E) \cdot P(F)$.

EXAMPLE 5.19

Suppose that 20% of all teenage drivers in a certain county received a citation for a moving violation within the past year. Assume in addition that 80% of those receiving such a citation attended traffic school so that the citation would not appear on their permanent driving records. If a teenage driver from this county is randomly selected, what is the probability that he or she received such a citation and attended traffic school?

Let's define two events E and F by

F = selected driver received such a citation

E = selected driver attended traffic school

The question posed can then be answered by calculating $P(E \text{ and } F)$. The percentages given in the problem statement imply that

$$P(F) = .20, \qquad P(E|F) = .80$$

Invoking the multiplication rule now gives

$$\begin{aligned} P(E \text{ and } F) &= P(E|F) \cdot P(F) \\ &= (.80) \cdot (.20) \\ &= .16 \end{aligned}$$

Thus 16% of all registered teenage drivers received a citation and subsequently attended traffic school.

EXAMPLE 5.20

The accompanying table gives information on VCRs sold by a certain appliance store.

	Percentage of customers purchasing	Percentage buying an extended warranty among those who purchase
Brand 1	70%	20%
Brand 2	30%	40%

A purchaser is randomly selected from among all those having bought a VCR from the store. What is the probability that he or she purchased a brand 1 model and an extended warranty?

To answer this question, let

B_1 = the event that brand 1 is purchased

E = the event that an extended warranty is purchased

The tabulated information implies that

$$P(B_1) = P(\text{brand 1 purchased}) = .70$$
$$P(E|B_1) = P(\text{ext. warranty purchased}|\text{brand 1 purchased}) = .20$$

Notice that the 20% is identified with a *conditional* probability: among purchasers of brand 1, it is the percentage opting for an extended warranty. Substituting these numbers into the multiplication rule (with B_1 replacing F) yields

$$
\begin{aligned}
P(B_1 \text{ and } E) &= P(E|B_1) \cdot P(B_1) \\
&= (.20)(.70) \\
&= .14
\end{aligned}
$$

Thus 14% of all purchasers selected brand 1 and bought an extended warranty.

The tree diagram of Figure 5.12 gives a nice visual display of how the multiplication rule is used here. The two first-generation branches are labeled with events B_1 and B_2 along with their probabilities. There are two second-generation branches leading out from each first-generation branch. These correspond to the two events E and *not E*, and the *conditional* probabilities $P(E|B_1)$, $P(\text{not } E|B_1)$, $P(E|B_2)$, $P(\text{not } E|B_2)$ appear on these branches. The multiplication rule amounts to nothing more than multiplying probabilities across the tree diagram. For example,

$$
\begin{aligned}
P(B_2 \text{ and } E) &= P(\text{brand 2 } and \text{ warranty purchased}) \\
&= P(E|B_2) \cdot P(B_2) \\
&= (.4)(.3) \\
&= .12
\end{aligned}
$$

and this probability is displayed to the right of the E branch that comes from the B_2 branch.

FIGURE 5.12
A tree diagram for
probability calculations

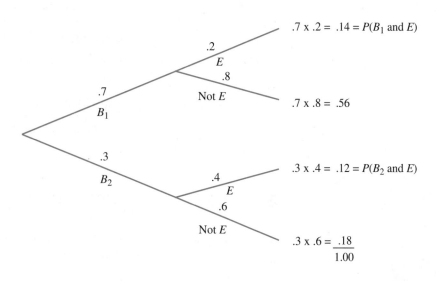

We can now easily calculate $P(E)$, the probability that an extended warranty is purchased. The event E can occur in two different ways:

buy brand 1 and warranty = B_1 and E

buy brand 2 and warranty = B_2 and E

Furthermore, the two events B_1 and E, B_2 and E are disjoint (each customer purchased a single VCR, so it can't be both brand 1 and brand 2). Thus

$$P(E) = P(B_1 \text{ and } E) + P(B_2 \text{ and } E)$$
$$= P(E|B_1) \cdot P(B_1) + P(E|B_2) \cdot P(B_2)$$
$$= (.2)(.7) + (.4)(.3)$$
$$= .14 + .12$$
$$= .26$$

This probability is the sum of two of the probabilities shown on the right side of the tree diagram. Thus 26% of all VCR purchasers selected an extended warranty.

The multiplication rule can be extended to give an expression for the probability that several events occur together. In the case of three events E, F, and G, we have

$$P(E \text{ and } F \text{ and } G) = P(E|F \text{ and } G) \cdot P(F|G) \cdot P(G)$$

When the events are all independent, $P(E|F \text{ and } G) = P(E)$ and $P(F|G) = P(F)$, so the right-hand side is just the product of three unconditional probabilities.

EXAMPLE 5.21

Twenty percent of all passengers who fly from Los Angeles to New York do so on airline G. This airline misplaces luggage for 10% of its passengers, and 90% of this lost luggage is subsequently recovered. If a passenger who has flown from L.A. to N.Y. is randomly selected, what is the probability that the selected individual flew on airline G (event G), had luggage misplaced (event F) and subsequently recovered the misplaced piece(s) (event E)? The stated percentages imply that

$$P(G) = .20, \qquad P(F|G) = .10, \qquad P(E|F \text{ and } G) = .90$$

Thus

$$P(E \text{ and } F \text{ and } G) = (.90)(.10)(.20) = .018$$

EXERCISES 5.37–5.44   SECTION 5.4

5.37   There are two traffic lights on the route used by a certain individual to go from home to work. Let E denote the event that the individual must stop at the first light, and define the event F in a similar manner for the second light. Suppose that $P(E) = .4$, $P(F) = .3$, and $P(E \ and \ F) = .15$.

a. What is the probability that the individual must stop at at least one light; that is, what is the probability of the event $E \ or \ F$?

b. What is the probability that the individual needn't stop at either light?

c. What is the probability that the individual must stop at exactly one of the two lights?

d. What is the probability that the individual must stop just at the first light? (Hint: How is the probability of this event related to $P(E)$ and $P(E \ and \ F)$? A Venn diagram might help.)

5.38 A family with two automobiles is to be randomly selected. Let A be the event that the older car has an automatic transmission and let B be the event that the newer car has an automatic transmission. Suppose that $P(A) = .7$ and $P(B) = .8$.

a. Can $P(A \ or \ B)$ be calculated from the given information? Explain.

b. Could it be the case that $P(A \ and \ B) = .75$? Explain.

c. If the probability is .9 that the selected family owns at least one car with an automatic transmission, what is the probability that both cars owned by the selected family have automatic transmissions? That at least one car has a manual transmission?

5.39 Exercise 5.28 presented the accompanying table giving proportions of insured individuals with various automobile and homeowner's deductible levels.

Auto	Homeowner's				
	N	L	M	H	
L	.04	.06	.05	.03	.18
M	.07	.10	.20	.10	.47
H	.02	.03	.15	.15	.35
	.13	.19	.46	1.28	

Suppose that an individual having both types of policies is randomly selected.

a. What is the probability that the individual has a medium auto deductible and a high homeowner's deductible?

b. What is the probability that the individual has a low auto deductible? A low homeowner's deductible?

c. What is the probability that the individual is in the same category for both auto and homeowner's deductibles?

d. Based on your answer in part (c), what is the probability that the two categories are different?

e. What is the probability that the individual has at least one low deductible level?

f. Using the answer in part (e), what is the probability that neither deductible level is low?

5.40 Let F denote the event that a randomly selected registered voter in a certain city has signed a petition to recall the mayor. Also let E denote the event that a randomly selected registered voter actually votes in the recall election. Describe the event E and F in words. If $P(F) = .10$ and $P(E|F) = .80$, determine $P(E \ and \ F)$.

5.41   Only .1 of 1% of the individuals in a certain population have a particular disease (an incidence rate of .001). Of those having the disease, 95% test positive when a certain diagnostic test is applied. Of those not having the disease, 90% test negative when the test is applied. Suppose that an individual from this population is randomly selected and given the test.

   a. Construct a tree diagram having two first-generation branches, for "has disease" and "doesn't have disease," and two second-generation branches leading out from each of these, for "positive test" and "negative test." Then enter appropriate probabilities on the four branches.
   b. Use the multiplication rule to calculate P(has disease *and* positive test).
   c. Calculate P(positive test).
   d. Use the definition of conditional probability along with the results of parts (b) and (c) to calculate P(has disease|positive test). Does the result surprise you? Give an intuitive explanation for the size of this probability.

5.42   A company uses three different assembly lines—A_1, A_2, and A_3—to manufacture a particular component. Of those manufactured by line A_1, there are 5% that need rework to remedy a defect, whereas 8% of A_2's components need rework and 10% of A_3's need rework. Suppose that 50% of all components are produced by line A_1, whereas 30% are produced by line A_2 and 20% come from line A_3.

   a. Construct a tree diagram with first-generation branches corresponding to the three lines. Leading from each one, draw one branch for rework (R) and another for no rework (N). Then enter appropriate probabilities on the branches.
   b. What is the probability that a randomly selected component came from line 1 and needed rework?
   c. What is the probability that a randomly selected component needed rework?

5.43   A certain company sends 40% of its overnight mail parcels via express mail service E_1. Of these parcels, 2% arrive after the guaranteed delivery time (denote by L the event "late delivery"). If a record of an overnight mailing is randomly selected from the company's file, what is the probability that the parcel went via E_1 and was late?

5.44   Return to Exercise 5.43, and suppose that 50% of the overnight parcels are sent via express mail service E_2 and the remaining 10% are sent via E_3. Of those sent via E_2, only 1% arrive late, whereas 5% of the parcels handled by E_3 arrive late.

   a. What is the probability that a randomly selected parcel arrived late? (Hint: A tree diagram should help.)
   b. Suppose that the selected record shows that the parcel arrived late, but the name of the service does not appear on the record. What is the probability that the parcel was handled by E_1? That is, what is the *posterior* probability of E_1 given L, denoted $P(E_1|L)$? What is $P(E_2|L)$? $P(E_3|L)$?

5.5 Some Counting Rules Useful in Probability (Optional)

We saw earlier that in the case of equally likely outcomes,

$$P(E) = \frac{\text{number of outcomes in } E}{N}$$

where N is the total number of possible experimental outcomes. When N is quite large, constructing a complete listing of all possibilities is obviously tedious. The application of some clever counting methods often makes such a listing unnecessary.

Multiplication Rules

RULE 1

Consider an experiment for which each outcome consists of a pair of the form (first element, second element). Suppose that there are n_1 possibilities for the first element, and for each such possibility, there are n_2 choices for the second element. Then

$$N = \text{total number of outcomes} = (n_1)(n_2)$$

EXAMPLE 5.22

Your local audio-video store has a display in which each of 10 receivers A_1, A_2, $\ldots$, A_{10} can be connected to any of 15 pairs of speakers B_1, $\ldots$, B_{15}. If a receiver and pair of speakers are randomly selected, one possible outcome is (A_3, B_7) and another is (A_{10}, B_2). Application of rule 1 gives

$$N = \text{number of (receiver, speaker) pairs}$$
$$= (n_1)(n_2) = (10)(15) = 150$$

Suppose that three of the receivers and four sets of speakers are made by Sony. Then the number of (Sony receiver, Sony speaker) pairs is $(3)(4) = 12$. Let

$$C = \text{the event that both receiver and speakers are Sony brand}$$

Assuming that any pair has the same chance of selection (equally likely outcomes),

$$P(C) = \frac{\text{number of outcomes in } C}{N} = \frac{12}{150} = .080$$

If n_1 and n_2 are small, the possible outcomes can be pictured in a tree diagram. Consider the previous example, in which there were $n_1 = 3$ Sony receivers and $n_2 = 4$ pairs of Sony speakers. The corresponding tree diagram appears in

Figure 5.13. Each of the 12 terminal points on the right corresponds to a different possible pair.

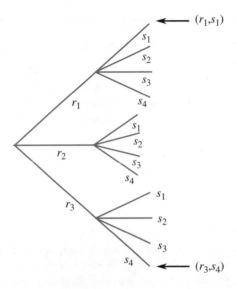

Rule 1 can be extended to the formation of triples, quadruples, and so on. For example, suppose that each outcome consists of a triple and that

1. The number of possibilities for the first element is n_1.
2. For each such choice, the number of possibilities for the second element is n_2.
3. For each way of selecting the first two elements, the number of possibilities for the third is n_3.

Then

$$N = \text{number of triples} = (n_1)(n_2)(n_3)$$

The corresponding tree diagram would have three generations of branches.

EXAMPLE 5.23

(*Example 5.22 continued*) Suppose that in addition to the 10 receivers and 15 sets of speakers, the store has 12 CD players. Then the total number of three-component systems is

$$N = (n_1)(n_2)(n_3) = (10)(15)(12) = 1800$$

If three of the CD players are Sony brand and the choice of each component is made in a completely random fashion, then

$$P(\text{all three components are Sony}) = \frac{(3)(4)(3)}{1800} = .02$$

The probability that at least one of the selected components is *not* a Sony is .98.

Permutations

Example 5.24 illustrates a problem situation that seems different from what we have considered so far, but an extension of rule 1 can still be applied.

EXAMPLE 5.24

Twelve players—A, B, C, . . . , L—have tried out for a junior high school basketball team. The players are similar in heights and abilities, so any player is a candidate for any of the five positions (center, power forward, small forward, shooting guard, and point guard). One possible team consists of players C, A, H, D, J in these positions, another is A, B, C, D, E, and yet another is C, A, B, E, D (same players as the previous team but occupying different positions). How many different teams can be formed?

Let

$$n_1 = \text{number of ways to select center} = 12$$

For any particular choice of center,

$$n_2 = \text{number of ways to select power forward} = 11$$

Similarly, once a center and power forward have been selected, there are $n_3 = 10$ choices for small forward, and so on. The number of possible teams is then

$$(n_1)(n_2)(n_3)(n_4)(n_5) = (12)(11)(10)(9)(8) = 95{,}040$$

In order to watch each team for 5 min, the coach would be in for a long evening!

Suppose now that n players have tried out for a sports team. The k available positions are to be filled by selecting an *ordered* subset of size k from the n players (in the previous example, $n = 12$ and $k = 5$). There are n ways to select the first position, $n - 1$ ways to select the second position once the first has been selected, and so on. After the first $k - 1$ have been selected, the last one can be chosen in any one of $n - (k - 1)$ ways.

RULE 2

Given a collection of n different individuals or objects, an ordered subset of these is called a **permutation.** Denote the number of permutations of size k by $P_{n,k}$. Then

$$P_{n,k} = (n)(n - 1)(n - 2) \cdots (n - (k - 1))$$

According to Example 5.24, the number of permutations of size 5 that can be formed from 12 distinct objects is 95,040. There is a more concise expression for $P_{n,k}$ that involves *factorial notation.*

> **DEFINITION**
>
> For any positive whole number m, the symbol $m!$, read **m factorial,** is defined by
>
> $$m! = (m)(m - 1)(m - 2) \cdots (2)(1)$$
>
> In addition, 0! is defined to be 1.

Thus

$$5! = (5)(4)(3)(2)(1) = 120$$

and

$$12! = (12)(11)(10) \cdots (2)(1) = 479{,}001{,}600$$

Clearly $m!$ grows very rapidly as m grows. In the previous example,

$$
\begin{aligned}
P_{12,5} &= (12)(11)(10)(9)(8) \\
&= \frac{(12)(11)(10)(9)(8)(7)(6)(5)(4)(3)(2)(1)}{(7)(6)(5)(4)(3)(2)(1)} \\
&= \frac{12!}{7!}
\end{aligned}
$$

More generally,

$$P_{n,k} = \frac{n!}{(n - k)!}$$

EXAMPLE 5.25

A friend of ours went to a wine-tasting event featuring Chardonnay wines. There were 20 wines available for tasting, and she decided to try 8. Assuming that the order of tasting is relevant, the number of possibilities is

$$P_{20,8} = \frac{20!}{(20 - 8)!} = \frac{20!}{12!} = 5{,}079{,}110{,}400$$

Combinations

In many situations the order in which objects or individuals are selected or listed is not important, only which individuals end up in the subset. For example, a bridge hand consists of 13 cards, and the order in which these cards are dealt does not matter. Therefore, a determination of the number of bridge hands should not take order into account.

EXAMPLE 5.26

A statistics department consists of five faculty members—individuals *A, B, C, D, E*—all of whom would like to attend a national meeting. Unfortunately there is enough money available for only three to go. How many different ways are there to select those three?

Suppose for the moment that order *is* important. Then the number of possibilities is $P_{5,3} = 60$. Among these are six that include *A*, *B*, and *C*:

$$ABC \quad ACB \quad BAC \quad BCA \quad CAB \quad CBA$$

There are also six that include *A*, *B*, and *D*:

$$ABD \quad ADB \quad BAD \quad BDA \quad DAB \quad DBA$$

In fact, for any particular three individuals, there are $3! = (3)(2)(1) = 6$ ways to form an ordered subset. Thus for every unordered subset, there are 3! ordered subsets; that is

$$\left(\begin{array}{c} \text{number of} \\ \text{ordered subsets} \end{array} \right) = 60 = \left(\begin{array}{c} \text{number of} \\ \text{unordered subsets} \end{array} \right)(3!)$$

implying that

$$\left(\begin{array}{c} \text{number of} \\ \text{unordered subsets} \end{array} \right) = \frac{60}{3!} = 10$$

These ten unordered subsets are, in fact,

ABC	ABD	ABE	ACD	ACE
ADE	BCD	BCE	BDE	CDE

RULE 3

Given a collection of *n* different individuals or objects, an unordered subset of these is called a **combination.** The number of combinations of size *k*, denoted by either $C_{n,k}$ or, more commonly, the symbol $\binom{n}{k}$, is given by

$$\binom{n}{k} = \frac{P_{n,k}}{k!} = \frac{n!}{k!(n-k)!}$$

The division by *k*! reflects the fact that any particular unordered set (combination) of size *k* may be ordered in *k*! ways.

EXAMPLE 5.27

Our wine-tasting friend of Example 5.25 is going to her cabin in the mountains and wants to take five bottles of Cabernet with her. She has 15 bottles of this variety, all from different wineries, among which is a bottle of Caparone and a bottle of Stag's Leap. Suppose that she randomly selects the five bottles in such a way that any group of five has the same chance of being selected (by, for example, selecting five slips from those with numbers $1, \ldots, 15$ on them). Let A be the event that both the Caparone and Stag's Leap bottles are selected. Because outcomes are equally likely,

$$P(A) = \frac{\text{number of outcomes in } A}{\text{number of ways of selecting five bottles}}$$

The denominator of $P(A)$ is just

$$\binom{15}{5} = \frac{15!}{(5!)(15-5)!} = \frac{15!}{(5!)(10!)}$$

$$= \frac{(15)(14)(13)(12)(11)}{5!} = 3003$$

How many outcomes are in A? Such an outcome must consist of the Caparone, the Stag's Leap, and any three other bottles. The number of outcomes in A is then the number of ways to select three other bottles from the remaining 13 to include with the Caparone and Stag's Leap wines. This number is

$$\binom{13}{3} = \frac{13!}{(3!)(10!)} = \frac{(13)(12)(11)}{3!} = 286$$

This gives

$$P(A) = \frac{286}{3003} = .095$$

EXERCISES 5.45–5.52   SECTION 5.5

5.45   Mozart wrote 27 piano concertos and 41 symphonies. How many ways are there to listen first to a Mozart piano concerto and then to a symphony?

5.46   A local appliance store offers ten different washer models and eight different dryer models.
   a. How many possible washer-dryer pairs are there?
   b. Three of the washers and three of the dryers are made by GE. If one of the washer-dryer pairs is randomly selected (equally likely outcomes), what is the probability that both are GE models?
   c. Referring to (b), what is the probability that exactly one of the selected machines is a GE model?

5.47 A library has six Colin Dexter mysteries on the shelf, five by Tony Hillerman, and four by Arthur Upfield (all first-rate authors!).

    a. How many ways are there to select one book by each author?

    b. How many ways are there to select three books from among the 15 without regard to author? (Hint: Use combinations.)

    c. If three books are selected in a completely random fashion, what is the probability that the three are by different authors?

5.48 You have identified eight courses that you are seriously considering taking next term.

    a. How many ways are there to select five from among the eight without regard to order?

    b. Two of these are statistics courses, and you have definitely decided to take them (your friends are ready to have you committed!). How many ways are there now to select five courses to take?

    c. If you randomly select five from among the eight courses, what is the probability that both the statistics courses will be on your schedule?

5.49 A certain restaurant offers a three-course meal at a special price. Patrons can choose from among five appetizers, eight main courses, and six desserts. For how many nights could you eat at this restaurant without eating the same meal twice?

5.50 The new-release section of your favorite video store has eight dramas and six comedies.

    a. How many ways are there to select two movies of each type for a weekend of movie watching?

    b. If there are 25 movies in the new-release section and you randomly select four, what is the probability that all are dramas? What is the probability that none are dramas or comedies?

    c. If you select four movies as described in part (b), what is the probability that you end up with exactly two dramas? (Hint: How many ways are there to select two dramas and then two films that aren't dramas?)

5.51 A little league team consists of 15 players.

    a. How many ways are there to select a starting team (assuming each player can play each position)?

    b. If the starting nine are randomly selected from the 15 players, what is the probability that players A, B, C, and D will be left on the bench?

5.52 Here is a famous problem that shows coincidences are often not as unlikely to occur as you might think.

    a. Suppose that there are three people in a room. Disregarding the possibility of a February 29th birthday, how many possible "birthday triples" are there? (Hint: $n_1 = n_2 = n_3 = 365$.)

    b. As in (a), how many ways are there for the three people to have *different* birthdays? (Hint: $n_1 = 365$, but now what are n_2 and n_3?)

    c. If each individual is equally likely to be born on any one of the 365 days (so the outcomes in (a) are equally likely), what is the probability that all three people have different birthdays? That at least two have the same birthday? (Hint: If A and B denote the events whose probabilities are requested, then $B = not A$.)

    d. Answer the questions posed in (c) for a group of 10 people.

    e. How many people need to be in a room before the probability that at least two have the same birthday exceeds .5?

CHAPTER FIVE SUMMARY OF KEY CONCEPTS AND FORMULAS

Term or Formula	Comment

Chance experiment

Any experiment for which there is uncertainty concerning the resulting outcome.

Sample space

The collection of all possible outcomes of a chance experiment.

Event

Any collection of possible outcomes from a chance experiment.

Simple event

An event that consists of a single outcome.

Events   1. *not A*
       2. *A or B*
       3. *A and B*

1. The event consisting of all outcomes not in A.
2. The event consisting of all outcomes in at least one of the two events.
3. The event consisting of outcomes common to both events.

Disjoint (mutually exclusive) events

Events that have no outcomes in common.

Probability of an event E, denoted by $P(E)$

The long-run relative frequency of occurrence of E when the experiment is repeated indefinitely.

Basic properties of probability

The probability of any event must be a number between 0 and 1.
The sum of probabilities of all simple events in the sample space must be 1.
$P(E)$ is the sum of the probabilities of all simple events in E.
$P(E) + P(not\ E) = 1$.

$$P(E) = \frac{\text{no. of outcomes in } E}{N}$$

$P(E)$ when the outcomes are equally likely, where N is the number of outcomes in the sample space.

$P(E\ or\ F) = P(E) + P(F)$

$P(E_1\ or \ldots or\ E_k)$
  $= P(E_1) + \cdots + P(E_k)$

Addition rules when events are disjoint.

$$P(E|F) = \frac{P(E\ and\ F)}{P(F)}$$

The conditional probability of the event E given that the event F has occurred.

Independence of events E and F

$P(E|F) = P(E)$

Events E and F are independent if the probability that E has occurred given F is the same as the probability that E will occur with no knowledge of F.

$P(E\ and\ F) = P(E) \cdot P(F)$

$P(E_1\ and \ldots and\ E_k)$
  $= P(E_1) \cdots P(E_k)$

Multiplication rules for independent events.

Term or Formula	**Comment**
$P(E \text{ or } F) = P(E)$ $+ P(F) - P(E \text{ and } F)$	The general addition rule for two events.
$P(E \text{ and } F) = P(E\|F) \cdot P(F)$	The general multiplication rule for two events.
$(n_1)(n_2)$	The counting rule for determining the number of pairs.
$(n_1)(n_2)(n_3)$	The counting rule for determining the number of triples.
$P_{n,k} = \dfrac{n!}{(n-k)!}$	The number of permutations (ordered subsets) of size k from n different objects.
$\dbinom{n}{k} = \dfrac{n!}{k!(n-k)!}$	The number of combinations (unordered subsets) of size k from n different objects.

ENCORE

Let's reconsider the jury-selection problem posed in the Chapter Preview. The following events are relevant:

B_1 = the event that a randomly selected juror is unbiased
B_2 = the event that a randomly selected juror is biased against the prosecution
B_3 = the event that a randomly selected juror is biased against the defense
R = the event that an existing bias is revealed in the questioning
E = the event that the juror is excused for cause

Assumptions

1. $P(B_1) = .5$, $P(B_2) = .1$, $P(B_3) = .4$ (these probabilities are consistent with data obtained in Florida relating to the trial of serial killer Theodore Bundy).
2. $P(R|B_2) = P(R|B_3) = .85$; that is, among jurors who are biased, 85% will have their bias revealed (a high probability, corresponding to extensive questioning in a capital case).
3. $P(E|B_2 \text{ and } R) = P(E|B_3 \text{ and } R) = .7$; that is, among jurors who are biased and have their bias revealed, 70% will be excused for cause (this is for a "moderate" judge).

The accompanying tree diagram summarizes the situation.

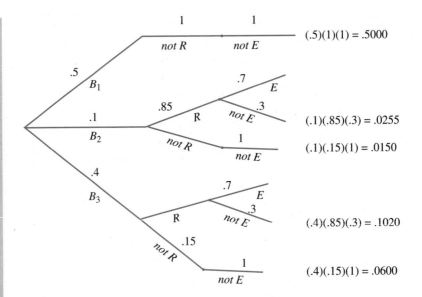

If there is no bias, none will be revealed and the juror will surely not be excused for cause. Also, if there is bias but it isn't revealed, the juror will surely not be excused for cause. Thus the probability 1 appears on many branches of the tree diagram. We have multiplied probabilities across the tree diagram for every possible way that a juror is *not* excused for cause. Adding these probabilities gives

$$P(not\ E) = .5000 + .0255 + .0150 + .1020 + .0600$$
$$= .7025$$

Now

$$P(\text{unbiased}\,|\,\text{not excused}) = \frac{P(B_1\ and\ not\ E)}{P(not\ E)}$$

$$= \frac{.5000}{.7025} = .71$$

$$P(\text{biased against prosecution}\,|\,\text{not excused}) = \frac{P(B_2\ and\ not\ E)}{P(not\ E)}$$

$$= \frac{.0255 + .0150}{.7025} = .06$$

and

$$P(\text{biased against defense}\,|\,\text{not excused}) = P(B_3\,|\,not\ E)$$
$$= 1 - P(B_1\,|\,not\ E) - P(B_2\,|\,not\ E)$$
$$= .23$$

Given the stated assumptions, there is obviously a substantial chance that a juror who survives the questioning (*voir dire*) process will still have a bias, particularly one favorable to the prosecution. The article "Fair Number of Peremptory Challenges in Jury Trials" (*J. Amer. Stat. Assoc.* (1979):747–753) extends these ideas by considering how many "without-cause" challenges should be given to each side to increase the likelihood of an unbiased jury being selected.

SUPPLEMENTARY EXERCISES 5.53–5.78

5.53 A student has a box containing 25 computer disks, of which 15 are blank and 10 are not. She randomly selects disks one by one and examines each one, terminating the process only when she finds a blank disk. What is the probability that she must examine at least two disks?

5.54 In a school machine shop, 60% of all machine breakdowns occur on lathes and 15% occur on drill presses. Let E denote the event that the next machine breakdown is on a lathe, and let F denote the event that a drill press is the next machine to break down. With $P(E) = .60$ and $P(F) = .15$, calculate:
a. $P(not\ E)$
b. $P(E\ or\ F)$
c. $P(not\ E\ and\ not\ F)$

5.55 There are five faculty members in a certain academic department. These individuals have 3, 6, 7, 10, and 14 years of teaching experience, respectively. Two of these individuals are randomly selected to serve on a personnel review committee. What is the probability that the chosen representatives have a total of at least 15 years of teaching experience? (Hint: Consider all possible committees.)

5.56 Automobiles coming to a certain intersection can either turn left (L), turn right (R), or go straight (S). Suppose that for a randomly selected car, $P(L) = .1$, $P(S) = .7$, and $P(R) = .2$, and suppose that cars turn or go straight ahead independently of one another.
a. Among four randomly selected cars, what is the probability that all go straight?
b. What is the probability that four randomly selected cars go in the same direction?
c. What is the probability that three randomly selected cars all go in a different direction?

5.57 The general addition rule for three events states that

$$P(A\ or\ B\ or\ C) = P(A) + P(B) + P(C) -$$
$$P(A\ and\ B) - P(A\ and\ C) -$$
$$P(B\ and\ C) +$$
$$P(A\ and\ B\ and\ C)$$

A new magazine publishes columns entitled "Art" (A), "Books" (B), and "Cinema" (C). Suppose that 14% of all subscribers read A, 23% read B, 37% read C, 8% read A and B, 9% read A and C, 13% read B and C, and 5% read all three columns. What is the probability that a randomly selected subscriber reads at least one of these three columns?

5.58 A theater complex is currently showing four R-rated movies, three PG-13 movies, two PG movies, and one G movie. The accompanying table gives the number of people at the first showing of each movie on a certain Saturday.

Theater	Rating	No. of viewers
1	R	600
2	PG-13	420
3	PG-13	323
4	R	196
5	G	254
6	PG	179
7	PG-13	114
8	R	205
9	R	139
10	PG	87

2517

Suppose that a single one of these viewers is randomly selected.

a. What is the probability that the selected individual saw a PG movie?
b. What is the probability that the selected individual saw a PG or a PG-13 movie?
c. What is the probability that the selected individual did not see an R movie?

5.59 Refer to Exercise 5.58, and suppose that two viewers are randomly selected. Let R_1 and R_2 denote the events that the first and second individuals, respectively, watched an R-rated movie. Are R_1 and R_2 independent events? Explain. From a practical point of view, can these events be regarded as independent? Explain.

5.60 A large department store sells sport shirts in three sizes (small, medium, and large), three patterns (plaid, print, and stripe), and two sleeve lengths (long and short). The accompanying tables give the proportions of shirts sold falling in the various category combinations.

Short-sleeved

Size	Pl	Pr	St
S	.04 -	.02	.05
M	.08	.07	.12
L	.03	.07	.08

Long-sleeved

Size	Pl	Pr	St
S	.03	.02	.03
M	.10	.05	.07
L	.04	.02	.08

a. What is the probability that the next shirt sold is a medium, long-sleeved, print shirt?
b. What is the probability that the next shirt sold is a medium print shirt?
c. What is the probability that the next shirt sold is a short-sleeved shirt? A long-sleeved shirt?
d. What is the probability that the size of the next shirt sold is medium? That the pattern of the next shirt sold is a print?

5.61 Refer to Exercise 5.60.
a. Given that the shirt just sold was a short-sleeved plaid, what is the probability that its size was medium?
b. Given that the shirt just sold was a medium plaid, what is the probability that it was short-sleeved? Long-sleeved?

5.62 One box contains six red balls and four green balls, and a second box contains seven red balls and three green balls. A ball is randomly chosen from the first box and placed in the second box. Then a ball is randomly selected from the second box and placed in the first box.
a. What is the probability that a red ball is selected from the first box and a red ball is selected from the second box?
b. At the conclusion of the selection process, what is the probability that the numbers of red and green balls in the first box are identical to the numbers at the beginning?

5.63 A bowl contains four slips of paper. One says "win prize 1," one says "win prize 2," one says "win prize 3," and the last slip says "win prizes 1, 2, and 3." You randomly select a single slip. Let E_1 be the event that you win prize 1, and define E_2 and E_3 analogously for prizes 2 and 3, respectively.
a. Can the event E_1 *and* E_2 occur? What is $P(E_1$ *and* $E_2)$? Are E_1 and E_2 independent events?
b. Are E_1 and E_3 independent events? Are E_2 and E_3 independent events?
c. Is it true that $P(E_1$ *and* E_2 *and* $E_3) = P(E_1) \cdot P(E_2) \cdot P(E_3)$? (Note: This shows that events can be "pairwise independent" without being "mutually" independent, as required by our definition.)

5.64 A quiz consists of five multiple choice questions. Suppose that in grading the quizzes, questions are marked independently of one another, and the probability that any particular question is marked correctly is .9.
a. What is the probability that all five questions on a particular quiz are marked correctly?
b. What is the probability that at least one marking error is made on a particular quiz?
c. What is the probability that all five questions are incorrectly marked?

5.65 At a certain gas station, 40% of all customers fill their tanks. Of those who fill their tanks, 80% pay with a credit card.
  a. What is the probability that a randomly selected customer fills his or her tank and pays with a credit card?
  b. If three customers are randomly selected, what is the probability that all three fill their tanks and pay with a credit card?

5.66 Components of a certain type are shipped to a supplier in batches of ten. Suppose that 50% of all batches contain no defective components, 30% contain one defective component, and 20% contain two defective components. Two components from a batch are randomly selected and tested.
  a. If the batch from which the components were selected actually contains two defectives, what is the probability that neither of these is selected for testing?
  b. What is the probability that the batch contains two defectives and neither of these is selected for testing?
  c. What is the probability that neither component selected for testing is defective? (Hint: This could happen with any one of the three types of batches. A tree diagram might help.)

5.67 On Monday morning a loan officer at a credit union is given 15 auto loan applications to process. Three of these are for 36 months, five are for 48 months, and the other seven are for 60 months. Only two applications can be processed that morning. Suppose that the two to be processed are randomly selected from among the 15.
  a. Let A_1 be the event that the first application processed is for 36 months, and let A_2 be the event that the second application processed is for 36 months. What is $P(A_1)$? What is $P(A_2|A_1)$? Describe the event A_1 *and* A_2 in words, and calculate the probability of this event.
  b. What is the probability that both applications processed that morning are for loans of the same duration?

5.68 A company has just placed an order with a supplier for two different products. Let

E = the event that the first product is out of stock

F = the event that the second product is out of stock

Suppose that $P(E) = .3$, $P(F) = .2$, and the probability that at least one product is out of stock is .4.
  a. What is the probability that both products are out of stock?
  b. Are E and F independent events?
  c. Given that the first product is in stock, what is the probability that the second is also?

5.69 An appliance dealer sells three different brands of refrigerator (B_1, B_2, and B_3). Each brand comes in either a side-by-side model (S) or a top-freezer model (T). The accompanying table provides information on probabilities of the various brand-model combinations for a randomly selected purchaser. In addition, $P(S) = .20$, $P(B_1|S) = .50$, and $P(T|B_2) = .76$.

	Model	
Brand	S	T
B_1	.10	.35 .45
B_2	.06	.19 .25
B_3	.04	.26
	.20 .80	

  a. Determine the probabilities of the remaining four brand-model combinations.
  b. Given that a randomly selected purchaser chose a top-freezer model, what is the probability that it was not a brand B_1 refrigerator?

5.70 Suppose that three cards are drawn without replacement from a well-mixed deck. Let E denote the event that the first card is a face card, let F be the event that the second card is a face card, and let G be the event that the third card is a face card.
  a. What is $P(E)$?
  b. What is $P(F|E)$?
  c. What is $P(G|E \text{ and } F)$?
  d. What is the probability that all three cards selected are face cards?

5.71 Suppose three cards are selected from a well-mixed deck without replacement.
  a. Use the general multiplication rule for three events to calculate the probability that all three cards are hearts.

b. Calculate the probability that all three cards come from the same suit.

c. If five cards are dealt from the deck (a poker hand), determine the probability that all are hearts. (Hint: Extend the multiplication rule again.)

5.72 A sales representative for a company that manufactures water-treatment systems can make sales presentations to either one or two potential customers on any given day. The probability that there will be a single presentation is .6. If just one presentation is made, it is successful with probability .8. If two presentations are made, the first is successful with probability .8, the second is successful with probability .8, and these two events ("success on 1st" and "success on 2nd") are independent.

a. What is the probability that just one presentation is made on a particular day and it is successful?

b. What is the probability that two presentations are made and both are successful?

c. What is the probability that two presentations are made and neither is successful?

d. What is the probability that the sales rep has no successful presentations on a given day? (Hint: Construct a tree diagram with first-generation branches for one presentation (E_1) and two presentations (E_2). The branches leading out from the E_2 branch should specify all possibilities for each presentation.)

5.73 A transmitter is sending a message by using a binary code, namely, a sequence of 0s and 1s. Each transmitted "bit" (0 or 1) must pass through three relays in order to reach the receiver. At each relay, the probability is .20 that the bit sent on will be different from the bit received (a reversal). Assume that the relays operate independently of one another.

transmitter → relay 1 → relay 2 → relay 3 → receiver

a. If a 1 is sent from the transmitter, what is the probability that a 1 is sent on by all three relays?

b. If a 1 is sent from the transmitter, what is the probability that a 1 is received by the receiver? (Hint: The eight experimental outcomes can be displayed on a tree diagram with three gen-

erations of branches, one generation for each relay.)

5.74 Referring to Exercise 5.73, suppose that 70% of all bits sent from the transmitter are 1s. If a 1 is received by the receiver, what is the probability that a 1 was sent?

5.75 A tennis coach has brought out 12 tubes of Penn balls and 8 tubes of Wilson balls for his class. If 5 tubes are needed at the outset and these are randomly selected, what is the probability that all 5 are of the same brand?

5.76 The "Ask Marilyn" column in a recent issue of *Parade Magazine* posed a question involving a game show that generated thousands of reader responses and much controversy. Suppose that you are a contestant and are confronted with three doors. There are goats behind two doors and an automobile behind the remaining door. You select door 1 and the host then says "at least one of the other doors has a goat behind it, so I am going to open such a door." The host opens door 3 and then asks if you now want to switch from 1 to 2. Should you do so? (Hint: Suppose that the auto is equally likely to be behind any of the three doors and also that when the auto is behind door 1, the host is equally likely to open 2 or 3. Possible outcomes are AGG2 (the auto is behind 1 and 2 is opened), AGG3, GAG3, and GGA2. What are $P(\text{auto behind } 1|3 \text{ opened})$ and $P(\text{auto behind } 2|3 \text{ opened})$?

5.77 Suppose that all outcomes in one event, *A,* are contained in another event, *B* (for example, $A =$ jack is selected and $B =$ face card is selected). The accompanying Venn diagram shows that *B* consists of two nonoverlapping pieces: one is *A,* and the other is (*not A*) *and B.*

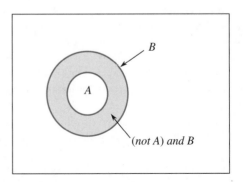

What is the relationship between $P(B)$, $P(A)$, and $P((\text{not } A) \text{ and } B)$? What does this imply about the relationship between $P(A)$ and $P(B)$?

5.78 If $P(A) = .5$, $P(B) = .4$, and A and B are independent, could they possibly be disjoint? Explain.

References

Devore, Jay L. *Probability and Statistics for Engineering and the Sciences,* 3rd ed. Pacific Grove, Calif.: Brooks/Cole Publishing Co., 1991. (The treatment of probability in this source is more comprehensive and at a somewhat higher mathematical level than is ours.)

Mosteller, Frederick, Robert Rourke, and George Thomas. *Probability with Statistical Applications.* Reading, Mass.: Addison-Wesley Publishing Co., 1970. (Although a bit old, there is no more recently published book that provides a better in-depth coverage of probability at a very modest mathematical level.)

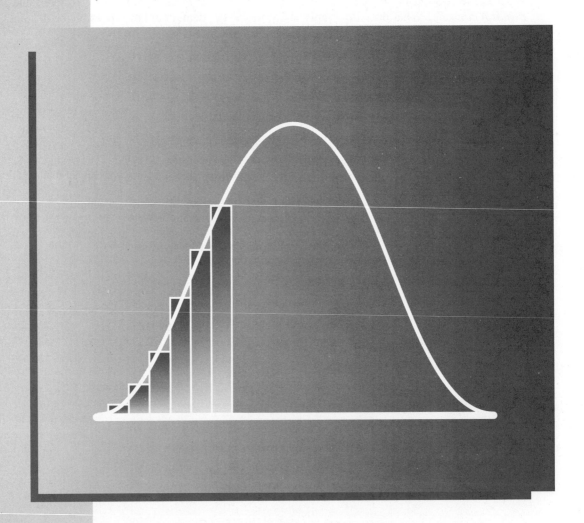

Random Variables and Discrete Probability Distributions

A substantial amount of empirical evidence suggests that most human beings are not good random number generators. That is, if an individual is asked to write down a "random" sequence of digits, each digit a 0, 1, . . . , or 9, chances are that the sequence would look rather different from what would be expected when a real random number generator (such as selecting numbered slips from a box) is employed. Similarly, consider the following sequence of 200 *H*'s and *T*'s:

```
T HHT HT HT HT T T T HHT T HHT T HHHT T HT HT T T HT T T T T HT HT T T HT T HHH
T HHHHT HT T T HHHHT HHT HT T T HHT HHHHT T HHHT T T HHHT HHHHT T T HT H
T HHT T T HHHT T T T HHHT HT HHHHT HHHT HHHHT T HT HHT HHHT T T HT HHH
HT T T T HHHHT HT HHHT T HHHHT T HHT T HHT T T T HT HT HT T HT HHT T HT T T
```

Is there a good way to tell whether this sequence resulted from actually tossing a coin 200 times or whether it was, instead, simply someone's idea of what could have resulted from performing such an experiment? The paper "The Longest Run of Heads" (*College Mathematics Journal* (1990):196–207) by Mark Schilling suggests that there tends to be more alternation between *H*'s and *T*'s in an artificial sequence than in a typical real sequence. In particular, consider the longest subsequence of consecutive *H*'s in the entire sequence—the longest head run. For our example, the length of this subsequence is 4—*HHHH* appears several different times. The number of *H*'s in the longest head run might be as small as 1 (*HTHTHT* . . . or *THTH* . . .), as large as 200 (*HHH* . . . *H*), or any whole number in between 1 and 200. The length of the longest head run is referred to as a *random variable,* because it is a variable quantity and its value is subject to uncertainty. How likely is it that the value of this random variable is equal to 4? Is at most 4? These types of questions can be answered by obtaining the *probability distribution* of the random variable, which specifies the probability associated with each possible value of the variable. We will consider such probability distributions and their characteristics in this chapter. Incidentally, the distribution of runs has applicability that goes beyond coin tossing. The cited paper refers to applications in handwriting analysis, hydrology (floods and droughts), and molecular biology.

Introduction

The focus of interest in a chance experiment is frequently on some numerical aspect of the outcome. An environmental scientist who obtains an air sample from a specified location might be especially concerned with the concentration of ozone (a major constituent of smog). A quality control inspector who must decide whether to accept a large shipment of components may base the decision on the number of defectives in a group of 20 components randomly selected from the shipment.

Prior to selection of the air sample, there is uncertainty as to what value of ozone concentration will result. Similarly, the number of defective components among the 20 selected might be any integer between 0 and 20. Because the value of a variable quantity such as ozone concentration or number of defectives is subject to uncertainty, it is called a *random variable*.

In this chapter we first distinguish between two general types of random variables, *discrete* and *continuous*. We then consider probability models for discrete variables. Special emphasis is given to the binomial probability distribution, the most widely used discrete probability model in statistics.

6.1   Random Variables

In most chance experiments there will be one or more variable quantities on which an investigator will focus attention. As an example, consider a management consultant who is studying the operation of a supermarket. The chance experiment might involve randomly selecting a customer leaving the store. One interesting numerical variable would be the number of items x purchased by the customer. Possible values of this variable are 0 (a frustrated customer), 1, 2, 3, and so on. Until a customer is selected and the number of items counted, there is uncertainty as to what value of x will result. Another variable of potential interest is the time y (min) spent in a checkout line. One possible y value is 3.0 and another 4.0, but *any* other number between 3.0 and 4.0 is also a possibility. Whereas possible values of x are isolated points on the number line, possible y values form an entire interval (a continuum) on the number line.

> **DEFINITION**
>
> A numerical variable whose value depends on the outcome of a chance experiment is called a **random variable**. A random variable is **discrete** if its set of possible values is a collection of isolated points on the number line. The variable is **continuous** if its set of possible values is an entire interval on the number line.

Figure 6.1 shows a set of possible values for each type of random variable.

FIGURE 6.1
Two different types
of random variables

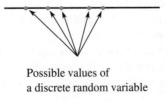

Possible values of
a discrete random variable

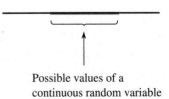

Possible values of a
continuous random variable

In practice, a discrete random variable almost always arises in connection with counting (the number of items purchased, the number of gas pumps in use, the number of broken eggs in a carton, and the like). A continuous random variable is one whose value is typically obtained by measurement (the temperature in a freezer compartment, the weight of a pineapple, the amount of time spent in the store, and so on). Because there is a limit to the accuracy of any measuring instrument, such as a watch or a scale, it may seem that any variable should be regarded as discrete. However, when there are a very large number of very closely spaced values, the variable's behavior is most easily studied by conceptualizing it as continuous. (This is one reason that the branch of mathematics called *calculus* was developed.)

EXAMPLE 6.1

Consider an experiment in which the type of dryer—electric (*E*) or gas (*G*)—chosen by each of three successive purchasers at a large appliance store is noted. Define a random variable x by

x = the number of gas dryers purchased by the three customers

The experimental outcome in which the first and third customers purchase a gas dryer and the second one an electric dryer can be abbreviated *GEG*. The associated x value is 2, since two of the three customers selected a gas model. Similarly, the x value for the outcome *GGG* (all three purchase a gas model) is 3. We display each of the eight possible experimental outcomes and the corresponding value of x.

Outcome	*EEE*	*GEE*	*EGE*	*EEG*	*GGE*	*GEG*	*EGG*	*GGG*
x value	0	1	1	1	2	2	2	3

There are only four possible x values—0, 1, 2, and 3—and these are isolated points on the number line. Thus, x is a discrete random variable.

In some situations the random variable of interest is discrete but the number of possible values is not finite. Here is an example.

EXAMPLE 6.2

Each trial run of a power generating unit can be either a success (*S*) or a failure (*F*). The unit's purchaser has specified that the unit will not be accepted until two consecutive successful trial runs have been observed. The random variable of interest is

x = the number of trial runs that must be made prior to acceptance
    of the unit

The simplest experimental outcome is *SS,* where the first two trial runs are both successful; in this case the associated x value is 2. There is also just one outcome for which $x = 3$, namely, *FSS* (for $x = 3$, the second and third runs must be *S*'s; if the first were also *S,* the experiment would have terminated with $x = 2$). Some possible x values and outcomes are as follows

x value	Outcomes
2	*SS*
3	*FSS*
4	*FFSS, SFSS*
5	*FFFSS, SFFSS, FSFSS*
6	*FFFFSS, SFFFSS, FSFFSS, SFSFSS, FFSFSS*
⋮	⋮
10	*FFFFFFFFSS* and many others
⋮	⋮

Any positive integer that is at least 2 (such as 2, 3, 4, 5) is a possible x value. For example, $x = 50$ if the first 48 trials result in F's and the 49th and 50th trials are S's. (There are many other outcomes for which $x = 50$.) Because the values 2, 3, 4, . . . are isolated points on the number line (x is determined by counting), x is a discrete random variable. But there is no upper limit to the number of possible x values.

Now consider an example of a continuous random variable.

EXAMPLE 6.3

A shot is fired at a circular target with a radius of 1 ft. Suppose that the shot is sure to land someplace on the target. As illustrated in Figure 6.2, the experimental outcome (landing point) can be described by a horizontal coordinate in combination with a vertical coordinate. Let x be the number on the horizontal axis that is directly below or above the landing point. Similarly, let y be the number on the vertical axis that is directly left or right of the landing point. Then the landing point is identified by the pair (x, y).

FIGURE 6.2
The circular target and experimental outcome $\left(\frac{1}{2}, \frac{1}{4}\right)$.

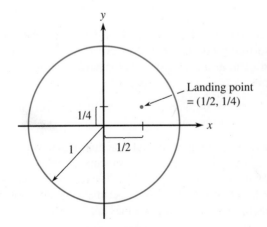

Define a random variable z by

> $z =$ the distance from the target's center to the point at which the shot lands

The relation between the outcome (x, y) and the corresponding z value is

$$z = \sqrt{(\text{horiz. coord.})^2 + (\text{vert. coord.})^2}$$

$$= \sqrt{x^2 + y^2}$$

Thus the outcome $\left(\frac{1}{2}, \frac{1}{4}\right)$ gives us

$$z = \sqrt{(\frac{1}{2})^2 + (\frac{1}{2})^2} = \sqrt{.3125} = .559$$

The smallest possible z value is 0, which occurs when the landing point is the center point. The maximum z value, 1, occurs if the landing point is anywhere on the edge of the target. Relative to these two extremes, z can be *any* number between 0 and 1, comprising an entire interval (continuum) on the number line. Thus z is a continuous random variable.

EXERCISES 6.1–6.7   SECTION 6.1

6.1   Say whether each of the following random variables is discrete or continuous.
   a. The number of defective tires on a car
   b. The body temperature of a hospital patient
   c. The number of pages in a book
   d. The number of draws with replacement from a deck of cards until a heart is selected
   e. The lifetime of a light bulb

6.2   Classify each of the following random variables as either discrete or continuous.
   a. The fuel efficiency (mi/gal) of an automobile
   b. The amount of rainfall at a particular location during the next year
   c. The distance that a person throws a baseball
   d. The number of questions asked during a one-hour lecture
   e. The tension (lb/in.^{2}) at which a tennis racket is strung
   f. The amount of water used by a household during a given month
   g. The number of traffic citations issued by the highway patrol in a particular county on a given day

6.3   Starting at a particular time, each car entering an intersection is observed to see whether it turns left (L), right (R), or goes straight ahead (S). The experiment terminates as soon as a car is observed to go straight. Let y denote the number of cars observed. What are possible y values? List five different outcomes and their associated y values.

6.4   A point is randomly selected from the interior of a square, as pictured. Let x denote the distance from the lower left corner A of the square to the selected point. What are possible values of x? Is x a discrete or continuous variable?

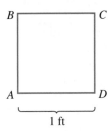

1 ft

6.5   A point is randomly selected on the surface of a lake that has maximum depth of 100 ft. Let y = the depth of the lake at the randomly chosen point. What are possible values of y? Is y discrete or continuous?

6.6   A person stands at the corner marked A of the square pictured in Exercise 6.4 and tosses a coin. If it lands H, the person moves one corner clockwise, to B. If the coin lands T, the person moves one corner counterclockwise, to D. This process is then repeated until the person arrives back at A. Let y denote the number of coin tosses. What are possible values of y? Is y discrete or continuous?

6.7   A box contains four slips of paper marked 1, 2, 3, and 4. Two slips are selected without replacement. List the possible values for each of the following random variables.

    a. x = the sum of the two numbers
    b. y = the difference between the first and second numbers
    c. z = the number of slips selected that show an even number
    d. w = the number of slips selected that show a 4

6.2 Probability Distributions for Discrete Random Variables

Let x be a discrete random variable associated with a particular chance experiment. The outcome that occurs when the experiment is performed determines which value of x is observed. The total probability for all outcomes is 1. The probability distribution of x describes how much of this probability is placed on each possible x value.

EXAMPLE 6.4

Six lots of components are ready to be shipped by a certain supplier. The number of defective components in each lot is as follows.

Lot:	1	2	3	4	5	6
Number of defectives:	0	2	0	1	2	0

One of these lots is to be randomly selected for shipment to a particular customer. Let x be the number of defectives in the selected lot. The three possible x values are 0, 1, and 2. Of the six equally likely simple events, three result in $x = 0$, one in $x = 1$, and the other two in $x = 2$. Thus

$$P(x = 0) = P(\text{lot 1 or 3 or 6 is sent}) = \frac{3}{6} = .500$$

$$P(x = 1) = P(\text{lot 4 is sent}) = \frac{1}{6} = .167$$

$$P(x = 2) = P(\text{lot 2 or 5 is sent}) = \frac{2}{6} = .333$$

That is, a probability of .500 is distributed to the x value 0, a probability of .167 is placed on the x value 1, and the remaining probability, .333, is associated with the x value 2.

DEFINITION

The **probability distribution of a discrete random variable x** gives the probability associated with each possible x value. Each probability is the limiting relative frequency of occurrence of the corresponding x value when the experiment is repeatedly performed.

If 2 is one possible value of x, we will often write $p(2)$ in place of $P(x = 2)$. Similarly, $p(5)$ will denote the probability that $x = 5$, and so on.

EXAMPLE 6.5

Each of four randomly selected customers purchasing a dryer at a certain store chooses either an electric (E) or a gas (G) model. Assume that these customers make their choices independently of one another and that 40% of all customers select an electric model. This implies that for any particular one of the four customers, $P(E) = .4$ and $P(G) = .6$. One possible experimental outcome is *EGGE*, where the first and fourth customers select electric models and the other two choose gas models. Independence of choice implies that

$$\begin{aligned} P(EGGE) = {}& P(\text{1st chooses } E \text{ and 2nd chooses } G \text{ and} \\ & \text{3rd chooses } G \text{ and 4th chooses } E) \\ = {}& P(E) \cdot P(G) \cdot P(G) \cdot P(E) \\ = {}& (.4)(.6)(.6)(.4) \\ = {}& .0576 \end{aligned}$$

Similarly,

$$P(EGEG) = P(E) \cdot P(G) \cdot P(E) \cdot P(G)$$
$$= (.4)(.6)(.4)(.6)$$
$$= .0576 \quad \text{(identical to } P(EGGE))$$

and

$$P(GGGE) = (.6)(.6)(.6)(.4) = .0864$$

Now, let the random variable of interest be

x = the number of electric dryers purchased by the four customers

Table 6.1 displays all 16 experimental outcomes, the probability of each one, and the x value associated with each outcome.

TABLE 6.1　Outcomes and probabilities for Example 6.5

Outcome	Probability	x value	Outcome	Probability	x value
GGGG	.1296	0	GEEG	.0576	2
EGGG	.0864	1	GEGE	.0576	2
GEGG	.0864	1	GGEE	.0576	2
GGEG	.0864	1	GEEE	.0384	3
GGGE	.0864	1	EGEE	.0384	3
EEGG	.0576	2	EEGE	.0384	3
EGEG	.0576	2	EEEG	.0384	3
EGGE	.0576	2	EEEE	.0256	4

The probability distribution of x is easily obtained from this information. Consider the smallest possible x value, 0. The only outcome for which $x = 0$ is GGGG, so

$$p(0) = P(x = 0) = P(GGGG) = .1296$$

There are four different outcomes for which $x = 1$, so $p(1)$ results from summing the four corresponding probabilities:

$$p(1) = P(x = 1) = P(EGGG \text{ or } GEGG \text{ or } GGEG \text{ or } GGGE)$$
$$= P(EGGG) + P(GEGG) + P(GGEG) + P(GGGE)$$
$$= .0864 + .0864 + .0864 + .0864$$
$$= 4(.0864)$$
$$= .3456$$

Similarly,

$$p(2) = P(EEGG) + \cdots + P(GGEE) = 6(.0576) = .3456$$
$$p(3) = 4(.0384) = .1536$$
$$p(4) = .0256$$

The probability distribution of x is summarized in the accompanying table.

x value	0	1	2	3	4
$p(x)$ = probability of value	.1296	.3456	.3456	.1536	.0256

To interpret $p(3) = .1536$, think of performing the experiment repeatedly, each time with a different group of four customers. In the long run, 15.36% of these groups will have exactly three customers purchasing an electric dryer.

The probability distribution can be used to determine probabilities of various events involving x. For example, the probability that at least two of the four customers choose electric models is

$$P(x \geq 2) = P(x = 2 \text{ or } 3 \text{ or } 4)$$
$$= p(2) + p(3) + p(4)$$
$$= .5248$$

Thus, in the long run, 52.48% of the time a group of four dryer purchasers will include at least two who select electric models.

In tabular form, the probability distribution for a discrete random variable looks exactly like a relative frequency distribution of the sort discussed in Chapter 2. There we introduced a histogram as a pictorial representation of a relative frequency distribution. An analogous picture for a discrete probability distribution is called a **probability histogram.** The picture has a rectangle centered above each possible value of x, and the area of each rectangle is the probability of the corresponding value. Figure 6.3 displays the probability histogram for the probability distribution of Example 6.5.

FIGURE 6.3
Probability histogram for the distribution of Example 6.5

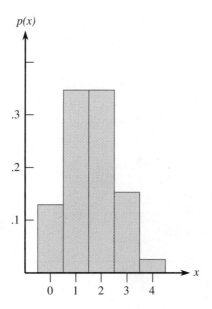

In the foregoing example, the probability distribution was derived by starting with a simple experimental situation and applying basic probability rules. Often such a derivation is not possible. Instead an investigator conjectures a probability distribution consistent with empirical evidence and prior knowledge. The only conditions that must be satisfied are

1. $p(x) \geq 0$ for every x value

2. $\sum\limits_{\substack{\text{all } x \\ \text{values}}} p(x) = 1$

EXAMPLE 6.6

A consumer organization that evaluates new automobiles customarily reports the number of major defects on each car examined. Let x denote the number of major defects on a randomly selected car of a certain type. One possible probability distribution is

x	0	1	2	3	4	5	6	7	8	9	10
$p(x)$	.041	.130	.209	.223	.178	.114	.061	.028	.011	.004	.001

The corresponding probability histogram appears in Figure 6.4.

FIGURE 6.4
Probability histogram for the distribution of the number of major defects

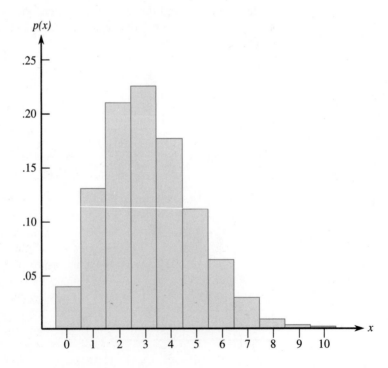

The probability that the number of major defects is between 2 and 5 inclusive is

$$P(2 \leq x \leq 5) = p(2) + p(3) + p(4) + p(5) = .724$$

If car after car of this type were examined, in the long run, 72.4% would have 2, 3, 4, or 5 major defects.

EXERCISES 6.8–6.19 SECTION 6.2

6.8 Let x be the number of courses for which a randomly selected student at a certain university is registered. The probability distribution of x appears in the accompanying table.

x	1	2	3	4	5	6	7
$p(x)$	.02	.03	.09	.25	.40	.16	.05

a. What is $P(x = 4)$?
b. What is $P(x \leq 4)$?
c. What is the probability that the selected student is taking at most five courses?
d. What is the probability that the selected student is taking at least five courses? More than five courses?
e. Calculate $P(3 \leq x \leq 6)$ and $P(3 < x < 6)$. Explain in words why these two probabilities are different.

6.9 Airlines sometimes overbook flights. Suppose that for a plane with 100 seats, an airline takes 110 reservations. Define the variable x as the number of people who actually show up for a sold-out flight. From past experience, the probability distribution of x is given in the following table.

x	95	96	97	98	99	100	101	102	103	104	105	106	107	108	109	110
$p(x)$	.05	.10	.12	.14	.24	.17	.06	.04	.03	.02	.01	.005	.005	.005	.0037	.0013

a. What is the probability that the airline can accommodate everyone who shows up for the flight?
b. What is the probability that not all passengers can be accommodated?
c. If you are trying to get a seat on such a flight and you are number 1 on the standby list, what is the probability that you will be able to take the flight? What if you are number 3?

6.10 Many manufacturers have quality control programs that include inspection of incoming materials for defects. Suppose that a computer manufacturer receives computer boards in lots of five. Two boards are selected from each lot for inspection. We can represent possible outcomes of the selection process by pairs. For example, the pair (1, 2) represents the selection of boards 1 and 2 for inspection.
a. List the ten different possible outcomes.
b. Suppose that boards 1 and 2 are the only defective boards in a lot of five. Two boards are to be chosen at random. Define x to be the number of defective boards observed among those inspected. Find the probability distribution of x.

6.11   Simulate the experiment described in Exercise 6.10 using five slips of paper with two marked defective and three marked nondefective. Place the slips in a box, mix them well, and draw out two. Record the number of defectives. Replace the slips and repeat until you have 50 observations on the variable x. Construct a relative frequency distribution for the 50 observations and compare this with the probability distribution obtained in Exercise 6.10.

6.12   Of all airline flight requests received by a certain discount ticket broker, 70% are for domestic travel and 30% are for international flights. Let x be the number of requests among the next three received that are for domestic flights. Assuming independence of successive requests, determine the probability distribution of x. (Hint: One possible outcome is *DID*, with the probability $(.7)(.3)(.7) = .147$.)

6.13   Some parts of California are particularly earthquake-prone. Suppose that in one such area, 20% of all homeowners are insured against earthquake damage. Four homeowners are to be selected at random; let x denote the number among the four who have earthquake insurance.

   a. Find the probability distribution of x. (Hint: Let S denote a homeowner who has insurance and F one who doesn't. Then one possible outcome is *SFSS*, with probability $(.2)(.8)(.2)(.2)$ and associated x value 3. There are 15 other outcomes.)

   b. What is the most likely value for x?

   c. What is the probability that at least two of the four selected have earthquake insurance?

6.14   Let x = the number of underinflated tires on a randomly selected automobile.

   a. Which of the following is a legitimate probability distribution for x, and why are the other two not allowed?

x	0	1	2	3	4
$p(x)$	.3	.2	.1	.05	.05
$p(x)$	.4	.1	.1	.1	.3
$p(x)$	.4	.1	.2	.1	.3

$\Sigma p(x) = 1$

   b. For the legitimate distribution of part (a), compute $P(2 \le x \le 4)$, $P(x \le 2)$, and $P(x \ne 0)$.

   c. If $p(x) = c \cdot (5 - x)$ for $x = 0, 1, \ldots, 4$, what is the value of the constant c? (Hint: $\Sigma p(x) = 1$.)

6.15   A box contains five slips of paper. These slips are marked $1, $1, $1, $10, and $25. The winner of a contest will select two slips of paper at random and will then get the larger of the dollar amounts on the two slips. Define a random variable w by

   w = the amount awarded

   Determine the probability distribution of w. (Hint: Think of the slips as numbered 1, 2, 3, 4, and 5, so that an outcome of the experiment consists of two of these numbers.)

6.16   Components coming off an assembly line are either free of defects (S, for success) or defective (F, for failure). Suppose that 70% of all such components are defect-free. Components are independently selected and tested one by one. Let y denote the number of components that must be tested until a defect-free component is obtained.

a. What is the smallest possible y value, and what experimental outcome gives this y value? What is the second smallest y value, and what outcome gives rise to it?

b. What is the set of all possible y values?

c. Determine the probability of each of the five smallest y values. You should see a pattern that leads to a simple formula for $p(y)$, the probability distribution of y.

6.17   A fair die is rolled. If the outcome is 1, 2, or 3, the die is rolled a second time, and this terminates the experiment. If the outcome of the first roll is 4, 5, or 6, the experiment terminates immediately. Let x denote the number on the upturned face of the die when the experiment terminates. Obtain the probability distribution of x. (Hint: A tree diagram might help; the initial branches should refer to the first roll, and some of these will have second-generation branches attached to them.)

6.18   A contractor is required by a county planning department to submit anywhere from one to five forms (depending on the nature of the project) in applying for a building permit. Let y = the number of forms required of the next applicant. The probability that y forms are required is known to be proportional to y; that is, $p(y) = ky$ for $y = 1, \ldots, 5$.

a. What is the value of k? (Hint: $\Sigma p(y) = 1$.)

b. What is the probability that at most three forms are required?

c. What is the probability that between two and four forms (inclusive) are required?

d. Could $p(y) = y^2/50$ for $y = 1, \ldots, 5$ be the probability distribution of y? Explain.

6.19   A library subscribes to two different weekly news magazines, each of which is supposed to arrive in Wednesday's mail. In actuality, each one could arrive on Wednesday, Thursday, Friday, or Saturday. Suppose that the two arrive independently of one another and that for each one,

$$P(W) = .4, \qquad P(T) = .3, \qquad P(F) = .2, \qquad P(S) = .1$$

Define a random variable y by y = the number of days beyond Wednesday that it takes for both magazines to arrive. For example, if the first arrives on Friday and the second on Wednesday, then $y = 2$, whereas $y = 1$ if both magazines arrive on Thursday. Obtain the probability distribution of y. (Hint: Draw a tree diagram with two generations of branches, the first labeled with arrival days for magazine 1 and the second for magazine 2.)

6.3   The Mean Value and the Standard Deviation

We study a random variable x, such as the number of insurance claims made by a homeowner (a discrete variable) or the tensile strength of wire (a continuous variable), to learn something about how its values are distributed along the measurement scale. The sample mean $\bar{x}$ and sample standard deviation s summarize center and spread in a sample of x values. Similarly, the mean value and standard deviation of a random variable describe where the variable's probability distribution is centered and the extent to which it spreads out about the center.

The Mean Value of a Discrete Random Variable

Consider the experiment consisting of the random selection of an automobile licensed in a particular state. Let the discrete random variable x be the number of low-beam headlights on the selected car that need adjustment. Possible x values are 0, 1, and 2, and the probability distribution of x and the corresponding probability histogram might look as follows:

x value	0	1	2
Probability	.5	.3	.2

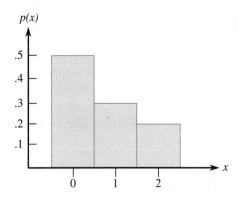

In a sample of 100 such cars, the sample relative frequencies might differ somewhat from these probabilities (which are the limiting relative frequencies). We might see

x value	0	1	2
Frequency	46	33	21

The sample average value of x for these 100 observations is then the sum of 46 zeros, 33 ones, and 21 twos, all divided by 100.

$$\bar{x} = \frac{(46)(0) + (33)(1) + (21)(2)}{100}$$

$$= \left(\frac{46}{100}\right)(0) + \left(\frac{33}{100}\right)(1) + \left(\frac{21}{100}\right)(2)$$

$$= \left(\begin{array}{c}\text{rel. freq.}\\\text{of }0\end{array}\right)(0) + \left(\begin{array}{c}\text{rel. freq.}\\\text{of }1\end{array}\right)(1) + \left(\begin{array}{c}\text{rel. freq.}\\\text{of }2\end{array}\right)(2) = .75$$

As the sample size increases, each relative frequency will approach the corresponding probability. In a very long sequence of experiments, the value of $\bar{x}$ will approach

$$\left(\begin{array}{c}\text{probability}\\\text{that }x = 0\end{array}\right)(0) + \left(\begin{array}{c}\text{probability}\\\text{that }x = 1\end{array}\right)(1) + \left(\begin{array}{c}\text{probability}\\\text{that }x = 2\end{array}\right)(2)$$

$$= (.5)(0) + (.3)(1) + (.2)(2)$$

$$= .70 = \text{mean value of }x$$

Notice that the expression for $\bar{x}$ here is a weighted average of possible x values; the weight for each value is the observed relative frequency. Similarly, the mean value of x is a weighted average, but now the weights are the probabilities from the probability distribution.

DEFINITION

The **mean value of a discrete random variable x,** denoted by μ_x (or just μ when the identity of x is obvious), is computed by first multiplying each possible x value by the probability of observing that value and then adding the resulting quantities. Symbolically,

$$\mu_x = \sum_{\substack{\text{all possible}\\ x \text{ values}}} x \cdot (\text{probability of } x) = \Sigma x \cdot p(x)$$

The phrase "expected value" is sometimes used in place of mean value, and $E(x)$ is alternative notation for μ_x.

EXAMPLE 6.7

Individuals applying for a certain license are allowed up to four attempts to pass the licensing exam. Let x denote the number of attempts made by a randomly selected applicant. The probability distribution of x is as follows:

x	1	2	3	4
$p(x)$	.10	.20	.30	.40

Thus x has mean value

$$\mu_x = \sum_{x=1,\ldots,4} x \cdot p(x)$$

$$= (1) \cdot p(1) + (2) \cdot p(2) + (3) \cdot p(3) + (4) \cdot p(4)$$

$$= (1)(.10) + (2)(.20) + (3)(.30) + (4)(.40)$$

$$= .10 + .40 + .90 + 1.60$$
$$= 3.00$$

It is no accident that the symbol μ for the mean value is the same symbol used earlier for a population mean. When the probability distribution describes how x values are distributed among the members of a population (so probabilities are population relative frequencies), the mean value of x is exactly the average value of x in the population.

EXAMPLE 6.8

At 1 min after birth and again at 5 min, each newborn child is given a numerical rating called an *Apgar score*. Possible values of this score are 0, 1, 2, . . . , 9, and 10. A child's score is determined by five factors: muscle tone, skin color, respiratory effort, strength of heartbeat, and reflex, with a high score indicating a healthy infant. Let the random variable x denote the Apgar score (at 1 min) of a randomly selected newborn infant at a particular hospital, and suppose that x has the following probability distribution.

x	0	1	2	3	4	5	6	7	8	9	10
$p(x)$	.002	.001	.002	.005	.02	.04	.17	.38	.25	.12	.01

The mean value of x is

$$\mu = (0) \cdot p(0) + (1) \cdot p(1) + \cdots + (9) \cdot p(9) + (10) \cdot p(10)$$

$$= (0)(.002) + (1)(.001) + \cdots + (9)(.12) + (10)(.01)$$

$$= 7.16$$

The average Apgar score for a *sample* of newborn children born at this hospital may be $\bar{x} = 7.05$, $\bar{x} = 8.30$, or any one of a number of other possible values between 0 and 10. However, as child after child is born and rated, the average score will approach the value 7.16. This value can be interpreted as the mean Apgar score for the population of all babies born at this hospital.

The Standard Deviation of a Discrete Random Variable

The mean value μ provides only a partial summary of a probability distribution. Two different distributions may both have the same value of μ, yet a long sequence of sample values from one distribution may exhibit considerably more variability than a long sequence of values from the other distribution.

EXAMPLE 6.9

A television manufacturer receives certain components in lots of four from two different suppliers. Let x and y denote the number of defective components in randomly selected lots from the first and second suppliers, respectively. The probability distributions and associated probability histograms for x and y are given in Figure 6.5.

x	0	1	2	3	4
$p(x)$	.4	.3	.2	.1	0

y	0	1	2	3	4
$p(y)$	.2	.6	.2	0	0

FIGURE 6.5
Probability distribution for the number of defective components
(a) In a lot from supplier 1
(b) In a lot from supplier 2

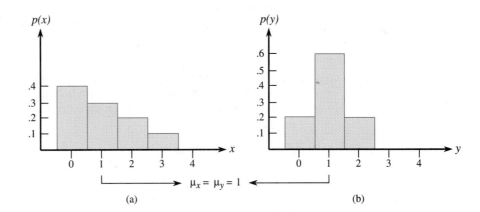

The mean values of both x and y are 1, so for either supplier the long-run average number of defectives per lot is 1. However, the two probability histograms show that the probability distribution for the second supplier is concentrated nearer the mean value than is the first supplier's distribution. The greater spread of the first distribution implies that there will be more variability in a long sequence of observed x values than in an observed sequence of y values. For example, the y sequence will contain no 3s, whereas in the long run, 10% of the observed x values will be 3.

As with s^2 and s, the variance and standard deviation of x involve squared deviations from the mean. A value far from the mean results in a large squared deviation. However, such a value contributes substantially to variability in x only if the probability associated with that value is not too small. For example, if $\mu_x = 1$ and $x = 25$ is a possible value, the squared deviation is $(25 - 1)^2 = 576$. If, however, $P(x = 25) = .000001$, the value 25 will hardly ever be observed, so it won't contribute much to variability in a long sequence of observations. This is why each squared deviation is multiplied by the probability associated with the value (and thus weighted) to obtain a measure of variability.

> **DEFINITION**
>
> The **variance of a discrete random variable x,** denoted by σ_x^2 or just σ^2, is computed by first subtracting the mean from each possible x value to obtain the deviations, then squaring each deviation and multiplying the result by the probability of the corresponding x value, and finally adding these quantities. Symbolically,
>
> $$\sigma^2 = \sum_{\substack{\text{all possible} \\ x \text{ values}}} (x - \mu)^2 \cdot p(x)$$
>
> The **standard deviation of x,** denoted by σ_x or just σ, is the square root of the variance.

When the probability distribution describes how x values are distributed among members of a population (so probabilities are population relative frequencies), σ^2 and σ are the population variance and standard deviation (of x), respectively.

EXAMPLE 6.10

(*Example 6.9 continued*) For $x =$ the number of defectives in a lot from the first supplier,

$$\sigma_x^2 = (0 - 1)^2 \cdot p(0) + (1 - 1)^2 \cdot p(1) + (2 - 1)^2 \cdot p(2) + (3 - 1)^2 \cdot p(3)$$
$$= (1)(.4) + (0)(.3) + (1)(.2) + (4)(.1)$$
$$= 1.0$$

so $\sigma_x = 1.0$. For $y =$ the number of defectives in a lot from the second supplier,

$$\sigma_y^2 = (0 - 1)^2 (.2) + (1 - 1)^2(.6) + (2 - 1)^2(.2)$$
$$= .4$$

Then $\sigma_y = \sqrt{.4} = .632$. The fact that $\sigma_x > \sigma_y$ confirms the impression conveyed by Figure 6.5 concerning the variability of x and y.

EXAMPLE 6.11

(*Example 6.8 continued*) Reconsider the distribution of Apgar scores for children born at a certain hospital. What is the probability that a child's score will be within two standard deviations of the mean score for the hospital? As Figure 6.6 shows, values of x within two standard deviations of the mean are those for which $\mu - 2\sigma < x < \mu + 2\sigma$.

FIGURE 6.6
Values within two standard
deviations of the mean

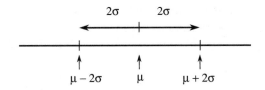

We already have $\mu = 7.16$. The variance is

$$\sigma^2 = \Sigma(x - \mu)^2 \cdot p(x) = \Sigma(x - 7.16)^2 \cdot p(x)$$
$$= (0 - 7.16)^2(.002) + (1 - 7.16)^2(.001) + \cdots + (10 - 7.16)^2(.01)$$
$$= 1.5684$$

$$\sigma = \sqrt{1.5684} = 1.25$$

This gives

$$P(\mu - 2\sigma \leq x \leq \mu + 2\sigma) = P(7.16 - 2.50 \leq x \leq 7.16 + 2.50)$$
$$= P(4.66 \leq x \leq 9.66)$$
$$= P(x = 5, 6, 7, 8, \text{ or } 9)$$
$$= p(5) + \cdots + p(9)$$
$$= .96$$

EXERCISES 6.20–6.31   SECTION 6.3

6.20   A personal computer salesperson working on a commission receives a fixed amount
for each system sold. Suppose that for a given month, the probability distribution
of $x = $ the number of systems sold is given in the accompanying table.

x	1	2	3	4	5	6	7	8
$p(x)$	.05	.10	.12	.30	.30	.11	.01	.01

a. Find the mean value of x (the mean number of systems sold).
b. What is the probability that x is within 2 of its mean value?

6.21   Refer to the previous exercise.
a. Find the variance and standard deviation of x. How would you interpret these
values?
b. What is the probability that the number of systems sold is within one standard
deviation of its mean value?
c. What is the probability that the number sold is more than two standard deviations from the mean?

6.22   A local television station sells 15-s, 30-s, and 60-s advertising spots. Let x denote the length of a randomly selected commercial appearing on this station, and suppose that the probability distribution of x is given in the accompanying table.

x	15	30	60
$p(x)$	.1	.3	.6

a. Find the average length for commercials appearing on this station.
b. If a 15-s spot sells for $500, a 30-s spot for $800, and a 60-s spot for $1000, find the average amount paid for commercials appearing on this station. (Hint: Consider a new variable, y = cost, and then find the probability distribution and mean value of y.)

6.23   An author has written a book and submitted it to a publisher. The publisher offers to print the book and gives the author the choice between a flat payment of $10,000 or a royalty plan. Under the royalty plan, the author would receive $1 for each copy of the book sold. The author thinks that the accompanying table gives the probability distribution of the variable x = the number of books that will be sold. Which payment plan should the author choose? Why?

x	1,000	5,000	10,000	20,000
$p(x)$	.05	.3	.4	.25

6.24   A grocery store has an express line for customers purchasing at most 5 items. Let x be the number of items purchased by a randomly selected customer using this line. Give examples of two different assignments of probabilities such that the resulting distributions have the same mean but have standard deviations that are quite different.

6.25   Refer to Exercise 6.9 and compute the mean value of the number of people holding reservations who show up for the flight.

6.26   Exercise 6.8 gave the following probability distribution for x, the number of courses for which a randomly selected student is registered.

x	1	2	3	4	5	6	7
$p(x)$	.02	.03	.09	.25	.40	.16	.05

a. Calculate the mean value of x.
b. Calculate the standard deviation of x.
c. What possible values of x are within two standard deviations of the mean value (that is, in the interval from $\mu - 2\sigma$ to $\mu + 2\sigma$)? What is the probability that the observed value of x is within two standard deviations of the mean value?

6.27   A gas station sells gasoline at the following prices (cents per gallon, depending on the type of gas and service) 115.9, 118.7, 129.9, 139.9, 144.9, and 159.7. Let y denote the price per gallon paid by a randomly selected customer.
a. Is y a discrete random variable? Explain.
b. Suppose that the probability distribution of y is as follows.

y	115.9	118.7	129.9	139.9	144.9	159.7
$p(y)$	.36	.24	.10	.16	.08	.06

What is the probability that a randomly selected customer has paid more than $1.20 per gallon? Less that $1.40 per gallon?

c. Refer to part (b), and calculate the mean value and standard deviation of y. Interpret these values.

6.28 A chemical supply company currently has in stock 100 lb of a certain chemical, which it sells to customers in 5-lb lots. Let x = the number of lots ordered by a randomly chosen customer. The probability distribution of x is as follows.

x	1	2	3	4
$p(x)$	.2	.4	.3	.1

a. Calculate the mean value of x.

b. Calculate the variance and standard deviation of x.

6.29 Return to Exercise 6.28, and let y denote the amount of material left (lb) after the next customer's order is shipped.

a. What are the possible values of y?

b. What is the probability associated with each possible y value (the probability distribution of y)?

c. Calculate μ_y.

6.30 Let x be a random variable with mean value μ_x and standard deviation σ_x. Define a new random variable $y = ax + b$, where a and b are numerical constants (for example, $y = 5x + 20$). Thus y is a linear function of x. It is then not difficult to show that

$$\mu_y = a\mu_x + b \qquad \sigma_y = |a| \cdot \sigma_x$$

(The absolute value of a is needed in case a is negative, since σ_y cannot be negative.)

a. Suppose x = the number of units sold, y = the resulting profit, $y = 20x - 100$, $\mu_x = 50$, and $\sigma_x = 10$. What is the mean value of the profit, and what is the standard deviation of the profit?

b. Return to Exercise 6.29, and use the fact that $\mu_x = 2.3$ to determine the mean value of the amount left after the next order has been shipped (x and y there *are* linearly related; what is the relationship?).

6.31 Frequently we are interested not so much in μ_x, the mean value of x, as in the mean value of a specified function of x. For example, x might be the number of units of a certain commodity sold; the function of interest would then be the resulting profit. Let $h(x)$ denote the function whose mean value is desired. Then

$$\mu_{h(x)} = \text{the mean value of the function } h(x) = \Sigma h(x) \cdot p(x)$$

That is, the mean value of x is a weighted average of x values, and the mean value of $h(x)$ is a weighted average of $h(x)$ values.

Example 6.7 gave the accompanying probability distribution for the variable x representing the number of attempts by a randomly selected applicant to pass a licensing exam. Suppose that someone who makes x attempts is charged x^2 dollars. Calculate the mean value of the amount charged, that is, the mean value of $h(x) = x^2$.

x	1	2	3	4
$p(x)$	.1	.2	.3	.4

6.4   The Binomial Distribution (Optional)

Suppose we decide to record the sex of each of the next 25 newborn children at a particular hospital. What is the chance that at least 15 are female? What is the chance that between 10 and 15 are female? How many among the 25 can we expect to be female? These and other similar questions can be answered by studying the *binomial probability distribution*. This distribution arises when the experiment of interest is a *binomial experiment,* one having the following characteristics.

PROPERTIES OF A BINOMIAL EXPERIMENT

1. It consists of a fixed number of smaller experiments called *trials.*
2. Each trial can result in one of only two outcomes, labeled *success* (*S*) and *failure* (*F*).
3. Outcomes of different trials are independent.
4. The probability that a trial results in *S* is the same for each trial.
5. The **binomial random variable** x is defined as

   x = the number of successes observed when the experiment is performed

The probability distribution of x is called the *binomial probability distribution.*

The assignment of the *S-F* labels in any particular problem context is arbitrary. In coin tossing, for example, *S* can be identified with either a head or a tail, as long as subsequent calculations are consistent with the assignment.

One illustration of a binomial probability distribution was given in Example 6.5. There we considered x = the number among four customers who selected an electric (as opposed to gas) dryer. This is a binomial experiment with

number of trials = 4, $P(\text{success}) = P(E) = .4$

The 16 ((2)(2)(2)(2)) possible outcomes, along with their probabilities, were displayed in Table 6.1.

Consider now the case of five customers, a binomial experiment with five trials. Here the binomial distribution will tell us how much probability is distributed to each of the possible x values 0, 1, 2, 3, 4, and 5. Five of the 32 possible outcomes yield $x = 1$:

$$SFFFF \quad FSFFF \quad FFSFF \quad FFFSF \quad FFFFS$$

By independence, the first of these has probability

$$
\begin{aligned}
P(SFFFF) &= P(S) \cdot P(F) \cdot P(F) \cdot P(F) \cdot P(F) \\
&= (.4)(.6)(.6)(.6)(.6) \\
&= (.4)(.6)^4 \\
&= .05184
\end{aligned}
$$

This is also the probability of each of the other four outcomes with $x = 1$; when the probabilities are multiplied, only the *number* of S's is relevant, not on which trials they occur. Thus

$$
\begin{aligned}
p(1) &= P(x = 1) \\
&= P(SFFFF \text{ or } FSFFF \text{ or } FFSFF \text{ or } FFFSF \text{ or } FFFFS) \\
&= .05184 + .05184 + .05184 + .05184 + .05184 \\
&= (5)(.05184) \\
&= .2592
\end{aligned}
$$

Similarly, there are ten outcomes for which $x = 2$, because there are ten ways to select two from among the five trials to be the S's: $SSFFF, SFSFF, \ldots$, and $FFFSS$. Each of these has probability

$$
\begin{aligned}
P(SSFFF) &= (.4)(.4)(.6)(.6)(.6) \\
&= (.4)^2(.6)^3 \\
&= .03456
\end{aligned}
$$

from which

$$
\begin{aligned}
p(2) &= P(x = 2) \\
&= P(SSFFF) + \cdots + P(FFFSS) \\
&= (10)(.4)^2(.6)^3 \\
&= .3456
\end{aligned}
$$

The general form of the distribution here is

$$
\begin{aligned}
p(x) &= P(x\ S\text{'s among the five trials}) \\
&= \binom{\text{no. of outcomes}}{\text{with } x\ S\text{'s}}\binom{\text{probability of any particular}}{\text{outcome with } x\ S\text{'s}} \\
&= \binom{\text{no. of outcomes}}{\text{with } x\ S\text{'s}} \cdot (.4)^x \cdot (.6)^{5-x}
\end{aligned}
$$

Let n denote the number of trials in the experiment. Then the number of outcomes with x S's is the number of ways of selecting x from among the n trials to be the success trials; from Section 5.5 on counting methods, this is just the number of combinations of size x that can be formed from n distinct objects (the trials). An expression for this quantity is

$$\text{number of outcomes with } x \text{ successes} = \frac{n!}{x!(n-x)!}$$

where for any positive whole number m, the symbol $m!$ (read "m factorial") is defined by

$$m! = m(m-1)(m-2) \cdots (2)(1)$$

and $0! = 1$ (see Section 5.5 for examples).

THE BINOMIAL PROBABILITY DISTRIBUTION

Let

n = the number of trials in the experiment

$\pi = P(S)$ (the probability that any
                    particular trial results in a success)

Then

$p(x) = P(x$ successes among the n trials)

$$= \frac{n!}{x!(n-x)!} \cdot \pi^x(1-\pi)^{n-x} \qquad x = 0, 1, 2, \ldots, n$$

EXAMPLE 6.12

Sixty percent of all watches sold by a large discount store have a digital display and 40% have an analog display. The type of watch purchased by each of the next 12 customers will be noted. Define a random variable x by

x = the number of watches among these 12 that have a digital display

Letting S denote the sale of a digital watch, x is a binomial random variable with $n = 12$ and $\pi = P(S) = .60$. The probability distribution of x is given by

$$p(x) = \frac{12!}{x!(12-x)!} \cdot (.6)^x(.4)^{12-x} \qquad x = 0, 1, 2, \ldots, 12$$

The probability that exactly four watches are digital is

$$p(4) = P(x = 4) = \frac{12!}{4!8!} \cdot (.6)^4(.4)^8$$

$$= \frac{(12)(11)(10)(9)(8)(7)(6) \cdots (2)(1)}{(4)(3)(2)(1) \cdot 8!} \cdot (.6)^4(.4)^8$$

$$= \frac{(12)(11)(10)(9)}{(4)(3)(2)(1)} \cdot (.6)^4(.4)^8$$

$$= (495)(.6)^4(.4)^8$$

$$= .042$$

If group after group of 12 purchases is examined, the long-run percentage of those with exactly four watches will be 4.2%. According to this calculation, 495 of the possible outcomes (there are $2^{12} = 4096$) have $x = 4$. Notice also how the larger factorial in the denominator cancels with a portion of the numerator factorial.

The probability that between four and seven (inclusive) of these watches are digital is

$$P(4 \leq x \leq 7) = P(x = 4 \text{ or } 5 \text{ or } 6 \text{ or } 7)$$

$$= p(4) + p(5) + p(6) + p(7)$$

$$= \frac{12!}{4!8!} \cdot (.6)^4(.4)^8 + \cdots + \frac{12!}{7!5!} \cdot (.6)^7(.4)^5$$

$$= .042 + .101 + .177 + .227$$

$$= .547$$

Notice that

$$P(4 < x < 7) = P(x = 5 \text{ or } 6)$$
$$= p(5) + p(6)$$
$$= .278$$

So the probability depends on whether $<$ or $\leq$ appears.

The binomial distribution formula can be tedious to use unless n is very small. We have included in the appendixes a tabulation (Table I) of binomial probabilities for selected n in combination with various values of π. This should help you practice using the binomial distribution without getting bogged down in arithmetic.

USING TABLE I

To find $p(x)$ for any particular value of x,

1. Locate the part of the table corresponding to your value of n (5, 10, 15, 20, or 25)
2. Move down to the row labeled with your value of x.
3. Go across to the column headed by the specified value of π.

The desired probability is at the intersection of the designated x row and π column. For example, when $n = 20$ and $\pi = .8$,

$$p(15) = P(x = 15)$$
$$= \text{the entry at the intersection of the } x = 15 \text{ row}$$
$$\text{and } \pi = .8 \text{ column}$$
$$= .175$$

Although $p(x)$ is positive for every possible x value, many probabilities are zero to three decimal places, so they appear as .000 in the table. There are much more extensive binomial tables available. Alternatively, it is easy to program a computer or some calculators to calculate these probabilities.

Suppose that a population consists of N individuals or objects, each one classified as an S or an F. If sampling is carried out without replacement (as it almost always is), then successive draws are dependent. However, when the sample size n is much smaller than N, the extent of this dependence is minimal.

Let x denote the number of S's in a sample of size n from a population containing N individuals or objects. If $n/N \leq .05$ (at most 5% of the population is sampled), then x has approximately a binomial distribution.

EXAMPLE 6.13

In recent years homeowners have become increasingly security conscious. A *Los Angeles Times* poll (November 10, 1991) reported that almost 20% of Southern California homeowners questioned had installed a home security system. Suppose that exactly 20% of all such homeowners have a system. Consider a random sample of $n = 20$ homeowners (much less than 5% of the population). Then x, the number of homeowners in the sample who have a security system, has (approximately) a binomial distribution with $n = 20$ and $\pi = .20$. The probability that five of those sampled have a system is

$$p(5) = P(x = 5)$$
$$= \text{the entry in the } x = 5 \text{ row and } \pi = .20 \text{ column from the}$$
$$n = 20 \text{ part of Table I}$$
$$= .175$$

The probability that at least 40% of those in the sample—that is, 8 or more—have a system is

$$P(x \geq 8) = P(x = 8, 9, 10, \ldots, 19, 20)$$
$$= p(8) + p(9) + \cdots + p(20)$$
$$= .022 + .007 + .002 + .000 + \cdots + .000$$
$$= .031$$

If, in fact, $\pi = .20$, only about 3% of all samples of size 20 would result in at least eight homeowners having a security system. Because $P(x \geq 8)$ is so small when $\pi = .20$, if $x \geq 8$ were actually observed, a reasonable conclusion would be that $\pi > .20$. In Chapter 10 we show how hypothesis-testing methods can be used to decide which of two contradictory claims about a population (for example, $\pi = .20$ or $\pi > .20$) is more plausible.

The Mean Value and the Standard Deviation of x

A binomial random variable x based on n trials has possible values $0, 1, 2, \ldots, n$, so the mean value is

$$\mu = \Sigma x \cdot p(x) = (0) \cdot p(0) + (1) \cdot p(1) + \cdots + n \cdot p(n)$$

and the variance of x is

$$\sigma^2 = \Sigma(x - \mu)^2 \cdot p(x)$$
$$= (0 - \mu)^2 \cdot p(0) + (1 - \mu)^2 \cdot p(1) + \cdots + (n - \mu)^2 \cdot p(n)$$

These expressions would appear to be very tedious to evaluate for any particular values of n and π. Fortunately, algebraic manipulation results in considerable simplification, so that summation is unnecessary.

The mean value and the standard deviation of a binomial random variable are

$$\mu = n\pi, \qquad \sigma = \sqrt{n\pi(1 - \pi)}$$

EXAMPLE 6.14

It has been reported (*Newsweek,* December 2, 1991) that one-third of all credit-card users pay their bills in full each month. This figure is, of course, an average across different cards and issuers. Suppose that 30% of all individuals holding Visa cards issued by a certain bank pay in full each month ($\pi = .30$, although the bank might not call such individuals successes). A random sample of $n = 25$ cardholders is to be selected. The mean value of the number x who pay in full each month is

$$\mu_x = n\pi = 25(.30) = 7.5$$

and the standard deviation is

$$\sigma_x = \sqrt{n\pi(1 - \pi)} = \sqrt{25(.30)(.70)} = \sqrt{5.25} = 2.29$$

The probability that x is further than one standard deviation from its mean value is

$$
\begin{aligned}
P(x < \mu - \sigma \text{ or } x > \mu + \sigma) &= P(x < 5.21 \text{ or } x > 9.79) \\
&= P(x \leq 5) + P(x \geq 10) \\
&= p(0) + \cdots + p(5) + p(10) + \cdots + p(25) \\
&= .382 \qquad \text{(using Table I)}
\end{aligned}
$$

The value of σ is zero when $\pi = 0$ or $\pi = 1$. In these two cases there is no uncertainty in x: we are sure to observe $x = 0$ when $\pi = 0$ and $x = n$ when $\pi = 1$. It is also easily verified that $\pi(1 - \pi)$ is largest when $\pi = .5$. Thus the binomial distribution spreads out the most when sampling from a 50-50 population. The farther π is from .5, the less spread out is the distribution.

EXERCISES 6.32–6.45   SECTION 6.4

6.32   **a.** In a binomial experiment consisting of six trials, how many outcomes have exactly one S, and what are these outcomes?
   b. In a binomial experiment consisting of 20 trials, how many outcomes have exactly ten S's? Exactly fifteen S's? Exactly five S's?

6.33   Twenty-five percent of the customers entering a grocery store between 5 P.M. and 7 P.M. use an express checkout. Consider five randomly selected customers, and let x denote the number among the five who use the express checkout.
   a. What is $p(2)$, that is, $P(x = 2)$?
   b. What is $P(x \leq 1)$?
   c. What is $P(2 \leq x)$? (Hint: Make use of your computation in part (b).)
   d. What is $P(x \neq 2)$?

6.34   The *Los Angeles Times* (December 13, 1983) reported that only 58% of the tenth graders in Los Angeles high schools graduate from those schools 3 years later. (Of the 42% who did not graduate from Los Angeles schools, some moved to other school districts, but most are presumed to have dropped out.) Suppose that four tenth graders are randomly selected from Los Angeles schools. This is a binomial experiment with $\pi = .58$, $n = 4$, and $x =$ the number among the four who graduate.
   a. What is the probability that all four students graduate 3 years later from a Los Angeles school (that is, that $x = 4$)?
   b. What is the probability that exactly three of the four graduate from Los Angeles schools?
   c. What is the probability that at least three graduate from Los Angeles schools?

d. What is the probability that none of the four graduate from Los Angeles schools?

6.35 A breeder of show dogs is interested in the number of female puppies in a litter. If a birth is equally likely to result in a male or female puppy, give the probability distribution of the variable

$$x = \text{the number of female puppies in a litter of size 5}$$

6.36 A manufacturer of camera flash bars notes that defective flash bulbs are sometimes produced. If the probability that any given bulb will be defective is .05, what is the probability that there are no defective flashes on a flash bar containing ten bulbs? What is the probability that at most one of the ten bulbs is defective?

6.37 Industrial quality control programs often include inspection of incoming materials from suppliers. If parts are purchased in large lots, a typical plan might be to select 20 parts at random from a lot and inspect them. A lot might be judged acceptable if one or fewer defective parts are found among those inspected. Otherwise, the lot is rejected and returned to the supplier. Use Table I to find the probability of accepting lots that have each of the following.
a. 5% defective parts
b. 10% defective parts
c. 20% defective parts
(Hint: Identify success with a defective part.)

6.38 In an experiment to investigate whether a graphologist (handwriting analyst) could distinguish a normal person's handwriting from that of a psychotic, a well-known expert was given ten files, each containing handwriting samples from a normal person and from a person diagnosed as psychotic. The graphologist was then asked to identify the psychotic's handwriting. The graphologist made correct identification in six of the ten trials (data taken from *Statistics in the Real World,* Larsen and Stroup. New York: MacMillan Publishing Co., 1976). Does this evidence indicate that the graphologist has an ability to distinguish the handwriting of psychotics? (Hint: What is the probability of correctly guessing six or more times out of ten? Your answer should depend on whether this probability is relatively small or large.)

6.39 If the temperature in Florida falls below 32° F during certain periods of the year, there is a chance that the citrus crop will be damaged. Suppose that the probability is .1 that any given tree will show measurable damage when the temperature falls to 30° F. If the temperature does drop to 30° F, what is the expected number of trees showing damage in an orchard of 2000 trees? What is the standard deviation of the number of trees that show damage?

6.40 Thirty percent of all automobiles undergoing a headlight inspection at a certain inspection station fail the inspection.
a. Among 15 randomly selected cars, what is the probability that at most five fail the inspection?
b. Among 15 randomly selected cars, what is the probability that between five and ten (inclusive) fail the inspection?
c. Among 25 randomly selected cars, what is the mean value of the number that *pass* the inspection, and what is the standard deviation of the number that pass the inspection?

d. What is the probability that among 25 randomly selected cars, the number that pass is within one standard deviation of the mean value?

6.41   You are to take a multiple choice exam consisting of 100 questions with five possible responses to each. Suppose that you have not studied and so must guess (select one of the five answers in a completely random fashion) on each question. Let x represent the number of correct responses on the test.
  a. What kind of probability distribution does x have?
  b. What is your expected score on the exam? (Hint: Your expected score is the mean value of the x distribution.)
  c. Compute the variance and standard deviation of x.
  d. Based on your answers to parts (b) and (c), is it likely that you would score over 50 on this exam? Explain the reasoning behind your answer.

6.42   Suppose that 20% of the 10,000 signatures on a certain recall petition are invalid. Would the number of invalid signatures in a sample of size 1000 have (approximately) a binomial distribution? Explain.

6.43   A coin is to be tossed 25 times. Let $x =$ the number of tosses that result in heads (H). Consider the following rule for deciding whether or not the coin is fair.

Judge the coin to be fair if $8 \le x \le 17$.
Judge it to be biased if either $x \le 7$ or $x \ge 18$.

  a. What is the probability of judging the coin to be biased when it is actually fair?
  b. What is the probability of judging the coin to be fair when $P(H) = .9$, so that there is a substantial bias? Repeat for $P(H) = .1$.
  c. What is the probability of judging the coin to be fair when $P(H) = .6$? When $P(H) = .4$? Why are the probabilities so large compared to the probabilities in part (b)?
  d. What happens to the "error probabilities" of parts (a) and (b) if the decision rule is changed so that the coin is judged fair if $7 \le x \le 19$ and unfair otherwise? Is this a better rule than the one first proposed?

6.44   A city ordinance requires that a smoke detector be installed in all residential housing. There is concern that too many residences are still without detectors, so a costly inspection program is being contemplated. Let $\pi =$ the proportion of all residences that have a detector. A random sample of 25 residences will be selected. If the sample strongly suggests that $\pi < .80$ (fewer than 80% have detectors), as opposed to $\pi \ge .80$, the program will be implemented. Let $x =$ the number of residences among the 25 that have a detector, and consider the following decision rule.

Reject the claim that $\pi \ge .8$ and implement the program if $x \le 15$.

  a. What is the probability that the program is implemented when $\pi = .80$?
  b. What is the probability that the program is not implemented if $\pi = .70$? If $\pi = .60$?
  c. How do the "error probabilities" of parts (a) and (b) change if the value 15 in the decision rule is changed to 14?

6.45   Exit polling has been a controversial practice in recent elections, since early release of the resulting information appears to affect whether or not those who have not yet voted will do so. Suppose that 90% of all registered California voters favor banning the release of information from exit polls in presidential elections until after the polls in California close. A random sample of 25 California voters is selected.

    a. What is the probability that more than 20 favor the ban?

    b. What is the probability that at least 20 favor the ban?

    c. What are the mean value and standard deviation of the number who favor the ban?

    d. If fewer than 20 in the sample favor the ban, is this at odds with the assertion that (at least) 90% of the populace favors the ban? (Hint: Consider $P(x < 20)$ when $\pi = .9$.)

CHAPTER SIX SUMMARY OF KEY CONCEPTS AND FORMULAS

Term or Formula	Comment
Random variable: discrete or continuous	A numerical variable with a value determined by the outcome of a chance experiment: it is discrete if its possible values are isolated points on the number line and continuous if its possible values form an entire interval on the number line.
Probability distribution $p(x)$ of a discrete random variable x	A formula, table, or graph that gives the probability associated with each x value. Conditions on $p(x)$ are (1) $p(x) \geq 0$, and (2) $\Sigma p(x) = 1$, where the sum is over all possible x values.
$\mu_x = \Sigma x \cdot p(x)$	The mean value of a discrete random variable x; it locates the center of the variable's probability distribution.
$\sigma_x^2 = \Sigma(x - \mu)^2 \cdot p(x)$ $\sigma_x = \sqrt{\sigma_x^2}$	The variance and standard deviation, respectively, of a discrete random variable; these are measures of the extent to which the variable's distribution spreads out about μ_x.
Binomial experiment	An experiment consisting of n smaller experiments called *trials*. Each trial results in one or two outcomes, "success" or "failure"; the trials are independent; and the probability of success, π, is the same on each trial.
Binomial probability distribution: $p(x) = \dfrac{n!}{x!(n-x)!} \cdot \pi^x(1 - \pi)^{n-x}$	This formula gives the probability of observing x successes ($x = 0, 1, \ldots, n - 1$, or n) among the n trials of a binomial experiment.
$\mu = n\pi$ $\sigma_x = \sqrt{n\pi(1 - \pi)}$	The mean and standard deviation of a binomial random variable.

ENCORE

T

he Chapter Preview suggested that one could differentiate between an actual sequence of coin tosses and an artificially generated sequence (obtained by asking someone to write down H's and T's) by examining the length of the longest head run. Let's suppose that a fair coin is to be tossed three times. The random variable of interest is

x = the largest number of consecutive H's in the resulting sequence

Possible outcomes and associated x values are as follows.

Outcome	TTT	HTT	THT	TTH	HTH	HHT	THH	HHH
x value	0	1	1	1	1	2	2	3

Fairness of the coin implies that the outcomes are equally likely, from which, for example,

$$p(1) = P(x = 1) = \frac{\text{no. of outcomes with } x = 1}{8} = \frac{4}{8}$$

The distribution of x appears in the accompanying table

x	0	1	2	3
$p(x)$	$\frac{1}{8}$	$\frac{4}{8}$	$\frac{2}{8}$	$\frac{1}{8}$

If the number of tosses n is at all large, it becomes very tedious to list the 2^n possible outcomes (for example, there are more than one billion when $n = 30$) to obtain the distribution of x. The cited paper presents a clever "recursive" method for determining cumulative probabilities of the form $P(x \le 0), P(x \le 1), P(x \le 2)$, and so on. For example, $P(x \le 3) = 1$ when $n = 1, 2,$ or 3. This information is used to obtain $P(x \le 3)$ when $n = 4$, then $P(x \le 3)$ when $n = 5$, and so on. After reaching the desired n,

$$p(3) = P(x = 3) = P(x \le 3) - P(x \le 2)$$

The result for $n = 200$ is as follows:

x	4	5	6	7	8	9	10	11	12
$p(x)$	.033	.165	.257	.224	.146	.083	.044	.023	.011

In addition,

$$P(x \le 3) = .001, P(x \ge 13) = .013$$

The sequence of length 200 in the preview had $x = 4$. Since

$$P(x \le 4) = P(x \le 3) + P(x = 4) = .034$$

it is very likely that the longest head run in 200 tosses will exceed 4. The given sequence appears to have been artificially generated.

The Schilling paper also gives general expressions for μ_x and σ_x, considers the longest run of *either* heads or tails, and generalizes to a coin for which $P(H)$ is something other than .5.

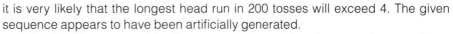

SUPPLEMENTARY EXERCISES 6.46–6.65

6.46 An article in the December 8, 1991 *Los Angeles Times* reported that there are 40,000 travel agencies nationwide, of which 11,000 are members of the American Society of Travel Agents (booking a tour through an ASTA member increases the likelihood of a refund in the event of cancellation).
   a. If x is the number of ASTA members among 5000 randomly selected agencies, could you use the methods of Section 6.4 to compute $P(1200 < x < 1400)$? Why or why not?
   b. In a random sample of 100 agencies, what are the mean value and standard deviation of the number of ASTA members?
   c. If the sample size in (b) is doubled, does the standard deviation double? Explain.

6.47 A soft-drink machine dispenses only regular Coke and diet Coke. Sixty percent of all purchases from this machine are diet drinks. The machine currently has ten cans of each type. If 15 customers want to purchase drinks prior to the machine being restocked, what is the probability that each of the 15 is able to purchase the type of drink desired? (Hint: Let x denote the number among the 15 who want a diet drink. For which possible values of x is everyone satisfied?)

6.48 A mail-order computer software business has six telephone lines. Let x denote the number of lines in use at a specified time. The probability distribution of x is as follows.

x	0	1	2	3	4	5	6
$p(x)$	.10	.15	.20	.25	.20	.06	.04

Write each of the following events in terms of x, and then calculate the probability of each one.
   a. At most three lines are in use.
   b. Fewer than three lines are in use.

   c. At least three lines are in use.
   d. Between two and five lines (inclusive) are in use.
   e. Between two and four lines (inclusive) are *not* in use.
   f. At least four lines are *not* in use.

6.49 Return to Exercise 6.48.
   a. Calculate the mean value and standard deviation of x.
   b. What is the probability that the number of lines in use is farther than three standard deviations from the mean value?

6.50 A new battery's voltage may be acceptable (A) or unacceptable (U). A certain flashlight requires two batteries, so batteries will be independently selected and tested until two acceptable ones have been found. Suppose that 80% of all batteries have acceptable voltages, and let y denote the number of batteries that must be tested.
   a. What is $p(2)$, that is, $P(y = 2)$?
   b. What is $p(3)$? (Hint: There are two different outcomes that result in $y = 3$.)
   c. In order to have $y = 5$, what must be true of the fifth battery selected? List the four outcomes for which $y = 5$, and then determine $p(5)$.
   d. Use the pattern in your answers for parts (a) through (c) to obtain a general formula for $p(y)$.

6.51 Each of the numbers 1, 2, 3, and 4 is to be assigned either a plus sign ($+$) or a minus sign ($-$). Once these have been assigned, the sum will be calculated. Let w denote the resulting sum. For example, if the "signed" numbers are -1, $+2$, -3, and -4, then $w = -1 + 2 - 3 - 4 = -6$. If the signs are assigned independently, and $P(+) = P(-) = .5$, determine the probability distribution of w. (Hint: Construct a tree diagram with two first-generation branches for the two signs that 1 can receive. From each of these, draw two second-generation branches corresponding to $+2$ and -2. Then draw third- and fourth-generation branches.) (Note: An important statistical procedure, the *signed-rank test*, is based on this type of distribution.)

6.52 Two sisters, Allison and Teri, have agreed to meet between 1 and 6 P.M. on a particular day. In fact, Allison is equally likely to arrive at exactly 1 P.M., 2 P.M., 3 P.M., 4 P.M., 5 P.M., or 6 P.M. Teri is also equally likely to arrive at each of these six times, and Allison's and Teri's arrival times are independent of one another. There are thus 36 equally likely (Allison, Teri) arrival-time pairs, for example, (2,3) or (6,1). Suppose the first person to arrive waits until the second person does also; let w be the amount of time the first person has to wait.
   a. What is the probability distribution of w?
   b. How much time do you expect to elapse between the two arrivals?

6.53 Four people—a, b, c, and d—are waiting to give blood. Of these four, a and b have type AB blood, whereas c and d do not. An emergency call has just come in for some type AB blood. If blood samples are taken one by one from the four in random order for blood typing, and x is the number of samples taken to obtain an AB individual (so possible x values are 1, 2, and 3), what is the probability distribution of x? (Hint: See the tree diagram of Example 6.2.)

6.54 Bob and Lygia are going to play a series of Trivial Pursuit games. The first person to win four games will be declared the winner. (This is the World Series of Trivial Pursuit.) Suppose that outcomes of successive games are independent and that the probability of Lygia winning any particular game is .6. Define a random variable x as the number of games played in the series.
   a. What is $p(4)$? (Hint: Either Bob or Lygia could win four straight.)
   b. What is $p(5)$? (Hint: For Lygia to win in exactly five games, what has to happen in the first four games and in game 5?)
   c. Determine the probability distribution of x.
   d. How many games can you expect the series to last?

6.55 Refer to Exercise 6.54, and let y be the number of games won by the series loser. Determine the probability distribution of y.

6.56 A sporting goods store has a special sale on three brands of tennis balls, call them D, P, and W. Because the sale price is so low, only one can of balls will be sold to each customer. If 40% of all customers buy brand W, 35% buy brand P, 25% buy brand D, and x is the number among three randomly selected customers who buy brand W, what is the probability distribution of x?

6.57 A small drugstore orders copies of a news magazine for its magazine rack each week. Let $x =$ the number of customers who come in to buy the magazine during a given week. The probability distribution of x is

x	1	2	3	4	5	6
$p(x)$	$\frac{1}{15}$	$\frac{2}{15}$	$\frac{3}{15}$	$\frac{4}{15}$	$\frac{3}{15}$	$\frac{2}{15}$

The store pays $.25 for each copy purchased, and the price of the magazine is $1. Any magazines unsold at the end of the week have no value.
   a. If the store orders three copies of the magazine, what is the mean value of the profit? (profit = revenue − cost)
   b. Answer the question posed in part (a) when four copies are ordered. Is it better to order three or four copies?

6.58 A student who must write a paper for a course has a choice of two topics. For the first topic, the student will have to request two books through interlibrary loan, or four books for the second topic. The student feels that there will be enough information only if at least half the books ordered arrive on time.
   a. If the books arrive independently of one another and the probability of a book arriving on time is .5, for which topic is there most likely to be sufficient information?
   b. Answer the question posed in part (a) if the on-time probability is .9 rather than .5.

6.59 The n candidates for a job have been ranked 1, 2, 3, . . . , n. Let x be the rank of a randomly selected candidate, so that x has probability distribution

$$p(x) = \begin{cases} \dfrac{1}{n} & \text{if } x = 1, 2, 3, \ldots, n \\ 0 & \text{otherwise} \end{cases}$$

a. Determine μ_x. (Hint: The sum of the first n positive integers, $1 + 2 + \cdots + n$, is $n(n + 1)/2$.)

b. A shortcut formula for the variance of a discrete random variable x is

$$\sigma_x^2 = [\Sigma\, x^2 \cdot p(x)] - \mu_x^2$$

(This is similar to the computational formula for the sample variance.) Use this to obtain σ_x^2 for x as defined at the beginning of the exercise. (Hint: The sum of the squares of the first n positive integers is

$$1^2 + 2^2 + \cdots + n^2 = \frac{n(n + 1)(2n + 1)}{6}\bigg)$$

c. What are μ_x and σ_x when $n = 10$?

6.60 Consider a disease that can be diagnosed by carrying out a blood test. Let π denote the probability that a randomly selected individual has the disease. Given a sample of n independently selected individuals, one way to proceed is by carrying out a separate test on each of the n blood samples. A potentially more economical approach, *group testing*, was introduced during World War II to identify syphilitic men among army inductees. First a part of each blood sample is taken, these are combined, and then a single test is carried out. If no one has the disease, the result will be negative, and only this test is required. If at least one individual is diseased, the group test will give a positive result, in which case the n individual tests are then carried out. Let $y = $ the number of tests performed.

a. What are the two possible values of y?

b. What is $p(1)$, the probability that just one test will suffice? What is the probability of the other possible y value?

c. If $\pi = .1$ and $n = 3$, what is the mean value of the number of tests performed? How does it compare with the number of tests required without group testing?

6.61 A stereo store is offering a special price on a complete system of components. A purchaser is offered a choice of manufacturers for each component:

Receiver: JVC, Kenwood, Pioneer, Sansui, Sony
CD player: BSR, Dual, Sony, Technics
Speakers: AR, KLH, JBL
Cassette deck: Advent, Sony, Teac

A switchboard in the store allows customers to hook together any selection of components (one of each type). Suppose that one component of each type is randomly selected in such a way that different selections are independent. Let x denote the number of Sony components selected.

a. What is $p(0)$, the probability that no Sony components are selected?

b. What is the probability that the only Sony component selected is the receiver? What is $p(1)$? (Hint: The 1 could refer to either the receiver, the CD player, or the deck.)

c. Obtain the probability distribution of x.

6.62 A plan for an executive traveler's club has been developed by an airline on the premise that 10% of its current customers would qualify for membership.

a. Assuming the validity of this premise, among 25 randomly selected current customers, what is the probability that between 2 and 6 (inclusive) qualify for membership?

b. Again assuming the validity of the premise, what are the expected number of customers who qualify and the standard deviation of the number who qualify in a random sample of 100 current customers?

c. Let x denote the number in a random sample of 25 current customers who qualify for membership. Consider rejecting the company's premise in favor of the claim that $\pi > .10$ if $x \geq 7$. What is the probability that the company's premise is rejected when it is actually valid?

d. Referring back to the decision rule introduced in part (c), what is the probability that the company's premise is not rejected even though $\pi = .20$ (that is, 20% qualify)?

6.63 A probability distribution that has been used with great success to model the number of events that occur during a specified time interval is the **Poisson distribution.** Here "events" could be accidents on a stretch of highway, telephone calls to a drug hotline, customers arriving at a service facility, occurrences of tornadoes, and so on. Let x denote the number of events that occur in a time interval of length t. The Poisson probability distribution is then

$$p(x) = P(x \text{ events occur in time } t)$$
$$= \frac{e^{-\alpha t}(\alpha t)^x}{x!}, \qquad x = 0, 1, 2, \ldots$$

where the letter e denotes a fixed number, called the *base of the natural logarithm system*, that has the approximate value 2.7182818. It can be shown that

$$\mu_x = \alpha t$$

so that when $t = 1$ (a one-unit time interval), $\mu_x = \alpha$. Thus α is the mean number of occurrences during a one-unit time interval; that is, it is the *rate* at which events occur over time.

Suppose that airplanes arrive at a certain airport according to a Poisson distribution with rate $\alpha = 2$ per minute.

a. What is the probability that exactly three planes arrive during a 1-min period? (Hint: $e^{-2} \approx$ .1353353.)

b. What is the probability that at least two airplanes arrive during a 1-min period? (Hint: Remember that $P(A) = 1 - P(not\ A)$.)

c. What is the probability that exactly five planes arrive during a 2-min period?

d. What is the mean value of the number of airplanes that arrive during a half-hour period?

6.64 Shortly after being put into service, some buses of a certain type develop cracks on the underside of the mainframe. A particular city has 20 buses of this type, 8 of which actually have cracks. Suppose that five buses are randomly selected for inspection in such a way that each sample of this size has the same chance of selection (by choosing five from among 20 numbered slips). Let x denote the number of buses in the sample that have cracks, and define the symbol $\binom{m}{k}$ by

$$\binom{m}{k} = \frac{m!}{k!(m - k)!}$$

Then counting rules can be used to show that

$p(x) = P(x$ buses in the sample have cracks)

$$= \frac{\text{no. of samples for which } x \text{ buses have cracks}}{\text{number of samples of size 5}}$$

$$= \frac{\binom{8}{x} \cdot \binom{12}{5 - x}}{\binom{20}{5}}$$

(This is called the **hypergeometric distribution**.)

a. What is $p(3)$?

b. What is $P(x \leq 1)$?

6.65 In one "pyramid scheme," a founder recruits someone else to sell a product, then another recruit is signed on by either the founder or the first recruit, then yet another individual is recruited by one of the first three, and so on. The accompanying figure illustrates two different recruitment patterns for the case of a founder plus three recruits. In (a), for example, the founder first recruited person 2; then the founder (rather than person 2) recruited person 3, who in turn recruited person 4.

(a)　　　　(b)

a. Draw a similar picture (a *rooted tree*) for each of the other possible patterns in this case.

b. A *leaf* is an individual who has not yet recruited anyone else (for example, 2 and 4 in (a)). Let x denote the number of leaves, and determine possible values of x for the case under consideration.

c. If at any stage the next person to enter the scheme is equally likely to be recruited by any of those already participating, then the different patterns themselves are equally likely. Use this to determine the probability distribution of x and its mean value.

d. How many different patterns (trees) are there corresponding to a founder plus four recruits? (Hint: How does such a pattern get formed from one corresponding to just three recruits?)

References

The books in the Chapter 5 References contain material on discrete probability distributions.

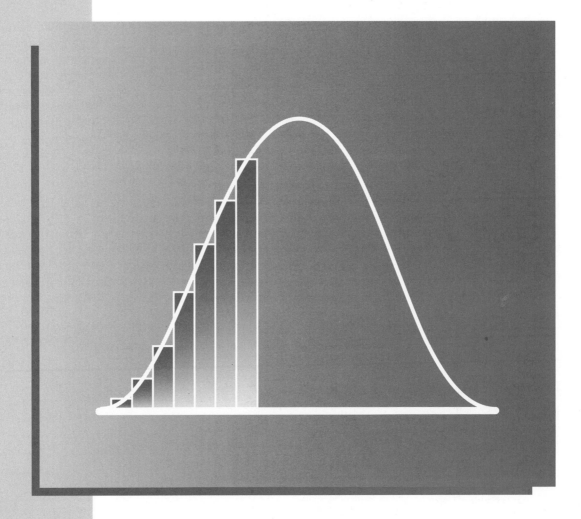

Continuous Probability Distributions

PREVIEW

Ⅰn order to stay profitable in a competitive marketplace, manufacturers are placing increasing emphasis on programs designed to enhance the quality of their products. A discussion of two such programs appeared in the paper "Quality Engineering Using Design of Experiments" (*Proc. of the Amer. Statistical Assoc. Section on Statistical Education* (1982):11–20). Sony color television sets are manufactured in Japan and also in the United States. One characteristic that affects the overall quality of the set is color density. The most desirable value of color density (t) is chosen as a target value, and a set is graded as A, B, C, or "defective," depending on how close its color density is to t. Defective sets are those whose color density differs from t by more than 5. (The value of t was not given in the paper—it must be a trade secret!)

At the time that this study was conducted, the Sony–USA plant focused attention solely on obtaining a color density in the $t \pm 5$ range, whereas the Sony–Japan plant emphasized trying to achieve a color density as close to 5 as possible. The authors noted that the distribution of color density for Sony–USA was more or less uniform (flat) over the range $t \pm 5$, whereas the color-density distribution for Sony–Japan was more mound-shaped. The accompanying picture is similar to one given in the paper and shows the two color-density distributions.

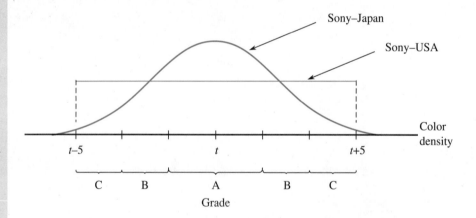

The two color-density distributions were used to justify the author's observations that while Sony–Japan produced more defective sets, they also produced more grade A and fewer grade C sets than did Sony–USA. In the Chapter Encore we will see how specific assumptions about the color-density distributions allow us to determine the proportions of grade A, B, and C sets produced by Sony–USA and Sony–Japan. We will also see how changes in the color-density distributions might affect these proportions.

Introduction

The previous chapter discussed probability distributions for discrete random variables. The other type of random variable is a continuous random variable. Here we will first present general properties of probability distributions for continuous random variables. We will then turn our attention to the most important distribution in all of statistics: The *normal distribution* and the corresponding *bell-shaped curve*.

7.1 Probability Distributions for Continuous Random Variables

A continuous random variable is one that has as its set of possible values an entire interval on the number line. An example is the weight x (lb) of a newborn child. Suppose for the moment that weight is recorded only to the nearest pound. Then possible x values are whole numbers, such as 4 or 9. The probability distribution can be pictured as a probability histogram in which the area of each rectangle is the probability of the corresponding weight value. The total area of all the rectangles is 1, and the probability that a weight (to the nearest pound) is between two values, such as 6 and 8, is the sum of the corresponding rectangular areas. Figure 7.1(a) illustrates this.

FIGURE 7.1
Probability distributions for birth weight:
shaded area = $P(6 \leq \text{weight} \leq 8)$
(a) Weight measured to the nearest pound
(b) Weight measured to the nearest tenth of a pound
(c) Limiting curve as measurement accuracy increases

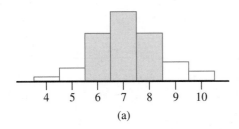
(a)

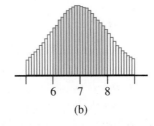
(b)

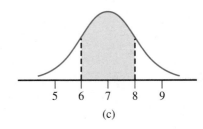
(c)

Now suppose that weight is measured to the nearest *tenth* of a pound. There are many more possible weight values than before, such as 5.0, 5.1, 5.7, 7.3, 8.9, and so on. As shown in Figure 7.1(b), the rectangles in the probability histogram are much narrower and this histogram has a much smoother appearance than the first one. Again, this histogram can be drawn so that area equals probability and the total area of all the rectangles is 1.

Figure 7.1(c) shows what happens as weight is measured to a greater and greater degree of accuracy. The sequence of probability histograms approaches a smooth curve. The curve can't go below the horizontal measurement scale, and the total area under the curve is 1 (because this is true of each probability histogram). The probability that x falls in an interval such as $6 \leq x \leq 8$ is the area under the curve and above that interval.

DEFINITION

A **probability distribution for a continuous random variable x** is specified by a mathematical function $f(x)$, called the **density function,** whose graph is a smooth curve (the **density curve**). It is required that

1. $f(x) \geq 0$ (so the curve cannot dip below the horizontal axis);

2. The total area under the density curve $= 1$.

    The probability that x falls in any particular interval is the area under the density curve and above the interval.

For any two numbers a and b with $a < b$, define three events as follows:

i. $a < x < b$ is the event that the value of x is between a and b.
ii. $x < a$ is the event that the value of x is less than a.
iii. $b < x$ is the event that the value of x exceeds b.

Figure 7.2 illustrates how the probabilities of these events are identified with areas under a density curve.

FIGURE 7.2
Probabilities as areas under a probability density curve

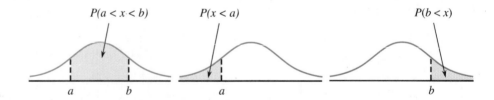

$P(a < x < b)$ $P(x < a)$ $P(b < x)$

                    a b a b

EXAMPLE 7.1

Define a continuous random variable x by

    $x =$ the amount of time (min) taken by a clerk to process a certain type of application form

Suppose that x has a "uniform" distribution with density function

$$f(x) = \begin{cases} .5 & 4 < x < 6 \\ 0 & \text{otherwise} \end{cases}$$

The graph of $f(x)$ (the density curve) is shown in Figure 7.3. It is especially easy to use, since calculating probabilities requires only finding areas of rectangles using the formula

$$\text{area} = (\text{base}) \cdot (\text{height})$$

FIGURE 7.3
The uniform distribution for Example 7.1

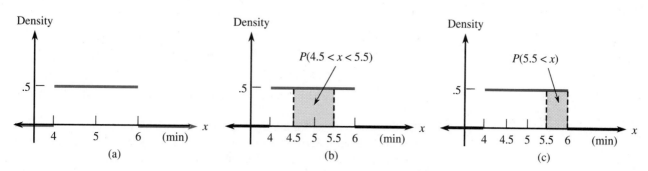

The curve has positive height only between $x = 4$ and $x = 6$, so according to this model, the smallest possible x value is 4 and the largest value is 6. The total area under the curve is just the area of the rectangle with base extending from 4 to 6 and with height .5. This gives

$$\text{area} = (6 - 4)(.5) = 1$$

as required.

As illustrated in Figure 7.3(b), the probability that x is between 4.5 and 5.5 is

$$
\begin{aligned}
P(4.5 < x < 5.5) &= \text{area of shaded rectangle} \\
&= (\text{base width}) \cdot (\text{height}) \\
&= (5.5 - 4.5)(.5) \\
&= .5
\end{aligned}
$$

Similarly, because $x > 5.5$ is equivalent here to $5.5 < x < 6$, we have

$$P(5.5 < x) = (6 - 5.5)(.5) = .25$$

According to this uniform model, in the long run, 25% of all forms that are processed will have processing times that exceed 5.5 min.

The probability that a *discrete* random variable x lies in the interval between two limits a and b depends on whether or not either limit is included in the interval. Suppose, for example, that x is the number of major defects on a new automobile. Then

$$P(3 \leq x \leq 7) = p(3) + p(4) + p(5) + p(6) + p(7)$$

whereas

$$P(3 < x < 7) = p(4) + p(5) + p(6)$$

If, however, x is a *continuous* random variable, such as task completion time, then $P(3 \le x \le 7) = P(3 < x < 7)$. The reason is that the area under a density curve and above a single value such as 3 or 7 is zero. The area above an interval of values therefore does not depend on whether either endpoint is included.

For any two numbers a and b with $a < b$,

$$P(a \le x \le b) = P(a < x \le b) = P(a \le x < b) = P(a < x < b)$$

when x is a continuous random variable.

Probability calculations for continuous random variables are often done using *cumulative* areas. A cumulative area is all the area under the density curve to the left of a particular value. Figure 7.4 illustrates the cumulative area to the left of .5, which is just $P(x < .5)$. The probability that x lies in any particular interval is the difference between two cumulative areas.

FIGURE 7.4
A cumulative area under
a density curve

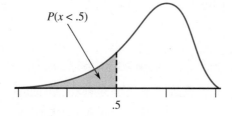

$P(x < .5)$

.5

The probability that a continuous random variable x lies between a lower limit a and an upper limit b is

$$P(a < x < b) = \left(\begin{array}{c} \text{cumulative area to} \\ \text{the left of } b \end{array} \right) - \left(\begin{array}{c} \text{cumulative area to} \\ \text{the left of } a \end{array} \right)$$

$$= P(x < b) - P(x < a)$$

The foregoing property is illustrated in Figure 7.5 for the case $a = .25$ and $b = .75$. We will use this result extensively in the next section when we do normal probability distribution calculations. For many distributions, cumulative areas can be calculated using methods from the branch of mathematics called *integral calculus*.

FIGURE 7.5
Calculation of $P(a < x < b)$ using cumulative areas

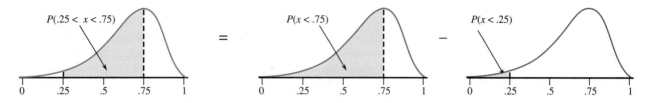

The Mean and the Standard Deviation When x Is Continuous

Figure 7.6 illustrates how the density curve for a continuous random variable can be approximated by a probability histogram of a discrete random variable. Computing the mean value and the standard deviation using this discrete distribution gives an approximation to μ and σ for the continuous random variable x. If an even more accurate approximating probability histogram is used (narrower rectangles), better approximations to μ and σ result.

FIGURE 7.6
Approximating a density curve by a probability histogram

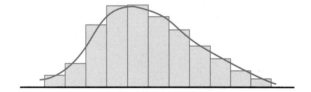

In practice, such an approximation method is often unnecessary. Instead, μ and σ can be defined and computed using methods from calculus. The details need not concern us; what is important is that μ and σ play exactly the same role here as they did in the discrete case. The mean value μ locates the center of the continuous distribution and gives the approximate long-run average of many observed x values. The standard deviation σ measures to what extent the continuous distribution (density curve) spreads out about μ and gives information about the amount of variability that can be expected in a long sequence of observed x values.

EXAMPLE 7.2

A company receives concrete of a certain type from two different suppliers. Define random variables x and y by

> x = compressive strength (lb/in.^{2}) of a randomly selected batch from supplier 1
>
> y = compressive strength of a randomly selected batch from supplier 2

Suppose that

$$\mu_x = 4650 \text{ lb/in.}^2 \qquad \sigma_x = 200 \text{ lb/in.}^2$$
$$\mu_y = 4500 \text{ lb/in.}^2 \qquad \sigma_y = 275 \text{ lb/in.}^2$$

The long-run average strength per batch for many, many batches from the first supplier will be roughly 4650 lb/in.^{2} This is 150 lb/in.^{2} greater than the long-run average for batches from the second supplier. In addition, a long sequence of batches from supplier 1 will exhibit substantially less variability in compressive strength values than will a similar sequence from supplier 2. The first supplier is preferred to the second both in terms of average value and variability. Figure 7.7 displays density curves that are consistent with this information.

FIGURE 7.7
Density curves for
Example 7.2

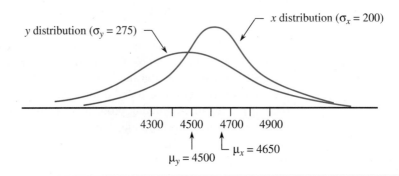

EXERCISES 7.1–7.8   SECTION 7.1

7.1   A particular professor never dismisses class early. (Do you know anyone like this?) Let x denote the amount of time past the hour (minutes) that elapses before the professor dismisses class. Suppose that x has a uniform distribution on the interval from 0 to 10 min. The density curve is shown in the accompanying figure.

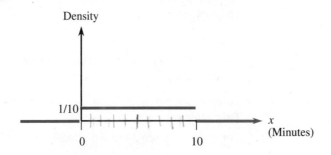

    a. What is the probability that at most 5 min elapse before dismissal?

    b. What is the probability that between 3 and 5 min elapse before dismissal?

    c. What is the mean value of the time that elapses before dismissal? Explain the reasoning you used to obtain your answer.

7.2   If x has a uniform distribution on the interval from A to B, it can be shown that $\sigma = (B - A)/\sqrt{12}$.

    a. Refer to Exercise 7.1. What is the standard deviation of elapsed time until dismissal?

    b. Refer to Exercise 7.1. What is the probability that the elapsed time is within one standard deviation of its mean value?

7.3   The article "Modeling Sediment and Water Column Interactions for Hydrophobic Pollutants" (*Water Research* (1984):1169–1174) suggests the uniform distribution on the interval from 7.5 to 20 as a model for x = depth (cm) of the bioturbation layer in sediment for a certain region. (Please don't ask us what the bioturbation layer is!)

    a. Draw the density curve for x.

    b. What must the height of the density curve be?

    c. What is the probability that x is at most 12?

    d. What is the probability that x is between 10 and 15? Between 12 and 17? Why are these two probabilities equal?

    e. What is the mean value of x?

    f. Use the formula for σ in Exercise 7.2 to calculate the standard deviation of x.

7.4   Let x denote the amount of gravel sales (tons) during a randomly selected week at a particular sales facility. Suppose that the density curve has height $f(x)$ above the value x, where

$$f(x) = \begin{cases} 2(1 - x) & 0 \le x \le 1 \\ 0 & \text{otherwise} \end{cases}$$

The density curve (the graph of $f(x)$) is shown in the accompanying figure. Use the fact that the area of a triangle $= (\frac{1}{2}) \cdot (\text{base}) \cdot (\text{height})$ to calculate each of the following probabilities.

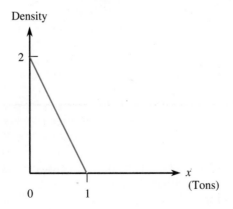

Density

2

0   1

x
(Tons)

    a. $P(x < \frac{1}{2})$

    b. $P(x \le \frac{1}{2})$

    c. $P(x < \frac{1}{4})$

    d. $P(\frac{1}{4} < x < \frac{1}{2})$ (Hint: Use the results of parts (a) through (c).)

    e. The probability that sales exceed $\frac{1}{2}$ ton.

    f. The probability that sales are at least $\frac{3}{4}$ ton.

7.5 Let x be the amount of time (min) that a particular San Francisco commuter must wait for a BART train. Suppose that the density curve is as pictured (a uniform distribution).

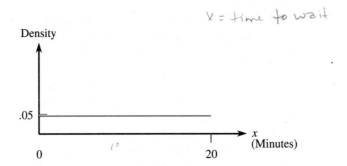

    a. What is the probability that x is less than 10 min? More than 15 min?

    b. What is the probability that x is between 7 and 12 min?

    c. Find the value c for which $P(x < c) = .9$.

7.6 Referring to Exercise 7.5, let x and y be waiting times on two independently selected days. Define a new random variable w by $w = x + y$, the sum of the two waiting times. The set of possible values for w is the interval from 0 to 40 (since both x and y can range from 0 to 20). It can be shown that the density curve of w is as pictured. (It is called a *triangular distribution* for obvious reasons!)

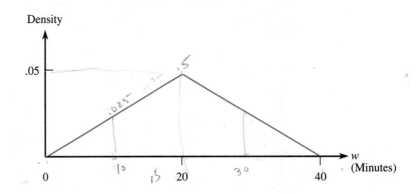

    a. Verify that the total area under the density curve is equal to 1. (Hint: The area of a triangle is .5(base) · (height).)

    b. What is the probability that w is less than 20? Less than 10? More than 30?

    c. What is the probability that w is between 10 and 30? (Hint: It might be easier first to find the probability that w is *not* between 10 and 30.)

7.7 In a certain coin-operated target game, the objective is to get as close as possible to the midpoint of a 2-ft-long horizontal line segment. Identify the midpoint with the value 0 on a measurement scale, and let x = the actual landing point. Any number between -1 and $+1$ is a possible value of x. The density curve for x is specified by the function

$$f(x) = \begin{cases} .75(1 - x^2) & -1 \le x \le 1 \\ 0 & \text{otherwise} \end{cases}$$

A graph of the density curve follows. For any x between -1 and $+1$, the area under the curve to the left of x is $.5 + .75(x - \frac{1}{3}x^3)$.

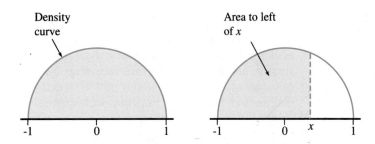

a. Verify that the total area under the density curve (the area to the left of 1) is 1.
b. Calculate $P(x < .5)$ (that is, the area under the density curve to the left of .5).
c. Calculate the probability that the landing point is within ½ foot of the target.
d. What is the mean value of x? (Hint: The density curve is symmetric.)

7.8 An express mail service charges a special rate for any package that weighs less than 1 lb. Let x denote the weight of a randomly selected parcel that qualifies for this special rate. The probability distribution of x is specified by the accompanying density curve.

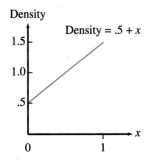

Use the fact that

area of a trapezoid = (base) · (average of two side lengths)

to answer each of the following questions.

a. What is the probability that a randomly selected package of this type is at most ½ lb? Between ¼ lb and ½ lb? At least ¾ lb?

b. It can be shown that $\mu_x = \frac{7}{12}$ and $\sigma_x^2 = \frac{11}{144}$. What is the probability that the value of x is more than one standard deviation from the mean value?

7.2   The Normal Distribution

A normal curve was first introduced in Chapter 2 as one with a shape that gives a very good approximation to histograms for many different data sets. There are actually many different normal curves rather than just one. Every one is bell-shaped, and a particular normal curve results from specifying where the curve is centered and how much it spreads out about its center. For a particular normal distribution, the density function, which gives the height of the curve above each value x on the measurement scale, is rather complicated. Fortunately we needn't deal with it explicitly. For our purposes, an acquaintance with some general properties and a table that gives certain normal curve areas will suffice.

DEFINITION

A continuous random variable x is said to have a **normal distribution** if the density curve of x is a normal curve.[1] The mean value μ determines where the curve is centered on the measurement axis, and the standard deviation σ determines the extent to which the curve spreads out about μ.

Figure 7.8 illustrates normal density curves for several different values of μ and σ. As with all density curves, the total area under each curve is 1.

---

[1]The density function for a normally distributed random variable is

$$f(x) = \frac{1}{\sqrt{2\pi\sigma^2}} \cdot e^{-(x-\mu)^2/2\sigma^2} \qquad \text{for } -\infty < x < \infty$$

where the symbols e and π represent numbers whose approximate values are

$$e \approx 2.7182818, \qquad \pi \approx 3.1415927$$

That is, for any number x, the value of $f(x)$ gives the height of the normal curve (with specified mean μ and standard deviation σ) above the value x on the number line.

FIGURE 7.8
Several normal
density curves

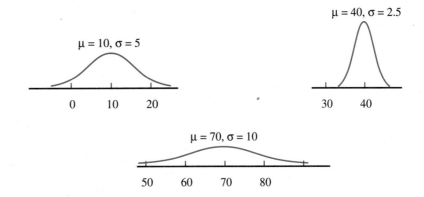

The value of μ is the number on the measurement axis lying directly below the top of the bell. The value of σ can also be ascertained from a picture of the curve. Consider the normal curve pictured in Figure 7.9. Starting at the top of the bell (above 100) and moving to the right, the curve turns downward until it is above the value 110. After that point it continues to decrease in height but is turning up rather than down. Similarly, to the left of 100 it turns down until it reaches 90 and then begins to turn up. The curve changes from turning down to turning up at a distance of 10 on either side of μ, and thus $\sigma = 10$. In general, σ is the distance to either side of μ at which a normal curve changes from turning downward to turning upward.

FIGURE 7.9
Pictorial identification
of μ and σ

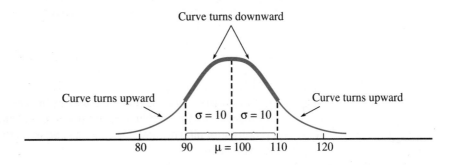

Consider a random variable x having a normal distribution with specified values of μ and σ. Then the probability that an observed x value falls in some interval is the area under the corresponding normal density curve and above that interval. For example, let x denote the number of miles per gallon achieved by a particular type of car in a fuel efficiency test. Suppose that x is a normally distributed variable with $\mu = 27.0$ mi/gal and $\sigma = 1.5$ mi/gal. Figure 7.10 illustrates the curve areas that correspond to various probabilities. It turns out that any normal probability of this sort can be calculated from a single table of cumulative areas.

FIGURE 7.10
Probabilities as curve
areas when x has a
normal distribution with
$\mu = 27.0$ and $\sigma = 1.5$

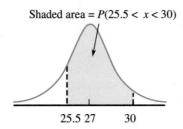

Shaded area $= P(25.5 < x < 30)$

25.5 27   30

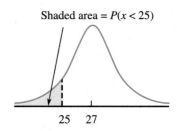

Shaded area $= P(x < 25)$

25   27

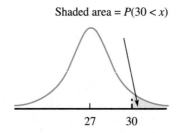

Shaded area $= P(30 < x)$

27   30

The Standard Normal Distribution

Rather than tabulate normal curve areas separately for each different combination of μ and σ, statisticians have chosen a particular normal curve as a reference curve. Once we learn to use the table containing areas (that is, probabilities) for this reference curve, it is easy to obtain areas under any other normal curve.

DEFINITION

A random variable z is said to have a **standard normal distribution** if it has a normal distribution with mean value $\mu = 0$ and standard deviation $\sigma = 1$. The corresponding normal curve is referred to as the **standard normal** or **z curve.**

The z curve is displayed in Figure 7.11(a). It is centered at $\mu = 0$ and the "turning points" are above $z = +1$ and $z = -1$. Appendix Table II, which also appears on the inside front cover, tabulates cumulative z curve areas of the sort shown in Figure 7.11(b) for many different values along the z axis. The smallest value for which the cumulative area is given is -3.49, a value quite far out in the lower tail of the z curve. The next smallest value for which the area appears is -3.48, then -3.47, then -3.46, and so on, in increments of .01, terminating with the cumulative area to the left of 3.49.

FIGURE 7.11
A standard normal (z) curve
and a cumulative area

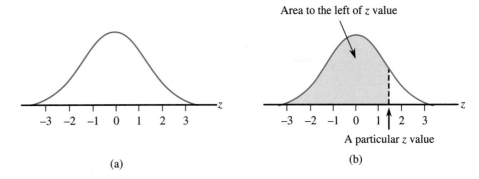

(a)

(b)

Area to the left of z value

A particular z value

USING THE TABLE OF STANDARD NORMAL CURVE AREAS

Let c denote a number between -3.49 and 3.49 that has two digits to
the right of the decimal point (such as -1.76 or 0.58). For each such c,
Appendix Table II gives

$$\begin{pmatrix} \text{area under } z \text{ curve} \\ \text{to the left of } c \end{pmatrix} = P(z < c) = P(z \le c)$$

To find this probability, locate

i. the row labeled with the sign of c and the digits to either side of the
    decimal point (for example, -1.7 or 0.5);
ii. the column identified with the second digit to the right of the decimal
    point in c (for example, $.06$ if $c = -1.76$).

The desired probability is the number at the intersection of this row and
column.

EXAMPLE 7.3

The probability $P(z < -1.76)$ is found at the intersection of the -1.7 row and the
$.06$ column of the z table. The result is

$$P(z < -1.76) = .0392$$

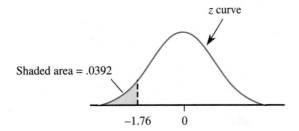

Shaded area = .0392

z curve

-1.76 0

In other words, in a long sequence of observations selected from the standard normal distribution, roughly 3.9% of the observed values will be smaller than -1.76. Similarly,

$$P(z \leq 0.58) = \begin{pmatrix} \text{entry in 0.5 row and} \\ \text{.08 column of Table II} \end{pmatrix} = .7190$$

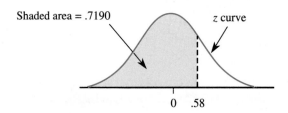

Consider now $P(z < -3.85)$. This probability does not appear in Appendix Table II (there is no -3.8 row). However, it must be true that

$$P(z < -3.85) < P(z < -3.49) \qquad \text{(draw a picture)}$$

Since $P(z < -3.49) = .0002$, it follows that $P(z < -3.85) < .0002$. In practice, we can say that

$$P(z < -3.85) \approx 0$$

Arguing in a similar fashion, $P(z \leq 4.18) > P(z \leq 3.49) = .9998$, from which we conclude that

$$P(z \leq 4.18) \approx 1$$

We can now use the probabilities tabulated in Appendix Table II to calculate other probabilities involving z. For example (see Figure 7.12), the probability that z falls in the interval between a lower limit a and an upper limit b is

FIGURE 7.12
$P(a < z < b)$ as the difference of two cumulative areas

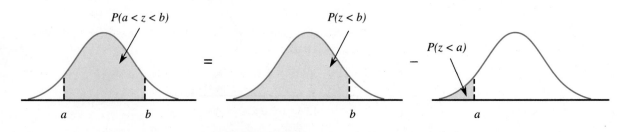

$$P(a < z < b) = \begin{pmatrix} \text{the area under the } z \text{ curve} \\ \text{and above the interval} \\ \text{from } a \text{ to } b \end{pmatrix} = P(z < b) - P(z < a)$$

That is, $P(a < z < b)$ is the difference between two cumulative areas.
Similarly, the probability that z exceeds a value c is

$$P(c < z) = \begin{pmatrix} \text{the area under the } z \text{ curve} \\ \text{to the right of } c \end{pmatrix} = 1 - P(z \le c)$$

In words, a "right-tail" area is 1 minus the corresponding cumulative area. This is illustrated in Figure 7.13.

FIGURE 7.13
Relationship between an upper-tail area and a cumulative area

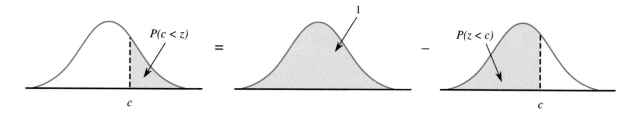

EXAMPLE 7.4

The probability that z is between -1.76 and 0.58 is

$$P(-1.76 < z < 0.58) = P(z < 0.58) - P(z < -1.76)$$
$$= .7190 - .0392$$
$$= .6798$$

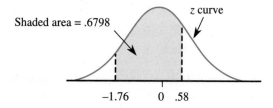

The probability that z is between -2 and $+2$ (within two standard deviations of its mean, since $\mu = 0$ and $\sigma = 1$) is

$$P(-2.00 < z < 2.00) = P(z < 2.00) - P(z < -2.00)$$
$$= .9772 - .0228$$
$$= .9544 \approx .95$$

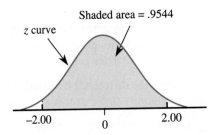

This last probability is the basis for one part of the Empirical Rule, which states that when a histogram is well approximated by a normal curve, roughly 95% of the values are within two standard deviations of the mean.

The probability that the value of z exceeds 1.96 is

$$P(1.96 < z) = 1 - P(z \leq 1.96)$$
$$= 1 - .9750$$
$$= .0250$$

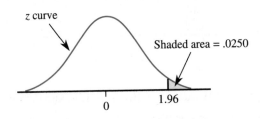

That is, 2.5% of the area under the z curve lies to the right of 1.96 in the upper tail. Similarly,

$$P(-1.28 < z) = \text{area to the right of } -1.28$$
$$= 1 - P(z \leq -1.28)$$
$$= 1 - .1003 = .8997 \approx .90$$

In some applications, the area to be captured under the z curve is specified. The problem is then to find the interval or limit that captures the desired area.

EXAMPLE 7.5

What value on the horizontal z axis is such that the area under the z curve to the left of that value is .67? If c denotes this value, then c must satisfy

$$P(z < c) = .67$$

The accompanying figure illustrates this relationship. The desired cumulative area is .6700, so we enter the "main body" of the z table and look for this value (or the closest one to it). The value .6700 does indeed appear—it is at the intersection of the row labeled 0.4 and the column labeled .04. Thus $c = .44$.

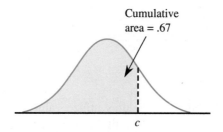

Cumulative
area = .67

To find a value of c for which the captured upper-tail area is .05, that is, for which

$$P(c < z) = .05$$

note that the cumulative area to the left of c must be .95 (see the next illustration).

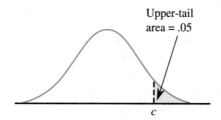

Upper-tail
area = .05

A search for .9500 in Appendix Table II reveals the following:

.9495 is in the 1.6 row and the .04 column.
.9505 is in the 1.6 row and the .05 column.

Because .9500 is halfway between these two areas, we use $c = 1.645$.

What interval, symmetrically placed about zero, captures a central z curve area of .95? That is, for what value of c do we have

$$P(-c < z < c) = .95?$$

As the following illustration shows, the cumulative area up to c must be .9750 (.025 + .95). The z table then reveals that $c = 1.96$. To check, note that

$$P(-1.96 < z < 1.96) = P(z < 1.96) - P(z < -1.96)$$
$$= .9750 - .0250$$
$$= .9500$$

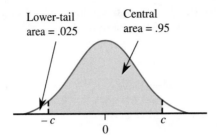

Many statistical procedures utilize values that capture either particular tail areas or central areas under the z curve. Such values are often referred to as **z critical values.** Table 7.1 displays the most frequently used z critical values.

TABLE 7.1   The most useful z critical values

Critical value, z	Area to the right of z	Area to the left of $-z$	Area between $-z$ and z
1.28	.10	.10	.80
1.645	.05	.05	.90
1.96	.025	.025	.95
2.33	.01	.01	.98
2.58	.005	.005	.99
3.09	.001	.001	.998
3.30	.0005	.0005	.999

Probabilities for an Arbitrary Normal Distribution

Calculation of any probability involving a normal random variable can be reduced to a z curve calculation by means of the following result.

Let x be a normally distributed random variable with mean value μ and standard deviation σ. Then the *standardized variable*

$$z = \frac{x - \mu}{\sigma}$$

obtained by first subtracting the mean value and then dividing by the standard deviation, has a standard normal distribution; that is, the probability distribution of z is given by the standard normal curve.

To see how this result is used, suppose x has a normal distribution with $\mu = 30$ and $\sigma = 2$. Let's first consider $P(27 < x < 36)$. Subtracting 30 from each term inside the parentheses and dividing by 2 gives an equivalent event:

$$27 < x < 36 \quad \text{if and only if} \quad \frac{27 - 30}{2} < \frac{x - 30}{2} < \frac{36 - 30}{2}$$

Since the events are equivalent, the probabilities are the same. Because $z = (x - 30)/2$ has a standard normal distribution, we have

$$P(27 < x < 36) = P\left(\frac{27 - 30}{2} < \frac{x - 30}{2} < \frac{36 - 30}{2}\right)$$

$$= P(-1.50 < z < 3.00)$$

The desired probability is therefore the area under the z curve and above the interval from -1.50 to 3.00. Similarly,

$$x < 29 \quad \text{if and only if} \quad \frac{x - 30}{2} < \frac{29 - 30}{2}$$

so

$$P(x < 29) = P\left(\frac{x - 30}{2} < \frac{29 - 30}{2}\right) = P(z < -.50)$$

In general, **standardizing** the limit or limits on x—by subtracting the mean and dividing by the standard deviation—gives the corresponding limit or limits on a standard normal random variable.

When x has a normal distribution with mean μ and standard deviation σ,

$$P(a < x < b) = P\left(\frac{a - \mu}{\sigma} < z < \frac{b - \mu}{\sigma}\right) = \quad \text{z curve area between the standardized limits}$$

$$P(x < a) = P\left(z < \frac{a - \mu}{\sigma}\right) = \quad \text{z curve area to the left of the standardized limit}$$

$$P(b < x) = P\left(\frac{b - \mu}{\sigma} < z\right) = \quad \text{z curve area to the right of the standardized limit}$$

EXAMPLE 7.6

Let x denote the systolic blood pressure (mm) of an individual selected at random from a certain population. Suppose that x has a normal distribution with mean $\mu = 120$ mm and standard deviation $\sigma = 10$ mm. (The article "Oral Contraceptives, Pregnancy, and Blood Pressure" (*J. Amer. Med. Assoc.* 222 (1972):1507–1510) reported on the results of a large study in which a sample histogram of blood pressures among women of similar ages was found to be well approximated by a normal curve.) To find the probability that x is between 110 and 140, we first standardize these limits:

$$\text{standardized lower limit} = \frac{110 - 120}{10} = -1.00$$

$$\text{standardized upper limit} = \frac{140 - 120}{10} = 2.00$$

Then

$$
\begin{aligned}
P(110 < x < 140) &= P(-1.00 < z < 2.00) \\
&= P(z < 2.00) - P(z < -1.00) \\
&= .9772 - .1587 \\
&= .8185
\end{aligned}
$$

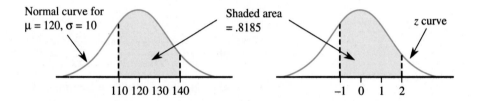

Thus if blood pressure values for many, many women from this population were determined, roughly 82% of the values would fall between 110 and 140 mm. Similarly,

$$P(125 < x) = P\left(\frac{125 - 120}{10} < z\right)$$

$$
\begin{aligned}
&= P(.50 < z) \\
&= 1 - P(z \le .50) \\
&= 1 - .6915 \\
&= .3085
\end{aligned}
$$

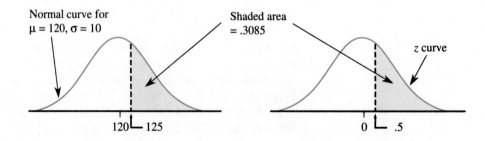

Since $\mu - 4\sigma = 120 - 40 = 80$, the probability that x falls more than four standard deviations below its mean is

$$P(x < 80) = P\left(z < \frac{80 - 120}{10}\right) = P(z < -4) \approx 0$$

If an individual's blood pressure is reported as less than 80, it is highly unlikely that the value was selected from the normal distribution specified here.

EXAMPLE 7.7

One method for determining the hardness of a metal involves impressing a hardened point into the surface of the metal and measuring the depth of penetration. Suppose that the hardness of a particular alloy is normally distributed with a mean value of 70 and a standard deviation of 4.

What is the probability that the hardness of a randomly selected specimen is between 60 and 65? Is at least 50? To answer these questions, let

x = hardness of a randomly selected specimen

Then x has a normal distribution with $\mu = 70$ and $\sigma = 4$, so

$$P(60 < x < 65) = P\left(\frac{60 - 70}{4} < z < \frac{65 - 70}{4}\right)$$

$$= P(-2.50 < z < -1.25)$$

$$= \left(\begin{array}{c}\text{area to the left} \\ \text{of} -1.25\end{array}\right) - \left(\begin{array}{c}\text{area to the left} \\ \text{of} -2.50\end{array}\right)$$

$$= (-1.25\ z\text{ table entry}) - (-2.50\ z\text{ table entry})$$

$$= .1056 - .0062$$

$$= .0994$$

Note that $P(60 \le x \le 65) = .0994$ also, since x is a continuous random variable.

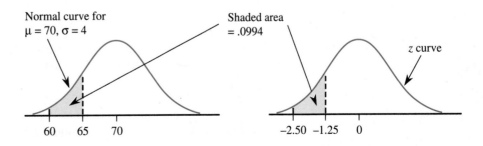

Normal curve for $\mu = 70$, $\sigma = 4$

Shaded area $= .0994$

z curve

Similarly,

$$P(50 \le x) = P\left(\frac{50 - 70}{4} \le z\right)$$
$$= P(-5.00 \le z)$$
$$= 1 - P(z < -5.00)$$
$$\approx 1 - 0$$
$$= 1$$

Thus there is almost no chance that hardness will be smaller than 50 (more than five standard deviations below the mean value).

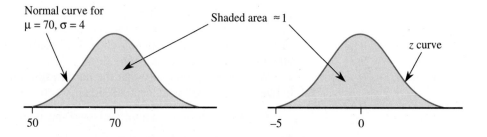

Suppose that four specimens are independently selected. What is the probability that hardness exceeds 65 for exactly two of the four specimens? Let's call a specimen a success S if its hardness exceeds 65. Then

$$\pi = P(S) = P(65 < x) = P(-1.25 < z)$$
$$= 1 - (\text{area to the left of } -1.25) = .8944$$

The event of interest is that there are exactly two S's in a binomial experiment with $n = 4$ trials and success probability $\pi = .8944$. Using the binomial probability distribution formula gives us

$$p(2) = \left(\frac{4!}{2!2!}\right)(.8944)^2(.1056)^2$$
$$= (6)(.8944)^2(.1056)^2$$
$$= .0535$$

The process of standardizing a value is just a way of reexpressing a distance. If we standardize the value 34 using $\mu = 30$ and $\sigma = 2$, the result is

$$\frac{34 - 30}{2} = \frac{4}{2} = 2$$

This says that 34 is two standard deviations "above" (to the right of) the mean.

Similarly,

$$\frac{27.5 - 30}{2} = \frac{-2.5}{2} = -1.25$$

so 27.5 is 1.25 standard deviations "below" (to the left of) the mean.

> Standardizing a value tells how many standard deviations the value is from the mean. A value above the mean yields a positive standardized value, and a value below the mean yields a negative standardized value.

EXAMPLE 7.8

If reaction time x to a certain stimulus is normally distributed, what is the probability that x is observed to be within one standard deviation of its mean? The value $\mu - \sigma$ is one standard deviation below the mean, and $\mu + \sigma$ is one standard deviation above the mean. Therefore,

$$P\left(\begin{array}{c}x \text{ is within 1 standard} \\ \text{deviation of its mean}\end{array}\right) = P(\mu - \sigma < x < \mu + \sigma)$$

Standardizing limits gives us

$$\frac{(\mu + \sigma) - \mu}{\sigma} = \frac{\sigma}{\sigma} = 1.00, \qquad \frac{(\mu - \sigma) - \mu}{\sigma} = \frac{-\sigma}{\sigma} = -1.00$$

from which we obtain

$$
\begin{aligned}
P(\mu - \sigma < x < \mu + \sigma) &= P(-1.00 < z < 1.00) \\
&= .8413 - .1587 \\
&= .6826 \\
&\approx .68
\end{aligned}
$$

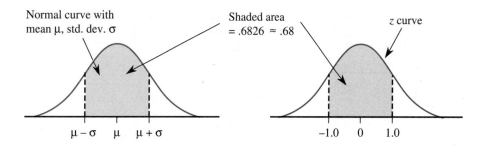

Normal curve with mean μ, std. dev. σ

Shaded area = .6826 ≈ .68

z curve

$\mu - \sigma$ μ $\mu + \sigma$

-1.0 0   1.0

Similarly,

$$P(\mu - 2\sigma < x < \mu + 2\sigma) = P(-2 < z < 2) = .9544 \approx .95$$

and

$$P(\mu - 3\sigma < x < \mu + 3\sigma) = P(-3 < z < 3) = .9974 \approx .997$$

Multiplication of these three probabilities by 100 gives the percentages quoted earlier in the Empirical Rule. Notice that these probabilities do not depend on μ or σ.

We saw that in some z problems, a probability (curve area) is specified and the corresponding limit is requested. This also occurs in other normal distribution settings.

EXAMPLE 7.9

The Environmental Protection Agency has in recent years developed a testing program to monitor vehicle emission levels of several pollutants. The article "Determining Statistical Characteristics of a Vehicle Emissions Audit Procedure" (*Technometrics* (1980):483–493) describes the program, which involves using different vehicle configurations (combinations of weight, engine type, transmission, and axle ratios) and a fixed driving schedule (including cold- and hot-start phases, idling, accelerating, and decelerating). Data presented in the paper suggests that the normal distribution is a plausible model for the amount of oxides of nitrogen (g/mi) emitted. Let x denote the amount of this pollutant emitted by a randomly selected vehicle with a particular configuration. Suppose that x has a normal distribution with $\mu = 1.6$ and $\sigma = .4$. What pollution level c is such that 99% of all such vehicles emit pollution amounts less than c and only 1% exceed it? The distribution of x appears in Figure 7.14, with c identified on the measurement scale.

FIGURE 7.14
The normal distribution
for Example 7.9

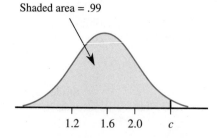

Shaded area = .99

1.2   1.6   2.0 c

The value c satisfies $P(x < c) = .99$. By standardizing, this can be related to a z critical value:

$$P(x < c) = P\left(z < \frac{c - 1.6}{.4}\right) = .99$$

From Table 7.1 (given earlier in this section) or Appendix Table II, the z critical value that captures a cumulative area of .99 is 2.33, that is, $P(z < 2.33) = .99$.

Thus

$$\frac{c - 1.6}{.4} = 2.33$$

from which

$$c = 1.6 + (.4)(2.33) = 2.532$$

EXERCISES 7.9–7.29   SECTION 7.2

7.9   Determine the following standard normal (z) curve areas.
   a. The area under the z curve to the left of 1.75
   b. The area under the z curve to the left of $-.68$
   c. The area under the z curve to the right of 1.20
   d. The area under the z curve to the right of -2.82
   e. The area under the z curve between -2.22 and .53
   f. The area under the z curve between -1 and 1
   g. The area under the z curve between -4 and 4

7.10   Determine each of the areas under the standard normal (z) curve.
   a. To the left of -1.28
   b. To the right of 1.28
   c. Between -1 and 2
   d. To the right of 0
   e. To the right of -5
   f. Between -1.6 and 2.5
   g. To the left of .23

7.11   Let z denote a random variable having a standard normal distribution. Determine each of the following probabilities.
   a. $P(z < 2.36)$
   b. $P(z \leq 2.36)$
   c. $P(z < -1.23)$
   d. $P(1.14 < z < 3.35)$
   e. $P(-.77 < z < -.55)$
   f. $P(-2.90 < z \leq 1.15)$
   g. $P(2 < z)$
   h. $P(-3.38 \leq z)$
   i. $P(z < 4.98)$

7.12   Let z denote a random variable having a normal distribution with $\mu = 0$ and $\sigma = 1$. Determine each of the following probabilities.
   a. $P(z < .10)$
   b. $P(z < -.10)$
   c. $P(.40 < z < .85)$
   d. $P(-.85 < z < -.40)$

e. $P(-.40 < z < .85)$
f. $P(-1.25 < z)$
g. $P(z < -1.50 \text{ or } z > 2.50)$

7.13 Determine a number c to satisfy each of the following conditions (where z has a standard normal distribution).
a. $P(z < c) = .5910$
b. $P(z < c) = .4090$
c. $P(c < z) = .0030$
d. $P(-c < z < c) = .7540$

7.14 Determine the value c for which each of the following probabilities involving a standard normal random variable is as specified.
a. $P(z < c) = .0075$
b. $P(c < z) = .0040$ $z > c$
c. $P(c < z) = .9830$
d. $P(-c < z < c) = .9940$
e. $P(z < -c \text{ or } c < z) = .0160$

7.15 Each of the following probabilities P involves a standard normal random variable z. Determine the value of c in each case so that P is as specified.
a. $P(z < c) = .975$
b. $P(z < c) = .90$
c. $P(c < z) = .90$
d. $P(c < z) = .005$
e. $P(-c < z < c) = .99$
f. $P(z > c \text{ or } z < -c) = .002$

7.16 Because $P(z < 0.44) = .67$, the value 0.44 is the 67th percentile of the standard normal distribution. Determine the value of each of the following percentiles for the standard normal distribution. (If the cumulative area that you must look for does not appear in the z table, use the closest entry.)
a. The 91st percentile (Hint: Look for area .9100)
b. The 77th percentile
c. The 50th percentile
d. The 9th percentile
e. How are the percentiles of (a) and (d) related? If p denotes a number between 0 and 1, what is the relationship between the $100p$th percentile and the $100(1 - p)$th percentile? What property of the z curve justifies your assertion?

7.17 Let x denote the amount of dye (ml) dispensed into one gallon of paint when mixing a certain shade. Suppose that x has a normal distribution with $\mu = 5$ ml and $\sigma = .2$ ml. Calculate the following probabilities.
a. $P(x < 5.0)$
b. $P(x < 5.4)$
c. $P(x \leq 5.4)$
d. $P(4.6 < x < 5.2)$
e. $P(4.5 < x)$
f. $P(4.0 < x)$

7.18 Let x be the weight (lb) of a certain type of fish caught at a particular location. If x is normally distributed with a mean value of 3.8 lb and a standard deviation of 1.1 lb, calculate the following probabilities.

a. $P(x < 4.0)$

b. $P(3.25 < x)$

c. $P(3 < x < 5)$

d. $P(x < 8)$

e. $P(8 < x)$

f. $P(x < 6.363)$

g. $P(1.644 < x < 5.956)$

7.19 A gasoline tank for a certain car is designed to hold 15 gal. Suppose that the actual capacity x of a randomly chosen tank has a normal distribution with mean value 15.0 gal and standard deviation .10 gal.

   a. What is the probability that a randomly selected tank will hold at most 14.8 gal?

   b. What is the probability that a randomly selected tank will hold between 14.7 and 15.1 gal?

7.20 Refer to Exercise 7.19, and suppose that the car on which the randomly selected tank is mounted gets exactly 25 mi/gal on a trip. What is the probability that the car can travel 370 mi without refueling? (Hint: At 25 mi/gal, a trip of 370 mi requires how much gasoline?)

7.21 Suppose that the force acting on a column that provides support for a building is normally distributed with mean 15.0 Kips and standard deviation 1.25 Kips. What is the probability that the force

   a. is at most 17 Kips?

   b. is less than 17 Kips?

   c. is between 12 and 17 Kips?

   d. differs from 15.0 Kips by more than two standard deviations?

7.22 Stress resistance x (lb/in.^{2}) for a certain type of plastic sheet is normally distributed with mean value 30 and standard deviation .6.

   a. Calculate $P(29 < x < 32)$.

   b. Calculate $P(x < 28.2)$

   c. Calculate the probability that x is farther than 1.2 from its mean value.

7.23 Return to Exercise 7.22, involving stress resistance of a plastic sheet.

   a. Find the number c for which $P(x < c) = .01$. (Hint: $P(z < -2.33) = .01$.)

   b. Find the value of c for which 95% of all such sheets have stress resistances within c of the mean value, that is, for which $P(30 - c < x < 30 + c) = .95$. (Hint: $P(-1.96 < z < 1.96) = .95$.)

7.24 What is the probability that the value of a normally distributed random variable is observed to lie

   a. within 1.5 standard deviations of its mean value?

   b. farther than 2.5 standard deviations from its mean value?

   c. between 1 and 2 standard deviations from its mean value?

7.25 The air pressure in a randomly selected tire put on a certain model new car is normally distributed with mean value 31 lb/in.^{2} and standard deviation .2 lb/in.^{2}

   a. What is the probability that the pressure for a randomly selected tire exceeds 30.5 lb/in.^{2}?

   b. What is the probability that the pressure for a randomly selected tire is between 30.5 and 31.5 lb/in.^{2}? Is between 30 and 32 lb/in.^{2}?

   c. Suppose a tire is classed as underinflated if its pressure is less than 30.4 lb/in.^{2}

What is the probability that at least one of the four tires on a car is under-inflated? (Hint: If A = at least 1 tire is underinflated, what is *not A*?)

✓ 7.26   The time that it takes a randomly selected job applicant to perform a certain task is normally distributed with a mean value of 120 sec and a standard deviation of 20 sec. The fastest 10% are to be given advanced training. What task times qualify individuals for such training?

7.27   A machine that produces ball bearings has initially been set so that the true average diameter of the bearings it produces is .500 in. A bearing is acceptable if its diameter is within .004 in. of this target value. Suppose, however, that the setting has changed during the course of production, so that the bearings have normally distributed diameters with mean value .499 in. and standard deviation .002 in. What percentage of the bearings produced will not be acceptable?

✓ 7.28   Suppose that net typing rate in words per minute (wpm) for experienced electric-typewriter touch typists is approximately normally distributed with a mean value of 60 wpm and a standard deviation of 15 wpm. (The paper "Effects of Age and Skill in Typing" (*J. of Exper. Psych.* (1984):345–371) describes how net rate is obtained from gross rate by using a correction for errors.)

a. What is the probability that a randomly selected typist's net rate is at most 60 wpm? Less than 60 wpm?

b. What is the probability that a randomly selected typist's net rate is between 45 and 90 wpm?

c. Would you be surprised to find a typist in this population whose net rate exceeded 105 wpm? (Note: The largest net rate in a sample described in the paper cited is 104 wpm.)

d. Suppose that two typists are independently selected. What is the probability that both their typing rates exceed 75 wpm?

7.29   Because $P(z \leq 2.33) = .9901 \approx .99$, the value 2.33 is the 99th percentile of the standard normal distribution. That is, 99% of the area under the z curve lies to the left of 2.33. Let x have a normal distribution with mean value μ and standard deviation σ.

a. Show that $P(x \leq \mu + 2.33\sigma) = .99$, so that $\mu + 2.33\sigma$ is the 99th percentile of this normal distribution.

b. In Exercise 7.25, tire pressure $x(\text{lb/in.}^2)$ was assumed to be normally distributed with mean 31.0 and standard deviation .2. What is the 99th percentile of the tire pressure distribution (the value below which 99% of such tires have tire pressure)?

c. What is the 90th percentile of the tire pressure distribution? (Hint: First find the 90th percentile for z.)

d. What is the first percentile for the tire pressure distribution?

7.3   Further Applications of the Normal Distribution (Optional)

In this section we first show how probabilities for some discrete random variables can be approximated using a normal curve. The most important case of this concerns the approximation of binomial probabilities. Finally, as a prelude to statistical analysis, we present a method for judging whether it is plausible that a given sample has come from a normal population distribution.

The Normal Curve and Discrete Variables

The probability distribution of a discrete random variable x is represented pictorially by a probability histogram. The probability of a particular value is the area of the rectangle centered at that value. Possible values of x are isolated points on the number line, usually whole numbers. For example, if $x =$ the IQ of a randomly selected 8-year-old child, then x is a discrete random variable, since an IQ score must be a whole number.

Often a probability histogram can be very well approximated by a normal curve, as illustrated in Figure 7.15. In such cases, it is customary to say that x has *approximately* a normal distribution. The normal distribution can then be used to calculate approximate probabilities of events involving x.

FIGURE 7.15
A normal curve approximation
to a probability histogram

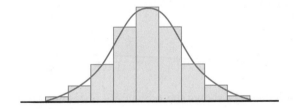

EXAMPLE 7.10

The number of express mail packages mailed at a certain post office on a randomly selected day is approximately normally distributed with mean value 18 and standard deviation 6. Let's first calculate the approximate probability that $x = 20$. Figure 7.16(a) shows a portion of the probability histogram for x with the approximating normal curve superimposed. The area of the shaded rectangle is $P(x = 20)$.

FIGURE 7.16
The normal approximation
for Example 7.10

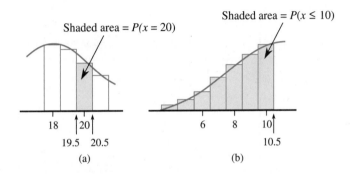

The left edge of this rectangle is at 19.5 on the horizontal scale, and the right edge is at 20.5. Therefore, the desired probability is approximately the area under the normal curve between 19.5 and 20.5. Standardizing these limits gives us

$$\frac{20.5 - 18}{6} = .42, \qquad \frac{19.5 - 18}{6} = .25$$

from which we get

$$P(x = 20) \approx P(.25 < z < .42) = .6628 - .5987 = .0641$$

In a similar fashion, Figure 7.16(b) shows that $P(x \le 10)$ is approximately the area under the normal curve to the left of 10.5. Thus,

$$P(x \le 10) \approx P\left(z \le \frac{10.5 - 18}{6}\right) = P(z \le -1.25) = .1056$$

The calculation of probabilities in Example 7.10 illustrates the use of a **continuity correction.** Because the rectangle for $x = 10$ extends to 10.5 on the right, we use the normal curve area to the left of 10.5 rather than just 10. In general, if possible x values are consecutive whole numbers, then $P(a \le x \le b)$ will be approximately the normal curve area between limits $a - \frac{1}{2}$ and $b + \frac{1}{2}$.

The Normal Approximation to a Binomial Distribution

Figure 7.17 shows the probability histograms for two binomial distributions, one with $n = 25$, $\pi = .4$ and the other with $n = 25$, $\pi = .1$. For each distribution we computed

$$\mu = n\pi \quad \text{and} \quad \sigma = \sqrt{n\pi(1 - \pi)}$$

and then we superimposed a normal curve with this μ and σ on the corresponding probability histogram. A normal curve fits the probability histogram very well in the first case. When this happens, binomial probabilities can be accurately approx-

FIGURE 7.17
Normal approximations to
binomial distributions

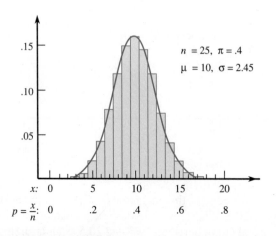
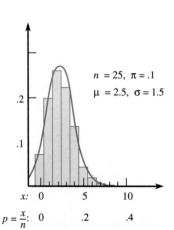

imated by areas under the normal curve. Because of this, statisticians say that both x (the number of S's) and x/n (the proportion of S's) are "approximately normally distributed." In the second case, the normal curve does not give a good approximation because the probability histogram is quite skewed, whereas the normal curve is symmetric.

Let x be a binomial random variable based on n trials and success probability π, so that

$$\mu = n\pi, \qquad \sigma = \sqrt{n\pi(1 - \pi)}$$

If n and π are such that both

$$n\pi \geq 5 \qquad \text{and} \qquad n(1 - \pi) \geq 5$$

then x has approximately a normal distribution. This along with the continuity correction implies that

$$P(a \leq x \leq b) \approx P\left(\frac{a - \frac{1}{2} - \mu}{\sigma} \leq z \leq \frac{b + \frac{1}{2} - \mu}{\sigma}\right)$$

That is, the probability that x is between a and b inclusive is approximately the area under the approximating normal curve between $a - \frac{1}{2}$ and $b + \frac{1}{2}$. Similarly,

$$P(x \leq b) \approx P\left(z \leq \frac{b + \frac{1}{2} - \mu}{\sigma}\right)$$

$$P(a \leq x) \approx P\left(\frac{a - \frac{1}{2} - \mu}{\sigma} \leq z\right)$$

When either $n\pi < 5$ or $n(1 - \pi) < 5$, the binomial distribution is too skewed for the normal approximation to give accurate results.

EXAMPLE 7.11

Premature babies are those born more than three weeks early. *Newsweek* (May 16, 1988) reports that 10% of the live births in this country are premature. Suppose that 250 live births are randomly selected and the number x of "preemies" is determined. Since

$$n\pi = 250(.10) = 25 \geq 5$$
$$n(1 - \pi) = 250(.90) = 225 \geq 5$$

x has approximately a normal distribution, with

$$\mu = 250(.10) = 25, \qquad \sigma = \sqrt{250(.1)(.9)} = 4.743$$

The probability that x is between 15 and 30 (inclusive) is

$$P(15 \leq x \leq 30) = P\left(\frac{14.5 - 25}{4.743} < z < \frac{30.5 - 25}{4.743}\right)$$

$$= P(-2.21 < z < 1.16)$$
$$= .8770 - .0136$$
$$= .8634$$

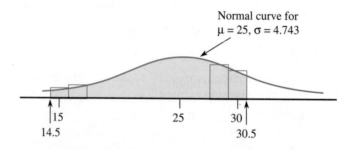

Normal curve for
$\mu = 25$, $\sigma = 4.743$

The event that *fewer than* 20 births are premature includes x values 19, 18, 17, ..., 1, and 0, so

$$P(x < 20) = P(x \leq 19) \approx P\left(z < \frac{19.5 - 25}{4.743}\right)$$
$$= P(z < -1.16)$$
$$= .1230$$

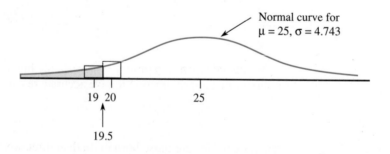

Normal curve for
$\mu = 25$, $\sigma = 4.743$

Checking for Normality

Some of the most frequently used statistical methods are valid only when a sample $x_1, x_2, \ldots, x_n$ has come from a population distribution that is (at least approximately) normal. One way to see whether an assumption of population normality is plausible is to construct a **normal probability plot.** This plot utilizes certain quantities called **normal scores.** The values of the normal scores depend on the sample size n. For example, the normal scores when $n = 10$ are as follows.

−1.539	−1.001	−.656	−.376	−.123
.123	.376	.656	1.001	1.539

To interpret these numbers, think of selecting sample after sample from a standard normal distribution, each one consisting of $n = 10$ observations. Then −1.539 is the long-run average of the smallest observation from each sample, −1.001 is the long-run average of the second smallest observation from each sample, and so on. Said another way, −1.539 is the mean value of the smallest observation in a sample of size 10 from the z distribution, −1.001 is the mean value of the second smallest observation, and so on.

   After ordering the sample observations from smallest to largest, the smallest normal score is paired with the smallest observation, the second smallest normal score with the second smallest observation, and so on. The first number in a pair is the normal score and the second is the observed x value. Each such pair can be represented as a point on a two-dimensional coordinate system. Consider, for example, the pair (1.001, 35.0). The corresponding point lies above 1.001 on the horizontal axis and to the right of 35.0 on the vertical axis. This is illustrated in Figure 7.18.

FIGURE 7.18
Representing a pair of
numbers as a point

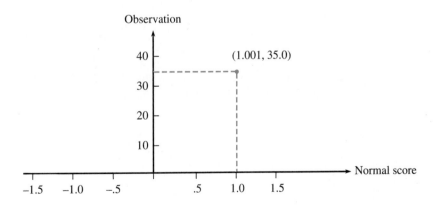

If the sample has actually been selected from a *standard* normal distribution, the second number in each pair should be reasonably close to the first number (ordered observation ≈ corresponding mean value). Then the n plotted points will fall near a line with slope equal 1 (a 45° line) passing through (0, 0). When the sample has been obtained from *some* normal population distribution, the plotted points should be close to *some* straight line.

> A substantial linear pattern in a normal probability plot suggests that population normality is plausible. On the other hand, a systematic departure from a straight-line pattern (such as curvature in the plot) casts doubt on the legitimacy of assuming a normal population distribution.

Appendix Table III contains normal scores for selected values of n.

EXAMPLE 7.12

The following ten observations are widths of contact windows in integrated circuit chips:

| 3.21 | 2.49 | 2.94 | 4.38 | 4.02 | 3.62 | 3.30 | 2.85 | 3.34 | 3.81 |

The ten pairs for the normal probability plot are then

(−1.539, 2.49)	(.123, 3.34)
(−1.001, 2.85)	(.376, 3.62)
(−.656, 2.94)	(.656, 3.81)
(−.376, 3.21)	(1.001, 4.02)
(−.123, 3.30)	(1.539, 4.38)

The normal probability plot is shown in Figure 7.19. The linearity of the plot supports the assumption that the window width distribution from which these observations were drawn is normal.

FIGURE 7.19
A normal probability plot
for Example 7.12

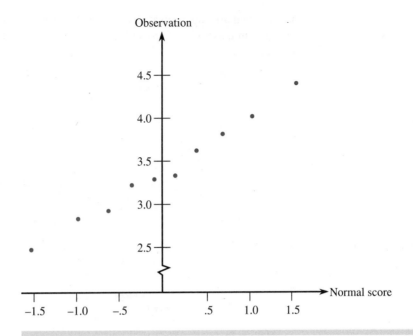

Extensive tabulations of normal scores for many different sample sizes are available. Alternatively, the better packages of statistical programs (such as MINI-TAB and SAS) can compute these scores on request and then construct a normal probability plot.

The judgment as to whether a plot does or doesn't show a substantial linear pattern is somewhat subjective. Particularly when n is small, normality should not be ruled out unless the departure from linearity is very clear cut. Figure 7.20 displays several plots that suggest a nonnormal population distribution.

FIGURE 7.20
Plots suggesting nonnormality
(a) Indication that
the population distribution
is skewed;
(b) Indication that
the population distribution
has "heavier tails" than
a normal curve;
(c) Presence of an outlier

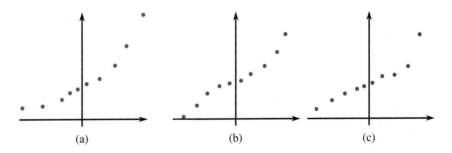

EXAMPLE 7.13

Example 2.17 presented data on cell interdivision times (IDTs). A sample histogram of the original data was quite skewed, but transforming by logarithms yielded a reasonably bell-shaped histogram. Figure 7.21 displays normal probability plots for the original data and for the log-transformed data. The latter plot is clearly much more linear in appearance than is the former. Not only has a log transformation resulted in a symmetric histogram but also in one that is very well fit by a normal curve.

FIGURE 7.21
MINITAB generated
normal probability plots
(a) Original IDT data
(b) Log-transformed IDT data

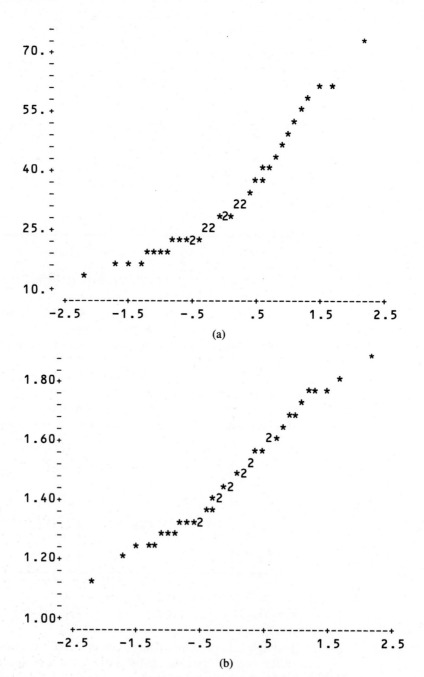

FIGURE 7.21
MINITAB generated
normal probability plots
(a) Original IDT data
(b) Log-transformed IDT data

Using the Correlation Coefficient to Check Normality

The correlation coefficient r was introduced in Chapter 4 as a quantitative measure of the extent to which the points in a scatter plot fall close to a straight line. Let's denote the n (normal score, observation) pairs as follows:

$$(x_1, y_1) = \text{(smallest normal score, smallest observation)}$$
$$\vdots$$
$$(x_n, y_n) = \text{(largest normal score, largest observation)}$$

Then the correlation coefficient can be computed using the defining equation for r given in Chapter 4. The normal probability plot always slopes upward (since it is based on values ordered from smallest to largest), so r will be a positive number. A value of r quite close to 1 indicates a very strong linear relationship in the normal probability plot. If r is too much smaller than 1, normality of the underlying distribution is questionable.

How far below 1 does r have to be before we begin to doubt seriously the plausibility of normality? The answer depends on the sample size n. If n is small, an r value somewhat below 1 would not be surprising even when the distribution is normal, but if n is large, only an r value very close to 1 would support the assumption of normality. For selected values of n, Table 7.2 gives critical values to which r can be compared in checking for normality.

TABLE 7.2   Values to which r can be compared to check for normality

n	5	10	15	20	25	30	40	50	60	75
Critical r	.832	.880	.911	.929	.941	.949	.960	.966	.971	.976

SOURCE: MINITAB User's Manual.

> If
>
> $$r < \text{critical } r \text{ for corresponding } n$$
>
> considerable doubt is cast on the assumption of population normality.

If your sample size is in between two tabled values of n, use the critical value for the larger sample size (for example, if $n = 46$, use the value .966 for sample size 50). In addition to providing a normal probability plot, MINITAB will automatically compute r upon request.

EXAMPLE 7.14

(*Example 7.13 continued*) The sample size for the IDT data is $n = 40$.

	r	Critical r
Original data	.950	.960
Log-transformed data	.988	.960

Since $.950 < .960$, it is doubtful that the IDT distribution itself is normal. But the normality of $\log_{10}(\text{IDT})$ is strongly supported by the very high value of r, much larger than the critical value.

How were the critical values in Table 7.2 obtained? Consider the critical value .941 for $n = 25$. Suppose the underlying distribution is actually normal. Consider obtaining a large number of different samples, each one consisting of 25 observations, and computing the value of r for each one. Then it can be shown that only 1% of the samples result in an r value less than the critical value .941. That is, .941 was chosen to guarantee a 1% error rate—in only 1% of all cases will we judge normality implausible when the distribution really is normal. The other critical values are also chosen to yield a 1% error rate for the corresponding sample sizes. It might have occurred to you that another type of error is possible—obtaining a large value of r and concluding that normality is a reasonable assumption when the distribution is actually quite nonnormal. This type of error is more difficult to control than the type mentioned above, but the procedure we have described does a good job in both respects.

EXERCISES 7.30–7.44   SECTION 7.3

7.30   Let x denote the IQ score for an individual selected at random from a certain population. The value of x must be a whole number. Suppose that the distribution of x can be approximated by a normal distribution with mean value 100 and standard deviation 15. Calculate (approximations to) the following probabilities.
   a. $P(x = 100)$
   b. $P(x \leq 110)$
   c. $P(x < 110)$ (Hint: $x < 110$ is the same as $x \leq 109$.)
   d. $P(75 \leq x \leq 125)$

7.31   Suppose that the distribution of the number of items x produced by an assembly line during an 8-hour shift can be approximated by a normal distribution with mean value 150 and standard deviation 10.
   a. What is the probability that the number of items produced is at most 120?
   b. What is the probability that at least 125 items are produced?
   c. What is the probability that between 135 and 160 (inclusive) items are produced?

7.32   The number of vehicles leaving a turnpike at a certain exit during a particular time period has approximately a normal distribution with mean value 500 and standard deviation 75. What is the probability that the number of cars exiting during this period is

a. at least 650?

b. strictly between 400 and 550? ("Strictly" means that the values 400 and 550 are not included.)

c. between 400 and 550 (inclusive)?

7.33   Let x have a binomial distribution with $n = 50$ and $\pi = .6$, so that $\mu = n\pi = 30$ and $\sigma = \sqrt{n\pi(1 - \pi)} = 3.4641$. Calculate the following probabilities using the normal approximation with the continuity correction.

a. $P(x = 30)$

b. $P(x = 25)$

c. $P(x \le 25)$

d. $P(25 \le x \le 40)$

e. $P(25 < x < 40)$ (Hint: $25 < x < 40$ is the same as $26 \le x \le 39$.)

7.34   Seventy percent of the bicycles sold by a certain store are mountain bikes. Among 100 randomly selected bike purchases, what is the approximate probability that

a. at most 75 are mountain bikes?

b. between 60 and 75 (inclusive) are mountain bikes?

c. more than 80 are mountain bikes?

d. at most 30 are *not* mountain bikes?

7.35   Suppose that 25% of the fire alarms in a large city are false alarms. Let x denote the number of false alarms in a random sample of 100 alarms. Give approximations to the following probabilities.

a. $P(20 \le x \le 30)$

b. $P(20 < x < 30)$

c. $P(35 \le x)$

d. The probability that x is farther than two standard deviations from its mean value

7.36   Suppose that 65% of all registered voters in a certain area favor a 7-day waiting period prior to purchase of a handgun. Among 225 randomly selected voters, what is the probability that

a. at least 150 favor such a waiting period?

b. more than 150 favor such a waiting period?

c. fewer than 125 favor such a waiting period?

7.37   Flash bars manufactured by a certain company are sometimes defective.

a. If 5% of all such bars are defective, could the techniques of this section be used to approximate the probability that at least five of the bars in a random sample of size 50 are defective? If so, calculate this probability; if not, explain why not.

b. Reconsider the question posed in part (a) for the probability that at least 20 bars in a random sample of size 500 are defective.

7.38   A company that manufactures mufflers for cars offers a lifetime warranty on its products provided that ownership of the car does not change. Suppose that only 20% of its mufflers are replaced under this warranty.

a. In a random sample of 400 purchases, what is the approximate probability that between 75 and 100 (inclusive) are replaced under warranty?

b. Among 400 randomly selected purchases, what is the probability that at most 70 are ultimately replaced under warranty?

c. If you were told that fewer than 50 among 400 randomly selected purchases were ever replaced under warranty, would you question the 20% figure? Explain.

7.39   Ten measurements of the steam rate (lb/h) of a distillation tower were used to construct the given normal probability plot ("A Self-Descaling Distillation Tower" (*Chem. Eng. Process* (1968):79–84)). Based on this plot, do you think it is reasonable to assume that the normal distribution provides an adequate description of the steam rate distribution? Explain.

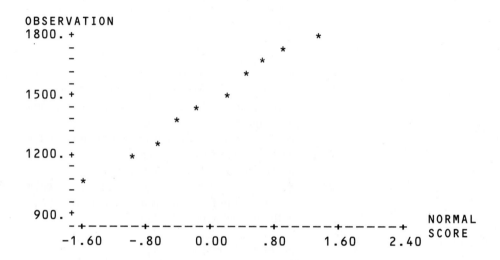

7.40   The accompanying normal probability plot was constructed using part of the data appearing in the paper "Trace Metals in Sea Scallops" (*Environ. Concentration and Toxicology* 19:1326–1334). The variable under study was the amount of cadmium in North Atlantic scallops. Does the sample data suggest that the cadmium concentration distribution is not normal? Explain.

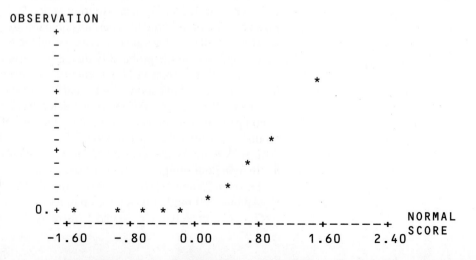

Did we go over this?

7.41 Consider the following ten observations on the lifetime (hr) for a certain type of component: 152.7, 172.0, 172.5, 173.3, 193.0, 204.7, 216.5, 234.9, 262.6, 422.6. Construct a normal probability plot, and comment on the plausibility of a normal distribution as a model for component lifetime.

7.42 The paper "The Load-Life Relationship for M50 Bearings with Silicon Nitride Ceramic Balls" (*Lubric. Eng.* (1984):153–159) reported the accompanying data on bearing load life (million revs.); the corresponding normal scores are also given. Construct a normal probability plot. Is normality plausible?

x	Normal score	x	Normal score
47.1	−1.867	240.0	.062
68.1	−1.408	240.0	.187
68.1	−1.131	278.0	.315
90.8	−.921	278.0	.448
103.6	−.745	289.0	.590
106.0	−.590	289.0	.745
115.0	−.448	367.0	.921
126.0	−.315	385.9	1.131
146.6	−.187	392.0	1.408
229.0	−.062	505.0	1.867

7.43 The accompanying observations are DDT concentrations in the blood of 20 people.

24	26	30	35	35	38	39	40	40	41
42	42	52	56	58	61	75	79	88	102

Use the normal scores from Exercise 7.42 to construct a normal probability plot, and comment on the appropriateness of a normal probability model.

7.44 Consider the following sample of 25 observations on the diameter x (cm) of a disk used in a certain system:

16.01	16.08	16.13	15.94	16.05	16.27	15.89	15.84	16.15
16.19	16.22	15.95	16.10	15.92	16.04	15.82	16.15	16.06
15.66	16.07	16.13	16.11	15.78	15.99	16.29		

The 13 largest normal scores for a sample of size 25 are 1.965, 1.524, 1.263, 1.067, .905, .764, .637, .519, .409, .303, .200, .100, and 0. The 12 smallest scores result from placing a minus sign in front of each of the given nonzero scores. Construct a normal probability plot. Does it appear plausible that disk diameter is normally distributed? Explain.

CHAPTER SEVEN SUMMARY OF KEY CONCEPTS AND FORMULAS

Term or Formula	Comment
Probability distribution of a continuous random variable x	Specified by a smooth (density) curve for which the total area under the curve is 1. The probability $P(a < x < b)$ is the area under the curve and above the interval from a to b; this is also $P(a \le x \le b)$.
μ_x **and** σ_x	The mean and standard deviation, respectively, of a continuous random variable x. These quantities describe the center and extent of spread about the center of the variable's probability distribution.
Normal distribution	A continuous probability distribution that has a bell-shaped density curve specified by a certain mathematical function. A particular normal distribution is determined by specifying values of μ and σ.
Standard normal distribution	This is the normal distribution with $\mu = 0$ and $\mu = 1$. The density curve is called the z curve, and z is the letter commonly used to denote a variable having this distribution. Areas under the z curve to the left of various values are given in Appendix Table II, which also appears on the inside front cover.
z critical value	A number on the z measurement scale that captures a specified tail area or central area.
$z = \dfrac{x - \mu}{\sigma}$	z is obtained from x by "standardizing": subtracting the mean and then dividing by the standard deviation. When x has a normal distribution, z has a standard normal distribution. This fact implies that probabilities involving *any* normal random variable (any μ or σ) can be obtained from z curve areas.
Normal approximation to the binomial distribution	When both $n\pi \ge 5$ and $n(1 - \pi) \ge 5$, binomial probabilities are well-approximated by corresponding areas under a normal curve with $\mu = n\pi$ and $\sigma = \sqrt{n\pi(1 - \pi)}$.
Normal probability plot	A picture used to judge the plausibility of the assumption that a sample has been selected from a normal population distribution. If the plot is reasonably straight, this assumption is reasonable.

ENCORE

In the chapter preview, we saw that the distribution of color density was uniform for Sony–USA and mound-shaped for Sony–Japan. Suppose that (consistent with information given in the paper mentioned in the preview) sets are graded as follows.

Grade A: Any set with color density in the range $t \pm 1.67$
Grade B: Any set with color density in the range $t + 1.67$ to $t + 3.33$ or in the range $t - 3.33$ to $t - 1.67$
Grade C: Any set with color density in the range $t + 3.33$ to $t + 5$ or in the range $t - 5$ to $t - 3.33$
Defective: Any set with color density outside the range $t \pm 5$

Let x represent the color density of a randomly selected Sony color TV.

The color-density distribution for Sony–USA is shown here. Since this is a uniform distribution over an interval of length 10 ($t - 5$ to $t + 5$), the height of the density curve must be $1/10$, as shown.

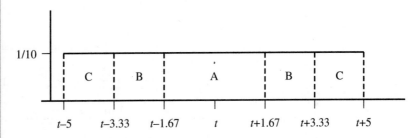

Since areas under the density curve are just areas of rectangles, we can easily compute

$$P(\text{grade A}) = P(t - 1.67 < x < t + 1.67)$$
$$= \text{area under curve and above interval from } t - 1.67 \text{ to } t + 1.67$$
$$= \tfrac{1}{10}(3.34)$$
$$= .334$$

Similarly,

$$P(\text{grade B}) = P(t - 3.33 < x < t - 1.67) + P(t + 1.67 < x < t + 3.33)$$
$$= \tfrac{1}{10}(1.66) + \tfrac{1}{10}(1.66)$$
$$= .332$$

and

$$P(\text{grade C}) = .334$$

In addition, for Sony–USA,

$$P(\text{defective}) = P(x < t - 5) + P(x > t + 5)$$
$$= 0$$

The color-density (x) distribution for Sony–Japan was approximately normal with $\mu = t$, the desired value of color density. Suppose that the standard deviation of the distribution was 2. (A value of $\sigma = 2$ is consistent with graphs appearing in the cited paper.) To compute the proportion of sets that would meet the specifications for grade A sets, we must find the area under the normal curve (with $\mu = t$ and $\sigma = 2$) above the interval $t - 1.67$ and $t + 1.67$, as shown in the accompanying picture.

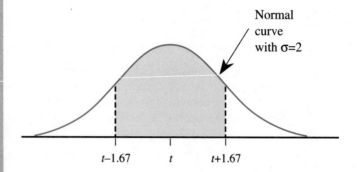

Converting $t + 1.67$ and $t - 1.67$ to z values, we get

$$z_1 = \frac{t + 1.67 - \mu}{\sigma} = \frac{t + 1.67 - t}{2} = \frac{1.67}{2} = .84$$

$$z_2 = \frac{t - 1.67 - \mu}{\sigma} = \frac{t - 1.67 - t}{2} = \frac{-1.67}{2} = -.84$$

Then, using Appendix Table II,

$$
\begin{aligned}
P(\text{grade A}) &= P(t - 1.67 < x < t + 1.67) \\
&= P(-.84 < z < .84) \\
&= .7995 - .2005 \\
&= .5990
\end{aligned}
$$

Similar computations result in

$$P(\text{grade B}) = .3060$$
$$P(\text{grade C}) = .0826$$
$$P(\text{defective}) = .0124$$

The probability calculations for Sony–USA and Sony–Japan are summarized in the accompanying table.

	Grade			
	A	B	C	Defective
Sony–USA	33%	33%	33%	0%
Sony–Japan	60%	31%	8%	1%

This table clearly shows how the two manufacturing plants differ. Even though Sony–USA is not producing any "defective" sets, if grade B and C sets are of less value than grade A sets, the Sony–Japan focus on closeness to target may be a better approach.

We can also look at the potential effects of a proposed improvement to the manufacturing process. Suppose the Sony–Japan process could be modified in such a way that the set-to-set variability in color density (as measured by σ) would be decreased. If the new process had a standard deviation of 1.5 (rather than 2), we would find that

$$P(\text{grade A}) = .7330$$
$$P(\text{grade B}) = .2406$$
$$P(\text{grade C}) = .0256$$
$$P(\text{defective}) = .0008$$

As a result of this process improvement, the proportion of grade C and defective sets would be greatly reduced.

SUPPLEMENTARY EXERCISES 7.45–7.63

7.45 A pizza company advertises that it puts .5 lb of real mozzarella cheese on its medium pizzas. In fact, the amount of cheese on a randomly selected medium pizza is normally distributed with a mean value of .5 lb and a standard deviation of .025 lb.
  a. What is the probability that the amount of cheese on a medium pizza is between .525 and .550 lb?
  b. What is the probability that the amount of cheese on a medium pizza exceeds the mean value by more than two standard deviations?
  c. What is the probability that three randomly selected medium pizzas all have at least .475 lb of cheese?

7.46 There are at least two things to keep in mind when interpreting EPA fuel efficiency ratings (mi/gal) for different automobiles. The first is that their values are determined under experimental conditions that are not necessarily representative of actual driving conditions. Second, each reported value is an average, so fuel efficiency for a randomly selected car may differ (considerably) from the average. Suppose, then, that fuel efficiency for a particular model car under specified conditions is normally

distributed with mean 30.0 mi/gal and standard deviation 1.2 mi/gal.
  a. What is the probability that the fuel efficiency for a randomly selected car of this type is between 29 and 31 mi/gal?
  b. Would it surprise you to find that the efficiency of a randomly selected car of this model is less than 25 mi/gal?
  c. If three cars of this model are randomly selected, what is the probability that all three have efficiencies exceeding 32 mi/gal?
  d. Find a number c such that 95% of all cars of this model have efficiencies exceeding c (that is, $P(x > c) = .95$).

7.47 The amount of time spent by a statistical consultant with a client at their first meeting is a random variable (what else!) having a normal distribution with mean value 60 min and standard deviation 10 min.
  a. What is the probability that more than 45 min is spent at the first meeting?
  b. What amount of time is exceeded by only 10% of all clients?
  c. If the consultant assesses a fixed charge of $10

(for overhead) and then charges $50 per hour, what is the mean revenue from a client?

7.48 The lifetime of a certain brand of battery is normally distributed with mean value 6 h and standard deviation .8 h when it is used in a particular cassette player. Suppose two new batteries are independently selected and put into the player. The player will cease to function as soon as one of the batteries fails.

    a. What is the probability that the player functions for at least 4 h?

    b. What is the probability that the cassette player works for at most 7 h?

    c. Find a number c such that only 5% of all cassette players will function without battery replacement for more than c hours.

7.49 A machine producing vitamin E capsules operates so that the actual amount of vitamin E in each capsule is normally distributed with mean 5 mg and standard deviation .05 mg. What is the probability that a randomly selected capsule contains less than 4.9 mg of vitamin E? At least 5.2 mg?

7.50 Accurate labeling of packaged meat is difficult because of weight decrease due to moisture loss (defined as a percentage of the package's original net weight). Suppose that moisture loss for a package of chicken breasts is normally distributed with mean value 4.0% and standard deviation 1.0%. (This model is suggested in the paper "Drained Weight Labeling for Meat and Poultry: An Economic Analysis of a Regulatory Proposal" (*J. of Consumer Affairs* (1980):307–325).) Let x denote the moisture loss for a randomly selected package.

    a. What is the probability that x is between 3.0% and 5.0%?

    b. What is the probability that x is at most 4.0%?

    c. What is the probability that x is at least 7.0%?

    d. Find a number c such that 90% of all packages have moisture losses below c %.

    e. What is the probability that moisture loss differs from the mean value by at least 1%?

7.51 The *Wall Street Journal* (February 15, 1972) reported that General Electric was being sued in Texas for sex discrimination over a minimum height requirement of 5 ft 7 in. The suit claimed that this restriction eliminated more than 94% of adult females from consideration. Let x represent the height of a randomly selected adult woman. Suppose that x is approximately normally distributed with mean 66 in. (5 ft 6 in.) and standard deviation 2 in.

    a. Is the claim that 94% of all women are shorter than 5 ft 7 in. correct?

    b. What proportion of adult women would be excluded from employment due to the height restriction?

7.52 Suppose that your statistics professor tells you that the scores on a midterm exam were approximately normally distributed with a mean of 78 and a standard deviation of 7. The top 15% of all scores have been designated as A's. Your score is 89. Did you receive an A? Explain.

7.53 Suppose that the pH of soil samples taken from a certain geographic region is normally distributed with a mean pH of 6.00 and a standard deviation of .10. If the pH of a randomly selected soil sample from this region is determined, answer the following questions about it.

    a. What is the probability that the resulting pH is between 5.90 and 6.15?

    b. What is the probability that the resulting pH exceeds 6.10?

    c. What is the probability that the resulting pH is at most 5.95?

    d. What value will be exceeded by only 5% of all such pH values?

7.54 The light bulbs used to provide exterior lighting for a large office building have an average lifetime of 700 h. If length of life is approximately normally distributed with a standard deviation of 50 h, how often should all of the bulbs be replaced so that no more than 20% of the bulbs will have already burned out?

7.55 Soaring insurance rates have made it difficult for many people to afford automobile insurance. Suppose that 16% of all those driving in a certain city are uninsured. Consider a random sample of 200 drivers.

    a. What is the mean value of the number who are uninsured, and what is the standard deviation of the number who are uninsured?

    b. What is the (approximate) probability that between 25 and 40 (inclusive) drivers in the sample were uninsured?

c. If you learned that more than 50 among the 200 were uninsured, would you doubt the 16% figure? Explain.

7.56 Let x denote the duration of a randomly selected pregnancy (the time elapsed between conception and birth). Accepted values for the mean value and standard deviation of x are 266 days and 16 days, respectively. Suppose that the probability distribution of x is (approximately) normal.

a. What is the probability that the duration of pregnancy is between 250 and 300 days?

b. What is the probability that the duration of pregnancy is at most 240 days?

c. What is the probability that the duration of pregnancy is within 16 days of the mean duration?

d. A *Dear Abby* column dated January 20, 1973, contained a letter from a woman who stated that the duration of her pregnancy was exactly 310 days. (She wrote that the last visit with her husband, who was in the navy, occurred 310 days prior to birth.) What is the probability that the duration of pregnancy is at least 310 days? Does this probability make you a bit skeptical of the claim?

e. Some insurance companies will pay the medical expenses associated with childbirth only if the insurance has been in effect for more than 9 months (275 days). This restriction is designed to ensure that the insurance company has to pay benefits only for those pregnancies where conception occurred during coverage. Suppose that conception occurred two weeks after coverage began. What is the probability that the insurance company will refuse to pay benefits because of the 275-day insurance requirement?

7.57 A machine that cuts corks for wine bottles operates so that the diameter of the corks produced is approximately normally distributed with mean 3 cm and standard deviation .1 cm. The specifications call for corks with diameters between 2.9 and 3.1 cm. A cork not meeting the specifications is considered defective. (A cork that is too small leaks and causes the wine to deteriorate, while a cork that is too large doesn't fit in the bottle.) What proportion of corks produced by this machine are defective?

7.58 Refer to Exercise 7.57. Suppose that there are two machines available for cutting corks. The one de-

scribed in the preceding problem produces corks with diameters normally distributed with mean 3 cm and standard deviation .1 cm. The second machine produces corks with diameters normally distributed with mean 3.05 cm and standard deviation .01 cm. Which machine would you recommend? (Hint: Which machine would produce the fewest defective corks?)

7.59 Suppose that SAT math and verbal scores are approximately normally distributed. Both the math and verbal sections of the test have a distribution of scores with an average of 500 and a standard deviation of 100.

a. If a student scored 620 on the verbal section, what percentile is associated with his or her score?

b. If the same student scored 710 on the math section, what is the corresponding percentile?

c. What score does a student have to achieve in order to be at the 90th percentile?

7.60 A certain bookstore deals exclusively in mysteries. Let x denote the number of pages in a book randomly selected from the store's inventory. Suppose that x has approximately a normal distribution with a mean value of 240 pages and a standard deviation of 40 pages.

a. What is the probability that x is at least 250 pages?

b. What is the probability that x is more than 250 pages?

c. What is the probability that x is between 200 and 250 pages (inclusive)?

d. If two books are independently selected, what is the probability that at least one has fewer than 200 pages?

7.61 The weight of parcels sent with a certain service has a normal distribution with mean value 10 lb and standard deviation 2 lb. This parcel service wishes to establish a weight limit w beyond which there will be a surcharge. What value w is such that 99% of all parcels are at least one pound under the surcharge weight w?

7.62 Suppose that only 40% of all drivers in a certain region regularly wear a seat belt. A random sample of 500 drivers is selected.

a. What is the probability that at least half of those in the sample regularly wear seat belts?

b. What is the probability that between 25% and 50% (inclusive) of those in the sample regularly wear a seat belt?

7.63 A probability distribution that has been very widely used to model lifetimes and various other phenomena is the *exponential distribution*. The corresponding density curve has height

$$f(x) = \begin{cases} (1/\mu)e^{-x/\mu} & x \geq 0 \\ 0 & \text{otherwise} \end{cases}$$

where μ is the mean value of x and $e \approx 2.71828$. The corresponding density curve follows. For any value $x > 0$, the area under the curve to the left of x is $1 - e^{-x/\mu}$.

Density

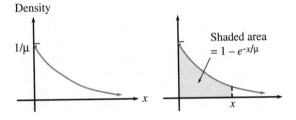

Suppose that the lifetime of a particular component has an exponential distribution with mean value 1000 h.

a. What is the probability that the lifetime is at most 2000 h?

b. What is the probability that the lifetime is at most 1000 h? Why is this probability not .5?

c. What is the probability that the lifetime is between 500 and 2000 h?

References

The books referenced in Chapter 5 contain material on probability distributions. The book by Chambers et al. listed in the Chapter 2 References is a good source for more information on probability plotting.

CHAPTER

8

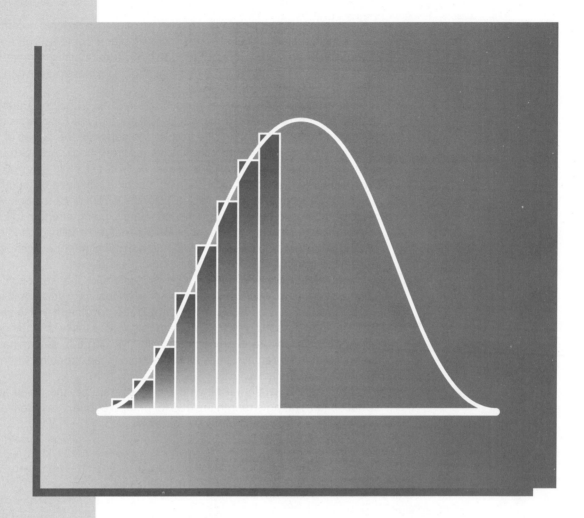

Sampling Distributions

PREVIEW

Manufacturing processes are often monitored in order to determine whether unusual circumstances (such as inferior raw materials or tool wear) are influencing the quality of the manufactured product. Important quality characteristics are recorded over time so that any change that affects process output can be detected quickly and corrective action taken.

For example, one characteristic of interest to a textbook publisher is the strength of the bindings on the books it manufactures. This strength could be measured by recording the force required to separate the pages of a book from its cover. The strength of the binding varies from book to book due to normal variability in the manufacturing process, but occasionally external factors may affect the binding process. If the binding machine is in need of servicing, strength may become more erratic and vary substantially from book to book. A low-quality batch of glue used in binding might cause the binding strength to be lower than normal. Either of these occurrences would affect the quality of the finished book, and the publisher would like to detect and correct either one as soon as possible in order to limit the number of inferior bindings produced.

To accomplish this, a sample of ten books could be taken each shift and the binding strength for each book determined. The resulting data could then be used to decide whether the values in the sample are consistent with a stable binding process and the result of normal manufacturing variability or whether the sample values indicate abnormal process behavior. Making this determination requires that we be able to identify values that differ from those expected when the process is behaving normally.

Suppose that when the binding process is stable, the mean and standard deviation for binding strength are 180 lb/in.^{2} and 3 lb/in.^{2}, respectively. A sample of 10 books resulted in binding strengths of

179.0	181.5	179.4	179.7	181.5
178.0	184.0	183.9	178.1	175.6

and a sample mean strength of 180.1, whereas a second sample of 10 books from the next shift resulted in strengths of

176.7	182.6	184.9	177.7	178.7
177.3	179.2	180.6	177.3	180.4

and a sample mean strength of 179.5. Is this second sample consistent with normal process behavior, or has some external force adversely influenced the process?

Results introduced in this chapter form the basis for a graphical technique called a *control chart*. A control chart is employed to monitor a process over time and is the most widely used tool for detecting abnormal process behavior. The construction of one type of control chart, called an X-bar chart, is illustrated in the Chapter Encore.

Introduction

The inferential methods presented in subsequent chapters will use information contained in a sample to reach conclusions about one or more characteristics of the whole population. As an example, let μ denote the true mean nicotine content (in mg) for a particular brand of cigarette. To learn something about μ, a sample of $n = 4$ cigarettes might be obtained, resulting in

$$x_1 = 1.68, \qquad x_2 = 1.89, \qquad x_3 = 1.73, \qquad \text{and} \qquad x_4 = 1.95$$

from which we calculate the sample mean, $\bar{x} = 1.813$. How close is this sample mean to the true population mean, μ? If another sample of 4 were selected and $\bar{x}$ computed, would this second $\bar{x}$ value be near 1.813 or might it be quite different?

These issues can be addressed by studying what is called the *sampling distribution* of $\bar{x}$. Just as the probability distribution of a numerical variable describes long-run behavior, the sampling distribution of $\bar{x}$ provides information about the long-run behavior of $\bar{x}$ based on many different samples, each of size n.

Properties of $\bar{x}$'s sampling distribution can be used to develop inferential procedures for drawing conclusions about μ. In a similar manner, we will study the sampling distribution of a *sample proportion* (the fraction of individuals in a sample who have some specified property). This will enable us to describe procedures for making inferences about the corresponding population proportion π.

8.1 Statistics and Random Samples

The objective of many investigations and research projects is to draw conclusions about how the values of some numerical variable x are distributed in a population. Although many aspects of the distribution might be of interest, attention is often focused on one particular population characteristic. Examples include:

1. $x =$ fuel efficiency (mi/gal) for a 1992 Honda Accord, with interest centered on the mean value μ of fuel efficiency for all such cars;
2. $x =$ thickness of a printed circuit board used in a personal computer, with interest focused on the variability in thickness as described by σ, the standard deviation of x;

3. x = time to first recurrence of skin cancer for a patient who was successfully treated using a particular therapy, with attention focused on the proportion π of such individuals whose first recurrence is within five years of original treatment.

Statistics

Statistical methods for drawing conclusions about the distribution of a variable x are based on obtaining a sample of x values. As in earlier chapters, the letter n denotes the number of observations in the sample (the sample size). The observations themselves are denoted by $x_1, x_2, \ldots, x_n$. Once these values are available, an investigator must decide which computed quantities will be most informative in drawing the desired type of conclusion. For example, we shall see in the next few chapters that several standard statistical procedures for drawing conclusions about μ utilize calculated values of both $\bar{x}$ and s.

DEFINITION

Any quantity computed from values in a sample is called a **statistic.**

Several statistics other than $\bar{x}$ and s were introduced in Chapter 3. They included the *sample median* (the middle value in the ordered list of sample observations), the *sample range* (the difference between the largest and smallest sample values), a *trimmed mean,* and a *sample percentile.*

It is very important to appreciate the distinction between a population characteristic (that is, a characteristic of the x distribution) and a statistic, which is a sample characteristic. The mean value of x, or the population mean, μ, is a population characteristic. The value of μ is a fixed number, such as 1.75 mg for nicotine content or 28.5 mi/gal for fuel efficiency. However, the value of μ is generally not known, which is why we take a sample of x values. The sample mean, $\bar{x}$, is a characteristic of the sample. Its value is a fixed number for any particular sample, but different samples typically result in different $\bar{x}$ values. It would be nice if the value of $\bar{x}$ turned out to be exactly μ; in practice, however, this almost never happens because of sampling variability. Some samples yield x values that are not very representative of the population distribution. Thus the value of μ might be 1.75, but one sample might yield $\bar{x} = 1.63$, whereas another might result in $\bar{x} = 2.04$.

Sampling Distributions

The value of a statistic varies from one sample to another. This variability may cause different samples to result in different conclusions about the population, and there is a risk that sample information will lead us to an incorrect conclusion. In order to evaluate this risk, information about a statistic's long-run behavior is needed. This information is obtained by using probability concepts to determine a statistic's sampling distribution.

DEFINITION

The value of a statistic depends on the particular sample selected from the population and changes from sample to sample. A statistic is therefore a random variable and as such has a probability distribution. The probability distribution of a statistic is called its **sampling distribution.** The sampling distribution of a statistic describes the long-run behavior of the statistic's values when many different samples, each of size *n,* are obtained and the value of the statistic is computed for each one.

EXAMPLE 8.1

The library of a particular classical music radio station contains five different recordings of Beethoven's Fifth Symphony (a population of size 5). Because listener polls have identified this as the most popular classical work, the station manager has insisted that three different recordings of this symphony be played each month. The recordings all differ somewhat in playing time (due to differences in interpretations by conductors and orchestras). These times are 29.6, 29.9, 30.0, 30.2, and 30.8 min.

Suppose that the three recordings to be played in a given month are determined by writing each of the five playing times on a different slip of paper, mixing up the slips, and selecting three at random. Then any set of three times has the same chance of selection as any other set. Suppose that the statistic of interest here is the sample median playing time. We list each of the ten possible samples (ordered for convenience) and the corresponding value of this statistic.

Sample	Sample median	Sample	Sample median
29.6, 29.9, 30.0	29.9	29.6, 30.2, 30.8	30.2
29.6, 29.9, 30.2	29.9	29.9, 30.0, 30.2	30.0
29.6, 29.9, 30.8	29.9	29.9, 30.0, 30.8	30.0
29.6, 30.0, 30.2	30.0	29.9, 30.2, 30.8	30.2
29.6, 30.0, 30.8	30.0	30.0, 30.2, 30.8	30.2

Each sample has the same chance of occurring as any other sample, so the probability of any particular one is $\frac{1}{10}$, or .10. That is, in a very long sequence of months, each sample would occur about $\frac{1}{10}$ (or 10%) of the time. The only three possible values of the sample median are 29.9, 30.0, and 30.2. Since 30.0 is the sample median for four of the possible samples,

$$P(\text{sample median} = 30.0) = \frac{4}{10} = .4$$

Similarly,

$$P(\text{sample median} = 29.9) = .3$$

and

$$P(\text{sample median} = 30.2) = .3$$

The sampling distribution of the sample median can now be summarized in a probability distribution table:

Value of sample median	29.9	30.0	30.2
Probability of value	.3	.4	.3

Thus, in the long run, 40% of all months result in a sample median playing time of 30.0. Notice that the population median time is 30.0 (the middle value when all five possible times are ordered). In 40% of all months, the sample median equals the population median, but in 60% of all months the two differ. The population median remains fixed in value, but the sample median varies in value from sample to sample.

There are several interesting things to notice about Example 8.1. First of all, even though this experiment involved relatively few outcomes, obtaining the sampling distribution required some careful thought and calculation. Things would have been much worse if the radio station owned ten different recordings (a larger population) and five (a larger sample) were to be played each month. Just listing the possible outcomes would be extremely tedious. (There are 252 of them!) Second, the same reasoning could be used to obtain the sampling distribution of any other statistic. For example, replacing the value of the sample median by the value of $\bar{x}$ (29.83 for the first ordered sample, and so on) would lead to the sampling distribution of $\bar{x}$. Third, the calculations were done for sampling without replacement. If sampling had been with replacement, the same time might have been chosen twice or even on all three selections. Additional samples and corresponding values of the sample median would be possible, resulting in a more complicated sampling distribution. In conclusion, the sampling distribution depends not only on which statistic is under consideration but also on the sample size and the method of sampling.

EXAMPLE 8.2

A company maintains three offices in a certain area, each staffed by two employees. Information concerning yearly salaries (in thousands of dollars) is as follows.

Office	1		2		3	
Employee	1	2	3	4	5	6
Salary	14.7	18.6	15.2	18.6	10.8	14.7

A survey will be conducted to obtain information on average salary levels. Two of the six employees will be selected for inclusion in the survey. Suppose that six slips of paper numbered 1, 2, . . . , 6 are placed in a box and two are drawn without replacement. This ensures that each of the 15 possible employee pairs has probability $\frac{1}{15}$ of being chosen. Computing the sample average salary $\bar{x}$ for each possible pair leads to the sampling distribution of $\bar{x}$ shown. For example, $\bar{x} = 16.65$ occurs for the four pairs (1, 2), (1, 4), (2, 6), and (4, 6), so

$$P(\bar{x} = 16.65) = \frac{4}{15} = .267$$

$\bar{x}$ value	12.75	13.00	14.70	14.95	16.65	16.90	18.60
Probability	.133	.067	.200	.133	.267	.133	.067

Thus if this experiment is performed over and over again, each time with a new selection of two employees, in the long run the value $\bar{x} = 14.70$ will occur 20% of the time, the value $\bar{x} = 18.60$ only 6.7% of the time, and so on.

Now consider what happens if the method for obtaining a sample is changed. Suppose this time one of the three offices is selected at random (using just three slips of paper), and both employees from that office are included. This is called a *cluster sample* because a cluster (in this case an office) is selected at random and all individuals in the cluster are included in the sample. There are only three possible employee pairs, each one having probability $\frac{1}{3}$ (or .333) of occurring. The resulting sampling distribution of $\bar{x}$ is now as follows.

$\bar{x}$ value	12.75	16.65	16.90
Probability	.333	.333	.333

If this experiment is repeated many times over, each of these three $\bar{x}$ values will occur approximately 33.33% of the time. These two sampling distributions of $\bar{x}$ are obviously quite different. Clearly the sampling distribution depends on the method of sampling used.

Random Samples

When an investigator takes a sample from a population of interest, the sampling is usually done without replacement. This implies that the results of successive selections are dependent. (See the discussion on sampling in Chapter 5.) The dependence will be quite negligible, however, when the sample size is small relative to the population size. Sampling without replacement is then almost like sampling with replacement, for which there is no dependence in successive draws and the distribution of possible values is identical on each selection.

> **DEFINITION**
>
> A sample $x_1, x_2, \ldots, x_n$ of values of a numerical variable x is called a
> **(simple) random sample** if the sampled values are selected independently
> from the same population distribution.

In most applications, selection is random and without replacement, but the sample size is much smaller than the population size (at most 5% of the population is sampled). For practical purposes, the successive observations can be regarded as independent, so the sample can be considered a random sample as we have defined it. The x values in a random sample are usually obtained by first selecting n individuals or objects and then observing or determining the value of x for each one. *It is customary to refer to the selected individuals or objects, as well as to the x values themselves, as a random sample.* Thus we may speak of a "random sample of students" when the variable of interest is $x =$ grade point average, or a "random sample of houses" when a study is concerned with $x =$ January electricity usage.

Methods for analyzing both random samples and other types of samples are based on concepts of probability and results concerning the sampling distributions of various statistics. However, the statistics and methods employed are most easily understood in the case of random samples. The inferential methods introduced in Chapters 9 through 16 are based on random sampling. Chapter 17 introduces some alternative sampling techniques.

EXERCISES 8.1–8.13   SECTION 8.1

8.1   Explain the difference between a population characteristic and a statistic.

8.2   What is the difference between $\bar{x}$ and μ? Between σ and s?

8.3   For each of the following statements, identify the number that appears in boldface type as either the value of a population characteristic or a statistic.

   a. A department store reports that **84%** of all customers who use the store's credit plan pay their bills on time. *P*

   b. A sample of 100 students at a large university had a mean age of **24.1** years. *S*

   c. The Department of Motor Vehicles reports that **22%** of all vehicles registered in a particular state are imports. *P*

   d. A hospital reports that, based on the ten most recent cases, the mean length of stay for surgical patients is **6.4** days. *S*

   e. A consumer group, after testing 100 batteries of a certain brand, reported an average life of **63** h of use. *S*

8.4   Assume that the 435 members of the U.S. House of Representatives are listed in alphabetical order. Explain how you would select a random sample of 20 members.

8.5   Describe how you might go about selecting a random sample of each of the following.

    a. Doctors practicing in Los Angeles County
    b. Students enrolled at a particular university
    c. Boxes in a warehouse
    d. Registered voters in your community
    e. Subscribers to a local newspaper
    f. Radios from a shipment of 1000

8.6   Consider the following "population": $\{1, 2, 3, 4\}$. Note that the population mean is

$$\mu = \frac{1 + 2 + 3 + 4}{4} = 2.5$$

    a. Suppose that a random sample of size two is to be selected without replacement from this population. There are twelve possible samples (provided that the order in which observations are selected is taken into account).

1, 2	1, 3	1, 4
2, 1	2, 3	2, 4
3, 1	3, 2	3, 4
4, 1	4, 2	4, 3

    Compute the sample mean for each of the 12 possible samples. Use this information to construct the sampling distribution of $\bar{x}$. (Display it in table form.)

    b. Suppose that a random sample of size two is to be selected, but this time sampling will be done *with* replacement. Using a method similar to that of part (a), construct the $\bar{x}$ sampling distribution. (Hint: There are 16 different possible samples in this case.)

    c. In what ways are the two sampling distributions of parts (a) and (b) similar? In what ways are they different?

8.7   Simulate sampling from the population of Exercise 8.6 by using four slips of paper individually marked 1, 2, 3, and 4. Select a sample of size 2 without replacement, and compute $\bar{x}$. Repeat this process 50 times, and construct a relative frequency distribution of the fifty $\bar{x}$ values. How does the relative frequency distribution compare to the sampling distribution of $\bar{x}$ derived in 8.6(a)?

8.8   Use the method of Exercise 8.6 to find the sampling distribution of the sample range when a random sample of size 2 is to be selected with replacement from the population $\{1, 2, 3, 4\}$. (Recall that sample range = largest observation − smallest observation.)

8.9   On four different occasions you have borrowed money from a friend in the amounts $1, $5, $10, and $20. The friend has four IOU slips with each of these amounts written on a different slip and will randomly select two slips from among the four and ask that those IOU's be repaid immediately. Let t (the sample total) denote the amount that you must repay immediately.

    a. List all possible outcomes, the value of t for each, and then determine the sampling distribution of t.

    b. Calculate the mean value of t. How does μ_t relate to the "population" mean μ?

8.10   Refer to Exercise 8.9. Suppose that instead of asking that the total amount on the two selected slips be repaid immediately, the maximum m of the two selected amounts is to be repaid immediately (for example, $m = 10$ if the \$5 and \$10 slips are drawn). Obtain the sampling distribution of m if the two slips are selected
    a. without replacement;
    b. with replacement.

8.11   Consider the following "population": {2, 3, 3, 4, 4}. The value of μ is 3.2, but suppose this is not known to an investigator who therefore wants to estimate μ from sample data. Three possible statistics for estimating μ are:

statistic 1: the sample mean, $\bar{x}$
statistic 2: the sample median
statistic 3: the average of the largest and smallest values in the sample

A random sample of size 3 will be selected without replacement. Provided that we disregard the order in which observations are selected, there are ten possible samples that might result (writing 3 and 3*, 4 and 4* to distinguish the two 3's and the two 4's):

2, 3, 3*	2, 3, 4	2, 3, 4*
2, 3*, 4	2, 3*, 4*	2, 4, 4*
3, 3*, 4	3, 3*, 4*	3, 4, 4*
3*, 4, 4*		

For each of these ten samples, compute statistics 1, 2, and 3. Construct the sampling distribution of each of these statistics. Which statistic would you recommend for estimating μ? Explain the reasons for your choice.

8.12   The three offices in Example 8.2 can be regarded as distinct segments, or *strata*, of the population. A *stratified sample* involves selecting a specified number of individuals from each stratum. When values within a stratum are similar but values in some strata differ substantially from those in other strata, stratified sampling can help ensure a representative sample. In the context of Example 8.2, suppose that a stratified sample consists of one of the two individuals from each stratum (each selected by tossing a fair coin). There are then eight possible samples. List them, and obtain the sampling distribution of $\bar{x}$.

8.13   Suppose that you have four books on your shelf that you are planning to read in the near future. Two are fictional works, containing 212 and 379 pages, respectively, and the other two are nonfiction, with 350 and 575 pages, respectively.
    a. Suppose that you randomly select two books from among these four to take on a one-week ski trip (in case you injure yourself). Let $\bar{x}$ denote the sample average number of pages for the two books selected. Obtain the sampling distribution of $\bar{x}$ and determine the mean of the $\bar{x}$ distribution.
    b. Suppose that you randomly select one of the two fiction books and also randomly select one of the two nonfiction books. Determine the sampling distribution of $\bar{x}$ and then calculate the mean of the $\bar{x}$ distribution.

8.2   A Sampling Experiment

Consider a small population consisting of the 20 students enrolled in an upper-division class. The students are numbered from 1 to 20, and the amounts spent on textbooks for the current semester are shown in the accompanying table.

Student	Amount spent on books	Student	Amount spent on books
1	267	11	319
2	258	12	263
3	342	13	265
4	261	14	262
5	275	15	333
6	295	16	184
7	222	17	231
8	270	18	159
9	278	19	230
10	168	20	323

For this population

$$\mu = \frac{267 + 258 + \cdots + 323}{20} = 260.25$$

Suppose that the value of the population mean is unknown to us and that we want to estimate μ by taking a random sample of 5 students and computing the sample mean amount spent on textbooks, $\bar{x}$. Is this a reasonable thing to do? Will the estimate that we produce be close in value to the true population mean? To answer these questions, we can perform a simple experiment that allows us to look at the behavior of the statistic $\bar{x}$ when random samples of size 5 are taken from this population. (Note that this is not a realistic example, since if a population consisted of only 20 individuals, we would probably conduct a census rather than select a sample. However, this small population size makes it easier to work with as we develop the ideas of sampling distributions.)

   Let's select a random sample of size 5 from this population. This can be done by writing the numbers from 1 to 20 on slips of paper, mixing them well, and then selecting 5 slips without replacement. The numbers on the slips selected identify which of the 20 students will be included in our sample. Alternatively, either a table of random digits or a computer random-number generator can be used to determine which 5 should be selected. MINITAB has such a random-number generator, and we used it to obtain 5 numbers between 1 and 20, resulting in

17   20   7   11   9

Selecting students numbered 17, 20, 7, 11, and 9 gives the following sample of amounts spent on books:

231   323   222   319   278

For this sample

$$\bar{x} = \frac{1373}{5} = 274.60$$

The sample mean is larger than the population mean of 260.25 by about \$15. Is this typical, or is this sample mean unusually far away from μ? Taking additional samples could provide some insight.

Four more random samples from this same population are shown next.

Sample 2		Sample 3		Sample 4		Sample 5	
Student	x	Student	x	Student	x	Student	x
4	261	15	333	20	323	18	159
15	333	12	263	16	184	8	270
12	263	3	342	19	230	9	278
1	267	7	222	1	267	7	222
18	159	18	159	8	270	14	262

The value of $\bar{x}$ can be computed for each sample to obtain

Sample	2	3	4	5
$\bar{x}$	256.60	263.80	254.80	238.20

Since $\mu = 260.25$, we can see the following:

1. The value of $\bar{x}$ differs from one random sample to another (sampling variability).
2. Some samples produced $\bar{x}$ values larger than μ (samples 1 and 3), whereas others produced $\bar{x}$ values smaller than μ (samples 2, 4, and 5).
3. Samples 2, 3, and 4 produced $\bar{x}$ values that were fairly close to the population mean, but sample 5 resulted in an $\bar{x}$ value that was \$22 below the population mean.

Continuing with the experiment, we selected 40 additional random samples (each of size 5). The resulting sample means are as follows.

Sample	$\bar{x}$	Sample	$\bar{x}$	Sample	$\bar{x}$
6	275.6	8	126.0	10	215.4
7	279.2	9	270.0	11	266.2

(continued)

Sample	$\bar{x}$	Sample	$\bar{x}$	Sample	$\bar{x}$
12	241.6	25	301.0	38	261.4
13	255.4	26	247.0	39	275.0
14	263.8	27	273.8	40	301.4
15	239.6	28	282.8	41	237.0
16	248.2	29	220.4	42	287.4
17	330.8	30	213.6	43	249.2
18	288.8	31	287.6	44	236.8
19	252.8	32	214.8	45	264.6
20	225.0	33	253.4		
21	307.2	34	279.6		
22	280.0	35	252.6		
23	277.4	36	242.2		
24	241.2	37	262.6		

The MINITAB histogram (produced using the GHIST command) of the 45 sample means given in Figure 8.1 provides us with a lot of information about the behavior of the statistic $\bar{x}$. Most samples resulted in sample means that were reasonably near $\mu = 260.25$, falling between 235 and 295. A few samples, however, produced $\bar{x}$ values that were very far from μ. If we were to take a sample of size 5 from this population and use $\bar{x}$ as an estimate of the population mean μ, we should not expect $\bar{x}$ to be really close to μ.

If we had continued sampling indefinitely, the resulting histogram of $\bar{x}$ values would be a picture of the sampling distribution of $\bar{x}$ for samples of size 5 from this population. The information provided by this sampling distribution enables us to

FIGURE 8.1
$\bar{x}$ values from 45 random samples

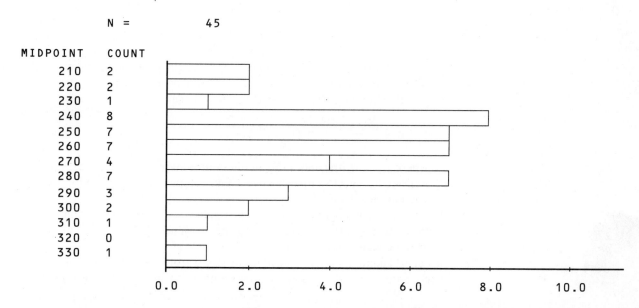

evaluate the behavior of the statistic $\bar{x}$ and is critical for developing inferential procedures based on $\bar{x}$. Fortunately, some general patterns emerge when this type of sampling experiment is conducted for different sample sizes and different populations, so we don't actually have to carry out such experiments on a regular basis! These general results are described in the next section.

EXERCISES 8.14–8.17   SECTION 8.2

 8.14 Consider a population consisting of the following five values, which represent the number of video rentals during the academic year for each of five students.

8   14   16   10   11

a. Compute the mean of this population.
b. Select a random sample of size 2 by writing the numbers from 1 to 5 on slips of paper and selecting two. Compute the mean of your sample.
c. Repeatedly select samples of size 2 and compute the associated $\bar{x}$ values until you have looked at 25 samples.
d. Construct a histogram using the 25 $\bar{x}$ values. Are most of the sample $\bar{x}$ values near the population mean? Do the $\bar{x}$ values differ a lot from sample to sample, or do they tend to be similar?

8.15 Refer to Exercise 8.14. For the population of size 5 given there, the population variance is $\sigma^2 = 8.16$.
a. When the entire population is known, the population variance is found using the formula

$$\sigma^2 = \frac{1}{n}\Sigma(x - \mu)^2$$

Use this formula to verify that $\sigma^2 = 8.16$ for the given population.
b. Select a random sample of size 2 in the manner described in Problem 8.14, part (b). Compute the value of the sample variance, s^2. Note that for $n = 2$,

$$s^2 = \frac{\Sigma(x - \bar{x})^2}{n - 1} = (x_1 - \bar{x})^2 + (x_2 - \bar{x})^2$$

where x_1 is the first data value in the sample and x_2 is the second.
c. Repeatedly select samples of size 2 and compute the associated s^2 values until you have looked at 25 samples.
d. Construct a histogram using the 25 s^2 values. Are most of the sample s^2 values near the population variance? Do the s^2 values differ a lot from sample to sample, or are they similar?

8.16 Select 10 additional random samples of size 5 from the population of 20 students given in the text and compute the mean amount spent on books for each of the 10 samples. Are the $\bar{x}$ values consistent with the results of the sampling experiment summarized in Figure 8.1?

8.17   Suppose the sampling experiment described in the text had used samples of size 10 rather than size 5. If 45 samples of size 10 were selected, $\bar{x}$ computed, and a histogram constructed, how do you think this histogram would differ from that for samples of size 5 (Figure 8.1)? In what way would it be similar?

8.3   The Sampling Distribution of a Sample Mean

When the objective of a statistical investigation is to make an inference about the population mean, μ, it is natural to consider the sample mean, $\bar{x}$. In order to understand how inferential procedures based on $\bar{x}$ work, we must first study how sampling variability causes $\bar{x}$ to differ in value from one sample to another. The behavior of $\bar{x}$ is described by its sampling distribution. The sample size n and characteristics of the population—its shape, mean value μ, and standard deviation σ—are important in determining properties of the sampling distribution of $\bar{x}$.

It is helpful to begin by looking at the results of some sampling experiments. In the two examples that follow, we start with a specified x population distribution, fix a sample size n, and select 500 different random samples of this size. We then compute $\bar{x}$ for each sample and construct a sample histogram of these 500 $\bar{x}$ values. Because 500 is reasonably large (a reasonably long sequence of samples), the sample histogram should rather closely resemble the true sampling distribution of $\bar{x}$ (obtained from an unending sequence of $\bar{x}$ values). We repeat the experiment for several different values of n to see how the choice of sample size affects the sampling distribution. Careful examination of these sample histograms will aid in understanding the general results to be stated shortly.

EXAMPLE 8.3

The paper "Platelet Size in Myocardial Infarction" (*Brit. Med. J.* (1983): 449–451) presented evidence that suggests that the distribution of platelet volume was approximately normal in shape both for patients after acute myocardial infarction (a heart attack) and for control subjects who had no history of serious illness. The

FIGURE 8.2
Normal distribution of platelet volume x with $\mu = 8.25$ and $\sigma = .75$

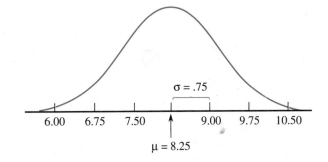

FIGURE 8.3
Sample histograms for $\bar{x}$ based on 500 samples, each consisting of n observations
(a) $n = 5$ (b) $n = 10$ (c) $n = 20$ (d) $n = 30$

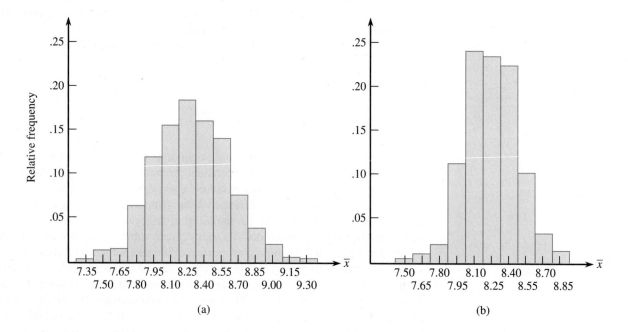

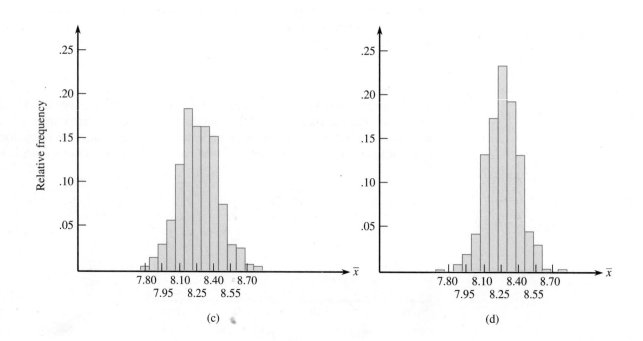

suggested values of μ and σ for the control-subject distribution were $\mu = 8.25$ and $\sigma = .75$. Figure 8.2 pictures the corresponding normal curve. The curve is centered at 8.25, the mean value of platelet volume. The value of the population standard deviation, .75, determines the extent to which the x distribution spreads out about its mean value.

We first used MINITAB to select 500 random samples from this normal distribution, each one consisting of $n = 5$ observations. A histogram of the resulting 500 $\bar{x}$ values appears in Figure 8.3(a). This procedure was repeated for samples of size $n = 10$, again for $n = 20$, and finally for $n = 30$. The resulting sample histograms of $\bar{x}$ values are displayed in Figure 8.3 (b), (c), and (d).

The first thing to notice about the histograms is their shape. To a reasonable approximation, each of the four looks like a normal curve. The resemblance would be even more striking if each histogram had been based on many more than 500 $\bar{x}$ values. Second, each histogram is centered approximately at 8.25, the mean of the population being sampled. Had the histograms been based on an unending sequence of $\bar{x}$ values, their centers would have been exactly the population mean, 8.25.

The final aspect of the histograms to note is their spread relative to one another. The smaller the value of n, the greater the extent to which the sampling distribution spreads out about the mean value. This is why the histograms for $n = 20$ and $n = 30$ are based on narrower class intervals than those for the two smaller sample sizes. For the larger sample sizes, most of the $\bar{x}$ values are quite close to 8.25. This is the effect of averaging. When n is small, a single unusual x value can result in an $\bar{x}$ value far from the center. With a larger sample size, any unusual x values, when averaged in with the other sample values, still tend to yield an $\bar{x}$ value close to μ. Combining these insights yields a result that should appeal to your intuition: $\bar{x}$ **based on a large n tends to be closer to μ than does $\bar{x}$ based on a small n.**

EXAMPLE 8.4

Now consider properties of the $\bar{x}$ sampling distribution when the population distribution is quite skewed (and thus very unlike a normal distribution). The May 8, 1983, issue of the *Los Angeles Times* contained data on the amount spent per pupil by each of 254 school districts located in Southern California. Figure 8.4 displays a histogram of the data. The histogram has a very long upper tail.

Let's now regard the 254 values as comprising a population, so that the histogram of Figure 8.4 shows the distribution of values in the population. The skewed shape makes identification of the mean value from the picture more difficult than for a normal distribution. We found the average of these 254 values to be $\mu = 1864$, so that is the balance point for the population histogram. The median population value is 1818, less than μ and reflective of the distribution's positively skewed nature.

For each of the sample sizes $n = 5, 10, 20$, and 30, as well as for $n = 50$, we selected 500 random samples of size n. This was done with replacement to approximate more nearly the usual situation in which the sample size n is only a small fraction of the population size. (Without replacement, $n = 30$ results in more than

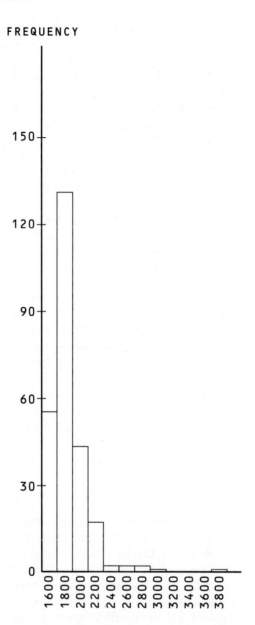

FIGURE 8.4
The population distribution for
Example 8.4 ($\mu = 1864$)

10% of the population being sampled; see the discussion at the end of Section 8.1.)
We then constructed a histogram of the 500 $\bar{x}$ values for each of the five sample
sizes. These histograms are displayed in Figure 8.5 (a) through (e).

Unlike the normal population case, these histograms all differ in shape. In
particular, the histograms become progressively less skewed as the sample size, n,
increases. The averages of the 500 $\bar{x}$ values for the five different sample sizes are
all quite close to the population mean $\mu = 1864$. If each histogram had been based
on an unending sequence of $\bar{x}$ values rather than just 500 values, each histogram

FIGURE 8.5
Histograms of 500 $\bar{x}$ values, each based on n observations
(a) $n = 5$ (average $\bar{x} = 1863.5$)
(b) $n = 10$ (average $\bar{x} = 1865.4$)

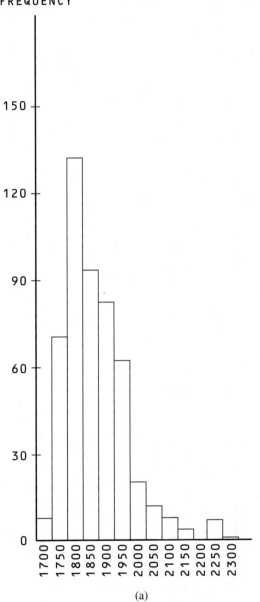

(a)

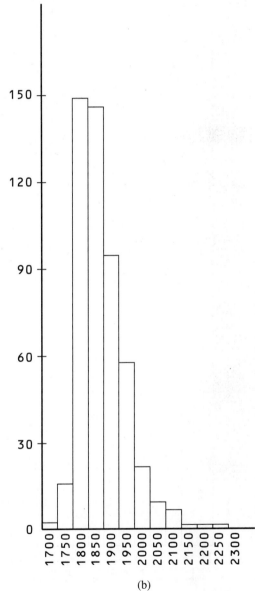

(b)

FIGURE 8.5 (continued)
Histograms of 500 $\bar{x}$ values, each based on n observations
(c) $n = 20$ (average $\bar{x} = 1865.0$)
(d) $n = 30$ (average $\bar{x} = 1862.1$)

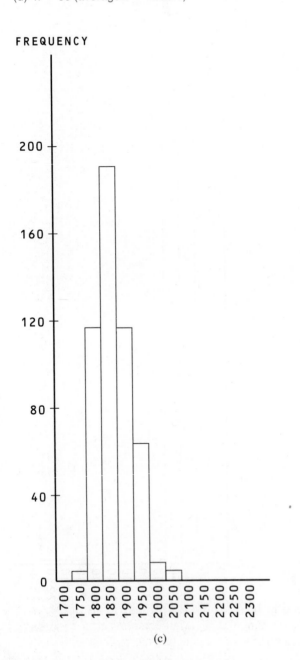

(c)

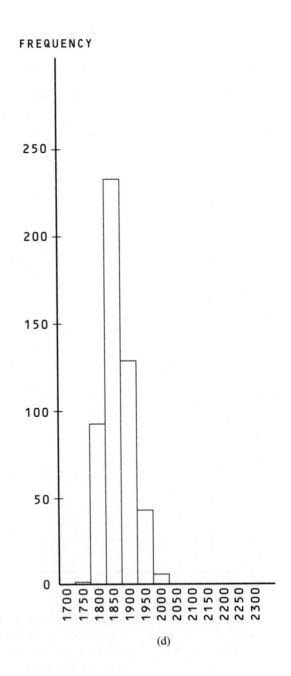

(d)

FIGURE 8.5 (continued)
Histograms of 500 $\bar{x}$ values,
each based on n observations
(e) $n = 50$
(average $\bar{x} = 1864.5$)

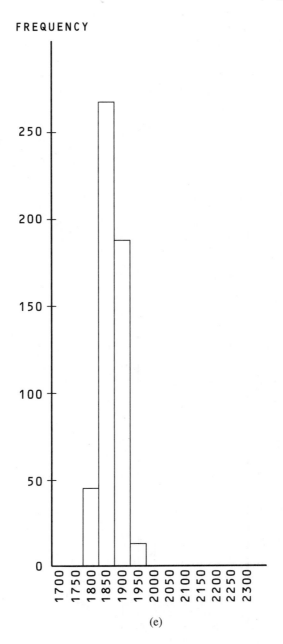

(e)

would have been centered at exactly 1864. Thus different values of n change the shape but not the center of $\bar{x}$'s sampling distribution. Comparison of the five $\bar{x}$ histograms in Figure 8.5 also shows that as n increases, the extent to which the histogram spreads out about its center decreases markedly. Increasing n both changes the shape of the distribution and squeezes it in toward the center, so that $\bar{x}$ based on a large n is a less variable quantity than is $\bar{x}$ based on a small value of n.

All five of the histograms in Figure 8.5 were drawn using the same horizontal scale so that the decrease in spread as n increases would be easy to see. However, this makes it hard to see what is happening to the shape of the histograms as the sample size changes. Figure 8.6 is a histogram based on narrower class intervals for the $\bar{x}$ values from samples of size 50. This picture shows that for $n = 50$, the histogram has a shape much like a normal curve. This is the effect of averaging. Even when n is large, one of the few large x values in the population appears only infrequently in the sample. When one does appear, its contribution to $\bar{x}$ is swamped

FIGURE 8.6
Histogram of 500 x values, each based on a sample of 50 observations

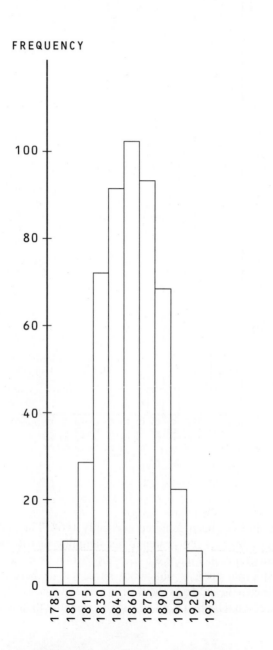

by the contributions of more typical sample values. The normal curve shape of the histograms for $n = 30$ and $n = 50$ are exactly what is predicted by the Central Limit Theorem, to be introduced shortly. According to this theorem, even if the population distribution bears no resemblance whatsoever to a normal curve, the $\bar{x}$ sampling distribution is approximately normal when the sample size n is reasonably large.

General Rules Concerning the Sampling Distribution of $\bar{x}$

Examples 8.3 and 8.4 suggest that for any n, the center of the $\bar{x}$ distribution (the mean value of $\bar{x}$) coincides with the mean of the population being sampled, but the spread of the $\bar{x}$ distribution decreases as n increases. The histograms indicate that the standard deviation of $\bar{x}$ is smaller for large n than for small n. The sample histograms also suggest that in some cases, the $\bar{x}$ distribution is approximately normal in shape. These observations are stated more formally in the following general rules.

GENERAL RULES CONCERNING THE $\bar{x}$ SAMPLING DISTRIBUTION

Let $\bar{x}$ denote the mean of the observations in a random sample of size n from a population having mean μ and standard deviation σ. Denote the mean value of the $\bar{x}$ distribution by $\mu_{\bar{x}}$ and the standard deviation of the $\bar{x}$ distribution by $\sigma_{\bar{x}}$. Then the following rules hold.

Rule 1. $\mu_{\bar{x}} = \mu$

Rule 2. $\sigma_{\bar{x}} = \sigma/\sqrt{n}$

Rule 3. When the population distribution is normal, the sampling distribution of $\bar{x}$ is also normal for any sample size n.

Rule 4. When n is sufficiently large, the sampling distribution of $\bar{x}$ is well approximated by a normal curve, even when the population distribution is not itself normal.

Rule 1, $\mu_{\bar{x}} = \mu$, says that the $\bar{x}$ distribution is always centered at the mean of the population sampled. Rule 2, $\sigma_{\bar{x}} = \sigma/\sqrt{n}$, not only says that the spread of the $\bar{x}$ distribution decreases as n increases but also gives a precise relationship between the standard deviation of the $\bar{x}$ distribution and the population standard deviation. When $n = 4$, for example,

$$\sigma_{\bar{x}} = \frac{\sigma}{\sqrt{n}} = \frac{\sigma}{\sqrt{4}} = \frac{\sigma}{2}$$

so that the $\bar{x}$ distribution has a standard deviation only half as large as the population standard deviation. Rules 3 and 4 specify circumstances under which the $\bar{x}$ distribution is normal or approximately normal: when the population is normal or when the sample size is large. Figure 8.7 illustrates these rules by showing several $\bar{x}$ distributions superimposed over a graph of the population distribution.

FIGURE 8.7
Population distribution and
sampling distributions of $\bar{x}$
(a) A symmetric
population distribution
(b) A skewed
population distribution

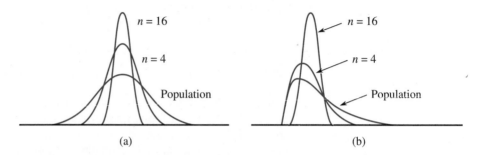

Rule 4 is the statement of a very important result called the **Central Limit Theorem.** This theorem says that when n is sufficiently large, the $\bar{x}$ distribution is approximately normal, no matter what the population distribution looks like. This result has enabled statisticians to develop some large-sample procedures for making inferences about a population mean μ even when the shape of the population distribution is unknown.

Recall that a variable is standardized by subtracting the mean value and then dividing by its standard deviation. Using rules 1 and 2 to standardize $\bar{x}$ gives an important consequence of the last two rules.

If n is large or the population distribution is normal, the standardized variable

$$z = \frac{\bar{x} - \mu_{\bar{x}}}{\sigma_{\bar{x}}} = \frac{\bar{x} - \mu}{\sigma/\sqrt{n}}$$

has (approximately) a standard normal (z) distribution.

Application of the Central Limit Theorem in specific problem situations requires a rule of thumb for deciding whether n is indeed sufficiently large. Such a rule is not as easy to come by as you might think. Look again at Figure 8.5, which shows the approximate sampling distribution of $\bar{x}$ for $n = 5, 10, 20, 30,$ and 50 when the population distribution is quite skewed. Certainly the histogram for $n = 10$ is not well described by a normal curve, and this is still true of the histogram for $n = 20$, particularly in the tails of the histogram (far away from the mean value). Among the five histograms, only the ones for $n = 30$ and $n = 50$ have reasonably normal shapes.

On the other hand, when the population distribution is normal, the sampling distribution of $\bar{x}$ is normal for any n. If the population distribution is somewhat skewed but not to the extent of Figure 8.4, we might expect the $\bar{x}$ sampling distribution to be a bit skewed for $n = 5$ but quite well fit by a normal curve for n as small as 10 or 15. The value of n required for a normal curve to give a good approximation to $\bar{x}$'s sampling distribution will depend on how much the population distribution differs from a normal distribution. The closer the population distribution is to being normal, the smaller the value of n necessary for the Central Limit Theorem approximation to be accurate.

The rule that many statisticians recommend is conservative.

> The Central Limit Theorem can safely be applied if n exceeds 30.

If the population distribution is believed to be reasonably close to a normal distribution, an n of 15 or 20 is often large enough for $\bar{x}$ to have approximately a normal distribution. At the other extreme, we can imagine a distribution with a much longer tail than that of Figure 8.4, in which case even $n = 40$ or 50 would not suffice for approximate normality of $\bar{x}$. In practice, however, very few population distributions are likely to be this badly behaved.

To see how information regarding the sampling distribution of $\bar{x}$ can be used, consider the following three examples.

EXAMPLE 8.5

Let x denote the duration of a randomly selected song (in minutes) for a certain type of songbird. Suppose that the mean value of song duration is $\mu = 1.5$ min and that the standard deviation of song duration is $\sigma = .9$ min. (These values are suggested by the results of a large random sample of house finch songs, as reported in "Song Dialects and Colonization in the House Finch" (*Condor* (1975):407–422).) The sampling distribution of $\bar{x}$ based on a random sample of $n = 25$ song durations then also has mean value

$$\mu_{\bar{x}} = 1.5 \text{ min}$$

That is, the sampling distribution of $\bar{x}$ is centered at 1.5. The standard deviation of $\bar{x}$ is

$$\sigma_{\bar{x}} = \frac{\sigma}{\sqrt{n}} = \frac{.9}{\sqrt{25}} = .18$$

only one-fifth as large as the population standard deviation, σ.

EXAMPLE 8.6

A meat market claims that the average fat content of its ground chuck is 12%. Let x denote the fat content of a randomly selected package of ground chuck. Suppose that x is normally distributed, with $\sigma = 1.6\%$. Consider selecting $n = 16$ packages and determining the fat content of each one (observations $x_1, x_2, \ldots, x_{16}$), and let $\bar{x}$ denote the resulting sample average fat content. Because the x distribution is normal, $\bar{x}$ is also normally distributed. If the market's claim is correct, the $\bar{x}$ sampling distribution has mean value

$$\mu_{\bar{x}} = \mu = 12$$

and standard deviation

$$\sigma_{\bar{x}} = \frac{\sigma}{\sqrt{n}} = \frac{1.6}{\sqrt{16}} = .40$$

To calculate a probability involving $\bar{x}$, we simply standardize by subtracting the mean value, 12, and dividing by the standard deviation (of $\bar{x}$), which is .40. For example, the probability that the sample average fat content is between 11.6% and 12.8% is calculated by first standardizing the interval limits:

$$\text{lower limit:} \quad \frac{11.6 - 12}{.40} = -1.0$$

$$\text{upper limit:} \quad \frac{12.8 - 12}{.40} = 2.0$$

Then

$$P(11.6 \leq \bar{x} \leq 12.8) = \left(\begin{array}{c} \text{area under the } z \text{ curve} \\ \text{between } -1.0 \text{ and } 2.0 \end{array} \right)$$

$$= \left(\begin{array}{c} \text{area to the} \\ \text{left of } 2.0 \end{array} \right) - \left(\begin{array}{c} \text{area to the} \\ \text{left of } -1.0 \end{array} \right)$$

$$= .9772 - .1587$$

$$= .8185$$

The probability that the sample average fat content is at least 13% is, since $(13 - 12)/.40 = 2.5$,

$$P(13 \leq \bar{x}) = \left(\begin{array}{c} \text{area under the } z \text{ curve} \\ \text{to the right of } 2.5 \end{array} \right) = .0062$$

If the x distribution is as described and the claim is correct, a sample average fat content based on 16 observations exceeds 13% for less than 1% of all such samples. Thus, observation of an $\bar{x}$ value that exceeds 13% casts doubt on the market's claim that the average fat content is 12%.

EXAMPLE 8.7

A cigarette manufacturer asserts that one of its brands of cigarettes has an average nicotine content of $\mu = 1.8$ mg per cigarette. Smokers of this brand would probably not be disturbed if the mean were less than 1.8 but would be unhappy if it exceeded

1.8. Let x denote the nicotine content of a randomly selected cigarette and suppose that σ, the standard deviation of the x distribution, is .4.

An independent testing organization is asked to analyze a random sample of 36 cigarettes. Let $\bar{x}$ be the average nicotine content for this sample. The sample size, $n = 36$, is large enough to invoke the Central Limit Theorem and regard the $\bar{x}$ distribution as being approximately normal. The standard deviation of the $\bar{x}$ distribution is

$$\sigma_{\bar{x}} = \frac{\sigma}{\sqrt{n}} = \frac{.4}{\sqrt{36}} = .0667 \text{ mg}$$

If the manufacturer's claim is correct, we know that

$$\mu_{\bar{x}} = \mu = 1.8 \text{ mg}$$

Suppose the sample resulted in a mean of $\bar{x} = 1.84$. Does this result indicate that the manufacturer's claim is incorrect?

We can answer this question by looking at the sampling distribution of $\bar{x}$. Due to sampling variability, even if $\mu = 1.8$ we know that $\bar{x}$ will deviate somewhat from this value. Is it likely that we would see a sample mean as large as 1.84 when the true population mean is 1.8? If the company's claim is correct,

$$P(\bar{x} \geq 1.84) \approx P\left(z > \frac{1.84 - 1.8}{.0667}\right)$$

$$= P(z > .6)$$

$$= \left(\begin{array}{c}\text{area under the } z \text{ curve} \\ \text{to the right of } .6\end{array}\right)$$

$$= .2743$$

The value of $\bar{x} = 1.84$ does not exceed 1.8 by enough to cast substantial doubt on the manufacturer's claim. Values of $\bar{x}$ as large as 1.84 will be observed about 27.43% of the time when a random sample of size 36 is taken from a population with mean 1.8 and standard deviation .4.

Other Cases

We now know a great deal about the sampling distribution of $\bar{x}$ in two cases, that of a normal population distribution and that of a large sample size. What happens when the population distribution is not normal and n is small? Unfortunately, while it is true that $\mu_{\bar{x}} = \mu$ and $\sigma_{\bar{x}} = \sigma/\sqrt{n}$, there is no general result about the shape of the $\bar{x}$ distribution. When the objective is to make an inference about the center of such a population, one way to proceed is to replace the normality assumption with some other distributional model for the population. Statisticians have proposed and studied a number of such models. Then theoretical methods or simulation can be used to describe the $\bar{x}$ distribution corresponding to the assumed model. An alternative path is to use an inferential procedure based on statistics other than $\bar{x}$.

EXERCISES 8.18–8.29   SECTION 8.3

8.18 A random sample is to be selected from a population with mean $\mu = 100$ and standard deviation $\sigma = 10$. Determine the mean and standard deviation of the $\bar{x}$ sampling distribution for each of the following sample sizes.

    a. $n = 9$ **b.** $n = 15$ **c.** $n = 36$
    d. $n = 50$ **e.** $n = 100$ **f.** $n = 400$

8.19 For which of the sample sizes given in Exercise 8.18 would it be reasonable to think that the $\bar{x}$ sampling distribution will be approximately normal in shape?

8.20 Explain the difference between σ and $\sigma_{\bar{x}}$. Between μ and $\mu_{\bar{x}}$.

8.21 Suppose that a random sample of size 64 is to be selected from a population with mean 40 and standard deviation 5.

    a. What are the mean and standard deviation of the $\bar{x}$ sampling distribution? Describe the shape of the $\bar{x}$ sampling distribution.

    b. What is the approximate probability that $\bar{x}$ will be within .5 of the population mean μ?

    c. What is the approximate probability that $\bar{x}$ will differ from μ by more than .7?

8.22 The time that a randomly selected individual waits for an elevator in an office building has a uniform distribution over the interval from 0 to 1 min. (The uniform distribution is discussed briefly in Example 7.1.) It can be shown that, for this distribution, $\mu = .5$ and $\sigma = .289$.

    a. Let $\bar{x}$ be the sample average waiting time for a random sample of 16 individuals. What are the mean value and standard deviation of $\bar{x}$'s sampling distribution?

    b. Answer part (a) for a random sample of 50 individuals. In this case, sketch a picture of a good approximation to the actual $\bar{x}$ distribution.

8.23 Let x denote the time (min) that it takes a fifth grade student to read a certain passage. Suppose that the mean value and standard deviation of x are $\mu = 2$ min and $\sigma = .8$ min, respectively.

    a. If $\bar{x}$ is the sample average time for a random sample of $n = 9$ students, where is the $\bar{x}$ distribution centered and how much does it spread out about the center (as described by its standard deviation)?

    b. Repeat part (a) for a sample of size of $n = 20$ and again for a sample of size $n = 100$. How do the centers and spreads of the three $\bar{x}$ distributions compare to one another? Which sample size would be most likely to result in an $\bar{x}$ value close to μ, and why?

8.24 Suppose that the mean value of interpupillary distance for all adult males is 65 mm and the population standard deviation is 5 mm.

    a. If the distribution of interpupillary distance is normal and a sample of $n = 25$ adult males is selected, what is the probability that the sample average distance $\bar{x}$ for these 25 will be between 64 and 67 mm? At least 68 mm?

b. Suppose that a sample of 100 adult males is obtained. Without assuming that interpupillary distance is normally distributed, what is the approximate probability that the sample average distance is between 64 and 67 mm? At least 68 mm?

8.25   Suppose that a sample of size 100 is to be drawn from a population with standard deviation 10.

a. What is the probability that the sample mean will be within 2 of the value of μ?

b. For this example ($n = 100$, $\sigma = 10$), complete each statement by computing the appropriate value.

    i. Approximately 95% of the time, $\bar{x}$ is within ____ of μ.

    ii. Approximately .3% of the time, $\bar{x}$ is farther than ____ from μ.

8.26   A manufacturing process is designed to produce bolts with a .5-in. diameter. Once each day, a random sample of 36 bolts is selected and the diameters recorded. If the resulting sample mean is less than .49 in. or greater than .51 in., the process is shut down for adjustment. The standard deviation for diameter is .02 in. What is the probability that the manufacturing line will be shut down unnecessarily? (Hint: Find the probability of observing an $\bar{x}$ in the shut-down range when the true process mean really is .5 in.)

8.27   College students with a checking account typically write relatively few checks in any given month, while full-time residents typically write many more checks during a month. Suppose that 50% of a bank's accounts are held by students and 50% by full-time residents. Let x denote the number of checks written in a given month by a randomly selected bank customer.

a. Give a sketch of what the probability distribution of x might look like.

b. Let the mean value of x be 22.0 and the standard deviation 16.5. If a random sample of $n = 100$ customers is selected and $\bar{x}$ denotes the sample average number of checks written during a particular month, where is the sampling distribution of $\bar{x}$ centered, and what is the standard deviation of the $\bar{x}$ distribution? Sketch a rough picture of the sampling distribution.

c. Referring to part (b), what is the approximate probability that $\bar{x}$ is at most 20? At least 25? What result are you using to justify your computations?

8.28   An airplane with room for 100 passengers has a total baggage limit of 6000 lb. Suppose that the total weight of the baggage checked by an individual passenger is a random variable x with mean value 50 lb and standard deviation 20 lb. If 100 passengers board a flight, what is the approximate probability that the total weight of their baggage will exceed the limit? (Hint: With $n = 100$, the total weight exceeds the limit precisely when the average weight $\bar{x}$ exceeds 6000/100.)

8.29   The thickness of the coating (mm) applied to disk drives is a characteristic that determines the usefulness of the product. When no unusual circumstances are present, the thickness (x) has a normal distribution with mean 3 mm and standard deviation .05 mm. Suppose the process will be monitored by selecting a random sample of 16 drives from each shift's production and determining $\bar{x}$, the mean coating thickness for the sample.

a. Describe the sampling distribution of $\bar{x}$ (for a sample size 16).

b. When no unusual circumstances are present, we expect $\bar{x}$ to be within $3\sigma_{\bar{x}}$ of 3 mm, the desired value. An $\bar{x}$ value farther from 3 than $3\sigma_{\bar{x}}$ is interpreted as an indication of a problem that needs attention. Compute $3 \pm 3\sigma$. (A plot over time of $\bar{x}$ values with horizontal lines drawn at the limits $\mu \pm 3\sigma_{\bar{x}}$ is called a *process control chart.*)

c. Referring to part (b), what is the probability that a sample mean will be outside $3 \pm 3\sigma_{\bar{x}}$ just by chance (that is, when there are no unusual circumstances)?

d. Suppose that a machine used to apply the coating is out of adjustment, resulting in a mean coating thickness of 3.05 mm. What is the probability that a problem will be detected when the next sample is taken? (Hint: This will occur if $\bar{x} > 3 + 3\sigma_{\bar{x}}$ or $\bar{x} < 3 - 3\sigma_{\bar{x}}$ when $\mu = 3.05$.)

8.4 The Sampling Distribution of a Sample Proportion

The objective of many statistical investigations is to draw a conclusion about the proportion of individuals or objects in a population that possess a specified property; for example, Maytag washers that don't require service during the warranty period, Europeans who favor the deployment of a certain type of missile, or smokers who regularly smoke nonfilter cigarettes. In such situations, any individual or object that possesses the property of interest is labeled a success (*S*), and one that does not possess the property is termed a failure (*F*). The letter π denotes the proportion of *S*'s in the population. The value of π is a number between 0 and 1, and 100π is the percentage of *S*'s in the population. Thus $\pi = .75$ means that 75% of the population members are *S*'s, while $\pi = .01$ identifies a population containing only 1% *S*'s and 99% *F*'s.

The value of π is usually unknown to an investigator. When a random sample of size *n* is selected from this type of population, some of the individuals in the sample are *S*'s and the remaining individuals in the sample are *F*'s. The statistic that will provide a basis for making inferences about π is *p*, the **sample proportion of *S*'s**:

$$p = \frac{\text{the number of } S\text{'s in the sample}}{n}$$

For example, if $n = 5$ and three *S*'s result, then $p = \frac{3}{5} = .6$.

Just as making inferences about μ requires knowing something about the sampling distribution of the statistic $\bar{x}$, making inferences about π requires first learning about properties of the sampling distribution of the statistic *p*. For example, when $n = 5$, possible values of *p* are 0, .2 (from $\frac{1}{5}$), .4, .6, .8, and 1. The sampling distribution of *p* gives the probability of each of these six possible values (the long-run proportion of the time that each value would occur if samples with $n = 5$ were selected over and over again). Similarly, when $n = 100$, the 101 possible values of *p* are 0, .01, .02, . . . , .98, .99, and 1. The sampling distribution of *p* can then be used to calculate probabilities such as $P(.3 \le p \le .7)$ and $P(.75 \le p)$.

Before stating some general rules concerning the sampling distribution of *p*, we present the results of two sampling experiments as aids to developing an intuitive understanding of the rules. In each example, we selected a population having a specified value of π and obtained 500 random samples, each of size n, from the population. We then computed p for each sample and constructed a sample histogram of these 500 values. As with $\bar{x}$, this was repeated for several different values of n to show how the sampling distribution changes with increasing sample size.

EXAMPLE 8.8

The percentage of females in the European labor force varies widely from country to country. The publication *European Marketing Data and Statistics* (17th ed., 1981) reports that Ireland's work force had the lowest percentage of females, 26.5%, whereas the (former) U.S.S.R. had the highest, with 50.4%. We decided to simulate sampling from Ireland's labor force with S denoting a female worker and F a male worker, so $\pi = .265$. A computer was used to select 500 samples of size $n = 5$, then 500 samples of size $n = 10$, then 500 samples with $n = 25$, and finally 500 samples with $n = 50$. The sample histograms of the 500 values of p for the four sample sizes are displayed in Figure 8.8.

FIGURE 8.8
Histograms of 500 values of p, each based on a random sample of size n ($\pi = .265$)
(a) $n = 5$
(b) $n = 10$
(c) $n = 25$
(d) $n = 50$

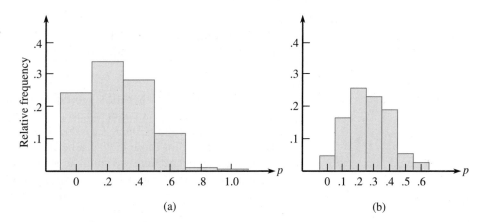

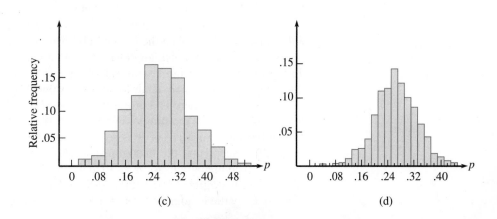

The most noticeable feature of the histogram shapes is the progression toward the shape of a normal curve as n increases. The histogram for $n = 5$ is definitely skewed. The two smallest possible values of p, which are 0 and .2, occurred 122 and 174 times, respectively, in the 500 samples, while the two largest values, .8 and 1, occurred only 3 and 1 times, respectively. The histogram for $n = 10$ is considerably more bell-shaped, although it still has a slight positive skew. The histogram for $n = 25$ exhibits very little skewness, and the histogram for $n = 50$ looks like a normal curve.

Although the skewness of the first two histograms makes the location of their centers (balance points) a bit difficult, all four histograms appear to be centered at roughly .265, the value of π for the population being sampled. Had the histograms been based on an unending sequence of samples (or, equivalently, on theoretical calculations using the binomial probability distribution) instead of just 500 samples, each histogram would have been centered at exactly .265. Finally, taking note of the different horizontal scales for (a)–(d), the histograms spread out more for small n than for large n (as was the case for $\bar{x}$). The value of p based on a large sample size tends to be closer to π, the population proportion of S's, than does p from a small sample.

Our next example shows what happens to the sampling distribution of p when π is either quite close to 0 or quite close to 1.

EXAMPLE 8.9

The development of viral hepatitis subsequent to a blood transfusion can cause serious complications for a patient. The paper "Hepatitis in Patients with Acute Nonlymphatic Leukemia" (*Amer. J. of Med.* (1983):413–421) reported that in spite of careful screening for those having a hepatitis antigen, viral hepatitis occurs in 7% of blood recipients. Here we simulate sampling from the population of blood recipients, with S denoting a recipient who contracts hepatitis (not the sort of characteristic one thinks of identifying as a success, but the S–F labeling is arbitrary), so that $\pi = .07$. Figure 8.9 displays histograms of 500 values of p for the four sample sizes $n = 10, 25, 50$, and 100.

As was the case in Example 8.8, all four histograms are centered at approximately the value of π for the population being sampled. (The average values of p are .0690, .0677, .0707, and .0694.) If the histograms had been based on an unending sequence of samples, they would all have been centered at exactly $\pi = .07$. Again the spread of a histogram based on a large n is smaller than the spread of a histogram resulting from a small sample size. The larger the value of n, the closer the sample proportion, p, tends to be to the value of the population proportion, π.

Furthermore, there is a progression toward the shape of a normal curve as n increases. However, the progression is much slower here than in the previous example because the value of π is so extreme. (The same thing would happen for $\pi = .93$, except that the histograms would be negatively rather than positively skewed.) The histograms for $n = 10$ and $n = 25$ exhibit substantial skew, and the skew of the histogram for $n = 50$ is still moderate (compare Figure 8.9(c) to Figure 8.8(d)). Only the histogram for $n = 100$ is reasonably well fit by a normal curve. It

FIGURE 8.9
Histograms of 500 values of *p*,
each based on a random
sample of size *n* ($\pi = .07$)
(a) *n* = 10
(b) *n* = 25
(c) *n* = 50
(d) *n* = 100

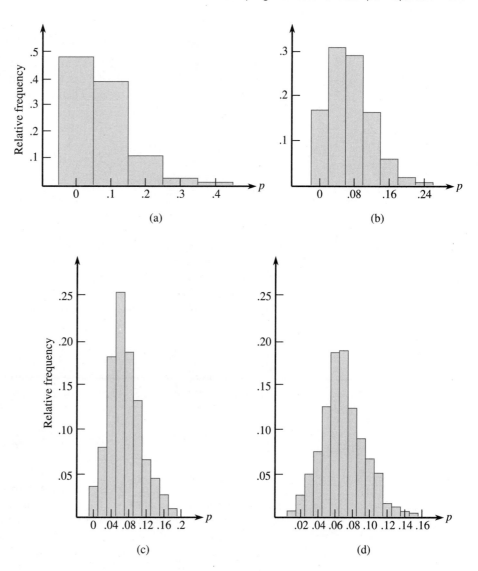

appears that whether a normal curve provides a good approximation to the sampling distribution of *p* depends on the values of both *n* and π. Knowing just that *n* = 50 is not enough to guarantee that the shape of the histogram is approximately normal.

The previous two examples suggest that the sampling distribution of *p* depends both on *n*, the sample size, and on π, the proportion of *S*'s in the population. These results are stated more formally in the following general rules.

GENERAL RULES CONCERNING THE p SAMPLING DISTRIBUTION

Let p be the proportion of successes in a random sample of size n from a population whose proportion of S's is π. Denote the mean value of p by μ_p and the standard deviation by σ_p. Then the following rules hold.

Rule 1. $\mu_p = \pi$

Rule 2. $\sigma_p = \sqrt{\pi(1 - \pi)/n}$

Rule 3. When n is sufficiently large, the sampling distribution of p is approximately normal.

Thus the sampling distribution of p is always centered at the value of the population success proportion π, and the extent to which the distribution spreads out about π decreases as the sample size n increases.

Examples 8.8 and 8.9 indicate that both π and n must be considered in judging whether p's sampling distribution is approximately normal.

The farther the value of π is from .5, the larger the value of n must be in order for the normal approximation to the sampling distribution of p to be accurate. A conservative rule of thumb is that if

$$n\pi \geq 5 \quad \text{and} \quad n(1 - \pi) \geq 5$$

then the sampling distribution of p is approximately normal.

A sample size of $n = 100$ is not by itself sufficient to justify the use of the normal approximation. If $\pi = .01$, the distribution of p will be very positively skewed, so a bell-shaped curve will not give a good approximation. Similarly, if $n = 100$ and $\pi = .99$ (so $n(1 - \pi) = 1 < 5$), the distribution of p will have a substantial negative skew. The conditions $n\pi \geq 5$ and $n(1 - \pi) \geq 5$ ensure that the sampling distribution of p is not too skewed. If $\pi = .5$, the normal approximation can be used for n as small as 10, while for $\pi = .05$ or $.95$, n should be at least 100.

EXAMPLE 8.10

The proportion of all blood recipients stricken with viral hepatitis was given as .07 in the paper referenced in Example 8.9. Suppose that a new treatment is developed that is believed to reduce the incidence rate of viral hepatitis. This treatment is given to $n = 200$ blood recipients. Only six of the 200 patients contract hepatitis. This appears to be a favorable result, since $p = 6/200 = .03$. The question of interest to medical researchers is: Does this result indicate that the true (long-run) proportion of patients who contract hepatitis after the experimental treatment will be less than .07, or could this result be plausibly attributed to sampling variability (that is, the fact that p will typically deviate from its mean value, π)? If the treatment is ineffective,

$$\mu_p = \pi = .07$$

$$\sigma_p = \sqrt{\pi(1 - \pi)/200} = \sqrt{(.07)(.93)/200} = .018$$

Furthermore, since

$$n\pi = 200(.07) = 14 \geq 5$$

and

$$n(1 - \pi) = 200(.93) = 186 \geq 5,$$

the sampling distribution of p is approximately normal. Then

$$P(p < .03) = P\left(z < \frac{.03 - .07}{.018}\right)$$

$$= P(z < -2.2)$$
$$= \text{area to the left of } -2.2 \text{ under the } z \text{ curve}$$
$$= .0139$$

Thus, it is unlikely that a sample proportion .03 or smaller would be observed if the treatment really is ineffective. The new treatment appears to yield a smaller incidence rate for the disease than occurs without any treatment.

EXERCISES 8.30–8.36   SECTION 8.4

8.30   A random sample is to be selected from a population that has a proportion of successes $\pi = .65$. Determine the mean and standard deviation of the sampling distribution of p for each of the following sample sizes.
   a. $n = 10$ **b.** $n = 20$ **c.** $n = 30$
   d. $n = 50$ **e.** $n = 100$ **f.** $n = 200$

8.31   For which of the sample sizes given in Exercise 8.30 would the sampling distribution of p be approximately normal if $\pi = .65$? If $\pi = .2$?

8.32   A certain chromosome defect occurs in only one out of 200 Caucasian adult males. A random sample of $n = 100$ such individuals is obtained.
   a. What is the mean value of the sample proportion p, and what is the standard deviation of the sample proportion?
   b. Does p have approximately a normal distribution in this case? Explain.
   c. What is the smallest value of n for which the sampling distribution of p is approximately normal?

8.33 A column in the April 22, 1985, issue of *Newsweek* reported that 55% of all women in the U.S. work force regard themselves as underpaid. Although this conclusion was based on sample data, suppose that, in fact, $\pi = .55$, where π represents the true proportion of working women who believe that they are underpaid.

    a. Would p based on a random sample of only ten working women have approximately a normal distribution? Explain why or why not.

    b. What are the mean value and standard deviation of p based on a random sample of size 400?

    c. When $n = 400$, what is $P(.5 \le p \le .6)$?

    d. Suppose now that $\pi = .4$. For a random sample of $n = 400$ working women, what is $P(.5 < p)$?

8.34 The article "Thrillers" (*Newsweek,* April 22, 1985) states, "Surveys tell us that more than half of America's college graduates are avid readers of mystery novels." Let π denote the actual proportion of college graduates who are avid readers of mystery novels. Consider p to be based on a random sample of 225 college graduates.

    a. If $\pi = .5$, what are the mean value and standard deviation of p? Answer this question when $\pi = .6$. Does p have approximately a normal distribution in both cases? Explain.

    b. Calculate $P(p \ge .6)$ both when $\pi = .5$ and when $\pi = .6$.

    c. Without doing any calculations, how do you think the probabilities in part (b) would change if n were 400 rather than 225?

8.35 Suppose that a particular candidate for public office is in fact favored by 48% of all registered voters in the district. A polling organization takes a random sample of 500 voters and will use p, the sample proportion, to estimate π. What is the approximate probability that p will be greater than .5, causing the polling organization to incorrectly predict the result of the upcoming election?

8.36 A manufacturer of electric typewriters purchases plastic print wheels from a vendor. When a large shipment is received, a random sample of 200 print wheels is selected and each is inspected. If the sample proportion of defectives is more than .02, the entire shipment will be returned to the vendor.

    a. What is the approximate probability that the shipment will be returned if the true proportion of defectives in the shipment is .05?

    b. What is the approximate probability that the shipment will not be returned when the true proportion of defectives in the shipment is .10?

CHAPTER EIGHT SUMMARY OF KEY CONCEPTS AND FORMULAS

Term or Formula	Comment
Statistic	Any quantity whose value is computed from sample data.
Sampling distribution	The probability distribution of a statistic: the sampling distribution describes the long-run behavior of the statistic.

Term or Formula	Comment
Random sample	A sample for which values are selected independently from the same population distribution.
Sampling distribution of $\bar{x}$	The probability distribution of the sample mean $\bar{x}$, based on a random sample of size n. Key properties of the $\bar{x}$ sampling distribution are $\mu_{\bar{x}} = \mu$ and $\sigma_{\bar{x}} = \sigma/\sqrt{n}$ (where μ and σ are the population mean and standard deviation, respectively). In addition, when the population distribution is normal or the sample size is large, the sampling distribution of $\bar{x}$ is (approximately) normal.
Central Limit Theorem	This important theorem states that when n is sufficiently large, the $\bar{x}$ distribution will be approximately normal. The standard rule of thumb is that the theorem can safely be applied when n exceeds 30.
Sampling distribution of p	The probability distribution of the sample proportion p, based on a random sample of size n. When the sample size is sufficiently large, the sampling distribution of p is approximately normal, with $\mu_p = \pi$ and $\sigma_p = \sqrt{\pi(1 - \pi)/n}$ (where π is the true population proportion).

ENCORE

The book-binding process described in the Chapter Preview is designed to produce binding strengths with a mean of 180 lb/in.^{2} and a standard deviation of 3 lb/in.^{2} In order to monitor the process over time, a sample of 10 books is selected from each shift and the sample mean computed. If the value of the sample mean is not what would be expected as a result of sampling variability alone, some external factor may be influencing the process. We can use what is known about the behavior of $\bar{x}$ to decide when this might be the case.

When the process is behaving properly ($\mu = 180$, $\sigma = 3$), the $\bar{x}$ distribution for samples of size 10 will have

$$\mu_{\bar{x}} = 180, \quad \sigma_{\bar{x}} = \frac{\sigma}{\sqrt{n}} = \frac{3}{\sqrt{10}} = .95$$

If the binding strength distribution is approximately normal, the $\bar{x}$ distribution will also be approximately normal; thus we would expect almost all (99.7%) $\bar{x}$ values to be within $3\sigma_{\bar{x}}$ of the process mean, 180. Even if the binding strength distribution is not normal, Chebyshev's Rule ensures that *at least* 89% of all possible samples will produce an $\bar{x}$ value within $3\sigma_{\bar{x}}$ of 180. As a result, we expect to see $\bar{x}$ values in the range

$$\mu_{\bar{x}} \pm 3\sigma_{\bar{x}} = 180 \pm 3(.95) = (177.15, 182.85)$$

An $\bar{x}$ value between 177.15 and 182.85 is considered consistent with proper process behavior, whereas an $\bar{x}$ value outside this range can be interpreted as indicative of a problem.

As sample data is collected over time, each $\bar{x}$ value is compared to the limits 177.15 and 182.85. These comparisons are often displayed graphically as an $\bar{x}$ control chart. To construct an $\bar{x}$ chart, the sample means are plotted over time along a horizontal axis. The limits $\mu_{\bar{x}} \pm 3\sigma_{\bar{x}}$ (called *control limits*) are shown along the vertical axis of the plot. For our example, the basic design of the plot is illustrated next.

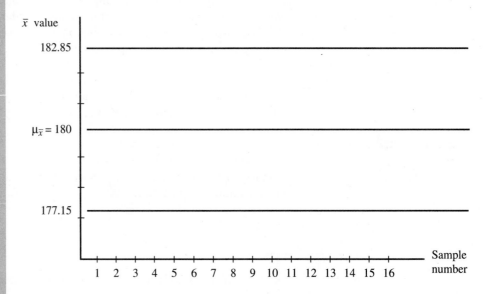

As each successive sample is obtained, $\bar{x}$ is computed, and its value is entered as a point on the control chart. If the point falls between the control limits, no action is taken. If the $\bar{x}$ value falls outside the control limits (something that is not expected to occur when the process is behaving normally), action can be taken to determine if a problem exists.

To illustrate the use of a control chart, consider the means of twenty samples of size 10 shown here. The first 17 samples were taken from a binding process where the mean strength was 180. At time period 18 the mean strength slipped to 175. We will see how the control chart signals this change in the process.

Sample number	$\bar{x}$	Sample number	$\bar{x}$	Sample number	$\bar{x}$
1	180.1	8	180.3	15	180.7
2	179.5	9	180.7	16	181.3
3	179.7	10	180.8	17	180.3
4	180.3	11	180.2	18	173.9
5	180.2	12	179.2	19	176.2
6	181.2	13	179.4	20	175.6
7	179.0	14	177.5		

Plotting these sample means against the control limits results in the following chart. Note that starting at sample number 18, the $\bar{x}$ values fall outside the control limits.

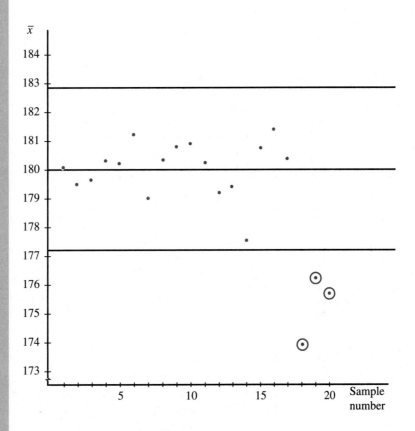

Many statistical computer packages will construct control charts. Shown on the following page is an $\bar{x}$ chart from MINITAB.

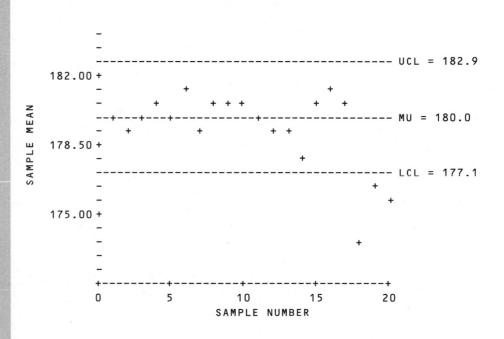

Control charts provide a great deal of useful information about manufacturing processes. Process characteristics other than the mean can be monitored by plotting sample statistics such as the sample range, standard deviation, or median on control charts that are designed using the same line of reasoning that leads to the $\bar{x}$ control chart.

SUPPLEMENTARY EXERCISES 8.37–8.43

8.37 The nicotine content in a single cigarette of a particular brand is a random variable with mean .8 mg and standard deviation .1 mg. If 100 of these cigarettes are analyzed, what is the probability that the resulting sample mean nicotine content will be less than .79? Less than .77?

8.38 Let $x_1, x_2, \ldots, x_{100}$ denote the actual net weights (in lb) of 100 randomly selected bags of fertilizer. Suppose that the weight of a randomly selected bag is a random variable with mean 50 lb and variance 1 lb². Let $\bar{x}$ be the sample mean weight ($n = 100$).

a. Describe the sampling distribution of $\bar{x}$.

b. What is the probability that the sample mean is between 49.75 lb and 50.25 lb?

c. What is the probability that the sample mean is less than 50 lb?

8.39 Suppose that 20% of the subscribers of a cable television company watch the shopping channel at least once a week. The cable company is trying to decide whether to replace this channel with a new local station. A survey of 100 subscribers will be undertaken. The cable company has decided to keep the shopping channel if the sample proportion is greater than .25. What is the approximate probability that the cable company will keep the shopping channel, even though the true proportion who watch it is only .20?

8.40 Although a lecture period at a certain university lasts exactly 50 minutes, the actual lecture time of a statistics instructor on any particular day is a random variable with mean value 52 min and standard deviation 2 min. Suppose that times of different lectures are independent of one another. Let $\bar{x}$ represent the mean of 36 randomly selected lecture times.

a. What are the mean value and standard deviation of the sampling distribution of $\bar{x}$?

b. What is the probability that the sample mean exceeds 50 min? 55 min?

8.41 Water permeability of concrete is an important characteristic in assessing suitability for various applications. Permeability can be measured by letting water flow across the surface and determining the amount lost (in./hr). Suppose that the permeability index x for a randomly selected concrete specimen of a particular type is normally distributed with mean value 1000 and standard deviation 150.

a. How likely is it that a single specimen will have a permeability index between 850 and 1300?

b. If the permeability index is determined for each specimen in a random sample of size 10, how likely is it that the sample average permeability index will be between 950 and 1100? Between 850 and 1300?

8.42 Suppose that 60% of all students taking Elementary Statistics write their names in their textbooks. A random sample of 100 students is selected.

a. What is the mean value of the proportion among the 100 sampled who have their names in their texts? What is the standard deviation of the sample proportion?

b. What is the chance that at most 50% of those sampled have their names in their texts?

c. Answer part (b) if there are 400 students in the random sample.

8.43 The amount of money spent by a customer at a discount store has a mean of $100 and a standard deviation of $30. What is the probability that a randomly selected group of 50 shoppers will spend a total of more than $5300? (Hint: The total will be more than $5300 when the sample average exceeds what value?)

References

The books by Freedman et al. and by Moore, both listed in the Chapter 2 References, give excellent informal discussions of sampling distributions at a very elementary level.

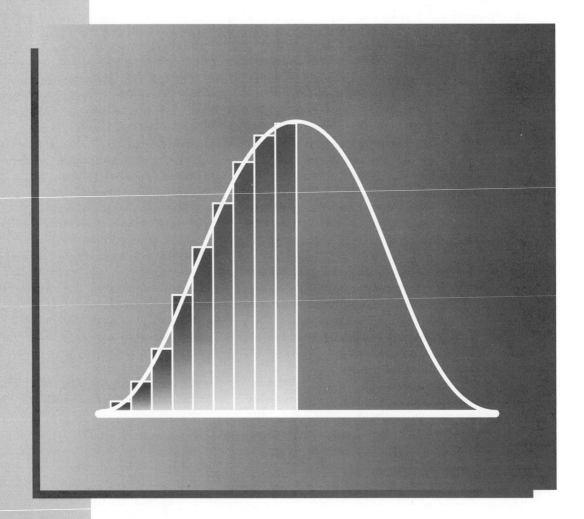

Estimation Using a Single Sample

PREVIEW

December 15, 1991, marked the 200th anniversary of the ratification of the Bill of Rights. Prompted by the resulting attention focused on the Bill of Rights, the American Bar Association conducted a survey of 507 U.S. adults in order to estimate the proportion of all U.S. adults who can correctly describe the Bill of Rights and the proportion who know its original purpose. The survey was multiple choice. Possible answers to the question that asked respondents to describe the Bill of Rights were as follows:

1. The first 10 amendments to the Constitution
2. The preamble of the Constitution
3. Any rights bill passed by Congress
4. A message of rebellion from the founding fathers to the British monarchy
5. Don't know

Possible answers to the question asking about the original purpose of the Bill of Rights were these:

1. To limit abuses by the federal government
2. To ensure equality for all citizens
3. To limit abuses by states
4. All of the above
5. Don't know

   The methods introduced in this chapter can be used to produce the desired estimates. Since the estimates are based only on a sample rather than a census of all U.S. adults, it will also be important that we estimate in a way that conveys information about anticipated accuracy.

Introduction

The objective of inferential statistics is to use sample data to increase our knowledge about the corresponding population. Often, data is collected to obtain information that allows the investigator to estimate the value of some population characteristic, such as population mean, μ, or a population proportion, π. This could be accomplished by using the sample data to arrive at a single number that represents a plausible value for the characteristic of interest. Alternatively, one could construct an entire interval of plausible values for the characteristic. These two estimation techniques, *point estimation* and *interval estimation,* are introduced in this chapter.

9.1   Point Estimation

The simplest approach to estimating a population characteristic involves using sample data to compute a single number that can be regarded as a plausible value of the characteristic. For example, sample data might suggest that 1.1 mg is a plausible value for μ, the true mean nicotine content of Players 100-mm cigarettes. (This is the value stated on the package.) In a different setting, a sample survey of students at a particular university might lead to the statement that .41 is a plausible value for π, the true proportion of students who favor a fee for recreational activities.

> **DEFINITION**
>
> A **point estimate** of a population characteristic is a single number that is based on sample data and represents a plausible value of the characteristic.

In the examples just given, 1.1 is a point estimate of μ and .41 is a point estimate of π. The adjective *point* reflects the fact that the estimate is a single point on the number line.

A point estimate is obtained by first selecting an appropriate statistic. The estimate is then the value of the statistic for the given sample. Thus the computed value of the sample mean $\bar{x}$ could provide a point estimate of a population mean μ.

EXAMPLE 9.1

Radon, an odorless gas that can cause lung cancer, is released in the decay of radium, which is naturally present in soil and rocks. The Environmental Protection Agency considers radon to be the second leading cause of lung cancer (behind cigarette smoking). One radon hot spot has been identified on the Spokane Indian reservation in Washington. The Associated Press (June 10, 1991) reported that of 270 randomly selected homes on the reservation, 68 showed radon readings above 4 pCi (the level that the EPA considers hazardous). Suppose that we would like to estimate π, where

$\pi = $ proportion of all homes on the reservation with radon
levels above 4 pCi

With "success" identified as a radon reading above 4 pCi, π is then just the population proportion of successes. The statistic

$$p = \frac{\text{number of successes in the sample}}{n}$$

which is the sample proportion of successes, is an obvious choice for obtaining a point estimate of π. Based on the reported information, the point estimate of π, the proportion of all homes on the reservation whose radon readings exceed 4 pCi, is

$$p = \frac{68}{270} = .252$$

For purposes of estimating a population proportion π, it would be difficult to suggest a statistic other than p that could reasonably be used. In other situations there are several statistics that can be used to obtain an estimate. The following example presents such a case.

EXAMPLE 9.2

The paper "Effects of Roadside Conditions on Plants and Insects" (*J. Appl. Ecology* (1988):709–715) reported the results of an experiment to evaluate the effect of nitrous oxide from automobile exhaust on roadside soil. The concentration of soluble nitrogen (in mg/g) was recorded at 20 roadside locations. Suppose that the observed readings are as given, along with a dot diagram of the data. (This data is compatible with summary values given in the paper.)

| 1.7 | 1.9 | 2.0 | 1.7 | 1.6 | 1.7 | 1.8 | 1.7 | 1.8 | 1.8 |
| 1.6 | 1.7 | 2.1 | 1.7 | 1.8 | 1.7 | 1.8 | 1.4 | 1.9 | 1.7 |

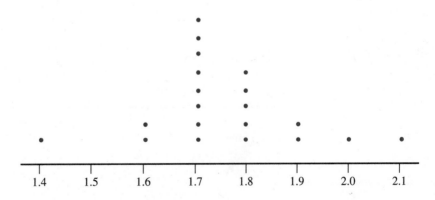

Suppose that a point estimate of μ, the true mean soluble nitrogen concentration, is desired. An obvious choice of a statistic for estimating μ is the sample mean, $\bar{x}$. However, there are other possibilities. We might consider using a trimmed mean or even the sample median, since the data set exhibits some symmetry. (If the corresponding population distribution is symmetric, μ is also the population median.)

The three statistics and the resulting estimates of μ are

$$\text{sample mean} = \bar{x} = \frac{\Sigma x}{n} = \frac{35.1}{20} = 1.76$$

$$\text{sample median} = \frac{1.7 + 1.7}{2} = 1.70$$

$$10\% \text{ trimmed mean} = \left(\begin{array}{c}\text{average of middle} \\ \text{16 observations}\end{array}\right) = \frac{28.0}{16} = 1.75$$

The estimates differ somewhat from one another. The choice among them should depend on which statistic tends to produce an estimate closest to the true value. The following subsection discusses criteria for choosing among competing statistics.

Choosing a Statistic for Computing an Estimate

The point of the previous example is that there may be more than one statistic that can reasonably be used to obtain a point estimate of a specified population characteristic. Loosely speaking, the statistic used should be one that tends to yield an accurate estimate, that is, an estimate close to the value of the population characteristic. Information on the accuracy of estimation for a particular statistic is provided by the statistic's sampling distribution. Figure 9.1 pictures the sampling distributions of three different statistics. The value of the population characteristic, which we refer to as the *true value,* is marked on the measurement axis.

FIGURE 9.1
Sampling distributions of three different statistics for estimating a population characteristic

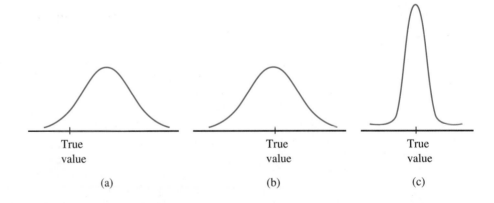

The distribution pictured in Figure 9.1(a) is that of a statistic unlikely to yield an estimate close to the true value. The distribution is centered to the right of the true value, making it very likely that an estimate (a value of the statistic for a particular sample) will be substantially larger than the true value. If this statistic is used to compute an estimate based on a first sample, then another estimate based on a second sample, and another estimate based on a third sample, and so on, the long-run average value of these estimates will considerably exceed the true value.

The sampling distribution of Figure 9.1(b) is centered at the true value. Thus, while one estimate may be smaller than the true value and another may be larger, when this statistic is used many times over with different samples, there will be no long-run tendency to over- or underestimate the true value. However, while this sampling distribution is correctly centered, it spreads out quite a bit about the true value. Because of this, some estimates resulting from the use of this statistic will be far above or below the true value—even though there is no systematic tendency to underestimate or overestimate the true value. In contrast, the mean value of the statistic with the distribution appearing in Figure 9.1(c) is exactly the true value of the population characteristic (implying no systematic estimation error), and the statistic's standard deviation is relatively small. Estimates using this third statistic will almost always be quite close to the true value, certainly more often than estimates resulting from the statistic with the sampling distribution shown in Figure 9.1(b).

> **DEFINITION**
>
> A statistic with mean value equal to the value of the population characteristic being estimated is said to be an **unbiased statistic**. A statistic that is not unbiased is said to be **biased.**

Let $x_1, x_2, \ldots, x_n$ represent the values in a random sample. One of the general results concerning the sampling distribution of $\bar{x}$, the sample mean, is that $\mu_{\bar{x}} = \mu$. This result says that the $\bar{x}$ values from many different random samples of size n center around μ, the population mean. For example, if $\mu = 100$, the $\bar{x}$ distribution is centered at 100, whereas if $\mu = 5200$, then the $\bar{x}$ distribution is centered at 5200. Therefore, $\bar{x}$ is an unbiased statistic for estimating μ. Similarly, since the sampling distribution of p is centered at π ($\mu_p = \pi$), it follows that p is an unbiased statistic for estimating a population proportion.

Using an unbiased statistic that has a small standard deviation guarantees that there will be no systematic tendency to under- or overestimate the value of the population characteristic and that estimates will almost always be relatively close to the true value.

> Given a choice between several unbiased statistics that could be used for estimating a population characteristic, the best statistic to use is the one with the smallest standard deviation.

Consider the problem of estimating a population mean, μ. The obvious choice of statistic for obtaining a point estimate of μ is the sample mean, $\bar{x}$, an unbiased statistic for this purpose. However, when the population distribution is symmetric, $\bar{x}$ is not the only choice. Other unbiased statistics for estimating μ in this case include the sample median and any trimmed mean (with the same number of observations trimmed from each end of the ordered sample). Which statistic should be used? The following result is helpful in making a choice.

1. If the population distribution is normal, then $\bar{x}$ has a smaller standard deviation than any other unbiased statistic for estimating μ. However, in this case, a

trimmed mean with a small trimming percentage (such as 10%) performs almost as well as $\bar{x}$.

2. When the population distribution is symmetric with heavy tails compared to the normal curve, a trimmed mean is a better statistic than $\bar{x}$ for estimating μ.

When the population distribution is unquestionably normal, the choice is clear: Use $\bar{x}$ to estimate μ. But with a heavy-tailed distribution, a trimmed mean gives protection against one or two outliers in the sample that might otherwise drastically affect the value of the estimate.

Now consider estimating the population variance σ^2. The sample variance

$$s^2 = \frac{\Sigma(x - \bar{x})^2}{n - 1}$$

is a good choice for obtaining a point estimate of the population variance σ^2. It can be shown that s^2 is an unbiased statistic for estimating σ^2; that is, whatever the value of σ^2, the sampling distribution of s^2 is centered at that value. It is precisely for this reason—to obtain an unbiased statistic—that the divisor $n - 1$ is used. An alternative statistic is the average squared deviation

$$\frac{\Sigma(x - \bar{x})^2}{n}$$

which has a more natural divisor than s^2. However, the average squared deviation is biased, with its values tending to be smaller than σ^2.

EXAMPLE 9.3

The paper "Sensory and Mechanical Assessment of the Quality of Frankfurters" (*J. of Texture Studies* (1990):395–409) reported the following salt content (percent by weight) for ten frankfurters:

2.26	2.11	1.64	1.17	1.64
2.36	1.70	2.10	2.19	2.40

Then

$$\Sigma x = 19.57 \qquad \Sigma x^2 = 39.7335 \qquad n = 10$$

and

$$\Sigma(x - \bar{x})^2 = \Sigma x^2 - \frac{(\Sigma x)^2}{n}$$

$$= 39.7335 - \frac{(19.57)^2}{10}$$

$$= 1.435$$

Let σ^2 denote the true variance in salt content for frankfurters. Using the sample variance s^2 to provide a point estimate of σ^2 yields

$$s^2 = \frac{\Sigma(x - \bar{x})^2}{n - 1} = \frac{1.435}{9} = .1594$$

Using the average squared deviation (with divisor $n = 10$), the resulting point estimate is

$$\frac{\Sigma(x - \bar{x})^2}{n} = \frac{1.435}{10} = .1435$$

Because s^2 is an unbiased statistic for estimating σ^2, most statisticians would recommend using the point estimate, .1594.

An obvious choice of a statistic for estimating the population standard deviation σ is the sample standard deviation s. For the data given in Example 9.3,

$$s = \sqrt{.1594} = .3992$$

Unfortunately, the fact that s^2 is an unbiased statistic for estimating σ^2 does not imply that s is an unbiased statistic for estimating σ. The sample standard deviation tends to underestimate slightly the true value of σ. However, unbiasedness is not the only criterion by which a statistic can be judged, and there are other good reasons for using s to estimate σ. In what follows, whenever we need to estimate σ based on a single random sample, we use the statistic s to obtain a point estimate.

EXERCISES 9.1–9.10   SECTION 9.1

9.1   Three different statistics are being considered for estimating a population characteristic. The sampling distributions of the three statistics are shown below.

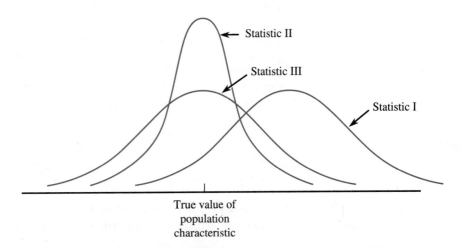

True value of
population
characteristic

Which statistic would you recommend? Explain your choice.

9.2   Why is an unbiased statistic generally preferred over a biased statistic for estimating a population characteristic? Does unbiasedness by itself guarantee that the estimate will be close to the true value? Explain. Under what circumstances might you choose a biased statistic over an unbiased statistic if two statistics are available for estimating a population characteristic?

9.3   The sale of human organs for transplantation raises some difficult ethical issues for the medical community. Let π denote the true proportion of all U.S. doctors who oppose the sale of organs. The *Los Angeles Times* (November 24, 1978) reported that in a random sample of 244 doctors, 184 opposed the sale of organs. Give a point estimate of π.

9.4   The paper "Diallel Analysis of Pod Length and Shelling Percent of Winged Beans" (*Field Crops Research* (1987):209–216) reported the following lengths for nine winged bean pods.

12.1	18.5	17.2	27.7	17.9	12.9	17.0	15.0	14.5

a. Use the given data to produce a point estimate of μ, the true mean length for winged bean pods.
b. Use the given data to produce a point estimate of σ^2, the variance of pod length for all winged bean pods.
c. Use the given data to produce an estimate of σ, the standard deviation of pod length. Is the statistic you used to produce your estimate unbiased?

9.5   The accompanying radiation readings (in mR/h) were obtained from television display areas in a sample of ten department stores ("Many Color TV Set Lounges Show Highest Radiation," *J. of Environ. Health* (1969):359–360).

.40	.48	.60	.15	.50	.80	.50	.36	.16	.89

$\xi x = 4,84$

.16   .2304   .36   .0225   .25   .64   .25   .1296   .0256   .7921

a. Assuming that the distribution of radiation readings is approximately normal, give a point estimate of μ, the true mean radiation level for TV lounges.
b. The recommended limit for this type of radiation is .5 mR/h. Use the given data to estimate the proportion of TV lounges with radiation levels exceeding the recommended limit.

9.6   A random sample of $n = 12$ four-year-old red pine trees was selected, and the diameter (in.) of each tree's main stem was measured. The resulting observations were as follows.

11.3	10.7	12.4	15.2	10.1	12.1	16.2	10.5	11.4	11.0	10.7	12.0

a. Compute a point estimate of σ, the population standard deviation of main stem diameter. What statistic did you use to obtain your estimate?

b. Making no assumption whatsoever about the shape of the population distribution of diameter, give a point estimate for the population median diameter (that is, for the middle diameter value in the entire population of four-year-old red pine trees). What statistic did you use to obtain the estimate?

c. Suppose that the population distribution of diameter is symmetric but with heavier tails than the normal distribution. Give a point estimate of the population mean diameter based on a statistic that gives some protection against the presence of outliers in the sample. What statistic did you use?

d. Suppose that the diameter distribution is normal. Then the 90th percentile of the diameter distribution is $\mu + 1.28\sigma$ (so 90% of all trees have diameters less than this value). Compute a point estimate for this percentile. (Hint: First compute an estimate of μ in this case; then use it along with your estimate of σ from part (a).)

9.7   Each person in a random sample of 20 students at a particular university was asked whether he or she was registered to vote. The responses were (with R = registered, N = not registered)

R	R	N	R	N	N	R	R	R	N
N	R	R	R	R	R	N	R	R	R

Use this data to estimate π, the true proportion of all students at the university who are registered to vote.

9.8   **a.** A random sample of ten houses in a particular area, each of which is heated with natural gas, is selected and the amount of gas (therms) used during the month of January is determined for each house. The resulting observations are

103	156	118	89	125	147	122	109	138	99

Let μ_J denote the average gas usage during January by all houses in this area. Compute a point estimate of μ_J.

b. Suppose that there are 10,000 houses in this area that use natural gas for heating. Let τ denote the total amount of gas used by all of these houses during January. Estimate τ using the data of part (a). What statistic (sample-based quantity) did you use in computing your estimate?

c. Use the data in part (a) to estimate π, the proportion of all houses that used at least 100 therms.

d. Give a point estimate of the population median usage (the middle value in the population of all houses) based on the sample of part (a). What statistic did you use?

9.9   Referring to Exercise 9.8, suppose that August gas usage is determined for these same ten houses, yielding the observations (in the same order)

42	57	50	26	43	62	68	50	47	29

Let μ_d denote the average difference between January and August usage for all houses in this area. Use this data along with that of Exercise 9.8(a) to compute a point estimate of μ_d. What statistic did you use?

9.10 After taking a random sample of 80 components of a certain type, 12 are found to be defective.

a. Give a point estimate of the proportion of all such components that are *not* defective.

b. A system is to be constructed by randomly selecting two of these components and connecting them in series, as shown here.

The series connection implies that the system will function if and only if neither component is defective (that is, both components work properly). Estimate the proportion of all such systems that work properly. (Hint: If π denotes the probability that a component works properly, how can $P(\text{system works})$ be expressed in terms of π?)

9.2 A Large-Sample Confidence Interval for a Population Mean

Section 9.1 discussed how to estimate a population characteristic using a point estimate (a single number). A point estimate results from selecting an appropriate statistic and computing its value for the given sample. It would be nice if a statistic could be found for which the resulting point estimate was exactly the value of the characteristic being estimated. However, the estimate (the value of the statistic) depends on which sample is selected. Different samples generally yield different estimates, due to sampling variability. In practice, only rarely is a sample selected for which the estimate is exactly equal to the value of the population characteristic. We can only hope that the chosen statistic produces an estimate close to the value of the population characteristic. These considerations suggest the desirability of indicating how precisely the population characteristic has been estimated. The point estimate by itself conveys no information about its closeness to the value of the population characteristic. While a point estimate may represent our best guess for the value of μ, it is not the only plausible value.

Suppose that, instead of reporting a point estimate as the single most credible value for the population characteristic, we report an entire interval of reasonable values based on the sample data. We might, for example, be confident that for some population, the value of the average serum cholesterol level, μ, is in the interval from 156.4 to 158.8. The narrowness of this interval implies that we have rather precise information about the value of μ. If, with the same high degree of confidence, we could state only that μ was between 145.3 and 169.9, it would be clear that our knowledge concerning the value of μ is relatively imprecise.

DEFINITION

A **confidence interval** for a population characteristic is an interval of plausible values for the characteristic. It is constructed so that, with a chosen degree of confidence, the value of the characteristic will be captured inside the interval.

Associated with each confidence interval is a **confidence level.** The confidence level provides information on how much "confidence" we can have in the *method* used to construct the interval estimate. Usual choices for confidence levels are 90%, 95%, and 99%, although other levels are also possible. If we were to construct a 95% confidence interval using the technique to be described shortly, we would be using a method that is "successful" 95% of the time. That is, if this method were used to generate an interval estimate over and over again with different samples, in the long run, 95% of the resulting intervals would capture the true value of the characteristic being estimated. Similarly, a 99% confidence interval is one that is constructed using a method that is, in the long run, successful in capturing the true value of the population characteristic 99% of the time.

We will discuss factors that affect the choice of confidence level after we examine the method for constructing confidence intervals. We begin by considering a large-sample confidence interval for a population mean μ. Let $x_1, x_2, \ldots, x_n$ denote a random sample from a population with mean μ and standard deviation σ.

In this section, **we assume that n is large enough for the Central Limit Theorem to apply.** Then the sampling distribution of $\bar{x}$ is described approximately by a normal curve with mean $\mu_{\bar{x}} = \mu$ and standard deviation $\sigma_{\bar{x}} = \sigma/\sqrt{n}$.

The development of a confidence interval for μ is easiest to understand if we select a particular confidence level, say 95%. Appendix Table II, the table of standard normal (z) curve areas, can be used to determine a value of z such that a central area of .95 falls between $-z$ and z. In this case, the remaining area of .05 is divided equally between the two tails, as shown in Figure 9.2.

Note that the total area to the left of the desired z is .975 (.95 central area + .025 area below $-z$). Locating .9750 in the body of Appendix Table II, we find that the corresponding z critical value is 1.96.

Generalizing this result to normal distributions other than the standard normal tells us that for *any* normal distribution, about 95% of the values are within 1.96 standard deviations of the mean. Since for large samples the $\bar{x}$ distribution is

FIGURE 9.2
Capturing a central area of .95
under the *z* curve

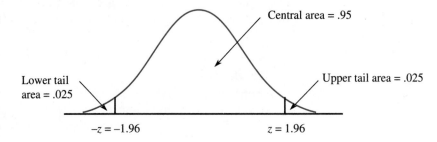

approximately normal with mean $\mu_{\bar{x}} = \mu$ and $\sigma_{\bar{x}} = \sigma/\sqrt{n}$, we get the following result.

> Approximately 95% of all samples will result in an $\bar{x}$ value that is within $1.96\sigma_{\bar{x}} = 1.96\sigma/\sqrt{n}$ of the true population mean μ.

If $\bar{x}$ is within $1.96\sigma/\sqrt{n}$ of μ, the interval

$$\bar{x} - 1.96 \cdot \frac{\sigma}{\sqrt{n}} \quad \text{to} \quad \bar{x} + 1.96 \cdot \frac{\sigma}{\sqrt{n}}$$

will capture μ (and this will happen for 95% of all possible samples). However, if $\bar{x}$ is farther away from μ than $1.96\sigma/\sqrt{n}$ (which will happen for about 5% of all possible samples), this interval will not include the true value of μ. This is pictured in Figure 9.3.

FIGURE 9.3
The mean μ is captured in the interval from $\bar{x} - 1.96\sigma/\sqrt{n}$ to $\bar{x} + 1.96\sigma/\sqrt{n}$ when $\bar{x}$ is within $1.96\sigma/\sqrt{n}$ of μ

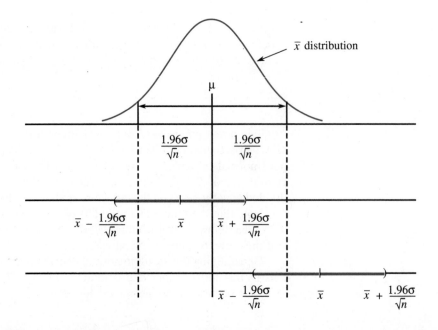

> When n is large, a **95% confidence interval for μ** is
>
> $$\left(\bar{x} - 1.96 \cdot \frac{\sigma}{\sqrt{n}}, \; \bar{x} + 1.96 \cdot \frac{\sigma}{\sqrt{n}} \right)$$
>
> An abbreviated formula for the interval is
>
> $$\bar{x} \pm 1.96 \cdot \frac{\sigma}{\sqrt{n}}$$
>
> where $+$ gives the upper limit and $-$ gives the lower limit of the interval.

EXAMPLE 9.4

Public Citizens, a consumer group, ranks the 111 U.S. nuclear reactors according to employee exposure to radiation. Based on a sample of workers at Diablo Canyon Nuclear Power Plant, Public Citizens rated Diablo's Unit 2 reactor as the 28th worst in the country. They reported (*San Luis Obispo Telegram-Tribune,* April 11, 1990) a mean annual radiation exposure of .481 rems for a sample of Unit 2 workers. Suppose that the mean was based on a sample of 400 workers and that the sample standard deviation was .33 rems (these values are compatible with other summary statistics given in the article).

Let μ denote the true mean radiation exposure for Unit 2 workers at Diablo Canyon. Although σ, the true population standard deviation, is not usually known, for illustrative purposes suppose that $\sigma = .35$. Then a 95% confidence interval for μ is

$$\bar{x} \pm 1.96\left(\frac{\sigma}{\sqrt{n}} \right) = .481 \pm 1.96\left(\frac{.35}{\sqrt{400}} \right)$$

$$= .481 \pm .034$$
$$= (.447, .515)$$

Based on the sample, plausible values of μ, the true mean annual radiation exposure for Diablo's Unit 2 workers, are those between .447 and .515 rems. A 95% confidence level is associated with the method used to produce this interval estimate.

The 95% confidence interval for μ in Example 9.4 is (.447, .515). It is tempting to say that there is a 95% chance that μ is between .447 and .515. Do not yield to this temptation! The 95% refers to the percentage of *all* possible samples resulting in an interval that includes μ. Said another way, if we take sample after sample from the population and use each one separately to compute a 95% confidence interval, in the long run roughly 95% of these intervals will capture μ. Figure 9.4 illustrates this for 100 intervals; 93 of the intervals include μ, whereas 7 do not. Our interval (.447, .515) either includes μ or it does not (remember, the value of μ is fixed but not known to us). We cannot make a chance (probability) statement

FIGURE 9.4
One hundred 95% confidence intervals for μ computed from 100 different samples (* identifies intervals that don't include μ)

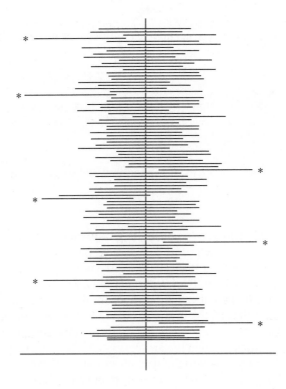

concerning this particular interval. *The confidence level 95% refers to the **method** used to construct the interval rather than to any particular interval, such as the one we obtained.*

The formula given for a 95% confidence interval can easily be adapted to other confidence levels. The choice of a 95% confidence level led to the use of the z value 1.96 (chosen to achieve a central area of .95 under the standard normal curve) in the formula. Any other confidence level can be obtained by using an appropriate z critical value in place of 1.96. For example, suppose we wanted to achieve a confidence level of 99%. To obtain a central area of .99, the appropriate z critical value would have a cumulative area (area to the left) of .995, as illustrated in Figure 9.5.

FIGURE 9.5
Finding the z critical value for a 99% confidence level

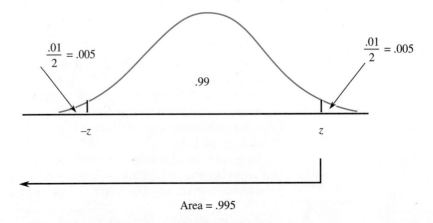

From Appendix Table II, we find that the corresponding z critical value is 2.58. A 99% confidence interval for μ is then obtained by using 2.58 in place of 1.96 in the formula for the 95% confidence interval.

The general formula for a **large-sample confidence interval for μ** (when the value of σ is known) is

$$\bar{x} \pm (z \text{ critical value}) \cdot \frac{\sigma}{\sqrt{n}}$$

The desired confidence level determines which z critical value is used.

The three most commonly used confidence levels, 90%, 95%, and 99%, use z critical values 1.645, 1.96, and 2.58, respectively.

Why settle for 95% confidence when 99% confidence is possible? The higher confidence level comes with a price tag: The resulting interval is wider than the 95% interval. The width of the 95% interval is $2(1.96\sigma/\sqrt{n})$, whereas the 99% interval has width $2(2.58\sigma/\sqrt{n})$. The higher *reliability* of the 99% interval (where "reliability" is specified by the confidence level) entails a loss in precision (as indicated by the wider interval). Many investigators think that a 95% interval gives a reasonable compromise between reliability and precision.

A Confidence Interval When σ Is Unknown

The confidence interval just developed still has one major drawback: in order to compute the interval limits, σ must be known. Unfortunately, this is rarely true in practice. However, when n is large, it is legitimate to replace σ in our previous formula by the sample standard deviation s. This is because when n is large, the value of s is likely to be close to the value of σ. Replacing σ by s introduces very little extra variability, so no other change in the interval is required.

A **large-sample confidence interval for a population mean μ** is given by the formula

$$\bar{x} \pm (z \text{ critical value}) \cdot \frac{s}{\sqrt{n}}$$

As a rule of thumb, this interval is appropriate when the sample size exceeds 30.

For a confidence level of approximately 95%, the z critical value 1.96 should be used; for a 90% confidence level, the value 1.645 is appropriate; and for a 99% confidence level, the value 2.58 is used.

EXAMPLE 9.5

A primary cause of hearing loss in many individuals is exposure to noise. The paper "Effects of Steady State Noise upon Human Hearing Sensitivity from 8,000 to 20,000 Hz" (*Amer. Indus. Hygiene Assoc. J.* (1980):427–432) reported on a study involving a sample of 44 individuals who had substantial exposure to industrial noise (jet engines, turbines, and the like). Each individual was asked to identify the loudness level at which signals at various frequencies became audible. For a frequency of 10 kz,

$$\text{sample size} = n = 44$$
$$\text{sample average loudness level} = \bar{x} = 32.0 \text{ dB}$$
$$\text{sample standard deviation} = s = 22.0 \text{ dB}$$

A 90% confidence interval for μ, the mean detection level for the population of all individuals exposed to noise of this type, is

$$\bar{x} \pm (1.645) \cdot \frac{s}{\sqrt{n}} = 32.0 \pm (1.645) \cdot \frac{22.0}{\sqrt{44}}$$
$$= 32.0 \pm 5.5$$
$$= (26.5, 37.5)$$

Even though the confidence level is only 90% rather than 95%, the resulting interval is rather wide because s is quite large—there is much variability in detection level—and n is not terribly large. However, individuals with minimal noise exposure have an average detection level on the order of 20 dB. So even though our estimate of μ is relatively imprecise, it is clear that noise exposure can have negative effects.

The variable of interest in each of these examples (time in Example 9.4 and loudness level in Example 9.5) is continuous. The large-sample confidence interval formulas are valid not only in this case but also when μ is the mean value of a discrete variable. The following example illustrates its use with discrete data.

EXAMPLE 9.6

The behavior of bats has long been a fascinating subject to many people. One aspect of particular interest has been roosting behavior. Individuals of most species do not forage continuously at night. Instead, they commonly return to the roost for varying amounts of time between foraging periods. The paper "Night Roosting Behavior of the Little Brown Bat" (*J. of Mammology* (1982):464–474) reported that when bats of this species return to the roost, they often have trouble gaining a foothold to hang in their usual upside-down position. Let x denote the number of attempts made by a randomly selected little brown bat before gaining a foothold, and let μ denote the mean value of x. (If you picture a population of bats returning to roost, μ is the mean value of x in the population.) For a sample of $n = 48$ bats attempting to roost,

$$\text{sample mean number of attempts} = \bar{x} = 13.7$$
$$\text{sample standard deviation} = s = 14.1$$

A 95% confidence interval for μ is then

$$\bar{x} \pm (1.96) \cdot \frac{s}{\sqrt{n}} = 13.7 \pm (1.96) \cdot \frac{14.1}{\sqrt{48}}$$

$$= 13.7 \pm 4.0$$

$$= (9.7, 17.7)$$

Although this interval estimate is not terribly precise, one would presumably go batty acquiring enough data to increase the precision substantially.

The General Form of a Confidence Interval

Many confidence intervals have the same general form as the large-sample intervals for μ that we just considered. We started with a statistic $\bar{x}$ from which a point estimate for μ was obtained. The standard deviation of this statistic is $\sigma/\sqrt{n}$, which can be computed when the value of σ is known. This resulted in a confidence interval of the form

$$\left(\begin{array}{c} \text{point estimate using} \\ \text{a specified statistic} \end{array} \right) \pm \left(\begin{array}{c} \text{critical} \\ \text{value} \end{array} \right) \cdot \left(\begin{array}{c} \text{standard deviation} \\ \text{of the statistic} \end{array} \right)$$

When σ was unknown, we estimated the standard deviation of the statistic by $s/\sqrt{n}$, yielding the interval

$$\left(\begin{array}{c} \text{point estimate using} \\ \text{a specified statistic} \end{array} \right) \pm \left(\begin{array}{c} \text{critical} \\ \text{value} \end{array} \right) \cdot \left(\begin{array}{c} \text{estimated standard} \\ \text{deviation of the} \\ \text{statistic} \end{array} \right)$$

For a population characteristic other than μ, a statistic for estimating the characteristic will be selected. Then (drawing on statistical theory) a formula for the standard deviation of the statistic will be given. In practice it will almost always be necessary to estimate this standard deviation (using something analogous to $s/\sqrt{n}$ rather than $\sigma/\sqrt{n}$), so the second interval will be the prototype confidence interval. The estimated standard deviation of the statistic is usually referred to as the **standard error** in the statistical literature.

Choosing the Sample Size

When σ is known, the 95% confidence interval for μ is based on the fact that, for approximately 95% of all random samples, $\bar{x}$ will be within $1.96\sigma/\sqrt{n}$ of μ. The quantity $1.96\sigma/\sqrt{n}$ is sometimes called the **bound on the error of estimation** associated with a 95% confidence level—with 95% confidence, the point estimate $\bar{x}$ will be no further than this from μ. Before collecting any data, an investigator may wish to determine a sample size for which a particular value of the bound is achieved. For example, with μ representing the average fuel efficiency in mi/gal for all cars of a certain type, the objective of an investigation may be to estimate μ to within 1 mi/gal with 95% confidence. The value of n necessary to achieve this is obtained by equating 1 to $1.96\sigma/\sqrt{n}$ and solving for n.

In general, suppose it is desired to estimate μ to within an amount B (the specified error of estimation) with 95% confidence. Finding the necessary sample size requires solving the equation $B = 1.96\sigma/\sqrt{n}$ for n. The result is

$$n = \left[\frac{1.96\sigma}{B} \right]^2$$

Notice that a large value of σ forces n to be large, as does a small value of B.

Use of the sample-size formula requires that σ be known. Of course, this is rarely the case. One possibility is to carry out a preliminary study and use the resulting sample standard deviation (or a somewhat larger value, to be conservative) to determine n for the main part of the study. Another possibility is simply to make an educated guess about what value of σ might result and use it in calculating n. For a population distribution that is not too skewed, dividing the range (the difference between the largest and smallest values) by 4 often gives a rough idea of the standard deviation.

> The sample size required to estimate a population mean μ to within an amount B with 95% confidence is
>
> $$n = \left[\frac{1.96\sigma}{B} \right]^2$$
>
> If σ is unknown, it may be estimated based on previous information or, for a population that is not too skewed, by using $\dfrac{(\text{range})}{4}$.

EXAMPLE 9.7

The financial aid office wishes to estimate the mean cost of textbooks per quarter for students at a particular university. In order for the estimate to be useful, they want the estimate to be within $20 of the true population mean. How large a sample should be used in order to be 95% confident of achieving this level of accuracy?

In order to determine the required sample size, we must first estimate σ. The financial aid office is pretty sure that the amount spent on books varies widely, with most values between $50 and $450. A reasonable estimate of σ is then

$$\frac{\text{range}}{4} = \frac{450 - 50}{4} = \frac{400}{4} = 100$$

The required sample size is

$$n = \left[\frac{1.96\sigma}{B}\right]^2 = \left[\frac{(1.96)(100)}{20}\right]^2 = [9.8]^2 = 96.04$$

A sample size of 97 or larger would be recommended.

EXERCISES 9.11–9.28   SECTION 9.2

9.11   Discuss how each of the following factors affects the width of the large-sample confidence interval for μ when σ is known.
   a. Confidence level
   b. Sample size
   c. Population standard deviation

9.12   The formula used to compute a confidence interval for μ when n is large and σ is known is

$$\bar{x} \pm (z \text{ critical value}) \cdot \frac{\sigma}{\sqrt{n}}$$

What is the appropriate z critical value for each of the following confidence levels?
   a. 95%   **b.** 90%   **c.** 99%   **d.** 80%   **e.** 85%

9.13   Suppose that a random sample of 50 bottles of a particular brand of cough medicine is selected and the alcohol content of each bottle is determined. Let μ denote the average alcohol content for the population of all bottles of the brand under study. Suppose that the sample of 50 results in a 95% confidence interval for μ of (7.8, 9.4).
   a. Would a 90% confidence interval have been narrower or wider than the given interval? Explain your answer.
   b. Consider the following statement: There is a 95% chance that μ is between 7.8 and 9.4. Is this statement correct? Why or why not?
   c. Consider the following statement: If the process of selecting a sample of size 50 and then computing the corresponding 95% confidence interval is repeated 100 times, 95 of the resulting intervals will include μ. Is this statement correct? Why or why not?

9.14   The McClatchy News Service (*San Luis Obispo Telegram-Tribune,* June 13, 1991) reported on a sample of prime-time television hours. The following table summarizes the information reported for four networks.

Network	Mean number of violent acts per hour
ABC	15.6
CBS	11.9
FOX	11.7
NBC	11.0

Suppose that each of these sample means was computed on the basis of viewing $n = 50$ randomly selected prime-time hours and that the population standard deviation for each of the four networks is known to be 5.

a. Compute a 95% confidence interval for μ_{ABC}, the true mean number of violent acts per prime-time hour for ABC.

b. Compute 95% confidence intervals for the mean number of violent acts per prime-time hour for each of the other three networks.

c. The National Coalition on Television Violence claims that shows on ABC are more violent than the other networks. Based on the confidence intervals from parts (a) and (b), do you agree with this conclusion? Explain.

9.15 Many of those who watch television think that far too much time is devoted to commercials. People involved in various aspects of television advertising obviously have a different perspective. The paper "The Impact of Infomercials: Perspectives of Advertisers and Advertising Agencies" (*J. of Ad. Research* (1983):25–32) reported on a survey of $n = 62$ such individuals. Each person was asked what he or she believed to be the optimum amount of allocated time per hour for commercials during prime time. The resulting sample average was $\bar{x} = 8.20$ min. Let μ denote the average allocation of time believed optimal for the population of all individuals involved in television advertising. Suppose that $\sigma = 4.5$. Compute and interpret a 99% confidence interval for μ.

9.16 *U.S.A. Today* (January 15, 1986) reported on a study of medical costs incurred by automobile accident victims. A survey of 135 accident victims resulted in an average medical cost of $565 for motorists wearing seat belts and an average of $1200 for motorists who were not wearing seat belts. Suppose that the sample sizes and standard deviations for the two groups were as given in the accompanying table.

	Sample size n	Medical cost $\bar{x}$	Medical cost s
Wearing seat belts	90	565	268
No seat belts	45	1200	506

a. Construct a 90% confidence interval for the mean medical cost for accident victims who were wearing seat belts.

b. Construct a 90% confidence interval for the mean medical cost for accident victims who were not wearing seat belts.

9.17 A manufacturer of video recorder tapes sells tapes labeled as giving 6 h of playing time. Sixty-four of these tapes are selected and the actual playing time for each is determined. If the mean and standard deviation of the 64 observed playing times are 352 min and 8 min, respectively, construct a 99% confidence interval for μ, the true average playing time for 6-h tapes made by this manufacturer. Based on your interval, do you think that the manufacturer could be accused of false advertising? Explain.

9.18 Computer equipment can be very sensitive to high temperatures. As a result, when testing computer components, the temperature at which a malfunction occurs is of interest. Let μ denote the average temperature at which components of a certain type fail. A random sample of 49 components was tested by exposing the components to increasing temperatures and recording the temperature at which each component first failed. The resulting observations were used to compute $\bar{x} = 89°$ F and $s = 14°$ F. Find a 95% confidence interval for μ.

9.19 The Bureau of Alcohol, Tobacco, and Firearms (BATF) has been concerned about the lead levels in California wines. In a previous testing of wine specimens, lead levels ranging from 50 to 700 parts per billion were recorded (*San Luis Obispo Telegram-Tribune,* June 11, 1991). How many wine specimens should be tested if BATF wishes to estimate the true mean lead level for California wines to within 10 parts per billion with 95% confidence?

9.20 The amount of time spent on housework by women who work outside the home was examined in the paper "The Effects of Wife's Employment Time on Her Household Work Time" (*Home Econ. Research J.* (1983):260–265). Each person in a sample of 362 working women was asked to indicate how much time she spent each day on certain household activities. Some of the results are summarized in the accompanying table.

Activity	Average (min/day)	Standard deviation
All housework	348.95	176.9
Food preparation	74.43	50.4
Cleaning	72.09	72.6

a. Construct a 90% confidence interval for the average amount of time that all working women spend on housework.

b. Construct a 95% confidence interval for the mean time that working women spend on food preparation.

c. Would a 95% confidence interval for the average amount of time spent on cleaning be wider or narrower than the 95% interval for the average amount of time spent in food preparation? Explain.

d. How would you explain the very large standard deviation for the amount of time spent on cleaning?

9.21 The current version of a certain bias-ply tire is known to give an average of 20,000 mi of tread wear with a standard deviation of 2000 mi. A change in the manufacture of the tire has been proposed that, it is hoped, will increase the average tread wear without changing the standard deviation. How many prototypes of the new tire should be manufactured and tested in order to estimate the true mean tread life to within 500 mi with 95% confidence?

9.22 The paper "External Search Effort: An Investigation Across Several Product Categories" (*J. of Consumer Research* (1987):83–91) reported on the results of a survey on buying habits.

a. For a sample of buyers of small TVs, it was reported that the mean number of visits to retail stores prior to making a purchase was 2.29. Suppose that this mean was based on a sample of size 100 and that the sample standard deviation was 1.6. Construct a 95% confidence interval for the true mean number of retail visits made by buyers of small TVs.

b. For a sample of buyers of large TVs, the mean number of retail visits was reported to be 3.25. Assuming the sample size was also 100 and that the sample standard deviation was 1.7, obtain a 95% confidence interval for the true mean number of retail visits made by buyers of large TVs.

c. Do the intervals constructed in parts (a) and (b) overlap? Based on these two intervals, would you conclude that buyers of large TVs make more retail visits, on the average, than buyers of small TVs? Explain your answer.

9.23 Anyone who has owned a dog or cat knows that caring for a pet can be expensive. The paper "Veterinary Health Care Market for Dogs" (*J. of Amer. Vet. Med. Assoc.* (1984):207–208) studied annual veterinary expenditures for households owning dogs. The average veterinary expenditure was reported as $74 per year, and the corresponding standard deviation was (approximately) $40. Suppose that these statistics had been calculated based on a random sample of size 144 (the actual sample was much larger). Construct a 90% confidence interval for the average yearly veterinary expenditure for dog-owning households.

9.24 A manufacturer of college textbooks is interested in estimating the strength of the bindings produced by a particular binding machine. Strength can be measured by recording the force required to pull the pages from the binding. If this force is measured in pounds, how many books should be tested in order to estimate with 95% confidence to within .1 lb the average force required to break the binding? Assume that σ is known to be .8 lb.

9.25 The paper "The Variability of Blood Pressure Measurements in Children" (*Amer. J. of Public Health* (1983):1207–1211) reported the results of a study of 99 third-grade children. The sample consisted of 53 boys and 46 girls. The values of several variables, including systolic blood pressure, diastolic blood pressure, and pulse, were recorded for each child. Means and standard deviations are given in the accompanying table.

	Boys		Girls	
	Average	Standard deviation	Average	Standard deviation
Systolic blood pressure	101.7	9.8	101.8	9.8
Diastolic blood pressure	59.2	9.8	60.3	10.1
Pulse	86.7	10.3	86.7	10.2

a. Construct 90% confidence intervals for the mean systolic blood pressure for boys and for girls. Are the intervals similar? Based on your intervals, do you think that there is a difference in mean systolic blood pressure for boys and girls? Explain.

b. Construct a 99% confidence interval for boys' average pulse rate.

9.26 Suppose that the study discussed in the previous problem is to be considered a pilot study and that a large-scale study will follow.

a. The researchers would like to estimate the true average pulse rate for girls to within 1 beat/min with 95% confidence. How many girls should be included in the study?

b. Suppose that in addition to estimating the average pulse rate for girls to within 1 beat/min, the researchers also want to be able to estimate both the average systolic blood pressure and the average diastolic blood pressure for girls to within 1.5 with 95% confidence. How many girls should be studied in order to achieve all of these goals?

9.27 The paper "National Geographic, the Doomsday Machine," which appeared in the *Journal of Irreproducible Results* (yes, there really is a journal by that name—it's a spoof of technical journals!) predicted dire consequences resulting from a nationwide buildup of *National Geographic*. The author's predictions are based on the observation that the number of subscriptions for *National Geographic* is on the rise and that no one ever throws away a copy of the *National Geographic*. A key to the analysis presented in the paper is the weight of an issue of the magazine. Suppose that you were assigned the task of estimating the average weight of a particular issue of the *National Geographic*. How many copies should you sample in order to estimate the average weight to within .1 oz with 95% confidence? Assume that σ is known to be 1 oz.

9.28 The formula described in this section for determining sample size corresponds to a confidence level of 95%. What would be the appropriate formula for determining sample size when the desired confidence level is 90%? 99%?

9.3 A Large-Sample Confidence Interval for a Population Proportion

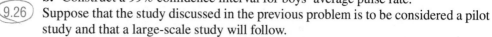

Often an investigator wishes to make an inference about the proportion of individuals or objects in a population that possesses a particular property of interest. For example, a university administrator might be interested in the proportion of students who prefer a new on-line computer registration system to the previous registration method. In a different setting, a quality control engineer might be concerned about the proportion of defective parts manufactured using a particular process.

Let

π = proportion of the population that possesses the property of interest

In this section, we consider the problem of estimating π using information in a random sample of size n from the population. Previously, we used the sample proportion

$$p = \frac{\text{number in sample that possess property of interest}}{n}$$

to calculate a point estimate of π. We can also use p to form a confidence interval for π.

Although there is a small-sample confidence interval for π, our focus will be on the large-sample case. The justification for the large-sample interval rests on properties of the sampling distribution of the statistic p:

1. The sampling distribution of p is centered at π, that is, $\mu_p = \pi$. Therefore, p is an unbiased statistic for estimating π.
2. The standard deviation of p is $\sigma_p = \sqrt{\pi(1 - \pi)/n}$
3. As long as n is large ($n\pi \geq 5$ and $n(1 - \pi) \geq 5$), the sampling distribution of p is well approximated by a normal curve.

The accompanying box summarizes these properties.

> When n is large, the statistic p has a sampling distribution that is approximately normal with mean π and standard deviation $\sqrt{\pi(1 - \pi)/n}$

The same line of reasoning that we used to develop the large-sample confidence interval for μ gives us the interval estimate

$$p \pm (z \text{ critical value}) \sqrt{\frac{\pi(1 - \pi)}{n}}$$

Since π is unknown, $\sigma_p = \sqrt{\pi(1 - \pi)/n}$ must be estimated. As long as the sample size is large, the value of $\sqrt{p(1 - p)/n}$ should be close to $\sqrt{\pi(1 - \pi)/n}$ and can be used in its place.

> **A large-sample confidence interval for π is**
>
> $$p \pm (z \text{ critical value}) \cdot \sqrt{\frac{p(1 - p)}{n}}$$
>
> This interval can be used as long as $np \geq 5$ and $n(1 - p) \geq 5$. The appropriate z critical value depends on the confidence level specified.

EXAMPLE 9.8

The 1983 Tylenol poisoning episode focused attention on the desirability of packaging various commodities in a tamper-resistant manner. The article "Tamper-Resistant Packaging: Is It Really?" (*Package Engr.* (June 1983):96–104) reported the results of a survey dealing with consumer attitudes toward such packaging. One question asked of the sample of 270 consumers was, "Would you be willing to pay extra for tamper-resistant packages?" The number of yes responses was 189. Let π denote the proportion of all consumers who would pay extra for such packaging. A point estimate of π is

$$p = \frac{189}{270} = .700$$

Since

$$np = (270)(.700) = 189 \geq 5$$
$$n(1 - p) = (270)(.300) = 81 \geq 5$$

the large-sample interval can be used. A 95% confidence interval requires the z critical value 1.96. The required computations follow.

$$p \pm 1.96 \sqrt{\frac{p(1 - p)}{n}} = .700 \pm 1.96 \sqrt{\frac{(.700)(.300)}{270}}$$
$$= .700 \pm (1.96)(.028)$$
$$= .700 \pm .055$$
$$= (.645, .755)$$

We can be 95% confident that π, the proportion of consumers who would pay extra for tamper-resistant packaging, is between .645 and .755. This result should be encouraging to those manufacturers who want to pass on extra packaging costs to the consumer.

Choosing the Sample Size

When estimating μ using a large sample, $1.96\sigma_{\bar{x}} = 1.96\sigma/\sqrt{n}$ is called the *bound on the error of estimation* because, for 95% of all samples, $\bar{x}$ is within this distance of μ. Similarly, when p is used to estimate π,

$$\text{bound on error} = 1.96\sigma_p = 1.96 \sqrt{\frac{\pi(1 - \pi)}{n}}$$

For 95% of all samples, p is within $1.96\sqrt{\pi(1 - \pi)/n}$ of π.

Suppose that an investigator wishes to estimate π to within B (a specified error bound) with 95% confidence. Then the sample size n should be chosen to satisfy

$$B = 1.96 \sqrt{\frac{\pi(1 - \pi)}{n}}$$

Solving this equation for n results in

$$n = \pi(1 - \pi)\left(\frac{1.96}{B}\right)^2$$

Unfortunately, the use of this formula requires the value of π, which is unknown. A conservative solution follows from the observation that $\pi(1 - \pi)$ is never larger than .25 (its value when $\pi = .5$). Replacing $\pi(1 - \pi)$ by .25, the maximum value, yields

$$n = .25\left(\frac{1.96}{B}\right)^2$$

Using this formula to obtain n gives us a sample size with which we can be 95% confident that p will be within B of π, no matter what the value of π.

The sample size required to estimate a population proportion π to within an amount B with 95% confidence is

$$n = \pi(1 - \pi)\left[\frac{1.96}{B}\right]^2$$

The value of π may be estimated using prior information. In the absence of any such information, using $\pi = .5$ in this formula gives a conservatively large value for the required sample size (this value of π gives a larger n than would any other value).

EXAMPLE 9.9

The 1991 publication of the book *Final Exit*, which includes chapters on doctor-assisted suicide, caused a great deal of controversy in the medical community. The Society for the Right to Die and the American Medical Association quoted very different figures regarding the proportion of primary-care physicians who have participated in some form of doctor-assisted suicide for terminally ill patients (*USA Today*, July 1991). Suppose that a survey of physicians is to be designed in order to estimate this proportion to within .05 with 95% confidence. How many primary-care physicians should be included in a random sample?

Using a conservative value of $\pi = .5$ in the formula for required sample size gives

$$n = \pi(1 - \pi)\left(\frac{1.96}{B}\right)^2 = .25\left(\frac{1.96}{.05}\right)^2 = 384.16$$

Thus a sample of at least 385 doctors should be used.

9.29   The use of the interval

$$p \pm (z \text{ critical value}) \cdot \sqrt{\frac{p(1-p)}{n}}$$

requires a large sample. For each of the following combinations of n and p, indicate whether the given interval would be appropriate.

a. $n = 50$ and $p = .30$ **b.** $n = 50$ and $p = .05$
c. $n = 15$ and $p = .45$ **d.** $n = 100$ and $p = .01$
e. $n = 100$ and $p = .70$ **f.** $n = 40$ and $p = .25$
g. $n = 60$ and $p = .25$ **h.** $n = 80$ and $p = .10$

9.30   Discuss how each of the following factors affects the width of the confidence interval for π.

a. The confidence level
b. The sample size
c. The value of p

9.31   Retailers report that the use of cents-off coupons is increasing. The Scripps Howard News Service (July 9, 1991) reported the proportion of all households that use coupons as .77. Suppose that this estimate was based on a random sample of 800 households. Construct a 95% confidence level for π, the true proportion of all households that use coupons.

9.32   A sample of 481 historians responded to questions about the performance of various U.S. presidents, and the results were presented at the annual conference of the Organization of American Historians (Associated Press, March 28, 1991). Of the 481 surveyed, 433 responded that Ronald Reagan lacked the proper intellect for the presidency. Construct a 90% confidence interval for π, the true proportion of all historians who believe that Reagan lacked the proper intellect for the presidency. (Note: In constructing this interval, we are assuming that the sample of 481 is a random sample of all historians. Do you think this is plausible?)

9.33   In 1988, the *Dallas Morning News* contacted 162 randomly selected people whose names appeared on nominating petitions for Democratic presidential candidate Jesse Jackson (*Austin American-Statesman*, January 23, 1988). One hundred sixteen of those contacted confirmed that they had signed the petitions, whereas the remaining individuals denied signing the petition and said that their names had been forged. Estimate the proportion of valid signatures on the nominating petitions using a 99% confidence interval.

9.34   The article "What Kinds of People Do Not Use Seat Belts" (*Amer. J. of Public Health* (1977):1043–1049) reported on a survey with the objective of studying characteristics of drivers and seat belt usage. Let π denote the proportion of all drivers of cars with seat belts who use them. Suppose that at the outset of the study, the investigators wished to estimate π to within an amount .02 with 95% confidence. What is the required sample size? Why is the recommended sample size so large?

9.35   In recent years, a number of student deaths have been attributed to participation in high-school sports. The paper "Concussion Incidences and Severity in Secondary

School Varsity Football Players" (*Amer. J. of Public Health* (1983):1370–1375) reported the results of a survey of 3063 high-school varsity football players. Each participant was asked to provide information on injuries and illnesses incurred as a result of participation in the 1977 football season. Loss of consciousness due to concussion was reported by 528 players. Use this information to construct a 90% confidence interval for π, the proportion of high-school football players who suffer loss of consciousness due to concussion.

9.36   The *Los Angeles Times* (January 6, 1987) reported on a survey of 200 patients at Boston's Brigham Woman's Hospital and San Francisco's H. C. Moffitt Hospital. Eighty of the patients surveyed said they prefer that doctors call them by their first name. Use this information to construct a 95% confidence interval for π, the proportion of all patients at these two hospitals who prefer doctors to address them by their first names.

9.37   The article referenced in Exercise 9.36 reported that of the 200 patients surveyed, 110 thought a doctor should wear a white coat when seeing patients and 96 said it was acceptable for a doctor to wear tennis shoes.
   a. Construct a 90% confidence interval for the proportion of all patients at these two hospitals who believe that a doctor should wear a white coat.
   b. Construct a 95% confidence interval for the proportion of all patients at these two hospitals who think it is acceptable for a doctor to wear tennis shoes.

9.38   The attitudes of classroom teachers are important when introducing a new technology into the classroom. The paper "Attitudes towards Microcomputers in Learning" (*Educ. Research* (1987):137–145) reported that 67% of teachers surveyed think that computers are now essential tools in the classroom. Suppose that this information was based on a random sample of $n = 200$ elementary schoolteachers. Calculate a 90% confidence interval for π, the true proportion of elementary schoolteachers who think the computer is an essential classroom tool.

9.39   Many universities allow courses to be taken on a credit/no credit basis. This encourages students to take courses outside their areas of emphasis without having to worry about the effect on their grade-point averages. The paper "Effects of Transition from Pass/No Credit to Traditional Letter Grade System" (*J. of Exper. Educ.* (Winter 1981/82):88–90) compared student performance under the pass/no credit and letter-grade systems. Sixty-three university professors who had taught under both grading systems participated in the study. Thirty-five responded "yes" when asked whether they felt that students under the letter-grade system performed better on tests and assignments. Construct a 99% confidence interval for π, the proportion of university professors who have taught under both systems and feel that student performance is better under the letter-grade system.

9.40   The paper "Worksite Smoking Cessation Programs: A Potential for National Impact" (*Amer. J. of Public Health* (1983):1395–1396) investigated the effectiveness of smoking cessation programs that appeal to all smokers at a particular worksite and not just those who have expressed an interest in giving up smoking. The program tested involved group meetings and monetary incentives for attending meetings and for not smoking. Of those who chose to participate in the experiment, 91% successfully stopped smoking and were still abstinent 6 months later. Suppose that 70 people were involved in the experiment and that these 70 are considered to be a sample of all people who participate in such a program. Let π denote the success rate (the proportion of participants who are still nonsmokers 6 months after completing the program) for this program. Find a 99% confidence interval for π.

9.41   In order to estimate the proportion of students at a particular university who favor the sale of beer on campus, a random sample of 100 students is selected. Of the selected students, 43 support the sale of beer. Let π denote the true proportion of the university's students who favor the sale of beer on campus. Estimate π using a 90% confidence interval. Does the width of the interval suggest that precise information about π is available? Why or why not?

9.42   Steroid use among athletes is currently a controversial issue. The paper "Anabolic Steroid Use among 1010 College Men" (*The Physician and Sports Medicine* (1988):75–79) reported that 17 of 1010 college men surveyed used steroids. Assuming the 1010 men surveyed were selected randomly, estimate the true proportion of college men who use steroids by obtaining a 99% confidence interval.

9.43   The paper "Television and Human Values: A Case for Cooperation" (*J. of Home Econ.* (Summer 1982):18–23) reported that 48% of U.S. homes had more than one television set.

   a. Suppose that the statistic reported in this paper was based on a random sample of 200 homes. Construct a 95% confidence interval for π, the proportion of all U.S. homes that have more than one television set.

   b. The same paper reported that the average viewing time per household was about 6 hours per day. If you wanted to construct an interval estimate for the average television viewing time for all U.S. households, would you use the following interval?

$$p \pm (z \text{ critical value}) \cdot \sqrt{\frac{p(1 - p)}{n}}$$

   Explain your answer.

9.44   A consumer group is interested in estimating the proportion of packages of ground beef sold at a particular store that have an actual fat content exceeding the fat content stated on the label. How many packages of ground beef should be tested in order to estimate this proportion to within .05 with 95% confidence?

9.45   A manufacturer of small appliances purchases plastic handles for coffeepots from an outside vendor. If a handle is cracked, it is considered defective and must be discarded. A very large shipment of plastic handles is received. The proportion of defective handles, π, is of interest. How many handles from the shipment should be inspected in order to estimate π to within .1 with 95% confidence?

9.46   Cornell University's Cooperative Education Department conducted a study of soda consumption among children (*Consumer's Research* (November 1983)). An estimate of the proportion of children under age 3 who drink soda at least every 3 days was desired. How large a sample should be selected in order to obtain an estimate within .05 of the true value with 95% confidence?

9.47   The formula given in the text for computing the sample size necessary to estimate π to within an amount B has an associated confidence level of 95%. How would you modify the formula to obtain the sample size required for 99% confidence? Will the value of n for 99% confidence be larger than that for 95% confidence (based on the same B)? Explain.

9.4   A Small-Sample Confidence Interval for the Mean of a Normal Population

The large-sample confidence interval for μ discussed in Section 9.2 is appropriate whatever the shape of the population distribution. This is because it is based on the Central Limit Theorem, which says that when n is sufficiently large, the $\bar{x}$ sampling distribution is approximately normal for any population distribution. When n is small, the Central Limit Theorem does not apply and the interval we developed earlier should not be used. One way to proceed in the small-sample case is to make a specific assumption about the shape of the population distribution and then to use an interval that is valid only under this assumption. The confidence interval we will develop in this section is based on the assumption that the population distribution is normal.

In order to understand the derivation of this confidence interval, it is instructive to begin by taking another look at the large-sample 95% confidence interval. We know that $\mu_{\bar{x}} = \mu$ and that $\sigma_{\bar{x}} = \sigma/\sqrt{n}$; also, when n is large, the $\bar{x}$ distribution is approximately normal. These facts imply that the standardized variable

$$z = \frac{\bar{x} - \mu}{\sigma/\sqrt{n}}$$

has approximately a standard normal distribution. Since the interval from -1.96 to 1.96 captures an area of .95 under the z curve, approximately 95% of all samples result in an $\bar{x}$ value satisfying

$$-1.96 < \frac{\bar{x} - \mu}{\sigma/\sqrt{n}} < 1.96$$

Manipulating these inequalities to isolate μ in the middle results in the equivalent inequalities

$$\bar{x} - 1.96 \cdot \frac{\sigma}{\sqrt{n}} < \mu < \bar{x} + 1.96 \cdot \frac{\sigma}{\sqrt{n}}$$

The term $\bar{x} - 1.96(\sigma/\sqrt{n})$ is the lower limit of the 95% large-sample confidence interval for μ, and $\bar{x} + 1.96(\sigma/\sqrt{n})$ is the upper limit. If σ is unknown, the sample standard deviation, s, is used. When n is large, the substitution of s for σ has little effect.

When n is small, the shape of the $\bar{x}$ distribution may not be approximately normal and depends on the shape of the population distribution. However, when the population distribution is itself normal, the $\bar{x}$ distribution is normal even for small sample sizes. It follows that

$$z = \frac{\bar{x} - \mu}{\sigma/\sqrt{n}}$$

has a standard normal distribution. But, since σ will usually be unknown, we must estimate σ with the sample standard deviation, resulting in the standardized variable

$$t = \frac{\bar{x} - \mu}{s/\sqrt{n}}$$

The value of s may not be all that close to σ when n is small. As a consequence, the use of s in place of σ introduces extra variability, so the distribution of t is more spread out than the standard normal (z) curve. (The value of z will vary from sample to sample, because different samples generally result in different $\bar{x}$ values. There is even more variability in t, because different samples may result in different values of both $\bar{x}$ and s.)

In order to develop an appropriate confidence interval, we need to know about the probability distribution of the standardized variable t for a small sample from a normal population. This requires that we first learn about probability distributions called t distributions.

t Distributions

Just as there are many different normal distributions, there are also many t distributions. While normal distributions are distinguished from one another by their mean μ and standard deviation σ, the t distributions are distinguished by a positive whole number called *degrees of freedom* (df). There is a t distribution with 1 df, another with 2 df, and so on.

IMPORTANT PROPERTIES OF t DISTRIBUTIONS

1. The t curve corresponding to any fixed number of degrees of freedom is bell-shaped and centered at zero, just as is the standard normal (z) curve.
2. Any t curve is more spread out than the z curve.
3. As the number of degrees of freedom increases, the spread of the corresponding t curve decreases.
4. As the number of degrees of freedom increases, the corresponding sequence of t curves approaches the z curve.

These properties are illustrated in Figure 9.6, which shows several t curves along with the z curve.

FIGURE 9.6
Comparison of the z curve and t curves for 12 df and 4 df

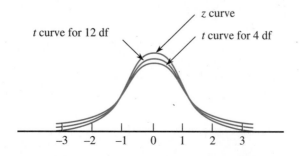

Appendix Table IV (which also appears inside the back cover) gives selected upper-tail critical values for various t distributions. The central areas for which values are tabulated are .80, .90, .95, .98, .99, .998, and .999. To find a particular critical value, go down the left margin of the table to the row labeled with the desired number of degrees of freedom. Then move over in that row to the column headed by the desired central area. For example, the value in the 12-df row under the column corresponding to central area .95 is 2.18, so 95% of the area under the t curve with 12 df lies between -2.18 and 2.18. Moving over two columns, the critical value for central area .99 (still with 12 df) is 3.06. Moving down the .99 column to the 20-df row, the critical value is 2.85, so the area between -2.85 and 2.85 is .99 under the t curve with 20 df. Notice that the critical values increase as you move to the right in each row. This is necessary in order to capture a larger central area and a smaller tail area. In each column, the critical values decrease as you move downward, reflecting decreasing spread for t distributions with larger degrees of freedom.

The larger the number of degrees of freedom, the more closely the t curve resembles the z curve. To emphasize this, we have included the z critical values as the last row of the t table. Furthermore, once the number of degrees of freedom exceeds 30, the critical values change very little as the number of degrees of freedom increases. For this reason, Table IV jumps from 30 df to 40 df, then to 60 df, then to 120 df, and finally to the row of z critical values. If we need a critical value for a number of degrees of freedom between those tabulated, we just use the critical value for the closest df. For df > 120, we use the z critical values.

The t Confidence Interval

The fact that the sampling distribution of $(\bar{x} - \mu)/(\sigma/\sqrt{n})$ is approximately the z (standard normal) distribution when n is large is what led to the large-sample z interval. In the same way, the following proposition provides the key to obtaining a small-sample confidence interval when the population distribution is normal.

Let $x_1, x_2, \ldots, x_n$ constitute a random sample from a normal population distribution. Then the sampling distribution of the standardized variable

$$t = \frac{\bar{x} - \mu}{s/\sqrt{n}}$$

is the t distribution with $n - 1$ df.

To see how this result leads to the desired confidence interval, consider the case $n = 25$, so that df $= 24$. From Table IV, the interval between -2.06 and 2.06 captures a central area of .95 under the t curve with 24 df. Then 95% of all samples (with $n = 25$) from a normal population result in values of $\bar{x}$ and s for which

$$-2.06 < \frac{\bar{x} - \mu}{s/\sqrt{n}} < 2.06$$

Manipulating these inequalities to isolate μ yields

$$\bar{x} - 2.06 \cdot \frac{s}{\sqrt{25}} < \mu < \bar{x} + 2.06 \cdot \frac{s}{\sqrt{25}}$$

The 95% confidence interval for μ in this situation extends from the lower limit $\bar{x} - 2.06(s/\sqrt{25})$ to the upper limit $\bar{x} + 2.06(s/\sqrt{25})$. This interval can be written

$$\bar{x} \pm 2.06 \cdot \frac{s}{\sqrt{25}}$$

The major difference between this interval and the large-sample interval is the use of the t critical value 2.06 rather than the z critical value 1.96. The extra uncertainty that results from estimating σ using a small sample causes the t interval to be wider than the z interval.

If the sample size is something other than 25 or if the desired confidence level is something other than 95%, a different t critical value (obtained from Table IV) is used in place of 2.06.

THE ONE-SAMPLE t CONFIDENCE INTERVAL

Let $x_1, x_2, \ldots, x_n$ be a random sample from a normal population distribution with mean value μ. Then a t **confidence interval for μ** has the form

$$\bar{x} \pm (t \text{ critical value}) \cdot \frac{s}{\sqrt{n}}$$

where the critical value is based on $n - 1$ df. Appendix Table IV gives critical values appropriate for each of the confidence levels 90%, 95%, and 99%, as well as several other less frequently used confidence levels.

This confidence interval is appropriate for small n only when the population distribution is (at least approximately) normal. If this is not the case, as might be suggested by a normal probability plot or box plot, another method should be used.

EXAMPLE 9.10

The use of synthetic male hormones (technically, anabolic steroids) is widespread in sports that require great muscular strength. The article "Side Effects of Anabolic Steroids in Weight Trained Men" (*The Physician and Sports Med.* (December 1983):87–98) reported on a study of a sample of 20 bodybuilders who were current users of such steroids. The sample average weekly dose for oral agents was $\bar{x} = 173$ mg, and the sample standard deviation was $s = 45$ mg. Suppose that, in the population of all bodybuilders who use oral steroids, the distribution of the weekly dose is normal with mean value μ. To compute a 95% confidence interval for μ, the t critical value for $n - 1 = 19$ df is needed. From Table IV, this value is 2.09. The 95% confidence interval is then

$$\bar{x} \pm (t \text{ critical value}) \cdot \frac{s}{\sqrt{n}} = 173 \pm (2.09) \cdot \frac{45}{\sqrt{20}}$$

$$= 173 \pm 21.0$$

$$= (152, 194)$$

We can be highly confident that the true average weekly dose is somewhere between 152 mg and 194 mg. The article reports that a manufacturer's recommended dose for a certain oral steroid is between 35 mg and 70 mg per week, so our analysis certainly suggests excessive steroid use among bodybuilders.

EXAMPLE 9.11

Chronic exposure to asbestos fiber is a well-known health hazard. The paper "The Acute Effects of Chrysotile Asbestos Exposure on Lung Function" (*Environ. Research* (1978):360–372) reported results of a study based on a sample of construction workers who had been exposed to asbestos over a prolonged period. Among the data given in the article were the following (ordered) values of pulmonary compliance (cm^3/cm H_2O) for each of 16 subjects 8 months after the exposure period. (Pulmonary compliance is a measure of lung elasticity, or how effectively the lungs are able to inhale and exhale.)

167.9	180.8	184.8	189.8	194.8	200.2	201.9	206.9
207.2	208.4	226.3	227.7	228.5	232.4	239.8	258.6

A normal probability plot of this data is quite straight, so it seems plausible that the population pulmonary compliance distribution is approximately normal. For this data set, we have

$$n = 16 \qquad \Sigma x = 3356.0 \qquad \Sigma x^2 = 712{,}673.82$$

$$\bar{x} = \frac{3356.0}{16} = 209.75$$

$$s^2 = \frac{\Sigma x^2 - \dfrac{(\Sigma x)^2}{n}}{n - 1}$$

$$= \frac{712{,}673.82 - \dfrac{(3356.0)^2}{16}}{15}$$

$$= 583.52$$

$$s = \sqrt{583.52} = 24.16$$

Let μ denote the mean pulmonary compliance for the population of all men who have extensive exposure to asbestos. The t critical value for a 90% confidence interval when df $= 16 - 1 = 15$ is 1.75. The confidence interval is then obtained as follows:

$$\bar{x} \pm (1.75)\frac{s}{\sqrt{n}} = 209.75 \pm (1.75)\frac{(24.16)}{\sqrt{16}}$$

$$= 209.75 \pm 10.57$$

$$= (199.18, 220.32)$$

With 90% confidence, the mean pulmonary compliance μ is between 199.18 and 220.32 cm^3/cm H$_2$O. Remember that the 90% confidence level implies that 90% of the time, the method used to construct this interval successfully captures μ.

EXERCISES 9.48–9.59   SECTION 9.4

9.48   Given a variable that has a t distribution with the specified degrees of freedom, what percentage of the time will its value fall in the indicated region?
  a. 10 df, between -1.81 and 1.81
  b. 10 df, between -2.23 and 2.23
  c. 24 df, between -2.06 and 2.06
  d. 24 df, between -2.80 and 2.80
  e. 24 df, outside the interval from -2.80 and 2.80
  f. 24 df, to the right of 2.80
  g. 10 df, to the left of -1.81

9.49   The formula used to compute a confidence interval for the mean of a normal population when n is small is

$$\bar{x} \pm (t \text{ critical value}) \cdot \frac{s}{\sqrt{n}}$$

What is the appropriate t critical value for each of the following confidence levels and sample sizes?
  a. 95% confidence, $n = 17$ **b.** 90% confidence, $n = 12$
  c. 99% confidence, $n = 24$ **d.** 90% confidence, $n = 25$
  e. 90% confidence, $n = 13$ **f.** 95% confidence, $n = 10$

9.50   The eating habits of 12 bats were examined in the paper "Foraging Behavior of the Indian False Vampire Bat" (*Biotropica* (1991):63–67). These bats consume insects and frogs. For these 12 bats, the mean time to consume a frog was 21.9 min. Suppose the standard deviation was 7.7 min. Construct and interpret a 90% confidence interval for the mean suppertime of a vampire bat whose meal consists of a frog.

9.51   Fat content (in percent) for ten hot dogs was given in the paper "Sensory and Mechanical Assessment of the Quality of Frankfurters" (*Journal of Texture Studies* (1990):395–409). Use the given data to construct a 90% confidence interval for the true mean fat percentage of hot dogs.

25.2	21.3	22.8	17.0	29.8
21.0	25.5	16.0	20.9	19.5

9.52   Family food expenditures were investigated in the paper "Household Production of Food: Expenditures, Norms, and Satisfaction" (*Home Econ. Research J.* (March 1983):27). A sample of Iowa homes resulted in an average weekly food expenditure of $164 and a standard deviation of $85. Assuming these results were based on a random sample of size 25, construct a 95% confidence interval for μ, the mean weekly food expenditure for Iowa families. Interpret your interval.

9.53   Blood concentrations of growth hormone and glucose levels were measured for 16 low-birth-weight infants 4 days after birth ("Serum Concentrations of Growth Hormone, Insulin, Free Thyroxine, Thyrotropin, and Cortisol in Very Low Birth Weight Infants Receiving Total Parenteral Nutrition" *Amer. J. of Diseases of Children* (1988):993–995).

Growth hormone (μg/L)		Glucose (mmol/L)	
$\bar{x}$	s	$\bar{x}$	s
40.3	16.0	6.6	3.2

a. Assuming that the glucose level distribution is approximately normal, construct a 90% confidence interval for the true mean glucose level of low-birth-weight infants at 4 days after birth.

b. Calculate a 95% confidence interval for the true mean growth hormone level of low-birth-weight infants at 4 days after birth. What assumptions about the growth hormone distribution are required for the validity of the interval computed?

9.54   A triathlon consisting of swimming, cycling, and running is one of the more strenuous amateur sporting events. The paper "Cardiovascular and Thermal Response of Triathlon Performance" (*Medicine and Science in Sports and Exercise* (1988): 385–389) reported on a research study involving nine male triathletes. Maximum heart rate (beats/min) was recorded while performing each of the three events.

	$\bar{x}$	s
Swimming	188	7.2
Biking	186	8.5
Running	194	7.8

a. Assuming that the heart rate distribution for each event is approximately normal, construct 95% confidence intervals for the true mean heart rate of triathletes for each event.

b. Do the intervals in part (a) overlap? Based on the computed intervals, do you think there is evidence that the mean maximum heart rate is higher for running than for the other two events? Explain.

9.55   Authors of the paper "Quality of Carrots Dehydrated by Three Home Methods" (*Home Econ. Research J.* (September 1983):81) examined the time and energy required to dehydrate carrots. Five 1-qt containers of sliced carrots were dehydrated by each method, and the accompanying data was reported.

Method	Time required for dehydration (min)		Energy required for dehydration (W·hr)	
	Mean	(Approximate) Standard deviation	Mean	(Approximate) Standard deviation
Convection oven	428	35	2199	100
Food dehydrator	513	20	3920	170
Microwave oven	135	4	1431	30

a. Compute a 90% confidence interval for the average time required to dehydrate 1 qt of carrots using a convection oven.

b. Given that the method of dehydration is by food dehydrator, would a 90% confidence interval for the average time required be wider or narrower than the 90% interval for the convection oven method computed in part (a)? Explain without actually computing the interval.

c. Construct a 95% confidence interval for the average energy required to dehydrate 1 qt of carrots with each of the three methods. Based on these intervals, what conclusions can you draw about the relative efficiency of the three methods?

9.56   The effectiveness of various drugs used to treat horses is discussed in the paper "Factors Involved in the Choice of Routes of Administration of Antimicrobial Drugs" (*J. of Amer. Vet. Med. Assoc.* (1984):1076–1082). One characteristic of interest is the *half-life* of a drug (the length of time until the concentration of the drug in the blood is one-half of the initial value). Given here are the reported values of the sample size and the half-life sample mean and standard deviation for three drugs under study.

Drug	n	Sample mean	Sample standard deviation
Gentamicin	7	1.85 h	.231 h
Trimethoprin	6	3.16 h	.845 h
Sulfadimethoxine	6	10.62 h	2.560 h

a. Construct a 90% confidence interval for the mean half-life of gentamicin. Is this confidence interval valid whatever the distribution of half-lives? Explain.

b. Construct individual 90% confidence intervals for the average half-lives of trimethoprin and sulfadimethoxine.

c. Interpret each of the intervals in parts (a) and (b). Do any of the intervals overlap? If a shorter half-life is desirable (since it would indicate quicker absorption of the drug), based on your confidence intervals would you be able to recommend one of the three drugs over the others? Explain.

9.57   The paper "Surgeons and Operating Rooms: Underutilized Resources" (*Amer. J. of Public Health* (1983):1361–1365) investigated the number of operations per year performed by doctors in various medical specialties.

a.   Nine plastic surgeons were asked to indicate the number of operations performed in the previous year. The resulting sample mean was 263.7 operations. If the sample standard deviation was 50.4, find a 90% confidence interval for the average number of operations per year for the population of all plastic surgeons.

b.   Twenty-two neurosurgeons were also surveyed concerning the number of operations performed during the previous year. The sample mean was 58.5 operations. If the sample standard deviation was 12.1, find a 99% confidence interval for μ, the mean number of operations performed per year by neurosurgeons.

c.   What assumptions are required about the distribution of the number of operations performed in one year for the two populations of doctors in order for the intervals in parts (a) and (b) to be appropriate?

 9.58   A wine manufacturer sells a Cabernet with a label that asserts an alcohol content of 11%. Sixteen bottles of this Cabernet are randomly selected and analyzed for alcohol content. The resulting observations are

10.8	9.6	9.5	11.4	9.8	9.1	10.4	10.7
10.2	9.8	10.4	11.1	10.3	9.8	9.0	9.8

a.   Construct a 95% confidence interval for μ, the average alcohol content of the bottles of Cabernet produced by this manufacturer. (Assume that alcohol content is normally distributed.)

b.   Based on your interval in part (a), do you think that the manufacturer is incorrect in its label claim? Explain.

9.59   Five students visiting the student health center for a free dental examination during National Dental Hygiene Month were asked how many months had passed since their last visit to a dentist. Their responses were as follows.

6   17   11   22   29

If these five students can be considered to be a random sample of all students participating in the free check-up program, construct a 95% confidence interval for the mean number of months elapsed since the last visit to a dentist for the population of students participating in the program.

CHAPTER NINE SUMMARY OF KEY CONCEPTS AND FORMULAS

Term or Formula	Comment
Point estimate	A single number, based on sample data, that represents a plausible value of a population characteristic.

Term or Formula	Comment
Unbiased statistic	A statistic that has a sampling distribution with a mean equal to the value of the population characteristic to be estimated.
Confidence interval	An interval that is computed from sample data and provides plausible values for a population characteristic.
Confidence level	A number that provides information on how much "confidence" we can have in the method used to construct a confidence interval estimate. The confidence level specifies the percentage of all possible samples that will produce an interval containing the true value of the population characteristic.
$\bar{x} \pm (z \text{ critical value}) \cdot \dfrac{s}{\sqrt{n}}$	A formula used to construct a confidence interval for μ when the sample size is large.
$n = \left[\dfrac{1.96\sigma}{B}\right]^2$	A formula used to compute the sample size necessary for estimating μ to within an amount B with 95% confidence.
$p \pm (z \text{ critical value}) \cdot \sqrt{\dfrac{p(1-p)}{n}}$	A formula used to construct a confidence interval for π when the sample size is large.
$n = \pi(1-\pi)\left[\dfrac{1.96}{B}\right]^2$	A formula used to compute the sample size necessary for estimating π to within an amount B with 95% confidence.
$\bar{x} \pm (t \text{ critical value}) \cdot \dfrac{s}{\sqrt{n}}$	A formula used to construct a confidence interval for μ when the sample size is small and when it is reasonable to assume that the population distribution is normal.

ENCORE

The results of the American Bar Association survey mentioned in the Chapter Preview were published by the Associated Press (December 16, 1991). It was reported that of the 507 people surveyed, 142 correctly described the Bill of Rights as the first ten amendments to the Constitution and only 46 correctly responded that the original purpose of the Bill of Rights was to limit abuses by the federal government.

Let

π_1 = proportion of all U.S. adults who can correctly describe the Bill of Rights

and

π_2 = proportion of all U.S. adults who know the original purpose of the Bill of Rights

We will construct confidence intervals to estimate π_1 and π_2. Let's begin by calculating p_1 and p_2, the two sample proportions.

p_1 = sample proportion who correctly identified the Bill of Rights

$$= \frac{142}{507}$$

$$= .280$$

p_2 = sample proportion who knew the original purpose of the Bill of Rights

$$= \frac{46}{507}$$

$$= .091$$

The value of $p_1 = .280$ is a point estimate of π_1. Since this estimate by itself does not convey any information about the accuracy of estimation, we will proceed to an interval estimate. A 95% confidence interval for π_1 is

$$p_1 \pm (z \text{ critical value}) \sqrt{\frac{p_1(1 - p_1)}{n}}$$

This interval is appropriate because the sample size is large ($np_1 = 507(.280) = 142 > 5$ and $n(1 - p_1) = 507(.720) = 365 > 5$). For a confidence level of 95%, the appropriate z critical value is 1.96. Substituting into the confidence interval formula gives

$$.280 \pm 1.96 \sqrt{\frac{(.280)(.720)}{507}}$$

$$= .280 \pm .039$$

$$= (.241, .319)$$

Based on the sample, we believe that the proportion of all U.S. adults who can correctly identify the Bill of Rights, π_1, is between .241 and .319. We have used a method to produce this estimate that has a 5% error rate (in the long run, only 5% of intervals constructed using this method will fail to include the true value).

A 95% confidence interval for π_2 is

$$p_2 \pm (z \text{ critical value}) \sqrt{\frac{p_2(1 - p_2)}{n}}$$

$$= .091 \pm 1.96 \sqrt{\frac{(.091)(.909)}{507}}$$

$$= .091 \pm .025$$

$$= (.066, .116)$$

Based on this sample of 507 U.S. adults, we believe that the true proportion of all U.S. adults who know the original purpose of the Bill of Rights, π_2, is between .066 and .116.

The results of this survey, released on the 200th anniversary of the Bill of Rights, were described as depressing by those coordinating the anniversary celebration!

SUPPLEMENTARY EXERCISES 9.60–9.75

9.60 Scripps News Service (September 14, 1991) reported that 4% of the members of the American Bar Association (ABA) are African-Americans. Suppose that this figure is based on a random sample of 400 ABA members.
  a. Is the sample size large enough to justify the use of the large-sample confidence interval for a population proportion?
  b. Construct and interpret a 90% confidence interval for π, the true proportion of all ABA members who are African-American.

9.61 The Center for Urban Transportation Research released a report stating that the average commuting distance in the United States is 10.9 mi (*USA Today* August 13, 1991). Suppose that this average is actually the mean of a sample of 300 commuters and that the sample standard deviation was 6.2 mi. Estimate the true mean commuting distance using a 99% confidence interval.

9.62 In 1991 California imposed a "snack tax" (a sales tax on snack food) in an attempt to help balance the state budget. A proposed alternative tax was a 12¢-per-pack increase in the cigarette tax. In a poll of 602 California registered voters, 445 responded that they would have preferred the cigarette tax increase to the snack tax (*Reno Gazette-Journal* August 26, 1991). Estimate the true proportion of California registered voters who prefer the cigarette tax increase using a 95% confidence interval.

9.63 Television advertisers are becoming concerned about the use of video cassette recorders (VCRs) to tape television shows, since many viewers fast-forward through the commercials when viewing taped shows. A survey conducted by A. C. Nielsen Co. of 1100 VCR owners found that 715 used the fast-forward feature to avoid commercials on taped programs (the *Los Angeles Times*, September 2, 1984). Construct and interpret a 95% confidence interval for the proportion of all VCR owners who use the fast-forward feature to avoid advertisements.

9.64 Stock researcher Norman Fosback published a study assessing the effect of stock tips that appeared in the *Wall Street Journal*. A sample of companies receiving favorable mention showed a mean 1-day price increase of 5.5 points (the *Los Angeles Times*, April 30, 1984). Suppose the sample consisted of 100 observations and that the sample standard deviation was 3.6. Construct a 95% confidence interval for μ, the true mean 1-day increase of companies receiving positive mention.

9.65 The paper "The Market for Generic Brand Products" (*J. of Marketing* (1984):75–83) reported that in a random sample of 1442 shoppers, 727 purchased generic brands. Estimate the true proportion of all shoppers who purchase generic brands by using a 99% confidence interval.

9.66 Each year as Thanksgiving draws near, inspectors from the Department of Weights and Measures weigh turkeys randomly selected from grocery store freezers to see if the marked weight is accurate. The *San Luis Obispo Telegram-Tribune* (November 22, 1984) reported that of 1000 birds weighed, 486 required remarking. Use a 95% confidence interval to estimate π, the true proportion of all frozen turkeys with an incorrectly marked weight. Based on your interval, do you think that it is plausible that more than half of all frozen turkeys are incorrectly marked? Explain.

9.67 About 14% of all dogs suffer from an infection of the urinary tract sometime during their lifetime. The preferred treatment for an infection caused by the urinary bacteria *pseudomonas* is the antibiotic tetracycline. In a study of healthy adult dogs who received a daily dose of tetracycline of 55 mg/kg body weight, the mean concentration of tetracycline in the urine was 138 μg/mL and the sample standard deviation was 65 μg/mL ("Therapeutic Strategies Involving Antimicrobial Treatment of the Canine Urinary Tract," *J. of Amer. Vet. Med. Assoc.* (1984):1162–1164). Suppose the mean and standard deviation given had been computed using a sample of $n = 10$ observations. Construct and interpret a 95% confidence interval for the mean concentration of tetracycline in the urine of dogs receiving daily tetracycline (55mg/kg body weight).

9.68 The paper "Chlorinated Pesticide Residues in the Body Fat of People in Iran" (*Environ. Research* (1978):419–422) summarized the results of an Iranian study of a sample of $n = 170$ tissue specimens. It was found that the sample mean DDT concentration and sample standard deviation were 8.13 ppm and 8.34 ppm, respectively.

  a. Construct and interpret a 95% confidence interval for μ, the true mean DDT concentration.

  b. If the above summary data had resulted from a sample of only $n = 15$ specimens, do you think a t interval would have been appropriate? Explain.

9.69 In a survey of 1515 people, 606 said they thought that autoworkers were overpaid (Associated Press, August 15, 1984). Treating the 1515 people as a random sample of the American public, use a 90% confidence interval to estimate the true proportion of Americans who think autoworkers are overpaid.

9.70 The effect of anaesthetic on the flow of aqueous humour (a fluid of the eye) was investigated in the paper "A Method for Near-Continuous Determination of Aqueous Humour Flow: Effects of Anaesthetics, Temperature and Indomethacin" (*Exper. Eye Research* (1984):435–453). Summary quantities for aqueous flow rate (μL/min) observed under three different anaesthetics are given.

Anaesthetic	n	Mean flow rate	Standard deviation
Pentobarbitol	191	.99	.235
Urethane	13	1.47	.314
Ketamine	16	.99	.164

  a. Construct a 95% confidence interval for the true mean flow rate when under the effects of pentobarbitol.

  b. Construct a 95% confidence interval for the true mean flow rate under urethane. Give two reasons why this interval is wider than that in part (a).

  c. Construct a 95% confidence interval for the true mean flow rate under the anaesthetic ketamine. Note that the sample mean was the same for the pentobarbitol and the ketamine samples and yet the corresponding 95% confidence intervals are different. What factors contribute to this difference? Explain.

9.71 In a random sample of 31 inmates selected from residents of the prison in Angola, Louisiana ("The Effects of Education on Self-Esteem of Male Prison Inmates," *J. of Correctional Educ.* (1982):12–18), 25 were Caucasian. Use a 90% confidence interval to estimate the true proportion of inmates (at this prison) who are Caucasian.

9.72 When n is large, the statistic s is approximately unbiased for estimating σ and has approximately a normal distribution. The standard deviation of this statistic when the population distribution is normal is $\sigma_s \approx \sigma/\sqrt{2n}$, which can be estimated by $s/\sqrt{2n}$. A large-sample confidence interval for the population standard deviation σ is then

$$s \pm (z \text{ critical value}) \cdot \frac{s}{\sqrt{2n}}$$

Use the data of Exercise 9.70 to obtain a 95% confidence interval for the true standard deviation of flow rate under pentobarbitol.

9.73 The interval from -2.33 to 1.75 captures an area of .95 under the z curve. This implies that another large-sample 95% confidence interval for μ has lower limit $\bar{x} - 2.33(s/\sqrt{n})$ and upper limit $\bar{x} + 1.75(s/\sqrt{n})$. Would you recommend using this 95% interval over the 95% interval $\bar{x} \pm 1.96(s/\sqrt{n})$ discussed in the text? Explain. (Hint: Look at the width of each interval.)

9.74 Suppose that an individual's morning waiting time for a certain bus is known to have a uniform distribution on the interval from 0 min to an unknown upper limit θ min. A 95% confidence interval for θ based on a random sample of n waiting times can be shown to have lower limit $\max(x)$ and upper limit $\max(x)/(.05)^{1/n}$. If $n = 5$ and the resulting waiting times are 4.2, 3.5, 1.7, 1.2, and 2.4, obtain the confidence interval. (Hint: $(0.5)^{1/5} = .5493.$) Notice that the confidence interval here is not of the form (estimate) $\pm$ (critical value)(standard deviation).

9.75 As an example of a situation in which several different statistics could reasonably be used to calculate a point estimate, consider a population of N invoices. Associated with each invoice is its "book value," the recorded amount of that invoice. Let T denote the total book value, a known amount. Some of these book values are erroneous. An audit will be carried out by randomly selecting n invoices and determining the audited (correct) value for each one. Suppose that the sample gives the following results (in dollars).

Invoice	1	2	3	4	5
Book value	300	720	526	200	127
Audited value	300	520	526	200	157
Error	0	200	0	0	−30

Let

$$\bar{y} = \text{sample mean book value}$$
$$\bar{x} = \text{sample mean audited value}$$
$$\bar{d} = \text{sample mean error}$$

Several different statistics for estimating the total audited (correct) value have been proposed (see "Statistical Models and Analysis in Auditing," *Statistical Science* (1989):2–33). These include

$$\text{mean per unit statistic} = N\bar{x}$$
$$\text{difference statistic} = T - N\bar{d}$$
$$\text{ratio statistic} = T \cdot (\bar{x}/\bar{y})$$

If $N = 5000$ and $T = 1,761,300$, calculate the three corresponding point estimates. (The cited paper also discusses confidence intervals.)

References

Again, the books by Freedman et al. and by Moore listed in the Chapter 2 References contain very informal and lucid discussions of confidence intervals at a level comparable to that of this text. The Devore book referenced in Chapter 5 gives a somewhat more general introduction to confidence intervals.

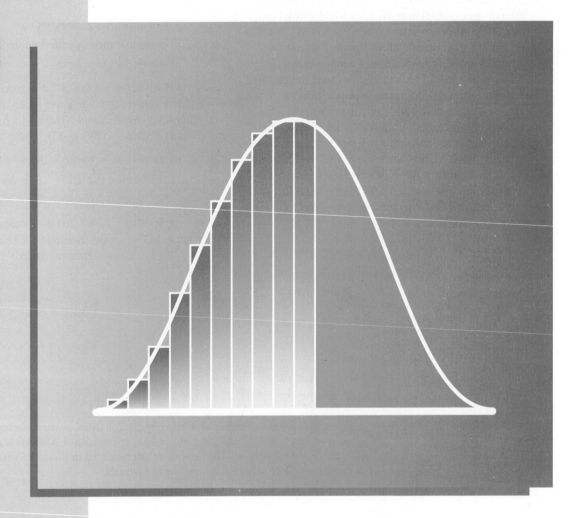

Hypothesis Testing Using a Single Sample

PREVIEW

In order to qualify an initiative to appear on an election ballot, backers must collect signatures of registered voters. The number of signatures required is usually a specified percentage of the number who voted in the last election. To qualify for a state ballot in a large state, such as California or New York, many signatures are needed. For example, to qualify for the 1988 California election, 654,954 signatures of registered voters were required. (*Los Angeles Times,* January 20, 1988).

When petitions with signatures are submitted, the secretary of state must decide if there are enough valid signatures. Each signature could be checked against voter-registration records, the invalid signatures removed, and the total determined. This process would be very time-consuming and expensive to implement. The actual procedure in California is to select a random sample of signatures. Each signature in the sample is then checked, and the resulting data is used to decide whether the proportion of valid signatures is high enough for the initiative to qualify.

In 1988, petitions supporting an initiative that would modify a previously approved voter-imposed spending limit were submitted to the State of California. The petitions contained approximately 1,000,000 signatures. Since 654,954 valid signatures were required, the initiative would qualify if the proportion of valid signatures was greater than .655 ($654,954/1,000,000 \approx .655$). Suppose that a sample of 5000 randomly selected signatures included 3605 that were valid. (This is consistent with summary values reported in the *Los Angeles Times.*)

Does this sample provide convincing evidence that the initiative qualifies for the ballot? The sample proportion of valid signatures is $3605/5000 = .721$, but we know that the proportion of valid signatures in the sample generally differs from the true proportion valid for all signatures submitted. Is it possible that the true proportion of valid signatures is less than .655 and that the sample proportion of .721 can be explained by the chance differences that occur from one sample to another? Or, should a sample proportion of .721 lead us to the conclusion that the true proportion valid for all signatures is greater than .655 and that the initiative should be placed on the ballot? Methods introduced in this chapter can be used to answer these questions.

Introduction

In the last chapter, we considered problems in which the primary goal was to estimate the unknown value of some population characteristic. Sample data may also be collected in order to decide whether some claim or statement about a population characteristic is plausible. For example, a consumer group investigating claims made by the pharmaceutical company that makes a prescription pain reliever might want to determine if the mean dosage per capsule is in fact 5 mg, as asserted by the manufacturer.

A *hypothesis* is a claim or a statement about one or more population characteristics. The hypothesis $\mu = 5$ mg, where μ is the true mean dosage, corresponds to the manufacturer's claim in the preceding example. The consumer group would like to use data resulting from a sample of capsules to make a decision between the two rival hypotheses $\mu = 5$ mg (the assertion that the manufacturer's claim is correct) and $\mu \neq 5$ mg (which says that the manufacturer's claim is incorrect). This chapter presents hypothesis-testing procedures that facilitate making such decisions.

10.1 Hypotheses and Test Procedures

A **hypothesis** is a claim or statement either about the value of a single population characteristic or about the values of several characteristics. The following are some examples of legitimate hypotheses:

1. $\mu = 100$, where μ is the average IQ for all first-born children
2. $\pi > .1$, where π is the proportion of all television sets of a certain brand that need repair while under warranty

The statements $\bar{x} > 110$ and $p = .15$ are not hypotheses because neither $\bar{x}$ nor p is a *population* characteristic.

In any hypothesis-testing problem, there are two contradictory hypotheses under consideration. One hypothesis might be $\mu = 100$ and the other $\mu \neq 100$, or one might be $\pi = .1$ and the other $\pi > .1$. The objective is to decide, based on sample information, which of the two hypotheses is correct. A criminal trial is a familiar situation in which a choice between two contradictory claims must be made. The person accused of the crime must be judged either innocent or guilty. Under the U.S. system of justice, the individual on trial is initially presumed innocent. Only strong evidence to the contrary will cause the innocence claim to be rejected in favor of a guilty verdict. The burden is thus put on the prosecution to prove the guilty claim. The French perspective in criminal proceedings is the opposite of ours. There, once enough evidence has been presented to justify bringing an individual to trial, the initial assumption is that the accused is guilty. The burden of proof then falls on the accused to establish innocence.

A **test of hypotheses** is a method for deciding which of the two contradictory claims (hypotheses) is the correct one. As in a judicial proceeding, we shall initially assume that a particular one of the two hypotheses is the correct one. In carrying out a test, this claim will be rejected in favor of the second (alternative) claim only if sample evidence is incompatible with the initial assumption.

DEFINITION

The **null hypothesis,** denoted by H_0, is the claim that is initially assumed to be true. The other hypothesis is referred to as the **alternative hypothesis** and is denoted by H_a.

In carrying out a test of H_0 versus H_a, the hypothesis H_0 will be rejected in favor of H_a only if sample evidence strongly suggests that H_0 is false. If the sample does not contain such evidence, H_0 will not be rejected. The two possible conclusions are then *reject H_0* or *fail to reject H_0*.

EXAMPLE 10.1

Consider a machine that produces ball bearings. Because of variation in the machining process, bearings produced by this machine do not have identical diameters. Let μ denote the true average diameter for bearings currently being produced. Suppose that the machine was initially calibrated to achieve the design specification $\mu = .5$ in. However, the manufacturer is now concerned that the diameters no longer conform to this specification. That is, the hypothesis $\mu \neq .5$ in. must now be considered a possibility. If sample evidence suggests that $\mu \neq .5$ in., the production process will have to be halted while recalibration takes place. Because this is costly, the manufacturer wants to be quite sure that $\mu \neq .5$ in. before undertaking recalibration. Under these circumstances, a sensible choice of hypotheses is

H_0: $\mu = .5$ (the specification is being met, so
recalibration is unnecessary)

H_a: $\mu \neq .5$

Only compelling sample evidence would then result in H_0 being rejected in favor of H_a.

EXAMPLE 10.2

A pack of a certain brand of cigarettes displays the statement, "1.5 mg nicotine average per cigarette by FTC method." Let μ denote the mean nicotine content per cigarette for all cigarettes of this brand. Then the advertised claim is that $\mu = 1.5$ mg. People who smoke this brand would probably be unhappy if it turned out that μ exceeded the advertised value. Suppose a sample of cigarettes of this brand is selected, and the nicotine content of each cigarette is determined. The sample results can then be used to test the hypothesis $\mu = 1.5$ mg against the hypothesis $\mu > 1.5$ mg. The accusation that the company is understating mean nicotine content is a serious one, and it is reasonable to require compelling sample evidence before concluding that $\mu > 1.5$. This suggests that the claim $\mu = 1.5$ should be selected as the null hypothesis and $\mu > 1.5$ selected as the alternative hypothesis. Then H_0: $\mu = 1.5$ would be rejected in favor of H_a: $\mu > 1.5$ only when sample evidence strongly suggests that the initial assumption $\mu = 1.5$ mg is no longer tenable.

Because the alternative of interest in Example 10.1 was $\mu \neq .5$, it was natural to state H_0 as the equality claim $\mu = .5$. However, the alternative hypothesis in Example 10.2 was stated as $\mu > 1.5$ (true average nicotine content exceeds the advertised level), from which it might seem more reasonable to state H_0 as $\mu \leq 1.5$ rather than $\mu = 1.5$. After all, the average level might actually be less than what the company advertises! Suppose, though, that sample evidence leads to the rejection of $\mu = 1.5$ in favor of the claim $\mu > 1.5$. Then, intuitively, the sample would offer even less support to values of μ smaller than 1.5 when compared to the claim $\mu > 1.5$. Thus, explicitly testing H_0: $\mu = 1.5$ is equivalent to implicitly testing the null hypothesis $\mu \leq 1.5$. We have chosen to state a null hypothesis as an equality claim.

The form of a null hypothesis is

H_0: population characteristic = hypothesized value

where the hypothesized value is a specific number determined by the problem context. The alternative hypothesis then has one of the following three forms:

H_a: population characteristic > hypothesized value
H_a: population characteristic < hypothesized value
H_a: population characteristic ≠ hypothesized value

Thus we might test H_0: $\pi = .1$ versus H_a: $\pi < .1$; but we will not consider testing H_0: $\mu = 50$ versus H_a: $\mu > 100$. The number appearing in the alternative hypothesis must be identical to the hypothesized value in H_0.

We previously noted that the American and French judicial systems operate from different perspectives when it comes to the initial presumption of innocence or guilt. Similarly, the selection of a null hypothesis—the claim that is initially assumed true—sometimes depends on the viewpoint of the investigator.

EXAMPLE 10.3

A customer is considering the purchase of many components of a certain type from a particular manufacturer and so is concerned about the long-run percentage of defective components. After reflection, the customer decides that 1% is the dividing line between acceptable and unacceptable defective rates. Let π denote the true proportion of this manufacturer's components that are defective. The manufacturer may be the only one currently making this component or may have offered the customer favorable purchase terms. In that case, the customer would want to purchase from this manufacturer unless sample evidence strongly suggests an unacceptable defective rate. It is then sensible to test

H_0: $\pi = .01$ versus H_a: $\pi > .01$

so that the alternative hypothesis is identified with an unacceptable defective percentage.

On the other hand, the customer might wish to place the burden of proof on the manufacturer and require them to show that its defective rate is acceptable. This suggests testing

H_0: $\pi = .01$ versus H_a: $\pi < .01$

with the alternative now stating that the defective rate is acceptable. The purchase from this manufacturer would then not be made unless sample evidence strongly suggested rejecting H_0 in favor of H_a.

Once H_0 and H_a have been formulated, we need a method for using sample data to determine whether H_0 should be rejected. This is accomplished through the use of a **test procedure.** Just as an incorrect verdict may be handed down in a criminal trial, there is some chance that when a test procedure is applied to sample data, the wrong conclusion may be drawn. In the next section, we examine the issue of errors in hypothesis testing.

EXERCISES 10.1–10.10 SECTION 10.1

10.1 Explain why the statement $\bar{x} = 50$ is not a legitimate hypothesis.

10.2 For the following pairs, indicate which don't comply with our rules for setting up hypotheses and explain why:

    a. H_0: $\mu = 15$, H_a: $\mu = 15$ **b.** H_0: $\pi = .4$, H_a: $\pi > .6$

    c. H_0: $\mu = 123$, H_a: $\mu < 123$ **d.** H_0: $\mu = 123$, H_a: $\mu = 125$

    e. H_0: $p = .1$, H_a: $p \neq .1$

10.3 In order to determine whether the pipe welds in a nuclear power plant meet specifications, a random sample of welds is selected, and tests are conducted on each weld in the sample. Weld strength is measured as the force required to break the weld. Suppose that the specifications state that the mean strength of welds should exceed 100 lb/in². The inspection team decides to test H_0: $\mu = 100$ versus H_a: $\mu > 100$. Explain why it might be preferable to use this H_a rather than $\mu < 100$.

10.4 Researchers have postulated that, due to differences in diet, Japanese children have a lower mean blood cholesterol level than U.S. children. Suppose that the mean level for U.S. children is known to be 170. Let μ represent the true mean blood cholesterol level for Japanese children. What hypotheses should the researchers test?

10.5 A certain university has decided to implement plus/minus grading as long as there is evidence that more than 60% of the faculty favor the change. A random sample of faculty will be selected and the resulting data used to test the relevant hypotheses. If π represents the true proportion of all faculty that favor a change to $+/-$ grading, which of the following pair of hypotheses should the administration test?

$$H_0: \pi = .6 \quad \text{versus} \quad H_a: \pi < .6$$

or

$$H_0: \pi = .6 \quad \text{versus} \quad H_a: \pi > .6$$

Explain your choice.

10.6   A large manufacturing plant monitors the proportion of defective items produced. In an effort to reduce this proportion, the plant has implemented a program of statistical quality control (SQC). Assuming that the proportion of defectives before SQC was .01, what hypotheses should the plant managers test to determine if the program has been effective?

10.7   A water-quality control board reports that the water is unsafe for drinking if the mean nitrate concentration exceeds 30 ppm. Water specimens from a well will be analyzed and appropriate hypotheses tested to determine if the well should be closed. If your drinking water comes from this well, what hypotheses would you want the water-quality board to test? Explain.

10.8   A county commissioner must make a decision on a resolution that would commit substantial resources to the construction of a sewer in an outlying residential area. Her fiscal decisions have been criticized in the past and so she decides to take a survey of constituents to find out whether they favor spending money for a sewer system. She will vote to appropriate funds only if she can be fairly certain that a majority of the people in her district favor the measure. What hypotheses should she test?

10.9   Many older homes have electrical systems that use fuses rather than circuit breakers. A manufacturer of 40-A fuses wants to make sure that the mean amperage at which its fuses burn out is in fact 40. If the mean amperage is lower than 40, customers will complain because the fuses require replacement too often. If the mean amperage is higher than 40, the manufacturer might be liable for damage to an electrical system due to fuse malfunction. In order to verify the mean amperage of the fuses, a sample of fuses is to be selected and inspected. If a hypothesis test is to be performed on the resulting data, what null and alternative hypotheses would be of interest to the manufacturer?

10.10   An automobile manufacturer offers a 50,000-mi extended warranty on its new cars. You plan on buying one of these cars and must decide whether to purchase the extended warranty. (The ordinary warranty is for 12,000 mi.) Suppose that a recent magazine article has reported the number of miles at which 30 of this manufacturer's cars first needed repair. This information can be used to conduct a test of hypotheses that will aid you in your decision.
  a. What hypotheses would you test in each of the following two cases?
    i. The extended warranty is very expensive.
    ii. The extended warranty is not very expensive.
  b. Explain your choice of hypotheses in part (a).

10.2 Errors in Hypothesis Testing

Hypothesis testing, like estimation, involves making an inference about a population characteristic. Since inferences are generally based on information from a sample rather than a census, they are subject to error. Before an inferential procedure is employed, it is important to understand the potential errors that might occur and to know something about the likelihood of making such errors.

In reaching a judgment on the innocence or guilt of a defendant in a criminal trial, two different types of errors must be considered. The defendant may be found guilty when in fact he or she is innocent. Alternatively, the defendant may be found innocent even though guilty. Similarly, there are two different types of errors that might be made when making a decision in a hypothesis-testing problem. One type of error involves rejecting H_0 even though H_0 is true. The second type of error results from failing to reject H_0 when it is false.

DEFINITION

The error of rejecting H_0 when H_0 is true is called a **type I error.** The error in which H_0 is not rejected when it is false is called a **type II error.**

No reasonable test procedure comes with a guarantee that neither type of error will be made: this is the price paid for basing an inference on a sample. With any procedure, there is some chance that a type I error will be made, and there is also some chance that a type II error will result.

EXAMPLE 10.4

In the fall of 1987, the U.S. Department of Transportation released information on the proportion of airline flights that were "on time." An on-time arrival is one that arrives within 15 min of its scheduled arrival time (Associated Press, November 11, 1987). Overall, 77% of all September (1987) flights arrived on time. Suppose an airline that performed poorly during September were to offer its employees incentives for improved performance. Monetary rewards will be paid if, in an upcoming month, the airline's proportion of on-time flights exceeds the overall industry rate of .77. Let π be the true proportion of the airline's flights that are on time during the month of interest. A random sample of flights might be selected and used as a basis for choosing between

$$H_0: \pi = .77 \quad \text{and} \quad H_a: \pi > .77$$

In this context, a type I error (rejecting a true H_0) would result in the airline's rewarding its employees when in fact their true proportion of on-time flights did not exceed .77. A type II error (not rejecting a false H_0) would result in the airline employees *not* receiving a reward that in fact they deserved.

EXAMPLE 10.5

(*Example 10.2 continued*) With μ denoting the true mean nicotine content (in mg) for cigarettes of the brand under study, the hypotheses to be tested are

$$H_0: \mu = 1.5 \quad \text{versus} \quad H_a: \mu > 1.5$$

The null hypothesis states that the manufacturer's advertised claim of 1.5 mg is correct. The alternative hypothesis states that the true mean nicotine content exceeds the value claimed by the manufacturer.

In this context, a type I error would mean concluding that μ is greater than 1.5 when in fact it is not. A possible consequence of this type of error is that the manufacturer would be falsely accused of misleading advertising. A type II error would result when the true mean nicotine content in fact exceeds 1.5 but this is not detected, so we fail to reject H_0. A consequence of a type II error is that the manufacturer is allowed to continue advertising a value that understates the true mean nicotine content.

Examples 10.4 and 10.5 illustrate the two different types of error that might occur when testing hypotheses. Note that type I and type II errors, and the associated consequences of making such errors, are quite different.

In choosing a test procedure (a method for deciding whether or not to reject H_0), we would like a small probability of drawing an incorrect conclusion. Some commonly used notation will facilitate a discussion of error probabilities.

DEFINITION

The probability of a type I error is denoted by α and is called the **level of significance** of the test. Thus a test with $\alpha = .01$ is said to have a level of significance of .01, or to be a level .01 test. The probability of a type II error is denoted by β.

EXAMPLE 10.6

A new type of lie detector that measures brain waves has been developed by a professor of neurobiology at Northwestern University (Associated Press, July 7, 1988). He says, "It would probably not falsely accuse any innocent people and it would probably pick up 70% to 90% of guilty people." Suppose that the result of this lie detector was allowed as evidence in a criminal trial and was to be the sole basis of a decision between two rival hypotheses:

H_0: accused is innocent

H_a: accused is guilty

(Note: although these are not "statistical hypotheses" (statements about a population characteristic), this example is useful in the discussion of type I and type II errors.)

In this situation, a type I error would be finding an innocent person guilty—rejecting the null hypothesis of innocence when it was, in fact, true. A type II error would be finding a guilty person innocent—not rejecting the null hypothesis of innocence when it was, in fact, false. If the developer of the lie detector is correct in his statements, the probability of a type I error, α, is approximately 0 and β, the probability of type II error is somewhere between .1 and .3.

The ideal test procedure has both $\alpha = 0$ and $\beta = 0$. However, since we must base our decision on incomplete information—a sample rather than a census—it is impossible to achieve this ideal. The standard test procedures do allow the user to control α, but provide no direct control over β.

Since α represents the probability of rejecting a true null hypothesis, selecting $\alpha = .05$ results in a test procedure that, used over and over with different samples, rejects a true H_0 about five times in a hundred. Selecting $\alpha = .01$ results in a test procedure with a type I error rate of 1% in long-term repeated use. Choosing a small value for α implies that the user wants to employ a procedure for which the risk of a type I error is quite small.

A natural question that arises at this point is the following: If the user can select α, the probability of making a type I error, why would anyone ever select $\alpha = .05$ rather than $\alpha = .01$? Why not always select a very small value for α? In order to achieve a small probability of making a type I error, the corresponding test procedure will require the evidence against H_0 to be very strong before the null hypothesis can be rejected. While this makes a type I error unlikely, it increases the risk of a type II error (*not* rejecting H_0 when it should have been rejected). Therefore, if a type II error has serious consequences, it may be a good idea to select a somewhat larger value for α.

In general, there is a compromise between small α and small β, leading to the following widely accepted principle for specifying a test procedure.

> After thinking about the consequences of type I and type II errors, identify the largest α that is tolerable for the problem. Then employ a test procedure that uses this maximum acceptable value—rather than anything smaller—as the level of significance (because using a smaller α increases β).

Thus if you decide that $\alpha = .05$ is tolerable, you should not use a test with $\alpha = .01$, because the smaller α inevitably results in larger β. The values of α most frequently used in practical problems are .05 and .01 (a 1-in-20 or 1-in-100 chance of rejecting H_0 when it is actually true), but the choice in any given problem depends on the seriousness of a type I error relative to a type II error in that context.

EXAMPLE 10.7

A television manufacturer claims that (at least) 90% of its sets will need no service during the first 3 years of operation. A consumer agency wishes to check this claim, so it obtains a random sample of $n = 100$ purchasers and asks each whether or not the set purchased needed repair during the first three years. Let p be the sample proportion of responses indicating no repair (so that no repair is identified with a success). Let π denote the true proportion of successes. The agency does not want to claim false advertising unless sample evidence strongly suggests that $\pi < .9$. The appropriate hypotheses are then

$$H_0: \pi = .9 \quad \text{versus} \quad H_a: \pi < .9$$

In this context, a type I error consists of saying that the manufacturer's claim is fallacious ($\pi < .9$) when in fact the manufacturer is correct in its claim. A type II error occurs if the manufacturer's claim is incorrect but the consumer agency fails to detect it. Since a type I error has quite serious consequences, the consumer agency may decide that a type I error probability of .01, but no larger, can be tolerated. They would then use a test procedure with $\alpha = .01$.

We are now ready to take a formal look at some general hypothesis-testing procedures. In the remainder of this chapter, we will consider testing hypotheses about either a population mean μ or a population proportion π.

EXERCISES 10.11–10.18   SECTION 10.2

10.11   The National Cancer Institute conducted a 2-year study to determine if cancer death rates for areas near nuclear power plants were higher than for areas without nuclear facilities (*San Luis Obispo Telegram-Tribune*, September 17, 1990). A spokesperson for the Cancer Institute said, "From the data at hand, there was no convincing evidence of any increased risk of death from any of the cancers surveyed due to living near nuclear facilities. However no study can prove the absence of an effect."

a. Let π denote the true proportion of the population in areas near nuclear power plants who die of cancer during a given year. The researchers at the Cancer Institute might have considered the two rival hypotheses of the form

H_0: $\pi =$ value for areas without nuclear facilities

H_a: $\pi >$ value for areas without nuclear facilities

Did the Cancer Institute reject H_0 or fail to reject H_0?

b. If the Cancer Institute was incorrect in its conclusion that there is no increased cancer risk associated with living near a nuclear power plant, would they be making a type I or a type II error? Explain.

c. Comment on the spokesperson's last statement that no study can *prove* the absence of an effect. Do you agree with this statement?

 10.12   A manufacturer of handheld calculators receives very large shipments of printed circuits from a supplier. It is too costly and time-consuming to inspect all incoming circuits, so when each shipment arrives, a sample is selected for inspection. Information from the sample is then used to test H_0: $\pi = .05$ versus H_a: $\pi < .05$, where π is the true proportion of defectives in the shipment. If the null hypothesis is rejected, the shipment is accepted and the circuits are used in the production of calculators. If the null hypothesis cannot be rejected, the entire shipment is returned to the supplier due to inferior quality. (A shipment is defined to be of inferior quality if it contains 5% or more defectives.)

a. In this context, define type I and type II errors.

b. From the calculator manufacturer's point of view, which type of error would be considered more serious?

c. From the printed circuit supplier's point of view, which type of error would be considered more serious?

10.13   Water samples are taken from water used for cooling as it is being discharged from a power plant into a river. It has been determined that as long as the mean temperature of the discharged water is at most 150° F, there will be no negative effects on the river's ecosystem. To investigate whether the plant is in compliance with regulations that prohibit a mean discharge water temperature above 150°, 50 water samples will be taken at randomly selected times, and the temperature of each sample recorded. The resulting data will be used to test the hypotheses

$$H_0: \mu = 150° \quad \text{versus} \quad H_a: \mu > 150°$$

In the context of this example, describe type I and type II errors. Which type of error would you consider to be more serious? Explain.

10.14   The purchasing manager for a large office complex must decide between two competing brands of fluorescent light bulbs. One is the brand currently used in the building and has a mean life of 900 h. The new brand is more expensive, but the manufacturer claims that the mean life exceeds that of the current brand.

a. What hypotheses about μ, the true mean life for the new brand, should the purchasing manager test? Explain your choice.

b. For the hypotheses of part (a), describe type I and type II errors.

10.15   The marketing department for a computer company must determine the selling price for a new model of personal computer. In order to make a reasonable profit, the company would like the computer to sell for $3200. If more than 30% of the potential customers would be willing to pay this price, the company will adopt it. A survey of potential customers is to be carried out; it will include a question asking the maximum amount that the respondent would be willing to pay for a computer with the features of the new model. Let π denote the proportion of all potential customers who would be willing to pay $3200 or more. Then the hypotheses to be tested are

$$H_0: \pi = .3 \quad \text{versus} \quad H_a: \pi > .3$$

In the context of this example, describe type I and type II errors. Discuss the possible consequences of each type of error.

10.16   Occasionally, warning flares of the type contained in most automobile emergency kits fail to ignite. A consumer advocacy group is to investigate a claim against a manufacturer of flares brought by a person who claims that the proportion of defectives is much higher than the value of .1 claimed by the manufacturer. A large number of flares will be tested and the results used to decide between $H_0: \pi = .1$ and $H_a: \pi > .1$, where π represents the true proportion of defectives for flares made by this manufacturer. If H_0 is rejected, charges of false advertising will be filed against the manufacturer.

a. Explain why the alternative hypothesis was chosen to be $H_a: \pi > .1$.

b. In this context, describe type I and type II errors and discuss the consequences of each.

10.17   Suppose that you are an inspector for the Fish and Game Department, and you are given the task of determining whether to prohibit fishing along part of the California coast. You will close an area to fishing if it is determined that fish in that region have an unacceptably high mercury content.

   a. If a mercury concentration of 5 ppm is the maximum considered safe, which pair of hypotheses would you test?

$$H_0: \mu = 5 \quad \text{versus} \quad H_a: \mu > 5$$

or

$$H_0: \mu = 5 \quad \text{versus} \quad H_a: \mu < 5$$

   Give the reasons for your choice.

   b. Would you prefer a significance level of .1 or .01 for your test? Explain.

10.18   An automobile manufacturer is considering using robots for part of its assembly process. Converting to robots is an expensive process, so it will be undertaken only if there is strong evidence that the proportion of defective installations is lower for the robots than for human assemblers. Let π denote the true proportion of defective installations for the robots. It is known that human assemblers have a defect proportion of .02.

   a. Which of the following pairs of hypotheses should the manufacturer test?

$$H_0: \pi = .02 \quad \text{versus} \quad H_a: \pi < .02$$

or

$$H_0: \pi = .02 \quad \text{versus} \quad H_a: \pi > .02$$

   Explain.

   b. In the context of this example, describe type I and type II errors.

   c. Would you prefer a test with $\alpha = .01$ or $\alpha = .1$? Explain your reasoning.

10.3   Large-Sample Hypothesis Tests for a Population Mean

Now that some general concepts of hypothesis testing have been introduced, we are ready to turn our attention to the development of test procedures. A preliminary example will aid in understanding the general method.

EXAMPLE 10.8

The Food and Nutrition Board of the National Academy of Sciences reports that the mean daily sodium intake should not exceed 3300 mg. In a study of sodium intake (*Consumer Reports* (1984):17–22), a sample of U.S. residents was found to have a mean daily sodium intake of 4600 mg. Suppose that this result was based on a sample of size 100 and that the population standard deviation is $\sigma = 1100$ mg. The researchers were interested in determining whether the mean daily sodium intake for U.S. residents exceeded the maximum recommended level.

Let μ represent the true mean sodium intake for all U.S. residents. The hypotheses to be tested are

$$H_0: \mu = 3300 \quad \text{versus} \quad H_a: \mu > 3300$$

The null hypothesis will be rejected only if there is strong evidence indicating that $\mu > 3300$ mg.

Suppose that H_0 is in fact true, so that $\mu = 3300$ mg. Even when this is the case, the sample mean $\bar{x}$ might differ somewhat from 3300 due simply to sampling variability. The researcher's sample resulted in $\bar{x} = 4600$ mg, a value larger than 3300. Is the difference between $\bar{x}$ and 3300 reasonably attributable to chance variation from sample to sample, or is $\bar{x}$ so much larger than 3300 that the only plausible conclusion is that $\mu > 3300$?

This question can be answered by examining the sampling distribution of $\bar{x}$. Since the sample size is large ($n = 100$), if H_0 is true the $\bar{x}$ sampling distribution is approximately normal, with

$$\mu_{\bar{x}} = \mu = 3300$$

and

$$\sigma_{\bar{x}} = \frac{\sigma}{\sqrt{n}} = \frac{1100}{\sqrt{100}}$$

It follows that when H_0 is true, the standardized variable

$$z = \frac{\bar{x} - 3300}{1100/\sqrt{100}}$$

has approximately a standard normal distribution (one described by the standard normal curve). For our sample,

$$z = \frac{4600 - 3300}{1100/\sqrt{100}} = \frac{1300}{110} = 11.82$$

Based on what we know about the standard normal distribution, 11.82 is an extremely unusual value. There are two possible explanations for this. Either H_0 is true and we have seen something incredibly rare (an $\bar{x}$ that is more than 11 standard deviations above what would be expected were H_0 true), or H_0 is false and the reason the observed sample mean is so large is because μ actually exceeds 3300. Because it would be so surprising to see an $\bar{x}$ value as large as 4600 when $\mu = 3300$, the sample provides quite convincing evidence against H_0. The null hypothesis should therefore be rejected.

Suppose that the sample had instead resulted in an $\bar{x}$ value of 3375 mg. Then

$$z = \frac{\bar{x} - 3300}{1100/\sqrt{100}} = \frac{3375 - 3300}{110} = .68$$

If $\mu = 3300$ mg, the observed $\bar{x}$ is less than one standard deviation above what would be expected. This is not an unusual occurrence for a normal random variable, and so the sample results are compatible with H_0. The null hypothesis would not be rejected in this case.

The preceding example illustrates the rationale behind large-sample procedures for testing hypotheses about μ. We begin by assuming that the null hypothesis is true. The sample is then examined in light of this assumption. Either the sample mean has a value that is compatible with H_0 or it has a value much different from what would be expected were H_0 true. Based on this assessment, a decision to reject or fail to reject H_0 can be made.

In the previous example, we calculated

$$z = \frac{\bar{x} - 3300}{1100/\sqrt{n}}$$

and used its value to decide between H_0 and H_a. This z is an example of a *test statistic*. Notice that the value of σ was assumed known. In practice, this is seldom the case. When the sample size is large, the statistic obtained by using s in place of σ still has approximately a standard normal distribution.

A **test statistic** is a quantity calculated from sample data that is used as a basis for reaching a decision in a hypothesis test.

When using a large sample ($n > 30$) to test a null hypothesis of the form

$$H_0\text{: } \mu = \text{hypothesized value}$$

the appropriate test statistic is

$$z = \frac{\bar{x} - \text{hypothesized value}}{s/\sqrt{n}}$$

This test statistic has (approximately) a standard normal distribution when H_0 is true.

As you probably noticed, the two cases examined in Example 10.8 ($z = 11.82$ and $z = .68$) were such that the decision between rejecting or not rejecting H_0 was very clear-cut. A decision in other cases may not be so obvious. For example, what if the sample had resulted in $z = 2.0$? Because the area under the standard normal curve to the right of 2.0 is .0228, a value as large or larger than 2.0 would occur for only about 2.3% of all samples when H_0 is true. Is this unusual enough to warrant rejection of H_0? How extreme must the value of z be before H_0 should be rejected?

This question is answered by specifying what is called a **rejection region.** Then H_0 is rejected if the computed value of the test statistic falls within the rejection region.

The appropriate rejection region for a hypothesis test is determined both by the form of the alternative hypothesis H_a and by the value of α (the probability of a type I error) selected by the person conducting the test. Since the test statistic

$$z = \frac{\bar{x} - \text{hypothesized value}}{s/\sqrt{n}}$$

has (approximately) a standard normal distribution when H_0 is true and n is large, we know how the z statistic will behave in this case. We can then determine which values are consistent with H_0 and which values are quite unusual. This is precisely what is needed for selecting a rejection region.

The alternative hypothesis will contain one of the three inequalities $>$, $<$, or $\neq$. If the alternative is

H_a: $\mu >$ hypothesized value

then H_0 should be rejected in favor of H_a if $\bar{x}$ considerably exceeds the hypothesized value. This is equivalent to rejecting H_0 if the value of z is quite large and positive (a z value far out in the upper tail of the z curve). The desired α is then achieved by using the z critical value that captures an upper-tail z curve area α as the cutoff value for the rejection region. Similarly, if

H_a: $\mu <$ hypothesized value

then H_0 should be rejected if $\bar{x}$ is considerably less than the hypothesized value or, equivalently, if z is too far out in the lower tail of the z curve to be consistent with H_0. In the case

H_a: $\mu \neq$ hypothesized value

rejection of H_0 is appropriate if the computed value of z is too far out in either tail of the z curve. Figure 10.1 (on page 440) illustrates the choice of rejection region for a given α in each case.

The z critical value that determines the boundary of the rejection region can be found by using Appendix Table II (the z curve table) or by using the bottom row of Appendix Table IV. This row contains z critical values corresponding to the most frequently used significance levels and is a little easier to use than Table II.

Suppose, for example, that the null hypothesis is H_0: $\mu = 25$ and that $\alpha = .05$ is specified. If the alternative is H_a: $\mu > 25$, the appropriate test procedure is upper-tailed. We are looking for the z critical value that captures an area of .05 in the upper tail, as illustrated.

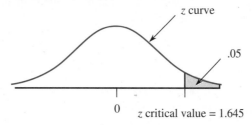

FIGURE 10.1
Alternative hypothesis,
rejection region, and α for a
large-sample z test
(a) Upper-tailed test
(b) Lower-tailed test
(c) Two-tailed test

Alternative Hypothesis

Rejection Region and α = P(type I error)

(a) H_a: μ > hypothesized value

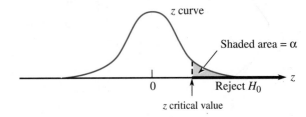

(b) H_a: μ < hypothesized value

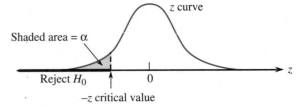

(c) H_a: $\mu \neq$ hypothesized value

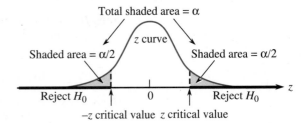

The level α = .05 is then located in the "level of significance for a one-tailed test" row along the bottom margin of Table IV. The desired critical value, 1.645, appears directly above α = .05 in the "z critical value" row. In this case, H_0 will be rejected if z > 1.645 but not otherwise. Similarly, if the alternative is H_a: μ < 25, the test is lower-tailed and, therefore, one-tailed, so for α = .05 the same critical value, 1.645, is used. Here H_0 will be rejected if z < -1.645.

A two-tailed rejection region would be used for testing H_0: μ = 25 versus H_a: $\mu \neq 25$. The correct critical value for this test when α = .05 is not 1.645 because, as illustrated, the value .05 must be divided equally between the two tails, giving an area of .025 for each tail.

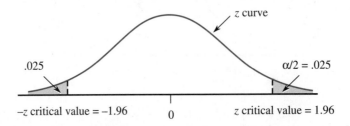

The critical value capturing an upper-tail z curve area of .025 is then identified. This is accomplished by entering the "level of significance for a two-tailed test" row along the bottom margin of Table IV, moving over to $\alpha = .05$, and looking directly above to the corresponding entry in the "z critical value" row. The resulting z critical value is 1.96, so H_0 will be rejected in favor of H_a: $\mu \neq 25$ either if $z > 1.96$ or if $z < -1.96$.

Once the inequality in H_a is identified and a value of α selected, the appropriate rejection region can be specified. Procedures for large-sample tests of hypotheses about a population mean are summarized in the accompanying box.

SUMMARY OF LARGE-SAMPLE z TESTS FOR μ

Null hypothesis: H_0: μ = hypothesized value

Test statistic: $z = \dfrac{\bar{x} - \text{hypothesized value}}{s/\sqrt{n}}$

Alternative Hypothesis	**Rejection Region**
H_a: $\mu >$ hypothesized value	Reject H_0 if $z > z$ critical value (upper-tailed test)
H_a: $\mu <$ hypothesized value	Reject H_0 if $z < -z$ critical value (lower-tailed test)
H_a: $\mu \neq$ hypothesized value	Reject H_0 if either $z > z$ critical value or $z < -z$ critical value (two-tailed test)

The z critical value in the rejection region is determined by the desired level of significance α. The bottom row of Appendix Table IV contains critical values corresponding to the most frequently used significance levels. These test procedures are valid without any restriction on the shape of the population distribution as long as n is large (the usual rule of thumb is $n > 30$).

EXAMPLE 10.9

In recent years, a substantial amount of research has focused on possible relationships between chemical contamination of various sorts and mental retardation. The article "Increased Lead Burdens and Trace-Mineral Status in Mentally Retarded Children" (*J. of Special Educ.* (1982):87–89) reported data on hair-lead concentration for a sample of mentally retarded children for which the cause of retardation was unknown. Summary quantities were

$$n = 40 \qquad \bar{x} = 15.90 \text{ ppm} \qquad s = 8.40 \text{ ppm}$$

The paper states that 15 ppm is considered the acceptable upper limit of hair-lead concentration. Does the given sample data support the research hypothesis that true average hair-lead concentration for all such mentally retarded children exceeds the acceptable upper limit?

In answering this type of question, it is helpful to proceed in an organized manner by following a fixed sequence of steps.

1. Population characteristic of interest: μ = the average hair-lead concentration for all mentally retarded children with the cause of retardation unknown.
2. Null hypothesis: $H_0: \mu = 15$
3. Alternative hypothesis: $H_a: \mu > 15$
4. Test statistic: $z = \dfrac{\bar{x} - 15}{s/\sqrt{n}}$

5. Rejection region: The inequality in H_a is >, so the test is upper-tailed with rejection region $z > z$ critical value. Using $\alpha = .01$ for the level of significance, Table IV yields the critical value 2.33. Then H_0 will be rejected in favor of H_a if $z > 2.33$ and not rejected otherwise.
6. Computations: The values of n, $\bar{x}$, and s are provided. Thus

$$z = \frac{15.90 - 15}{8.40/\sqrt{40}} = \frac{.90}{1.33} = .68$$

7. Conclusion: Since .68 is less than 2.33, the computed value of z does not fall into the rejection region. At level of significance .01, the hypothesis H_0 is not rejected. The data does not provide support for concluding that true average hair-lead concentration exceeds 15 ppm. A reasonable explanation for the observed difference between $\bar{x} = 15.9$ and the hypothesized value 15 is sampling variation.

We recommend that the sequence of steps illustrated in Example 10.9 be used in any hypothesis-testing analysis.

STEPS IN A HYPOTHESIS-TESTING ANALYSIS

1. Describe the population characteristic about which hypotheses are to be tested.
2. State the null hypothesis, H_0.
3. State the alternative hypothesis, H_a.
4. Display the test statistic to be used, with substitution of the hypothesized value identified in step 2 but *without* any computation at this point.
5. Identify the rejection region. This is accomplished by first using the inequality in H_a to determine whether an upper, lower, or two-tailed test is appropriate and then going to an appropriate table to obtain the critical value corresponding to the selected level of significance α.

(continued)

6. Compute all quantities appearing in the test statistic; then compute the value of the test statistic itself.
7. State the conclusion (which will be to reject H_0 if the value of the test statistic falls in the rejection region and not to reject H_0 otherwise). The conclusion should be stated in the context of the problem, and the level of significance used should be included.

Steps 1–3 constitute a statement of the problem, steps 4 and 5 state how the conclusion will be reached, and steps 6 and 7 give the analysis and conclusion.

EXAMPLE 10.10

Almost every student has experienced some degree of test anxiety at one time or another. The authors of the paper "Cultural and Sexual Differences in Test Anxiety, Trait Anxiety and Arousability" (*J. Cross-Cultural Psychology* (1991):238–249) hypothesized that students in countries where high-school testing had important consequences in terms of future opportunities (such as Egypt) would experience a greater level of test anxiety than do students in the United States. Test-anxiety scores were recorded for a sample of Egyptian high school students. For this sample,

$$n = 277 \qquad \bar{x} = 50.0 \qquad s = 12.7$$

For U.S. high school students, the mean test anxiety score is thought to be 41. Does the sample data support the researcher's theory? We will answer this question by carrying out a hypothesis test using a .05 level of significance.

1. μ = true mean test anxiety score for Egyptian high school students
2. H_0: $\mu = 41$
3. H_a: $\mu > 41$ (the mean for Egyptian students is higher than the U.S. value)

4. Test statistic: $\quad z = \dfrac{\bar{x} - 41}{s/\sqrt{n}}$

5. Because $>$ appears in the alternative hypothesis, an upper-tailed rejection region is used. For $\alpha = .05$, the appropriate one-tailed critical value (from Table II or from the z critical value row of Table IV) is 1.645. Therefore, we will reject H_0 if $z > 1.645$.
6. $n = 277, \bar{x} = 50.0$, and $s = 12.7$, so

$$z = \frac{50 - 41}{12.7/\sqrt{277}} = \frac{9}{.763} = 11.80$$

7. Since $11.80 > 1.645$, H_0 is rejected at the .05 level of significance. We conclude that the mean test-anxiety score for Egyptian high school students is higher than 41 (the mean for U.S. students). This provides support for the author's theory.

EXAMPLE 10.11

Speed, size, and strength are thought to be important factors in football performance. The paper "Physical and Performance Characteristics of NCAA Division I Football Players" (*Research Quarterly for Exercise and Sport* (1990):395–401) reported on physical characteristics of division I starting football players in the 1988 football season. Information for teams ranked in the top 20 was easily obtained, and it was reported that the mean weight of starters on top 20 teams was 105 kg. A sample of 33 starting players (various positions were represented) from division I teams that were not ranked in the top 20 resulted in a sample mean weight of 103.3 kg and a sample standard deviation of 16.3 kg. Is there sufficient evidence to conclude that the mean weight for non–top 20 starters is less than 105, the known value for top 20 teams?

The relevant hypotheses will be tested using a .01 level of significance.

1. μ = true mean weight of starters on teams that are not ranked in the top 20
2. $H_0: \mu = 105$
3. $H_a: \mu < 105$

4. Test statistic: $z = \dfrac{\bar{x} - 105}{s/\sqrt{n}}$

5. The alternative hypothesis uses $<$, so the test is a lower-tailed test. With $\alpha = .01$, the appropriate z critical value is -2.33, and so we will reject H_0 if $z < -2.33$.
6. $n = 33, \bar{x} = 103.3$, and $s = 16.3$, so

$$z = \frac{103.3 - 105}{16.3/\sqrt{33}} = \frac{-1.7}{2.838} = -.60$$

7. Since $-.60 \not< -2.33$, we fail to reject H_0. There is not sufficient evidence to conclude that the mean weight of non–top 20 starters is below that of top 20 teams.

Statistical versus Practical Significance

Carrying out a test amounts to deciding whether the value obtained for the test statistic could plausibly have resulted when H_0 is true. If the value doesn't deviate too much from what is expected when H_0 is true, there is no compelling reason for rejecting H_0 in favor of H_a. But suppose that the observed value is quite far out in the appropriate tail of the test statistic's sampling distribution when H_0 is true (for example, a large positive value of z when H_a contains the inequality $>$). One could continue to believe that H_0 is true and that such a value arose just through chance variation (a very unusual and "unrepresentative" sample). However, in this case a more plausible explanation for what was observed is that H_0 is false and H_a is true.

When the value of the test statistic falls in the rejection region, it is customary to say that the result is **statistically significant** at the chosen level α. The finding of statistical significance means that, in the investigator's opinion, the observed deviation from what was expected under H_0 cannot plausibly be attributed just to chance variation. Unfortunately, though, statistical significance cannot be equated with the conclusion that the true situation differs from what H_0 states in any practical sense. That is, even after H_0 has been rejected, the data may suggest that there is no *practical* difference between the true value of the population characteristic and what the null hypothesis states that value to be.

EXAMPLE 10.12

Let μ denote the true average IQ for children in a certain region of the United States. The average IQ for all children in the U.S. is 100. Education authorities are interested in testing

$$H_0: \mu = 100 \quad \text{versus} \quad H_a: \mu > 100$$

Using a significance level of $\alpha = .001$, the hypothesis H_0 will be rejected if $z > 3.09$. A sample of 2500 children resulted in the values

$$n = 2500 \qquad \bar{x} = 101.0 \qquad s = 15.0$$

Then

$$z = \frac{101.0 - 100}{15/\sqrt{2500}} = 3.33$$

Because $3.33 > 3.09$, we reject H_0. The true average IQ for this region does appear to exceed 100.

However, with $n = 2500$, the point estimate $\bar{x} = 101.0$ is almost surely very close to the true value of μ. So, it looks as though H_0 was rejected because $\mu \approx 101$ rather than 100. And, from a practical point of view, a 1-point IQ difference has no significance. So the statistically significant result does not have any practical consequences.

EXERCISES 10.19–10.35   SECTION 10.3

10.19   Let μ denote the true average amount of surface area in square feet covered by 1 gal of a particular oil-based paint. A researcher wishes to test the pair of hypotheses $H_0: \mu = 400$ versus $H_a: \mu > 400$ using a sample size of 50. Give the appropriate test statistic and rejection region for each of the given significance levels.
   a. .01   **b.** .05   **c.** .10   **d.** .13

10.20   A sample of size 75 is to be used to decide between the hypotheses $H_0: \mu = 14$ and $H_a: \mu \neq 14$, where μ is the true average filled weight in ounces for containers coming off a certain production line. Give the test statistic and rejection region associated with each of the given significance levels.

a. .05   **b.** .01   **c.** .10   **d.** .24

10.21   A scale for rating a politician's image solicits responses from -5 (very negative) to 5 (very positive). Let μ denote the true average image rating of a particular politician. A large-sample z statistic is to be used to test the hypotheses H_0: $\mu = 0$ versus H_a: $\mu < 0$. Determine the appropriate rejection region for each of the given significance levels.

a. .01   **b.** .05   **c.** .10

10.22   The desired percentage of silicon dioxide in a certain type of cement is 5.5. A random sample of $n = 36$ specimens gave a sample average percentage of $\bar{x} = 5.21$ and a sample standard deviation of $s = .38$. Let $\mu =$ the true average percentage of silicon dioxide in this type of cement. Test H_0: $\mu = 5$ versus H_a: $\mu \neq 5$ using a significance level of .01.

10.23   A coating designed to retard corrosion is applied to 35 metal bars. These bars are buried in soil for a specified time, and the maximum penetration (in mils) is then determined. The resulting summary data is $\bar{x} = 52.7$ and $s = 4.8$. Let μ denote the true average maximum penetration, and test H_0: $\mu = 50$ versus H_a: $\mu > 50$, using $\alpha = .05$.

10.24   The Environmental Protection Agency sets limits on the maximum allowable concentration of certain chemicals in drinking water. For the substance PCB, the limit has been set at 5 ppm. A random sample of 36 water specimens from the same well results in a sample mean PCB concentration of 4.82 ppm and sample standard deviation of .6 ppm.

a. Is there sufficient evidence to substantiate the claim that the well water is safe? Use a .01 level of significance.

b. Would you recommend using a significance level greater than .01? Why or why not?

10.25   Are young women delaying marriage and marrying at a later age? This question was addressed in a report issued by the U.S. Bureau of the Census (Associated Press, June 8, 1991). The report stated that in 1970 (based on census results) the mean age of brides marrying for the first time was 20.8 years. In 1990 (based on a sample, since census results were not yet available) the mean was 23.9. Suppose that the 1990 sample mean had been based on a sample of size 100 and that the sample standard deviation was 6.4. Is there sufficient evidence to support the claim that women are now marrying later in life? Test the relevant hypotheses using $\alpha = .01$. (Note: It is probably not reasonable to think that the distribution of age at first marriage is normal in shape.)

10.26   A certain type of brick is being considered for use in a particular construction project. It is decided that the brick will be used unless sample evidence strongly suggests that the true average compressive strength is below 3200 lb/in.^{2} A random sample of 36 bricks is selected and each is subjected to a compressive strength test. The resulting sample average compressive strength and the sample standard deviation of compressive strength are 3109 lb/in.^{2} and 156 lb/in.^{2}, respectively. State the relevant hypotheses and carry out a test to reach a decision using level of significance .05.

10.27   An automobile manufacturer recommends that any purchaser of one of its new cars bring it in to a dealer for a 3000-mi checkup. The company wishes to know whether the true average mileage at this initial servicing differs from 3000. A random sample of 50 recent purchasers resulted in a sample average mileage of 3208 mi and a sample standard deviation of 273 mi. Does the data strongly suggest that the true average mileage for this checkup is something other than the value recommended by the company? State and test the relevant hypotheses, using a level of significance of .01.

10.28 The paper "Undergraduate Marijuana Use and Anger" (*J. of Psych.* (1988): 343–347) reported that the mean and standard deviation on an anger expression scale were $\bar{x} = 42.72$ and $s = 6.05$, respectively, for a sample of $n = 47$ frequent marijuana users. Suppose that the population mean score for nonusers is 41.5.

a. Does the data indicate that frequent users have a mean anger expression score that is higher than for nonusers? State and test the relevant hypotheses using $\alpha = .05$.

b. Describe type I and type II errors for the hypotheses tested in part (a).

10.29 Data resulting from a study on white rabbit fertility appears in the paper "Genetic Analysis of Litter Traits in Bauscat and Giza White Rabbits" (*Animal Production* (1987):123–134). For the Giza white rabbit, a sample of 59 litters resulted in a mean litter weight of 1888 g and a standard deviation of 99 g. Does this data provide sufficient evidence to conclude that the true mean litter weight is less than 2000 g? Use a test with $\alpha = .05$.

10.30 Forty-eight 7-year-old children who were reading at below grade level were asked to read a passage aloud. The number of corrections and omissions were noted. ("Strategies Used in the Early Stages of Learning to Read: A Comparison of Children and Adults," *Educ. Research* (1987):83–93). The sample mean number of corrections and omissions was 17.68. Suppose that the sample also resulted in a standard deviation of 4.2.

a. If the population mean number of corrections and omissions for children who are reading at grade level is 19.9, does the data provide sufficient evidence that the mean number of corrections and omissions for children who are reading below grade level is different from 19.9? Carry out a test using a significance level of .01.

b. Would your conclusion have been different if a significance level of .05 had been used?

10.31 Each plant in a sample of 79 soybean plants grown in a particular soil type was analyzed to determine an iron-deficiency score ("Evaluation of Soybean Genotypes for Iron-Deficiency Chlorosis in Potted Calcareous Soil," *Crop Sci.* (1987): 953–957). The resulting sample mean and standard deviation were 4.2 and .6, respectively. Is there sufficient evidence to indicate that the iron-deficiency score for all soybean plants grown in this soil type exceeds 4.0? Use $\alpha = .01$.

10.32 The chemical Permethrin has been recommended as a way of controlling insects on plant leaves. One study on the effectiveness of Permethrin was summarized in the paper "Evaluation of Nonlethal Side Effects of Permethrin Used in Predator Exclusion Experiments" (*Environ. Entomol.* (1987):1012–1018). An inspection of 96 plants resulted in a mean of 7.2 insects per plant, with a standard deviation of 6.3.

a. Is there sufficient evidence to indicate that the true mean number of insects per plant is less than 8? Use $\alpha = .05$.

b. Would your conclusion in part (a) have been different if a significance level of .01 had been used?

10.33   Minor surgery on horses under field conditions requires a reliable short-term an-esthetic producing good muscle relaxation, minimal cardiovascular and respiratory changes, and a quick, smooth recovery with minimal aftereffects so that horses can be left unattended. The article "A Field Trial of Ketamine Anesthesia in the Horse" (*Equine Vet. J.* (1984):176–179) reported that for a sample of $n = 73$ horses to which ketamine was administered under certain conditions, the sample average lateral recumbency (lying-down) time was 18.86 min and the standard deviation was 8.6 min. Does this data suggest that true average lateral recumbency time under these conditions is less than 20 min? Use the seven-step procedure to test the appropriate hypotheses at level of significance .10.

10.34   One of the biggest problems facing researchers who must solicit survey data by mail is that of nonresponse. One method that has been proposed as a way of increas-ing both the response rate and the quality of responses is to offer a monetary incentive for returning a questionnaire. The paper "The Effect of Monetary In-ducement on Mailed Questionnaire Response Quality" (*J. of Marketing Research* (1980):265–268) examines some of these issues. One hypothesis of interest to the researchers was that providing a cash incentive for completing a survey would lead to fewer questions left unanswered. An appliance warranty questionnaire contain-ing 17 questions that had been used extensively was mailed to people who had purchased a major appliance during the previous year. A $.25 payment was in-cluded with each questionnaire. In the past, when no money was included with the survey, the mean number of questions left unanswered on returned forms was 1.38. In this experiment, 174 surveys were returned and the number of unanswered questions was determined for each one. The resulting sample mean was .81. Sup-pose that the sample standard deviation was 1.8. Using a level .01 test, can you conclude that including $.25 with each survey results in a mean number of unan-swered questions that is smaller than 1.38?

10.35   To check a manufacturer's claim that its audio tapes have an average playing time of at least 90 min, 900 tapes are randomly selected and timed. These yield a sample average playing time of 89.95 min and a sample standard deviation of .3 min. Does the data refute the manufacturer's claim? Comment on the statistical and practical significance of this result.

10.4   *P*-Values

One way to report the result of a hypothesis test is to simply say whether or not the null hypothesis was rejected at a specified level of significance. Thus an investiga-tor might state that H_0 was rejected at level of significance .05 or that use of a significance level of .01 resulted in failure to reject H_0. This type of statement is somewhat inadequate because nothing is said about whether the computed value of the test statistic just barely fell into the rejection region or whether it exceeded the critical value by a very large amount. A related difficulty is that such a report imposes the specified significance level on other decision makers. There are many decision situations in which individuals might have different views concerning the consequences of type I and type II errors. Each individual would then want to select his or her own personal significance level—some selecting $\alpha = .05$, others .01, and so on—and reach a conclusion accordingly. This could result in some individuals rejecting H_0, whereas others might conclude that the evidence against H_0 is not sufficient to justify its rejection.

EXAMPLE 10.13

The true average time to the initial relief of pain for the current best-selling pain reliever is known to be 10 min. Let μ denote the true average time to relief for a company's newly developed pain reliever. The company wishes to produce and market this product only if it provides quicker relief than does the current best seller, so it wishes to test

$$H_0: \mu = 10 \quad \text{versus } H_a: \mu < 10.$$

Only if experimental evidence leads to rejection of H_0 will the new pain reliever be introduced. After weighing the relative seriousness of the two types of errors, a single level of significance must be agreed upon and a decision—to reject H_0 and introduce the pain reliever or not to do so—must be made at that level.

Now suppose that the new product has been introduced. The company supports its claim of quicker relief by stating, based on an analysis of experimental data, that $H_0: \mu = 10$ was rejected in favor of $H_a: \mu < 10$, using a level of significance of $\alpha = .10$. Any particular individual contemplating a switch to this new pain reliever would naturally want to reach his or her own conclusion concerning the validity of the claim. Individuals who are satisfied with the current best seller would view a type I error (concluding that the new product provides quicker relief when it actually doesn't) as serious, so they might wish to use $\alpha = .05, .01$, or an even smaller level. Unfortunately, the nature of the company's statement prevents an individual decision maker from reaching a conclusion at such a level. The company has imposed its own choice of significance level on others. The report could have been done in a manner that allowed each individual flexibility in drawing a conclusion at a personally selected α.

A more informative way to report the result of a test is to give the *P*-value associated with the test. A *P*-value conveys a great deal of information about the strength of the evidence against H_0 and allows an individual decision maker to draw a conclusion at any specified level α. Before giving a general definition, consider how the conclusion in a hypothesis-testing problem depends on the selected α.

EXAMPLE 10.14

The nicotine-content problem discussed in Example 10.2 involved testing

$$H_0: \mu = 1.5 \quad \text{versus} \quad H_a: \mu > 1.5$$

The rejection region was upper-tailed, with H_0 rejected if $z > z$ critical value. Suppose that $z = 2.10$. The accompanying table displays the rejection region for each of four different values of α along with the resulting conclusion.

Level of significance α	Rejection region	Conclusion for $z = 2.10$
.05	$z > 1.645$	Reject H_0
.025	$z > 1.96$	Reject H_0
.01	$z > 2.33$	Don't reject H_0
.005	$z > 2.58$	Don't reject H_0

For α relatively large, the z critical value is not very far out in the upper tail; 2.10 exceeds the critical value, and so H_0 is rejected. However, as α decreases, the critical value increases. For small α the z critical value is large; 2.10 does not exceed it, and H_0 is not rejected.

Recall that for an upper-tailed z test, α is just the area under the z curve to the right of the critical value. That is, once α is specified, the critical value is chosen to capture upper-tail area α. Table II shows that the area to the right of 2.10 is .0179. Using an α larger than .0179 would result in a z critical value that is smaller than 2.10, so 2.10 would fall into the rejection region. An α less than .0179 would not result in rejection, since the corresponding z critical value is larger than 2.10.

FIGURE 10.2
Relationship between α and tail area captured by computed z
(a) Tail area captured by computed z
(b) When $\alpha > .0179$, z critical value < 2.10 and H_0 is rejected
(c) When $\alpha < .0179$, z critical value > 2.10 and H_0 is not rejected

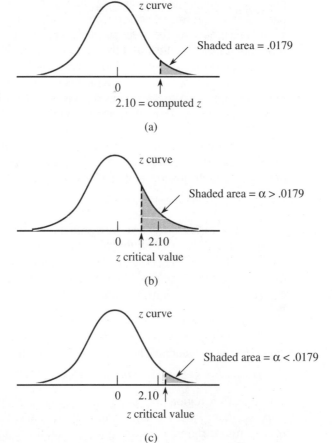

The decision at a particular level α thus depends on how the selected α compares to the tail area captured by the computed z. This is illustrated in Figure 10.2. Notice in particular that .0179, the captured tail area, is the smallest level α at which H_0 can be rejected, because using any smaller α results in a z critical value that exceeds 2.10, so that 2.10 is then not in the rejection region.

In general, suppose that the sampling distribution of a test statistic has been determined when H_0 is true. Then for a specified α, the rejection region is determined by finding a critical value or values that capture a tail area of α (upper-, lower-, or two-tailed, whichever is appropriate) under the sampling distribution curve. The smallest α for which H_0 could be rejected is determined by the tail area captured by the computed value of the test statistic. This smallest α is the *P*-value.

DEFINITION

The ***P*-value** is the smallest level of significance at which H_0 can be rejected. Once the *P*-value has been determined, the conclusion at any particular level α results from comparing the *P*-value to α:

1. If *P*-value $\leq \alpha$, then reject H_0 at level α.
2. If *P*-value $> \alpha$, then do not reject H_0 at level α.

For most statistical computer packages, the *P*-value is the way in which the result of a hypothesis-testing analysis is reported.

EXAMPLE 10.15

Let μ denote the true average stopping distance in feet of a particular type of car under certain specified conditions. An investigator tested

$$H_0: \mu = 125 \quad \text{versus} \quad H_a: \mu < 125$$

and reported that the *P*-value $= .0372$. What conclusion is appropriate at significance level .01? By the definition of the *P*-value, the *smallest* α at which H_0 can be rejected is .0372; any smaller α results in H_0 not being rejected. Since $\alpha = .01$ is smaller than the *P*-value, H_0 shouldn't be rejected.

Calculating the *P*-Value for a *z* Test

With the aid of Table II the (approximate) *P*-value can be calculated for any z test (not only for the large-sample z test concerning μ discussed in Section 10.3 but also others presented in later sections and chapters). The test of Example 10.14 is upper-tailed, so the *P*-value is the area captured under the z curve to the right of the computed value of z. If the test had been lower-tailed, the *P*-value would have been the area under the z curve to the left of the computed z (the lower-tail area). For a two-tailed test, finding the area captured in the tail in which z falls—for example, the upper tail when $z = 2.43$ or the lower tail when $z = -.92$—determines $\alpha/2$ (because α is the sum of the upper- and lower-tail areas). In this case the P-value is twice the captured area. This is summarized in the accompanying box.

TYPE OF z TEST	P-VALUE
Upper-tailed	Area under the z curve to the right of computed z
Lower-tailed	Area under the z curve to the left of computed z
Two-tailed	Twice the area captured in the tail determined by the computed z

EXAMPLE 10.16

Suppose that a z test for testing

$$H_0: \mu = 10 \quad \text{versus} \quad H_a: \mu < 10$$

results in the value $z = -1.49$. Since this is a lower-tail test, the associated P-value is the area under the standard normal curve and to the left of -1.49. From Table II, the desired area is .0681. This is illustrated in the accompanying picture. Therefore, the P-value $= .0681$. At significance level .10, the hypothesis H_0 will be rejected (since $.0681 < .10$), but rejection of H_0 is not justified at significance level .05.

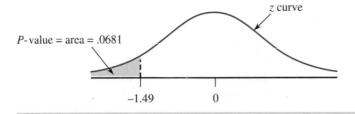

P-value = area = .0681

z curve

-1.49 0

The P-value can be used to carry out a hypothesis test. In the seven-step procedure previously employed, the appropriate test statistic was selected, a rejection region was identified, and then a conclusion was reached by determining whether the computed value of the test statistic fell into the rejection region. When using P-values, it is not necessary to set up a rejection region, since our decision will be based on comparing the P-value to α. After selecting a test statistic, we calculate the value of the test statistic and then obtain the associated P-value.

EXAMPLE 10.17

The mean systolic blood pressure for white males aged 35–44 in the United States is 127.2. The paper "Blood Pressure in a Population of Diabetic Persons Diagnosed after 30 Years of Age" (*Amer. J. of Public Health* (1984):336–339) reports that the mean blood pressure and standard deviation of a sample of 101 diabetic males aged 35–44 are 130 and 8, respectively. The researchers were interested in determining whether the mean systolic blood pressure of 35–44-year-old diabetic males differed from that of 35–44-year-old males in the general population. A significance level of .01 was selected. The analysis again proceeds via a sequence of steps.

1. Let μ denote the true mean systolic blood pressure for diabetic males aged 35–44.
2. H_0: $\mu = 127.2$
3. H_a: $\mu \neq 127.2$
4. Test statistic: $z = \dfrac{\bar{x} - 127.2}{s/\sqrt{n}}$
5. Calculations:

$$z = \frac{130 - 127.2}{8/\sqrt{101}} = \frac{2.80}{.796} = 3.52$$

6. Determination of the *P*-value: From Table II, the area under the *z* curve and to the right of 3.52 is .0002. Since this is a two-tailed test,

   P-value = 2(.0002) = .0004. $= .01$

7. Conclusion: The null hypothesis will be rejected at significance level .01 (since the *P*-value is smaller than the significance level).

There is sufficient evidence to conclude that the mean systolic blood pressure of 35–44-year-old diabetic males differs from that of 35–44-year-old males in the general population.

EXERCISES 10.36–10.45   SECTION 10.4

10.36 For which of the given *P*-values will the null hypothesis be rejected when performing a level .05 test?
   a. .001   **b.** .021   **c.** .078   **d.** .047   **e.** .148

10.37 Pairs of *P*-values and significance levels, α, are given. For each pair, state whether the observed *P*-value will lead to rejection of H_0 at the given significance level.
   a. *P*-value = .084, α = .05   **b.** *P*-value = .003, α = .001
   c. *P*-value = .498, α = .05   **d.** *P*-value = .084, α = .10
   e. *P*-value = .039, α = .01   **f.** *P*-value = .218, α = .10

10.38   Let μ denote the true average reaction time to a certain stimulus. For a large-sample z test of H_0: $\mu = 5$ versus H_a: $\mu > 5$, find the P-value associated with each of the given values of the test statistic.
   a. 1.4   **b.** .9   **c.** 1.9   **d.** 2.4   **e.** −.1

10.39   Newly purchased automobile tires of a certain type are supposed to be filled to a pressure of 30 lb/in.^{2} Let μ denote the true average pressure. Find the P-value associated with each given z statistic value for testing H_0: $\mu = 30$ versus H_a: $\mu \neq 30$.
   a. 2.1   **b.** −1.7   **c.** −.5   **d.** 1.4   **e.** −5

10.40   To assess the impact of quality circles (groups of employees who meet to discuss issues related to product quality) on employee job satisfaction, the authors of the paper "Consequences of Quality Circles in an Industrial Setting: A Longitudinal Assessment" (*Academy Mgmt. J.* (1988):338–358) studied 73 employees who were participating in quality circles. The mean job satisfaction score for this sample was 3.18 and the standard deviation was .99. Suppose that the mean score on this scale for all workers is known to be 3.12. (This is consistent with values given in the paper.)
   a. What hypotheses should be tested if the researcher wants to determine whether the mean job satisfaction score for employees participating in quality circles is higher than that of the general working population?
   b. Can the large-sample z test be used to test the hypotheses in part (a)?
   c. What is the value of the test statistic for this data?
   d. Find the P-value associated with the value of the test statistic computed in part (c).
   e. Will H_0 be rejected if a significance level of .05 is selected?
   f. Would the conclusion in part (e) have been different for a significance level of .01? Of .10?

10.41   A soda manufacturer is interested in determining whether its bottling machine tends to overfill. Each bottle is supposed to contain 12 oz of fluid. A random sample of size 36 is taken from bottles coming off the production line, and the contents of each bottle is carefully measured. It is found that the mean amount of soda for the sample of bottles is 12.1 oz and the sample standard deviation is .2 oz. The manufacturer will use this information to test H_0: $\mu = 12$ versus H_a: $\mu > 12$.
   a. What value does the z test statistic take for this data?
   b. Find the P-value associated with the value of z computed in part (a).
   c. If the manufacturer decides on a level .05 test, should H_0 be rejected in favor of the conclusion that the machine is overfilling?

10.42   A sample of 40 speedometers of a particular brand is obtained and each is checked for accuracy at 55 mi/h. The resulting sample average and sample standard deviation are 53.8 and 1.3, respectively. Let μ denote the true average reading when the actual speed is 55 mi/h. Compute a P-value and use it and a significance level of .01 to decide whether the sample evidence strongly suggests that μ is not 55.

10.43   The drying time of a particular brand and type of paint is known to have a mean of 75 min. In an attempt to improve drying time, a new additive has been developed. Use of the additive in 100 test samples of the paint yields an observed mean drying time of 68.5 min and a standard deviation of 9.4 min. Using a significance level of .01, does the experimental evidence indicate that the additive improves (shortens) drying time? Use a P-value to conduct your test.

10.44   The national mean cholesterol level is approximately 210 (*Science 84* (April 1984):16). Each person in a group of men with unusually high cholesterol levels (over 265) was treated with a new drug, cholestyramine. After taking the drug for a given length of time, cholesterol determinations were made. Suppose that 100 men participated in the study. After treatment with the drug, the mean cholesterol level for the 100 men was 228 and the sample standard deviation was 12. Let μ denote the average cholesterol level for all men taking the drug. One question of interest is whether men taking the drug still have a mean cholesterol level that exceeds the national average. Compute the *P*-value for this data. If a .05 significance level is chosen, what conclusion would you draw?

10.45   Student reading skills have long been a major focus of concern in the education community. The article "Can an Advance Organizer Technique Compensate for Poor Reading Performance?" (*J. of Exptl. Educ.* (Summer 1986):217–222) reported on one study of reading comprehension. A random sample of 100 students was selected, and each was shown an "organizer" (an introduction to orient students to the nature of the test material) prior to taking a test. The resulting sample mean test score was 32.96 and the sample standard deviation was 9.24. Suppose that through long experience with this test, it is known that the true average score without an organizer is 32. Does this data suggest that preliminary exposure to an organizer increases the true average score on this test?

   a.   Use a significance level of .05 to test the appropriate hypothesis.

   b.   Determine the *P*-value for the test of part (a), and then indicate for which significance levels the null hypothesis would be rejected.

10.5 Small-Sample Hypothesis Tests for the Mean of a Normal Population

The large-sample procedures for testing hypotheses about a population mean μ can be used without having to make any specific assumptions about the population distribution. However, the Central Limit Theorem, which provided the justification for large-sample tests, is not valid when n is small. As with confidence intervals, one way to proceed is to make a specific assumption about the nature of the population distribution and then to develop testing procedures that are valid in this more specialized situation. Here we shall restrict consideration to the case of a normal population distribution. The result on which a test procedure is based is then the same as the one we used in the previous chapter to obtain a t confidence interval.

When $x_1, x_2, \ldots, x_n$ constitute a random sample of size n from a normal distribution, the probability distribution of the standardized variable

$$t = \frac{\bar{x} - \mu}{s/\sqrt{n}}$$

is the t distribution with $n - 1$ df.

The null hypothesis is stated just as it was for the large-sample test concerning μ:

$H_0: \mu =$ hypothesized value

When H_0 is true, replacing μ by the hypothesized value gives a test statistic with a sampling distribution that is known (t with $n - 1$ df). A rejection region corresponding to the desired significance level is then obtained by using the appropriate t critical value from the $n - 1$ df row of Appendix Table IV.

SUMMARY OF t TEST FOR THE MEAN OF A NORMAL POPULATION

Null hypothesis: $H_0: \mu =$ hypothesized value

Test statistic: $t = \dfrac{\bar{x} - \text{hypothesized value}}{s/\sqrt{n}}$

Alternative Hypothesis	Rejection Region
$H_a: \mu >$ hypothesized value	Reject H_0 if $t > t$ critical value (upper-tailed test)
$H_a: \mu <$ hypothesized value	Reject H_0 if $t < -t$ critical value (lower-tailed test)
$H_a: \mu \neq$ hypothesized value	Reject H_0 if either $t > t$ critical value or $t < -t$ critical value (two-tailed test)

The t critical value in the rejection region is based on $n - 1$ degrees of freedom and is determined by the desired level of significance. Table IV contains one-tailed and two-tailed critical values corresponding to the most frequently used significance levels.

The test statistic here is the same as the large-sample z statistic of Section 10.3. It is labeled t to emphasize that it has a t distribution when H_0 is true, rather than the z distribution.

EXAMPLE 10.18

The low population density of the Amazon region has long puzzled geographers and other social scientists. Some have suggested that environmental conditions are inimical to support of a large population. The paper "Anthrosols and Human Carrying Capacity in Amazonia" (*Annals of the Assoc. of Amer. Geog.* (1980):553–566) suggests otherwise. The author's case for this viewpoint rests largely on an analysis of black-earth soil samples, which gives evidence of the presence of large and sedentary Indian populations prior to the European influx. The accompanying stem-and-leaf display gives pH values for the 29 black-earth soil samples discussed in the paper. (pH is a numerical measure of acidity and is related to availability of soil nutrients.) Does this data indicate that true average black-earth pH differs from 5.0, the pH value for many other types of soil in the region? The display gives evidence of a somewhat skewed distribution (confirmed by a normal probability plot) and the largest value, 7.9, is a mild outlier. However, $n = 29$ is close to the sample size required for the large-sample z test, which requires no specific assumption about the pH distribution, so it seems safe to use the t test here. Let's state and test the relevant hypotheses at a level of significance of .05.

4L	.2 .3
4H	.5 .6 .6 .6 .6 .6 .6 .9
5L	.3 .3 .3 .4 .4 .4
5H	.5 .5 .5 .6 .6 .6 .7 .9 .9
6L	.1 .2
6H	
7L	.0
7H	.9

1. μ = the true average black-earth soil pH in Amazonia
2. H_0: $\mu = 5.0$
3. H_a: $\mu \neq 5.0$ ($\neq$ because of the phrase *differs from*, which indicates a departure from H_0 in either direction)
4. Test statistic:

$$t = \frac{\bar{x} - 5.0}{s/\sqrt{n}}$$

5. Rejection region: Reject H_0 if either $t > t$ critical value or $t < -t$ critical value. Because the test is two-tailed, first locate .05 in the two-tailed significance level row along the bottom margin of Table IV. Moving up that column to the $n - 1$ = 28 df row gives critical value 2.05, so H_0 will be rejected if either $t > 2.05$ or $t < -2.05$.
6. $\Sigma x = 155.6$ and $\Sigma(x - \bar{x})^2 = 18.23$ (either from the deviations or by using the computational formula $\Sigma x^2 - (\Sigma x)^2/n$). Thus

$$\bar{x} = 155.6/29 = 5.37$$
$$s^2 = 18.23/28 = .651$$

so $s = .807$. The computed value of t is

$$t = \frac{5.37 - 5.0}{.807/\sqrt{29}} = \frac{.37}{.150} = 2.47$$

7. The value $t = 2.47$ is in the upper tail of the rejection region ($2.47 > 2.05$) so H_0 is rejected at level .05. The true average pH of black-earth soil does appear to be something other than 5.0.

EXAMPLE 10.19

Extensive data collected during the first half of this century showed clearly that in those years, American-born Japanese children grew faster than did Japanese-born Japanese children. A research paper "Do American-Born Japanese Children Still Grow Faster than Native Japanese?" *Amer. J. of Phys. Anthro.* (1975):187–194) conjectured that improved economic and environmental conditions in postwar Japan had greatly narrowed this gap. To investigate the validity of this conjecture, a large sample of Hawaiian-born Japanese children was obtained, and the children were categorized with respect to age. There were thirteen 11-year-old boys in the sample (most of the children sampled were older). The sample average height of these 13 boys was 146.3 cm and the sample standard deviation was 6.92 cm. The average height of native-born 11-year-old Japanese children at that time was known to be 139.7 cm. Does this data suggest that the true average height for Hawaiian-born male 11-year-olds exceeds that for their native-born counterparts? The investigators were willing to assume that the population height distribution was normal. The relevant hypotheses can then be tested using a t test with level of significance .01. The steps in the analysis are as follows.

1. μ = true average height for all Hawaiian-born 11-year-old male Japanese children
2. H_0: $\mu = 139.7$
3. H_a: $\mu > 139.7$
4. Test statistic: $t = \dfrac{\bar{x} - 139.7}{s/\sqrt{n}}$

5. Rejection region: because the inequality in H_a is $>$, an upper-tailed test is appropriate. The hypothesis H_0 should be rejected in favor of H_a if $t > t$ critical value. With df $= n - 1 = 13 - 1 = 12$, moving along the bottom margin of Table IV to one-tailed level of significance .01 and up to the 12 df row gives a t critical value of 2.68. The rejection region is therefore $t > 2.68$.

6. With $n = 13$, $\bar{x} = 146.3$, and $s = 6.92$, the computed value of t is

$$t = \frac{146.3 - 139.7}{6.92/\sqrt{13}} = \frac{6.60}{1.92} = 3.44$$

7. Since 3.44 is in the rejection region ($3.44 > 2.68$), at level of significance .01 we reject H_0 in favor of H_a. It seems clear that at this age, the average height of Hawaiian-born Japanese children exceeds that of their native-born counterparts.

Although the growth differential at age 11 appears to be substantial, analysis of data on older children suggests that the gap narrows considerably.

Strictly speaking, the validity of the one-sample t test requires that the population distribution be normal. In practice, the test can be used even when the population distribution is somewhat nonnormal as long as n is not too small. Statisticians say that the test is "robust" to mild departures from normality, by which they mean that error probabilities are still approximately what they would be in the case of a normal population distribution.

P-Values for *t* Tests

Table II can be used to compute the *P*-values for *z* tests. However, because Table IV gives only limited information on *t* distributions, the best that we can typically do (unless $t \approx t$ critical value) is to establish an upper and/or lower bound on the *P*-value for a *t* test. The procedure for doing this is summarized in the accompanying box.

PROCEDURE FOR CALCULATING BOUNDS ON THE *P*-VALUE FOR A *t* TEST

When the test is two-tailed, upper-tailed and *t* is positive, or lower-tailed and *t* is negative, bounds on the associated *P*-value are computed as follows.

1. Locate the row of Table IV corresponding to the df associated with the test.
2. Look across this row to determine where the computed value of *t* (or $|t|$ if *t* is negative) falls relative to the critical values.
3. Determine the bounds for the *P*-value by referring to one of the two *level of significance rows* at the bottom of the table, depending on whether the test is one- or two-tailed.
   a. If the computed *t* falls between two critical values in the table, the *P*-value will be between the corresponding levels of significance.
   b. If the computed *t* exceeds the largest critical value in the row, then the *P*-value is smaller than the level of significance for the largest critical value in the row.
   c. If the computed *t* is smaller than the smallest critical value in the row, then the *P*-value is larger than the significance level associated with the smallest critical value in the row.

The *P*-value is greater than .5 if the computed value of *t* is negative for an upper-tailed test or positive for a lower-tailed test.

Suppose, for example, that $t = 2.25$ for a two-tailed test based on 20 df. Table IV shows that

$$2.09 < 2.25 < 2.53$$

where 2.09 is the *t* critical value for a test with $\alpha = .05$ and 2.53 is used for $\alpha = .02$. The *P*-value then satisfies

$$.02 < P\text{-value} < .05$$

If instead $t = 4.37$, then since the largest critical value in the 20 df row is 3.85, corresponding to $\alpha = .001$, we have

$$P\text{-value} < .001$$

This would also be the case for $t = -4.37$.

EXAMPLE 10.20

Federal officials have investigated the problems associated with disposal of hazardous wastes. One disposal site is the abandoned Stringfellow acid pits in Riverside County, Calif. The EPA sampled water from 11 wells in nearby Glen Avon (*Los Angeles Times,* May 31, 1984). The EPA standard for maximum allowable radiation level of drinking water is 15pCi/L. Suppose that the sample of 11 water specimens resulted in a sample mean radiation level of 22.5pCi/L and a sample standard deviation of 8. Is this sufficient evidence to indicate that the water in Glen Avon has a mean radiation level that exceeds the EPA standard?

1. Let μ denote the true mean radiation level for well water in Glen Avon.
2. $H_0: \mu = 15$
3. $H_a: \mu > 15$
4. Test statistic: $t = \dfrac{\bar{x} - 15}{s/\sqrt{n}}$
5. Computations:

$$t = \frac{22.5 - 15}{8/\sqrt{11}} = \frac{7.5}{2.4} = 3.125$$

6. Determination of the *P*-value: Since the sample size is 11, df $= 10$. Looking in the 10 df row of Table IV, we find that

$$2.76 < 3.125 < 3.17$$

where 2.76 is the critical value associated with a one-tailed significance level of .01 and 3.17 is the critical value associated with significance level .005. Therefore,

$$.005 < P\text{-value} < .01$$

7. Conclusion: The null hypothesis will be rejected if $\alpha = .01$ or larger. It will not be rejected if $\alpha = .005$ or smaller.

Although our *t* table, like *t* tables in all other texts, limits us to bounds on the *P*-value, almost any good statistical computer package is programmed to calculate the *P*-value resulting from a *t* test. With this information, the *t* table is unnecessary—a conclusion can be drawn simply by comparing the *P*-value to the selected level of significance.

EXAMPLE 10.21

An automobile manufacturer who wishes to advertise that one of its models achieves 30 mi/gal decides to carry out a fuel efficiency test. Six nonprofessional drivers are selected and each one drives a car from Phoenix to Los Angeles. The resulting miles-per-gallon figures are

$$x_1 = 27.2, \qquad x_2 = 29.3, \qquad x_3 = 31.2$$
$$x_4 = 28.4, \qquad x_5 = 30.3, \qquad x_6 = 29.6$$

Assuming that fuel efficiency (mi/gal) is normally distributed under these circumstances, does the data contradict the claim that true average fuel efficiency is (at least) 30?

With μ denoting true average fuel efficiency, the hypotheses of interest are

$$H_0: \mu = 30 \quad \text{versus} \quad H_a: \mu < 30$$

The alternative statement is the contradiction of prior belief. We used MINITAB to perform a t test; the output is given here. ("SE MEAN" denotes the standard error of the mean, which is $s/\sqrt{n} = .57$.)

```
TEST OF MU = 30.0 VS MU L.T. 30.0

N     MEAN    STDEV    SE MEAN        T    P VALUE
6     29.33    1.41      0.57     -1.16      0.15
```

The P-value is .15, the smallest level at which H_0 can be rejected. Thus, even at level of significance .10, the hypothesis H_0 cannot be rejected ($\alpha < P$-value). The data does not contradict the prior belief.

EXERCISES 10.46–10.59   SECTION 10.5

10.46 Let μ denote the true average surface area covered by 1 gal of a certain paint. The hypothesis $H_0: \mu = 400$ is to be tested against $H_a: \mu > 400$. Assuming that paint coverage is normally distributed, give the appropriate test statistic and rejection region for each given sample size and significance level.
   a. $n = 10$, $\alpha = .05$ b. $n = 18$, $\alpha = .01$
   c. $n = 25$, $\alpha = .001$ d. $n = 50$, $\alpha = .10$

10.47 Suppose that, at a certain store, the amount of air pressure (lb/in.^{2}) in new tires of a particular type is normally distributed with mean value μ. For testing $H_0: \mu = 30$ versus $H_a: \mu \neq 30$, give the test statistic and rejection region for each sample size and significance level listed in Exercise 10.46.

10.48 The National Bureau of Standards previously reported the value of selenium content in orchard leaves to be .08 ppm. The paper entitled "A Neutron Activation Method for Determining Submicrogram Selenium in Forage Grasses" (*Soil Sci. Amer. J.* (1975):57–60) reported the following selenium content for five determinations:

.072   .073   .080   .078   .088

   a. What assumption about the selenium content distribution must you be willing to make in order to use a t test for testing $H_0: \mu = .08$ versus $H_a: \mu \neq .08$?
   b. Use a t test at level .01 to test the hypotheses stated in part (a).

10.49   The times of first sprinkler activation (s) for a series of tests of fire-prevention sprinkler systems that use an aqueous film-forming foam were

27   41   22   27   23   35   30   33   24   27   28   22   24

("Use of AFFF in Sprinkler Systems," *Fire Tech.* (1976):5). The system has been designed so that the true average activation time is supposed to be at most 25 s. Does the data strongly indicate that the design specifications have not been met? Test the relevant hypotheses using a significance level of .05. What assumption are you making about the distribution of activation times?

10.50   The paper "Distinguishing the Dimensions of Valence and Belief Consistency in Depressive and Nondepressive Information Processing" (*Cognitive Therapy and Research* (1988):391–407) reported that the mean and standard deviation of scores on a self-image scale for 13 clinically depressed women were 28.63 and 13.61, respectively.

   a. Suppose that the mean score for nondepressed women is 28.0. What hypotheses would you test to determine whether the mean score for depressed women differs from 28.0?

   b. Assuming that the self-image score distribution is approximately normal, use a significance level of .01 to test the hypotheses in part (a).

   c. In the context of this problem, describe type I and type II errors.

10.51   The paper "Orchard Floor Management Utilizing Soil-Applied Coal Dust for Frost Protection" (*Agric. and Forest Meteorology* (1988):71–82) reported the following values for soil heat flux of eight plots covered with coal dust.

34.7   35.4   34.7   37.7   32.5   28.0   18.4   24.9

The mean soil heat flux for plots covered only with grass is 29.0. Assuming that the heat flux distribution is approximately normal, does the data suggest that the coal dust is effective in increasing the mean heat flux over that for grass? Test the appropriate hypotheses using a .05 significance level.

10.52   A new method for measuring phosphorus levels in soil is described in the paper "A Rapid Method to Determine Total Phosphorus in Soils" (*Soil Sci. Amer. J.* (1988):1301–1304). Suppose a sample of 11 soil specimens, each with a true phosphorus content of 548 mg/kg, is analyzed using the new method. The resulting sample mean and standard deviation for phosphorus level are 587 and 10, respectively.

   a. Is there evidence that the mean phosphorus level reported by the new method differs significantly from the true value of 548 mg/kg? Use $\alpha = .05$.

   b. What assumptions must you make in order for the test in part (a) to be appropriate?

10.53   A number of veterinary procedures on pigs require the use of a general anesthetic. To evaluate the effects of a certain anesthetic, it was administered to four pigs and various bodily functions were measured. ("Xylazine-Ketamine-Oxymorphone: An Injectable Anesthetic Combination in Swine," *J. of Amer. Vet. Med. Assoc.* (1984):182–184). Average normal heart rate for pigs is considered to be 114 beats per minute. The heart rates for the four pigs under anesthesia were 116, 85, 118, and 118 beats/min. Use a level .10 test to determine whether the anesthetic results in a mean heart rate that differs significantly from the mean normal heart rate.

10.54   A certain type of soil was determined to have a natural mean pH of 8.75. The authors of the paper "Effects of Brewery Effluent on Agricultural Soil and Crop Plants" (*Environ. Pollution* (1984):341–351) treated soil samples with various dilutions of an acidic effluent. The mean and standard deviation of the five pH measurements were 8.00 and .05, respectively. Does this data indicate that at this concentration, the effluent results in a mean pH that is lower than the natural pH of the soil? Use a level .01 test.

10.55   Much concern has been expressed in recent years regarding the practice of using nitrates as meat preservatives. In one study involving possible effects of these chemicals, bacteria cultures were grown in a medium containing nitrates. The rate of uptake of radio-labeled amino acid was then determined for each one, yielding the accompanying observations.

7251	6871	9632	6866	9094	5849	8957	7978
7468	7064	7494	7883	8178	7523	8724	

Suppose it is known that true average uptake for cultures without nitrates is 8000. Does the data suggest that the addition of nitrates results in a decrease in true average uptake? Test the appropriate hypotheses using a significance level of .10. Be sure to state any assumptions that are necessary to validate the use of your test.

10.56   A researcher collected data in order to test H_0: $\mu = 17$ versus H_a: $\mu > 17$. Place bounds on the P-value for each of the given t test statistic values and associated degrees of freedom.
   a. $t = 1.84$, df $= 14$ **b.** $t = 3.74$, df $= 25$
   c. $t = 2.42$, df $= 13$ **d.** $t = 1.32$, df $= 8$
   e. $t = 2.67$, df $= 45$

10.57   Place bounds on the P-value for a two-tailed t test for each case.
   a. $t = 2.3$, df $= 6$ **b.** $t = -3.0$, df $= 14$
   c. $t = 4.2$, df $= 24$ **d.** $t = -1.3$, df $= 17$

10.58   One method for straightening wire prior to coiling it to make a spring is called "roller straightening." The paper "The Effect of Roller and Spinner Wire Straightening on Coiling Performance and Wire Properties" (*Springs* (1987):27–28) reported on the tensile properties of wire. Suppose that a sample of 16 wires is selected and each is tested to determine tensile strength (N/mm^2). The resulting sample mean and standard deviation are 2160 and 30, respectively.
   a. The mean tensile strength for springs made using spinner straightening is 2150 N/mm^2. What hypotheses should be tested to determine if the mean tensile strength for the roller method exceeds 2150?
   b. Assuming that the tensile strength distribution is approximately normal, what test statistic would you use to test the hypotheses in part (a)?
   c. What is the value of the test statistic for this data?
   d. Place bounds on the P-value associated with the value of the test statistic computed in part (c).
   e. For a level .05 test, what conclusion would you reach?

10.59 The accompanying times (s) to first sprinkler activation were first presented in Exercise 10.49.

| 27 | 41 | 22 | 27 | 23 | 35 | 30 | 33 | 24 | 27 | 28 | 22 | 24 |

(See "Use of AFFF in Sprinkler Systems," *Fire Tech.* (1976):5). The system has been designed so that the true average activation time is supposed to be at most 25 s. Does the data strongly indicate that the design specifications have not been met? Answer by computing bounds on the *P*-value. Use $\alpha = .01$.

10.6 Large-Sample Hypothesis Tests for a Population Proportion

Let π denote the proportion of individuals or objects in a specified population that possess a certain property. A random sample of n individuals or objects is to be selected from the population. The sample proportion

$$p = \frac{\text{number that possess property}}{n}$$

is the natural statistic for making inferences about π.

Consider testing hypotheses about π. The null hypothesis will be of the form

$$H_0: \pi = \text{hypothesized value}$$

and the alternative hypothesis will be similar, but with the $=$ in H_0 replaced by $>$, $<$, or $\neq$. For example, we might want to test

$$H_0: \pi = .25 \quad \text{versus} \quad H_a: \pi < .25$$

The rationale used to construct a test procedure is similar to that used in the previous sections. If H_0 is true and the sample size is large enough, the sampling distribution of p is approximately normal, with mean

$$\mu_p = \pi = \text{hypothesized value}$$

and standard deviation

$$\sigma_p = \sqrt{\frac{\pi(1 - \pi)}{n}}$$

$$= \sqrt{\frac{(\text{hypothesized value})(1 - \text{hypothesized value})}{n}}$$

In this case,

$$z = \frac{p - \text{hypothesized value}}{\sqrt{(\text{hypothesized value})(1 - \text{hypothesized value})/n}}$$

has approximately a standard normal distribution.

This z variable serves as the test statistic. Once a significance level α is selected, a rejection region can be determined. The nature of the rejection region —upper-tailed, lower-tailed, or two-tailed—depends on which of the three inequalities $>$, $<$, or $\neq$ (respectively) appears in H_a.

SUMMARY OF LARGE-SAMPLE z TESTS FOR π

Null hypothesis: $H_0: \pi = $ hypothesized value

Test statistic: $z = \dfrac{p - \text{hypothesized value}}{\sqrt{(\text{hypoth. value})(1 - \text{hypoth. value})/n}}$

Alternative Hypothesis	**Rejection Region**
$H_a: \pi > $ hypothesized value	Reject H_0 if $z > z$ critical value (upper-tailed test)
$H_a: \pi < $ hypothesized value	Reject H_0 if $z < -z$ critical value (lower-tailed test)
$H_a: \pi \neq $ hypothesized value	Reject H_0 if either $z > z$ critical value or $z < -z$ critical value (two-tailed test)

The z critical values corresponding to the most frequently used levels of significance appear in the bottom row of Appendix Table IV.

This test can be used if n satisfies both

$n(\text{hypothesized value}) \geq 5$ and

$n(1 - \text{hypothesized value}) \geq 5$

EXAMPLE 10.22

The article "Statistical Evidence of Discrimination" (*J. of Amer. Stat. Assoc.* (1982):773–783) discussed the court case *Swain v. Alabama* (1965), in which it was alleged that there was discrimination against blacks in grand jury selection. Census data suggested that 25% of those eligible for grand jury service were black, yet a random sample of 1050 individuals called to appear for possible duty yielded only 177 blacks. Using a level .01 test, does this data support a conclusion of discrimination?

1. The population characteristic of interest here is $\pi =$ the true proportion of all those called for possible grand jury service who are black.
2. $H_0: \pi = .25$
3. $H_a: \pi < .25$ (discrimination exists)
4. Since

$$n \cdot (\text{hypothesized value}) = 1050(.25) \geq 5$$
$$n \cdot (1 - \text{hypothesized value}) = 1050(.75) \geq 5$$

the large-sample test is appropriate. The test statistic is

$$z = \frac{(p - .25)}{\sqrt{(.25)(.75)/n}}$$

5. The inequality in H_a implies the use of a lower-tailed test, with H_0 rejected if $z < -z$ critical value. From the bottom row of Table IV, z critical value $= 2.33$ for a one-tailed, level .01 test. The rejection region is then $z < -2.33$.
6. The denominator of z is

$$\sqrt{\frac{(.25)(.75)}{1050}} = .0134$$

and

$$p = \frac{177}{1050} = .169$$

so

$$z = \frac{.169 - .250}{.0134} = \frac{-.081}{.0134} = -6.04$$

7. Since $-6.04 < -2.33$, the hypothesis H_0 is rejected at level .01. Evidence of discrimination seems very clear. Unfortunately, the court looked only at the numerator difference, $-.081$, rather than at z itself. In the court's view, the difference was not large enough to establish a *prima facie* (without further examination) case.

EXAMPLE 10.23

Environmental problems associated with leaded gasolines are well known. Many motorists have tampered with their cars' emission-control devices in order to save money by purchasing leaded rather than unleaded gas. A *Los Angeles Times* article (March 17, 1984) reported that 15% of all California motorists have engaged in such tampering. Suppose that after obtaining a random sample of 200 cars from one particular California county, the emission-control devices of 21 of them are found to have been modified. Does this suggest that the proportion of cars in this county with tampered devices differs from the statewide proportion? We will use a test with a significance level of .05.

1. π = the proportion of cars in this county with modified emission-control devices
2. H_0: π = .15
3. H_a: $\pi \neq$ .15
4. Since $(200)(.15) \geq 5$ and $(200)(.85) \geq 5$, the z test can be used. The test statistic is

$$z = \frac{(p - .15)}{\sqrt{(.15)(.85)/n}}$$

5. Table IV shows that the critical value for a two-tailed level .05 test is 1.96, so H_0 will be rejected if either $z > 1.96$ or $z < -1.96$.

6. $\sqrt{(.15)(.85)/200}$ = .0252 and p = 21/200 = .105, so

$$z = \frac{(.105 - .15)}{.0252} = \frac{-.045}{.0252} = -1.79$$

7. Since -1.79 is neither greater than 1.96 nor less than -1.96, the hypothesis H_0 cannot be rejected at level .05. The data does not suggest that the proportion of cars in this county having modified devices differs from the statewide proportion.

P-values for the z tests of this section are calculated in the same way as the earlier z tests concerning μ.

EXAMPLE 10.24

A woman who smokes during pregnancy increases health risks to the infant. ("Understanding the Intentions of Pregnant Nullipara to Not Smoke Cigarettes after Childbirth," *J. of Drug Educ.* (1988):115–120). Suppose that a sample of 300 pregnant women who smoked prior to pregnancy contained 51 who quit smoking during pregnancy. (This is consistent with summary data given in the paper.) Does this data support the theory that fewer than 25% of female smokers quit smoking during pregnancy? We will compute a P-value and use a significance level of .05 to reach a decision.

1. π = true proportion of female smokers who quit smoking during pregnancy
2. H_0: π = .25
3. H_a: $\pi <$ .25
4. Test statistic: $z = \dfrac{p - .25}{\sqrt{\dfrac{(.25)(.75)}{n}}}$

5. $p = \dfrac{51}{300} = .17$

so

$$z = \frac{.17 - .25}{\sqrt{\dfrac{(.25)(.75)}{300}}} = \frac{-.08}{.025} = -3.2$$

6. Since H_a indicates a lower-tail test, the P-value is the area under the z curve and to the left of -3.2. From Appendix Table II, this area is .0007, as illustrated.

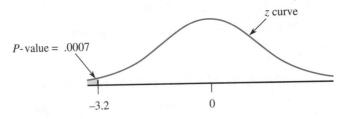

7. Since the P-value is smaller than the selected α, the null hypothesis is rejected, and we conclude that fewer than 25% of female smokers quit smoking while pregnant.

EXERCISES 10.60–10.74   SECTION 10.6

10.60 For which of the following null hypotheses H_0 and sample sizes n is the large-sample z test appropriate?
   a. $H_0: \pi = .2, n = 25$ **b.** $H_0: \pi = .6, n = 10$
   c. $H_0: \pi = .9, n = 100$ **d.** $H_0: \pi = .05, n = 75$

10.61 A pizza parlor is considering replacing its oven with a new one. The new oven is particularly suited to baking large (16-in.) pizzas. Let π denote the proportion of all pizzas ordered that are large. A random sample of $n = 150$ pizza orders yielded 120 that were large. Test $H_0: \pi = .75$ versus $H_a: \pi > .75$ using a significance level of .10.

10.62 A new edition of a certain textbook has been sent to 8000 faculty across the country for examination. Let π denote the proportion of these books that are sold to a book-buyer. (Such sales are a serious problem for publishers and authors.) If a random sample of 100 faculty members yields 28 who sold their examination copies, test $H_0: \pi = .40$ versus $H_a: \pi < .40$, using $\alpha = .05$.

10.63 A telephone company is trying to decide whether some new lines in a large community should be installed underground. Because a small surcharge will have to be added to telephone bills to pay for the extra installation costs, the company has decided to survey customers and proceed only if the survey strongly indicates that more than 60% of all customers favor underground installation. If 118 of 160 customers surveyed favor underground installation in spite of the surcharge, what should the company do? Test using a significance level of .05.

10.64 Duck hunting in populated areas faces opposition on the basis of safety and environmental issues. The *San Luis Obispo Telegram-Tribune* (June 18, 1991) reported the results of a survey to assess public opinion regarding duck hunting on Morro Bay (located along the central coast of California). A sample of 750 local residents included 560 who strongly opposed hunting on the bay. Does this sample provide sufficient evidence to conclude that the majority of local residents oppose hunting on Morro Bay? Test the relevant hypotheses using $\alpha = .01$.

10.65 Drug testing of job applicants is becoming increasingly more common. The Associated Press (May 24, 1990) reported that 12.1% of those tested in California tested positive. Suppose that this figure had been based on a sample of size 600, with 73 testing positive. Does this sample support a claim that more than 10% of job applicants in California test positive for drug use?

10.66 The incidence of a certain type of chromosome defect in the U.S. adult male population is believed to be 1 in 80. A random sample of 600 individuals in U.S. penal institutions revealed 12 men who have such defects. Can it be concluded that the incidence rate of this defect among prisoners differs from the presumed rate for the entire adult male population? State and test the relevant hypotheses using $\alpha = .05$. What type of error might you have made in reaching a conclusion?

10.67 Airport security checks were the subject of an Associated Press report (*San Luis Obispo Telegram-Tribune*, October 23, 1987). Tests were conducted in 1986–87. FAA officials tried to sneak concealed weapons through airport security checks at 136 different airports. Of 2419 attempts, 496 resulted in nondetection. Is there sufficient evidence to indicate that the proportion of weapons that would not be detected by airport security is greater than .15? Use a significance level of .01.

10.68 Many consumers are turning to generics as a way of reducing the cost of prescription medications. The paper "Commercial Information on Drugs: Confusing to the Physician?" (*J. of Drug Issues* (1988):245–257) gave the results of a survey of 102 doctors. Only 47 of those surveyed knew the generic name for the drug methadone. Does this data support the hypothesis that fewer than half of all physicians know the generic name for methadone? Test the appropriate hypotheses using a .01 significance level.

10.69 The *Los Angeles Times* (December 11, 1984) reported that 32% of all adult Americans have attended at least one year of college. Suppose that a random sample of 200 adults in the western United States included 82 with one or more years of college. (This is consistent with summary values reported.) Does this data support the assertion that a higher proportion of westerners (as compared to the United States as a whole) have attended at least one year of college? Test the appropriate hypotheses using a significance level of .01.

10.70 How do young people make decisions? This question was examined in the paper "Decision Making and Young People" (*J. of Drug Educ.* (1988):109–113). Each person in a random sample of 216 seventh graders was asked whether they agreed with the statement, "It is best for me to do the first thing that comes into my mind." A total of 107 agreed with that statement. Based on this information, would you conclude that the true proportion of seventh graders who think it best to do the first thing that comes to mind is different from .5? Test the relevant hypotheses, using $\alpha = .05$.

10.71   A statewide health-care poll revealed that 484 of 1008 Californians surveyed felt that their lives contain a great deal of stress ("Poll: Laid-Back Californians Also Get Stressed, Depressed," Associated Press, March 29, 1988). Is there sufficient evidence to conclude that fewer than half of all Californians feel that their life is stressful? Use $\alpha = .05$.

10.72   The psychological impact of subliminal advertising has been the subject of much speculation. To decide whether people believe that the use of subliminal advertising is ethical, the authors of the paper "Public Perceptions of Subliminal Advertising" (*J. of Adver.* (January 1984):40–44) conducted a survey of 145 residents of Washington, D.C. Of those surveyed, 58 felt that the use of subliminal advertising was acceptable. Does this data provide sufficient evidence to conclude that fewer than half of Washington's residents find subliminal advertising acceptable? Use a level .05 test.

10.73   A U.S. House of Representatives subcommittee has been hearing testimony on a possible link between problem pregnancies and working with video display terminals (VDTs). A survey of United Airlines employees who work full-time on VDTs found that of 48 pregnancies, 15 resulted in miscarriage (*Los Angeles Times*, March 11, 1984). According to the March of Dimes, there is a 10% miscarriage rate for the general population.
    a. Does the data strongly indicate that the miscarriage rate of women who work full-time on VDTs is higher than that of the general female population? Use a level .01 test.
    b. On the basis of your work in part (a), can it be concluded that full-time work on VDTs tends to *cause* miscarriages? Explain.

10.74   Is it appropriate for a physician to help a gravely ill person die? In a survey of 588 doctors, 365 responded that it was sometimes right to agree to hasten a patient's death ("Hemlock Poll: Doctors Favor Mercy Killing," Associated Press, February 19, 1988). Based on this information, would you conclude that more than 60% of all doctors feel it is sometimes appropriate to help a seriously ill person die?
    a. Test the relevant hypotheses using a .01 level of significance.
    b. Would your conclusion have been different if a significance level of .05 had been employed?

10.7   Type II Error Probabilities for Selected Tests (Optional)

The test procedures presented in this chapter are designed to control the probability of a type I error (rejecting H_0 when H_0 is true) at the desired level α. However, little has been said so far about β, the probability of a type II error (not rejecting H_0 when H_0 is false). Remember that to control α, we needed to know the sampling distribution of the test statistic when H_0 is true. This allowed us to select a critical value to capture tail area α under the sampling distribution curve. Computation of β is more difficult than determination of α because the sampling distribution of a test statistic when H_0 is false is usually substantially more complicated than when H_0 is true. Fortunately, statisticians have managed to surmount these difficulties in the case of some commonly used test procedures. Here we consider the determination of β for the hypothesis tests introduced in this chapter.

When we carry out a hypothesis test, we specify the desired value of α, the probability of a type I error. The probability of a type II error, β, is the probability of not rejecting H_0, even though it is false. Suppose we are testing

$$H_0: \mu = 1.5 \quad \text{versus} \quad H_a: \mu > 1.5$$

If H_0 is true, $\mu = 1.5$ and we know that the $\bar{x}$ distribution is centered at 1.5. This enables us to set up a rejection region that will result in the desired probability of incorrect rejection of H_0 (α). On the other hand, if H_0 is false, we know that $\mu > 1.5$. The value of β, the probability of nonrejection of H_0, depends on the actual value of μ. If μ is only slightly larger than 1.5, it is likely that the observed $\bar{x}$ value will be near 1.5 and that we will not interpret its value as one that should lead us to reject $H_0: \mu = 1.5$. In this case, the value of β is probably quite large. If the true value of μ is much larger than 1.5, the value of $\bar{x}$ will probably be enough larger than 1.5 that we would not mistake the sample as one from a population with $\mu = 1.5$. It would be unlikely that a type II error would occur and β would be small. Since we don't know the true value of μ (if we did, we wouldn't be carrying out the hypothesis test!) we can't calculate the actual value of β. However, we can get some idea of the magnitude of β by determining what the value would have been for several different alternative possibilities for μ. We might, for example, determine the value of β in the case of $\mu = 1.55$ and also in the cases $\mu = 1.6$ and $\mu = 1.65$. The following example illustrates this process.

EXAMPLE 10.25

(*Example 10.2 continued*) A cigarette manufacturer claims that the mean nicotine content of its cigarettes is 1.5 mg. In Example 10.2, we proposed investigating this claim by testing the hypotheses

$$H_0: \mu = 1.5 \quad \text{versus} \quad H_a: \mu > 1.5$$

where μ = true mean nicotine content. A random sample of $n = 36$ cigarettes is to be selected and the resulting data used to reach a conclusion. Suppose that the standard deviation of nicotine content (σ) is known to be approximately .20 mg and that a significance level of .01 is to be used.

The significance level of .01 and the fact that H_a indicates an upper-tailed test leads to the rejection region $z > 2.33$. Our test statistic is (since $\sigma = .20$)

$$z = \frac{\bar{x} - 1.5}{.20/\sqrt{n}} = \frac{\bar{x} - 1.5}{.20/\sqrt{36}} = \frac{\bar{x} - 1.5}{.0333}$$

The rejection region $z > 2.33$ is then equivalent to

$$\frac{\bar{x} - 1.5}{.0333} > 2.33$$

which can be rewritten as

$$\bar{x} > 1.5 + 2.33(.0333)$$

or

$$\bar{x} > 1.578$$

So, if $\bar{x} > 1.578$, we will reject H_0, and if $\bar{x} \leq 1.578$, we will fail to reject H_0. This decision rule corresponds to $\alpha = .01$ and gives us a .01 probability of rejecting H_0 when it is true (a type I error).

Let's now investigate the chance of making a type II error. Suppose that $\mu = 1.6$. Then H_0 is false, and the correct decision would be to reject H_0. If we fail to reject H_0, which happens if we see an $\bar{x}$ value that is 1.578 or smaller, we would be making a type II error. What is the probability that this occurs? If $\mu = 1.6$, the $\bar{x}$ distribution is approximately normal, centered at 1.6, and has a standard deviation of .0333. The probability of observing an $\bar{x}$ value 1.578 or less can then be determined by finding an area under a normal curve, as illustrated in the accompanying picture.

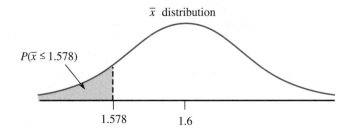

Since this is not the standard normal (z) curve, we must first convert to a z score before using Appendix Table II to find the area. Here

$$z = \frac{1.578 - 1.6}{.0333} = -.66$$

From Table II, the area to the left of $z = -.66$ under the standard normal curve is .2546. So, if $\mu = 1.6$, $\beta = .2546$. This means that if μ is 1.6, about 25% of all samples would result in $\bar{x}$ values 1.578 or smaller and nonrejection of H_0.

Figure 10.3 shows the $\bar{x}$ distribution for the case where H_0 is true ($\mu = 1.5$) and also for the cases $\mu = 1.6$ and $\mu = 1.65$. Also shown in this figure is the probability of type II error when $\mu = 1.6$ and also when $\mu = 1.65$. This probability is smaller for $\mu = 1.65$ than for the case $\mu = 1.6$ because $\bar{x} \leq 1.578$ ($z \leq 2.33$) is less likely when $\mu = 1.65$ than when $\mu = 1.60$. Put another way, the chance of a type II error is smaller for a value of μ far from the hypothesized value 1.5 than for a value of μ closer to 1.5. Although we illustrated P(type II error) only for the alternative values $\mu = 1.6$ and $\mu = 1.65$, this probability can also be computed for any other value of μ exceeding 1.5 (that is, any other value for which H_0 is false and H_a is true).

FIGURE 10.3
The sampling distribution of $\bar{x}$ and error probabilities for Example 10.25
(a) $\mu = 1.5$ (H_0 true)
(b) $\mu = 1.6$ (H_0 false)
(c) $\mu = 1.65$ (H_0 false)

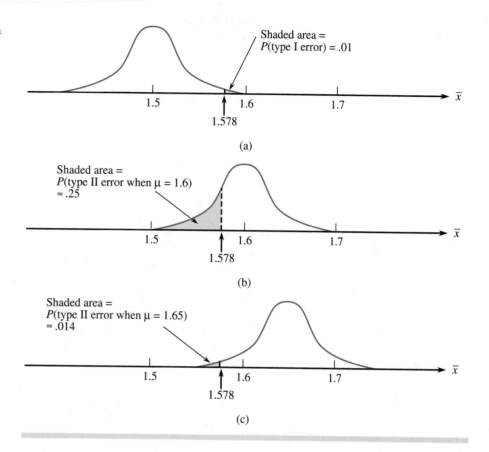

The probability of a type II error for z tests concerning a population proportion π is calculated in a similar manner. To see how this error probability is determined, consider testing

$$H_0: \pi = .5 \quad \text{versus} \quad H_a: \pi > .5$$

based on a random sample of size $n = 100$. The appropriate test statistic is

$$z = \frac{p - .5}{\sqrt{\dfrac{(.5)(.5)}{100}}} = \frac{p - .5}{.05}$$

A test with $\alpha = .01$ rejects H_0 if $z > 2.33$ or, equivalently,

$$\frac{p - .5}{.05} > 2.33$$

This can be rewritten as $p > .617$. Therefore, we reject H_0 if $p > .617$ and fail to reject H_0 if $p \leq .617$.

Suppose that, in fact, $\pi = .7$ and so H_0 is false. What is the probability that we will fail to reject H_0, committing a type II error? If $\pi = .7$, the sampling distribution of p is approximately normal, centered at $\mu_p = .7$, and has standard deviation $\sigma_p = \sqrt{(.7)(.3)/100} = .0458$. Then β, the probability of type II error, can be found by evaluating $P(p \le .617)$, as illustrated in the accompanying figure.

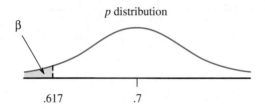

p distribution

β

.617   .7

To find this area, we convert to a z score:

$$z = \frac{.617 - .7}{.0458} = -1.81$$

and locate the corresponding area in Appendix Table II. The result is that if $\pi = .7$, $\beta = .0351$. That is, when $\pi = .7$, only 3.5% of all samples with $n = 100$ will result in failure to reject H_0 (a type II error). This probability is small because $\pi = .7$ is quite far from .5, and such a departure from H_0 is easy to detect when $n = 100$.

EXAMPLE 10.26

A package delivery service advertises that at least 90% of all packages brought to its office by 9 A.M. for delivery in the same city are delivered by noon that day. Let π denote the proportion of all such packages actually delivered by noon. The hypotheses of interest are

$$H_0: \pi = .9 \quad \text{versus} \quad H_a: \pi < .9$$

where the alternative hypothesis states that the company's claim is untrue. The value $\pi = .8$ represents a substantial departure from the company's claim. If the hypotheses are tested at level .01 using a sample of $n = 225$ packages, what is the probability that the departure from H_0 represented by this alternative value will go undetected?

At significance level .01, H_0 is rejected if $z < -2.33$. This is equivalent to rejecting H_0 if

$$\frac{p - .9}{\sqrt{\dfrac{(.9)(.1)}{225}}} = \frac{p - .9}{.02} < -2.33$$

or equivalently, if

$$p < .853$$

When $\pi = .8$, p has approximately a normal distribution with mean

$$\mu_p = .8$$

and standard deviation

$$\sigma_p = \sqrt{\frac{(.8)(.2)}{225}} = .0267$$

Then β is the probability of obtaining a sample proportion greater than or equal to .853, as illustrated in the accompanying figure.

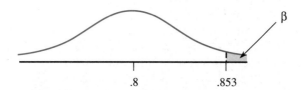

Converting to a z score results in

$$z = \frac{.853 - .8}{.0267} = 1.99$$

and Table II gives

$$\beta = 1 - .9767 = .0233$$

When $\pi = .8$ and a level .01 test is used, less than 3% of all samples of size $n = 225$ will result in a type II error.

β for the t Test

Determining β values for t tests is accomplished by using a set of graphs specially constructed for this purpose. The value of β depends not only on the true value of μ, but also on the selected significance level α—β increases as α is made smaller. This implies that for any fixed alternative value, β for a level .01 test is larger than β for a level .05 test. In addition, β depends on the number of degrees of freedom, $n - 1$. For any fixed level α, it should be easier for the test to detect a specific departure from H_0 when n is large than when n is small. This is indeed the case; for a fixed alternative value, β decreases as $n - 1$ increases.

There is unfortunately one other quantity on which β depends—the population standard deviation σ. Consider testing

$$H_0: \mu = 100 \quad \text{versus} \quad H_a: \mu > 100$$

and focus on the alternative value $\mu = 110$. Figure 10.4 pictures the population distribution both when $\mu = 110$, $\sigma = 10$ and when $\mu = 110$, $\sigma = 2.5$. In both cases, H_0 is false and we would like β to be small. When $\sigma = 2.5$, virtually all the sampled observations considerably exceed 100, making it rather obvious that H_0 is false. But when $\sigma = 10$, there is a good chance that some of the observations will fall considerably below 110, resulting in a sample whose $\bar{x}$ value does not strongly

FIGURE 10.4
Two normal population
distributions for which
$H_0: \mu = 100$ is false
because $\mu = 110$

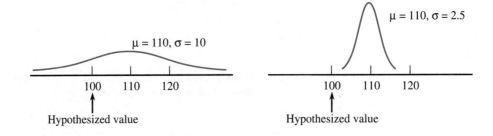

contradict H_0. That is, it will be easier to detect a departure from H_0 when σ is small (in which case β will be small) than when σ is relatively large.

Once α is specified and n is fixed, the determination of β at a particular alternative value of μ requires that a value of σ be chosen, since each different value of σ yields a different value of β. If the investigator can specify a range of plausible values for σ, then using the largest such value will give a pessimistic β (one on the high side).

Figure 10.5 pictures three different β curves for a one-tailed t test (appropriate for $H_a: \mu >$ hypothesized value or for $H_a: \mu <$ hypothesized value). A more complete set of curves for both one- and two-tailed tests when $\alpha = .05$ and when $\alpha = .01$ appear in Table V of the appendices. To determine β, first compute the quantity

$$d = \frac{|\text{alternative value} - \text{hypothesized value}|}{\sigma}$$

Then locate d on the horizontal axis, move directly up to the curve for $n - 1$ df, and move over to the vertical axis to read β.

FIGURE 10.5
β curves for the one-tailed
t test

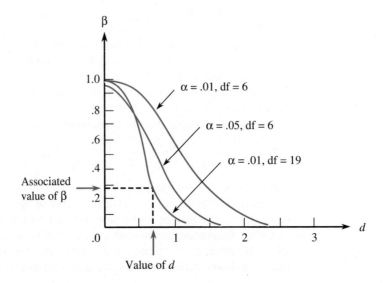

EXAMPLE 10.27

Consider testing

$$H_0: \mu = 100 \quad \text{versus} \quad H_a: \mu > 100$$

and focus on the alternative value $\mu = 110$. Suppose $\sigma = 10$, the sample size is $n = 7$, and that a significance level of .01 has been selected. For $\sigma = 10$,

$$d = \frac{|110 - 100|}{10} = \frac{10}{10} = 1$$

Figure 10.5 (using df $= 7 - 1 = 6$) gives $\beta \approx .6$. The interpretation is that if $\sigma = 10$ and a level .01 test based on $n = 7$ is used, when H_0 is false because $\mu = 110$, roughly 60% of all samples will result in erroneously not rejecting H_0! If a level .05 test is used instead, then $\beta \approx .3$, which is still rather large. Using a level .01 test with $n = 20$ (df $= 19$) yields, from Figure 10.5, $\beta \approx .05$. At the alternative 110, for $\sigma = 10$ the level .01 test based on $n = 20$ has smaller β than the level .05 test with $n = 7$. Substantially increasing n counterbalances using the smaller α.

Now consider the alternative $\mu = 105$, again with $\sigma = 10$, so that

$$d = \frac{|105 - 100|}{10} = \frac{5}{10} = .5$$

Then from Figure 10.5, $\beta \approx .95$ when $\alpha = .01$, $n = 7$; $\beta \approx .7$ when $\alpha = .05$, $n = 7$; and $\beta \approx .65$ when $\alpha = .01$, $n = 20$. These values of β are all quite large; with $\sigma = 10$, $\mu = 105$ is too close to the hypothesized value of 100 for any of these three tests to have a good chance of detecting such a departure from H_0. A substantial decrease in β necessitates using a much larger sample size. For example, from Table V, $\beta \approx .08$ when $\alpha = .05$ and $n = 40$.

The curves in Figure 10.5 also give β when testing $H_0: \mu = 100$ versus $H_a: \mu < 100$. If the alternative value $\mu = 90$ is of interest and $\sigma = 10$,

$$d = \frac{|90 - 100|}{10} = \frac{10}{10} = 1$$

and values of β are the same as those given in the first paragraph of this example. For the alternative $\mu = 95$,

$$d = \frac{|95 - 100|}{10} = .5$$

and values of β are as given in the second paragraph.

Since curves for only selected degrees of freedom appear in Table V, other degrees of freedom require a visual approximation. For example, the 27-df curve (for $n = 28$) would lie between the 19- and 29-df curves, which do appear, and would be closer to the latter. This type of approximation is adequate because it is the general magnitude of β—large, small, or moderate—that is of primary concern.

The curves can also be used to find a value of $n - 1$ (and thus n) for which β has a specified value at a particular alternative. Find the point at which a vertical line through the value of d and a horizontal line through the specified value of β intersect. The nearest curve passing below this point gives the necessary value of $n - 1$. This is pictured in Figure 10.6 where visual approximation is used to identify the closest curve.

FIGURE 10.6
Determining $n - 1$ for a
specified d and β

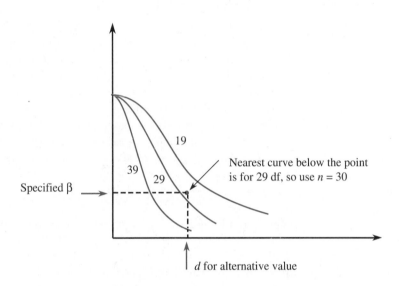

EXAMPLE 10.28

A farm supply store that packs its own fertilizer in 50-lb bags is being investigated for underfilling the bags. With μ denoting the true average net weight of all bags, the hypotheses of interest are H_0: $\mu = 50$ versus H_a: $\mu < 50$. Only if H_0 can be rejected will the store be formally accused of cheating its customers. To avoid an erroneous accusation of cheating (a very serious error), a small level of significance is appropriate. Suppose that $\alpha = .01$ is selected. The investigators feel that the alternative value $\mu = 49.8$ represents a substantial departure from H_0, so they are concerned that β should be small for this alternative. Assuming that net weight is normally distributed and that $\sigma = .25$, what would β be if the test is based on the contents of $n = 15$ bags? What value of n would be required to have $\beta = .05$ for this alternative?

The d value for this alternative and σ is

$$d = \frac{|49.8 - 50|}{.25} = \frac{.20}{.25} = .8$$

Using the β curves for a level .01 one-tailed test gives $\beta \approx .33$ from the $n - 1 = 15 - 1 = 14$-df curve. To obtain $\beta = .05$ at this alternative (value of d), a much larger value of n than 15 is clearly required. A horizontal line at height $\beta = .05$ and vertical line through $d = .8$ intersect right on the 29-df curve. Thus $n = 30$ is sufficient to obtain a suitably small β at the alternative of interest, provided that σ = .25. If σ is actually larger than .25, then n = 30 will, of course, not suffice.

The β curves in Table V are those for t tests. When the alternative corresponds to a value of d relatively close to zero, β for a t test may be rather large. One might ask whether there is another type of test that has the same level of significance α as does the t test and smaller values of β. For example, in Example 10.28 we had $\beta \approx$ .33 for a hypothesized value of 50, alternative μ = 49.8, σ = .25 (so d = .8), and a level .01 one-tailed t test. Is there some other test procedure, based on a different test statistic and rejection region, that has α = .01 and β < .33 under these circumstances? The following result provides the answer to this question.

> When the population distribution is normal, the level α t test for testing hypotheses about μ has smaller β than does any other test procedure that has the same level of significance α.

Stated another way, among all tests with level of significance α, the t test makes β as small as it can possibly be. In this sense, the t test is a best test. Statisticians have also shown that when the population distribution is not too far from a normal distribution, no test procedure can improve on the t test (have the same α and substantially smaller β) by very much. But when the population distribution is believed to be very nonnormal (heavy-tailed, highly skewed, or multimodal), the t test should not be used. Then it's time to consult your friendly neighborhood statistician, who could provide you with alternative methods of analysis.

EXERCISES 10.75–10.79   SECTION 10.7

10.75   Water samples are taken from water used for cooling as it is being discharged from a power plant into a river. It has been determined that as long as the mean temperature of the discharged water is at most 150° F, there will be no negative effects on the river ecosystem. To investigate whether the plant is in compliance with regulations that prohibit a mean discharge water temperature above 150°, 50 water samples will be taken at randomly selected times, and the water temperature of each sample will be recorded. A z statistic

$$z = \frac{\bar{x} - 150}{\sigma/\sqrt{n}}$$

will then be used to decide between the hypotheses

$$H_0: \mu = 150 \quad \text{and} \quad H_a: \mu > 150$$

where μ is the true mean temperature of discharged water. Assume that σ is known to be 10.

a. Explain why use of the z statistic would be appropriate in this setting.

b. Describe type I and type II errors in this context.

c. The rejection of H_0 when $z > 1.8$ corresponds to what value of α (the probability of making a type I error)?

d. Suppose that the true value for μ is 153 and that the rejection region $z > 1.8$ is used. Draw a sketch (similar to that of Figure 10.1) of the sampling distribution of $\bar{x}$ and shade the region that would represent β, the probability of making a type II error.

e. For the hypotheses and rejection region described, compute the value of β when $\mu = 153$.

f. For the hypotheses and rejection region described, what value would β take if $\mu = 160$?

g. If the rejection region $z > 1.8$ is used and $\bar{x} = 152.4$, what is the appropriate conclusion? What type of error might have been made in reaching this conclusion?

10.76   A maker of aspirin claims that, when placed in water, its tablets dissolve completely in at most 2 min. Fifty randomly selected tablets are to be examined. Each will be dropped into a beaker of water and the time until the tablet completely dissolves will be recorded. The resulting data will be used to test $H_0: \mu = 2$ versus $H_a: \mu > 2$, where μ represents the true mean dissolving time for aspirin tablets made by this particular manufacturer. Since $n = 50$ is large, the test statistic $z = (\bar{x} - 2)/\sigma_{\bar{x}}$ will have approximately a standard normal distribution when H_0 is true.

a. Consider rejecting H_0 when $z > 1.9$. What is the level of significance for this test?

b. The value 1.9 given in (a) is called the critical value for the test. If the critical value were changed to 2.2, so that H_0 is rejected if $z > 2.2$, would the significance level be larger or smaller than that corresponding to the critical value of 1.9? Explain.

c. If H_0 is rejected when $z > 1.645$, the corresponding level of significance would be .05. If a smaller significance level were desired, would a critical value greater than or less than 1.645 be required? Explain.

d. Would the type II error probability be larger for $\mu = 2.5$ or $\mu = 3.0$ (irrespective of which α is used)? Explain.

10.77   The city council in a large city has become concerned about the trend toward exclusion of renters with children in apartments within the city. The housing coordinator has decided to select a random sample of 125 apartments and determine for each whether or not children would be permitted. Let π be the true proportion of apartments that prohibit children. If π exceeds .75, the city council will consider appropriate legislation.

a. If 102 of the 125 sampled exclude renters with children, would a level .05 test lead you to the conclusion that more than 75% of all apartments exclude children?

b. What is the probability of a type II error when $\pi = .8$?

10.78   The amount of shaft wear after a fixed mileage was determined for each of seven internal combustion engines, resulting in a mean of .0372 in. and a standard deviation of .0125 in.

a. Assuming that the distribution of shaft wear is normal, test at level .05 the hypotheses $H_0: \mu = .035$ versus $H_a: \mu > .035$.

b. Using $\sigma = .0125$, $\alpha = .05$, and Table V, what is the value of β, the probability of a type II error, when $\mu = .04$?

10.79   Optical fibers are used in telecommunications to transmit light. Current technology allows production of fibers that will transmit light about 50 km (*Research at Rensselaer,* 1984). Researchers are trying to develop a new type of glass fiber that will increase this distance. In evaluating a new fiber, it would be of interest to test $H_0: \mu = 50$ versus $H_a: \mu > 50$, with μ denoting the true average transmission distance for the new optical fiber.

a. If a level .05 test is to be used and 10 measurements are to be made ($n = 10$), what would be the rejection region for the test?

b. Assuming $\sigma = 10$ and $n = 10$, use Table V to find β, the probability of a type II error, for each of the given alternative values of μ when a level .05 test is employed.

i. 52   **ii.** 55   **iii.** 60   **iv.** 70

CHAPTER TEN SUMMARY OF KEY CONCEPTS AND FORMULAS

Term or Formula	Comment
Hypothesis	A claim about the value of a population characteristic.
Null hypothesis, H_0	The hypothesis initially assumed to be true. It has the form H_0: population characteristic = hypothesized value.
Alternative hypothesis, H_a	A hypothesis that specifies a claim that is contradictory to H_0 and is judged the more plausible claim when H_0 is rejected.
Type I error	Rejection of H_0 when H_0 is true; the probability of a type I error is denoted by α.
Type II error	Nonrejection of H_0 when H_0 is false; the probability of a type II error is denoted by β.
Test statistic	The quantity computed from sample data for making a decision between H_0 and H_a.
Rejection region	Specifies values of the test statistic for which H_0 should be rejected.
P-value	The smallest significance level at which H_0 can be rejected.
$z = \dfrac{\bar{x} - \text{hypothesized value}}{s/\sqrt{n}}$	A test statistic for testing $H_0: \mu = $ hypothesized value when the sample size is large.
$t = \dfrac{\bar{x} - \text{hypothesized value}}{s/\sqrt{n}}$	A test statistic for testing $H_0: \mu = $ hypothesized value when the sample size is small and it is reasonable to assume that the population distribution is normal.

Term or Formula	**Comment**
$z = \dfrac{p - \textbf{hypothesized value}}{\sqrt{\dfrac{\textbf{(hyp. val.)}(1 - \textbf{hyp. val.})}{n}}}$	A test statistic for testing H_0: π = hypothesized value when the sample size is large.

ENCORE

The problem posed in the Chapter Preview is that of deciding whether an initiative qualifies for the ballot. One million signatures were submitted; in order to qualify, 654,954 of the signatures must be valid (a legitimate signature of a registered voter). Let π denote the true proportion of all signatures submitted that are valid. If $\pi > .655$, the initiative qualifies for the ballot.

A sample of 5000 signatures included 3605 that were valid. We will use this sample information to test

$$H_0: \pi = .655 \quad \text{versus} \quad H_a: \pi > .655$$

If we are able to reject the null hypothesis, there is sufficient evidence to conclude that the initiative qualifies. The steps in a hypothesis test with significance level .01 follow.

1. π = true proportion of valid signatures
2. H_0: $\pi = .655$
3. H_a: $\pi > .655$
4. Test statistic: $z = \dfrac{p - .655}{\sqrt{\dfrac{(.655)(.345)}{n}}}$
5. Since H_a: $\pi > .655$, this is an upper-tail test. With $\alpha = .01$, we will reject H_0 if $z > 2.33$.
6. $p = \dfrac{3605}{5000} = .721$

   $z = \dfrac{.721 - .655}{\sqrt{\dfrac{(.655)(.345)}{5000}}} = \dfrac{.066}{.0067} = 9.85$

7. Reject H_0. The sample provides strong evidence against H_0. We conclude that $\pi > .655$ and that the initiative should be placed on the ballot.

This is consistent with the conclusion of March Fong Eu, California's Secretary of State in 1988. She stated that a random sampling of signatures showed the number of valid signatures to be "well in excess of the 654,954 signatures required" (*Los Angeles Times,* January 20, 1988).

SUPPLEMENTARY EXERCISES 10.80–10.92

10.80 Sixty-five clerical workers at a large financial service organization participated in a health-risk analysis, and the resulting data was summarized in the paper "Workplace Stress and Indicators of Coronary-Disease Risk" (*Acad. Mgmt. J.* (1988):686–698). For systolic blood pressure, the sample mean and standard deviation were 111.63 and 11.94, respectively. Is there sufficient evidence to conclude that the mean systolic blood pressure for all clerical workers at this business exceeds 110? Test the relevant hypotheses using a .01 significance level.

10.81 A Norwegian study of 105 males born in 1962 with birth weights of 2500 g or less was described in the article "Males with Low Birth Weight Examined at 18 Years of Age" (*J. of Amer. Med. Assoc.* (1984):3248). When examined in 1981 by the Norwegian military draft board, 7 of the 105 were declared unfit for military service. The Norwegian draft board declared 6.2% (a proportion of .062) of all 18-year-olds examined in 1981 unfit for military service. Does the data provide sufficient evidence to indicate that the true proportion of males with birth weights of 2500 g or less who are unfit is higher than that of the general population? Use a .01 significance level.

10.82 A standard method for recovering minerals and metals from biological materials results in a mean copper recovery of 63 ppm when used to treat oyster tissue. A new treatment method was described in the paper "Simple Sample Digestion of Sewage and Sludge for Multi-Element Analysis" (*J. Environ. Sci. and Health* (1984):959–972). Suppose this new treatment is used to treat $n = 40$ bits of oyster tissue, resulting in a sample mean copper recovery and a sample standard deviation of 62.6 ppm and 3.7 ppm, respectively. Is there evidence to suggest that the mean copper recovery is lower for the new method than for the standard one? Use a .01 significance level.

10.83 Past experience has indicated that the true response rate is 40% when individuals are approached with a request to fill out and return a particular questionnaire in a stamped and addressed envelope. An investigator believes that if the person distributing the questionnaire is stigmatized in some obvious way, potential respondents would feel sorry for the distributor and thus tend to respond at a rate higher than 40%. To investigate this theory, a distributor is fitted with an eyepatch. Of the 200 questionnaires distributed by this individual, 109 were returned. Does this strongly suggest that the response rate in this situation does exceed the rate in the past?
  a. State and test the appropriate hypotheses at significance level .05.
  b. Compute the *P*-value for this data and then use it to carry out a test.

10.84 The drug cibenzoline is currently being investigated for possible use in controlling cardiac arrhythmia. The paper "Quantification of Cibenzoline in Human Plasma by Gas Chromatography-Negative Ionization Mass Spectrometry" (*J. of Chromatography* (1984):403–409) describes a new method of determining the concentration of cibenzoline in a solution. After 5 ng of cibenzoline was added to a solution, the concentration was measured by the new method. This process was repeated three times, resulting in $n = 3$ concentration readings. The sample mean and standard deviation were reported to be 4.59 ng and .08 ng, respectively. Does this data suggest that the new method produces a mean concentration reading that is too small (less than 5 ng)? Use a .05 significance level and test the appropriate hypotheses.

10.85 The increasing number of senior citizens has made this group an attractive target market for retailers. An understanding of how the elderly feel about various consumer problems is, therefore, important to retailers. The paper "Consumer Problems and Complaint Actions of Older Americans" (*J. of Retailing* (1981):107–123) reported that in a sample of 404 elderly individuals who shop for grocery items, 270 were satisfied with their purchases, whereas 134 were dissatisfied. Suppose that the proportion of all individuals who are satisfied with grocery items is .8 (a value suggested in the paper). Does the sample data suggest that the proportion of elderly people who are satisfied is smaller than the proportion of all individuals who are satisfied? State the relevant hypotheses and carry out the appropriate test using a .01 significance level.

10.86 Police departments across the country have recently voiced concerns that too many calls to the 911 emergency telephone number are not true emergencies. Suppose that the police chief in a particular city is contemplating an advertising campaign to warn of the consequences of abusing the 911 number. Because of the cost, the campaign can be justified only if more than 25% of all 911 calls are not emergencies. A random sample of 200 recent calls to the 911 number is selected, and it is determined that 56 were nonemergency calls. Does this sample data support going ahead with the ad campaign? Test the relevant hypotheses using significance level .10.

10.87 To investigate whether sudden infant death syndrome (SIDS) might be related to an imbalance between peptides affecting respiration, the authors of the paper "Postmortem Analysis of Neuropeptides in Brains from Sudden Infant Death Victims" (*Brain Research* (1984):279–285) measured cortex met-enkephalin levels (pmol/g wet weight) in brain tissue of 12 SIDS victims. The resulting sample mean and standard deviation were 7.66 and 3.78, respectively. The mean level for children who are not victims of SIDS was reported to be 7.48. Using a .05 significance level, test to determine if the true mean met-enkephalin level of SIDS victims is higher than that of children who are not victims of SIDS.

10.88 The effect of discharging wastewater from a dairy processing plant into groundwater used to irrigate kidney beans was examined in the paper "Effect of Industrial Dairy Processing Effluent on Soil and Crop Plants" (*Environ. Pollution* (1984):97–106). The wastewater was rich in bicarbonates and calcium, so it was thought that irrigating with a 50% solution of wastewater might promote growth. Suppose that 40 kidney bean plants were irrigated with this mixture, resulting in a sample mean root length of 5.46 cm and a sample standard deviation of .55 cm. The mean root length for kidney bean plants irrigated with uncontami-

nated water is known to be 5.20 cm. Does this data support the hypothesis that irrigation with the 50% wastewater solution results in a mean root length that is greater than 5.20? Use a .05 significance level.

10.89 The paper referenced in Exercise 10.88 also gave information on root length for pearl millet. When irrigated with uncontaminated water, the mean root length is 6.40 cm. A sample of 40 plants irrigated with a 50% wastewater solution resulted in a sample mean root length of 4.76 cm and a sample standard deviation of .48 cm. Does the data strongly suggest that irrigation with the wastewater mixture results in a mean root length that differs from 6.40? Use a .05 level test.

10.90 A student organization uses the proceeds from a particular soft-drink dispensing machine to finance its activities. The price per can has been $.40 for a long time, and the average daily revenue during that period had been $50.00. The price was recently increased to $.45 per can. A random sample of $n = 20$ days subsequent to the price increase yielded a sample average revenue and sample standard deviation of $47.30 and $4.20, respectively. Does this data suggest that the true average daily revenue has decreased from its value prior to the price increase? Test the appropriate hypotheses using $\alpha = .05$.

10.91 A hot-tub manufacturer advertises that with its heating equipment, a temperature of 100° F can be achieved in at most 15 min. A random sample of 32 tubs is selected and the time necessary to achieve a 100° F temperature is determined for each tub. The sample average time and sample standard deviation are 17.5 min and 2.2 min, respectively. Does this data cast doubt on the company's claim?

a. Carry out a test of hypotheses using significance level .05.

b. Compute the *P*-value, and use it to reach a conclusion at level .05.

10.92 Let π denote the probability that a coin will land heads side up. The coin is tossed 10,000 times and 5100 heads result. Using a significance level of .05, would you reject the assertion that the coin is fair? From a practical point of view, does the unfairness of the coin bother you?

References

The books by Freedman et al. and by Moore, listed in earlier chapter references, are excellent sources. Their orientation is primarily conceptual with a minimum of mathematical development, and both sources offer many valuable insights. The introduction to hypothesis testing in the Devore book (Chapter 5 References) is more comprehensive than the present text, especially with respect to type II error probabilities and determination of sample size.

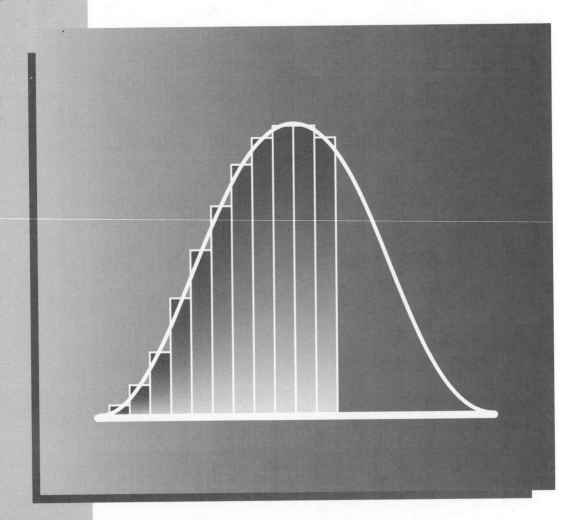

Inferences Using Two Independent Samples

A number of studies have focused on the question of whether children born to women who smoke differ physiologically from children born to nonsmokers. Two such investigations were described in the papers "Smoking during Pregnancy and Lactation and Its Effects on Breast-Milk Volume" (*American J. of Clinical Nutrition* (1991):1011–1016) and "Placental Transfer of Lead, Mercury, Cadmium, and Carbon Monoxide in Women" (*Environ. Research* (1978):494–503). The first study included ten lactating women who had never smoked and ten who smoked during pregnancy and continued to do so while breast-feeding. Breast-milk volume was measured, resulting in data that led the researchers to conclude that nonsmoking mothers had a significantly greater breast-milk volume than did smokers. The second study used samples that were much larger and looked at the lead concentration in the blood of babies born to smokers and to nonsmokers. The authors concluded that the mean blood lead concentration is, in fact, higher for the children of smokers than for the children of nonsmokers.

To reach these conclusions, hypothesis tests that compare the means of two different populations were used. The two-sample *z* test for large samples and the two-sample *t* test for small samples from normal populations are among the inferential methods introduced in this chapter.

Introduction

Many investigations are carried out for the purpose of comparing two populations. For example, hospital administrators might want to compare the average length of hospitalization for those patients having private health insurance with that for those covered by Medicare. Such a study would involve a comparison of two population means. A consumer organization might wish to determine whether there is a difference between two manufacturers of personal computers with respect to the proportion of machines that need repair during the first two years of use. This would require comparison of two population proportions. This chapter introduces hypothesis tests and confidence intervals that can be used when comparing two populations on the basis of either means or proportions if the samples are selected independently of one another.

11.1 Large-Sample Inferences Concerning the Difference between Two Population Means

An investigator who wishes to compare two populations is often interested either in estimating the difference between the two population means or in testing hypotheses about this difference. In order to accomplish either task, information (in the form of a sample) must be obtained from each population. The sample information is then used to make inferences about the difference between the population means.

In earlier chapters, μ was used to denote the mean of the single population under study. When comparing two populations, it is necessary to use notation that distinguishes between the characteristics of the first population and those of the second. This is accomplished by using subscripts on quantities such as μ and σ^2. Similarly, subscripts on sample statistics such as $\bar{x}$ indicate to which sample these quantities refer.

NOTATION

	Mean value	Variance	Standard deviation
Population 1	μ_1	σ_1^2	σ_1
Population 2	μ_2	σ_2^2	σ_2

	Sample size	Mean	Variance	Standard deviation
Sample from population 1	n_1	$\bar{x}_1$	s_1^2	s_1
Sample from population 2	n_2	$\bar{x}_2$	s_2^2	s_2

We will compare the means of two populations by focusing on their difference, $\mu_1 - \mu_2$. Note that when $\mu_1 - \mu_2 = 0$, the two population means are identical. That is,

$$\mu_1 - \mu_2 = 0 \quad \text{is equivalent to} \quad \mu_1 = \mu_2$$

Similarly,

$$\mu_1 - \mu_2 > 0 \quad \text{is equivalent to} \quad \mu_1 > \mu_2$$

and

$$\mu_1 - \mu_2 < 0 \quad \text{is equivalent to} \quad \mu_1 < \mu_2$$

Before developing inferential procedures concerning $\mu_1 - \mu_2$, we need to consider how the two samples, one from each population, are selected. Two samples are said to be **independent** if the selection of the individuals or objects that make up one sample has no bearing on the selection of those in the other sample. However, when observations from the first sample are paired in some meaningful way with observations in the second sample, the data is said to be **paired.** For example, to study the effectiveness of a speed-reading course, the reading speed of subjects could be measured prior to taking the class and again after completion of the course. This gives rise to two related samples—one from the population of individuals who have not taken this particular course (the "before" measurements) and one from the population of individuals who have had such a course (the "after" measurements). These samples are paired. The two samples are not independently chosen, since the selection of individuals from the first (before) population completely determines which individuals make up the sample from the second (after) population. In this chapter, we consider procedures based on independent samples. Methods for analyzing data resulting from paired samples are presented in the next chapter.

Because $\bar{x}_1$ provides an estimate of μ_1 and $\bar{x}_2$ gives an estimate of μ_2, it is natural to use $\bar{x}_1 - \bar{x}_2$ as a point estimate of $\mu_1 - \mu_2$. The value of $\bar{x}_1$ varies from sample to sample (it is a *statistic*), as does the value of $\bar{x}_2$. Thus $\bar{x}_1 - \bar{x}_2$ is itself a statistic and therefore has a sampling distribution. Our inferential methods will be based on information about the sampling distribution of $\bar{x}_1 - \bar{x}_2$. The next box summarizes what is known about the $\bar{x}_1 - \bar{x}_2$ distribution if the two samples are independently chosen.

PROPERTIES OF THE SAMPLING DISTRIBUTION OF $\bar{x}_1 - \bar{x}_2$

If the samples on which $\bar{x}_1$ and $\bar{x}_2$ are based are selected independently of one another, then

1. $\mu_{\bar{x}_1 - \bar{x}_2} = \left(\begin{array}{c} \text{the mean value} \\ \text{of } \bar{x}_1 - \bar{x}_2 \end{array} \right) = \mu_{\bar{x}_1} - \mu_{\bar{x}_2} = \mu_1 - \mu_2$

   Thus the $\bar{x}_1 - \bar{x}_2$ sampling distribution is always centered at the value of $\mu_1 - \mu_2$, so $\bar{x}_1 - \bar{x}_2$ is an unbiased statistic for estimating $\mu_1 - \mu_2$.

2. $\sigma^2_{\bar{x}_1 - \bar{x}_2} = \left(\begin{array}{c} \text{variance of} \\ \bar{x}_1 - \bar{x}_2 \end{array} \right) = \sigma^2_{\bar{x}_1} + \sigma^2_{\bar{x}_2} = \dfrac{\sigma_1^2}{n_1} + \dfrac{\sigma_2^2}{n_2}$

   and

   $\sigma_{\bar{x}_1 - \bar{x}_2} = \left(\begin{array}{c} \text{standard deviation} \\ \text{of } \bar{x}_1 - \bar{x}_2 \end{array} \right) = \sqrt{\dfrac{\sigma_1^2}{n_1} + \dfrac{\sigma_2^2}{n_2}}$

3. When n_1 and n_2 are both large, $\bar{x}_1$ and $\bar{x}_2$ each have approximately normal distributions (the Central Limit Theorem). This implies that the sampling distribution of $\bar{x}_1 - \bar{x}_2$ is also approximately normal (even if the two population distributions themselves are not normal).

Properties 1 and 2 in the box follow from these general results:

1. The mean value of a difference is the difference of the two individual mean values.
2. The variance of a difference of independent quantities is the *sum* of the two individual variances.

When the sample sizes are large, the properties of the $\bar{x}_1 - \bar{x}_2$ distribution imply that $\bar{x}_1 - \bar{x}_2$ can be standardized to obtain a variable with a sampling distribution that is approximately the standard normal (z) curve. Unfortunately, the values of σ_1^2 and σ_2^2 will rarely be known, but if n_1 and n_2 are both large (typically at least 30), s_1^2 and s_2^2 can be used in their places. This gives the following key result, on which large-sample tests and confidence intervals are based.

When n_1 and n_2 are both large, the distribution of

$$z = \frac{\bar{x}_1 - \bar{x}_2 - (\mu_1 - \mu_2)}{\sqrt{\dfrac{s_1^2}{n_1} + \dfrac{s_2^2}{n_2}}}$$

is described approximately by the standard normal (z) distribution.

Test Procedures

In a test designed to compare two population means, the null hypothesis will be of the form

$H_0: \mu_1 - \mu_2 =$ hypothesized value

Often the hypothesized value will be zero, with the null hypothesis then saying that there is no difference between the population means. The alternative hypothesis will involve the same hypothesized value but will use one of the three inequalities $>$, $<$, or $\neq$. As an example, let μ_1 and μ_2 denote the average fuel efficiencies (mi/gal) for two models of a certain type of car, equipped with 4-cylinder and 6-cylinder engines, respectively. The hypotheses under consideration might be

$H_0: \mu_1 - \mu_2 = 5$

versus

$H_a: \mu_1 - \mu_2 > 5$

This null hypothesis claims that average efficiency for the 4-cylinder engine exceeds the average efficiency for the 6-cylinder engine by exactly 5 mi/gal. The alternative hypothesis states that the difference between the true average efficiencies is more than 5 mi/gal.

A test statistic is obtained by replacing $\mu_1 - \mu_2$ in the standardized z variable (given in the previous box) by the hypothesized value, which appears in H_0. Thus the z statistic for testing $H_0: \mu_1 - \mu_2 = 5$ is

$$z = \frac{\bar{x}_1 - \bar{x}_2 - 5}{\sqrt{\dfrac{s_1^2}{n_1} + \dfrac{s_2^2}{n_2}}}$$

When H_0 is true, the sampling distribution of this z statistic is approximately the standard normal (z) curve. The type I error probability can now be controlled by using an appropriate z critical value to determine the rejection region for the test.

LARGE-SAMPLE z TESTS FOR $\mu_1 - \mu_2$

Null hypothesis: $H_0: \mu_1 - \mu_2 =$ hypothesized value

Test statistic: $z = \dfrac{\bar{x}_1 - \bar{x}_2 - \text{hypothesized value}}{\sqrt{\dfrac{s_1^2}{n_1} + \dfrac{s_2^2}{n_2}}}$

Alternative Hypothesis	Rejection Region
$H_a: \mu_1 - \mu_2 >$ hypothesized value	$z > z$ critical value (upper-tailed test)
$H_a: \mu_1 - \mu_2 <$ hypothesized value	$z < -z$ critical value (lower-tailed test)
$H_a: \mu_1 - \mu_2 \neq$ hypothesized value	Either $z > z$ critical value or $z < -z$ critical value (two-tailed test)

The appropriate z critical value is determined by the choice of significance level. Critical values for the most frequently used values of α appear in the bottom row of Table IV.

EXAMPLE 11.1

Are male college students more easily bored than their female counterparts? This question was examined in the paper "Boredom in Young Adults—Gender and Cultural Comparisons" (*J. of Cross-Cultural Psych.* (1991):209–223). The authors administered a scale called the Boredom Proneness Scale to 97 male and 148 female U.S. college students. Does the accompanying data support the research hypothesis that the mean Boredom Proneness Rating is higher for males than for females? We will test the appropriate hypotheses using a .05 significance level.

	Sample size	$\bar{x}$	s
Males	97	10.40	4.83
Females	148	9.26	4.68

1. $\mu_1 =$ mean boredom proneness score for all college males
    $\mu_2 =$ mean boredom proneness score for all college females
    $\mu_1 - \mu_2 =$ difference in mean boredom proneness scores

2. $H_0: \mu_1 - \mu_2 = 0$

3. $H_a: \mu_1 - \mu_2 > 0$

4. Test statistic:

$$z = \frac{\bar{x}_1 - \bar{x}_2 - 0}{\sqrt{\dfrac{s_1^2}{n_1} + \dfrac{s_2^2}{n_2}}}$$

5. Since this is an upper-tailed test, using a .05 level of significance ($\alpha = .05$) leads to the rejection region $z > 1.645$.

6. Computations:

$$z = \frac{10.40 - 9.26 - 0}{\sqrt{\dfrac{(4.83)^2}{97} + \dfrac{(4.68)^2}{148}}} = \frac{1.14}{.623} = 1.83$$

7. Since $1.83 > 1.645$, we reject H_0. The data supports the claim that the mean boredom proneness score is higher for male than for female college students. (Note that we would not have reached this conclusion had we selected $\alpha = .01$).

Comparing Treatments

Often an experiment is carried out in order to compare two different treatments or to compare the effect of a treatment with the effect of no treatment ("treatment versus control"). For example, an agricultural experimenter might wish to compare weight gains for animals on two different diets. Let μ_1 denote the mean weight gain (average response) for an animal on diet (treatment) 1. That is, if the population of all animals were placed on diet 1, then μ_1 would be the population average weight gain. This population does not actually exist, but we can conceptualize it—and the observed weight gains constitute a random sample from this conceptual population. Similarly, μ_2 can be viewed either as the mean weight gain for an animal fed diet 2 or as the average weight gain for the conceptual population consisting of all animals that could receive diet 2. Again, the observed weight gains represent a random sample from this conceptual population. The important point is that our two-sample z test (as well as other two-sample procedures) can be applied to compare conceptual populations.

EXAMPLE 11.2

The paper "Testing vs. Review: Effects on Retention" (*J. of Educ. Psych.* (1982): 18–22) reported on an experiment designed to compare several different methods ("treatments") for enhancing retention of school material just studied. After high-school students studied a brief history text, each one either took a test (method 1) or spent equivalent time reviewing selected passages (method 2). Two weeks afterward, each student took a retention test. Summary data from the experiment follows. Does retention appear to be better with one method than with the other?

Treatment	Sample size	Sample mean	Sample SD
Method 1 (test)	31	12.4	4.5
Method 2 (review)	34	11.0	3.1

1. Let μ_1 denote the true average retention score for all high school students who might be assigned to method 1 (the mean of a conceptual population) and define μ_2 analogously for method 2. Then $\mu_1 - \mu_2$ is the difference between the true average retention scores for the two methods.
2. $H_0: \mu_1 - \mu_2 = 0$ (no difference between methods)
3. $H_a: \mu_1 - \mu_2 \neq 0$ (the methods differ)
4. Test statistic:

$$z = \frac{\bar{x}_1 - \bar{x}_2 - 0}{\sqrt{\dfrac{s_1^2}{n_1} + \dfrac{s_2^2}{n_2}}}$$

5. Using $\alpha = .05$, H_0 will be rejected if $z > 1.96$ or if $z < -1.96$
6. Computations:

$$z = \frac{12.4 - 11.0 - 0}{\sqrt{\dfrac{(4.5)^2}{31} + \dfrac{(3.1)^2}{34}}}$$

$$= \frac{1.4}{.967}$$

$$= 1.45$$

7. Since 1.45 is between -1.96 and 1.96, we do not reject H_0. Retention does not seem to depend on which method is used.

P-Values

Because the test procedure presented in this section is based on a z test statistic, P-values can be computed using the same method as for the one-sample z tests of the previous chapter. This is illustrated in the following example.

EXAMPLE 11.3

The authors of the paper "Hostility, Aggression, and Anxiety Levels of Divorce and Nondivorce Children as Manifested in Their Responses to Projective Tests" (*J. of Personality Assessment* (1991):438–452) speculated that children of divorced parents would show higher levels of hostility than children of married parents. To test this theory, Rorschach tests were used to compute a measure of hostility for 54 children of divorced parents and 54 children of married parents. All children who participated were between 10 and 12 years of age and lived in Sweden. Does the accompanying data support the researchers' theory? We will use a .01 significance level.

	$\bar{x}$	s
Children of divorced parents	5.38	3.96
Children of married parents	1.94	3.10

1. μ_1 = mean hostility score for children of divorced parents
      μ_2 = mean hostility score for children of married parents
   $\mu_1 - \mu_2$ = difference in mean hostility scores

2. $H_0: \mu_1 - \mu_2 = 0$

3. $H_a: \mu_1 - \mu_2 > 0$

4. Test statistic:

$$z = \frac{\bar{x}_1 - \bar{x}_2 - 0}{\sqrt{\dfrac{s_1^2}{n_1} + \dfrac{s_2^2}{n_2}}}$$

5. Computations:

$$z = \frac{5.38 - 1.94 - 0}{\sqrt{\dfrac{(3.96)^2}{54} + \dfrac{(3.10)^2}{54}}} = \frac{3.44}{.684} = 5.03$$

6. Since this is an upper-tailed test, the associated P-value is the area under the z curve and to the right of the computed z value of 5.03. Since this area is approximately 0,

   P-value ≈ 0

7. The P-value is smaller than the selected significance level of .01, so we reject H_0. This data does support the researchers' hypothesis that the mean hostility score is higher for children of divorced parents than for children of married parents.

Comparisons and Causation

If the assignment of treatments to the individuals or objects used in a comparison of treatments is not made by the investigators, the study is said to be **observational.**

As an example, the article "Lead and Cadmium Absorption among Children near a Nonferrous Metal Plant" (*Environ. Research* (1978):290–308) reported data on blood–lead concentrations for two different samples of children. The first sample was drawn from a population residing within 1 km of a lead smelter, whereas those in the second sample were selected from a rural area much farther from the smelter. It was the parents of children, rather than the investigators, who determined whether the children would be in the close-to-smelter group or the far-from-smelter group. As a second example, a letter in the *Journal of the American Medical Association* (May 19, 1978) reported on a comparison of doctors' longevity after medical school graduation for those with an academic affiliation and those in private practice. (The letter writer's stated objective was to see whether "publish or perish" really meant "publish *and* perish.") Here again, an investigator did not start out with a group of doctors and assign some to academic and others to nonacademic careers. The doctors themselves selected their groups.

The difficulty with drawing conclusions based on an observational study is that a statistically significant difference may be due to some underlying factors that have not been controlled rather than to conditions that define the groups. Does the type of medical practice itself have an effect on longevity, or is the observed difference in lifetimes caused by other factors, which themselves led graduates to choose academic or nonacademic careers? Similarly, is the observed difference in blood–lead concentration levels due to proximity to the smelter? Perhaps there are other physical and socioeconomic factors related both to choice of living area and to concentration.

In general, rejection of $H_0: \mu_1 - \mu_2 = 0$ in favor of $H_a: \mu_1 - \mu_2 > 0$ suggests that, on the average, higher values of the variable are *associated* with individuals in the first population or receiving the first treatment than with those in the second population or receiving the second treatment. But *association does not imply causation*. Strong statistical evidence for a causal relationship can be built up over time through many different comparative studies that point to the same conclusions (as in the many investigations linking smoking to lung cancer). A **randomized controlled experiment,** in which investigators assign subjects in some prescribed random fashion to the treatments or conditions being compared, is particularly effective in suggesting causality. With such random assignment, the investigator and other interested parties will have more confidence in the conclusion that an observed difference was caused by the difference in treatments or conditions. Such carefully controlled studies are more easily carried out in the hard sciences than in social-science contexts, which may explain why the use of statistical methods is less controversial in the former than the latter disciplines.

A Confidence Interval

A large-sample confidence interval for $\mu_1 - \mu_2$ can be obtained from the same z variable on which the test procedures were based. When n_1 and n_2 are both large, approximately 95% of all samples from the two populations will be such that

$$-1.96 < \frac{\bar{x}_1 - \bar{x}_2 - (\mu_1 - \mu_2)}{\sqrt{\dfrac{s_1^2}{n_1} + \dfrac{s_2^2}{n_2}}} < 1.96$$

The 95% confidence interval results from manipulations that isolate $\mu_1 - \mu_2$ in the middle (just as isolating μ in $-1.96 < (\bar{x} - \mu)/(s/\sqrt{n}) < 1.96$ led to the large-sample interval for μ in Chapter 9):

$$\bar{x}_1 - \bar{x}_2 - 1.96\sqrt{\frac{s_1^2}{n_1} + \frac{s_2^2}{n_2}} < \mu_1 - \mu_2 < \bar{x}_1 - \bar{x}_2 + 1.96\sqrt{\frac{s_1^2}{n_1} + \frac{s_2^2}{n_2}}$$

A confidence level other than 95% is achieved by using an appropriate z critical value in place of 1.96.

The **large-sample confidence interval for $\mu_1 - \mu_2$** is

$$\bar{x}_1 - \bar{x}_2 \pm (z \text{ critical value})\sqrt{\frac{s_1^2}{n_1} + \frac{s_2^2}{n_2}}$$

The z critical values associated with the most frequently used confidence levels appear in the bottom row of Table IV.

EXAMPLE 11.4

U.S.A. Today (January 15, 1986) described a study of automobile accident victims at Newton–Wellesley Hospital in Massachusetts. The mean cost for medical treatment for a motorist wearing a seat belt at the time of the accident was $565, while the mean cost for a motorist who was not wearing a seat belt was $1200. Suppose that sample sizes and standard deviations were as given in the accompanying table.

	n	$\bar{x}$	s
Seat belts	45	565	220
No seat belts	90	1200	540

We will estimate the difference in the mean cost of medical treatment for belted and unbelted accident victims, using a 95% confidence interval.

Let

μ_1 = mean cost of treatment for a belted accident victim

μ_2 = mean cost of treatment for an unbelted accident victim

Then a 95% confidence interval for the difference $\mu_1 - \mu_2$ is

$$(\bar{x}_1 - \bar{x}_2) \pm 1.96 \sqrt{\frac{s_1^2}{n_1} + \frac{s_2^2}{n_2}}$$

$$= (565 - 1200) \pm 1.96 \sqrt{\frac{(220)^2}{45} + \frac{(540)^2}{90}}$$

$$= -635 \pm 1.96 \, (65.693)$$

$$= -635 \pm 128.758$$

$$= (-763.758, -506.242)$$

Based on the sample data, we are highly confident that $\mu_1 - \mu_2$ is between -763.758 and -506.242. Therefore, we believe that the mean cost of treatment for belted accident victims is less than that of unbelted accident victims by somewhere between $506.24 and $763.76.

EXERCISES 11.1–11.17   SECTION 11.1

11.1   Consider two populations for which $\mu_1 = 30$, $\sigma_1 = 2$, $\mu_2 = 25$, and $\sigma_2 = 3$. Suppose that two independent random samples of sizes $n_1 = 40$ and $n_2 = 50$ are selected. Describe the approximate sampling distribution of $\bar{x}_1 - \bar{x}_2$ (center, spread, and shape).

11.2   An article in the November 1983 *Consumer Reports* compared various types of batteries. The average lifetimes of Duracell Alkaline AA batteries and Eveready Energizer Alkaline AA batteries were given as 4.1 h and 4.5 h, respectively. Suppose that these are the population average lifetimes.

a. Let $\bar{x}_1$ be the sample average lifetime of 100 Duracell batteries and $\bar{x}_2$ be the sample average lifetime of 100 Eveready batteries. What is the mean value of $\bar{x}_1 - \bar{x}_2$ (that is, where is the sampling distribution of $\bar{x}_1 - \bar{x}_2$ centered)? How does your answer depend on the specified sample sizes?

b. Suppose that population standard deviations of lifetime are 1.8 h for Duracell batteries and 2.0 h for Eveready batteries. With the sample sizes as given in part (a), what is the variance of the statistic $\bar{x}_1 - \bar{x}_2$, and what is its standard deviation?

c. For the sample sizes as given in part (a), draw a picture of the approximate sampling distribution curve of $\bar{x}_1 - \bar{x}_2$ (include a measurement scale on the horizontal axis). Would the shape of the curve necessarily be the same for sample sizes of 10 batteries of each type? Explain.

11.3   Leucocyte (white blood cell) counts in thoroughbred horses have recently been studied as a possible aid to the diagnosis of respiratory viral infections. The accompanying data on neutrophils (the most numerous kind of leucocyte) was reported in a comparative study of counts in horses of different ages ("Leucocyte Counts in the Healthy English Thoroughbred in Training" *Equine Vet. J.* (1984):207–209).

Age	Sample size	Sample mean	Sample standard deviation
2-year-olds	197	51	5.6
4-year-olds	77	56	4.3

Does this data suggest that the true average neutrophil count for 4-year-olds exceeds that for 2-year-olds? Let μ_1 and μ_2 denote the true average counts for 2- and 4-year-old horses, respectively. Carry out a test of

$$H_0: \mu_1 - \mu_2 = 0 \quad \text{versus} \quad H_a: \mu_1 - \mu_2 < 0$$

using level of significance .001. Be sure to give the test statistic, rejection region, computations, and conclusion (stated in the problem context).

11.4   The Associated Press reported on the spending patterns of single Americans (*San Luis Obispo Telegram-Tribune,* April 12, 1988). The mean amount of money spent each year on clothing was $657 for women and $735 for men. Suppose that these means had been computed based on information obtained from independently chosen random samples of 500 women and 300 men, and that the two sample standard deviations were $260 (for women) and $320 (for men). Is there sufficient evidence to conclude that the average amount of money spent on clothes differs for single men and women? Test the appropriate hypotheses using a significance level of .01.

11.5   The paper "The Relationship of Task and Ego Orientation to Sportsmanship Attitudes and the Perceived Legitimacy of Injurious Acts" (*Research Quarterly for Exercise and Sport* (1991):79–87) examined the extent of approval of unsporting play and cheating. High school basketball players completed a questionnaire that was used to arrive at an approval score, with higher scores indicating greater approval. A sample of 56 male players resulted in a mean approval rating for unsportsmanlike play of 2.76, whereas the mean for a sample of 67 female players was 2.02. Suppose that the two sample standard deviations were .44 for males and .41 for females. Is it reasonable to conclude that the mean approval rating is higher for male players than for female players? Use $\alpha = .05$.

11.6   Various measures of flexibility were examined in the paper "On the Generality of the 'Sit and Reach' Test: An Analysis of Flexibility Data for an Aging Population" (*Research Quarterly for Exercise and Sport* (1990):326–330). Shoulder extension was measured for 41 women and 39 men aged 45 to 75 years. For the men the mean shoulder extension was 12.0° and the standard deviation was 4.9. For women, the mean and standard deviation were 10.3 and 3.7, respectively. Is there evidence that the mean shoulder extension for 45- to 75-year-old men exceeds that for women? Test the relevant hypotheses using $\alpha = .01$.

11.7   The number of friends consulted for advice before purchasing a large TV or a VCR was examined by the authors of the paper "External Search Effort: An Investigation across Several Product Categories" (*J. of Consumer Research* (1987):83–93).

Summary statistics consistent with information in the paper are given in the accompanying table.

Type of purchase	Number of purchasers (n)	Mean number of friends consulted	Standard deviation
Large TV	50	1.65	.4
VCR	50	3.26	.6

Does this data indicate that the average number of friends consulted prior to purchase is higher for those purchasing a VCR than for those purchasing a large TV? Test the relevant hypotheses using a level .01 test.

11.8   Much attention has been focused in recent years on merger activity among business firms. Many business analysts are interested in knowing how various characteristics of merged firms compare to those of nonmerged firms. The article "Abnormal Returns from Merger Profiles" (*J. of Finan. Quant. Analysis* (1983):149–162) reported the accompanying sample data on price–earnings ratios for two samples of firms.

Type of firm	Sample size	Sample mean	Sample standard deviation
Merged	44	7.295	7.374
Nonmerged	44	14.666	16.089

Let μ_1 and μ_2 denote the true average price–earnings ratios for all merged and nonmerged firms, respectively. Estimate $\mu_1 - \mu_2$ using a 99% confidence interval.

11.9   The paper "Blood Pressure in Japanese Children during the First Three Years of Life" (*Amer. J. of Diseases of Children* (1988):875–881) gave the accompanying data on systolic blood pressure (mm Hg).

Age	Sex	n	Sample mean	Sample standard deviation
1 year	M	74	93	9
	F	72	92	8
3 years	M	86	96	10
	F	66	96	10

a. Construct a 90% confidence interval estimate for the true difference in mean systolic blood pressure for 1-year-old males and 1-year-old females.
b. Using a significance level of .05, test to determine if the mean systolic blood pressure of 1-year-old males differs from that of 3-year-old males.
c. Repeat part (b) for females.

11.10   Do teenage boys worry more than teenage girls? This is one of the questions addressed by the authors of the paper "The Relationship of Self-Esteem and Attributional Style to Young People's Worries" (*J. of Psych.* (1987):207–215). A scale called the "Worries Scale" was administered to a group of teenagers, and the results are summarized in the accompanying table.

	n	Sample mean score	Sample standard deviation
Girls	108	62.05	9.5
Boys	78	67.59	9.7

Is there sufficient evidence to conclude that teenage boys score higher on the Worries Scale than teenage girls? Use a significance level of $\alpha = .05$.

11.11   The accompanying data on water salinity(%) was obtained during a study of seasonal influence of Amazon River water on biological production in the western tropical Atlantic ("Influence of Amazon River Discharge on the Marine Production System off Barbados, West Indies" *J. of Marine Research* (1979):669–681). Let μ_1 denote the true average salinity level of water samples collected during the summer, and define μ_2 analogously for samples collected during the winter. Compute a 99% confidence interval for $\mu_1 - \mu_2$. Is it necessary to make any assumptions about the two salinity distributions? Explain.

Period	Sample size	Sample mean	Sample standard deviation
Summer	51	33.40	.428
Winter	54	35.39	.294

11.12   Some astrologists have speculated that people born under certain sun-signs are more extroverted than people born under other signs. The accompanying data was taken from the paper "Self-Attribution Theory and the Sun-Sign" (*J. of Social Psych.* (1984):121–126). The Eysenck Personality Inventory (EPI) was used to measure extroversion and neuroticism.

	Sample size	Extroversion		Neuroticism	
Sun-sign	n	$\bar{x}$	s	$\bar{x}$	s
Water signs	59	11.71	3.69	12.32	4.15
Other signs	186	12.53	4.14	12.23	4.11
Winter signs	73	11.49	4.28	11.96	4.22
Summer signs	49	13.57	3.71	13.27	4.04

a. Is there sufficient evidence to indicate that those born under water signs have a lower mean extroversion score than those born under other (nonwater) signs? Use a level .01 test.

b. Does the data strongly suggest that those born under winter signs have a lower mean extroversion score than those born under summer signs? Use a level .05 test.

c. Does the data indicate that those born under water signs differ significantly from those born under other signs with respect to mean neuroticism score? Use $\alpha = .05$.

d. Do those born under winter signs differ from those born under summer signs with respect to mean neuroticism score? Compute the *P*-value associated with the test statistic and use it to state a conclusion for significance level .01.

11.13 Recorded speech can be compressed and played back at a faster rate. The paper "Comprehension by College Students of Time-Compressed Lectures" (*J. of Exper. Educ.* (Fall 1975):53–56) gave the results of a study designed to test comprehension of time-compressed speech. Fifty students listened to a 60-min lecture and took a comprehension test. Another 50 students heard the same lecture time-compressed to 40 min. The sample mean and standard deviation of comprehension scores for the normal speed group were 9.18 and 4.59, respectively, and those for the time-compressed group were 6.34 and 4.93, respectively.

a. Use a level .01 test to determine if the true mean comprehension score for students hearing a time-compressed lecture is significantly lower than the true mean score for students who hear a lecture at normal speed.

b. Estimate the difference in the true mean comprehension scores for normal and time-compressed lectures using a 95% confidence interval.

11.14 In a study of attrition among college students, 587 students were followed through their college years ("The Prediction of Voluntary Withdrawal from College: An Unsolved Problem" *J. of Exper. Educ.* (Fall 1980):29–45). Of the 587 students in the sample, 87 withdrew from college for various reasons (although none were dismissed for academic reasons). The accompanying table gives summary statistics on SAT scores for the "persisters" and the "withdrawers."

	SAT verbal score	
	Persisters	Withdrawers
n	500.0	87.0
$\bar{x}$	491.0	503.0
s	80.6	78.8

Is there sufficient evidence to indicate a difference in true mean SAT verbal scores for students who withdraw from college and those who graduate? Perform the relevant hypothesis test using a significance level of .10.

11.15 The earning gap between men and women has been the subject of many investigations. One such study ("Sex, Salary, and Achievement: Reward-Dualism in

Academia" *Sociology of Educ.* (1981):71–85) gave the accompanying information for samples of male and female college professors. Suppose that these statistics were based on samples of size 50 chosen from the populations of all male and all female college professors.

	Males		Females	
	Mean	Standard deviation	Mean	Standard deviation
Salary	1634.10	715.00	1091.80	418.80
Years at univ.	7.93	8.04	6.25	7.65

a. Does the data strongly suggest that the mean salary for women is lower than the mean salary for men? Use a level .05 test. Does the resulting conclusion by itself point to discrimination against female professors, or are there some possible nondiscriminating explanations for the observed difference?

b. If the results of the test in part (a) were to be summarized using a *P*-value, what value should be reported?

c. Estimate the difference in the mean number of years at the university for men and women using a 90% confidence interval. Based on your interval, do you think that there is a significant difference between the true mean number of years at the university for men and women? Explain.

11.16   Should quizzes be given at the beginning or the end of a lecture period? The paper "On Positioning the Quiz: An Empirical Analysis" (*Accounting Review* (1980): 664–670) provides some insight. Two sections of an introductory accounting class were given identical instructions to read and study assigned text materials. Three quizzes and a final exam were given during the term, with one section taking quizzes at the beginning of the lecture and the other section taking quizzes at the end. Final exam scores for the two groups are summarized. Does the accompanying data indicate that there is a significant difference in the true mean final exam scores for students who take quizzes at the beginning of class and those who take quizzes at the end?

	Quiz at beginning	Quiz at end
Sample size	40	40
Mean	143.7	131.7
Standard deviation	21.2	20.9

11.17   Celebrity endorsement of products is a common advertising technique. A group of 98 people was shown an ad containing a celebrity endorsement, and a second group of 98 was shown the same ad but using an unknown actor ("Effectiveness of Celebrity Endorsees" *J. of Ad. Research* (1983):57–62). Each participant rated the commercial's believability on a scale of 0 (not believable) to 10 (very believable). Results were as follows.

	Believability of ad	
Type of ad	Mean	Standard deviation
Celebrity ad	3.82	2.63
Noncelebrity ad	3.97	2.51

Is there sufficient evidence to indicate that use of a celebrity endorsement results in a true mean believability rating that differs from the true mean rating for non-celebrity endorsements? Use a level .05 test.

11.2 Small-Sample Inferences Concerning a Difference between Two Normal Population Means

The z test and confidence interval discussed in Section 11.1 were large-sample procedures. Their use required no specific assumptions about the population distributions, as long as n_1 and n_2 were large enough to ensure that the sampling distributions of $\bar{x}_1$ and $\bar{x}_2$ were approximately normal. When one or both of the sample sizes are small, the z procedures are not appropriate.

In order to proceed in the small-sample case, we make some assumptions about the population distributions and then develop procedures that are known to perform well when these assumptions are met.

> **BASIC ASSUMPTIONS IN THIS SECTION**
> 1. Both population distributions are normal.
> 2. The two population standard deviations are identical ($\sigma_1 = \sigma_2$), with σ denoting the common value.

Figure 11.1 pictures four different pairs of population distributions. Only Figure 11.1(a) is consistent with the basic assumptions. If you believe that the relevant picture for your problem is given in Figure 11.1(b)—normal population distributions but σ_1 substantially different from σ_2—then the methods of this section are inappropriate. There are several possible inferential procedures in this case, but (unlike the procedures of this section) there is still controversy among statisticians about which one should be used. The distributions in Figure 11.1(c) have exactly the same shape and spread, but one is shifted so that it is centered to the right of the other one. Appropriate inferential procedures in this case are presented in Section 11.4. Finally, inference involving population distributions with very different

FIGURE 11.1
Four possible population
distribution pairs
(a) Both normal, $\sigma_1 = \sigma_2$
(b) Both normal, $\sigma_1 \neq \sigma_2$
(c) Same shape and spread,
differing only in location
(d) Very different shapes
and spreads

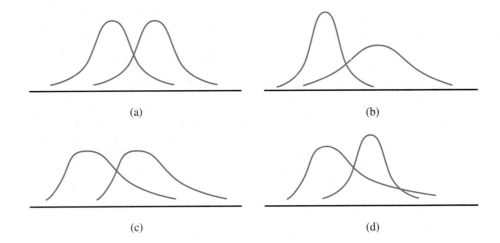

(a)   (b)

(c)   (d)

shapes and spreads, as in Figure 11.1(d), can be very complicated. Good advice
from a statistician is particularly important here.

In Chapter 8 we saw that if the population distribution is normal, the sampling
distribution of $\bar{x}$ is also normal for *any* sample size. This fact was important in the
development of the one-sample t test and confidence interval. In this section, both
population distributions are assumed normal, so the sampling distributions of both
$\bar{x}_1$ and $\bar{x}_2$ are normal, even for small samples. This in turn implies that the sampling
distribution of $\bar{x}_1 - \bar{x}_2$ is also normal for any n_1 and n_2.

The facts concerning the mean value and standard deviation of $\bar{x}_1 - \bar{x}_2$ given
in Section 11.1 remain valid here. We know that

$$\mu_{\bar{x}_1 - \bar{x}_2} = \mu_1 - \mu_2$$

which says that the $\bar{x}_1 - \bar{x}_2$ distribution is centered at $\mu_1 - \mu_2$. We are still
assuming that the two random samples are obtained independently of one another
and, in addition, that $\sigma_1 = \sigma_2 = \sigma$. The common standard deviation σ is then
used in place of σ_1 and σ_2 in the formula for the standard deviation of $\bar{x}_1 - \bar{x}_2$, resulting in

$$\sigma_{\bar{x}_1 - \bar{x}_2} = \sqrt{\frac{\sigma_1^2}{n_1} + \frac{\sigma_2^2}{n_2}}$$

$$= \sqrt{\frac{\sigma^2}{n_1} + \frac{\sigma^2}{n_2}}$$

$$= \sqrt{\sigma^2 \left(\frac{1}{n_1} + \frac{1}{n_2}\right)}$$

If $\bar{x}_1 - \bar{x}_2$ is now standardized by subtracting $\mu_{\bar{x}_1 - \bar{x}_2}$ and dividing by $\sigma_{\bar{x}_1 - \bar{x}_2}$, the result is a variable with a standard normal distribution:

$$z = \frac{\bar{x}_1 - \bar{x}_2 - (\mu_1 - \mu_2)}{\sqrt{\sigma^2 \left(\dfrac{1}{n_1} + \dfrac{1}{n_2} \right)}}$$

Estimating σ^2

Before this new standardized variable can be used as a test statistic or manipulated to yield a confidence interval, it is necessary to estimate σ^2. An obvious way to estimate σ^2 from the first sample alone is to use s_1^2, the sample variance of the n_1 observations in that sample. Similarly, the sample variance for the n_2 observations in the second sample also gives an estimate of σ^2. Intuitively, combining s_1^2 and s_2^2 in some fashion should lead to an estimate that is better than either one individually. A first thought might be to use $(s_1^2 + s_2^2)/2$, the ordinary average of the two variances. However, if n_1 is larger than n_2, the estimate s_1^2 will tend to be closer to σ^2 than will s_2^2. That is, the sample variance associated with the larger sample size tends to be more accurate than the one based on the smaller sample size. This fact suggests that a weighted average should be used, with the variance from a larger sample receiving heavier weight.

DEFINITION

The statistic for estimating the common variance σ^2 is

$$s_p^2 = \left(\frac{n_1 - 1}{n_1 + n_2 - 2} \right) s_1^2 + \left(\frac{n_2 - 1}{n_1 + n_2 - 2} \right) s_2^2$$

The computed value of s_p^2 is called the **pooled estimate of σ^2** (*pooled* is synonymous with *combined*).

The two quantities in parentheses in the formula for s_p^2 always have a sum of 1. If $n_1 = n_2$, then $s_p^2 = (\frac{1}{2})s_1^2 + (\frac{1}{2})s_2^2$, the ordinary average of the two sample variances. But whenever $n_1 \neq n_2$, the s^2 based on the larger sample size will receive more weight (be multiplied by a larger number) than will the other s^2. The multipliers of s_1^2 and s_2^2 in s_p^2 might at first seem unnatural. The reason for using them has to do with degrees of freedom. The first sample contributes $n_1 - 1$ df to the estimation of σ^2, and the second contributes $n_2 - 1$ df. The two samples are independent, so the number of degrees of freedom associated with s_p^2 is the sum $(n_1 - 1) + (n_2 - 1) = n_1 + n_2 - 2$.

EXAMPLE 11.5

Tennis elbow is thought to be aggravated by the impact experienced when hitting the ball. The paper "Forces on the Hand in the Tennis One-Handed Backhand" (*Int. J. of Sport Biomechanics* (1991):282–292) reported the force (N) on the hand just after impact on a one-handed backhand drive for six advanced players and for eight intermediate players. Summary data appears in the accompanying table.

	n	$\bar{x}$	s
Advanced	6	40.3	11.3
Intermediate	8	21.4	8.3

The authors of the paper assumed in their analysis of the data that both force distributions (advanced and intermediate) were normal with the same standard deviation, σ. The pooled estimate of σ^2 is then

$$s_p^2 = \left(\frac{n_1 - 1}{n_1 + n_2 - 2} \right) s_1^2 + \left(\frac{n_2 - 1}{n_1 + n_2 - 2} \right) s_2^2$$

$$= \left(\frac{5}{12} \right)(11.3)^2 + \left(\frac{7}{12} \right)(8.3)^2$$

$$= (.417)(127.69) + (.583)(68.89)$$

$$= 53.247 + 40.163$$

$$= 93.410$$

This gives

$$s_p = \sqrt{93.410} = 9.665$$

as the pooled estimate of σ. Notice that $s_p^2 = 93.410$ is between $s_1^2 = 127.69$ and $s_2^2 = 68.89$. It is closer to s_2^2 because s_2^2 is based on a larger sample size than is s_1^2.

When σ^2 is replaced by its estimate, s_p^2, the result is a standardized variable having a t distribution.

The standardized variable

$$t = \frac{\bar{x}_1 - \bar{x}_2 - (\mu_1 - \mu_2)}{\sqrt{s_p^2 \left(\dfrac{1}{n_1} + \dfrac{1}{n_2} \right)}}$$

has t distribution with df $= n_1 + n_2 - 2$ (provided the basic assumptions of this section are met).

Testing Hypotheses about $\mu_1 - \mu_2$

As in the previous section, we consider testing a null hypothesis of the form

H_0: $\mu_1 - \mu_2$ = hypothesized value

The test statistic results from replacing $\mu_1 - \mu_2$ in t by the hypothesized value (which often is zero). When H_0 is true, the sampling distribution of the test statistic is the t distribution with $n_1 + n_2 - 2$ df. The type I error probability is then controlled by using an appropriate t critical value to specify the rejection region.

SUMMARY OF THE POOLED t TEST

Null hypothesis: H_0: $\mu_1 - \mu_2$ = hypothesized value

Test statistic: $t = \dfrac{\bar{x}_1 - \bar{x}_2 - \text{hypothesized value}}{\sqrt{s_p^2\left(\dfrac{1}{n_1} + \dfrac{1}{n_2}\right)}}$

Alternative Hypothesis	**Rejection Region**
H_a: $\mu_1 - \mu_2$ > hypothesized value	$t > t$ critical value
H_a: $\mu_1 - \mu_2$ < hypothesized value	$t < -t$ critical value
H_a: $\mu_1 - \mu_2 \neq$ hypothesized value	Either $t > t$ critical value or $t < -t$ critical value

The test is based on $n_1 + n_2 - 2$ df, so the t critical value is obtained from the corresponding row and the appropriate column (depending on choice of α and whether the test is one-tailed or two-tailed) of Appendix Table IV.

EXAMPLE 11.6

The paper "Affective Variables Related to Mathematics Achievement among High-Risk College Freshmen" (*Psych. Reports* (1991):399–403) examines the relationship between attitudes toward mathematics and success at college level mathematics. Twenty men and thirty-eight women identified as being at high risk of failure (because they did not meet the usual admission requirements for the university) participated in the study. Each student was asked to respond to a series of questions, and then answers were used to obtain a math anxiety score. For this particular scale, the higher the score, the lower the level of anxiety toward mathematics. Summary values appear in the accompanying table. Does this data suggest that, as many researchers have hypothesized, the mean anxiety score for women is different than that for men? We will test the relevant hypotheses using a .05 level of significance.

	n	$\bar{x}$	s
Males	20	35.9	11.9
Females	38	36.6	12.3

Note that even though the sample size for the second sample is greater than 30, the fact that $n_1 = 20$ necessitates using the test developed for small samples. Since the two sample standard deviations are quite similar, the assumption $\sigma_1 = \sigma_2$ seems reasonable.

1. μ_1 = true mean math anxiety score for male at-risk students
    μ_2 = true mean math anxiety score for female at-risk students
    $\mu_1 - \mu_2$ = difference in mean math anxiety scores

2. $H_0: \mu_1 - \mu_2 = 0$

3. $H_a: \mu_1 - \mu_2 \neq 0$

4. Test statistic:

$$t = \frac{\bar{x}_1 - \bar{x}_2 - 0}{\sqrt{s_p^2\left(\dfrac{1}{n_1} + \dfrac{1}{n_2}\right)}}$$

5. The form of the alternative hypothesis ($\neq$) implies that a two-tailed rejection region should be used. With $\alpha = .05$ and

$$df = n_1 + n_2 - 2 = 20 + 38 - 2 = 56$$

Table IV gives the t critical value 2.00. H_0 will be rejected if either $t > 2.00$ or $t < -2.00$.

6. Based on the given sample standard deviations,

$$s_1^2 = (11.9)^2 = 141.61$$
$$s_2^2 = (12.3)^2 = 151.29$$

and

$$s_p^2 = \left(\frac{n_1 - 1}{n_1 + n_2 - 2}\right)s_1^2 + \left(\frac{n_2 - 1}{n_1 + n_2 - 2}\right)s_2^2$$

$$= \left(\frac{19}{56}\right)141.61 + \left(\frac{37}{56}\right)151.29$$

$$= 48.05 + 99.96$$
$$= 148.01$$

Then

$$t = \frac{35.9 - 36.6 - 0}{\sqrt{148.01\left(\dfrac{1}{20} + \dfrac{1}{38}\right)}} = \frac{-.70}{3.36} = -.21$$

7. Since $-.21$ is not in the rejection region, we fail to reject H_0. There is no reason to believe that the mean math anxiety score of at-risk males differs from that of at-risk females.

The pooled t test is highly recommended by virtually all statisticians when the two basic assumptions of this section are at least approximately satisfied. Normal probability plots can be used to check the plausibility of the normality assumptions. There is a formal test procedure, called an F test, for testing H_0: $\sigma_1^2 = \sigma_2^2$ versus H_a: $\sigma_1^2 \neq \sigma_2^2$. Some statisticians suggest that this test be carried out as a preliminary to the pooled t test, with the latter test used only if H_0: $\sigma_1^2 = \sigma_2^2$ is not rejected. But for technical reasons, we (along with many other statisticians) do not recommend this approach.[1]

Suppose that an investigator believes, prior to collecting data, that variability is roughly the same in the two populations or for the two treatments. Then, if calculated values of s_1^2 and s_2^2 are of roughly the same order of magnitude, use of the pooled t test is reasonable (particularly if the two sample sizes are not too different). This was certainly the case in Example 11.6.

P-Values

Rather than specifying a rejection region corresponding to a fixed significance level, we can compute the value of t and then obtain bounds on the associated P-value. If t is between two consecutive critical values in the $(n_1 + n_2 - 2)$ df row of the t table, the associated levels of significance (along the bottom margin) give upper and lower bounds. Only an upper bound is given if the computed t exceeds the largest critical value in the row, and only a lower bound is given when t is smaller than the smallest tabled value in the row.

EXAMPLE 11.7

(*Example 11.5 continued*) Example 11.5 gave summary statistics for two samples of tennis players. We will use the given information to determine if the mean force after impact is greater for advanced tennis players than it is for intermediate players.

---

[1]Both the pooled t test and the F test are based on the assumption of normal population distributions. But the F test is much more sensitive to departures from this assumption than is the t test. A significant value of the F statistic might result not because σ_1^2 and σ_2^2 differ greatly but because the population distributions are slightly nonnormal.

1. μ_1 = mean force after impact for advanced players
         μ_2 = mean force after impact for intermediate players
     $\mu_1 - \mu_2$ = difference in mean force

2. $H_0: \mu_1 - \mu_2 = 0$

3. $H_a: \mu_1 - \mu_2 > 0$

4. Test statistic

$$t = \frac{\bar{x}_1 - \bar{x}_2 - 0}{\sqrt{s_p^2 \left(\dfrac{1}{n_1} + \dfrac{1}{n_2} \right)}}$$

5. Calculations: From Example 11.5,

$$n_1 = 6 \qquad n_2 = 8$$
$$\bar{x}_1 = 40.3 \qquad \bar{x}_2 = 21.4$$
$$s_p^2 = 93.41$$

$$t = \frac{40.3 - 21.4 - 0}{\sqrt{93.41 \left(\dfrac{1}{6} + \dfrac{1}{8} \right)}} = \frac{18.9}{5.22} = 3.62$$

6. Since df $= n_1 + n_2 - 2 = 6 + 8 - 2 = 12$, we look at the 12-df row of Table IV. The computed value of t falls between 3.06 and 3.93, the t critical values corresponding to .005 and .001 one-tailed significance levels. Therefore,

     $.001 < P\text{-value} < .005$

7. We will now use a significance level of .01 to reach a conclusion. Since P-value $< .01$, we reject H_0. There is sufficient evidence to conclude that the mean force after impact is greater for advanced players than it is for intermediate players.

A Small-Sample Confidence Interval

A small-sample confidence interval for $\mu_1 - \mu_2$ is easily obtained from the basic t variable of this section. Both the derivation of and formula for the interval are very similar to that of the large-sample z interval discussed in the previous section.

> The **pooled t confidence interval for $\mu_1 - \mu_2$**, which is valid when both population distributions are normal and $\sigma_1 = \sigma_2$, is
>
> $$\bar{x}_1 - \bar{x}_2 \pm (t \text{ critical value}) \sqrt{s_p^2 \left(\frac{1}{n_1} + \frac{1}{n_2} \right)}$$
>
> The t critical value is based on $n_1 + n_2 - 2$ degrees of freedom. Critical values associated with the most frequently used confidence levels appear in Table IV.

EXAMPLE 11.8

Much research effort has been expended in studying possible causes of the pharmacological and behavioral effects resulting from smoking marijuana. The article "Intravenous Injection in Man of Δ^9THC and 11–OH–Δ^9THC" (*Science* (1982): 633) reported on a study of two chemical substances thought to be instrumental in marijuana's effects. Subjects were given one of the two substances in increasing amounts and asked to say when the effect was first perceived. Data values are necessary dose to perception per kilogram of body weight.

Δ^9THC	19.54	14.47	16.00	24.83	26.39	11.49
		($\bar{x}_1 = 18.79$,	$s_1 = 5.91$)			
11–OH–Δ^9THC		15.95	25.89	20.53	15.52	14.18	16.00
		($\bar{x}_2 = 18.01$,	$s_2 = 4.42$)			

From these values, $s_p^2 = 27.23$. Assuming normality of the two distributions and $\sigma_1 = \sigma_2$, we will calculate a 95% confidence interval for $\mu_1 - \mu_2$, the difference in mean dose to perception for the two substances. From the 10-df row of the t table, the t critical value is 2.23. The interval is, therefore,

$$(18.79 - 18.01) \pm 2.23 \sqrt{27.23 \left(\frac{1}{6} + \frac{1}{6} \right)} = .78 \pm 6.72$$

$$= (-5.94, 7.50)$$

This interval is rather wide because s_p^2 is large and the two sample sizes are small. Notice that the interval includes 0, so 0 is one of the many plausible values for $\mu_1 - \mu_2$. That is, it is plausible that there is no difference in the mean dose necessary for perception for the two substances.

EXERCISES 11.18–11.42   SECTION 11.2

11.18   Let μ_1 and μ_2 denote true average stopping distances (feet) for two different types of cars traveling at 50 mi/h. Assuming normality and $\sigma_1 = \sigma_2$, test

$$H_0: \mu_1 - \mu_2 = 0 \quad \text{versus} \quad H_a: \mu_1 - \mu_2 \neq 0$$

at level .05 using the following data: $n_1 = 6$, $\bar{x}_1 = 122.7$, $s_1 = 5.59$, $n_2 = 5$, $\bar{x}_2 = 129.3$, and $s_2 = 5.25$.

11.19   Suppose that μ_1 and μ_2 are true mean stopping distances (feet) at 50 mi/h for cars equipped with disk brakes and with pneumatic brakes, respectively. Use the pooled t test at significance level .01 to test

$$H_0: \mu_1 - \mu_2 = -10 \quad \text{versus} \quad H_a: \mu_1 - \mu_2 < -10$$

for the following data: $n_1 = 6$, $\bar{x}_1 = 115.7$, $s_1 = 5.03$, $n_2 = 6$, $\bar{x}_2 = 129.3$, and $s_2 = 5.38$.

11.20   Here's one to sink your teeth into: The authors of the paper "Analysis of Food Crushing Sounds During Mastication: Total Sound Level Studies" (*J. of Texture Studies* (1990):165–178) studied the nature of sounds generated during eating. Peak loudness (in decibels at 20 cm away) was measured for both open-mouth and closed-mouth chewing of potato chips and of tortilla chips. Forty subjects participated, with ten in each combination of conditions (such as closed-mouth, potato chip, and so on). We are not making this up! Summary values taken from plots given in the paper appear in the accompanying table.

	n	$\bar{x}$	s
Potato chip			
Open mouth	10	63	13
Closed mouth	10	54	16
Tortilla chip			
Open mouth	10	60	15
Closed mouth	10	53	16

a. Construct a 95% confidence interval for the difference in mean peak loudness between open-mouth and closed-mouth chewing of potato chips. Interpret the resulting interval.

b. For closed-mouth chewing (the recommended method!), is there sufficient evidence to indicate that there is a difference between potato and tortilla chips with respect to mean peak loudness? Test the relevant hypotheses using $\alpha = .01$.

c. The means and standard deviations given here were actually for stale chips. When ten measurements of peak loudness were recorded for closed-mouth chewing of *fresh* tortilla chips, the resulting mean and standard deviation were 56 and 14, respectively. Is there sufficient evidence to conclude that fresh tortilla chips are louder than stale chips? Use $\alpha = .05$.

11.21 The authors of the paper "Dynamics of Canopy Structure and Light Interception in *Pinus elliottii,* North Florida" (*Ecological Monographs* (1991):33–51) planned an experiment to determine the effect of fertilizer on a measure of leaf area. A number of plots were available for the study, and half were selected at random to be fertilized. In order to assure that the plots to receive the fertilizer and the control plots were similar, prior to beginning the experiment tree density (the number of trees per hectare) was recorded for eight plots to be fertilized and eight control plots, resulting in the given data.

Fertilizer plots:	1024	1216	1312	1280
	1216	1312	992	1120
Control plots:	1104	1072	1088	1328
	1376	1280	1120	1200

Based on this data, would you conclude that there is a significant difference in the mean tree density for fertilizer and control plots? Use $\alpha = .05$.

11.22 Thirteen males and fourteen females participated in a study of grip and leg strength ("Sex Differences in Static Strength and Fatigability in Three Different Muscle Groups," *Research Quarterly for Exercise and Sport* (1990):238–242). Right-leg strength (in newtons) was recorded for each participant, resulting in the values given here. Estimate the difference in mean right-leg strength between males and females using a 95% confidence interval. Interpret the resulting interval.

	n	$\bar{x}$	s
Males	13	2127	513
Females	14	1843	446

11.23 Spreading fires tend to do more damage to hardwood forests than do spot fires. Data on the percent of trees scarred by fire that appeared in the paper "Natural Disturbance Regimes in Hemlock-Hardwood Forests of the Upper Great Lakes Region" (*Ecological Monographs* (1991):145–164) can be used to quantify the difference in the extent of damage. The accompanying data was used to construct a 90% confidence interval for the difference in mean percent of trees scarred by fire for spreading and spot fires. Construct normal probability plots for each of the two samples. Do you think that use of the pooled t confidence interval was justified? Explain.

	Percent scarred				
Spreading fires	21.9	26.7	9.2	6.7	29.2
	26.7	6.7	8.3	18.4	4.9
Spot fires	1.6	4.6	1.1	1.2	21.1
	11.9	1.8	14.7	7.5	

11.24   Rainfall specimens from various sites in New Zealand were analyzed to determine the amount of sulfur in the rainwater. The sites were classified according to whether they were closer to the east or west coast of the islands. Is there sufficient evidence to conclude that the mean sulfur concentration in rainwater differs for the eastern and western parts of the island? Use $\alpha = .05$.

Eastern sites: .26   .13   .62   .40   .28   .23   .80   .32   .08   .09   .19   .21
                .58   .17   .61

Western sites: 1.15   1.20   .43   .46   .44   .25   .43   .43   .25   .43   .83   .11
              .60   .43   .23   .30   .22   .08   .07   .28

11.25   Are very young infants more likely to imitate actions that are modeled by a person or simulated by an object? This question was the basis of a research study summarized in the paper "The Role of Person and Object in Eliciting Early Imitation" (*J. Experimental Child Psych.* (1991):423–433). One action examined was mouth opening. This action was modeled repeatedly by either a person or a doll, and the number of times that the infant imitated the behavior was recorded. Twenty-seven infants participated, with 12 exposed to a human model and 15 exposed to the doll. Summary values are given here. Is there sufficient evidence to conclude that the mean number of imitations is higher for infants who watch a human model than for infants who watch a doll? Test the relevant hypotheses using a .01 significance level.

	Person model	Doll model
$\bar{x}$	5.14	3.46
s	1.6	1.3

11.26   The authors of the paper "The Color-a-Person Body Dissatisfaction Test" (*J. of Personality Assessment* (1991):395–413) used a nonverbal measure of body dissatisfaction to compare students at two different universities. A sample of 47 women at the University of Cincinnati and a sample of 24 women at the University of New Mexico participated in the study. Mean and standard deviations for a measure of self-esteem are given in the accompanying table. Is it reasonable to conclude that women at the two universities differ with respect to mean self-esteem score? Use $\alpha = .05$.

	Self-esteem score	
	$\bar{x}$	s
University of Cincinnati	32.55	4.41
University of New Mexico	31.25	4.92

11.27   In an experiment to study the effects of exposure to ozone, 20 rats were exposed to ozone in the amount of 2 ppm for a period of 30 days. The average lung volume for these rats after exposure was determined to be 9.28 mL with a standard deviation of .37, whereas the average lung volume for a control group of 17 rats with similar initial characteristics was 7.97 mL with a standard deviation of .41 ("Effect of Chronic Ozone Exposure on Lung Elasticity in Young Rats" *J. Appl. Physiology* (1974):92–97). Does this data indicate that there is an increase in true average lung volume associated with ozone? Letting μ_1 and μ_2 denote the true average lung volumes for the exposed and unexposed conditions, test

$$H_0: \mu_1 - \mu_2 = 0 \quad \text{versus} \quad H_a: \mu_1 - \mu_2 > 0$$

Use a level .01 test.

11.28   A paper in the *Journal of Nervous and Mental Disorders* ((1968):136–146) reported the following data on the amount of dextroamphetamine excreted by a sample of children having organically related disorders and a sample of children with nonorganic disorders. (Dextroamphetamine is a drug commonly used to treat hyperkinetic children.) Use a level .05 test to decide whether the data suggests a difference in mean dextroamphetamine excretion for children with organic and nonorganic disorders.

Organic	17.53	20.60	17.62	28.93	27.10
Nonorganic	15.59	14.76	13.32	12.45	12.79

11.29   An experiment to assess the effects of automobile pollution was described in the paper "Effects of Roadside Conditions on Plants and Insects" (*J. of Appl. Ecology* (1988):709–715). Twenty soil specimens taken .6 m from the roadside resulted in a mean nitrogen concentration of 1.70 mg/g. Twenty soil specimens taken 6 m from the roadside resulted in a mean nitrogen concentration of 1.35 mg/g. Suppose that the sample standard deviations were .4 (at .6 m) and .3 (at 6 m). Is there sufficient evidence to conclude that the mean nitrogen concentration in soil .6 m from the roadside is higher than that at 6 m? Test the relevant hypotheses using $\alpha = .01$.

11.30   The paper "Effect of Carbohydrate and Vitamin B_6 on Fuel Substrates during Exercise in Women" (*Medicine and Science in Sports and Exercise* (1988): 223–239) compared a group of women who participated in regular aerobic exercise with a group who did not. Data on percent body fat was obtained by skinfolds measured at seven sites and is summarized in the following table.

	Sample size	Mean percent body fat	Sample standard deviation
Aerobic exercise	5	20.1	4.2
No aerobic exercise	5	20.4	3.4

a. Estimate the true mean difference in percent body fat between the two groups using a 90% confidence interval.

b. Does your interval in part (a) contain zero? How would you interpret the interval?

    c. What assumptions about the two populations are necessary in order for the interval of part (a) to be valid?

11.31   The accompanying table gives data that appeared in the paper "Development and Clinical Trial of a Minimal-Contact, Cognitive-Behavioral Treatment for Tension Headache" (*Cognitive Therapy and Research* (1988):325–339). Two different treatments for headache (a relaxation therapy and a cognitive-behavioral therapy) were compared. Is there sufficient evidence to support the researchers' claim that the cognitive-behavioral therapy is more effective than relaxation in increasing the mean number of headache-free days (for a one-week period)? Test the relevant hypotheses using a level .05 test.

Therapy	Sample size	Mean number of headache-free days	Sample standard deviation
Relaxation	24	3.82	1.75
Cognitive-behavioral	24	5.71	1.43

11.32   Toxaphene is an insecticide that has been identified as a pollutant in the Great Lakes ecosystem. To investigate the effect of toxaphene exposure on animals, groups of rats were given toxaphene in their diet. The paper "Reproduction Study of Toxaphene in the Rat" (*J. of Environ. Sci. Health* (1988):101–126) reported weight gains (in grams) for rats given a low dose (4 ppm) and for control rats whose diet did not include the insecticide. The accompanying table gives data for both male and female rats.

	Males			Females		
	n	$\bar{x}$	s	n	$\bar{x}$	s
Control	15	529	66	23	237	32
Low dose	15	551	71	20	249	54

    a. Is there sufficient evidence to conclude that a low dose of toxaphene increases mean weight gain for male rats? Use a significance level of .05.

    b. Do you reach the same conclusion as in part (a) for female rats?

11.33   In an effort to assess the risk of brain damage in infants, the authors of the paper "Neuropathologic Documentation of Prenatal Brain Damage" (*Amer. J. of Diseases of Children* (1988):858–866) studied both infants born with brain damage and infants born without brain damage. They also looked at premature babies as well as those carried to term.

	Sample size	Mean birth weight (g)	Sample standard deviation
Term			
Brain damage	12	2998	707
No brain damage	13	2704	627
Premature			
Brain damage	10	1541	448
No brain damage	54	1204	656

a. Does the data indicate that the true mean birth weight for premature infants with brain damage differs from that of premature infants without brain damage? Test the relevant hypotheses using a significance level of .05.

b. Repeat part (a) for infants carried to term.

c. Use a 90% confidence interval to estimate the difference in mean weight between term and premature infants without brain damage.

d. Repeat part (c) for infants with brain damage.

11.34 The effect of plant diversity on beetle density was examined in a series of experiments described in the paper "Effects of Plant Diversity, Host Density, and Host Size on Population Ecology of the Colorado Potato Beetle" (*Environ. Entomology* (1987):1019–1026). Potatoes grown in fallow plots and potatoes grown in plots that also included bean plants and weeds (called a *triculture*) were compared on the basis of the number of beetle eggs found on the plant leaves. Data is given in the following table.

Plots	Number of plants inspected	Mean number of beetle eggs found	Sample standard deviation
Fallow	4	7.1	5.40
Triculture	4	14.6	8.30

Is there sufficient evidence to conclude that potatoes grown in fallow plots have a smaller mean number of eggs per plant than those grown in a triculture? Use a .05 level of significance.

11.35 Unionization of university faculty is a fairly recent phenomenon. There has been much speculation about the effect of collective bargaining on faculty and student satisfaction. Eighteen unionized and 23 nonunionized campuses participated in a study described in the paper "The Relationship between Faculty Unionism and Organizational Effectiveness" (*Academy of Management J.* (1982):6–24). The participating schools were scored on a number of dimensions. Summary statistics on faculty satisfaction and student academic development are given.

Campus	Student academic development		Faculty satisfaction	
Unionized ($n = 18$)	$\bar{x} = 3.71$	$s = .49$	$\bar{x} = 4.49$	$s = .56$
Nonunionized ($n = 23$)	$\bar{x} = 4.36$	$s = .88$	$\bar{x} = 4.85$	$s = .39$

a. Let μ_1 be the mean score on student academic development for all unionized schools and μ_2 the corresponding mean for nonunionized schools. Use a level .05 test to determine if there is a significant difference in mean student academic development score between unionized and nonunionized colleges.

b. Does the data indicate that unionized and nonunionized schools differ significantly with respect to mean faculty satisfaction score? Use a significance level of .05.

c. What P-value is associated with the value of the test statistic computed in part (b)?

11.36 Measurements on a number of physiological variables for samples of 8 male and 8 female adolescent tennis players were reported in "Physiological and Anthropometric Profiles of Elite Prepubescent Tennis Players" (*Sportsmed.* (1984): 111–116). Results are summarized in the accompanying table.

	Boys		Girls	
	$\bar{x}$	s	$\bar{x}$	s
Shoulder flexibility	214.4	12.9	216.3	20.0
Ankle flexibility	71.4	4.6	72.5	8.9
Grip strength	23.9	2.5	22.2	4.1

a. Estimate the difference in true mean grip strength for boys and girls using a 95% confidence interval. Does the confidence interval indicate that precise information about this difference is available?

b. Construct 95% confidence intervals for the difference between boys and girls with respect to both true mean shoulder flexibility and ankle flexibility. Interpret each of the intervals.

11.37 A study concerning the sublethal effects of insecticides ("Effects of Sublethal Doses of DDT and Three Other Insecticides on Tribolium Confusum" *J. of Stored Products Research* (1983):43–50) reported the accompanying data on oxygen consumption for flour beetles ten days after DDT treatment and for a control sample of untreated beetles.

Group	Sample size	Sample mean	Sample standard deviation
Untreated	25	5.02	.94
Treated	25	4.37	.98

a. Does the use of the pooled t test seem reasonable in determining whether DDT treatment results in a decrease in average oxygen consumption? Explain.
b. Test the hypotheses suggested in part (a) using a significance level of .05.
c. Obtain as much information as you can about the P-value for the test in part (b), and use the result to reach a conclusion at significance level .01.

11.38 Do certain behaviors result in a severe drain on energy resources because a great deal of energy is expended in comparison to energy intake? The paper "The Energetic Cost of Courtship and Aggression in a Plethodontid Salamander" (*Ecology* (1983):979–983) reported on one of the few studies concerned with behavior and energy expenditure. The accompanying data is on oxygen consumption (mL/g/h) for male–female salamander pairs. (The determination of consumption values was rather complicated, and it is partly for this reason that so few studies of this type have been carried out.) Compute a 95% confidence interval for the difference between true average consumption for noncourting pairs and true average consumption for courting pairs. What assumptions about the two consumption distributions are necessary for the validity of the interval?

Behavior	Sample size	Sample mean	Sample standard deviation
Noncourting	11	.072	.0066
Courting	15	.099	.0071

11.39 The establishment and maintenance of vegetation is an important component in most metalliferous mine waste–reclamation schemes. The ecological consequences for animal populations exposed to pollutants at contaminated reclamation sites is of concern. The paper "Cadmium in Small Mammals from Grassland Established on Metalliferous Mine Waste" (*Environ. Pollution* (1984):153–162) reported on cadmium concentrations in various body organs for several species of small mammals. The accompanying data is for skull concentrations in samples of one such species both at a reclamation site and at a control site.

Site	Sample size	Sample mean	Sample standard deviation
Control	20	.59	.13
Reclamation	21	.72	.18

a. Would you recommend using a z test from the previous section to analyze this data? Why or why not?
b. Use the test procedure discussed in *this* section to decide whether true mean cadmium concentrations in skulls differ at the two sites.

11.40 The paper "Pine Needles as Sensors of Atmospheric Pollution" (*Environ. Monitoring* (1982):273–286) reported on the use of neutron activity analysis to determine pollutant concentrations in pine needles. According to the paper's authors, "These observations strongly indicated that for those elements which are determined well by the analytical procedures, the distribution of concentrations is log-normal. Accordingly, in tests of significance the logarithms of concentrations will be used." The given data refers to bromine concentration in needles taken from a site near an oil-fired steam plant and from a relatively clean site. The summary values are means and standard deviations of the log-transformed observations. Let μ_1 be the true average log concentration at the first site and define μ_2 analogously for the second site. Test for equality of the two concentration distribution means against the alternative that they are different, by using the pooled t test at level .05 with the log-transformed data.

Site	Sample size	Mean log concentration	Standard deviation of log concentration
Steam plant	8	18	4.9
Clean	9	11	4.6

11.41   Information concerning the extent to which various agricultural products are affected by drought can have a great bearing on planting decisions. The paper "Varietal Differences in the Response of Potatoes to Repeated Periods of Water Stress in Hot Climates" (*Potato Research* (1983):315–321) reported the accompanying data on tuber yield (g/plant) for one particular potato variety.

Treatment	Sample size	Mean	Standard deviation
Unstressed	6	376	78.4
Stressed	12	234	65.8

    a. Assuming that the yield distributions for the two treatments have the same variance σ^2, compute the pooled estimate of this variance.

    b. Does the data suggest that true average yield under water stress is less than for the unstressed condition? Test at level of significance .01.

    c. Based on the computed value of the test statistic in part (b), what can you say about the P-value?

11.42   Referring to Exercise 11.41, suppose that the investigator wished to know whether water stress lowered true average yield by more than 50 g/plant. State and test the appropriate hypotheses at level .01.

11.3 Large-Sample Inferences Concerning a Difference between Two Population Proportions

Large-sample methods for estimating and testing hypotheses about a single population proportion, π, were presented in Chapters 9 and 10. The symbol π was used to represent the true proportion of individuals in the population who possess some characteristic (the "successes"). Inferences about the value of π were based on p, the corresponding sample proportion of successes.

Many investigations are carried out to compare the proportion of successes in one population (or resulting from one treatment) to the proportion of successes in a second population (or from a second treatment). As was the case for means, the subscripts 1 and 2 are used to distinguish between the two population proportions, samples sizes, and sample proportions.

NOTATION

Population 1: Proportion of "successes" = π_1
Population 2: Proportion of "successes" = π_2

	Sample size	Proportion of successes
Sample from population 1	n_1	p_1
Sample from population 2	n_2	p_2

When comparing two populations on the basis of "success" proportions, it is natural to focus on the quantity $\pi_1 - \pi_2$, the difference between the two population proportions. Since p_1 provides an estimate of π_1 and p_2 provides an estimate of π_2, the obvious choice for an estimate of $\pi_1 - \pi_2$ is $p_1 - p_2$.

Because p_1 and p_2 each vary in value from sample to sample, so will the difference $p_1 - p_2$. For example, a first sample from each of two populations might yield

$$p_1 = .74 \qquad p_2 = .63 \qquad p_1 - p_2 = .11$$

A second sample from each might result in

$$p_1 = .79 \qquad p_2 = .67 \qquad p_1 - p_2 = .12$$

and so on. Since the statistic $p_1 - p_2$ will be the basis for drawing inferences about $\pi_1 - \pi_2$, we need to know something about its behavior.

PROPERTIES OF THE SAMPLING DISTRIBUTION OF $p_1 - p_2$

If the two samples are selected independently of one another, the following properties hold:

1. $\mu_{p_1-p_2} = \pi_1 - \pi_2$

   This says that the sampling distribution of $p_1 - p_2$ is centered at $\pi_1 - \pi_2$, so $p_1 - p_2$ is an unbiased statistic for estimating $\pi_1 - \pi_2$.

2. $\sigma^2_{p_1-p_2} = \sigma^2_{p_1} + \sigma^2_{p_2} = \dfrac{\pi_1(1 - \pi_1)}{n_1} + \dfrac{\pi_2(1 - \pi_2)}{n_2}$

(continued)

and

$$\sigma_{p_1 - p_2} = \sqrt{\frac{\pi_1(1 - \pi_1)}{n_1} + \frac{\pi_2(1 - \pi_2)}{n_2}}.$$

3. If both n_1 and n_2 are large [$n_1\pi_1 \geq 5$, $n_1(1 - \pi_1) \geq 5$, $n_2\pi_2 \geq 5$, and $n_2(1 - \pi_2) \geq 5$], then p_1 and p_2 each have approximately normal sampling distributions, so their difference, $p_1 - p_2$, also has approximately a normal sampling distribution.

The properties in the box imply that when the samples are independently selected and both sample sizes are large, the distribution of the standardized variable

$$z = \frac{p_1 - p_2 - (\pi_1 - \pi_2)}{\sqrt{\frac{\pi_1(1 - \pi_1)}{n_1} + \frac{\pi_2(1 - \pi_2)}{n_2}}}$$

is described approximately by the standard normal (z) curve.

A Large-Sample Test Procedure

Comparisons of π_1 and π_2 are often based on large, independently selected samples, and we restrict ourselves to this case. The most general null hypothesis of interest has the form

$$H_0: \pi_1 - \pi_2 = \text{hypothesized value}$$

However, when the hypothesized value is something other than zero, the appropriate test statistic differs somewhat from the test statistic used for $H_0: \pi_1 - \pi_2 = 0$. Since this latter H_0 is almost always the relevant one in applied problems, we will focus exclusively on it.

Our basic testing principle has been to use a procedure that controls the probability of a type I error at the desired level α. This requires using a test statistic with a sampling distribution that is known when H_0 is true. That is, the test statistic should be developed under the assumption that $\pi_1 = \pi_2$ (as specified by the null hypothesis $\pi_1 - \pi_2 = 0$). In this case, π can be used to denote the common value of the two population proportions. The z variable obtained by standardizing $p_1 - p_2$ then simplifies to

$$z = \frac{p_1 - p_2}{\sqrt{\frac{\pi(1 - \pi)}{n_1} + \frac{\pi(1 - \pi)}{n_2}}}$$

Unfortunately, this cannot serve as a test statistic because the denominator cannot be computed: H_0 says that there is a common value π but it does not specify what that value is. A test statistic can be obtained, though, by first estimating π from the sample data and then using this estimate in the denominator of z.

When $\pi_1 = \pi_2$, either p_1 or p_2 separately gives an estimate of the common proportion π. A better estimate than either of these is a weighted average of the two, in which more weight is given to the sample proportion based on the larger sample.

DEFINITION

The **combined estimate of the common population proportion** is

$$p_c = \left(\frac{n_1}{n_1 + n_2}\right) p_1 + \left(\frac{n_2}{n_1 + n_2}\right) p_2$$

The test statistic for testing $H_0: \pi_1 - \pi_2 = 0$ results from using p_c in place of π in the standardized variable z given previously. This z statistic has approximately a standard normal distribution when H_0 is true, so a test that has the desired level of significance α uses the appropriate z critical value to specify the rejection region.

SUMMARY OF LARGE-SAMPLE z TESTS FOR $\pi_1 - \pi_2$

Null hypothesis: $H_0: \pi_1 - \pi_2 = 0$

Test statistic: $z = \dfrac{p_1 - p_2}{\sqrt{\dfrac{p_c(1 - p_c)}{n_1} + \dfrac{p_c(1 - p_c)}{n_2}}}$

Alternative Hypothesis	**Rejection Region**
$H_a: \pi_1 - \pi_2 > 0$	$z > z$ critical value
$H_a: \pi_1 - \pi_2 < 0$	$z < -z$ critical value
$H_a: \pi_1 - \pi_2 \neq 0$	Either $z > z$ critical value or $z < -z$ critical value

The z critical values corresponding to the most frequently used significance levels appear in the bottom row of Table IV. This test requires large samples and should be used only when all the quantities $n_1 p_1$, $n_1(1 - p_1)$, $n_2 p_2$, and $n_2(1 - p_2)$ are at least 5.

EXAMPLE 11.9

Many investigators have studied the effect of the wording of questions on survey responses. Consider the following two versions of a question concerning gun control.

1. Would you favor or oppose a law that would require a person to obtain a police permit before purchasing a gun?
2. Would you favor or oppose a law that would require a person to obtain a police permit before purchasing a gun, or do you think that such a law would interfere too much with the right of citizens to own guns?

The extra phrase in Question 2 reminding individuals of the right to bear arms might tend to elicit a smaller proportion of favorable responses than would the first question without the phrase. Does the data suggest that this is the case? We will test the relevant hypotheses using $\alpha = .01$.

Let π_1 denote the proportion of all adults who would respond *favor* when asked Question 1, and define π_2 similarly for Question 2. The paper "Attitude Measurement and the Gun Control Paradox" (*Public Opinion Quarterly* (1977–1978): 427–438) reported the accompanying sample data.

Sample size	$n_1 = 615$	$n_2 = 585$
Number who favor	463	403
Sample proportion	$p_1 = \dfrac{463}{615} = .753$	$p_2 = \dfrac{403}{585} = .689$

Suppose that $\pi_1 = \pi_2$; let π denote the common value. Then the combined estimate of π (since $n_1 + n_2 = 1200$) is

$$p_c = \frac{615}{1200}(.753) + \frac{585}{1200}(.689) = .722$$

The seven-step procedure can now be used to perform the hypothesis test.

1. $\pi_1 - \pi_2$ is the difference between the true proportions of favorable responses to Questions 1 and 2.

2. $H_0: \pi_1 - \pi_2 = 0 \qquad (\pi_1 = \pi_2)$

3. $H_a: \pi_1 - \pi_2 > 0 \qquad (\pi_1 > \pi_2)$, in which case the extra phrase *does* result in proportionately fewer favorable responses.

4. Test statistic:

$$z = \frac{p_1 - p_2}{\sqrt{\dfrac{p_c(1 - p_c)}{n_1} + \dfrac{p_c(1 - p_c)}{n_2}}}$$

5. The appropriate test is upper-tailed, and for $\alpha = .01$, Table IV gives the z critical value 2.33. In other words, H_0 will be rejected in favor of H_a if $z > 2.33$.

6. $n_1 = 615, n_2 = 585, p_1 = .753, p_2 = .689$, and $p_c = .722$, so

$$z = \frac{.753 - .689}{\sqrt{\dfrac{(.722)(.278)}{615} + \dfrac{(.722)(.278)}{585}}} = \frac{.064}{.0259} = 2.47$$

7. Since $2.47 > 2.33$, the hypothesis H_0 is rejected at level .01. Inclusion of the extra phrase about the right to bear arms *does* seem to result in fewer favorable responses than would be elicited without the phrase.

Because the large-sample test procedure here is a z test, we can compute a P-value in exactly the same way as we did for other z tests. For an upper-tailed test, the P-value is the area under the z curve to the right of the computed z. In the last example, $z = 2.47$ and the 2.47 entry of Table II is .9932, so

$$P\text{-value} = 1 - .9932 = .0068.$$

Since $.0068 < .01$, the hypothesis H_0 would be rejected at significance level .01 but would not be rejected at level .005 or .001.

EXAMPLE 11.10

Do teachers find their work rewarding and satisfying? The paper "Work-Related Attitudes" (*Psychological Reports* (1991):443–450) reported the results of a survey of 395 elementary school teachers and 266 high school teachers. Of the elementary school teachers, 224 said they were very satisfied with their jobs, whereas 126 of the high school teachers were very satisfied with their work. Based on this data, is it reasonable to conclude that the proportion very satisfied is different for elementary school teachers than it is for high school teachers? We will test the appropriate hypotheses using a .05 significance level.

1. π_1 = proportion of elementary school teachers who are very satisfied
   π_2 = proportion of high school teachers who are very satisfied

2. $H_0: \pi_1 - \pi_2 = 0$

3. $H_a: \pi_1 - \pi_2 \neq 0$

4. Test statistic:

$$z = \frac{p_1 - p_2}{\sqrt{\dfrac{p_c(1 - p_c)}{n_1} + \dfrac{p_c(1 - p_c)}{n_2}}}$$

5. $p_1 = \dfrac{224}{395} = .567; \qquad p_2 = \dfrac{126}{266} = .474$

The combined estimate of the common population proportion is

$$p_c = \left(\frac{n_1}{n_1 + n_2}\right)p_1 + \left(\frac{n_2}{n_1 + n_2}\right)p_2$$

$$= \left(\frac{395}{661}\right)(.567) + \left(\frac{266}{661}\right)(.474)$$

$$= .339 + .191$$

$$= .530$$

$$z = \frac{.567 - .474}{\sqrt{\dfrac{(.530)(.470)}{395} + \dfrac{(.530)(.470)}{266}}} = \frac{.093}{.040} = 2.33$$

6. The P-value associated with this test is twice the area under the standard normal (z) curve and to the right of the computed value of the test statistic, 2.33.

$$P\text{-value} = 2(.0099) = .0198$$

7. Since P-value $< \alpha$ (.0198 < .05), we reject H_0. The data supports the claim that the proportion very satisfied is different for elementary-school than for high-school teachers.

A Confidence Interval

A large-sample confidence interval for $\pi_1 - \pi_2$ is a special case of the general z interval formula

point estimate $\pm$ (z critical value)(estimated standard deviation)

The statistic $p_1 - p_2$ gives a point estimate of $\pi_1 - \pi_2$, and the standard deviation of this statistic is

$$\sigma_{p_1-p_2} = \sqrt{\frac{\pi_1(1 - \pi_1)}{n_1} + \frac{\pi_2(1 - \pi_2)}{n_2}}$$

An estimated standard deviation is obtained by using the sample proportions p_1 and p_2 in place of π_1 and π_2, respectively, under the square root symbol. Notice that this estimated standard deviation differs from the one used earlier in the test statistic. Here there isn't a null hypothesis that claims $\pi_1 = \pi_2$, so there is no common value of π to estimate.

A large-sample confidence interval for $\pi_1 - \pi_2$ is given by

$$(p_1 - p_2) \pm (z \text{ critical value}) \sqrt{\frac{p_1(1 - p_1)}{n_1} + \frac{p_2(1 - p_2)}{n_2}}$$

The interval is valid whenever $n_1 p_1$, $n_1(1 - p_1)$, $n_2 p_2$, and $n_2(1 - p_2)$ are at least 5.

EXAMPLE 11.11

Researchers at the National Cancer Institute released the results of a study that examined the effect of weed-killing herbicides on house pets. (Associated Press, September 4, 1991). The following data is compatible with summary values given in the report. Dogs, some of whom were from homes where the herbicide was used on a regular basis, were examined for the presence of malignant lymphoma. We will use the given data to estimate the difference between the proportion of exposed dogs that develop lymphoma and the proportion of unexposed dogs that develop lymphoma.

Group	Sample size	Number with lymphoma	p
Exposed	827	473	.57
Unexposed	130	19	.15

Let π_1 denote the proportion of exposed dogs that develop lymphoma, and define π_2 similarly for unexposed dogs. The sample sizes are large enough for the large-sample interval to be valid ($n_1 p_1 = 827(.57) \geq 5$, $n_1(1 - p_1) = 827(.43) \geq 5$, and so on). A 90% confidence interval for $\pi_1 - \pi_2$ is

$$(.57 - .15) \pm (1.645) \sqrt{\frac{(.57)(.43)}{827} + \frac{(.15)(.85)}{130}}$$

$$= .42 \pm (1.645)(.0357)$$

$$= .42 \pm .06$$

$$= (.36, .48)$$

Based on the observed sample, we believe that the proportion of exposed dogs that develop lymphoma exceeds that for unexposed dogs by somewhere between .36 and .48.

EXERCISES 11.43–11.60   SECTION 11.3

11.43   Let π_1 and π_2 denote the proportions of all male and all female shoppers, respectively, who buy only name-brand grocery products (as opposed to generic or store brands).

a. Test H_0: $\pi_1 - \pi_2 = 0$ versus H_a: $\pi_1 - \pi_2 \neq 0$ at level .05, using the following data: $n_1 = 200$, number of successes (only name-brand purchases) $= 87$, $n_2 = 300$, number of successes $= 96$.

b. Use the data of part (a) to compute a 95% confidence interval for $\pi_1 - \pi_2$.

11.44 Some defendants in criminal proceedings plead guilty and are sentenced without a trial, whereas others plead innocent, are subsequently found guilty, and then are sentenced. In recent years legal scholars have speculated as to whether the sentences of those who plead guilty differ in severity from the sentences of those who plead innocent and are subsequently judged guilty. Consider the accompanying data on a group of defendants from San Francisco County, all of whom were accused of robbery and had previous prison records ("Does It Pay to Plead Guilty? Differential Sentencing and the Functioning of Criminal Courts" *Law and Society Rev.* (1981–1982):45–69).

	Plea	
	Guilty	Not guilty
Number judged guilty	$n_1 = 191$	$n_2 = 64$
Number sentenced to prison	101	56
Sample proportion	$p_1 = .529$	$p_2 = .875$

Does this data suggest that the proportion of all defendants in these circumstances who plead guilty and are sent to prison differs from the proportion who are sent to prison after pleading innocent and being found guilty? Use $\alpha = .01$.

11.45 It is thought that the front cover and the nature of the first question on mail surveys influence the response rate. The paper "The Impact of Cover Design and First Questions on Response Rates for a Mail Survey of Skydivers" (*Leisure Sciences* (1991):67–76) tested this theory by experimenting with different cover designs. One cover was plain; the other used a picture of a skydiver. The researchers speculated that the return rate would be lower for the plain cover.

Cover	Number sent	Number returned
Plain	207	104
Skydiver	213	109

Does this data support the researchers' hypothesis? Test the relevant hypotheses using $\alpha = .10$.

11.46 Using an electronic process called time compression, a 30-s television commercial can be broadcast in its entirety in only 24 s. There is no shift in voice pitch and subjects are not aware that commercials have been altered. The article "Reducing the Costs of TV Commercials by Use of Time Compressions" (*J. of Marketing Research* (1980):52–57) reported on a study involving recall ability for subjects watching compressed as compared to noncompressed commercials. For one commercial, 15 of the 57 subjects viewing the normal version could subsequently recall the commercial, whereas 32 of the 74 subjects viewing the compressed version could subsequently recall it. Does this data suggest any difference between true recall proportions for the two versions?

    a. Verify that the sample sizes are large enough to justify using the large-sample procedures.

    b. Carry out a test at level .05 to answer the question posed.

    c. Compute the *P*-value. Based on this value, what would you conclude at level .10?

11.47   The Associated Press (June 8, 1991) reported the results of surveys conducted in 1970 and 1990. In each survey, women in their early 30s were asked whether they had ever been married. In the 1970 survey, 6% of those surveyed responded that they had never married, whereas 16% of the respondents in the 1990 survey had never married. The article didn't give sample sizes, but suppose that each survey had included 200 women. Would this data lead to the conclusion that the proportion of all women who have never married is higher in 1990 than it was in 1970? Use a test with significance level .01.

11.48   The paper "Foraging Behavior of the Indian False Vampire Bat" (*Biotropica* (1991):63–67) reported that 36 of 193 female bats in flight spent more than 5 min in the air before locating food. For male bats, 64 of 168 spent more than 5 min in the air. Is there sufficient evidence to conclude that the proportion of flights longer than 5 min in length differs for males and females? Test the relevant hypotheses using $\alpha = .01$.

11.49   The *Los Angeles Times* (March 1, 1987) reported that 70% of women motorists and 85% of male motorists pump their own gas. Suppose that these percentages were computed using samples of 100 males and 100 females. Use a 90% confidence interval to estimate the difference between the proportion of males and the proportion of females who pump their own gas. *so use this # first*

11.50   A person released from prison before completing the original sentence is placed under the supervision of a parole board. If that person violates specified conditions of good behavior during the parole period, the board can order a return to prison. To what extent is the frequency of parole violations related to the type of crime and various other factors? The paper "Impulsive and Premeditated Homicide: An Analysis of the Subsequent Parole Risk of the Murderer" (*J. of Criminal Law and Criminology* (1978):108–114) reported the accompanying data on parole behavior. One sample of individuals had served time in prison for impulsive murder and the other sample had served time for premeditated murder.

	Crime	
	Impulsive	Premeditated
Sample size	$n_1 = 42$	$n_2 = 40$
Number with no violation	13	22
Sample proportion	$p_1 = .310$	$p_2 = .550$

    Construct a 98% confidence interval for the difference in the proportion who successfully completed parole for impulsive and premeditated murderers.

11.51   The paper "Softball Sliding Injuries" (*Amer. J. of Diseases of Children* (1988): 715–716) provided a comparison of break-away bases (designed to reduce injuries) and stationary bases. Consider the following data (which agrees with summary values given in the paper).

	Number of games played	Number of games where a player suffered a sliding injury
Stationary bases	1250	90
Break-away bases	1250	20

Does the use of break-away bases reduce the proportion of games with a player suffering a sliding injury? Answer by performing a level .01 test.

11.52   An experiment to determine the effects of temperature on the survival of insect eggs was described in the paper "Development Rates and a Temperature-Dependent Model of Pales Weevil" (*Environ. Entomology* (1987):956–962). At 11° C, 73 of 91 eggs survived to the next stage of development. At 30° C, 102 of 110 eggs survived. Do the results of this experiment suggest that the survival rate (proportion surviving) differs for the two temperatures? Test the relevant hypotheses using $\alpha = .05$.

11.53   Ionizing radiation is being given increasing attention as a method for preserving horticultural products. The paper "The Influence of Gamma-Irradiation on the Storage Life of Red Variety Garlic" (*J. of Food Processing and Preservation* (1983):179–183) reported that 153 of 180 irradiated garlic bulbs were marketable (no external sprouting, rotting, or softening) 240 days after treatment, but only 119 of 180 untreated bulbs were marketable after this length of time. Does this data suggest that the true proportion of marketable irradiated bulbs exceeds that for untreated bulbs? Test the relevant hypotheses at level .01.

11.54   The positive effect of water fluoridation on dental health is well documented. One study that validates this is described in the paper "Impact of Water Fluoridation on Children's Dental Health: A Controlled Study of Two Pennsylvania Communities" (*Amer. Stat. Assoc. Proc. of the Social Statistics Section* (1981):262–265). Two communities were compared. One had adopted fluoridation in 1966, whereas the other had no fluoridation program. Of 143 children from the town without fluoridated water, 106 had decayed teeth, and 67 of 119 children from the town with fluoridated water had decayed teeth. Let π_1 denote the true proportion of children drinking fluoridated water who have decayed teeth and let π_2 denote the analogous proportion for children drinking unfluoridated water. Estimate $\pi_1 - \pi_2$ using a 90% confidence interval. Does the interval contain 0? Interpret the interval.

11.55   What psychological factors contribute to the success of competitive athletes? Numerous possibilities are examined in the paper "Elite Divers and Wrestlers: A Comparison between Open- and Closed-Skill Athletes" (*J. of Sport Psych.* (1983):390–409). Competitive divers participating in qualifying trials were asked whether they exercised within 1 h of a competition. Suppose that of 20 qualifying divers, 7 exercised within 1 h of a competition, whereas 12 of 25 nonqualifying divers exercised within 1 h of a meet. Is there sufficient evidence to indicate that the true proportion of qualifying divers who exercise within 1 h of a competition differs from the corresponding proportion for nonqualifying divers? Use a level .10 test.

11.56   As part of a class project, two college students from Florida found that people are willing to help strangers in quite surprising circumstances (Associated Press, May 10, 1984). The two students splashed their faces and hands and rinsed their mouths with gin. They told passersby that they were too drunk to unlock their car doors and asked for help. One student was dressed in a business suit, whereas the other wore a dirty T-shirt. Of 50 people approached by the student in the suit, 21 helped unlock the car door and aided him in getting into the car! The student in the T-shirt also approached 50 people and was assisted by 23 of them! Does the data suggest that the true proportion of people that would assist a well-dressed drunk into a car differs significantly from the true proportion who would assist a drunk in dirty clothes? Use a level .05 test.

11.57   The Associated Press (*Corvallis Gazette Times,* May 12, 1986) reported that "infants whose mothers use cocaine during pregnancy are far more likely than other babies to fall victim to sudden infant death syndrome." This statement was based on the data in the accompanying table. Does the data support the statement made? Test the relevant hypotheses using a .01 significance level.

	n	Number whose infants died
Mothers using cocaine	60	10
Mothers with no cocaine use	1600	5

11.58   How common is driving under the influence of alcohol among teenagers? This question was examined in the paper "Predictors of Driving While Intoxicated Among Teenagers" (*J. of Drug Issues* (1988):367–384). The accompanying data is compatible with summary statistics in the paper. Is there sufficient evidence to conclude that the proportion of girls who have driven while intoxicated in the past year is smaller than the corresponding proportion of boys? Use a .01 significance level.

	Number surveyed	Number who have driven while intoxicated
Boys	100	28
Girls	100	17

11.59   The *San Francisco Chronicle* (May 27, 1983) reported the results of a poll designed to assess public opinion on legalized gambling. Of 750 Californians interviewed, 578 favored a state lottery. A similar survey in 1971 found that of 750 people contacted, 518 favored a state lottery.

a. Does the data strongly suggest that the true 1983 proportion of Californians who favored a state lottery exceeds the corresponding 1971 proportion? Use a level .01 test.

b. What P-value is associated with the value of the test statistic in part (a)?

11.60   The article "New Stance Taken on Blood Cholesterol" (*Los Angeles Times*, February 12, 1984) stated: "Ten thousand patients have been treated surgically and 10,000 comparable patients have been treated medically. Five years later, 91% of the surgical patients are alive and 90% of the medical patients are alive. No difference."

a. Use the preceding information to test H_0: $\pi_1 - \pi_2 = 0$, where π_1 is the true proportion of patients who survive 5 years when treated surgically and π_2 is defined analogously for those treated medically.

b. Does the result of your hypothesis test in part (a) agree with the statement of "no difference" that appeared in the article? Do you think this is a case of statistical rather than practical significance? Explain.

11.4   Distribution-Free Procedures for Inferences Concerning a Difference between Two Population Means

One approach to making inferences about $\mu_1 - \mu_2$ when n_1 and n_2 are small is to assume that the two population distributions are normal with $\sigma_1 = \sigma_2$ and then use the pooled t test or confidence interval developed in Section 11.2. In some situations, though, the normality assumption may not be reasonable. The procedures to be presented in this section are valid under the following less-restrictive conditions on the population distributions.

> **BASIC ASSUMPTIONS IN THIS SECTION**
>
> The two population distributions have the same shape and spread. The only possible difference between the distributions is that one may be shifted to one side of the other.

Distributions consistent with these assumptions were pictured in Figure 11.1(c). A procedure that is valid whenever the basic assumptions are met is one whose use does not depend on any overly specific assumptions about the population distributions. Such a procedure is said to be **distribution-free** (some texts use the phrase *nonparametric* instead of distribution-free). The pooled t test is not distribution-free because its use is predicated on the specific assumption of (at least approximate) normality.

Inferences about $\mu_1 - \mu_2$ will be made from information in two independent random samples, one consisting of n_1 observations from the first population and the other consisting of n_2 observations from the second population. Suppose that we are trying to decide whether or not the two distributions are identical (because of our basic assumptions, this becomes $\mu_1 = \mu_2$ versus $\mu_1 \neq \mu_2$). When they are identical, each of the $n_1 + n_2$ observations is actually drawn from the same population distribution. The distribution-free procedure presented here is based on regarding the $n_1 + n_2$ observations as a single data set and assigning ranks to the ordered values. The assignment is easiest when there are no ties among the $n_1 + n_2$ values (each observation is different from every one of the others), so assume for the moment that this is the case. Then the smallest among the $n_1 + n_2$ values receives rank 1, the second smallest rank 2, and so on, until finally the largest value is assigned rank $n_1 + n_2$.

EXAMPLE 11.12

An experiment to compare fuel efficiencies for two types of subcompact automobiles was carried out by first randomly selecting $n_1 = 5$ cars of type 1 and $n_2 = 5$ cars of type 2. Each car was then driven from Phoenix to Los Angeles by a nonprofessional driver, after which the fuel efficiency (in mi/gal) was determined. The resulting data, with observations in each sample ordered from smallest to largest, is given here.

Type 1	39.3	41.0	42.4	43.0	44.4
Type 2	37.8	39.0	39.8	40.7	42.1

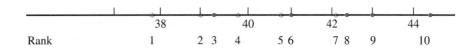

38		40	42	44
Rank 1	2 3 4	5 6	7 8 9	10

•   Sample 1

*   Sample 2

The ranks of the five observations in the first sample are 3, 6, 8, 9, 10. If these five observations had all been larger than every value in the second sample, the corresponding ranks would have been 6, 7, 8, 9, and 10. On the other hand, if all five sample 1 observations had been less than each value in the second sample, the ranks would have been 1, 2, 3, 4, and 5. The ranks of the five observations in the first sample might be any set of five numbers from among 1, 2, 3, ..., 9, 10—there are actually 252 possibilities.

Testing Hypotheses

Let's first consider testing

$$H_0: \mu_1 - \mu_2 = 0 \qquad (\mu_1 = \mu_2)$$

versus

$$H_a: \mu_1 - \mu_2 \neq 0 \qquad (\mu_1 \neq \mu_2)$$

When H_0 is true, all $n_1 + n_2$ observations in the two samples are actually drawn from identical population distributions. We would then expect that the observations in the first sample would be intermingled with those of the second sample when plotted along the number line. In this case, the ranks of the observations should also be intermingled. For example, with $n_1 = 5$ and $n_2 = 5$, the set of sample 1 ranks 2, 3, 5, 8, 10 would be consistent with $\mu_1 = \mu_2$, as would the set 1, 4, 7, 8, 9. However, when $\mu_1 = \mu_2$, it would be quite unusual for all five values from sample 1 to be smaller than every value in sample 2, resulting in the set 1, 2, 3, 4, 5 of sample 1 ranks. Similarly, we would not expect to observe 6, 7, 8, 9, 10 as the sample 1 ranks when the population distributions are identical.

A convenient measure of the extent to which the ranks are intermingled is the sum of the sample 1 ranks. These ranks in Example 11.12 were 3, 6, 8, 9, and 10, so

$$\begin{aligned} \text{rank sum} &= 3 + 6 + 8 + 9 + 10 \\ &= 36 \end{aligned}$$

The smallest possible rank sum when $n_1 = n_2 = 5$ is $1 + 2 + 3 + 4 + 5 = 15$, and the largest possible sum is $6 + 7 + 8 + 9 + 10 = 40$. If μ_1 and μ_2 differ greatly, we would expect the rank sum to be near either its smallest possible value (if $\mu_1 < \mu_2$) or its largest possible value (if $\mu_1 > \mu_2$). This suggests selecting both an upper-tail critical value and a lower-tail critical value and then rejecting H_0 in favor of H_a if either *rank sum* $\geq$ *upper-tail critical value* or *rank sum* $\leq$ *lower-tail critical value*. The two critical values should be chosen so that the probability of rejecting H_0 when H_0 is true (the type I error probability) has a specified value α. This requires information about the sampling distribution of the rank sum statistic when H_0 is true.

Consider again the case $n_1 = n_2 = 5$. There are 252 different sets of 5 from among the 10 ranks 1, 2, 3, . . . , 9, 10. The key point is that when H_0 is true, any one of these 252 sets has the same chance of being the sample 1 ranks as does any other set because all 10 observations come from the same population distribution. The chance under H_0 that any particular set occurs is 1/252 (because the possibilities are equally likely). Table 11.1 displays the seven sets of sample 1 ranks yielding the smallest rank sum values and the seven sets yielding the largest rank sum values. Each one of the other 238 possible rank sets has a rank sum value between 19 and 36.

TABLE 11.1   The seven rank sets that have the smallest rank sums and the seven that have the largest rank sums when $n_1 = 5$, $n_2 = 5$

Sample 1 ranks	Rank sum	Sample 1 ranks	Rank sum
1 2 3 4 5	15	6 7 8 9 10	40
1 2 3 4 6	16	5 7 8 9 10	39
1 2 3 4 7	17	4 7 8 9 10	38
1 2 3 5 6	17	5 6 8 9 10	38
1 2 3 4 8	18	3 7 8 9 10	37
1 2 3 5 7	18	4 6 8 9 10	37
1 2 4 5 6	18	5 6 7 9 10	37

Suppose that we agree to reject H_0 if either

$$\text{rank sum} \geq 37 \quad \text{or} \quad \text{rank sum} \leq 18$$

The probability of a type I error is then

$$\alpha = P(\text{rank sum} \geq 37 \text{ or rank sum} \leq 18 \text{ when } H_0 \text{ is true})$$

$$= P(\text{rank set is one of the 14 displayed in Table 11.1 when } H_0 \text{ is true})$$

$$= \frac{14}{252} = .056 \approx .05$$

That is, when this test procedure is used, roughly 5% of all possible samples will result in H_0 being incorrectly rejected. The approximate level of significance for the test is .05.

The alternative hypothesis $H_a: \mu_1 - \mu_2 > 0$ states that the first population distribution is shifted to the right of the second one. Evidence supporting this claim is provided by samples for which most sample 1 observations are larger than most observations in the second sample, resulting in large sample 1 ranks and a relatively large rank sum value. Thus for this alternative, an upper-tailed test—reject H_0 in favor of H_a if rank sum $\geq$ upper-tail critical value—is appropriate. In the case $n_1 = n_2 = 5$, Table 11.1 implies that the upper-tail test with critical value 39 has

$$\alpha = P(\text{type I error})$$

$$= P(\text{rank sum} \geq 39 \text{ when } H_0 \text{ is true})$$

$$= \frac{2}{252}$$

$$= .008$$

$$\approx .01$$

There are 12 sets of rankings with rank sum greater than or equal to 36, so using upper-tail critical value 36 gives

$$\alpha = P(\text{rank sum} \geq 36 \text{ when } H_0 \text{ is true})$$

$$= \frac{12}{252}$$

$$= .048$$

$$\approx .05$$

A lower-tailed test is appropriate when the alternative hypothesis is $H_a\colon \mu_1 - \mu_2 < 0$. The test that rejects H_0 in favor of this H_a when rank sum ≤ 16 has (in the case $n_1 = n_2 = 5$) $\alpha \approx .01$, whereas using critical value 19 gives $\alpha \approx .05$.

It is not possible to obtain exactly level .05 or .01 because the rank sum statistic has a discrete sampling distribution that, at least for n_1 and n_2 small, associates probability with relatively few possible values. This contrasts with z and t tests for which these levels could be achieved exactly. The reason for this is that the t and z sampling distributions are continuous, so probability is the area under a curve, and a critical value that captures area .05 or .01 can always be found.

SUMMARY OF THE RANK SUM TEST[2]

  Null hypothesis: $H_0\colon \mu_1 - \mu_2 = 0$

  Test statistic: rank sum = the sum of ranks assigned to the n_1 observations in the first sample

Alternative Hypothesis	Rejection Region
$H_a\colon \mu_1 - \mu_2 > 0$	Rank sum $\geq$ upper-tail critical value
$H_a\colon \mu_1 - \mu_2 < 0$	Rank sum $\leq$ lower-tail critical value
$H_a\colon \mu_1 - \mu_2 \neq 0$	Either rank sum $\geq$ upper-tail critical value or rank sum $\leq$ lower-tail critical value

The critical values for the upper-, lower-, and two-tailed tests are given in Table VI for the levels of significance closest to $\alpha = .05$ and $\alpha = .01$.

EXAMPLE 11.13

The extent to which an infant's health is affected by parental smoking is an important public health concern. The paper "Measuring the Exposure of Infants to Tobacco Smoke" (*New Engl. J. of Med.* (1984):1075–1078) reported on a study in which various measurements were taken both from a random sample of infants who had been exposed to household smoke and from a sample of unexposed infants. The accompanying data consists of observations on urinary concentration of cotanine, a major metabolite of nicotine (the values constitute a subset of the original data and were read from a plot that appeared in the paper). Does the data suggest

---

[2]This test procedure is often called the *Wilcoxin rank sum test* or the *Mann-Whitney test,* after the statisticians who developed it. Some sources use a slightly different (but equivalent) test statistic formula and set of critical values.

that the true average cotanine level is higher for exposed than for unexposed infants? The investigators used the rank sum test to analyze the data, so we do also.

Unexposed ($n_1 = 7$)	8	11	12	14	20	43	111	
Rank	1	2	3	4	5	7	11	
Exposed ($n_2 = 8$)	35	56	83	92	128	150	176	208
Rank	6	8	9	10	12	13	14	15

1. $\mu_1 - \mu_2$ is the difference between true average cotanine concentration for unexposed and exposed infants.
2. $H_0: \mu_1 - \mu_2 = 0$
3. $H_a: \mu_1 - \mu_2 < 0$ (unexposed average is less than exposed average)
4. Test statistic: rank sum = sum of the sample 1 ranks
5. The form of H_a dictates the use of a lower-tailed test. The critical value for a level .01 test is, from Table VI, 36, so H_0 should be rejected at level .01 if rank sum ≤ 36.
6. Rank sum = $1 + 2 + 3 + 4 + 5 + 7 + 11 = 33$
7. Since $33 \leq 36$, the computed value of the test statistic falls in the rejection region. H_0 is therefore rejected at level .01 in favor of the conclusion that $\mu_1 < \mu_2$. Infants exposed to cigarette smoke do seem to have higher cotanine levels than do unexposed infants.

The test procedure just described is easily modified to handle a hypothesized value other than zero. Consider as an example testing $H_0: \mu_1 - \mu_2 = 5$. This hypothesis is equivalent to $H_0: (\mu_1 - 5) - \mu_2 = 0$. That is, if 5 is subtracted from each population 1 value, then according to H_0, the distribution of the resulting values coincides with the population 2 distribution. This suggests that if the hypothesized value of 5 is first subtracted from each sample 1 observation, the test can then be carried out as before.

> To test $H_0: \mu_1 - \mu_2 =$ hypothesized value, subtract the hypothesized value from each observation in the first sample and then determine the ranks of these when combined with the n_2 observations from the second sample.

EXAMPLE 11.14

(*Example 11.13 continued*) Reconsider the cotanine concentration data introduced in Example 11.13. Suppose a researcher wished to know whether average concentration for exposed children exceeds that for unexposed children by more than 25. Recalling that μ_1 is the true average concentration for unexposed children, the exposed average exceeds the unexposed average by 25 when $\mu_1 - \mu_2 = -25$ and by more than 25 when $\mu_1 - \mu_2 < -25$. The hypotheses of interest are, therefore,

$$H_0: \mu_1 - \mu_2 = -25$$
$$H_a: \mu_1 - \mu_2 < -25$$

These hypotheses can be tested by first subtracting -25 (or, equivalently, adding 25) to each sample 1 observation.

Sample 1							
Unexposed	8	11	12	14	20	43	111
Unexposed $-(-25)$	33	36	37	39	45	68	136
Rank	1	3	4	5	6	8	12

Sample 2							
Exposed	35	56	83	92	128	150	176	208
Rank	2	7	9	10	11	13	14	15

1. $\mu_1 - \mu_2 =$ difference in true mean cotanine concentration for unexposed and exposed infants
2. $H_0: \mu_1 - \mu_2 = -25$
3. $H_a: \mu_1 - \mu_2 < -25$
4. Test statistic: rank sum = sum of sample 1 ranks
5. Since this is a lower-tail test with $\alpha = .01$, $n_1 = 7$, and $n_2 = 8$, Table VI gives critical value 36. We will reject H_0 at level .01 if rank sum ≤ 36.
6. Rank sum $= 1 + 3 + 4 + 5 + 6 + 8 + 12 = 39$
7. Since $39 \nleq 36$, we fail to reject H_0. Sample evidence does not suggest that the difference between mean concentration levels exceeds 25.

Frequently the $n_1 + n_2$ observations in the two samples are not all different from one another. When this occurs, the rank assigned to each observation in a tied group is the average of the ranks that would be assigned if the values in the group all differed slightly from one another. Consider, for example, the 10 ordered values

5.6   6.0   6.0   6.3   6.8   7.1   7.1   7.1   7.9   8.2

If the two 6.0 values differed slightly from each other, they would be assigned ranks 2 and 3. Therefore, each one is assigned rank $(2 + 3)/2 = 2.5$. If the three 7.1 observations were all slightly different, they would receive ranks 6, 7, and 8, so each of the three is assigned rank $(6 + 7 + 8)/3 = 7$. The ranks for the above 10 observations are then

1   2.5   2.5   4   5   7   7   7   9   10

If the proportion of tied values is quite large, it is recommended that the rank sum statistic be multiplied by a *correction factor*. Several of the chapter references contain details on this.

The P-value for a given set of data and test procedure was defined earlier as the smallest level α at which H_0 could be rejected. Thus it makes sense to speak of the P-value when the rank sum test is used. However, because Table VI gives critical values only for $\alpha = .05$ and $.01$, an exact P-value or even an accurate bound is not available unless the computed rank sum value coincides with or is very close to a tabulated critical value. There are more detailed tables from which the P-value can be determined.

A Normal Approximation

Table VI contains critical values only for $n_1 \leq 8$ and $n_2 \leq 8$. There are more extensive tables of critical values for other sample-size combinations, but when both sample sizes exceed 8, an alternative approach is based on the following approximation.

If $n_1 > 8$ and $n_2 > 8$, the distribution of the rank sum statistic when H_0 is true is well approximated by a normal distribution having mean value $n_1(n_1 + n_2 + 1)/2$ and standard deviation $\sqrt{n_1 n_2(n_1 + n_2 + 1)/12}$. This implies that the standardized variable

$$z = \frac{\text{rank sum} - n_1(n_1 + n_2 + 1)/2}{\sqrt{n_1 n_2(n_1 + n_2 + 1)/12}}$$

can serve as a test statistic. The rejection region uses a z critical value that depends on α and is upper-, lower-, or two-tailed according to whether H_a contains the inequality $>$, $<$, or $\neq$.

EXAMPLE 11.15

To compare interest rates offered by California banking institutions with those offered by Midwestern banks, 10 institutions from each region were randomly selected and the current interest rate on a one-year certificate of deposit was determined for each one. Does the accompanying data suggest that true average rates differ for the two regions? Let's analyze the data using the rank sum test.

Region	M	M	M	C	M	C	M	M	C	C
Rate	5.7	5.8	6.0	6.0	6.2	6.25	6.4	6.5	6.5	6.5
Rank	1	2	3.5	3.5	5	6	7	9	9	9
Region	M	M	C	M	C	M	C	C	C	C
Rate	6.75	6.75	6.8	7	7	7.2	7.25	7.4	7.5	7.5
Rank	11.5	11.5	13	14.5	14.5	16	17	18	19.5	19.5

1. Let μ_1 = true average rate for California banks, μ_2 = the true average rate for Midwestern banks, and $\mu_1 - \mu_2$ = the difference in average rates.
2. $H_0: \mu_1 - \mu_2 = 0$
3. $H_a: \mu_1 - \mu_2 \neq 0$
4. Test statistic:

$$z = \frac{\text{rank sum} - n_1(n_1 + n_2 + 1)/2}{\sqrt{n_1 n_2 (n_1 + n_2 + 1)/12}}$$

5. The form of H_a necessitates using a two-tailed test. For $\alpha = .05$, the bottom row of Table IV gives the z critical value as 1.96. H_0 should be rejected in favor of H_a either if $z > 1.96$ or if $z < -1.96$.
6. With $n_1 = n_2 = 10$,

$$\frac{n_1(n_1 + n_2 + 1)}{2} = \frac{10(10 + 10 + 1)}{2} = 105$$

and

$$\sqrt{\frac{n_1 n_2 (n_1 + n_2 + 1)}{12}} = \sqrt{\frac{(10)(10)(21)}{12}} = 13.23$$

The rank sum value is

$$\text{rank sum} = 3.5 + 6 + 9 + 9 + 13 + 14.5 + 17 + 18 + 19.5 + 19.5$$
$$= 129$$

so

$$z = \frac{129 - 105}{13.23} = \frac{24}{13.23} = 1.81$$

7. Since 1.81 is not in the rejection region, H_0 should not be rejected. The sample data does not suggest that average rates for the two regions differ.

Ordering the observations can be tedious, especially when n_1 and n_2 are large. Fortunately all the standard statistical computer packages have a rank sum option that does the ordering, ranking, and computations automatically.

Comparing the Rank Sum and Pooled *t* Tests

The basic assumptions of this section (identical shapes and spreads) are satisfied when both population distributions are normal with $\sigma_1 = \sigma_2$—the "home ground" of the pooled *t* test. Although the rank sum test can be used in this situation, statisticians favor the pooled *t* test. This is because when both tests are used with the same prescribed level of significance (for example, $\alpha = .05$), the pooled *t* test has smaller type II error probabilities than does the rank sum test. However, even on the pooled t test's home ground, the rank sum doesn't fare too badly. Roughly speaking, the rank sum test requires slightly larger sample sizes than what is required by the pooled t test in order to obtain the same β's.

When the population distributions are nonnormal but satisfy the basic assumptions stated earlier in this section, the situation is different. The pooled t test can now suffer by comparison with the rank sum test in two different ways. First, at least for small samples the actual level α for the t test may be quite different from the α selected by the investigator. This is because the t statistic no longer has a t distribution with $n_1 + n_2 - 2$ df when H_0 is true (it does only for normal population distributions), so the t critical values tabulated in Table IV no longer capture the prescribed tail areas.

For moderate to large samples, the specification of α is correct for either test. Here, though, when both tests use the same α, the rank sum test may have substantially smaller β than does the pooled t test (remember, we are no longer in normal land). This is particularly true when the population distributions have markedly nonnormal shapes, such as substantial skews or very heavy tails compared to a normal curve. In summary, the rank sum test performs almost as well as the pooled t test for the case of normal distributions and may substantially outperform the t test in other cases—provided that the distributions still have the same shapes and spreads. When this is not the case, comparisons between these two tests and various others are necessary, and statisticians still don't have all the answers.

A Confidence Interval for $\mu_1 - \mu_2$

A confidence interval based on the rank sum statistic is not nearly as familiar to users of statistical methods as is the hypothesis-testing procedure. This is unfortunate because the confidence interval has the same virtues to recommend it as does the rank sum test. It is valid under more general circumstances than is the pooled t interval, and its performance as compared to the pooled t interval parallels the performance of the rank sum test vis-à-vis the pooled t test.

The key to obtaining a confidence interval lies in exploiting a relationship between confidence intervals and two-tailed tests. Consider as an example the one-sample t test for testing

$H_0: \mu = $ hypothesized value

versus

$H_a: \mu \neq $ hypothesized value

and the one-sample t interval

$$\bar{x} \pm (t \text{ critical value}) \cdot \frac{s}{\sqrt{n}}$$

If $n = 12, \bar{x} = 52.6$, and $s = 6.3$, the 95% interval is

$$52.6 \pm (2.20) \cdot \frac{6.3}{\sqrt{12}}$$

$$= 52.6 \pm 4.0$$

$$= (48.6, 56.6)$$

For a two-tailed level .05 test, the computed value of the test statistic

$$t = \frac{\bar{x} - \text{hypothesized value}}{s/\sqrt{n}}$$

is compared to critical values $+2.20$ and -2.20. Suppose that the hypothesized value is 50.0, a number inside the confidence interval. Then

$$t = \frac{52.6 - 50.0}{6.3/\sqrt{12}} = 1.43$$

This value is not in the rejection region, so H_0 is not rejected at level .05. Similarly, if the hypothesized value is any other number in the 95% interval, H_0 cannot be rejected. However, if the hypothesized value is outside the confidence interval (such as, 46 or 57), then it is easily checked that H_0 would be rejected. So the confidence interval consists of all hypothesized values for which H_0: $\mu = $ *hypothesized value* is not rejected in favor of H_a: $\mu \neq $ *hypothesized value*.

Suppose that a level .05 test is available for testing

   H_0: population characteristic $=$ hypothesized value

versus

   H_a: population characteristic $\neq$ hypothesized value

Then a 95% confidence interval for the population characteristic consists of all hypothesized values for which H_0 cannot be rejected. A 99% interval is associated with a level $\alpha = .01$ test.

The form of the rank sum confidence interval can be most easily understood if an alternative expression for the rank sum statistic is first presented. Recall that the test involving a particular hypothesized value (not necessarily zero) is carried out by first subtracting the hypothesized value from each sample 1 observation and then ranking and summing the n_1 ranks. Suppose instead that each observation in the second sample is subtracted from every observation in the first sample. This gives a set of $n_1 n_2$ differences. Then it can be shown that

$$\text{rank sum} = \frac{n_1(n_1 + 1)}{2} + \left(\begin{array}{c} \text{number of differences that are greater than} \\ \text{or equal to the hypothesized value} \end{array} \right)$$

For example, if $n_1 = n_2 = 4$, there are 16 differences, and

$$\text{rank sum} = \frac{4(4 + 1)}{2} + \left(\begin{array}{c}\text{number of differences greater than}\\\text{or equal to hypothesized value}\end{array}\right)$$

$$= \quad 10 \quad + \left(\begin{array}{c}\text{number of differences greater than}\\\text{or equal to hypothesized value}\end{array}\right)$$

Table VI gives 11 and 25 as the lower- and upper-tail critical values when $\alpha = .05$. Thus H_0 will not be rejected if

$$12 \leq \text{rank sum} \leq 24$$

or, equivalently, if

$$2 \leq \left(\begin{array}{c}\text{number of differences greater than}\\\text{or equal to hypothesized value}\end{array}\right) \leq 14$$

Figure 11.2 illustrates the interval of hypothesized values for which this is the case. The 95% confidence interval for $\mu_1 - \mu_2$ then extends from the second smallest difference to the second largest difference.

FIGURE 11.2
16 differences and the 95% rank sum confidence interval when $n_1 = n_2 = 4$

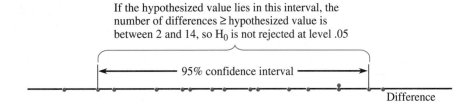

If the hypothesized value lies in this interval, the number of differences ≥ hypothesized value is between 2 and 14, so H_0 is not rejected at level .05

95% confidence interval

Difference

The **rank sum confidence interval for $\mu_1 - \mu_2$** is based on the $n_1 n_2$ differences that result from subtracting each sample 2 observation from each sample 1 observation. The confidence interval then has the form

(dth smallest difference, dth largest difference)

Table VII gives values of d corresponding to 90%, 95%, and 99% confidence levels.

EXAMPLE 11.16

The paper "Some Mechanical Properties of Impregnated Bark Board" (*Forest Products J.* (1977):31–38) reported the accompanying observations on crushing strength for epoxy-impregnated bark board (sample 1) and bark board impregnated with another polymer (sample 2). The sample values are displayed along the left and top margins in the accompanying table, and the differences appear in the main part of the table. From Table VII, a 95% confidence interval for $\mu_1 - \mu_2$, the difference between true average strengths, when $n_1 = 6$ and $n_2 = 5$ necessitates using $d = 5$. The five smallest and five largest differences are, respectively, 4350, 4470, 4610, 4730, 4830, and 8220, 8480, 8740, 9530, 9790. The confidence interval is then (4830, 8220).

		Differences				
			Second sample			
		4590	4850	5640	6390	6510
First sample	10,860	6270	6010	5220	4470	4350
	11,120	6530	6270	5480	4730	4610
	11,340	6750	6490	5700	4950	4830
	12,130	7540	7280	6490	5740	5620
	13,070	8480	8220	7430	6680	6560
	14,380	9790	9530	8740	7990	7870

In practice it is often not necessary to compute all $n_1 n_2$ differences but only some of the smallest and largest ones. Also, when n_1 and n_2 both exceed values for which d is tabulated, d is given approximately by the following formula (based on the normal approximation for the rank sum statistic):

$$d \approx \frac{n_1 n_2}{2} - \left(\begin{array}{c} z \text{ critical value for} \\ \text{desired confidence level} \end{array} \right) \sqrt{\frac{n_1 n_2 (n_1 + n_2 + 1)}{12}}$$

EXERCISES 11.61–11.71   SECTION 11.4

11.61   The urinary fluoride concentration (ppm) was measured both for a sample of live-stock that had been grazing in an area previously exposed to fluoride pollution and for a similar sample that had grazed in an unpolluted region. Does the data indicate strongly that the true average fluoride concentration for livestock grazing in the polluted region is larger than for the unpolluted region? Assume that the distributions of urinary fluoride concentration for both grazing areas have the same shape and spread, and use a level .05 rank sum test.

Polluted	21.3	18.7	23.0	17.1	16.8	20.9	19.7
Unpolluted	14.2	18.3	17.2	18.4	20.0		

11.62   A modification has been made to the process for producing a certain type of *time-zero* film (film that begins to develop as soon as a picture is taken). Because the modification involves extra cost, it will be incorporated only if sample data strongly indicates that the modification has decreased true average developing time by more than 1 s. Assuming that the developing-time distributions differ only with respect to location, if at all, use the rank sum test at level .05 on the given data to test the appropriate hypotheses.

Original process	8.6	5.1	4.5	5.4	6.3	6.6	5.7	8.5
Modified process	5.5	4.0	3.8	6.0	5.8	4.9	7.0	5.7

11.63   The study reported in "Gait Patterns During Free Choice Ladder Ascents" (*Human Movement Sci.* (1983):187–195) was motivated by publicity concerning the increased accident rate for individuals climbing ladders. A number of different gait patterns were used by subjects climbing a portable straight ladder according to specified instructions. The ascent times for seven subjects who used a lateral gait and six subjects who used a four-beat diagonal gait are given.

Lateral	.86	1.31	1.64	1.51	1.53	1.39	1.09
Diagonal	1.27	1.82	1.66	.85	1.45	1.24	

   a. Use the rank sum test to see if the data suggests any difference in the true average ascent times for the two gaits.

   b. Compute a 95% confidence interval for the difference between the true average gait times.

11.64   The paper "Histamine Content in Sputum from Allergic and Nonallergic Individuals" (*J. of Appl. Physiology* (1969):535–539) reported the accompanying data on sputum histamine level (μg/g) for a sample of 9 individuals classified as allergics and another sample of 13 individuals classified as nonallergics.

Allergics	67.6	39.6	1651.0	100.0	65.9	1112.0	31.0	102.4	64.7				
Nonallergics	34.3	27.3	35.4	48.1	5.2	29.1	4.7	41.7	48.0	6.6	18.9	32.4	45.5

   a. Define the two populations to be compared.

   b. Does the data indicate that there is a difference in true mean sputum histamine level between allergics and nonallergics? Use a level .01 rank sum test (as did the authors of the paper).

11.65   Many college professors are concerned about plagiarism by students. The paper "The Use of the Cloze Testing Procedure for Detecting Plagiarism" (*J. of Exper. Educ.* (1982):127) reported the results of an experiment designed to investigate one potential method for identifying papers that used plagiarized material. A cloze test involves reproducing a passage of text with certain words omitted. The author of the paper is to fill in the missing words. The test is then scored by counting the number of errors. The authors of this particular paper hypothesized that students should be better able to reproduce their own writing than something they had copied, and so nonplagiarists would tend to make fewer errors on a cloze test. To determine if this were in fact the case, sections of an English composition class were asked to write papers of 6 to 7 pages in length. Two sections were given specific instructions to plagiarize someone else's writing, and two other sections were given no special instructions. When papers were submitted, the purpose of the study was explained to the nonplagiarizing sections, and any student who had used the work of someone else was asked to withdraw his or her paper with no penalty. (Three students confessed!) Cloze tests were prepared for each paper submitted and given 1 week later. The number of errors on the cloze test for these students were as follows:

No plagiarism	1	1	2	2	3	3	3	4	4	4	4	4
	4	5	5	5	5	6	6	6	6	6	7	7
	7	8	8	9	9	9	10	10	10	11	13	
Plagiarism	1	2	3	4	4	4	5	6	6	6	7	7
	7	8	8	8	9	9	9	9	9	10	10	10
	10	11	12	13	13	13	13	14	14	15	17	17
	18	19	19									

Use the large-sample rank sum statistic at level .01 to determine whether the mean number of errors for students who plagiarize is significantly higher than the mean number of errors for students who do not plagiarize.

11.66   A blood-lead level of 70 mg/mL has been commonly accepted as safe. However, researchers have noted that some neurophysiological symptoms of lead poisoning appear in people whose blood-lead levels are below 70 mg/mL. The paper "Sub-clinical Neuropathy at Safe Levels of Lead Exposure" (*Arch. Environ. Health* (1975):180) gives the following nerve-conduction velocities for a group of workers who were exposed to lead in the workplace but whose blood-lead levels were below 70 mg/mL and for a group of controls who had no exposure to lead.

Exposed to lead	46	46	43	41	38	36	31
Control	54	50.5	46	45	44	42	41

Use a level .05 rank sum test to determine if there is a significant difference in mean conduction velocity between workers exposed to lead and those not exposed to lead.

11.67   The effectiveness of antidepressants in treating the eating disorder bulimia was examined in the paper "Bulimia Treated with Imipramine: A Placebo-Controlled Double-Blind Study" (*Amer. J. Psych.* (1983):554–558). A group of patients diagnosed as bulimic were randomly assigned to one of two treatment groups, one receiving imipramine and the other a placebo. One of the variables recorded was frequency of binging. The authors chose to analyze the data using a rank sum test because it makes no assumption of normality. They state: "Because of the wide range of some measures, such as frequency of binges, the rank sum is more appropriate and somewhat more conservative." Data consistent with the findings of this paper is given here.

Number of binges during one week							
Placebo	8	3	15	3	4	10	6	4
Imipramine	2	1	2	7	3	12	1	5

Does this data strongly suggest that imipramine is effective in reducing the mean number of binges per week? Use a level .05 rank sum test.

11.68   Researchers have noted that chickens fed a diet that is lacking in sodium and calcium become more active. To determine whether a sodium deficiency causes an increase in pecking activity, the authors of the paper "An Increase in Activity of Domestic Fowls Produced by Nutritional Deficiency" (*Animal Behavior* (1973): 10–17) observed 17 chickens who were deprived of sodium and 15 control chickens. They counted the number of pecks for each bird during a fixed period of time. Does the data strongly indicate that the mean number of pecks is higher for chickens whose diet lacks sufficient sodium? Use a large-sample rank sum test with $\alpha = .01$.

Sodium deprived	0	0	0	2	17	58	67	67	68	74	79
	85	92	95	97	150	181					
Control	0	0	0	0	0	8	13	13	20	33	34
	57	60	64	78							

11.69   The accompanying data resulted from an experiment to compare the effects of vitamin C in orange juice and in synthetic ascorbic acid on the length of odonto-blasts in guinea pigs over a 6-week period ("The Growth of the Odontoblasts of the Incisor Tooth as a Criterion of the Vitamin C Intake of the Guinea Pig" *J. Nutr.* (1947):491–504). Use the rank sum test at level .01 to decide whether or not true average length differs for the two types of vitamin C intake.

Orange juice	8.2	9.4	9.6	9.7	10.0	14.5	15.2
	16.1	17.6	21.5				
Ascorbic acid	4.2	5.2	5.8	6.4	7.0	10.1	11.2
	11.3	11.5					

11.70   In an experiment to compare the bond strength of two different adhesives, each adhesive was used in five bondings of two surfaces, and the force necessary to separate the surfaces was determined for each bonding. For adhesive 1, the resulting values were 229, 286, 245, 299, and 259, whereas the adhesive 2 observations were 213, 179, 163, 247, and 225. Let μ_1 and μ_2 denote the true average bond strengths of adhesives 1 and 2, respectively. Use a 90% distribution-free confidence interval to estimate $\mu_1 - \mu_2$.

11.71 The article "A Study of Wood Stove Particulate Emissions" (*J. Air Poll. Control Assoc.* (1979):724–728) reported the following data on burn time (h) for samples of oak and pine. Estimate the difference between mean burn time for oak and mean burn time for pine using a 95% distribution-free confidence interval. Interpret the interval.

Oak	1.72	.67	1.55	1.56	1.42	1.23	1.77	.48
Pine	.98	1.40	1.33	1.52	.73	1.20		

CHAPTER ELEVEN SUMMARY OF KEY CONCEPTS AND FORMULAS

Term or Formula	Comment
Independent samples	Two samples where the individuals or objects in the first sample are selected independently from those in the second sample.
Paired samples	Two samples for which each observation in the first sample is paired in a meaningful way with a particular observation in the second sample.
$z = \dfrac{(\bar{x}_1 - \bar{x}_2) - \text{hyp. value}}{\sqrt{\dfrac{s_1^2}{n_1} + \dfrac{s_2^2}{n_2}}}$	The test statistic for testing $$H_0: \mu_1 - \mu_2 = \text{hypothesized value}$$ when both sample sizes are large.
$(\bar{x}_1 - \bar{x}_2) \pm (z \text{ crit. value}) \sqrt{\dfrac{s_1^2}{n_1} + \dfrac{s_2^2}{n_2}}$	A formula for constructing a confidence interval for $\mu_1 - \mu_2$ when both sample sizes are large.
Pooled estimate of σ^2: $s_p^2 = \left(\dfrac{n_1 - 1}{n_1 + n_2 - 2}\right) s_1^2 + \left(\dfrac{n_2 - 1}{n_1 + n_2 - 2}\right) s_2^2$	s_p^2 is the statistic for estimating the common variance σ^2 when $\sigma_1^2 = \sigma_2^2 = \sigma^2$, a basic assumption required for use of the pooled t test and confidence interval.
$t = \dfrac{(\bar{x}_1 - \bar{x}_2) - \text{hyp. value}}{\sqrt{s_p^2 \left(\dfrac{1}{n_1} + \dfrac{1}{n_2}\right)}}$	The test statistic for testing $$H_0: \mu_1 - \mu_2 = \text{hypothesized value}$$ when it is reasonable to assume that both population distributions are normal and $\sigma_1^2 = \sigma_2^2$. It is used when at least one sample size is small.
$(\bar{x}_1 - \bar{x}_2) \pm (t \text{ crit. value}) \sqrt{s_p^2 \left(\dfrac{1}{n_1} + \dfrac{1}{n_2}\right)}$	A formula for constructing a confidence interval for $\mu_1 - \mu_2$ when it is reasonable to assume that the population distributions are normal and $\sigma_1^2 = \sigma_2^2$. It is used when at least one sample size is small.

Term or Formula	Comment
Combined estimate of the common population proportion:	p_c is the statistic for estimating the common population proportion when $\pi_1 = \pi_2$.

$$p_c = \left(\frac{n_1}{n_1 + n_2}\right)p_1 + \left(\frac{n_2}{n_1 + n_2}\right)p_2$$

$z = \dfrac{p_1 - p_2}{\sqrt{\dfrac{p_c(1 - p_c)}{n_1} + \dfrac{p_c(1 - p_c)}{n_2}}}$	The test statistic for testing $H_0: \pi_1 - \pi_2 = 0$ when both sample sizes are large.
$(p_1 - p_2) \pm (z \text{ crit. value})\sqrt{\dfrac{p_1(1 - p_1)}{n_1} + \dfrac{p_2(1 - p_2)}{n_2}}$	A formula for constructing a confidence interval for $\pi_1 - \pi_2$ when both sample sizes are large.

Rank sum = sum of sample 1 ranks	The test statistic for testing $$H_0: \mu_1 - \mu_2 = \text{hypothesized value}$$ when it is reasonable to assume that the two populations have the same shape and spread.
$z = \dfrac{\text{rank sum} - n_1(n_1 + n_2 + 1)/2}{\sqrt{n_1 n_2(n_1 + n_2 + 1)/12}}$	A standardized version of the rank sum for use when $n_1 > 8$ and $n_2 > 8$.
(dth smallest difference, dth largest difference)	The form of the rank sum confidence interval for $\mu_1 - \mu_2$, appropriate when the two populations have the same spread (the $n_1 n_2$ differences resulting from subtracting each sample 2 observation from every sample 1 observation). The value of d comes from Appendix Table VII.

ENCORE

The paper "Smoking During Pregnancy and Lactation and Its Effects on Breast-Milk Volume" introduced in the Chapter Preview states:

> Nonsmoking mothers had a significantly greater breast-milk volume than did smokers ($t = 5.21$, $p < .0001$).

Let's take a look at the data that was the basis for this conclusion. Breast-milk volume was recorded for ten smokers and ten nonsmokers.

	Volume (g)				
Smokers	621	793	593	545	753
	655	895	767	714	598
Nonsmokers	947	945	1083	1202	973
	981	930	745	903	899

Sample means and standard deviations (with smokers designated as sample 1 and nonsmokers as sample 2) were

Smokers	$\bar{x}_1 = 693.4$	$s_1 = 109.5$
Nonsmokers	$\bar{x}_2 = 960.8$	$s_2 = 119.6$

The two sample standard deviations are quite similar, making the assumption $\sigma_1 = \sigma_2$ plausible. The authors of the paper believed that the assumption of normal population distributions was also reasonable, and analyzed the data using the pooled t test. The steps in the analysis follow.

1. $\mu_1 - \mu_2 =$ difference in mean breast-milk volume for smokers and nonsmokers
2. $H_0: \mu_1 - \mu_2 = 0$
3. $H_a: \mu_1 - \mu_2 < 0$
4. Test statistic:

$$t = \frac{\bar{x}_1 - \bar{x}_2 - 0}{\sqrt{s_p^2 \left(\dfrac{1}{n_1} + \dfrac{1}{n_2} \right)}}$$

5. Calculations:

$$s_p^2 = \frac{9(109.5)^2 + 9(119.6)^2}{18}$$

$$= \frac{236,649.7}{18}$$

$$= 13,147.2$$

and so

$$t = \frac{693.4 - 960.8 - 0}{\sqrt{13,147.2(1/10 + 1/10)}} = \frac{-267.4}{51.28} = -5.21$$

(Our value of t is negative, since we chose sample 1 to be smokers. Had we designated nonsmokers as sample 1, we would have obtained $t = +5.21$, the value reported in the paper.)

6. P-value: For df $= n_1 + n_2 - 2 = 10 + 10 - 2 = 18$, we find that $t = 5.21$ is greater than all the values listed in the 18-df row of Table IV. Therefore,

P-value $< .0005$

MINITAB output shown here reports the P-value as .0000. This is consistent with the statement in the paper.

```
TWOSAMPLE T FOR smokers VS nonsmkrs
             N    MEAN   STDEV   SE MEAN
smokers     10     693     109        35
nonsmkrs    10     961     120        38
```

(continued)

```
95 PCT CI FOR MU smokers − MU nonsmkrs: (−375, −160)

TTEST MU smokers = MU nonsmkrs (VS LT): T= −5.21 P=0.0000 DF=18
POOLED STDEV = 115
```

7. Since the *P*-value associated with this test is so small, we would reject H_0 for almost any choice of α. Our conclusion is that the mean breast-milk volume is greater for nonsmokers than for smokers.

The paper also gave data on 15-day weight gains for the babies, reporting weights at the beginning of the study and again at the end. The methods of this chapter should not be used to analyze the "before" and "after" weight samples, since they are paired rather than independent samples.

The second study, described in the paper "Placental Transfer of Lead, Mercury, Cadmium, and Carbon Monoxide in Women," used data from 109 infants of mothers who smoked and 333 infants of mothers who didn't smoke to determine if the mean blood-lead concentration is higher for children born to smokers. Since both sample sizes are large, we use the two-sample *z* test to address this issue.

Sample	Sample size	Sample mean	Sample SD
Mothers who smoke	109	8.9	3.3
Mothers who don't smoke	333	8.1	3.5

1. μ_1 = average lead concentration for all newborns born to smoking mothers
       μ_2 = average lead concentration for all newborns born to nonsmoking mothers
     $\mu_1 - \mu_2$ = difference in average concentrations
2. H_0: $\mu_1 - \mu_2 = 0$
3. H_a: $\mu_1 - \mu_2 > 0$
4. Test statistic:

$$z = \frac{\bar{x}_1 - \bar{x}_2 - 0}{\sqrt{\dfrac{s_1^2}{n_1} + \dfrac{s_2^2}{n_2}}}$$

5. Using level of significance .05, the upper-tailed *z* critical value is 1.645. The hypothesis H_0 will be rejected if $z > 1.645$.
6. Computations:

$$z = \frac{8.9 - 8.1 - 0}{\sqrt{\dfrac{(3.3)^2}{109} + \dfrac{(3.5)^2}{333}}}$$

$$= .8/.37$$

$$= 2.16$$

7. Since 2.16 is greater than 1.645, we reject H_0 at level .05. The data supports the claim that the average lead concentration is higher for the children of smokers than for those of nonsmokers.

These studies (and others) indicate that smoking during pregnancy has consequences for both mother and infant. This is why most doctors recommend that expectant mothers refrain from smoking.

SUPPLEMENTARY EXERCISES 11.72–11.84

11.72 Meteorologists classify storms as either single-peak or multiple-peak. The total number of lightning flashes were recorded for seven single-peak and four multiple-peak storms, resulting in the given data ("Lightning Phenomenology in the Tampa Bay Area" *J. of Geophys. Research* (1984):11,789–11,805).

| Single-peak | 117 | 56 | 19 | 40 | 82 | 69 | 80 |
| Multiple-peak | 229 | 197 | 242 | 430 | | | |

a. Does the data suggest that the true mean number of lightning flashes differs for the two types of storms? Use a .05 significance level.
b. What assumptions about the distribution of number of flashes for each of the two types of storms are necessary in order that your test in part (a) be valid?

11.73 Nine observations of surface-soil pH were made at each of two different locations at the Central Soil Salinity Research Institute experimental farm, and the resulting data appeared in the article "Sodium–Calcium Exchange Equilibria in Soils as Affected by Calcium Carbonate and Organic Matter" (*Soil Sci.* (1984):109). Does the data suggest that the true mean soil pH values differ for the two locations? Test the appropriate hypotheses using a .05 significance level. Be sure to state any assumptions necessary for the validity of your test.

Site	pH
Location A	8.53 8.52 8.01 7.99 7.93 7.89 7.85 7.82 7.80
Location B	7.85 7.73 7.58 7.40 7.35 7.30 7.27 7.27 7.23

11.74 Reconsider the soil pH data given in Exercise 11.73.
a. Use a distribution-free procedure with significance level .05 to determine if the true mean soil pH is the same for both locations.
b. Construct and interpret a 95% distribution-free confidence interval for the difference in true mean soil pH values for the two locations.

11.75 The results of a study on job satisfaction among tenure-track faculty members and librarians employed by the California State University System were described in the paper "Job Satisfaction among Faculty and Librarians: A Study of Gender, Autonomy, and Decision-Making Opportunities" (*J. of Library Admin.* (1984):43–56). Random samples of 115 male and 105 female academic employees were selected. Each participant completed the Minnesota Satisfaction Questionnaire (MSQ) and was assigned a satisfaction score. The resulting mean and standard deviation were 75.43 and 10.53 for the males and 72.54 and 13.08 for the females. Does the data strongly suggest that male and female academic employees differ with respect to mean score on the MSQ? Use a .01 significance level.

11.76 The paper "An Evaluation of Football Helmets under Impact Conditions" (*Amer. J. of Sports Med.* (1984):233–237) reported that when 44 padded football helmets and 37 suspension-type helmets were subjected to an impact test (a drop of 1.5 m onto a hard surface), 5 of the padded and 24 of the suspension-type helmets showed damage. Using a .01 significance level, test appropriate hypotheses to determine if there is a difference between the two helmet types with respect to the true proportion of each type that would be damaged by a 1.5-m drop onto a hard surface.

11.77 The paper "Post-Mortem Analysis of Neuropeptides in Brains from Sudden Infant Death Victims" (*Brain Research* (1984):279–285) reported age (in days) at death for infants who died of sudden infant death syndrome (SIDS). Assuming that age at death for SIDS victims is normally distributed, use the given data to construct a 95% confidence interval for the difference in the true mean age at death for female and male SIDS victims. Interpret the resulting interval. How does the interpretation depend on whether zero is included in the interval?

Age at death (days)						
Females	55	120	135	154	54	
Males	56	60	60	60	105	140	147

11.78 The discharge of industrial wastewater into rivers affects water quality. To assess the effect of a particular power plant on water quality, 24 water specimens were taken 16 km upstream and 4 km downstream of the plant. Alkalinity (mg/L) was determined for each specimen, resulting in the given summary quantities. Does the data suggest that the true mean alkalinity is higher downstream than upstream? Use a .05 significance level.

Location	n	Mean	Standard deviation
Upstream	24	75.9	1.83
Downstream	24	183.6	1.70

11.79 The paper "Chronic 60-Hz Electric Field Exposure Induced Subtle Bioeffects on Serum Chemistry" (*J. of Environ. Sci. and Health* (1984): 865–885) described an experiment to assess the effects of exposure to a high-intensity electric field. A group of 45 rats exposed to an electric field from birth to 120 days of age was compared to a control group of 45 rats with no exposure. Summary quantities for various blood characteristics are given. Conduct the hypothesis tests necessary to determine whether the experimental treatment differs from no treatment with respect to true mean glucose, potassium, protein, or cholesterol levels. Use a .05 significance level for each test.

	Control		Experimental	
	Mean	s	Mean	s
Glucose (mg/dL)	136.30	12.70	139.20	16.10
Potassium (mg/dL)	7.44	.53	7.62	.54
Total protein (gm/dL)	6.63	.27	6.61	.34
Cholesterol (mg/dL)	69.00	11.40	67.80	9.38

11.80 The paper "Dyslexic and Normal Readers' Eye Movements" (*J. of Exper. Psych.* (1983):816–825) reported data on the number of eye movements while reading a particular passage for 34 dyslexic and 36 normal readers. The sample mean number of total movements and corresponding sample standard deviation were 8.6 and .30 for dyslexics and 9.2 and .16 for normal readers.

a. Does the data indicate a significant difference between dyslexic and normal readers with respect to true average number of eye movements? Use a level .10 test.

b. Give the *P*-value associated with the test statistic in part (a). Would your conclusions have been any different at significance levels .05 or .01?

11.81 The paper "The Effects of Education on Self-Esteem of Male Prison Inmates" (*J. Correlational Educ.* (1982):12–18) described the result of an experiment designed to ascertain whether mathematics education increases the self-esteem of prison inmates. Two random samples each of size

40 were selected from the population of prison inmates at Angola, Louisiana. One sample was designated as a control group and the other as an experimental group. Inmates in the experimental group received 18 weeks of mathematics tutoring, whereas those in the control group were not tutored. Both groups were given the Self-Esteem Inventory (SEI) at the beginning and end of the 18-week period. The mean and standard deviation of the change in SEI score were 2.9 and 5.4 for the experimental group and -1.3 and 5.6 for the control group.

a. Does the data provide sufficient evidence to conclude that mathematics tutoring is associated with a higher mean change in SEI score? Test the relevant hypotheses using a .01 significance level.

b. What is the *P*-value associated with the test in part (a)?

11.82 Two different methods (ampul and hot plate) for recovering metals from sewage were compared in the paper "Simple Sample Digestion of Sewage Sludge for Multi-Element Analysis" (*J. of Environ. Sci. and Health* (1984):959–972). Both methods were used to treat oyster tissue and the metal and mineral recovery were recorded. Answer the following questions, assuming that each method was used on 10 tissue specimens. Be sure to state any assumptions that must be true in order for the inferential procedure applied to be valid.

a. For iron, the mean recovery and standard deviation were 16 ppm and 2.5 ppm for the ampul method and 17.7 ppm and 1.2 ppm for the hot-plate method. Does the evidence suggest that the two methods differ with respect to mean iron recovery? Use a .05 significance level.

b. The sample mean and standard deviation for copper recovery were 62.6 ppm and 3.7 ppm for the ampul method and 65.0 and 3.8 for the hot-plate method. Estimate the true difference in mean copper recovery rate for the two methods using a 90% confidence interval. Does the interval include zero? Interpret the interval.

11.83 An electronic implant that stimulates the auditory nerve has been used to restore partial hearing to a number of deaf people. In a study of implant acceptability (*Los Angeles Times,* January 29, 1985), 250 adults born deaf and 250 adults who went deaf after learning to speak were followed for a period of time after receiving an implant. Of those deaf from birth, 75 had removed the implant, whereas only 25 of those who went deaf after learning to speak had done so. Does this suggest that the true proportion who remove the implants differs for those that were born deaf and those that went deaf after learning to speak? Test the relevant hypotheses using a .01 significance level.

11.84 The accompanying data appeared in the article "Effect of Exogenous Oestradiol-17B on Gonadatrophin Secretion in Postpartum Beef Cows" (*J. Reprod. and Fertility* (1984):473–478). Twelve cows between 10 and 17 days postpartum received one or two silicon rubber implants, each containing 45 mg of oestradiol (6 cows received one implant and the other 6 received two). The time (in days) to first rise in milk progesterone concentration was recorded. The experiment was terminated after 50 days, at which time 3 cows had not yet shown a rise in progesterone level.

Time (days)					
One implant	38	23	19	33	>50	>50
Two implants	24	34	30	42	35	>50

Use a distribution-free procedure to determine whether the data suggests a difference in true mean number of days to rise in progesterone level between cows receiving one implant and those receiving two implants. Assume that those sample values listed as > 50 are all tied, and assign each one the rank of 11 (the average of ranks 10, 11, and 12). Use a significance level of .05.

References

Daniel, Wayne. *Applied Nonparametric Statistics,* 2nd ed. Boston: PWS-Kent, 1990. (An elementary presentation of distribution-free methods, including the rank sum test discussed in the last section of this chapter.)

Devore, Jay. *Probability and Statistics for Engineering and the Sciences,* 3rd ed. Pacific Grove, Calif.: Brooks/Cole, 1991. (Contains a somewhat more comprehensive treatment of the inferential material presented in this and the previous two chapters, though the notation is a bit more mathematical than that of the present text.)

Mosteller, Frederick, and Richard Rourke. *Sturdy Statistics.* Reading, Mass.: Addison-Wesley, 1973. (A very readable intuitive development of distribution-free methods, including those based on ranks.)

12

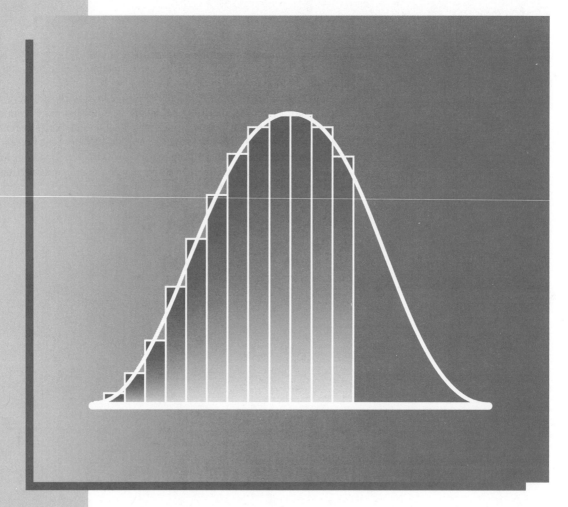

Inferences Using Paired Data

PREVIEW

Children with Down syndrome generally show a pattern of retarded mental development, although some achieve higher intellectual levels than others. The intellectual achievements of Down syndrome children have been studied by numerous investigators, and several different types of chromosomal abnormalities associated with the syndrome have been identified. Two such abnormalities are called trisomy 21 and mosaicism. The intellectual functionings of trisomy 21 and mosaic Down syndrome children were compared in the paper "Mental Development in Down Syndrome Mosaicism" (*American Journal on Mental Retardation* (1991): 345–351).

Thirty children with mosaic Down syndrome who were treated at USC Medical Center were selected to participate in the research project. The investigators then chose 30 children with trisomy 21 Down syndrome from among 350 that had been seen at the medical center. The 30 chosen were selected (with the help of a computer) to achieve the best possible matches for children in the mosaic group using age, sex, and parental socioeconomic status as the criteria for matching. The result was 30 matched pairs of children. IQ levels for all of the children were determined.

Pair	Mosaic	Trisomy 21
1	73	71
2	43	53
3	69	58
4	89	71
5	53	50
6	81	70
7	59	55
8	71	18
9	65	31
10	53	57
11	58	63
12	55	60
13	61	48
14	63	55
15	87	59
16	64	78
17	63	55
18	58	51
19	50	55
20	59	53
21	75	47
22	61	50
23	71	47
24	92	44
25	57	28
26	76	75
27	91	63
28	43	46
29	55	54
30	88	48

The researchers proposed using this data to test the theory that children with mosaic Down syndrome generally achieve higher intellectual levels. Although these samples provide information about the two types of Down syndrome, they were not independently chosen, since the 30 trisomy 21 children were specifically selected to match the children in the mosaic sample. Because the samples are not independently chosen, the two-sample techniques of the previous chapter are not appropriate. This chapter introduces methods for dealing with samples that are paired.

Introduction

The methods presented in Chapter 11 are appropriate when the individuals or objects in the sample from the first population are selected independently of those that constitute the sample from the second population. There are many situations, however, in which the two samples under study are related. One way in which this might occur is when the samples consist of pairs of observations on the same person or object. For example, to study the effectiveness of a speed-reading course, the reading speed of subjects could be tested prior to taking the class and again after completion of the course. This gives rise to two samples—one from the population of individuals who have not taken this particular course (the "before" measurements) and one from the population of individuals who have had such a course (the "after" measurements). Data of this type is said to be paired. The two samples are not independently chosen, since the selection of individuals from the first (before) population completely determines which individuals make up the sample from the second (after) population. This dependence invalidates the use of methods from Chapter 11 to draw conclusions about $\mu_1 - \mu_2$. In this chapter, we introduce methods for drawing inferences from paired data and also discuss why in some applications an experiment resulting in paired data might be preferable to an experiment involving independent samples.

12.1 Pairing versus Independent Samples

Two samples are said to be *independent* if the selection of the individuals or objects that make up one of the samples has no bearing on the selection of those in the other sample. However, in some situations an experiment with independent samples is not the best way to obtain information concerning any possible difference between the populations. For example, suppose that an investigator wants to determine if regular aerobic exercise affects blood pressure. A random sample of people who jog regularly and a second random sample of people who do not exercise regularly are selected independently of one another. The researcher then uses the pooled t test to conclude that a significant difference exists between the average blood pressures for joggers and nonjoggers. Is it reasonable to think that jogging influences blood pressure? It is known that blood pressure is related to both diet and body weight. Might it not be the case that joggers in the sample tend to be leaner and adhere to a healthier diet than the nonjoggers and that this might account for the observed differences? On the basis of this study, the researcher wouldn't be able to rule out the possibility that the observed difference in blood pressure is explained by weight differences between the two samples and that aerobic exercise in and of itself has no effect.

One way to avoid this difficulty would be to match subjects by weight. The researcher would find pairs of subjects so that the jogger and nonjogger in each pair were similar in weight (although weights for different pairs might vary widely). The factor *weight* could then be ruled out as a possible explanation for an observed difference in average blood pressure between the two groups. Matching the subjects by weight results in two samples for which each observation in the first sample is coupled in a meaningful way with a particular observation in the second sample. Such samples are said to be **paired.**

Experiments can be designed to yield paired data in a number of different ways. Some studies involve using the same group of individuals with measurements recorded both before and after some intervening treatment. Others use naturally occurring pairs such as twins or husbands and wives, and some construct pairs by matching factors whose effect might otherwise obscure differences (or the lack of them) between the two populations of interest (as might weight in the jogging example). Paired samples often provide more information than would independent samples because extraneous effects are screened out.

EXAMPLE 12.1

It has been hypothesized that strenuous physical activity affects hormone levels. The paper "Growth Hormone Increase During Sleep After Daytime Exercise" (*J. of Endocrinology* (1974):473–478) reported the results of an experiment involving six healthy male subjects. For each participant, blood samples were taken during sleep on two different nights using an indwelling venous catheter. The first blood sample was drawn after a day that included no strenuous activities, and the second was drawn after a day during which the subject engaged in strenuous exercise. The resulting data on growth hormone level (mg/mL) appears here. The samples are paired rather than independent since both samples consist of observations on the same men.

Subject	1	2	3	4	5	6
Postexercise	13.6	14.7	42.8	20.0	19.2	17.3
Control	8.5	12.6	21.6	19.4	14.7	13.6

Let μ_1 denote the mean nocturnal growth hormone level for the population of all healthy males who participated in strenuous activity on the previous day. Similarly, let μ_2 denote the mean nocturnal hormone level for the population consisting of all healthy males whose activities on the previous day did not include any strenuous physical exercise. The hypotheses of interest are then

$$H_0: \mu_1 - \mu_2 = 0 \quad \text{versus} \quad H_a: \mu_1 - \mu_2 \neq 0$$

Notice that in each of the six data pairs, the postexercise hormone level is higher than the corresponding control level. Intuitively this suggests that there may be a difference between the population means.

However, if the pooled t test for two independent samples is (incorrectly) employed, the resulting t test statistic is 1.28. This value does not allow for rejection of the hypothesis that $\mu_1 - \mu_2 = 0$ even at level of significance .10. This result might surprise you at first, but remember that this test procedure ignores the fact that the samples are paired. Two plots of the data are given in Figure 12.1. The first one ignores the pairing, and the two samples look quite similar. The plot in which pairs are identified does suggest a difference, since for each pair the exercise observation exceeds the no-exercise observation. Disregarding the paired nature of the samples results in a loss of information. Nocturnal growth hormone levels vary substantially from one individual to another. It is this variability that obscures the difference in hormone level associated with strenuous exercise.

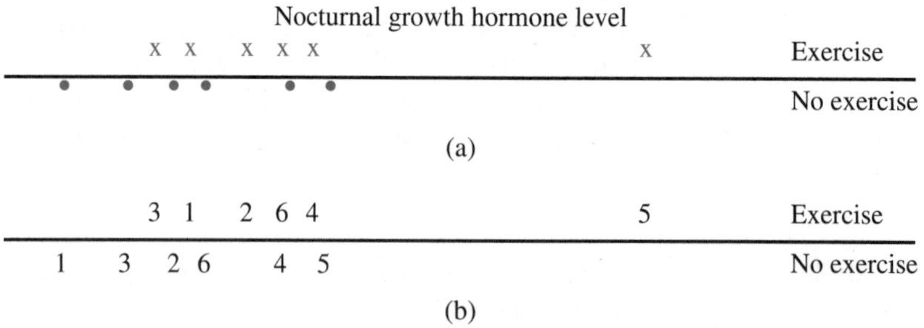

FIGURE 12.1
Two plots of the paired data
from Example 12.1
(a) pairing ignored
(b) pairs identified

In Example 12.1 an independent-samples experiment would not have been very effective in assessing whether exercise affects growth hormone levels. Hormone levels differ quite a bit from one person to another. With independent samples, we wouldn't know if any observed difference in the mean hormone level was a result of one sample by chance containing mostly people whose growth hormone level is naturally high. By using a paired-samples experiment, we are able to rule out this possibility.

EXAMPLE 12.2

Recent evidence suggests that nonsmokers who live with smokers and are therefore exposed to sidestream smoke (as opposed to mainstream smoke, which is inhaled by the smoker directly from the cigarette) may have an increased risk of lung disease. Mainstream and sidestream yields (in mg) of tar, nicotine, and carbon monoxide for eight nonfilter cigarettes appeared in the paper "Yields of Tar, Nicotine, and Carbon Monoxide in the Sidestream Smoke of Canadian Cigarettes" (*Amer. J. Public Health* (1984):228–231). Data on tar yield is given here.

Cigarette	Sidestream yield	Mainstream yield
1	15.8	18.5
2	16.9	17.0
3	21.6	17.2
4	18.8	19.4
5	29.3	15.6
6	20.7	16.4
7	18.9	13.3
8	25.0	10.2

Notice that the tar yield varies widely from one cigarette to another. For some cigarettes (but not all) sidestream yield is higher than mainstream yield. Since the data is paired (by cigarette), a method of analysis appropriate for paired data should be employed in order to determine if the mean tar yield of sidestream smoke differs from that of mainstream smoke.

These two examples suggest that the methods of inference developed for independent samples aren't adequate for dealing with paired samples. When samples are paired in a meaningful way, it is natural to focus on the differences between the observations making up each pair. In Example 12.1, the fact that all such differences are positive suggests that

$$H_0: \mu_1 - \mu_2 = 0$$

should probably be rejected. For Example 12.2, where some differences are positive and some are negative, the appropriate conclusion is not so obvious. In the next section, we will see a formal method for making inferences about $\mu_1 - \mu_2$ using paired samples.

EXERCISES 12.1–12.8 SECTION 12.1

12.1 Discuss the difference between independent samples and paired data.

12.2 Give an example of an experiment involving a comparison of two different brands of automobile tires that would result in paired data.

12.3 The director of a sports camp for swimmers would like to determine if its regimen of training is successful in improving performance. The director decides to focus attention on 100-m freestyle times. Describe how the camp director might go about collecting relevant data. Would the resulting samples be paired samples or independent samples?

12.4 In order to assess the effect of practice on the time required to assemble a chair from its component pieces, ten new employees of a furniture manufacturer are timed while assembling their first chairs and again while assembling their tenth chairs. This results in a sample of assembly times without benefit of practice (the ten first-chair measurements) and a sample of assembly times with benefit of practice (the ten tenth-chair times). Are these samples paired or independent? Explain.

12.5   Suppose you were interested in investigating the effect of a drug that is to be used in the treatment of patients who have glaucoma in both eyes. A comparison between the mean reduction in eye pressure for this drug and for a standard treatment is desired. Both treatments are applied directly to an eye.

   a. Describe how you would go about collecting data for your investigation.

   b. Does your method result in paired data?

   c. Can you think of a reasonable method of collecting data that would result in independent samples? Would such an experiment be as informative as a paired experiment? Comment.

12.6   Suppose you were interested in comparing the yield of two different irrigation methods (constant drip and intermittent) for watering avocado seedlings. Describe two possible methods of collecting data—one that would result in paired data and one that would result in independent samples.

12.7   Two different brands of shoes designed for marathon running are to be compared with respect to sole durability. Suppose that ten pairs of each brand, in any sizes, can be made available. How might an experiment resulting in paired data be carried out? How might an independent-samples experiment be carried out? Which would you recommend, and why?

12.8   Elected representatives are often criticized for missing important votes. Suppose that you would like to find out if members of the U.S. House of Representatives tend to miss more votes in nonelection years than in election years, where their performance might be more closely monitored. Describe how you might collect relevant information. Does your method involve paired samples of representatives?

12.2 Inferences Concerning a Difference between Two Population Means Using Paired Samples

An investigator who wishes to compare two population means is usually interested in estimating or testing a hypothesis about the difference $\mu_1 - \mu_2$. When sample observations from the first population are paired in some meaningful way with sample observations from the second population, inferences can be based on the differences between the two observations within the sampled pairs.

Suppose that there are n pairs in the sample. The sample mean and sample variance of the n observed x values were previously defined as $\bar{x} = \Sigma x/n$ and $s^2 = \Sigma(x - \bar{x})^2/(n - 1)$. If we compute the difference between the first and second observation for each pair, the result is a set of n sample differences. The **sample average difference** $\bar{x}_d$ and **sample variance of the differences** s_d^2 are then given by

$$\bar{x}_d = \frac{\Sigma(\text{difference})}{n} \qquad s_d^2 = \frac{\Sigma(\text{difference} - \bar{x}_d)^2}{n - 1}$$

The numerator of s_d^2 can be computed as

$$\Sigma(\text{difference})^2 - \frac{(\Sigma\text{difference})^2}{n}$$

EXAMPLE 12.3

(Example 12.2 continued) The following data on tar yield for sidestream and mainstream smoke for eight nonfilter cigarettes was first presented in Example 12.2. Since the data is paired (by cigarette), we can form differences by subtracting the mainstream yield from the sidestream yield for each cigarette. The resulting differences are displayed with the data pairs.

Cigarette	Sidestream yield	Mainstream yield	Difference
1	15.8	18.5	−2.7
2	16.9	17.0	−.1
3	21.6	17.2	4.4
4	18.8	19.4	−.6
5	29.3	15.6	13.7
6	20.7	16.4	4.3
7	18.9	13.3	5.6
8	25.0	10.2	14.8

The mean and variance of the sample of eight differences can now be computed:

$$\Sigma\text{difference} = (-2.7) + (-.1) + \cdots + 14.8 = 39.4$$

$$\Sigma(\text{difference})^2 = (-2.7)^2 + (-.1)^2 + \cdots + (14.8)^2 = 483.6$$

$$\bar{x}_d = \frac{\Sigma(\text{difference})}{n} = \frac{39.4}{8} = 4.93$$

$$s_d^2 = \frac{\Sigma(\text{difference})^2 - \frac{(\Sigma\text{difference})^2}{n}}{n-1}$$

$$= \frac{483.6 - \frac{(39.4)^2}{8}}{7}$$

$$= \frac{289.56}{7} = 41.37$$

Then

$$s_d = \sqrt{s_d^2} = \sqrt{41.37} = 6.43$$

We can regard the n sample differences as having been selected from a large population of differences. In Example 12.3, this population consists of differences (sidestream yield $-$ mainstream yield) for all cigarettes (from which the eight actually tested were chosen).

Let

μ_d = mean value of the difference population

and

σ_d = standard deviation of the difference population

The relationship between μ_d and the two individual population means is

$$\mu_d = \mu_1 - \mu_2$$

Therefore, when the samples are paired, inferences about $\mu_1 - \mu_2$ are equivalent to inferences about μ_d. Since inferences about μ_d can be based on the n observed sample differences, the original two-sample problem becomes a familiar one-sample problem.

The Paired t Test

To compare two population means when the samples are paired, we first translate the hypothesis of interest from one about the value of $\mu_1 - \mu_2$ to an equivalent one involving μ_d.

Hypothesis	**Equivalent Hypothesis when Samples Are Paired**
$H_0: \mu_1 - \mu_2 =$ hypothesized value	$H_0: \mu_d =$ hypothesized value
$H_a: \mu_1 - \mu_2 >$ hypothesized value	$H_a: \mu_d >$ hypothesized value
$H_a: \mu_1 - \mu_2 <$ hypothesized value	$H_a: \mu_d <$ hypothesized value
$H_a: \mu_1 - \mu_2 \neq$ hypothesized value	$H_a: \mu_d \neq$ hypothesized value

Sample differences (sample 1 value $-$ sample 2 value) are then computed and used as the basis for testing hypotheses about μ_d. When it is reasonable to assume that the population of differences is approximately normal, the one-sample t test, based on the differences, is the recommended test procedure. Generally speaking, the difference population will be normal if each of the two individual populations is normal. A normal probability plot of the differences can be used to validate this assumption.

THE PAIRED *t* TEST

> **Null hypothesis:** H_0: μ_d = hypothesized value
>
> **Test statistic:** $t = \dfrac{\bar{x}_d - \text{hypothesized value}}{s_d/\sqrt{n}}$

where n is the number of sample differences and $\bar{x}_d$ and s_d are the sample mean and standard deviation of these differences.

Alternative Hypothesis	**Rejection Region**
H_a: μ_d > hypothesized value	$t > t$ critical value (upper-tailed test)
H_a: μ_d < hypothesized value	$t < -t$ critical value (lower-tailed test)
H_a: μ_d ≠ hypothesized value	Either $t > t$ critical value or $t < -t$ critical value (two-tailed test)

Once the level of significance α has been specified, the appropriate t critical value can be obtained from the corresponding column and $(n - 1)$ df row of Appendix Table IV.

EXAMPLE 12.4

Trace metals in drinking water affect the flavor of the water, and unusually high concentrations can pose a health hazard. The paper "Trace Metals of South Indian River" (*Environ. Studies* (1982):62–66) reported trace-metal concentrations for both surface water and bottom water at six different river locations. Data on zinc concentration (mg/L) is given here.

Location	Bottom water	Top water
1	.430	.415
2	.266	.238
3	.567	.390
4	.531	.410
5	.707	.605
6	.716	.609

Although zinc concentration varies widely from one location to another, in every case the zinc concentration in bottom water is higher than that in top water. Since this data is paired (by location), we will employ a method of analysis appropriate for paired data.

We form the differences by subtracting top-water zinc concentration from the bottom-water concentration for each location.

Location	Difference
1	.430 − .415 = .015
2	.266 − .238 = .028
3	.567 − .390 = .177
4	.531 − .410 = .121
5	.707 − .605 = .102
6	.716 − .609 = .107

For the differences

$$\Sigma \text{difference} = .550$$
$$\Sigma(\text{difference})^2 = .068832$$

Then

$$\bar{x}_d = \frac{\Sigma \text{difference}}{n} = \frac{.550}{6} = .0917$$

$$s_d^2 = \frac{\Sigma(\text{difference})^2 - \dfrac{(\Sigma \text{difference})^2}{n}}{n-1}$$

$$= \frac{.068832 - \dfrac{(.550)^2}{6}}{5}$$

$$= .00368$$

$$s_d = \sqrt{s_d^2} = \sqrt{.00368} = .061$$

We now use the paired t test with significance level .05 to determine whether mean zinc concentration in bottom water exceeds that for top water.

1. $\mu_d = \mu_1 - \mu_2 =$ mean difference between bottom- and top-water zinc concentrations

2. $H_0\colon \mu_d = 0$
3. $H_a\colon \mu_d > 0$
4. Test statistic:

$$t = \frac{\bar{x}_d - 0}{s_d/\sqrt{n}} = \frac{\bar{x}_d}{s_d/\sqrt{n}}$$

5. The nature of H_a implies that a one-tailed rejection region should be used. With level of significance .05 and df $= n - 1 = 6 - 1 = 5$, Table IV gives 2.02 as the appropriate critical value. The null hypothesis will therefore be rejected if $t > 2.02$.

6. The values of $\bar{x}_d$ and s_d were previously computed to be $\bar{x}_d = .0917$ and $s_d = .061$. Substituting these values into the test-statistic formula yields

$$t = \frac{.0917}{.061/\sqrt{6}} = \frac{.0917}{.0249} = 3.68$$

7. The value $t = 3.68$ exceeds 2.02, implying that H_0 should be rejected in favor of H_a. The data suggests that mean zinc concentration for bottom water is higher than for top water.

Use of the pooled t test on the data in Example 12.4 would have been incorrect because the top- and bottom-water samples are not independent. Inappropriate use of the pooled t test in this setting would result in a computed t value of

$$t = \frac{(\bar{x}_1 - \bar{x}_2) - 0}{\sqrt{s_p^2\left(\dfrac{1}{n_1} + \dfrac{1}{n_2}\right)}} = \frac{.5362 - .4445}{\sqrt{.025\left(\dfrac{1}{6} + \dfrac{1}{6}\right)}} = \frac{.0917}{.091} = 1.01$$

The hypothesis of equal mean concentrations for top and bottom water would not be rejected. When the pairing is ignored, the difference between top- and bottom-water concentrations is obscured by the variability in zinc concentration from one location to another.

The numerators $\bar{x}_d$ and $\bar{x}_1 - \bar{x}_2$ of the two test statistics are always equal. The difference between paired t and pooled t lies in the denominator. The variability in differences is usually much smaller than the variability in each sample separately (because measurements in a pair tend to be similar). As a result, the value of the paired t statistic is usually larger in magnitude than the value of the pooled t statistic—3.68 versus 1.01 in the example we have just considered. Pairing typically reduces variability that might otherwise obscure small but nevertheless significant differences.

EXAMPLE 12.5

(*Example 12.3 continued*) The tar data of Example 12.3 can be used to test for any difference between mean tar yield for sidestream and mainstream smoke. We will use the paired t test with $\alpha = .05$.

1. $\mu_d = \mu_1 - \mu_2 =$ mean difference between tar yield for sidestream and mainstream smoke

2. $H_0: \mu_d = 0$
3. $H_a: \mu_d \neq 0$

4. Test statistic: $t = \dfrac{\bar{x}_d - 0}{s_d/\sqrt{n}}$

5. Since $\neq$ appears in the alternative hypothesis, this is a two-tailed test. With level of significance .05 and df $= n - 1 = 8 - 1 = 7$, Table IV gives 2.37 as the appropriate critical value. The null hypothesis will be rejected if $t > 2.37$ or $t < -2.37$.

6. From Example 12.3,

$$\bar{x}_d = 4.93 \qquad s_d = 6.43$$

This gives

$$t = \frac{4.93}{6.43/\sqrt{8}} = \frac{4.93}{2.27} = 2.17$$

7. Since 2.17 is not in the rejection region, we fail to reject H_0. There is not sufficient evidence to conclude that a difference in mean tar yield for sidestream and mainstream smoke exists.

Methods for computing β, the probability of making a type II error, for the one-sample t test were presented in Chapter 10. The curves given in Table V can be employed in a similar fashion to determine β for the paired t test. Also, when the sample size (the number of differences) is large, a one-sample z test is appropriate, and the normality assumption is no longer necessary.

P-Values

An alternative approach to initially fixing α when testing hypotheses is provided by P-values. The value of the paired t test statistic is computed and then an upper and/or lower bound on the associated P-value is obtained using Table IV. The investigator can then see what conclusion would be appropriate at any of the standard significance levels.

EXAMPLE 12.6

Douglas fir trees are an important source of wood products, so anything that affects tree growth is of interest to the lumber industry. To determine if fluoride contamination stunts growth, the authors of the paper "Patterns of Fluoride Accumulation and Growth Reduction Exhibited by Douglas Fir in the Vicinity of an Aluminum Reduction Plant" (*Environ. Pollution* (1984):221–235) compared trees within 8 km of an aluminum-processing plant to those farther than 8 km away. Tree growth for a given year can be determined by measuring the width of the trunk ring formed during that year. The accompanying data was collected for the years 1962 to 1975. The aluminum-processing plant went into operation in 1967.

	Preoperational Years			Operational Years		
	Mean ring size				Mean ring size	
Year	Within 8 km	Beyond 8 km	Year	Within 8 km	Beyond 8 km
1962	3.3	3.3	1967	2.6	3.2
1963	3.4	3.4	1968	2.4	3.1

(continued)

Preoperational Years			Operational Years		
	Mean ring size			Mean ring size	
Year	Within 8 km	Beyond 8 km	Year	Within 8 km	Beyond 8 km
1964	3.0	3.1	1969	2.0	2.9
1965	2.9	3.0	1970	2.3	3.2
1966	2.9	2.9	1971	2.2	3.1
			1972	2.1	2.9
			1973	1.9	2.6
			1974	2.2	2.8
			1975	2.0	2.9

To determine whether mean growth rates for trees within 8 km and those beyond 8 km differed significantly during the preoperational period, we test

$$H_0: \mu_d = 0 \quad \text{versus} \quad H_a: \mu_d \neq 0$$

The *within 8 − beyond 8* differences for the five preoperational years are 0, 0, −.1, −.1, and 0, yielding $\bar{x}_d = -.04$ and $s_d = .0548$.

The paired *t* test statistic is

$$t = \frac{\bar{x}_d - 0}{s_d/\sqrt{n}} = \frac{-.04 - 0}{.0548/\sqrt{5}} = \frac{-.04}{.0245} = -1.633$$

Since this is a two-tailed test, a bound on the *P*-value is determined from the two-tailed critical values in the *t* table. Using the 4-df row of Table IV, $t = 1.63$ falls between the critical values 1.53 ($\alpha = .20$) and 2.13 ($\alpha = .10$). Therefore

.10 < *P*-value < .20

For level of significance .1 or smaller, the null hypothesis would not be rejected, suggesting no difference between the preoperational mean growth rates.

We also carried out this test using MINITAB. There is no paired *t* command (although other packages do have such an option), so the analysis involves first computing the differences and then requesting a one-sample *t* test. Resulting computer output is given below. Note that MINITAB has calculated the *P*-value to be .18, which is consistent with the bounds obtained from the *t* table.

```
ROW     within 8     beyond 8     diff

 1         3.3          3.3        0.0
 2         3.4          3.4        0.0
 3         3.0          3.1       -0.1
 4         2.9          3.0       -0.1
 5         2.9          2.9        0.0

TEST OF MU = 0 VS MU N.E. 0
                N       MEAN      STDEV     SE MEAN         T      P VALUE
diff            5    -0.0400     0.0548       0.024     -1.63         0.18
```

A similar analysis of the postoperational years is appropriate for determining whether growth of trees near the site was reduced when the plant became operational. The hypotheses of interest are

$$H_0: \mu_d = 0 \quad \text{versus} \quad H_a: \mu_d < 0$$

The observed differences are

$$-.6 \quad -.7 \quad -.9 \quad -.9 \quad -.9 \quad -.8 \quad -.7 \quad -.6 \quad -.9$$

resulting in

$$\bar{x}_d = -.778 \qquad s_d = .130$$

The corresponding value of the paired t statistic is

$$t = \frac{-.778 - 0}{.130/\sqrt{9}} = \frac{-.778}{.0433} = -17.97$$

For a one-tailed test, the 8-df row of Table IV implies that P-value $< .0005$.

The accompanying MINITAB output indicates that the P-value is zero when rounded to four decimal places. A P-value this small very strongly indicates a reduction in growth rate near the plant.

```
ROW    within 8    beyond 8    diff

1         2.6         3.2      -0.6
2         2.4         3.1      -0.7
3         2.0         2.9      -0.9
4         2.3         3.2      -0.9
5         2.2         3.1      -0.9
6         2.1         2.9      -0.8
7         1.9         2.6      -0.7
8         2.2         2.8      -0.6
9         2.0         2.9      -0.9

TEST OF MU = 0 VS MU L.T. 0
```

	N	MEAN	STDEV	SE MEAN	T	P VALUE
diff	9	-0.778	0.130	0.043	-17.93	0.0000

A Confidence Interval for μ_d

The t confidence interval for μ given in Chapter 9 is easily adapted to obtain an interval estimate for μ_d.

> When it is reasonable to assume that the difference population is (approximately) normal, the **paired t confidence interval for μ_d** is
>
> $$\bar{x}_d \pm (t \text{ critical value}) \cdot \frac{s_d}{\sqrt{n}}$$
>
> For a specified confidence level, the $(n - 1)$df row of Table IV gives the appropriate t critical value.

EXAMPLE 12.7

Cushing's disease is characterized by muscular weakness due to adrenal or pituitary dysfunction. In order to provide effective treatment, it is important to detect childhood Cushing's disease as early as possible. Age at onset of symptoms and age at diagnosis for 15 children suffering from the disease is given in the paper "Treatment of Cushing's Disease in Childhood and Adolescence by Transphenoidal Microadenomectomy" (*New Eng. J. of Med.* (April 5, 1984):889). Since early diagnosis is crucial for successful treatment, the length of time (months) between onset of symptoms and diagnosis is of interest. Let μ_d be the mean difference between age at onset and age at diagnosis (so that μ_d is a negative number). We use the following data to estimate μ_d with a 90% confidence interval.

Patient	1	2	3	4	5	6	7	8
Onset	84	90	96	108	126	144	156	63
Diagnosis	108	102	151	123	156	204	170	84
Difference	−24	−12	−55	−15	−30	−60	−14	−21

Patient	9	10	11	12	13	14	15
Onset	119	120	132	144	144	144	144
Diagnosis	167	132	157	197	205	213	224
Difference	−48	−12	−25	−53	−61	−69	−80

The summary values are $\bar{x}_d = -38.6$ and $s_d = 23.18$. With $n - 1 = 14$ df, the t critical value for a 90% confidence level is 1.76 (from Table IV). The interval is therefore

$$-38.6 \pm (1.76)(23.18/\sqrt{15}) = -38.6 \pm 10.53$$
$$= (-49.13, -28.07)$$

Based on the sample data, we can be 90% confident that the mean elapsed time between onset of symptoms and diagnosis of childhood Cushing's disease is between 28.07 and 49.13 months. It appears that a great deal of time generally passes before Cushing's disease is diagnosed. This is probably due to the fact that child-hood Cushing's disease is very rare and so may be overlooked as a possibility until other more common illnesses are ruled out as causes of the symptoms.

When two populations are to be compared in order to draw a conclusion on the basis of sample data, a researcher might choose to use independent samples or paired samples. In many situations, paired data provides a more effective compar-ison by screening out the effects of extraneous variables that might obscure differ-ences between the two populations or that might suggest a difference when none exists.

EXERCISES 12.9–12.20   SECTION 12.2

12.9   The paper "Agronomic Performance of Winter versus Spring Wheat" (*Agronomy J.* (1991):527–531) described the results of an experiment to compare the yield (kg/ha) of Sundance winter wheat and Manitou spring wheat. Data for nine test plots is given next. Is there sufficient evidence to conclude that the mean yield for the Sundance winter wheat is higher than that for the Manitou spring wheat? Use $\alpha = .01$.

Location	1	2	3	4	5	6	7	8	9
Sundance	3201	3095	3297	3644	3604	2860	3470	2042	3689
Manitou	2386	2011	2616	3094	3069	2074	2308	1525	2779

12.10   The paper referenced in Exercise 12.9 also gave information on the protein con-centration of Sundance winter wheat and Manitou spring wheat grown at nine locations. Protein concentration was measured in grams of protein per kilogram of wheat.
   a. Use the accompanying data and $\alpha = .05$ to determine if there is a significant difference in protein concentration for the two varieties of wheat.
   b. Construct a 90% confidence interval for the true difference in mean protein concentration for the two varieties of wheat.

Location	1	2	3	4	5	6	7	8	9
Sundance	77	84	116	145	100	154	114	149	137
Manitou	125	111	144	171	133	166	143	176	170

12.11   Several methods of estimating the number of seeds in soil samples have been developed by ecologists. A paper that appeared in the *Journal of Ecology* ("A Comparison of Methods for Estimating Seed Numbers in the Soil" (1990):1079–1093) considered three such methods. The accompanying data gives number of seeds detected by the direct method and by the stratified method for 27 soil speci-mens. Does the data provide sufficient evidence to conclude that the mean number of seeds detected differs for the two methods? Test the relevant hypotheses using $\alpha = .05$.

Sample	Direct	Stratified	Sample	Direct	Stratified
1	24	8	15	32	28
2	32	36	16	0	0
3	0	8	17	36	36
4	60	56	18	16	12
5	20	52	19	92	92
6	64	64	20	4	12
7	40	28	21	40	48
8	8	8	22	24	24
9	12	8	23	0	0
10	92	100	24	8	12
11	4	0	25	12	40
12	68	56	26	16	12
13	76	68	27	40	76
14	24	52			

12.12   The effect of exercise on the amount of lactic acid in the blood was examined in the article "A Descriptive Analysis of Elite-Level Racquetball" (*Research Quarterly for Exercise and Sport* (1991):109–114). Eight men and seven women who were attending a week-long training camp participated in the experiment, and blood lactate levels were measured before and after playing three games of racquetball.

	Men			Women	
Player	Before	After	Player	Before	After
1	13	18	1	11	21
2	20	37	2	16	26
3	17	40	3	13	19
4	13	35	4	18	21
5	13	30	5	14	14
6	16	20	6	11	31
7	15	33	7	13	20
8	16	19			

   a. Estimate the mean change in blood lactate level for male racquetball players using a 95% confidence interval.

   b. Estimate the mean change for female players using a 95% confidence interval.

   c. Based on the intervals from parts (a) and (b), do you think the mean change in blood lactate level is the same for men as it is for women? Explain.

12.13   Researchers have long been interested in the effects of alcohol on the human body. The authors of the paper "Effects of Alcohol on Hypoxia" (*J. of Amer. Med. Assoc.* (December 13, 1965):135) examined the relationship between alcohol intake and the time of useful consciousness during high-altitude flight. Ten male subjects were taken to a simulated altitude of 25,000 ft and given several tasks to perform. Each was carefully observed for deterioration in performance due to lack of oxygen, and the time at which useful consciousness ended was recorded. Three days later, the experiment was repeated one hour after the subjects had ingested .5 cm^3 of 100-proof whiskey per pound of body weight. The time (in seconds) of useful consciousness was again recorded. The resulting data appears in the accompanying table.

Subject	No alcohol	Alcohol	Difference
1	261	185	76
2	565	375	190
3	900	310	590
4	630	240	390
5	280	215	65
6	365	420	−55
7	400	405	−5
8	735	205	530
9	430	255	175
10	900	900	0

Is there sufficient evidence to conclude that ingestion of .5 cm^3 of whiskey per pound of body weight reduces the mean time of useful consciousness? Use $\alpha = .05$.

12.14   Twelve infants paired according to birth weight were used to compare an enriched formula with a standard formula. Weight gains (g) are given.

Pair	Enriched formula	Standard formula
1	3604	3140
2	2950	3100
3	3344	2810
4	4022	3761
5	4316	3774
6	3077	2630

a. Let μ_d denote the true average difference in weight gain between the two formulas (enriched − standard). What alternative hypothesis suggests that the enriched formula is more effective than the standard formula in increasing weight? Test H_0: $\mu_d = 0$ against this alternative at significance level .05.

b. Why do you think a paired experiment was chosen for this study?

12.15   The paper "Relative Controllability of Dissimilar Cars" (*Human Factors* (1962): 375–380) reported results of an experiment to compare handling ability for two cars of different design. Time (in seconds) required to parallel park each car was recorded for 14 drivers. Does the data suggest that the mean time to parallel park differs significantly for the two designs? Test the relevant hypotheses using $\alpha = .10$.

Driver	Design 1	Design 2	Driver	Design 1	Design 2
1	37.0	17.8	8	58.2	32.2
2	25.8	20.2	9	33.6	27.8
3	16.2	16.8	10	24.4	23.2
4	24.2	41.4	11	23.4	29.6
5	22.0	21.4	12	21.2	20.6
6	33.4	38.4	13	36.2	32.2
7	23.8	16.8	14	29.8	53.8

12.16 The article "Action of Drugs on Movements of the Rat during Swimming" (*J. of Human Movement Studies* (1984):225–230) described the effects of the drug ephedrine. Rats were placed in a swimming apparatus where swimming movement triggered rotation of an exercise wheel. The number of revolutions during a fixed time interval was recorded both before and after administration of a dose of 5 mg of ephedrine per kilogram of body weight. The resulting data follows.

Before	15	30	3	16	11
After	6	5	3	6	2

Does the data suggest that ephedrine reduces the true mean number of revolutions? Test using a .05 significance level.

12.17 Dentists make many people nervous (even more so than statisticians!). To see if such nervousness elevates blood pressure, the blood pressure and pulse rates of 60 subjects were measured in a dental setting and in a medical setting ("The Effect of the Dental Setting on Blood Pressure Measurement" *Am. J. of Public Health* (1983):1210–1214). For each subject, the difference (dental-setting blood pressure minus medical-setting blood pressure) was formed. The analogous differences were also formed for pulse rates. Summary data follows.

	Mean difference	Standard deviation of differences
Systolic blood pressure	4.47	8.77
Pulse (beats/min)	−1.33	8.84

a. Does the data strongly suggest that true mean blood pressure is higher in a dental setting than in a medical setting? Use a level .01 test.

b. Is there sufficient evidence to indicate that true mean pulse rate in a dental setting differs from the true mean pulse rate in a medical setting? Use a significance level of .05.

12.18 Many people who quit smoking complain of weight gain. The results of an investigation into the relationship between smoking cessation and weight gain are given in the paper "Does Smoking Cessation Lead to Weight Gain?" (*Amer. J. of Public*

Health (1983):1303–1305). Three hundred twenty-two subjects who successfully participated in a program to quit smoking were weighed at the beginning of the program and again 1 year later. The mean change in weight was 5.15 lb and the standard deviation of the weight changes was 11.45 lb. Is there sufficient evidence to conclude that the true mean change in weight is positive? Use $\alpha = .05$.

12.19   In a study of memory recall, eight people were given 10 min to memorize a list of 20 nonsense words. Each was asked to list as many of the words as he or she could remember both 1 h and 24 h later.

Subject	1	2	3	4	5	6	7	8
1 h later	14	12	18	7	11	9	16	15
24 h later	10	4	14	6	9	6	12	12

Is there evidence to suggest that the mean number of words recalled after 1 h exceeds the mean recall after 24 h by more than 3? Use a level .01 test.

12.20   The paper "A Supplementary Behavioral Program to Improve Deficient Reading Performance" (*J. Abnormal Child Psych.* (1973):390–399) reported the results of an experiment in which seven pairs of children reading below grade level were obtained by matching so that within each pair the two children were equally deficient in reading ability. Then one child from each pair received experimental training, while the other received standard training. Based on the accompanying improvement scores, does the experimental training appear to be superior to the standard training? Use a .1 significance level.

Pair	1	2	3	4	5	6	7
Experimental	.5	1.0	.6	.1	1.3	.1	1.0
Control	.8	1.1	− .1	.2	.2	1.5	.8

12.3 Distribution-Free Procedures for Inferences Concerning a Difference between Two Population Means

In the previous section, the paired *t* test and paired *t* confidence interval were used to make inferences about μ_d, the population mean difference. These methods are appropriate when it is reasonable to assume that the difference population (from which the sample differences were randomly selected) is normal in shape. Since this may not always be the case, in this section we present an alternate test procedure, called the *signed-rank test,* and an associated confidence interval. These procedures are also based on the sample differences, but their validity requires only that the difference distribution be symmetric in shape. Symmetry is a weaker condition than normality (any normal distribution is symmetric, but there are many symmetric distributions which are not normal), so the signed-rank procedures are more widely valid than are the paired t procedures. Since the signed-rank procedures do not depend on specific distributional assumptions such as normality, they are distribution-free. A sufficient condition for the difference distribution to be symmetric is that the two population distributions (from which the first and second observations in each pair are drawn) are identical with respect to shape and spread.

As with the paired t test, we begin by forming differences. Next the absolute values of the differences are assigned ranks (this amounts to ignoring any negative signs when ranking). We then associate a $+$ or a $-$ sign with each rank, depending on whether the corresponding difference is positive or negative. For example, with $n = 5$, the differences might be

$$-17 \quad 12 \quad 3 \quad 10 \quad -6$$

The ordered absolute differences are then

$$3 \quad 6 \quad 10 \quad 12 \quad 17$$

and the corresponding signed ranks are

$$1 \quad -2 \quad 3 \quad 4 \quad -5$$
$$\uparrow \qquad\qquad\quad \uparrow$$

Negative because the corresponding difference is negative

If there are ties in the differences, the average of the appropriate ranks is assigned, as with the rank sum test in Chapter 11.

The signed-rank test statistic for testing H_0: $\mu_d = 0$ is the **signed-rank sum,** or the *sum of the signed ranks*. A large positive sum suggests that $\mu_d > 0$, since if this were the case, most differences would be positive and larger in magnitude than the few negative differences; most of the ranks, and especially the larger ones, would then be positively signed. Similarly, a large negative sum would suggest $\mu_d < 0$. A signed-rank sum near zero would be compatible with H_0: $\mu_d = 0$.

EXAMPLE 12.8

Treatment of terminal renal failure involves surgical removal of a kidney (a nephrectomy). The paper "Hypertension in Terminal Renal Failure, Observations Pre and Post Bilateral Nephrectomy" (*J. Chronic Diseases* (1973):471–501) gave the accompanying blood pressure readings for five terminal renal patients before and 2 months after surgery.

Patient	1	2	3	4	5
Before surgery	107	102	95	106	112
After surgery	87	97	101	113	80
Difference	20	5	−6	−7	32

We can determine whether the mean blood pressure before surgery exceeds the mean blood pressure two months after surgery by testing

$$H_0: \mu_1 - \mu_2 = 0 \quad \text{versus} \quad H_a: \mu_1 - \mu_2 > 0$$

where μ_1 denotes the true mean diastolic blood pressure for patients in renal failure and μ_2 denotes the true mean blood pressure for patients 2 months after surgery (equivalent hypotheses are $H_0: \mu_d = 0$ and $H_a: \mu_d > 0$ where μ_d is the mean difference in blood pressure).

A normal probability plot for this set of differences follows. Since the plot appears to be more S-shaped than linear, the assumption of a normal difference population is questionable. If it is reasonable to assume that the difference distribution is symmetric, a test based on the signed ranks can be used.

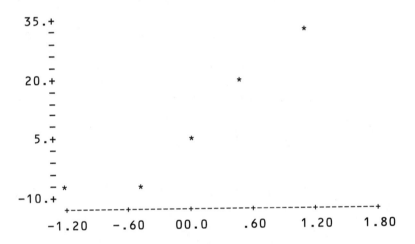

The absolute values of the differences and the corresponding ranks are as follows.

Absolute difference	5	6	7	20	32
Rank	1	2	3	4	5

Associating the appropriate sign with each rank then yields signed ranks 1, -2, -3, 4, and 5, and a signed-rank sum of $1 - 2 - 3 + 4 + 5 = 5$.

The largest possible value for this sum would be 15, occurring only when all differences are positive. There are 32 possible ways to associate signs with ranks 1, 2, 3, 4, and 5, and 10 of them have rank sums of at least 5. When the null hypothesis $H_0: \mu_d = 0$ is true, each of the 32 possible assignments is equally likely to occur, and so

$$P(\text{signed-rank sum} \geq 5 \text{ when } H_0 \text{ is true}) = \frac{10}{32} = .3125$$

Therefore, the observed sum of 5 is compatible with H_0—it does not provide evidence that H_0 should be rejected.

Testing Hypotheses Using Signed Ranks

Suppose we are interested in testing $H_0: \mu_d = 0$. Given a set of n pairs of observations, ranking the absolute differences requires using ranks 1 to n. Since each rank could then be designated as either a plus or a minus, there are 2^n different possible sets of signed ranks. When the null hypothesis is true, each of the 2^n signed rankings has the same chance of occurring. Examining these different signed rankings and the associated sums gives information about how the signed-rank sum behaves when the null hypothesis is true. In particular, by looking at the distribution of the sum when H_0 is true, we can determine which values are unusual enough to suggest rejection of H_0.

For example, when $n = 5$ there are 2^5 different signed-rank sets. A few of these and the associated sums are

$$1, 2, 3, 4, 5 \quad \text{sum} = 15$$
$$-1, 2, -3, 4, 5 \quad \text{sum} = 7$$
$$-1, -2, 3, 4, -5 \quad \text{sum} = -1$$

By systematically listing all 32 possible signed rankings, the following information is obtained:

Signed-rank sum	15	13	11	9	7	5	3	1
Number of rankings yielding sum	1	1	1	2	2	3	3	3

Signed-rank sum	-1	-3	-5	-7	-9	-11	-13	-15
Number of rankings yielding sum	3	3	3	2	2	1	1	1

If we were to reject $H_0: \mu_1 - \mu_2 = 0$ in favor of $H_a: \mu_1 - \mu_2 \neq 0$ whenever we observed a signed-rank sum greater than or equal to 13 or less than or equal to -13, the probability of incorrect rejection would be $4/32 = .125$ (since 4 of the possible signed rankings result in sums in the rejection region). Therefore, when $n = 5$, using the indicated rejection region gives a test with significance level .125.

For values of n larger than 5, finding the exact distribution of the signed-rank sum when H_0 is true is tedious and time-consuming, so tables have been developed. For selected sample sizes, Table VIII in the appendices gives critical values for the signed-rank test for levels of significance closest to the usual choices of .01, .05, and .10.

SUMMARY OF THE SIGNED-RANK TEST[1]

Null hypothesis: H_0: $\mu_d = 0$

Test statistic: signed-rank sum

Alternative Hypothesis	Rejection Region
H_a: $\mu_d > 0$	Signed-rank sum $\geq$ critical value
H_a: $\mu_d < 0$	Signed-rank sum $\leq$ $-$critical value
H_a: $\mu_d \neq 0$	Either signed-rank sum $\geq$ critical value or signed-rank sum $\leq$ $-$critical value

Selected critical values are given in Table VIII.

EXAMPLE 12.9

Some swimming races are won by less than .001 s. As a result, a technique that might give a competitive swimmer even a slight edge is given careful consideration. To determine which of two racing starts, the hole entry or the flat entry, is faster, the authors of the paper "Analysis of the Flat vs. the Hole Entry" (*Swimming Technique* (Winter 1980):112–117) studied ten college swimmers. A number of variables were measured for each type of start. The data for time to water entry appears here.

Swimmer	1	2	3	4	5	6	7	8	9	10
Flat entry	1.13	1.11	1.18	1.26	1.16	1.41	1.43	1.25	1.33	1.36
Hole entry	1.07	1.03	1.21	1.24	1.33	1.42	1.35	1.32	1.31	1.33
Difference	.06	.08	−.03	.02	−.17	−.01	.08	−.07	.02	.03

The authors of the paper used a level .05 signed-rank test to determine if there is a significant difference between the mean time to water entry for the two entry methods. Ordering the absolute differences results in the following assignment of signed ranks.

Difference	−.01	.02	.02	.03	−.03	.06	−.07	.08	.08	−.17
Signed rank	−1	2.5	2.5	4.5	−4.5	6	−7	8.5	8.5	−10

1. Let μ_d denote the mean difference in time to water entry for flat and hole entry.
2. H_0: $\mu_d = 0$
3. H_a: $\mu_d \neq 0$

---

[1]Alternative forms of the test statistic sometimes used are the sum of positive ranks, the sum of negative ranks, or the smaller of the sum of positive ranks and the sum of negative ranks. However, Table VIII should not be used to obtain critical values for these statistics.

4. Test statistic: signed-rank sum
5. With $n = 10$ and $\alpha = .05$, Table VIII gives 39 as the critical value for a two-tailed test. Therefore, H_0 will be rejected if either signed-rank sum ≥ 39 or signed-rank sum ≤ -39.
6. Signed-rank sum $= -1 + 2.5 + \cdots + (-10) = 10$
7. Since 10 does not fall in the rejection region, we do not reject H_0. There is not sufficient evidence to indicate that the mean time to water entry differs for the two methods.

The next example illustrates how zero differences are handled when performing a signed-rank test. Since zero is considered to be neither positive nor negative, zero values are generally excluded from a signed-rank analysis, and the sample size is reduced accordingly.

EXAMPLE 12.10

Two assay methods for measuring the level of vitamin B_{12} in red blood cells were compared in the paper "Noncobalimin Vitamin B_{12} Analogues in Human Red Cells, Liver and Brain" (*Am. J. of Clinical Nutrition* (1983):774–777). Blood samples were taken from 15 healthy adults, and, for each blood sample, the B_{12} level was determined using both methods. The resulting data is given here.

Subject	1	2	3	4	5	6	7	8
Method 1	204	238	209	277	197	227	207	205
Method 2	204	238	198	253	180	209	217	204
Difference	0	0	11	24	17	18	−10	1

Subject	9	10	11	12	13	14	15
Method 1	131	282	76	194	120	92	114
Method 2	137	250	82	165	79	100	107
Difference	−6	32	−6	29	41	−8	7

We assume that the difference distribution is symmetric and proceed with a signed-rank test to determine whether there is a significant difference between the two methods for measuring B_{12} content. A significance level of .05 will be used.

Two of the observed differences are zero. Eliminating the two zeros reduces the sample size from 15 to 13. Ordering the nonzero absolute differences results in the following assignment of signed ranks.

Difference	1	−6	−6	7	−8	−10	11	17	18	24	29	32	41
Signed rank	1	−2.5	−2.5	4	−5	−6	7	8	9	10	11	12	13

1. μ_d is the mean difference in B_{12} determination for the two methods.
2. $H_0: \mu_d = 0$
3. $H_a: \mu_d \neq 0$
4. Test statistic: signed-rank sum
5. The form of H_a indicates that a two-tailed test should be used. With $n = 13$ and $\alpha = .05$, Table VIII gives a critical value of 57 (corresponding to an actual significance level of .048). Therefore, H_0 will be rejected if either signed-rank sum ≥ 57 or signed-rank sum ≤ -57.
6. Signed-rank sum $= 1 + (-2.5) + (-2.5) + \cdots + 13 = 59$
7. Since 59 falls in the rejection region, H_0 is rejected in favor of H_a. We conclude that there is a significant difference in measurement of B_{12} level in red blood cells for the two assay methods.

The procedure for testing $H_0: \mu_d = 0$ just described can be easily adapted to test $H_0: \mu_d = $ hypothesized value, where the hypothesized value is something other than zero.

> To test $H_0: \mu_d = $ hypothesized value, subtract the hypothesized value from each difference prior to assigning signed ranks.

EXAMPLE 12.11

Tardive dyskinesia is a syndrome that sometimes follows long-term use of antipsychotic drugs. Symptoms include abnormal involuntary movements. In an experiment to evaluate the effectiveness of the drug Deanol in reducing symptoms, Deanol and a placebo treatment were each administered for four weeks to 14 patients. A Total Severity Index (TSI) score was used to measure improvement (larger TSI scores indicate greater improvement). The accompanying data comes from "Double Blind Evaluation of Deanol in Tardive Dyskinesia" (*J. Amer. Med. Assoc.* (1978):1997–1998). Let's use this data and a significance level of .01 to determine if the mean TSI score for people treated with Deanol exceeds the mean placebo TSI score by more than 1.

	TSI scores						
Patient	1	2	3	4	5	6	7
Deanol	12.4	6.8	12.6	13.2	12.4	7.6	12.1
Placebo	9.2	10.2	12.2	12.7	12.1	9.0	12.4
Difference	3.2	−3.4	.4	.5	.3	−1.4	−.3

Patient	8	9	10	11	12	13	14
Deanol	5.9	12.0	1.1	11.5	13.0	5.1	9.6
Placebo	5.9	8.5	4.8	7.8	9.1	3.5	6.4
Difference	0.0	3.5	−3.7	3.7	3.9	1.6	3.2

1. Let μ_d denote the mean difference in TSI score between Deanol and the placebo treatment.
2. H_0: $\mu_d = 1$
3. H_a: $\mu_d > 1$
4. Test statistic: signed-rank sum
5. An upper-tailed test is indicated by the form of H_a. For $n = 14$ and $\alpha = .01$, Table VIII gives a critical value of 73. Therefore, H_0 will be rejected in favor of H_a at level .01 if the signed-rank sum equals or exceeds 73.
6. Subtracting 1 from each difference results in the following set of values.

2.2	−4.4	−.6	−.5	−.7	−2.4	−1.3
−1	2.5	−4.7	2.7	2.9	.6	2.2

Ordering these values and associating signed ranks yields:

Sign	−	−	+	−	−	−	+
Absolute difference	.5	.6	.6	.7	1	1.3	2.2
Signed rank	−1	−2.5	2.5	−4	−5	−6	7.5

Sign	+	−	+	+	+	−	−
Absolute difference	2.2	2.4	2.5	2.7	2.9	4.4	4.7
Signed rank	7.5	−9	10	11	12	−13	−14

Then signed-rank sum $= -1 + (-2.5) + 2.5 + \cdots + (-14) = -4$.

7. Since $-4 < 73$, we fail to reject H_0. There is not sufficient evidence to indicate that the mean TSI score for the drug Deanol exceeds the mean TSI score for a placebo treatment by more than 1.

A Normal Approximation

Signed-rank critical values for sample sizes up to 20 are given in Table VIII. For larger sample sizes, the distribution of the signed-rank statistic when H_0 is true can be approximated by a normal distribution.

> If $n > 20$, the distribution of the signed-rank sum when H_0 is true is well approximated by the normal distribution with mean 0 and standard deviation $\sqrt{n(n + 1)(2n + 1)/6}$. This implies that the standardized statistic
>
> $$z = \frac{\text{signed-rank sum}}{\sqrt{n(n + 1)(2n + 1)/6}}$$
>
> has approximately a standard normal distribution. This z statistic can be used as a test statistic, with the rejection region based on an appropriate z critical value.

EXAMPLE 12.12

The exercise capability of people suffering chronic airflow obstruction (CAO) is severely limited. In order to determine maximum exercise ventilation under two different experimental conditions, 21 patients suffering from CAO exercised to exhaustion under each condition. Ventilation was then measured. The data is from "Exercise Performance with Added Dead Space in Chronic Airflow Obstruction" (*J. Applied Physiology* (1984):1020–1023).

Patient	1	2	3	4	5	6	7	8	9	10	11
Condition 1	62	57	56	55	50.5	50	47.2	43.5	40	40	41
Condition 2	52	46	51	52.4	55	51	43	40	34.2	34	33
Difference	10	11	5	2.6	−4.5	−1	4.2	3.5	5.8	6	8

Patient	12	13	14	15	16	17	18	19	20	21
Condition 1	33	31	28	27.1	27.5	27	25	19.2	17.5	12
Condition 2	32	38	26	28	28	18	21	18	16	15
Difference	1	−7	2	−.9	−.5	9	4	1.2	1.5	−3

Does this data suggest that the mean ventilation is different for the two experimental conditions? Let's analyze the data using a level .05 signed-rank test.

1. Let μ_d denote the true mean difference in ventilation between experimental conditions 1 and 2.
2. $H_0: \mu_d = 0$
3. $H_a: \mu_d \neq 0$
4. Test statistic:

$$z = \frac{\text{signed-rank sum}}{\sqrt{n(n + 1)(2n + 1)/6}}$$

5. With $\alpha = .05$, the bottom row of Table IV gives the z critical value for a two-tailed test as 1.96. H_0 will be rejected in favor of H_a if $z > 1.96$ or $z < -1.96$.

6. Ordering the absolute differences and assigning signed ranks yields

-1	-2	-3.5	3.5	5	6	7	8	-9	10	11
12	-13	14	15	16	-17	18	19	20	21	

The signed-rank sum is $-1 + (-2) + \cdots + 21 = 140$, and the denominator of z is

$$\sqrt{\frac{n(n + 1)(2n + 1)}{6}} = \sqrt{\frac{(21)(22)(43)}{6}} = 57.54$$

so

$$z = \frac{140}{57.54} = 2.43$$

7. Since 2.43 falls in the rejection region, we reject H_0 in favor of H_a. The sample data does suggest that the true mean ventilation rate differs for the two experimental conditions.

Comparing the Paired *t* and Signed-Rank Tests

In order for the paired t test to be an appropriate method of analysis, it must be assumed that the underlying difference distribution is normal. Proper use of the signed-rank test requires only that the difference distribution be symmetric. Since a normal distribution is symmetric, when the distribution of differences is normal, either the paired t or signed-rank test could be used. In this case, however, for a fixed significance level and sample size, the paired t test gives a slightly smaller type II error probability. Therefore, when the assumption of a normal difference distribution is met, the paired t test would be the preferred method for testing hypotheses about $\mu_1 - \mu_2$ using paired data. However, when the difference distribution is symmetric but not necessarily normal, the signed-rank test may prove to be a better choice.

A Distribution-Free Confidence Interval for μ_d

The distribution-free confidence interval for $\mu_1 - \mu_2$ discussed in Chapter 11 consisted of all hypothesized values for which $H_0: \mu_1 - \mu_2 =$ hypothesized value could not be rejected by the rank sum test. Similarly, the signed-rank sum confidence interval consists of those values for which $H_0: \mu_d =$ hypothesized value cannot be rejected by the signed-rank test. Unfortunately, in order to see the relation between the test procedure and confidence interval formula clearly, the test statistic must first be expressed in a different form, one that involves taking averages of all pairs of sample differences. We ask you to take it on faith that the procedure described below is correct (or consult one of the chapter references).

> A **signed-rank confidence interval for** μ_d is based on all possible pairwise averages of sample differences (including the average of each difference with itself). The confidence interval has the form
>
> (d^{th} smallest average, d^{th} largest average)
>
> The value of d is obtained from Appendix Table IX and depends on the specified confidence level and the sample size.

EXAMPLE 12.13

Elevated levels of growth hormone are characteristic of diabetic control. The paper "Importance of Raised Growth Hormone Levels in Medicating the Metabolic Derangements of Diabetes" (*N. Eng. J. of Med.* (March 29, 1981):810–815) reported the results of a comparison of growth hormone levels (mg/mL) for a conventional treatment and an insulin pump treatment for diabetes. Five diabetic patients participated in the study, with each patient receiving both treatments over a period of time. The resulting data is given. It would be useful to estimate the difference between mean growth hormone level for the two treatments.

Patient	1	2	3	4	5
Conventional	10	16	17	20	10
Pump	9	7	8	8	6
Difference	1	9	9	12	4

To compute the required pairwise averages, it is convenient to arrange the differences along the top and left of a rectangular table. Then the averages of the corresponding pairs of differences can be calculated and entered at the intersection of each row and column on or above the diagonal of the table.

Pairwise averages

		Difference				
		1	4	9	9	12
Difference	1	1	2.5	5	5	6.5
	4	—	4	6.5	6.5	8
	9	—	—	9	9	10.5
	9	—	—	—	9	10.5
	12	—	—	—	—	12

Arranging the pairwise averages in order yields

1   2.5   4   5   5   6.5   6.5   6.5   8   9   9   9   10.5   10.5   12

With a sample size of 5 and a 90% confidence level, Table IX gives $d = 2$ (corresponding to an actual confidence level of 87.5%). The confidence interval for $\mu_d = \mu_1 - \mu_2$ is then (2.5, 10.5).

As you can see, the calculations required in obtaining the pairwise averages can be tedious, especially for larger sample sizes. Fortunately, many of the standard computer packages calculate both the signed-rank sum and the signed-rank confidence interval. An approximate 90% signed-rank confidence interval from MINITAB is as follows.

```
       ESTIMATED
 N      CENTER  CONFIDENCE INTERVAL
 5      6.500  (   2.500,  10.500)
```

The Signed-Rank Test for Single-Sample Problems

Although we have introduced the signed-rank test in a two-sample context, it can also be used to test H_0: μ = hypothesized value, where μ is the mean value of a single population. In this setting, rather than forming differences and then associating signed ranks, a single sample is used and the hypothesized value from H_0 is subtracted from each observed sample value. Signed ranks are then associated with the resulting values. The rest of the test procedure (test statistic and rejection region) remains the same.

EXERCISES 12.21–12.31   SECTION 12.3

12.21   The effect of a restricted diet in the treatment of autistic children was examined in the paper "Gluten, Milk Proteins, and Autism: Dietary Intervention Effects on Behavior and Peptide Secretion" (*J. of Applied Nutrition* (1991):1–8). Ten children with autistic syndrome participated in the study. Peptide secretion was measured before diet restrictions and again after a period of restricted diet. The resulting data follows. Does this data suggest that the restricted diet was successful in reducing peptide secretion? Use the signed-rank test.

Subject	Before	After	Subject	Before	After
1	25	10	6	50	19
2	22	9	7	15	8
3	84	29	8	41	19
4	84	7	9	19	14
5	60	2	10	27	11

12.22   Peak force (N) on the hand was measured just prior to impact and just after impact on a backhand drive for six advanced tennis players. The resulting data, from the paper "Forces on the Hand in the Tennis One-Handed Backhand" (*Int. J. of Sport Biomechanics* (1991):282–292), is given in the accompanying table. Use the signed-rank test to determine if the postimpact mean force is greater than the preimpact force by more than 10.

Player	Preimpact	Postimpact
1	26.7	38.2
2	44.3	47.2
3	53.9	61.0
4	26.4	34.3
5	47.6	64.9
6	43.1	44.2

12.23   In an experiment to study the way in which different anesthetics affected plasma epinephrine concentration, 10 dogs were selected and concentration was measured while they were under the influence of the anesthetics isoflurane and halothane ("Sympathoadrenal and Hemodynamic Effects of Isoflurane, Halothane, and Cyclopropane in Dogs" *Anesthesiology* (1974):465–470). The resulting data is as follows.

Dog	1	2	3	4	5	6	7	8	9	10
Isoflurane	.28	.51	1.00	.39	.29	.36	.32	.69	.17	.33
Halothane	.30	.39	.63	.38	.21	.88	.39	.51	.32	.42

Use a level .05 signed-rank test to see whether the true mean epinephrine concentration differs for the two anesthetics. What assumptions must be made about the epinephrine concentration distributions?

12.24   The accompanying data refers to the concentration of the radioactive isotope strontium-90 in samples of nonfat and 2% fat milk from five dairies. Does the data strongly support the hypothesis that the true mean strontium-90 concentration is higher for 2% fat milk than for nonfat? Use a level .05 signed-rank test.

Dairy	1	2	3	4	5
Nonfat	6.4	5.8	6.5	7.7	6.1
2%	7.1	9.9	11.2	10.5	8.8

12.25   Both a gravimetric and a spectrophotometric method are under consideration for determining phosphate content of a particular material. Six samples of the material are obtained, each is split in half, and a determination is made on each half using one of the two methods, resulting in the following data. Use an approximate 95% distribution-free confidence interval to estimate the true mean difference for the two techniques. Interpret the interval.

Sample	1	2	3	4	5	6
Gravimetric	54.7	58.5	66.8	46.1	52.3	74.3
Spectrophotometric	55.0	55.7	62.9	45.5	51.1	75.4

12.26 The paper "Growth Hormone Treatment for Short Stature" (*N. Eng. J. Med.* (October 27, 1983):1016–1022) gives the accompanying data for height velocity before growth hormone therapy and during growth hormone therapy for 14 children with hypopituitarism.

Child	1	2	3	4	5	6	7
Before	5.3	3.8	5.6	2.0	3.5	1.7	2.6
During	8.0	11.4	7.6	6.9	7.0	9.4	7.9

Child	8	9	10	11	12	13	14
Before	2.1	3.0	5.5	5.4	2.1	3.0	2.4
During	7.4	7.4	7.5	11.8	6.4	8.8	5.0

a. Use a level .05 signed-rank test to decide if growth hormone therapy is successful in increasing the mean height velocity.

b. What assumptions about the height velocity distributions must be made in order that the analysis in (a) be valid?

12.27 The paper "Analysis of the Flat vs. the Hole Entry" cited in Example 12.9 of this section also gave the accompanying data on time from water entry to first stroke and initial velocity. The authors of the paper used signed-rank tests to analyze the data.

a. Use a level .01 test to ascertain whether there is a significant difference in true mean time from entry to first stroke for the two entry methods.

b. Does the data suggest a difference in true mean initial velocity for the two entry methods? Use a level .05 signed-rank test.

Swimmer	Time from entry to first stroke		Initial velocity	
	Hole	Flat	Hole	Flat
1	1.18	1.06	24.0	25.1
2	1.10	1.23	22.5	22.4
3	1.31	1.20	21.6	24.0

(continued)

Swimmer	Time from entry to first stroke		Initial velocity	
	Hole	Flat	Hole	Flat
4	1.12	1.19	21.4	22.4
5	1.12	1.29	20.9	23.9
6	1.23	1.09	20.8	21.7
7	1.27	1.09	22.4	23.8
8	1.08	1.33	22.9	22.9
9	1.26	1.27	23.3	25.0
10	1.27	1.38	20.7	19.5

12.28   The paper "Effects of a Rice-rich versus Potato-rich Diet on Glucose, Lipoprotein, and Cholesterol Metabolism in Noninsulin-Dependent Diabetics" (*Amer. J. Clinical Nutrition* (1984):598–606) gave the accompanying data on cholesterol synthesis rate for eight diabetic subjects. Subjects were fed a standardized diet with potato or rice as the major carbohydrate source. Participants received both diets for specified periods of time, with cholesterol synthesis rate (mmol/day) measured at the end of each dietary period. The analysis presented in this paper used the signed-rank test. Use such a test with significance level .05 to determine whether the true mean cholesterol synthesis rate differs significantly for the two sources of carbohydrates.

Subject	1	2	3	4	5	6	7	8
Potato	1.88	2.60	1.38	4.41	1.87	2.89	3.96	2.31
Rice	1.70	3.84	1.13	4.97	.86	1.93	3.36	2.15

12.29   The following pre- and postoperative lung capacities for 22 patients who underwent surgery as treatment for tuberculosis kyphosis of the spine appeared in the paper "Tuberculosis Kyphosis, Correction with Spinal Osteotomy, Halo-Pelvic Distractor, and Anterior and Posterior Fusion" (*J. Bone Joint Surgery* (1974):1419–1434). Does the data suggest that surgery increases the mean lung capacity? Use a level .05 large-sample signed-rank test.

Patient	1	2	3	4	5	6	7	8
Preoperative	1540	1160	1870	1980	1520	3155	1485	1150
Postoperative	1620	1500	2220	2080	2160	3040	2030	1370

Patient	9	10	11	12	13	14	15	16
Preoperative	1740	3260	4950	1440	1770	2850	2860	1530
Postoperative	2370	4060	5070	1680	1750	3730	3430	1570

Patient	17	18	19	20	21	22
Preoperative	3770	2260	3370	2570	2810	2990
Postoperative	3750	2840	3500	2640	3260	3100

12.30   Using the data of Exercise 12.26, estimate the true mean difference in height velocity before and during growth hormone therapy with a 90% distribution-free confidence interval.

12.31   The signed-rank test can be adapted for use in testing H_0: μ = hypothesized value, where μ is the mean of a single population (see the last part of this section). Suppose that the time required to process a request at a bank's automated teller machine is recorded for each of 10 randomly selected transactions, resulting in the following times (in min): 1.4, 2.1, 1.9, 1.7, 2.4, 2.9, 1.8, 1.9, 2.6, 2.2. Use the one-sample version of the signed-rank test and a .05 significance level to decide if the data indicates that the true mean processing time exceeds 2 min.

CHAPTER TWELVE SUMMARY OF KEY CONCEPTS AND FORMULAS

Term or Formula	Comment
$\bar{x}_d$	The sample mean difference.
s_d	The standard deviation of the sample differences.
μ_d	The mean value for the population of differences.
σ_d	The standard deviation for the population of differences.
$t = \dfrac{\bar{x}_d - \text{hypothesized value}}{s_d/\sqrt{n}}$	The paired t test statistic for testing H_0: $\mu_d = 0$.
$\bar{x}_d \pm (t\ \text{critical value}) \cdot \dfrac{s_d}{\sqrt{n}}$	The paired t confidence interval formula.
Signed-rank sum	The test statistic for a distribution-free test of H_0: $\mu_d = 0$.
$z = \dfrac{\text{signed-rank sum}}{\sqrt{n(n + 1)(2n + 1)/6}}$	A test statistic that can be used in place of the signed-rank sum statistic when the sample size is large.
(dth smallest average, dth largest average)	The form of the signed-rank confidence interval for μ_d (based on averages of pairs of differences). The value of d comes from Appendix Table IX.

ENCORE

T he Down syndrome data presented in the Chapter Preview will be used to test the theory that children with mosaic Down syndrome tend to achieve a higher intellectual level than children with trisomy 21 Down syndrome. Since the data is paired, our analysis will focus on the mosaic–trisomy 21 IQ differences, which are shown here.

Pair	Mosaic	Trisomy 21	Difference
1	73	71	2
2	43	53	−10
3	69	58	11
4	89	71	18
5	53	50	3
6	81	70	11
7	59	55	4
8	71	18	53
9	65	31	34
10	53	57	−4
11	58	63	−5
12	55	60	−5
13	61	48	13
14	63	55	8
15	87	59	28
16	64	78	−14
17	63	55	8
18	58	51	7
19	50	55	−5
20	59	53	6
21	75	47	28
22	61	50	11
23	71	47	24
24	92	44	48
25	57	28	29
26	76	75	1
27	91	63	28
28	43	46	−3
29	55	54	1
30	88	48	40

Let

μ_1 = mean IQ for children with mosaic Down syndrome
μ_2 = mean IQ for children with trisomy 21 Down syndrome

and

$\mu_d = \mu_1 - \mu_2$ = mean IQ difference between mosaic and trisomy 21 Down syndrome children

The question of interest can be answered by testing the hypothesis

$$H_0: \mu_d = 0 \quad \text{versus} \quad H_a: \mu_d > 0$$

The appropriate test statistic is

$$t = \frac{\bar{x}_d - 0}{s_d/\sqrt{n}}$$

Since H_a indicates a one-tailed test, with df $= 29$ and $\alpha = .05$, we will reject H_0 if $t > 1.70$. Using the 30 differences, we compute

$$\bar{x}_d = 12.33, \, s_d = 17.19$$

and so

$$t = \frac{12.33 - 0}{17.19/\sqrt{30}} = 3.93$$

Since 3.93 is greater than the t critical value of 1.70, the null hypothesis is rejected. The data supports the theory that the mean IQ for mosaic Down syndrome children is higher than the mean IQ for trisomy 21 Down syndrome children. Based on this finding, we would predict a higher level of intellectual functioning for Down syndrome children who are diagnosed as mosaic.

A confidence interval for μ_d would provide an estimate of the difference in mean IQ between mosaic and trisomy 21 Down syndrome children. A 90% confidence interval is obtained by substituting into the formula

$$\bar{x}_d \pm (t \text{ critical value}) \cdot \frac{s_d}{\sqrt{n}}$$

With df $= 29$, the appropriate t critical value for a 90% confidence level is 1.70. The resulting interval is

$$12.33 \pm 1.70\left(\frac{17.19}{\sqrt{30}}\right)$$

$$= 12.33 \pm 1.70(3.14)$$

$$= 12.33 \pm 5.34$$

$$= (6.99, 17.67)$$

We estimate that the mean IQ for mosaic Down syndrome children is higher than that for trisomy 21 children by between 6.99 and 17.67 points. The method used to produce this estimate has an error rate of 10%.

SUPPLEMENTARY EXERCISES 12.32–12.38

12.32 Two different underground pipe coatings for preventing corrosion are to be compared. Effect of a coating (as measured by maximum depth of corrosion penetration on a piece of pipe) may vary with depth, orientation, soil type, pipe composition, etc. Describe how an experiment that filters out the effects of these extraneous factors could be carried out.

12.33 A large amount of alcohol is known to reduce reaction time. To investigate the effects of small amounts of alcohol, reaction time (s) was recorded for seven individuals before and after 2 oz of 90-proof alcohol were consumed by each. Does the following data suggest that 2 oz of alcohol reduces mean reaction time? Use a significance level of .05.

Subject	1	2	3	4	5	6	7
Before	.6	.8	.4	.7	.8	.9	.7
After	.7	.8	.6	.8	.8	.8	.9

12.34 Samples of both surface soil and subsoil were taken from eight randomly selected agricultural locations in a particular county. The soil samples were analyzed to determine both surface pH and subsoil pH, with the following results.

Location	1	2	3	4	5	6	7	8
Surface pH	6.55	5.98	5.59	6.17	5.92	6.18	6.43	5.68
Subsoil pH	6.78	6.14	5.80	5.91	6.10	6.01	6.18	5.88

a. Compute a 90% confidence interval for the true average difference between surface and subsoil pH for agricultural land in this county.

b. What assumptions are necessary to validate the interval in part (a)?

12.35 The paper "Cardiac Output in Preadolescent Competitive Swimmers and in Untrained Normal Children" (*J. of Sports Med.* (1983):291–299) reported the results of an experiment designed to assess the effect of athletic training on cardiac output. Sixteen children participated in the study. Eight of the subjects were trained competitive swimmers. The other eight children were normal healthy untrained children selected from a large group of volunteers. An untrained subject was chosen to match each trained subject with respect to age, height, weight, and body surface area, giving eight matched pairs of subjects. Resting heart rate (beats/min) and cardiac output (1/min) were measured for each child, resulting in the accompanying data.

Pair	Heart rate		Cardiac output	
	Trained	Untrained	Trained	Untrained
1	90	95	3.2	2.9
2	85	75	5.9	5.4
3	75	80	4.2	3.4
4	120	65	7.4	2.8
5	95	82	5.5	4.3
6	105	80	4.5	4.8
7	85	100	4.3	4.3
8	75	85	5.3	4.9

a. Is there sufficient evidence to indicate a difference between trained and untrained children with respect to mean resting heart rate? Use a .05 significance level.

b. Does the data suggest that mean resting cardiac output differs for trained and untrained children? Test the appropriate hypotheses using a .01 significance level.

c. Explain why the researchers used paired samples rather than independent samples.

12.36 A famous paper on the effects of marijuana smoking ("Clinical and Psychological Effects of Marijuana in Man" *Science* (1968):1234–1241) described the results of an experiment in which the change in heart rate was measured for nine subjects who had never used marijuana before. Measurements were taken both 15 min after smoking at a low-dose level and 15 min after smoking a placebo (untreated) cigarette.

Subject	1	2	3	4	5	6	7	8	9
Placebo	16	12	8	20	8	10	4	−8	8
Low dose	20	24	8	8	4	20	28	20	20

a. Does the data suggest that marijuana smoking leads to a greater increase in heart rate than does smoking a placebo cigarette? Test using $\alpha = .01$.

b. Give as much information as you can about the P-value associated with the test in part (a).

12.37 The accompanying 1982 and 1983 net earnings (in millions of dollars) of ten food and beverage firms appeared in an article "Capital Expenditures Report" (*Food Engr.* (1984):93–101). Is there sufficient evidence to indicate that mean net earnings increased from 1982 to 1983? Assume that the ten companies represent a random sample of all food and beverage firms. Perform the appropriate hypothesis test using a .01 significance level.

Firm	1983	1982	Firm	1983	1982
Coors	89.0	33.0	Nestle	113.4	93.7
ConAgra	28.7	20.6	Beatrice	292.1	320.8
ADM	110.2	155.0	Carnation	155.0	137.6
Heinz	237.5	214.3	Hershey	100.2	94.2
General			Procter &		
Mills	130.7	134.1	Gamble	58.5	66.5

12.38 Many researchers have investigated the relationship between stress and reproductive efficiency. One such study is described in the paper "Stress or Acute Adrenocorticotrophin Treatment Suppresses LHRH-Induced LH Release in the Ram" (*J. of Reprod. and Fertility* (1984):385–393). Seven rams were used in the study, and LH (luteinizing hormone) release (ng/min) was recorded before and after treatment with ACTH (adrenocorticotrophin, a drug that results in stimulation of the adrenal gland). Use the accompanying data and $\alpha = .01$ to determine if there is a significant reduction in mean LH release following treatment with ACTH.

Ram	1	2	3	4	5	6	7
Before	2400	1400	1375	1325	1200	1150	850
After	2250	1425	1100	800	850	925	700

References

See the References at the end of Chapter 11.

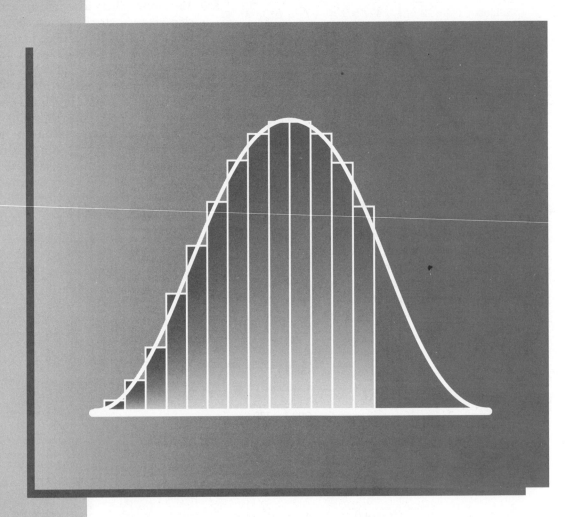

Simple Linear Regression and Correlation: Inferential Methods

PREVIEW

Computers seem to have invaded almost every aspect of our lives. This has led in recent years to an explosion in the number of investigations whose objective has been to study and document the varied effects of the computer revolution. Many of these have dealt with the work environment of people who spend a substantial amount of time staring at computer monitors. Image quality of monitors is an important characteristic, affecting—among other things—extent of eye strain and work efficiency. The paper "Image Quality Determines Differences in Reading Performance and Perceived Image Quality with CRT and Hard Copy Displays" (*Human Factors* (1991):459–469) reported on an experiment in which image quality (x) and average time for a group of subjects to read certain passages (y, in seconds) were determined. The accompanying data was read from a graph that appeared in the paper.

x	4.30	4.55	5.55	5.65	5.95	6.30	6.45	6.45
y	8.0	8.3	7.8	7.25	7.7	7.5	7.6	7.2

The authors fit a straight line to the data, carried out a formal test of hypotheses to see whether there was in fact a useful linear relationship between the two variables, and then proceeded to estimate the impact on reading time of increasing image quality by a specified amount. In this chapter we show how the simple linear regression model can be used as a basis for such inferences.

Introduction

Regression and correlation were introduced in Chapter 4 as tools for description and summarization. The general objective in a "simple" regression situation is to establish a relationship between a dependent variable y and an independent or predictor variable x. This would allow, among other things, for the prediction of y once a value of x is specified. The purpose of a correlation analysis is to assess how strongly two variables are related (there is no distinction here between independent and dependent variables). In this chapter we develop inferential methods for use in drawing conclusions from a regression or correlation analysis. As a first step, the simple linear regression model is introduced in Section 13.1. The model postulates that there is a *population regression line* such that when (x, y) observations are made, the resulting points in the scatter plot will be spread about the population line in a random fashion. The least squares line of Chapter 4 then becomes the estimate of the population line. Sections 13.2 and 13.3 present various methods for making inferences about model characteristics. Inferences about the population correlation coefficient are discussed in Section 13.4. The focus of Section 13.5 is on diagnostic techniques for deciding whether the simple linear regression model (or any other initially specified model) is appropriate.

13.1   The Simple Linear Regression Model

A *deterministic relationship* is one in which the value of y is completely determined by the value of an independent variable x. Such a relationship can be described using traditional mathematical notation such as $y = f(x)$, where $f(x)$ is a specified function of x. For example, we might have $y = 10 + 2x$ or $y = 4 - (10)^{2x}$. However, the variables of interest are often not deterministically related. The value of y = *first-year-college grade point average* is certainly not determined solely by x = *high-school grade point average*, and y = *crop yield* is determined partly by factors other than x = *amount of fertilizer used*.

A description of the relation between two variables x and y that are not deterministically related can be given by specifying a **probabilistic model.** The general form of an **additive probabilistic model** allows y to deviate from $f(x)$ by a random amount. The "model equation" is

y = deterministic function of x + random deviation

$\quad = f(x) + e$

Let x^* denote some particular value of x, and suppose that an observation on y is made when $x = x^*$. Then

If $e > 0$, $y > f(x^*)$.

If $e < 0$, $y < f(x^*)$.

If $e = 0$, $y = f(x^*)$.

Thinking geometrically, if $e > 0$, the observed point (x^*, y) will lie above the graph of $y = f(x)$, and $e < 0$ implies that this point will fall below the graph. This is illustrated in Figure 13.1. When $f(x)$ is a function used in a probabilistic model relating y to x and observations on y are made for various values of x, the resulting

FIGURE 13.1
A deviation from the
deterministic part of a
probabilistic model

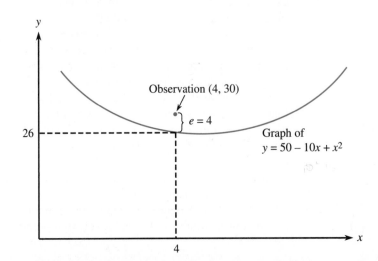

(*x, y*) points will be distributed about the graph of $f(x)$, some falling above it and others below it.

Simple Linear Regression

The simple linear regression model is a special case of the general probabilistic model in which the deterministic function $f(x)$ is linear (so its graph is a straight line).

DEFINITION

The **simple linear regression model** assumes that there is a line with slope β and vertical or y intercept α, called the **true** or **population regression line**. When a value of the **independent variable** x is fixed and an observation on the **dependent variable** y is made,

$$y = \alpha + \beta x + e$$

Because there is uncertainty about the value of the random deviation e (it is a random variable), y itself is a random variable. The assumptions about the distribution of e are as follows:

1. It has mean value 0 ($\mu_e = 0$).
2. It has standard deviation σ (which does not depend on x).
3. The distribution is normal.
4. The random deviations e_1, e_2, . . . , e_n associated with different observations are independent of one another.

Figure 13.2 shows several observations in relation to the population regression line.

FIGURE 13.2
Several observations resulting
from the simple linear
regression model

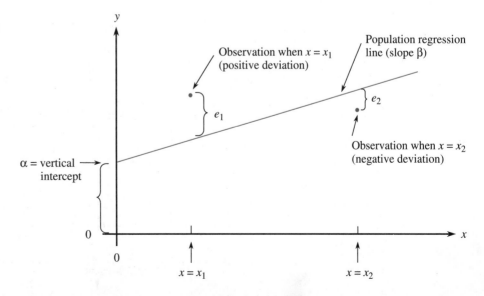

Consider properties of y when x has some fixed value x^*. Then

$$y = \alpha + \beta x^* + e$$

where $\alpha + \beta x^*$ is a fixed number. The sum of a fixed number and a normally distributed variable is again a normally distributed variable (the bell-shaped curve is simply relocated), so y itself has a normal distribution. Furthermore, $\mu_e = 0$ implies that the mean value of y is just $\alpha + \beta x^*$, the height of the population regression line above the value x^*. Lastly, because there is no variability in the fixed number $\alpha + \beta x^*$, the standard deviation of y is the same as that of e.

For any fixed x value, y itself has a normal distribution, with

$$\begin{pmatrix} \text{mean } y \text{ value} \\ \text{for fixed } x \end{pmatrix} = \begin{pmatrix} \text{height of the population} \\ \text{regression line above } x \end{pmatrix} = \alpha + \beta x$$

and

$$\text{standard deviation of } y = \sigma$$

The slope β of the population regression line is the *average* change in y associated with a one-unit increase in x, and the vertical intercept α is the height of the population line when $x = 0$.

The key features of the model are illustrated in Figure 13.3. Notice that the three normal curves in the figure have identical spreads. This is a consequence of $\sigma_e = \sigma$, which does not depend on x.

FIGURE 13.3
Illustration of the simple linear regression model

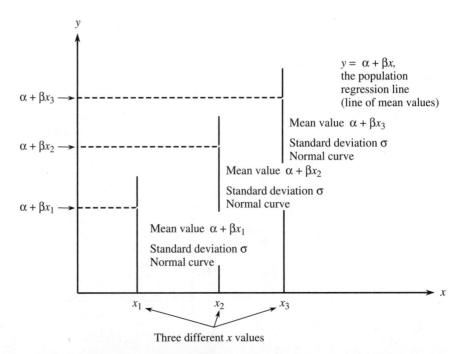

EXAMPLE 13.1

It is often important to have a preliminary assessment of material strength. The article "Some Field Experience in the Use of an Accelerated Method in Estimating 28-Day Strength of Concrete" (*J. of Amer. Concrete Inst.* (1969):895) suggests the simple linear regression model as a reasonable way to relate the variable

$$y = 28\text{-day cured strength of concrete} \quad (\text{lb/in.}^2)$$

to the variable

$$x = \text{accelerated strength} \quad (\text{lb/in.}^2)$$

Suppose that the actual model has

$$\beta = .25, \qquad \alpha = 1800, \qquad \sigma = 350 \text{ lb/in.}^2$$

The population regression line is shown in Figure 13.4.

FIGURE 13.4
The population regression line
for Example 13.1

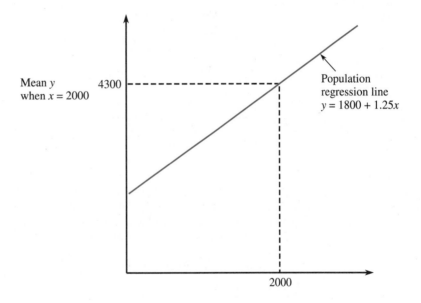

Thus for any fixed x, the variable y is normally distributed, with

$$\mu_y = 1800 + 1.25x$$
$$\sigma_y = 350$$

For example, when $x = 2000$, then 28-day strength has mean value

$$\mu_y = 1800 + (1.25)(2000) = 4300 \text{ lb/in.}^2$$

Because values between 3600 and 5000 are within 2σ of this mean value, roughly 95% of all 28-day strength observations made when accelerated strength is 2000 lb/in.^{2} will be between these limits. The slope $\beta = 1.25$ is the average increase in 28-day strength associated with a 1-lb/in.^{2} increase in accelerated strength.

We have seen that the model characteristics α and β determine the equation of the population regression line. The third model characteristic, σ, specifies the amount of variability about the population line.

> The value of σ determines the extent to which (x, y) observations deviate from the population line. When σ is small, most observations will be quite close to the line, but with large σ, there are likely to be some substantial deviations.

An illustration appears in Figure 13.5.

FIGURE 13.5
Data from the simple linear regression model
(a) σ small
(b) σ large

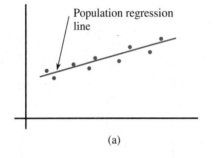
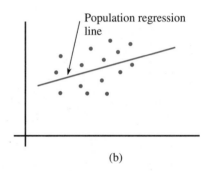

(a)   (b)

An intuitive way to appreciate the implications of the simple linear regression model is to think of the population of all (x, y) pairs as consisting of many smaller populations. Each one of these smaller populations contains pairs for which x has a fixed value. Suppose, for example, that the variables

x = grade point average in major courses

and

y = starting salary after graduation

are related according to the simple linear regression model. Then there is the population of all pairs with $x = 3.20$, the population of all pairs having $x = 2.75$, and so on. The model assumes that for each such population, y is normally distributed with the same standard deviation, and the *mean* y value (rather than y itself) is linearly related to x.

In practice, the judgment as to whether or not the simple linear regression model is appropriate must be based on sample data and a scatter plot. The plot should show a linear rather than a curved pattern, and the vertical spread of points should be relatively homogeneous throughout the range of x values. Figure 13.6 shows plots with three different patterns, only one of which is consistent with the model.

FIGURE 13.6
Some commonly encountered patterns in scatter plots
(a) a scatter plot consistent with the simple linear regression model
(b) a scatter plot that suggests a nonlinear probabilistic model
(c) a scatter plot that suggests that variability in y is not the same for all x values

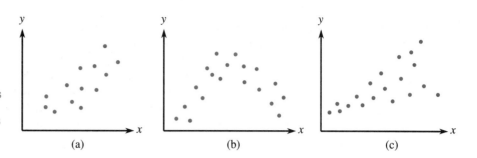

Estimating the Population Regression Line

The values of α and β (vertical intercept and slope of the population regression line) will almost never be known to an investigator. Instead, these values must first be estimated from the sample data $(x_1, y_1), \ldots, (x_n, y_n)$. We now assume that these n (x, y) pairs were obtained independently of one another, and that each observed y is related to the corresponding x via the model equation for simple linear regression.

Let a and b denote point estimates of α and β, respectively. These estimates come from applying the method of least squares.[1]

The point estimates of β, the slope, and α, the y intercept of the population regression line, are the slope and y intercept, respectively, of the least squares line. That is,

$$b = \text{point estimate of } \beta = \frac{\Sigma xy - [(\Sigma x)(\Sigma y)/n]}{\Sigma x^2 - [(\Sigma x)^2/n]}$$

$$a = \text{point estimate of } \alpha = \bar{y} - b\bar{x}$$

The estimated regression line is then just the least squares line

$$\hat{y} = a + bx$$

Let x^* denote a specified value of the predictor variable x. Then $a + bx^*$ has two different interpretations.

1. It is a (point) estimate of the mean y value when $x = x^*$.
2. It is a (point) prediction of an individual y value to be observed when $x = x^*$.

---

[1]As discussed in Chapter 4, the least squares line is the line that gives the smallest possible value of $\Sigma[y - (a + bx)]^2$, the sum of squared vertical deviations for points in the scatter plot.

EXAMPLE 13.2

When anthropologists analyze human skeletal remains, an important piece of information is living stature (the height of the person when alive). Since skeletons are usually quite incomplete, inferences about stature are commonly based on statistical methods that utilize measurements on small bones. The paper "The Estimation of Adult Stature from Metacarpal Bone Length" (*Amer. J. of Phys. Anthro.* (1978):113–120) presented data to validate one such method. Consider the accompanying representative data, where x = metacarpal bone I length (cm) and y = stature (cm).

	Observation									
	1	2	3	4	5	6	7	8	9	10
x	45	51	39	41	52	48	49	46	43	47
y	171	178	157	163	183	172	183	172	175	173

A scatter plot (Figure 13.7) strongly suggests the appropriateness of a linear relationship.

FIGURE 13.7
Scatter plot of the data
from Example 13.2

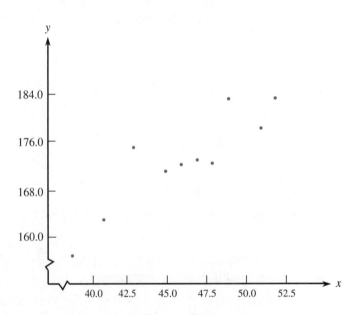

The summary statistics are

$$n = 10 \qquad \Sigma x = 461 \qquad \Sigma y = 1727$$
$$\Sigma x^2 = 21{,}411 \qquad \Sigma xy = 79{,}886 \qquad \Sigma y^2 = 298{,}843$$

The estimated slope is

$$b = \frac{\Sigma xy - [(\Sigma x)(\Sigma y)/n]}{\Sigma x^2 - [(\Sigma x)^2/n]} = \frac{79,886 - [(461)(1727)/10]}{21,411 - [(461)^2/10]}$$

$$= \frac{271.30}{158.90}$$

$$= 1.707363$$

$$\approx 1.707$$

and the estimated y intercept is

$$a = \bar{y} - b\bar{x} = 172.7 - (1.707363)(46.1)$$

$$= 93.990566$$

$$\approx 93.99$$

This gives us

$$\hat{y} = 93.99 + 1.707x$$

as the equation of the estimated regression line. A point estimate of the average stature for all population members having a metacarpal bone length of 45 cm results from substituting $x = 45$ into the estimated equation:

$$\left(\begin{array}{c}\text{estimate of average } y \\ \text{when } x = 45\end{array}\right) = a + b(45)$$

$$= 93.99 + (1.707)(45)$$

$$= 170.81 \text{ cm}$$

If an anthropologist obtains a 45-cm bone from an incomplete skeleton (of a population member), that individual's predicted stature would be

$$\left(\begin{array}{c}\text{predicted } y \text{ value} \\ \text{when } x = 45\end{array}\right) = a + b(45)$$

$$= 93.99 + (1.707)(45)$$

$$= 170.81 \text{ cm}$$

Notice that the point estimate and point prediction are identical because the same x value was used in each calculation.

The point estimate and point prediction $a + bx^*$ are not as informative as we might like, since no information about the precision of estimation or prediction is conveyed. In Section 13.3 we will present both a confidence interval and a prediction interval to remedy this defect.

In Example 13.2, the x values in the sample ranged from 39 to 52. An estimate or prediction should not be calculated for any x value much outside this range. Without sample data for such values, there is no hard evidence that the estimated linear relationship can be extrapolated very far. Statisticians refer to this potential pitfall as the **danger of extrapolation.**

Estimating σ^2 and σ

The value of σ determines the extent to which observed points (x, y) tend to fall close to or far away from the population regression line. A point estimate of σ is based on SSResid, the sum of squared residuals[2], which measures the extent to which the sample data spreads out about the estimated regression line.

DEFINITION

The statistic for estimating the variance σ^2 is

$$s_e^2 = \frac{\text{SSResid}}{n - 2}$$

where

$$\text{SSResid} = \Sigma(y - \hat{y})^2 = \Sigma y^2 - a\Sigma y - b\Sigma xy$$

The estimate of σ is the **estimated standard deviation**

$$s_e = \sqrt{s_e^2}$$

It is customary to call $n - 2$ the number of degrees of freedom associated with estimating σ^2 or σ in simple linear regression.

[handwritten note: Se = magnitude of a typical deviation of y from the least squares line]

The estimates and number of degrees of freedom here have analogues in our earlier work involving a single sample $x_1, x_2, \ldots, x_n$. The sample variance s^2 had numerator $\Sigma(x - \bar{x})^2$, a sum of squared deviations (residuals), and the denominator $n - 1$ was the number of degrees of freedom associated with s^2 and s. The use of $\bar{x}$ as an estimate of μ in the formula for s^2 reduces the number of degrees of freedom by one, from n to $n - 1$. In simple linear regression, estimation of α and β results in a loss of 2 degrees of freedom, leaving $n - 2$ as the df for SSResid, s_e^2, and s_e.

The coefficient of determination was defined earlier by

$$r^2 = 1 - \frac{\text{SSResid}}{\text{SSTo}}$$

where

$$\text{SSTo} = \Sigma(y - \bar{y})^2 = \Sigma y^2 - \frac{(\Sigma y)^2}{n}$$

---

[2]The residuals are $y_1 - \hat{y}_1, \ldots, y_n - \hat{y}_n$, where $\hat{y}_1 = a + bx_1, \hat{y}_2 = a + bx_2$, and so on.

The value of r^2 can now be interpreted as the proportion of observed y variation that can be explained by (or attributed to) the model relationship. The estimate s_e also gives another assessment of model performance. Roughly speaking, the value of σ represents the magnitude of a typical deviation of a point (x, y) in the population from the population regression line. Similarly, in a rough sense, s_e is the magnitude of a typical sample deviation (residual) from the least squares line. The smaller the value of s_e, the closer the points in the sample fall to the line, and the better the line does in predicting y from x.

EXAMPLE 13.3

Forest managers are increasingly concerned about the damage done to natural (animal) populations when forests are clearcut. Woodpeckers are a valuable forest asset both because they provide nest and roost holes for other animals and birds and because they prey on many forest insect pests. The paper "Artificial Trees as a Cavity Substrate for Woodpeckers" (*J. of Wildlife Mgmt.* (1983):790–798) reported on a study of how woodpeckers behaved when provided with polystyrene cylinders as an alternative roost and nest cavity substrate. We give selected values of x = ambient temperature (°C) and y = cavity depth (cm); these values were read from a scatter plot that appeared in the paper. Our plot (Figure 13.8), as well as the original plot, gives evidence of a strong negative linear relationship between x and y.

Row	Temp	Depth	Pred. y value	Residual
1	−6	21.1	22.195	−1.095
2	−3	26.0	21.160	4.840
3	−2	18.0	20.815	−2.815
4	1	19.2	19.780	−0.580
5	6	16.9	18.055	−1.155
6	10	18.1	16.675	1.425
7	11	16.8	16.330	0.470
8	19	11.8	13.569	−1.769
9	21	11.0	12.879	−1.879
10	23	12.1	12.189	−0.089
11	25	14.8	11.499	3.301
12	26	10.5	11.154	−0.654

The summary statistics are

$$n = 12 \qquad \Sigma x = 131 \qquad \Sigma y = 196.3$$
$$\Sigma x^2 = 2939 \qquad \Sigma xy = 1622.3 \qquad \Sigma y^2 = 3445.25$$

from which we calculate

$$b = -.345043 \qquad a = 20.125053$$
$$\text{SSResid} = 54.4655 \qquad \text{SSTo} = 234.1093$$

FIGURE 13.8
Scatter plot from MINITAB
for Example 13.3

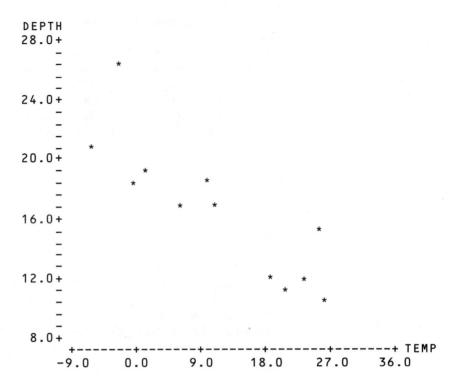

Thus

$$r^2 = 1 - \frac{\text{SSResid}}{\text{SSTo}} = 1 - \frac{54.4655}{234.1093} = 1 - .233 = .767$$

$$s_e^2 = \frac{\text{SSResid}}{n-2} = \frac{54.4655}{10} = 5.447$$

and

$$s_e = \sqrt{5.447} = 2.33$$

Approximately 76.7% of the observed variation in cavity depth y can be attributed to the probabilistic linear relationship with ambient temperature. The magnitude of a typical sample deviation from the least squares line is about 2.3, which is reasonably small in comparison to the y values themselves. The model appears to be useful for estimation and prediction.

A key assumption of the simple linear regression model is that the random deviation e in the model equation is normally distributed. In Section 13.5 we will indicate how the residuals can be used to check whether this is plausible.

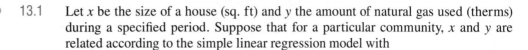

EXERCISES 13.1–13.12   SECTION 13.1

13.1   Let x be the size of a house (sq. ft) and y the amount of natural gas used (therms) during a specified period. Suppose that for a particular community, x and y are related according to the simple linear regression model with

$$\beta = \text{slope of population regression line} = .017$$

$$\alpha = y \text{ intercept of population regression line} = -5.0$$

a. What is the equation of the population regression line?
b. Graph the population regression line by first finding the point on the line corresponding to $x = 1000$ and then the point corresponding to $x = 2000$ and drawing a line through these points.
c. What is the mean value of gas usage for houses with 2100 sq. ft. of space?
d. What is the average change in usage associated with a one-sq. ft. increase in size?
e. What is the average change in usage associated with a 100-sq. ft. increase in size?
f. Would you use the model to predict usage for a 500-sq. ft. house? Why or why not? (Note: There are no small houses in the community in which this model is valid.)

13.2   The flow rate y (m³/min) in a device used for air-quality measurement depends on the pressure drop x (in. of water) across the device's filter. Suppose that for x values between 5 and 20, these two variables are related according to the simple linear regression model with true regression line $y = -.12 + .095x$.

a. What is the true average (that is, expected) flow rate for a pressure drop of 10 in.? A drop of 15 in.?
b. What is the true average change in flow rate associated with a 1-in. increase in pressure drop? Explain.
c. What change in flow rate can be expected when pressure drop decreases by 5 in.?

13.3   Data presented in the paper "Manganese Intake and Serum Manganese Concentration of Human Milk-Fed and Formula-Fed Infants" (*Amer. J. of Clinical Nutrition* (1984):872–878) suggests that a simple linear regression model is reasonable for describing the relationship between $y = $ serum manganese (Mn) and $x = $ Mn intake (μg/kg/day). Suppose that the true regression line is $y = -2 + 1.4x$ and that $\sigma = 1.2$. Then for a fixed x value, y has a normal distribution with mean $-2 + 1.4x$ and standard deviation 1.2.

a. What is the mean value of serum Mn when Mn intake is 4.0? When Mn intake is 4.5?
b. What is the probability that an infant whose Mn intake is 4.0 will have serum Mn greater than 5?
c. Approximately what proportion of infants whose Mn intake is 5 will have a serum Mn greater than 5? Less than 3.8?

13.4 Suppose that a simple linear regression model is appropriate for describing the relationship between y = house price and x = house size (sq. ft.) for houses in a large city. The true regression line is $y = 23{,}000 + 47x$ and $\sigma = 5000$.

a. What is the average (that is, expected) change in price associated with one extra sq. ft. of space? With 100 extra sq. ft. of space?

b. What proportion of 1800-sq. ft. homes would be priced over $110,000? Under $100,000?

13.5 a. Explain the difference between the line $y = \alpha + \beta x$ and the line $\hat{y} = a + bx$.

b. Explain the difference between β and b.

c. Let x^* denote a particular value of the independent variable. Explain the difference between $\alpha + \beta x^*$ and $a + bx^*$.

13.6 Explain the difference between σ and s_e.

13.7 Example 4.1 gave data from the paper "Influence of Wind Speed on Residence Time of "Uroleucon ambrosiae Alatae on Bean Plants" (*Envir. Entom.* (1991): 1375–1380) on x = wind speed (m/s) and y = residence half-time (time until half the pests deposited on a plant had departed). A computer analysis yielded the following information.

$$a = .0119 \qquad b = 3.4307 \qquad \text{SSTo} = 73.937 \qquad \text{SSResid} = 27.890$$

a. What percentage of observed variation in residence half-time can be attributed to the simple linear regression model?

b. Give a point estimate of σ and interpret the estimate.

c. Estimate the mean change in residence half-time associated with a 1-m/s increase in wind speed.

d. Calculate a point estimate of true average residence half-time when wind speed is 1 m/s.

13.8 The authors of the paper "Age, Spacing and Growth Rate of Tamarix as an Indication of Lake Boundary Fluctuations at Sebkhet Kelbia, Tunisia" (*J. of Arid Environ.* (1982):43–51) used a simple linear regression model to describe the relationship between y = vigor (average width in centimeters of the last two annual rings) and x = stem density (stems/m^2). Data on which the estimated model was based is as follows.

x	4	5	6	9	14	15	15	19	21	22
y	.75	1.20	.55	.60	.65	.55	0	.35	.45	.40

a. Construct a scatter plot for the data.

b. Summary quantities are

$$\Sigma x = 130 \qquad \Sigma x^2 = 2090 \qquad \Sigma y = 5.5 \qquad \Sigma y^2 = 3.875 \qquad \Sigma xy = 59.95$$

Find the estimated regression line and draw it on your scatter plot.

c. What is your estimate of the average change in vigor associated with a 1-unit increase in stem density?

d. What would you predict vigor to be for a plant whose density was 17 stems/m^2?

13.9 The accompanying summary quantities resulted from a study in which x was the number of photocopy machines serviced during a routine service call and y was the total service time (min):

$$n = 16 \qquad \Sigma(y - \bar{y})^2 = 22{,}398.05 \qquad \Sigma(y - \hat{y})^2 = 2620.57$$

a. What proportion of observed variation in total service time can be explained by a linear probabilistic relationship between total service time and the number of machines serviced?

b. Calculate the value of the estimated standard deviation s_e. What is the number of degrees of freedom associated with this estimate?

13.10 Exercise 4.44 described a regression situation in which y = hardness of molded plastic and x = amount of time elapsed since termination of the molding process. Summary quantities included $n = 15$, SSResid = 1235.470, and SSTo = 25,321.368.

a. Calculate a point estimate of σ. On how many degrees of freedom is the estimate based?

b. What percentage of observed variation in hardness can be explained by the simple linear regression model relationship between hardness and elapsed time?

13.11 The data below on x = advertising share and y = market share for a particular brand of cigarettes during ten randomly selected years appeared in the paper "Testing Alternative Econometric Models on the Existence of Advertising Threshold Effect" (*J. of Marketing Research* (1984):298–308).

x	.103	.072	.071	.077	.086	.047	.060	.050	.070	.052
y	.135	.125	.120	.086	.079	.076	.065	.059	.051	.039

a. Construct a scatter plot for this data. Do you think the simple linear regression model would be appropriate for describing the relationship between x and y?

b. Calculate the equation of the estimated regression line and use it to obtain the predicted market share when the advertising share is .09.

c. Compute r^2. How would you interpret this value?

d. Calculate a point estimate of σ. On how many degrees of freedom is your estimate based?

13.12 Periodic measurements of salinity and water flow were taken in North Carolina's Pamlico Sound, resulting in the given data (*J. Amer. Stat. Assoc.* (1980):828–838).

Water flow (x)	23	24	26	25	30	24	23	22
Salinity (y)	7.6	7.7	4.3	5.9	5.0	6.5	8.3	8.2

Water flow (x)	22	24	25	22	22	22	24
Salinity (y)	13.2	12.6	10.4	10.8	13.1	12.3	10.4

$$n = 15 \qquad \Sigma x = 358 \qquad \Sigma x^2 = 8608$$
$$\Sigma y = 136.3 \qquad \Sigma y^2 = 1362.59 \qquad \Sigma xy = 3195.0$$

a. Find the equation of the estimated regression line.
b. What would you predict salinity to be when water flow is 25?
c. Estimate the mean salinity for times when the water flow is 29.
d. What percentage of observed variation in salinity can be explained by the simple linear regression model?
e. Roughly speaking, what is the magnitude of a typical deviation from the estimated regression line?

13.2 Inferences Concerning the Slope of the Population Regression Line

The slope β in the simple linear regression model is the average or expected change in the dependent variable y associated with a one-unit increase in the value of the independent variable x. Examples include the average change in vocabulary size associated with an age increase of 1 year, the expected change in yield associated with the use of an additional gram of catalyst, and the average change in annual maintenance expense associated with using a computer system for one additional hour per week (all presuming that the simple linear regression model is appropriate).

Since the value of β is almost always unknown, it will have to be estimated from sample data: n independently selected observations $(x_1, y_1), \ldots, (x_n, y_n)$. The slope of the least squares line gives a point estimate. As with any point estimate, though, it is desirable to have some indication of how accurately b estimates β. In some situations, the value of the statistic b may vary greatly from sample to sample, so b computed from a single sample may well be rather different from β. In other situations, almost all possible samples yield b values quite close to β, so the error of estimation is almost sure to be small. To proceed further, we need some facts about the sampling distribution of the statistic b—information concerning the shape of the sampling distribution curve, where the curve is centered relative to β, and how much the curve spreads out about its center.

PROPERTIES OF THE SAMPLING DISTRIBUTION OF b

1. The mean value of b is β. That is, $\mu_b = \beta$, so the sampling distribution of b is always centered at the value of β. Thus b is an unbiased statistic for estimating β.
2. The standard deviation of the statistic b is

$$\sigma_b = \frac{\sigma}{\sqrt{\Sigma(x - \bar{x})^2}} = \frac{\sigma}{\sqrt{\Sigma x^2 - [(\Sigma x)^2/n]}}$$

3. The statistic b has a normal distribution (a consequence of assuming that the random deviation e is normally distributed).

Unbiasedness of b by itself is not a guarantee that the resulting estimate will be close to β. If σ_b is large, the normal sampling distribution curve will be quite spread out around β, and an estimate far from β may well result. For σ_b to be small, the numerator σ should be small (little variability about the population line) and/or the denominator should be large. This latter condition is equivalent to $\Sigma(x - \bar{x})^2$ being large. Because $\Sigma(x - \bar{x})^2$ is a measure of how much the observed x values spread out, we conclude that β will tend to be more precisely estimated when the x values in our sample are spread out than when they are close together.

Normality of b implies that the standardized variable $(b - \beta)/\sigma_b$ has a standard normal distribution. However, inferential methods cannot be based on this variable because the value of σ_b is not available (since the unknown σ appears in the numerator of σ_b). The obvious way out of this dilemma is to replace σ by s_e, yielding an estimated standard deviation.

The **estimated standard deviation of the statistic b** is

$$s_b = \frac{s_e}{\sqrt{\Sigma x^2 - [(\Sigma x)^2/n]}}$$

The probability distribution of the standardized variable

$$t = \frac{b - \beta}{s_b}$$

is the t distribution with $n - 2$ df.

In the same way that $t = (\bar{x} - \mu)/(s/\sqrt{n})$ was used in Chapter 9 to develop a confidence interval for μ, the t variable in the preceding box can be employed to give a confidence interval (interval estimate) for β.

A **confidence interval for β,** the slope of the population regression line, has the form

$$b \pm (t \text{ critical value}) \cdot s_b$$

where the t critical value is based on $n - 2$ degrees of freedom. Appendix Table IV gives critical values corresponding to the most frequently used confidence levels.

The interval estimate of β is centered at b and extends out from the center by an amount that depends on the sampling variability of b. When s_b is small, the interval will be narrow, implying that the investigator has precise knowledge of β.

EXAMPLE 13.4

Durable-press cotton fabric is produced by a chemical reaction involving formaldehyde. For economic reasons, finished fabric usually receives its first wash at home rather than at the manufacturing plant. Because the pH of in-home wash water varies greatly from location to location, textile researchers are interested in how pH affects different fabric properties. The paper "Influence of pH in Washing on the Formaldehyde-Release Properties of Durable-Press Cotton" (*Textile Research J.* (1981):263–270) reported the accompanying data, read from a scatter plot, on x = washwater pH and y = formaldehyde release (in ppm). The scatter plot (Figure 13.9) suggests the appropriateness of the simple linear regression model. The slope β in this context is the average change in formaldehyde release associated with a one-unit pH increase.

	Observation								
	1	2	3	4	5	6	7	8	9
x	5.3	6.8	7.1	7.1	7.2	7.6	7.6	7.7	7.7
y	545	770	780	790	680	760	790	795	935

	Observation								
	10	11	12	13	14	15	16	17	18
x	7.8	7.9	8.1	8.6	9.1	9.2	9.4	9.4	9.5
y	780	935	830	1015	1190	1030	1045	1250	1075

FIGURE 13.9
MINITAB scatter plot of the
data from Example 13.4

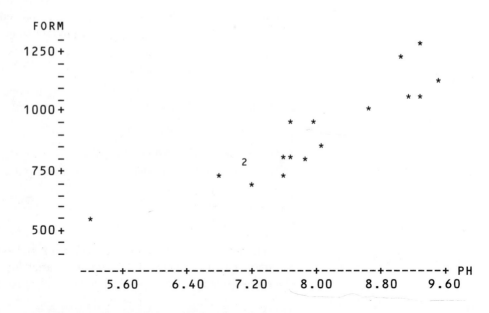

Straightforward calculation gives us

$$\Sigma x = 143.1 \qquad \bar{x} = 7.95 \qquad \Sigma y = 15{,}995 \qquad \bar{y} = 888.611111$$
$$\Sigma x^2 = 1158.33 \qquad \Sigma xy = 130{,}281.5 \qquad \Sigma y^2 = 14{,}781{,}675$$

$$b = 150.894368 \approx 150.894$$
$$a = -310.999115 \approx -311.00$$

$$\text{SSResid} = 97{,}361.24 \qquad \text{SSTo} = 568{,}340.2801$$

$$r^2 = .829$$

$$s_e^2 = 6085.0775 \qquad s_e = 78.01$$

$$s_b = \frac{s_e}{\sqrt{\Sigma x^2 - [(\Sigma x)^2/n]}} = \frac{78.01}{\sqrt{20.685}} = 17.152$$

Relative to the magnitude of b itself, this estimated standard deviation is not particularly large. The 95% confidence interval based on 16 degrees of freedom requires t critical value $= 2.12$. The resulting interval is then

$$b \pm (t \text{ critical value}) \cdot s_b \approx 150.89 \pm (2.12)(17.15)$$
$$\approx 150.89 \pm 36.36$$
$$= (114.53, 187.25)$$

The investigator can be quite confident that average formaldehyde release will increase by from 114.53 ppm to 187.25 ppm when the pH is increased by one unit.

Output from any of the standard statistical computer packages routinely includes the computed values of a, b, SSResid, s_e, SSTo, r^2, and s_b. Figure 13.10 displays partial MINITAB output for the data of Example 13.4. The format from other packages is very similar. Rounding will occasionally lead to small discrepancies between hand-calculated and computer-calculated values, but there are not such discrepancies for this example.

Hypothesis Tests Concerning β

Hypotheses about β can be tested using a t test very similar to the t tests discussed in earlier chapters. The null hypothesis states that β has a specific hypothesized value. The t statistic results from standardizing b, the point estimate of β, under the assumption that H_0 is true. When H_0 is true, the sampling distribution of this statistic is the t distribution with $(n - 2)$ df. The level of significance (type I error probability) is then controlled through the use of an appropriate t critical value from Table IV.

FIGURE 13.10
Partial MINITAB output for the
data of Example 13.4

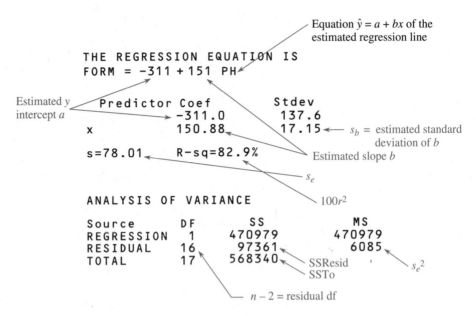

Equation $\hat{y} = a + bx$ of the
estimated regression line

THE REGRESSION EQUATION IS
FORM = −311 + 151 PH

Estimated y
intercept a

Predictor	Coef	Stdev
	−311.0	137.6
x	150.88	17.15

s_b = estimated standard
deviation of b

Estimated slope b

s=78.01   R−sq=82.9%

s_e

Estimated slope b

$100r^2$

ANALYSIS OF VARIANCE

Source	DF	SS	MS
REGRESSION	1	470979	470979
RESIDUAL	16	97361	6085
TOTAL	17	568340	

SSResid
SSTo

s_e^2

$n − 2$ = residual df

SUMMARY OF HYPOTHESIS TESTS CONCERNING β

Null hypothesis: H_0: β = hypothesized value

Test statistic: $t = \dfrac{b - \text{hypothesized value}}{s_b}$

Alternative Hypothesis	**Rejection Region**
H_a: β > hypothesized value	$t > t$ critical value
H_a: β < hypothesized value	$t < -t$ critical value
H_a: $\beta \neq$ hypothesized value	Either $t > t$ critical value or $t < -t$ critical value

The t critical value is based on $n - 2$ df.

Very frequently, the null hypothesis of interest is that $\beta = 0$. When this is the case, the population regression line is a horizontal line, and knowledge of x is of no use in predicting y. On the other hand, when $\beta \neq 0$ there *is* a useful linear relationship between x and y. The test of H_0: $\beta = 0$ versus H_a: $\beta \neq 0$ is often called the **model utility test** in simple linear regression. Since the hypothesized value is zero, the test statistic is the t ratio $t = b/s_b$. If a scatter plot and the value of r^2 do not provide convincing evidence for a useful linear relationship, it is recommended that the model utility test be carried out before the estimated model is used to make other inferences.

EXAMPLE 13.5

Exercise 4.39 described a study reported in the 1991 volume of the *Amer. J. of Phys. Anthropology* in which the objective was to predict age (y) from percentage of a tooth's root with transparent dentine. The accompanying data is for anterior teeth:

percentage x	15	19	31	39	41	44	47	48	55	65
age y	23	52	65	55	32	60	78	59	61	60

MINITAB output is displayed in Figure 13.11. In addition to b and s_b, the test statistic value for the model utility test appears in the "t-ratio" column, and the P-value for the test is given.

FIGURE 13.11
MINITAB output
for Example 13.5

```
The regression equation is
age = 32.1 + 0.555 percent

Predictor     Coef     Stdev    t-ratio      p
Constant      32.08    13.32     2.41     0.043
percent       0.5549   0.3101    1.79     0.111

s = 14.30   R-sq = 28.6%   R-sq (adj) = 19.7%

Analysis of Variance

SOURCE       DF       SS       MS       F       p
Regression    1     654.8    654.8    3.20    0.111
Error         8    1635.7    204.5
Total         9    2290.5
```

Does the simple linear regression model specify a useful relationship for predicting age from percent dentine? Let's carry out a test at significance level .05 using the sequence of steps employed in earlier chapters.

1. $\beta =$ the average change in age associated with a 1% increase in percentage tooth transparent dentine

2. $H_0: \beta = 0$ (no useful linear relationship)

3. $H_a: \beta \neq 0$

4. Test statistic: $t = \dfrac{b - 0}{s_b} = \dfrac{b}{s_b}$

5. Rejection region: The inequality in H_a calls for a two-tailed test. From Table IV, the required t critical value is 2.31. The null hypothesis should therefore be rejected if either $t > 2.31$ or $t < -2.31$.

6. From the MINITAB output, $b = .5549$, $s_b = .3101$, and
$$t = \frac{.5549}{.3101} = 1.79$$

7. Since 1.79 is not in the rejection region (it is neither larger than 2.31 nor less than -2.31), H_0 should not be rejected. The model does not appear to specify a useful way to predict age. The P-value .111 shows that this same conclusion would be reached for $\alpha = .10$.

When H_0: $\beta = 0$ cannot be rejected by the model utility test at a reasonably small significance level, the search for a useful model must continue. One possibility is to relate x to y via a nonlinear model, an appropriate strategy if the scatter plot shows curvature. Alternatively, a multiple regression model using more than one predictor variable can be developed. The next chapter introduces such models.

EXERCISES 13.13–13.28   SECTION 13.2

13.13   **a.** What is the difference between σ and σ_b?
      b. What is the difference between σ_b and s_b?

13.14   **a.** Suppose that a single y observation is made at each of the x values 5, 10, 15, 20, and 25. If $\sigma = 4$, what is σ_b, the standard deviation of the statistic b?
      b. Now suppose that a second y observation is made at every x value listed in part (a) (making a total of 10 observations). Is the resulting value of σ_b half of what it was in part (a)?
      c. How many observations at each x value in part (a) are required to yield a σ_b value that is half the value calculated in part (a)? Verify your conjecture.

13.15   Exercise 4.32 described an experiment carried out to study the relationship between $x = $ chlorine flow and $y = $ etch rate. Summary quantities included

$$n = 9 \qquad \Sigma x = 24.0 \qquad \Sigma x^2 = 70.50$$

If a primary objective had been to estimate β as accurately as possible, would it have been better to make $n = 8$ observations at x values $x_1 = 1.5$, $x_2 = 1.5$, $x_3 = 2.0$, $x_4 = 2.0$, $x_5 = 3.5$, $x_6 = 3.5$, $x_7 = 4.0$, $x_8 = 4.0$?

13.16   Exercise 13.10 of Section 13.1 presented information from a study in which y was the hardness of molded plastic and x was the time elapsed since termination of the molding process. Summary quantities included

$$n = 15 \qquad b = 2.50 \qquad \text{SSResid} = 1235.470 \qquad \Sigma(x - \bar{x})^2 = 4024.20$$

      a. Calculate s_b, the estimated standard deviation of the statistic b.
      b. Obtain a 95% confidence interval for β, the slope of the true regression line.
      c. Does the interval in part (b) suggest that β has been precisely estimated? Explain.

13.17   A study was carried out to relate sales revenue y (in thousands of dollars) to advertising expenditure x (also in thousands of dollars) for fast-food outlets during a three-month period. A sample of 15 outlets yielded the accompanying summary quantities.

$$\Sigma x = 14.10 \qquad \Sigma y = 1438.50 \qquad \Sigma x^2 = 13.92 \qquad \Sigma y^2 = 140,354$$
$$\Sigma xy = 1387.20 \qquad \Sigma(y - \bar{y})^2 = 2401.85 \qquad \Sigma(y - \hat{y})^2 = 561.46$$

a. What proportion of observed variation in sales revenue can be attributed to the linear relationship between revenue and advertising expenditure?

b. Calculate s_e and s_b.

c. Obtain a 90% confidence interval for β, the average change in revenue associated with a \$1000 (that is, one-unit) increase in advertising expenditure.

13.18   An experiment to study the relationship between $x = $ time spent exercising (min) and $y = $ amount of oxygen consumed during the exercise period resulted in the following summary statistics.

$$n = 20 \qquad \Sigma x = 50 \qquad \Sigma y = 16,705 \qquad \Sigma x^2 = 150$$
$$\Sigma xy = 44,194 \qquad\qquad \Sigma y^2 = 14,194,231$$

a. Estimate the slope and y intercept of the population regression line.

b. One sample observation on oxygen usage was 757 for a 2-min exercise period. What amount of oxygen would you predict for this exercise period, and what is the corresponding residual?

c. Compute a 99% confidence interval for the true average change in oxygen usage associated with a 1-min increase in exercise time.

13.19   Exercise 4.67 presented data on $x = $ average hourly wage and $y = $ quit rate for a sample of industries. Here is the MINITAB output.

```
The regression equation is
quit rate = 4.86 − 0.347 wage

Predictor       Coef      Stdev    t-ratio       p
Constant      4.8615     0.5201       9.35   0.000
wage         −0.34655    0.05866      −5.91   0.000

s = 0.4862        R-sq = 72.9%        R-sq (adj) = 70.8%

Analysis of Variance

SOURCE        DF        SS        MS        F       p
Regression     1    8.2507    8.2507    34.90   0.000
Error         13    3.0733    0.2364
Total         14   11.3240
```

a. Based on the given P-value, does there appear to be a useful linear relationship between average wage and quit rate? Explain your reasoning.

b. Calculate an estimate of the average change in quit rate associated with a \$1 increase in average hourly wage, and do so in a way that conveys information about the precision and reliability of the estimate.

13.20   The paper "Bumblebee Response to Variation in Nectar Availability" (*Ecology* (1981):1648–1661) reported a positive linear relationship between y, a measure of bumblebee abundance, and x, a measure of nectar availability. Representative data is given here.

x	3	8	11	10	23	23	30	35
y	4	6	12	18	11	24	22	37

Does the data support the paper's claim that there is evidence of a *positive* linear relationship between x and y (a tendency for y to increase linearly as x increases)? Use an appropriate inferential procedure to answer this question.

13.21   The paper "Effects of Enhanced UV-B Radiation on Ribulose-1,5-Biphosphate, Carboxylase in Pea and Soybean" (*Environ. and Exper. Botany* (1984):131–143) included the accompanying pea plant data, with $y =$ sunburn index and $x =$ distance (cm) from an ultraviolet light source.

x	18	21	25	26	30	32	36	40	40	50	51	54	61	62	63
y	4.0	3.7	3.0	2.9	2.6	2.5	2.2	2.0	2.1	1.5	1.5	1.5	1.3	1.2	1.1

$$\Sigma x = 609 \qquad \Sigma y = 33.1 \qquad \Sigma x^2 = 28{,}037$$
$$\Sigma xy = 1156.8 \qquad \Sigma y^2 = 84.45$$

Estimate the mean change in the sunburn index associated with an increase of 1 cm in distance in a way that includes information about the precision of estimation.

13.22   Exercise 13.17 described a regression analysis in which $y =$ sales revenue and $x =$ advertising expenditure. Summary quantities given there yield

$$n = 15 \qquad b = 52.57 \qquad s_b = 8.05$$

a. Test the hypotheses $H_0: \beta = 0$ versus $H_a: \beta \neq 0$ using a significance level of .05. What does your conclusion say about the nature of the relationship between x and y?

b. Consider the hypotheses $H_0: \beta = 40$ versus $H_a: \beta > 40$. The null hypothesis states that the average change in sales revenue associated with a one-unit increase in advertising expenditure is (at most) \$40,000. Carry out a test using significance level .01.

13.23   The accompanying data on fish survival and ammonia concentration is taken from the paper "Effects of Ammonia on Growth and Survival of Rainbow Trout in Intensive Static-Water Culture" (*Trans. of Amer. Fisheries Soc.* (1983):448–454). Let $x =$ ammonia exposure (mg/L) and $y =$ percent survival.

x	10	10	20	20	25	27	27	31	50
y	85	92	85	96	87	80	90	59	62

a. Estimate the slope and intercept of the true regression line.

b. Is the simple linear regression model useful for predicting survival from knowledge of ammonia exposure?

c. Predict percent survival when ammonia exposure is 30 mg/L.

d. Estimate β using a 90% confidence interval.

13.24   The paper "Technology, Productivity and Industry Structure" (*Tech. Forecasting and Social Change* (1983):1–13) included the accompanying data on $x =$ research and development expenditure and $y =$ growth rate for eight different industries.

x	2024	5038	905	3572	1157	327	378	191
y	1.90	3.96	2.44	.88	.37	$-.90$	.49	1.01

a. Would a simple linear regression model provide useful information for predicting growth rate from research and development expenditure? Use a .05 level of significance.

b. What can be said about the *P*-value associated with the test statistic value in part (a)?

c. Use a 90% confidence interval to estimate the average change in growth rate associated with a one-unit increase in expenditure. Interpret the resulting interval.

13.25 The paper "Effect of Temperature on the pH of Skim Milk" (*J. of Dairy Research* (1988):277–280) reported on a study involving x = temperature ($°$ C) under specified experimental conditions and y = milk pH. The accompanying data (read from a graph) is a representative subset of that which appeared in the paper.

x	4	4	24	24	25	38	38	40
y	6.85	6.79	6.63	6.65	6.72	6.62	6.57	6.52

x	45	50	55	56	60	67	70	78
y	6.50	6.48	6.42	6.41	6.38	6.34	6.32	6.34

$$\Sigma x = 678 \quad \Sigma y = 104.54 \quad \Sigma x^2 = 36{,}056$$
$$\Sigma xy = 4376.36 \quad \Sigma y^2 = 683.4470$$

Does this data strongly suggest that there is a negative (inverse) linear relationship between temperature and pH? State and test the relevant hypotheses using a significance level of .01.

13.26 The accompanying data on x = soil pH and y = Cl$^-$ ion retention (mL/100 g) is from the paper "Single Equilibration Method for Determination of Cation and Anion Retention by Variable Charge Soils" (*Soil Science Plant Nutrition* (1984):71–76).

x	6.15	6.11	5.88	6.45	5.80	6.06	5.83	6.33	7.35
y	0.14	0.37	1.47	1.12	2.08	1.79	3.18	2.15	0.51

x	8.18	7.69	7.29	6.53	5.01	5.34	6.19	5.81
y	0.32	0.76	2.13	2.75	6.69	5.59	2.87	4.22

$$n = 17 \quad \Sigma x = 108.00 \quad \Sigma x^2 = 697.2968$$
$$\Sigma y = 38.14 \quad \Sigma y^2 = 140.9262 \quad \Sigma xy = 225.3963$$

a. Obtain the equation of the estimated regression line.

b. Does the data indicate that the simple linear regression model is useful for predicting ion retention from pH? Use a level .01 test.

c. What can you say about the *P*-value associated with the computed value of the test statistic in part (b)?

13.27 In anthropological studies, an important characteristic of fossils is cranial capacity. Frequently skulls are at least partially decomposed, so it is necessary to use other characteristics to obtain information about capacity. One such measure that has been used is the length of the lambda-opisthion chord. A paper that appeared in the 1971 *Amer. Journal of Physical Anthropology* entitled "Vertesszollos and the Presapiens Theory" reported the following data for $n = 7$ *Homo erectus* fossils.

x (chord length in mm)	78	75	78	81	84	86	87
y (capacity in cm³)	850	775	750	975	915	1015	1030

Suppose that from previous evidence, anthropologists had believed that for each 1-mm increase in chord length, cranial capacity would be expected to increase by 20 cm³. Does this new experimental data strongly contradict prior belief? That is, should H_0: $\beta = 20$ be rejected in favor of H_a: $\beta \neq 20$? Use a .05 level of significance.

13.28 The article "Hydrogen, Oxygen, and Nitrogen in Cobalt Metal" (*Metallurgia* (1969): 121–127) contains a plot of the following data pairs, where x = pressure of extracted gas (μm) and y = extraction time (min).

x	40	130	155	160	260	275	325	370	420	480
y	2.5	3.0	3.1	3.3	3.7	4.1	4.3	4.8	5.0	5.4

a. Suppose that the investigators had believed prior to the experiment that $\beta = .006$. Does the data contradict this prior belief? Use a significance level of .10.

b. Give an upper and/or lower bound on the *P*-value associated with the test statistic value in part (a).

c. Compute and interpret a 95% confidence interval for the slope of the true regression line.

13.3 Inferences Based on the Estimated Regression Line

We have seen how, for any particular value of *x*, the estimated regression line $\hat{y} = a + bx$ gives either an estimate of the corresponding average *y* value or a prediction of a single *y* value. How precise is the resulting estimate or prediction? That is, how close might $a + bx$ be to the actual mean value $\alpha + \beta x$ or to a particular *y* observation? Because both *a* and *b* vary in value from sample to sample (each one is a statistic), for a fixed *x* the statistic $a + bx$ also has different values for different samples. The way in which this statistic varies in value with different samples is summarized by its sampling distribution. Properties of the sampling distribution are used to obtain both a confidence interval formula for $\alpha + \beta x$ and a prediction interval formula for a particular *y* observation. The narrowness of the corresponding interval conveys information about the precision of the estimate or prediction.

PROPERTIES OF THE SAMPLING DISTRIBUTION OF *a + bx* FOR A FIXED *x* VALUE

Let x^* denote a particular value of the independent variable x. Then the sampling distribution of the statistic $a + bx^*$ has the following properties:

1. The mean value of $a + bx^*$ is $\alpha + \beta x^*$, so that $a + bx^*$ is an unbiased statistic for estimating the average y value when $x = x^*$.
2. The standard deviation of the statistic $a + bx^*$, denoted by σ_{a+bx^*}, is given by

$$\sigma_{a+bx^*} = \sigma\sqrt{\frac{1}{n} + \frac{(x^* - \bar{x})^2}{\Sigma(x - \bar{x})^2}} = \sigma\sqrt{\frac{1}{n} + \frac{(x^* - \bar{x})^2}{\Sigma x^2 - [(\Sigma x)^2/n]}}$$

3. The assumption that the random deviation e in the model has a normal distribution implies that $a + bx^*$ is normally distributed.

The standard deviation of $a + bx^*$ is larger when $(x^* - \bar{x})^2$ is large than when it is small; that is, $a + bx^*$ tends to be a more precise estimate of $\alpha + \beta x^*$ when x^* is close to the center of the x values at which observations were made than when x^* is far from the center.

The standard deviation σ_{a+bx^*} cannot be calculated from the sample data because the value of σ is unknown. It can, however, be estimated by using s_e in place of σ. Using this estimated standard deviation to standardize $a + bx^*$ gives a variable with a t distribution.

The **estimated standard deviation of the statistic *a + bx****, denoted by s_{a+bx^*}, is given by

$$s_{a+bx^*} = s_e\sqrt{\frac{1}{n} + \frac{(x^* - \bar{x})^2}{\Sigma x^2 - [(\Sigma x)^2/n]}}$$

The probability distribution of the standardized variable

$$t = \frac{a + bx^* - (\alpha + \beta x^*)}{s_{a+bx^*}}$$

is the t distribution with $n - 2$ df.

Inferences about the Mean Value $\alpha + \beta x^*$

Previous z and t standardized variables were manipulated to give confidence intervals of the form

> (point estimate) $\pm$ (critical value) $\cdot$ (estimated standard deviation)

A parallel argument leads immediately to the following interval.

A **confidence interval for $\alpha + \beta x^*$**, the average y value when x has value x^*, is

$$a + bx^* \pm (t \text{ critical value}) \cdot s_{a+bx^*}$$

where the t critical value is based on $(n - 2)$ df. Table IV gives critical values corresponding to the most frequently used confidence levels.

Because of the dependence of s_{a+bx^*} on $(x^* - \bar{x})^2$, as discussed earlier, the confidence interval for $\alpha + \beta x^*$ gets wider as x^* moves farther from the center of the data.

EXAMPLE 13.6

Dairy scientists have recently carried out several studies on protein biosynthesis in milk and the accompanying decomposition of nucleic acids into various constituents. The paper "Metabolites of Nucleic Acids in Bovine Milk" (*J. of Dairy Science* (1984):723–728) reported the accompanying data on x = milk production (kg/day) and y = milk protein (kg/day) for Holstein-Friesan cows.

	Observation						
	1	2	3	4	5	6	7
x	42.7	40.2	38.2	37.6	32.2	32.2	28.0
y	1.20	1.16	1.07	1.13	.96	1.07	.85

	Observation						
	8	9	10	11	12	13	14
x	27.2	26.6	23.0	22.7	21.8	21.3	20.2
y	.87	.77	.74	.76	.69	.72	.64

A scatter plot (Figure 13.12) gives strong support for using the simple linear regression model.

FIGURE 13.12
MINITAB scatter plot of the
data from Example 13.6

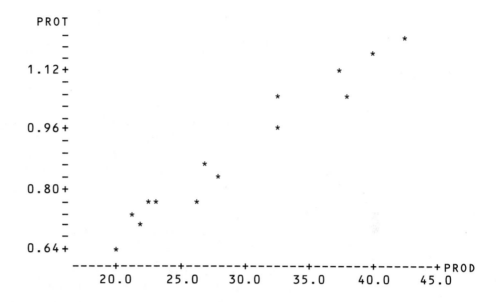

It is easily verified that

$$b = .024576 \qquad a = .175571 \qquad \text{SSResid} = .021140$$

$$\text{SSTo} = .481436 \qquad s_e = .0420 \qquad \Sigma x^2 - \frac{(\Sigma x)^2}{n} = 762.012$$

from which we get $r^2 = .956$ and the t ratio for testing model utility ($H_0: \beta = 0$):

$$t = \frac{b}{s_b} = \frac{.0246}{.042/\sqrt{762.012}} = \frac{.0246}{.00152} = 16.2$$

This calculated t considerably exceeds the upper-tail critical value 3.06 for a two-tailed test with significance level .01. This confirms the utility of the model, so further inferences can now be carried out.

Let's use the data to compute a 99% confidence interval for average milk protein when milk production is 30 kg/day, that is, for $\alpha + \beta(30)$. The point estimate of $\alpha + \beta(30)$ is

$$a + b(30) = .176 + (.0246)(30) = .914$$

With $\bar{x} = 29.564$, the estimated standard deviation of $a + b(30)$ is

$$s_{a+b(30)} = s_e \sqrt{\frac{1}{n} + \frac{(30 - \bar{x})^2}{\Sigma x^2 - [(\Sigma x)^2/n]}}$$

$$= .0420 \sqrt{\frac{1}{14} + \frac{(.436)^2}{762.012}}$$

$$= .0112$$

The t critical value for 99% confidence based on 12 df is 3.06. The confidence interval is

$$a + b(30) \pm (t \text{ critical value}) \cdot s_{a+b(30)} = .914 \pm (3.06)(.0112)$$
$$= .914 \pm .034$$
$$= (.880, .948)$$

We can be highly confident that when milk production is 30 kg/day, average milk protein is between .880 and .948 kg/day. Even with the very high confidence level, this interval is relatively narrow, partly because $x = 30$ is very close to $\bar{x}$ and partly because the model fits the data so well ($s_e = .0420$ and $r^2 = .956$).

A Prediction Interval for a Single y

Suppose that an investigator is contemplating making a single observation on y when x has the value x^* at some future time. Let y^* denote the resulting future observation. Recall that the point prediction for y^* is $a + bx^*$, and this is also the point estimate for $\alpha + \beta x^*$, the mean y value when $x = x^*$. Consider now the errors of estimation and prediction:

$$\text{estimation error} = \text{estimate} - \text{true value}$$
$$= a + bx^* - (\alpha + \beta x^*)$$

$$\text{prediction error} = \text{prediction} - \text{true value}$$
$$= a + bx^* - y^*$$

In the estimation error, only $a + bx^*$ is subject to sampling variability, since $\alpha + \beta x^*$ is a fixed (albeit unknown) number. However, both $a + bx^*$ and the observation y^* in the prediction error are subject to sampling variability. This implies that there is more uncertainty associated with predicting a single value y^* than with estimating a mean value $\alpha + \beta x^*$.

We can obtain an assessment of how precise the prediction $a + bx^*$ is by computing a prediction interval for y^*. If the resulting interval is narrow, there is little uncertainty in y^*, and the prediction $a + bx^*$ is quite precise. The interpretation of a prediction interval is very similar to the interpretation of a confidence interval. A 95% prediction interval for y^* is constructed using a method for which 95% of all possible samples would yield interval limits capturing y^*; only 5% of all samples would give an interval that did not include y^*.

Manipulation of a standardized variable similar to the one from which a confidence interval was obtained gives the following prediction interval.

> A **prediction interval for y^*,** a single y observation made when $x = x^*$, has the form
>
> $$a + bx^* \pm (t \text{ critical value}) \cdot \sqrt{s_e^2 + s_{a+bx^*}^2}$$

The prediction interval and confidence interval are centered at exactly the same place, $a + bx^*$. The inclusion of s_e^2 under the square root symbol makes the prediction interval wider—often substantially so—than the confidence interval.

EXAMPLE 13.7

(*Example 13.6 continued*) In Example 13.6 we computed a 99% confidence interval for average milk protein when milk production is 30 kg/day. Suppose that a single cow is randomly selected and its milk production on that day is found to be 30 kg. Let's compute a 99% prediction interval for y^*, the amount of protein in this milk. The necessary quantities are

$$a + b(30) = .176 + (.0246)(30) = .914$$
$$s_e^2 = (.0420)^2 = .001764$$
$$s_{a+b(30)}^2 = (.0113)^2 = .000128$$

The t critical value for 12 df and a 99% prediction level is 3.06. Substitution then gives the interval

$$.914 \pm (3.06)\sqrt{.001764 + .000128} = .914 \pm (3.06)(.0435)$$
$$= .914 \pm .133$$
$$= (.781, 1.047)$$

We can be quite confident that an individual cow with a daily milk production of 30 kg will have a daily milk protein yield of between .781 and 1.047 kg.

The confidence interval for the mean value $\alpha + \beta(30)$ is $.914 \pm .035$. The prediction interval is almost four times as wide as the confidence interval. Even with a rather precise estimate of $\alpha + \beta(30)$, there is a relatively wide range of plausible values for y^*.

Many statistical computer packages will give both the confidence interval and the prediction interval for a specified x^* upon request.

EXERCISES 13.29–13.44   SECTION 13.3

13.29   Explain the difference between a confidence interval and a prediction interval. How can a prediction level of 95% be interpreted?

13.30   Suppose that a regression data set is given and you are asked to obtain a confidence interval. How would you tell from the phrasing of the request whether the interval is for β or for $\alpha + \beta x^*$?

13.31   In Exercise 13.18, we considered a regression of y = oxygen consumption on x = time spent exercising. Summary quantities given there yield

$$n = 20 \qquad \bar{x} = 2.50 \qquad \Sigma x^2 - \frac{(\Sigma x)^2}{n} = 25$$

$$b = 97.26 \qquad a = 592.10 \qquad s_e = 16.486$$

a. Calculate $s_{a+b(2.0)}$, the estimated standard deviation of the statistic $a + b(2.0)$.

b. Without any further calculation, what is $s_{a+b(3.0)}$ and what reasoning did you use to obtain it?

c. Calculate the estimated standard deviation of the statistic $a + b(2.8)$.

d. For what value x^* is the estimated standard deviation of $a + bx^*$ smallest, and why?

13.32   The data of Exercise 13.25, in which x = milk temperature and y = milk pH, yields

$$n = 16 \qquad \bar{x} = 42.375 \qquad \Sigma x^2 - \frac{(\Sigma x)^2}{n} = 7325.75$$

$$b = -.00730608 \qquad a = 6.843345 \qquad s_e = .0356$$

a. Obtain a 95% confidence interval for $\alpha + \beta(40)$, the true average milk pH when the milk temperature is 40° C.

b. Calculate a 99% confidence interval for the true average milk pH when the milk temperature is 35° C.

c. Would you recommend using the data to calculate a 95% confidence interval for the true average pH when the temperature is 90° C? Why or why not?

 13.33   Return to the regression of y = milk pH on x = milk temperature described in Exercise 13.32.

a. Obtain a 95% prediction interval for a single pH observation to be made with milk temperature = 40° C.

b. Calculate a 99% prediction interval for a single pH observation when milk temperature = 35° C.

c. When the milk temperature is 60° C, would a 99% prediction interval be wider than the intervals of parts (a) and (b)? Answer without calculating the interval.

13.34   The sugar content of certain types of fruit is a critical factor in determining when harvesting should begin. One method for assessing sugar content involves taking a measurement using a refractometer. The paper "Use of Refractometer to Determine Soluble Solids of Astringent Fruits of Japanese Persimmons" (*J. of Horticultural Science* (1983):241–246) examined the relationship between y = total sugar content (%) and x = refractometer reading for persimmons. The estimated regression equation for predicting total sugar content from refractometer readings was given in the paper as $\hat{y} = -7.52 + 1.15x$. Suppose that $n = 50, \bar{x} = 17, s_e^2 = 1.1$, and $\Sigma(x - \bar{x})^2 = 112.5$.

a. Use a 95% confidence interval to estimate the mean percent of sugar for all persimmons with a refractometer reading of 18.

b. Construct a 90% prediction interval for the percent of sugar of an individual persimmon with a refractometer reading of 20.

c. Would a 90% prediction interval for the percent of sugar when the refractometer reading is 15 be narrower or wider than the interval of part (b)? Answer without computing the interval.

13.35   High blood-lead levels are associated with a number of different health problems. The paper "A Study of the Relationship between Blood Lead Levels and Occupational Lead Levels" (*Am. Stat.* (1983):471) gave data on x = air-lead level ($\mu g/m^3$) and y = blood-lead level ($\mu g/dL$). Summary quantities (based on a subset of the data given in a plot appearing in the paper) are

$$n = 15 \qquad \Sigma x = 1350 \qquad \Sigma y = 600$$
$$\Sigma x^2 = 155{,}400 \qquad \Sigma y^2 = 24{,}869.33 \qquad \Sigma xy = 57{,}760$$

a. Find the equation of the estimated regression line.
b. Estimate the mean blood-lead level for people who work where the air-lead level is 100 $\mu g/m^3$ using a 90% interval.
c. Construct a 90% prediction interval for the blood-lead level of a particular person who works where the air-lead level is 100 $\mu g/m^3$.
d. Explain the difference in interpretation of the intervals computed in parts (b) and (c).

13.36   The paper "Digestive Capabilities in Elk Compared to White-Tailed Deer" (*J. of Wildlife Mgmt.* (1982):22–29) examined the relationship between y = digestible amount of detergent-solubles (g) and x = amount of detergent-solubles in feed (%). Data for white-tailed deer is given.

x	30	40	40	48	56	60
y	15	28	27	29	33	38

a. Assuming that the simple linear regression model is appropriate, find a 95% confidence interval for the mean digestible amount of detergent-solubles when feed is composed of 36% detergent-solubles.
b. When x is 46%, would a 95% confidence interval for the mean y value be wider or narrower than the interval in part (a)? Explain.

13.37   The shelf life of packaged food depends on many factors. Dry cereal is considered to be a moisture-sensitive product (no one likes soggy cereal!) with the shelf life determined primarily by moisture content. In a study of the shelf life of one particular brand of cereal, x = time on shelf (stored at 73°F and 50% relative humidity) and y = moisture content were recorded. The resulting data is from "Computer Simulation Speeds Shelf Life Assessments" (*Package Engr.* (1983):72–73).

x	0	3	6	8	10	13	16
y	2.8	3.0	3.1	3.2	3.4	3.4	3.5

x	20	24	27	30	34	37	41
y	3.1	3.8	4.0	4.1	4.3	4.4	4.9

a. Summary quantities are

$$\Sigma x = 269 \qquad \Sigma y = 51 \qquad \Sigma xy = 1081.5$$
$$\Sigma x^2 = 7445 \qquad \Sigma y^2 = 190.78$$

Find the equation of the estimated regression line for predicting moisture content from time on the shelf.

b. Does the simple linear regression model provide useful information for predicting moisture content from knowledge of shelf time?

c. Find a 95% interval for the moisture content of an individual box of cereal that has been on the shelf 30 days.

d. According to the paper, taste tests indicate that this brand of cereal is unacceptably soggy when the moisture content exceeds 4.1. Based on your interval in part (c), do you think that a box of cereal that has been on the shelf 30 days will be acceptable? Explain.

13.38   For the cereal data of Exercise 13.37 the average x value is 19.21. Would a 95% confidence interval with $x^* = 20$ or $x^* = 17$ be wider? Explain. Answer the same question for a prediction interval.

13.39   Rhizobia is a small soil bacteria that forms nodules on the roots of legumes and aids in fixing nitrogen. The number of viable rhizobia per clover seed at the time of sowing is of interest to crop scientists. The paper "Survival of Rhizobia on Commercially Lime-Pelleted White Clover and Lucerne Seed" (*N. Zeal. J. of Exp. Agric.* (1983):275–278) gave the following data on $x =$ time stored (in weeks) and $y =$ number of viable rhizobia per seed for clover.

x	1	8	12	16	20	24	32	44
y	41	40	35	32	28	28	25	24

a. Find the equation of the estimated regression line.

b. Use a 95% confidence interval to estimate the mean number of rhizobia per seed for seeds stored 18 weeks.

c. Estimate the mean number of rhizobia for seed stored 22 weeks using a 95% confidence interval.

13.40   A regression of $y =$ sunburn index for a pea plant on $x =$ distance from an ultraviolet light source was considered in Exercise 13.21. The data and summary statistics presented there give

$$n = 15 \qquad \bar{x} = 40.60 \qquad \Sigma(x - \bar{x})^2 = 3311.60$$
$$b = -.0565 \qquad a = 4.500 \qquad \text{SSResid} = .8430$$

a. Calculate a 95% confidence interval for the true average sunburn index when the distance from the light source is 35 cm.

b. When two 95% confidence intervals are computed, it can be shown that the *simultaneous confidence level* is at least $[100 - 2(5)]\% = 90\%$. That is, if both intervals are computed for a first sample, then for a second sample, yet again for a third, and so on, in the long run at least 90% of the samples will result in intervals *both* of which capture the values of the corresponding population characteristics. Calculate confidence intervals for the true mean sunburn index when the distance is 35 cm and when the distance is 45 cm in such a way that the simultaneous confidence level is at least 90%.

c. If two 99% intervals were computed, what do you think could be said about the simultaneous confidence level?

13.41 The $n = 10$ observations from Exercise 13.28 on $x =$ pressure of extracted gas and $y =$ extraction time yield

$$b = .0068 \qquad a = 2.142 \qquad s_e = .106$$
$$s_{a+b(200)} = .0384 \qquad s_{a+b(250)} = .0349$$

a. Obtain a 95% prediction interval for a single observation to be made on extraction time when the pressure is 200 μm.

b. Obtain a 99% prediction interval for an observation on time when the pressure is 250 μm.

13.42 By analogy with the discussion in Exercise 13.40, when two different prediction intervals are computed, each at the 95% prediction level, the *simultaneous prediction level* is at least $[100 - 2(5)]\% = 90\%$.

a. Return to Exercise 13.41 and obtain prediction intervals for extraction time both when pressure is 200 μm and when pressure is 250 μm, so that the simultaneous prediction level is at least 90%.

b. If three different 99% prediction intervals are calculated for pressures of 200, 250, and 300 μm, what can be said about the simultaneous prediction level?

13.43 The article "Performance Test Conducted for a Gas Air-Conditioning System" (*Am. Soc. of Heating, Refrigerating, and Air Cond. Engr.* (1969):54) reported the following data on maximum outdoor temperature (x) and hours of chiller operation per day (y) for a 3-ton residential gas air-conditioning system.

x	72	78	80	86	88	92
y	4.8	7.2	9.5	14.5	15.7	17.9

Suppose that the system is actually a prototype model, and the manufacturer does not wish to produce this model unless the data strongly indicates that when maximum outdoor temperature is 82°F, the true average number of hours of chiller operation is less than 12. The appropriate hypotheses are then

$$H_0: \alpha + \beta(82) = 12 \qquad \text{versus} \qquad H_a: \alpha + \beta(82) < 12$$

Use the statistic

$$t = [a + b(82) - 12]/s_{a+b(82)}$$

which has a t distribution based on $(n - 2)$ df when H_0 is true, to test the hypotheses at significance level .01.

13.44 The paper "The Incorporation of Uranium and Silver by Hydrothermally Synthesized Galena" (*Econ. Geol.* (1964):1003–1024) reported on the determination of silver content of galena crystals grown in a closed hydrothermal system over a range of temperatures. With $x =$ crystallization temperature (°C) and $y =$ silver content (%), the data is

x	398	292	352	575	568	450	550
y	.15	.05	.23	.43	.23	.40	.44

x	408	484	350	503	600	600
y	.44	.45	.09	.59	.63	.60

Summary quantities are

$$\Sigma x = 6130 \qquad \Sigma y = 4.73 \qquad \Sigma xy = 2418.74$$
$$\Sigma x^2 = 3{,}022{,}050 \qquad\qquad \Sigma y^2 = 2.1785$$

When temperature equals 400° C, does the true average silver content appear to differ significantly from .25? Test the appropriate hypotheses at the .01 level of significance. (Hint: Examine the hypotheses and test procedure given in Problem 13.43.)

13.4   Inferences about the Population Correlation Coefficient

The sample correlation coefficient r, defined in Chapter 4, measures how strongly the x and y values in a *sample* of pairs are linearly related to one another. There is an analogous measure of how strongly x and y are related in the entire *population* of pairs from which the sample $(x_1, y_1), \ldots, (x_n, y_n)$ was obtained. It is called the **population correlation coefficient** and is denoted by ρ (notice again the use of a Greek letter for a population characteristic and Roman letter for a sample characteristic). Properties 1–5 of Section 4.2 remain valid if ρ is substituted for r in every statement. In particular, ρ measures the extent of any *linear* association in the population. To have $\rho = 1$ or -1, all (x, y) pairs in the population must lie exactly on a straight line.

The relationship between r and ρ is similar to the relationship between $\bar{x}$ and μ, between p and π, and between b and β. The first-listed quantity in each pair is a statistic with a value that varies from sample to sample. A first sample of pairs might yield $r = .57$, a second might give $r = .65$, a third $r = .48$, and so on. On the other hand, the second quantity in each case has a fixed value characteristic of the population being studied—for example, $\mu = 60.0$ or $\beta = 12.5$ or $\rho = .55$—but its value is typically unknown.

A Test for Independence ($\rho = 0$)

Investigators are often interested in detecting not just linear association but association of *any* kind. When there is no association of any type between x and y values, statisticians say that the two variables are *independent*. In general, $\rho = 0$ is not equivalent to the independence of x and y. However, there is one special, yet frequently occurring, situation in which the two conditions ($\rho = 0$ and independence) are identical. This is when the pairs in the population have what is called a **bivariate normal distribution.** The essential feature of such a distribution is that for *any* fixed x value, the distribution of associated y values is normal, *and* for any fixed y value, the distribution of x values is normal. As an example, suppose that height x and weight y have a bivariate normal distribution in the American adult male population. (There is good empirical evidence for this.) Then when $x = 68$ in., weight y has a normal distribution; when $x = 72$ in., weight is normally distributed; when $y = 160$ lb, height x has a normal distribution; when $y = 175$ lb, height has a normal distribution; and so on. In this example, of course, x and y are not independent, since a large height value tends to be associated with large weight values and a small height value with small weight values.

There is no easy way to check the assumption of bivariate normality, especially when the sample size n is small. A partial check can be based on the following property: If (x, y) has a bivariate normal distribution, then x alone has a normal distribution and so does y. This suggests doing a normal probability plot of x_1, $x_2, \ldots, x_n$ and a separate normal probability plot of $y_1, \ldots, y_n$. If either plot shows a substantial departure from a straight line, bivariate normality is a questionable assumption. If both plots are reasonably straight, bivariate normality is plausible, although no guarantee can be given.

The test of independence (zero correlation) is a t test. The formula for the test statistic essentially involves standardizing the estimate r under the assumption that $\rho = 0$.

A TEST FOR INDEPENDENCE IN A BIVARIATE NORMAL POPULATION

Null hypothesis: $H_0: \rho = 0$ (x and y are independent)

Test statistic: $t = \dfrac{r}{\sqrt{(1 - r^2)/(n - 2)}}$

Alternative Hypothesis	Rejection Region
$H_a: \rho > 0$ (positive dependence)	$t > t$ critical value
$H_a: \rho < 0$ (negative dependence)	$t < -t$ critical value
$H_a: \rho \neq 0$ (dependence)	Either $t > t$ critical value or $t < -t$ critical value

The t critical value is based on $n - 2$ df.

EXAMPLE 13.8

An accurate assessment of soil productivity is an essential input to rational land-use planning. Unfortunately, as the author argues in the article "Productivity Ratings Based on Soil Series" (*Prof. Geographer* (1980):158–163), an acceptable soil productivity index is not easy to come by. One difficulty is that productivity is determined partly by the crop that is planted, and the relationship between the yields of two different crops planted in the same soil may not be very strong. To illustrate, the paper presents the accompanying data on corn yield, x, and peanut yield, y (mT/Ha).

				Observation				
	1	2	3	4	5	6	7	8
x	2.4	3.4	4.6	3.7	2.2	3.3	4.0	2.1
y	1.33	2.12	1.80	1.65	2.00	1.76	2.11	1.63

The scatter plot in Figure 13.13 certainly casts doubt on the possibility of any relationship between the two yields.

FIGURE 13.13
Scatter plot of y = peanut yield versus x = corn yield

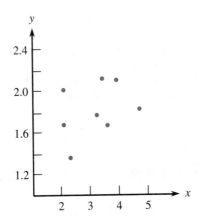

Assuming that the (x, y) pairs were drawn from a bivariate normal population, let's carry out a test of independence using significance level .10.

1. ρ = the correlation between corn yield and peanut yield in the population from which the given eight observations were selected.

2. H_0: $\rho = 0$

3. H_a: $\rho \neq 0$

4. Test statistic:

$$t = \frac{r}{\sqrt{(1 - r^2)/(n - 2)}}$$

5. The t critical value for a two-tailed test based on $n - 2 = 6$ df is 1.94, so H_0 will be rejected in favor of H_a if either $t > 1.94$ or $t < -1.94$.
6. Summary quantities are

$$\Sigma x = 25.7 \qquad \Sigma y = 14.40 \qquad \Sigma x^2 = 88.31$$
$$\Sigma y^2 = 26.4324 \qquad \Sigma xy = 46.856$$

from which, after some further calculation, we get

$$r = \frac{.5960}{\sqrt{5.74875}\ \sqrt{.51240}} = .347$$

The test statistic value is

$$t = \frac{.347}{\sqrt{[1 - (.347)^2]/6}} = \frac{.347}{\sqrt{.880/6}} = .91$$

7. Because .91 neither exceeds 1.94 nor is less than -1.94, it does not fall in the rejection region. The data is quite consistent with the assertion that $\rho = 0$, so there does not appear to be any dependence between the two yields.

In the context of regression analysis, the hypothesis of no linear relationship (H_0: $\beta = 0$) was tested using the t ratio b/s_b. Some algebraic manipulation shows that

$$\frac{r}{\sqrt{(1 - r^2)/(n - 2)}} = \frac{b}{s_b}$$

so the two test procedures are completely equivalent. The reason for using the formula for t that involves r is that when interest lies only in correlation, the extra effort involved in computing the regression quantities b, a, SSResid, s_e, and s_b need not be expended.

Other inferential procedures for drawing conclusions about ρ—a confidence interval or a test of hypotheses with nonzero hypothesized value—are somewhat complicated. One of the chapter references can be consulted for details.

EXERCISES 13.45–13.55   SECTION 13.4

13.45   Discuss the difference between r and ρ.

13.46   **a.** If the sample correlation coefficient is equal to 1, is it necessarily true that $\rho = 1$?
b. If $\rho = 1$, is it necessarily true that $r = 1$?

13.47   The paper "A Dual-Buffer Titration Method for Lime Requirement of Acid Mine-soils" (*J. of Environ. Qual.* (1988):452–456) reported on the results of a study relating to revegetation of soil at mine reclamation sites. With $x =$ KCl extractable aluminum and $y =$ amount of lime required to bring soil pH to 7.0, data in the paper resulted in the accompanying summary statistics.

$$n = 24 \qquad \Sigma x = 48.15 \qquad \Sigma x^2 = 155.4685$$
$$\Sigma y = 263.5 \qquad \Sigma y^2 = 3750.53 \qquad \Sigma xy = 658.455$$

Carry out a test at significance level .01 to see whether the population correlation coefficient is something other than zero.

13.48 The accompanying summary quantities for x = particulate pollution ($\mu g/m^3$) and y = luminance (.01 cd/m^2) were calculated from a representative sample of data that appeared in the paper "Luminance and Polarization of the Sky Light at Seville (Spain) Measured in White Light" (*Atmos. Environ.* (1988):595–599).

$$n = 15 \qquad \Sigma x = 860 \qquad \Sigma y = 348$$
$$\Sigma x^2 = 56,700 \qquad \Sigma y^2 = 8954 \qquad \Sigma xy = 22,265$$

a. Test to see whether there is a positive correlation between particulate pollution and luminance in the population from which the data was selected.

b. What proportion of observed variation in luminance can be attributed to the approximate linear relationship between luminance and particulate pollution?

13.49 In a study of bacterial concentration in surface and subsurface water ("Pb and Bacteria in a Surface Microlayer" *J. of Marine Research* (1982):1200–1206), the following data was obtained.

Concentration (x 10^6/mL)								
Surface	48.6	24.3	15.9	8.29	5.75	10.8	4.71	8.26	9.41
Subsurface	5.46	6.89	3.38	3.72	3.12	3.39	4.17	4.06	5.16

Summary quantities are

$$\Sigma x = 136.02 \qquad \Sigma y = 39.35 \qquad \Sigma xy = 673.65$$
$$\Sigma x^2 = 3602.65 \qquad \Sigma y^2 = 184.27$$

a. Using a significance level of .05, determine whether the data supports the hypothesis of a linear relationship between surface and subsurface concentration.

b. Give an upper and/or lower bound on the P-value associated with the computed test statistic value in part (a).

13.50 Physical properties of six flame-retardant fabric samples were investigated in the paper "Sensory and Physical Properties of Inherently Flame-Retardant Fabrics" (*Textile Research* (1984):61–68). Use the accompanying data and a .05 significance level to determine if a linear relationship exists between stiffness and thickness.

Stiffness (mg-cm)	7.98	24.52	12.47	6.92	24.11	35.71
Thickness (mm)	.28	.65	.32	.27	.81	.57

13.51 The April 11, 1983, issue of *Advertising Age* gave the accompanying data on x = memory size (K) and y = retail price (in dollars) for 13 of the many home computer systems on the market. Does this data suggest a linear relationship between x and y? Use a .10 significance level.

x	2	1	4	5	16	16	16
y	80	80	100	200	300	300	400

x	16	64	128	32	48	64
y	450	595	795	995	679	899

13.52   The paper "Chronological Trend in Blood Lead Levels" (*New Eng. J. of Med.* (1983):1373–1377) gave the following data on y = average blood-lead level of white children ages 6 months to 5 years and x = amount of lead used in gasoline production (in 1000 tons) for ten 6-month periods.

x	48	59	79	80	95	95	97	102	102	107
y	9.3	11.0	12.8	14.1	13.6	13.8	14.6	14.6	16.0	18.2

a. Construct separate normal probability plots for x and y. Do you think that it is reasonable to assume that the (x, y) pairs are from a bivariate normal population?

b. Does the data provide sufficient evidence to conclude that there is a linear relationship between blood-lead level and the amount of lead used in gasoline production? Use $\alpha = .01$.

c. If a simple linear regression analysis were carried out, what proportion of observed variation in blood-lead level could be explained by the model relationship?

13.53   The paper "The Mechanics of Swimming Muskrats" (*J. of Exp. Biology* (1984): 183–201) contained a scatter plot of y, the arc (in degrees) through which the hind feet were swept during the power phase, versus x, the swimming velocity (m/s). Selected data is given.

x	.25	.30	.35	.40	.45	.50	.50
y	98	92	87	97	101	116	96

x	.55	.55	.60	.65	.70	.75
y	115	114	110	115	123	133

$$\Sigma x = 6.55 \qquad \Sigma y = 1397 \qquad \Sigma x^2 = 3.5775$$
$$\Sigma y^2 = 152{,}283 \qquad \Sigma xy = 725.35$$

a. Compute the value of the sample correlation coefficient.

b. Does the data suggest that muskrats increase swimming speed in a linear fashion by increasing the sweep arc of their hind feet? State and test the appropriate hypotheses at level of significance .05.

c. What can you say about the P-value corresponding to the test statistic value computed in part (b)?

d. How would your conclusion change if x were expressed in feet per second? Explain.

13.54   A sample of $n = 500$ (x, y) pairs was collected and a test of H_0: $\rho = 0$ versus H_a: $\rho \neq 0$ was carried out. The resulting P-value was computed to be .00032.

a. What conclusion would be appropriate at level of significance .001?

b. Does this small *P*-value indicate that there is a very strong linear relationship between *x* and *y* (a value of ρ that differs considerably from zero)? Explain.

13.55 A sample of $n = 10{,}000$ (x, y) pairs resulted in $r = .022$. Test H_0: $\rho = 0$ versus H_a: $\rho \neq 0$ at level .05. Is the result statistically significant? Comment on the practical significance of your analysis.

13.5 Checking Model Adequacy Read.

The simple linear regression model equation, introduced in Section 13.1, is given by

$$y = \alpha + \beta x + e$$

where *e* represents the random deviation of an observed *y* value from the population regression line $y = \alpha + \beta x$. The inferential methods presented in the previous sections require some assumptions about *e*. Key assumptions are

1. *e* has a normal distribution;
2. The standard deviation of *e* is σ, which does not depend on *x*.

Inferences based on the simple linear regression model continue to be reliable when model assumptions are slightly violated (for example, mild nonnormality of the random deviation distribution). However, use of an estimated model in the face of grossly violated assumptions can result in very misleading conclusions being drawn. Therefore, it is desirable to have easily applied methods available for identifying such serious violations and for suggesting how a satisfactory model can be obtained.

Residual Analysis

If the deviations $e_1, e_2, \ldots, e_n$ from the population line were available, they could be examined for any inconsistencies with model assumptions. For example, a normal probability plot would suggest whether the normality assumption was tenable. But, since

$$e_1 = y_1 - (\alpha + \beta x_1)$$
$$\vdots$$
$$e_n = y_n - (\alpha + \beta x_n)$$

these deviations can be calculated only if the equation of the population line is known. In practice, this will never be the case. Instead, diagnostic checks must be based on the residuals

$$y_1 - \hat{y}_1 = y_1 - (a + bx_1)$$
$$\vdots$$
$$y_n - \hat{y}_n = y_n - (a + bx_n)$$

which are the deviations from the *estimated* line.

Before a sample has been selected, any particular residual $y_i - \hat{y}_i$ is a random variable because its value varies from sample to sample. When all model assumptions are met, the mean value of any residual is zero. Any observation that gives a very large positive or negative value should be examined carefully for any anomalous circumstances, such as a recording error or exceptional experimental conditions. Identifying residuals with unusually large magnitudes is made easier by inspecting **standardized residuals.**

Recall that a quantity is standardized by subtracting its mean value (zero in this case) and dividing by its standard deviation. Thus

$$\text{standardized residual} = \frac{\text{residual}}{\text{standard deviation of residual}}$$

The value of a standardized residual tells how many standard deviations the corresponding residual lies from its expected value, zero.

Since each residual $y_i - \hat{y}_i$ has a different standard deviation (depending on the value of x_i for that observation), computing the standardized residuals can be tiresome. Fortunately, many computer regression programs provide standardized residuals as part of the output.

In Section 7.3, the normal probability plot was introduced as a technique for deciding if the n observations in a random sample could plausibly have come from a normal population distribution. To check the assumption that $e_1, e_2, \ldots, e_n$ all come from the same normal distribution, we recommend a normal probability plot of the standardized residuals.

EXAMPLE 13.9

Landslides are common events in tree-growing regions of the Pacific Northwest, so their effect on timber growth is of special concern to foresters. The paper "Effects of Landslide Erosion on Subsequent Douglas Fir Growth and Stocking Levels in the Western Cascades, Oregon" (*Soil Science Soc. of Amer. J.* (1984):667–671) reported on the results of a study in which growth in a landslide area was compared with growth in a previously clear-cut area. We present data on clear-cut growth (see next page), with x = tree age (years) and y = 5-year height growth (cm). The scatter plot in Figure 13.14 supports the use of the simple linear regression model.

The residuals, their standard deviations, and the standardized residuals are given here in Table 13.1. Except for $x = 5$ and $x = 18$, the two most extreme values, the residuals have roughly equal standard deviations. The residual with the largest magnitude, -99.2, initially seems quite extreme, but the corresponding standardized residual is only -2.04. That is, the residual is approximately two standard deviations below its expected value zero, which is not terribly unusual in a sample this size. On the standardized scale, no residual here is surprisingly large. Before standardization, there are some large residuals simply because there

TABLE 13.1   Data, residuals, and standardized residuals for Example 13.9

Obs.	x	y	$\hat{y}$	Residual	Standard deviation of residual	Standardized residual
1	5	70	111.0	−41.0	40.9	−1.00
2	9	150	196.2	−46.2	48.1	−.96
3	9	260	196.2	63.8	48.1	1.33
4	10	230	217.6	12.4	49.0	.25
5	10	255	217.6	37.4	49.0	.76
6	11	165	238.9	−73.9	49.5	−1.49
7	11	225	238.9	−13.9	49.5	−.28
8	12	340	260.2	79.8	49.8	1.60
9	13	305	281.5	23.5	49.7	.47
10	13	335	281.5	53.5	49.7	1.08
11	14	290	302.9	−12.9	49.4	−.26
12	14	340	302.9	37.1	49.4	.75
13	15	225	324.2	−99.2	48.7	−2.04
14	15	300	324.2	−24.2	48.7	−.50
15	18	380	388.1	−8.1	44.6	−.18
16	18	400	388.1	11.9	44.6	.27

FIGURE 13.14
Scatter plot for the data
of Example 13.9

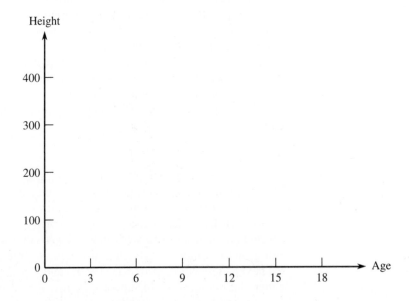

appears to be a substantial amount of variability about the true regression line ($s_e = 51.43$, $r^2 = .683$).

Figure 13.15 displays a normal probability plot of the standardized residuals. Few plots are straighter than this one! The plot casts no doubt on the normality assumption.

FIGURE 13.15
Normal probability plot of the
standardized residuals from
Example 13.9 (from MINITAB)

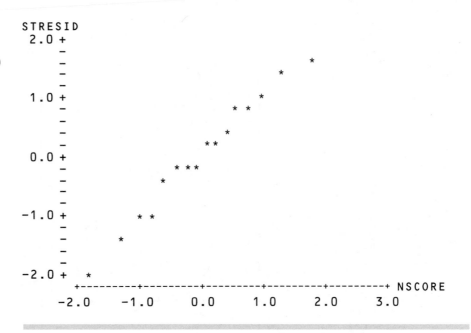

Plotting the Residuals

A plot of the (*x*, standardized residual) pairs, called a **standardized residual plot,** is often helpful in identifying unusual or highly influential observations and in checking for violations of model assumptions. A desirable plot is one that exhibits no particular pattern (such as curvature or a much greater spread in one part of the plot than in another), and one that has no point that is far removed from all the others. A point falling far above or below the horizontal line at height zero corresponds to a large standardized residual, which may indicate some kind of unusual behavior, such as a recording error, a nonstandard experimental condition, or an atypical experimental subject. A point that has an *x* value that differs greatly from others in the data set could have exerted excessive influence in determining the fitted line.

A plot such as the one pictured in Figure 13.16(a) is desirable, since no point lies much outside the horizontal band between -2 and 2 (so there is no unusually large residual corresponding to an outlying observation); there is no point far to the left or right of the others (thus no observation that might greatly influence the fit), and there is no pattern to indicate that the model should somehow be modified. When the plot has the appearance of Figure 13.16(b), the fitted model should be changed to incorporate curvature (a nonlinear model). One type of nonlinear model is discussed in the next chapter.

FIGURE 13.16
Examples of residual plots
(a) a satisfactory plot
(b) a plot suggesting that
a curvilinear regression model
is needed
(c) a plot indicating
nonconstant variance
(d) a plot showing a
large residual
(e) a plot showing a potentially
influential observation

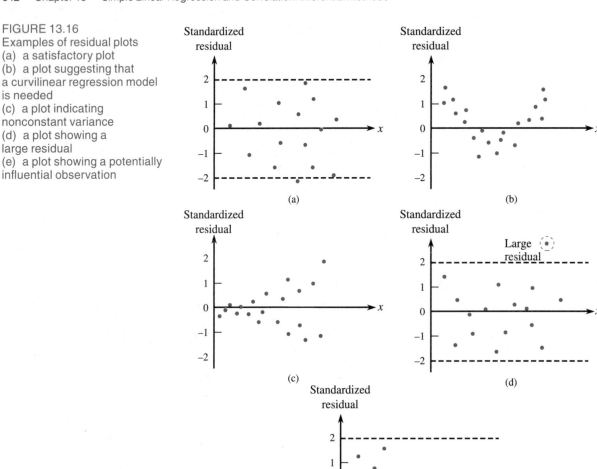

The increasing spread from left to right in Figure 13.16(c) suggests that the variance of y is not the same at each x value but rather increases with x. A straight-line model may still be appropriate, but the best-fit line should be selected by using weighted least squares rather than ordinary least squares. This involves giving more weight to observations in the region exhibiting low variability and less weight to observations in the region exhibiting high variability. A specialized regression analysis text or a knowledgeable statistician should be consulted for details.

The standardized residual plots of Figure 13.16(d) and (e) show an extreme outlier and a potentially influential observation, respectively. Consider deleting the observation corresponding to such a point from the data set and refitting the same model. Substantial changes in estimates and various other quantities warn of instability in the data. The investigator should certainly carry out a more careful analysis and perhaps collect more data before drawing any firm conclusions. Improved computing power has allowed statisticians to develop and implement a variety of diagnostics for identifying unusual observations in a regression data set.

EXAMPLE 13.10

Figure 13.17 displays a standardized residual plot for the tree age–5-year growth data of Example 13.9. The first observation was at $x_1 = 5$ and the corresponding standardized residual was -1.00, so the first plotted point is $(5, -1.00)$. Other points are similarly obtained and plotted. The plot shows no unusual behavior that might call for model modification or further analysis.

FIGURE 13.17
Standardized residual plot for the data of Example 13.10 (from MINITAB)

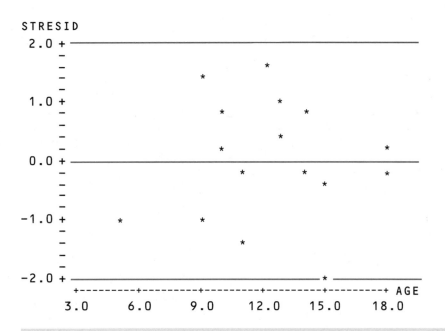

EXAMPLE 13.11

The paper "Snow Cover and Temperature Relationships in North America and Eurasia" (*J. of Climate and Appl. Meteorology* (1983):460–469) explored the relationship between October–November continental snow cover (*x*, in millions of km^2) and December–February temperature (*y*, in ° C). The given data refers to Eurasia during the $n = 13$ time periods 1969–1970, 1970–1971, ..., 1981–1982. A simple linear regression analysis done by the authors yielded $r^2 = .52$ ($r = -.72$), suggesting a substantial linear relationship. This is confirmed by a model utility test.

FIGURE 13.18
Plots for the data of
Example 13.11 (from
MINITAB)
(a) scatter plot
(b) standardized residual plot

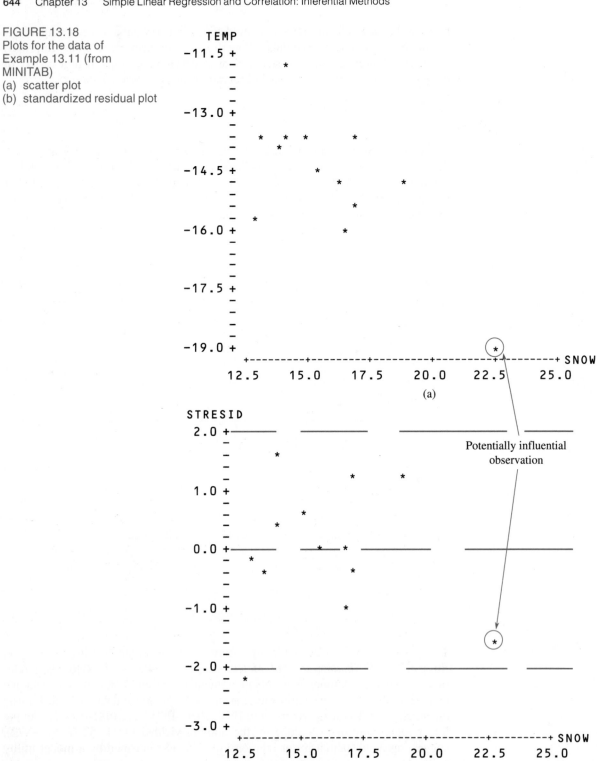

Potentially influential
observation

(a)

(b)

x	13.00	12.75	16.70	18.85	16.60	15.35	13.90
y	−13.5	−15.7	−15.5	−14.7	−16.1	−14.6	−13.4
St. resid.	−.11	−2.19	−.36	1.23	−.91	−.12	.34

x	22.40	16.20	16.70	13.65	13.90	14.75
y	−18.9	−14.8	−13.6	−14.0	−12.0	−13.5
St. resid.	−1.54	.04	1.25	−.28	1.54	.58

The scatter plot and standardized residual plot are displayed in Figure 13.18. There are no unusual patterns, though one standardized residual, −2.19, is a bit on the large side. The most interesting feature is the observation (22.40, −18.9) corresponding to a point far to the right of the others in these plots. This observation may have had a substantial influence on all aspects of the fit. The estimated slope when all 13 observations are included is $b = -.459$, and $s_b = .133$. When the potentially influential observation is deleted, the estimate of β based on the remaining 12 observations is $b = -.228$. Thus,

$$\begin{aligned}
\text{change in slope} &= \text{original } b - \text{new } b \\
&= -.459 - (-.228) \\
&= -.231
\end{aligned}$$

The change expressed in standard deviations is $-.231/.133 = -1.74$. Because b has changed by substantially more than one standard deviation, the observation under consideration appears to be highly influential.

Additionally, r^2 based just on the 12 observations is only .13, and the t ratio for β is not significant. Evidence for a linear relationship is much less conclusive in light of this analysis. The investigators should seek a climatological explanation for the influential observation and collect more data which can be used in seeking an effective relationship.

When the distribution of the random deviation e has heavier tails than does the normal distribution, observations with large standardized residuals are not that unusual. Such observations can have great effects on the estimated regression line when the least squares approach is used. In recent years, statisticians have proposed a number of alternative methods—called **robust**, or **resistant**, methods—for fitting a line. Such methods give less weight to outlying observations than does least squares without deleting them from the data set. The most widely used robust procedures require a substantial amount of computation, so a good computer program is necessary. Associated confidence-interval and hypothesis-testing formulas are still in the developmental stage.

EXERCISES 13.56–13.61   SECTION 13.5

13.56   Exercise 4.32 gave data on x = chlorine flow and y = etch rate. The x values and corresponding standardized residuals from a simple linear regression are as follows.

x	1.5	1.5	2.0	2.5	2.5	3.0	3.5	3.5	4.0
St. resid.	.31	1.02	−1.15	−1.23	.23	.73	−1.36	1.53	.07

Construct a standardized residual plot. Does the plot exhibit any unusual features?

13.57   The authors of the paper "Age, Spacing and Growth Rate of Tamarix as an Indication of Lake Boundary Fluctuations at Sebkhet Kelbia, Tunisia" (*J. of Arid Environ.* (1982):43–51) used a simple linear regression model to describe the relationship between y = vigor (average width in centimeters of the last two annual rings) and x = stem density (stems/m^2). The estimated model was based on the following data. Also given are the standardized residuals.

x	4	5	6	9	14	15	15	19	21	22
y	.75	1.20	.55	.60	.65	.55	0	.35	.45	.40
St. resid.	−.28	1.92	−.90	−.28	.54	.24	−2.05	−.12	.60	.52

a. What assumptions are required in order that the simple linear regression model be appropriate?

b. Construct a normal probability plot of the standardized residuals. Does the assumption that the random deviation distribution is normal appear to be reasonable? Explain.

c. Construct a standardized residual plot. Are there any unusually large residuals?

d. Is there anything about the standardized residual plot that would cause you to question the use of the simple linear regression model to describe the relationship between x and y?

13.58   The article "Effects of Gamma Radiation on Juvenile and Mature Cuttings of Quaking Aspen" (*Forest Science* (1967):240–245) reported the following data on x = exposure time to radiation (kR/16 hours) and y = dry weight of roots (mg × 10^{-1}).

x	0	2	4	6	8
y	110	123	119	86	62

a. Construct a scatter plot for this data. Does the plot suggest that the simple linear regression model might be appropriate?

b. The estimated regression line for this data is $\hat{y} = 127 - 6.65x$ and the standardized residuals are as given.

x	0	2	4	6	8
St. resid.	−1.55	.68	1.25	−.05	−1.06

Construct a standardized residual plot. What does the plot suggest about the adequacy of the simple linear regression model?

13.59 Carbon aerosols have been identified as a contributing factor in a number of air quality problems. In a chemical analysis of diesel engine exhaust, x = mass ($\mu g/cm^2$) and y = elemental carbon ($\mu g/cm^2$) were recorded ("Comparison of Solvent Extraction and Thermal Optical Carbon Analysis Methods: Application to Diesel Vehicle Exhaust Aerosol" *Environ. Science Tech.* (1984):231–234). The estimated regression line for this data set is $\hat{y} = 31 + .737x$. Given are the observed x and y values and the corresponding standardized residuals.

x	164.2	156.9	109.8	111.4	87.0	82.9	78.9
y	181	156	115	132	96	90	86
St. resid.	2.52	0.82	0.27	1.64	0.08	−0.18	−0.27

x	161.8	230.9	106.5	97.6	79.7	100.8	387.8
y	170	193	110	94	77	88	310
St. resid.	1.72	−0.73	0.05	−0.77	−1.11	−1.49	−0.89

x	118.7	248.8	102.4	64.2	89.4	117.9	135.0
y	106	204	98	76	89	130	141
St. resid.	−1.07	−0.95	−0.73	−0.20	−0.68	1.05	0.91

x	108.1	89.4	76.4	131.7
y	102	91	97	128
St. resid.	−0.75	−0.51	0.85	0.00

a. Construct a standardized residual plot. Are there any unusually large residuals? Do you think that there are any influential observations?

b. Is there any pattern in the standardized residual plot that would indicate that the simple linear regression model is not appropriate?

c. Based on your plot in part (a), do you think that it is reasonable to assume that the variance of y is the same at each x value? Explain.

13.60 An investigation of the relationship between traffic flow x (thousands of cars per 24 hr) and lead content y of bark on trees near the highway ($\mu g/g$ dry weight) yielded the accompanying data. A simple linear regression model was fit, and the resulting estimated regression line was $\hat{y} = 28.7 + 33.3x$. Both residuals and standardized residuals are also given.

x	8.3	8.3	12.1	12.1	17.0
y	227	312	362	521	640
Residual	−78.1	6.9	−69.6	89.4	45.3
St. resid.	−0.99	0.09	−0.81	1.04	0.51

x	17.0	17.0	24.3	24.3	24.3
y	539	728	945	738	759
Residual	−55.7	133.3	107.2	−99.8	−78.8
St. resid.	−0.63	1.51	1.35	−1.25	−0.99

a. Plot the (x, residual) pairs. Does the resulting plot suggest that a simple linear regression model is an appropriate choice? Explain your reasoning.

b. Construct a standardized residual plot. Does the plot differ significantly in general appearance from the plot in part (a)?

13.61   The accompanying data on x = U.S. population (millions) and y = crime index (millions) appeared in the paper "The Normal Distribution of Crime" (*J. of Police Science and Admin.* (1975):312–318).

Year	1963	1964	1965	1966	1967	1968	1969	1970	1971	1972	1973
x	188.5	191.3	193.8	195.9	197.9	199.9	201.9	203.2	206.3	208.2	209.9
y	2.26	2.60	2.78	3.24	3.80	4.47	4.99	5.57	6.00	5.89	8.64

The author comments that "The simple linear regression analysis remains one of the most useful tools for crime prediction." When observations are made sequentially in time, the residuals or standardized residuals should be plotted in time order (that is, first the one for time $t = 1$ (1963 here), then the one for time $t = 2$, and so on). Notice that here x increases with time, so an equivalent plot is of residuals or standardized residuals versus x. Using $\hat{y} = -47.26 + .260x$, calculate the residuals and plot the (x, residual) pairs. Does the plot exhibit a pattern that casts doubt on the appropriateness of the simple linear regression model? Explain.

CHAPTER THIRTEEN SUMMARY OF KEY CONCEPTS AND FORMULAS

Term or Formula	Comment
Simple linear regression model, $y = \alpha + \beta x + e$	This model assumes that there is a line with slope β and y intercept α, called the population (true) regression line, such that an observation deviates from the line by a random amount e. The random deviation is assumed to have a normal distribution with mean zero and standard deviation σ, and random deviations for different observations are assumed independent of one another.
Estimated regression line, $\hat{y} = a + bx$	The least squares line introduced in Chapter 4.
$s_e = \sqrt{\dfrac{\text{SSResid}}{n - 2}}$	The point estimate of the standard deviation σ, with associated degrees of freedom $n - 2$.
$s_b = \dfrac{s_e}{\sqrt{\Sigma x^2 - [(\Sigma x)^2/n]}}$	The estimated standard deviation of the statistic b.
$b \pm (t \text{ crit. val.}) \cdot s_b$	A confidence interval for the slope β of the population regression line, where the t critical value is based on $(n - 2)$ df.

Term or Formula	Comment

$$t = \frac{b - \text{hyp. value}}{s_b}$$

The test statistic for testing hypotheses about β. The calculated value of t is compared to a t critical value.

Model utility test, with

test statistic $t = \dfrac{b}{s_b}$

A test of $H_0\colon \beta = 0$, which asserts that there is no useful linear relationship between x and y, versus $H_a\colon \beta \neq 0$, the claim that there is a useful linear relationship.

$$s_{a+bx^*} = s_e \sqrt{\frac{1}{n} + \frac{(x^* - \bar{x})^2}{\Sigma x^2 - [(\Sigma x)^2/n]}}$$

The estimated standard deviation of the statistic $a + bx^*$, where x^* denotes a particular value of x.

$a + bx^* \pm (t \text{ crit. val.}) \cdot s_{a+bx^*}$ A confidence interval for $\alpha + \beta x^*$, the average value of y when $x = x^*$.

$a + bx^* \pm (t \text{ crit. val.}) \cdot \sqrt{s_e^2 + s_{a+bx^*}^2}$ A prediction interval for a single y value to be observed when $x = x^*$.

Population correlation coefficient ρ

A measure of the extent to which the x and y values in an entire population are linearly related.

$$t = \frac{r}{\sqrt{(1 - r^2)/(n - 2)}}$$

The test statistic for testing $H_0\colon \rho = 0$, according to which (assuming a bivariate normal population distribution) x and y are independent of one another.

Residual analysis

Methods based on the residuals for checking the assumptions of the simple linear regression model or any other regression model.

Standardized residual

A residual divided by its standard deviation.

Standardized residual plot

A plot of the $(x, \text{standard residual})$ pairs. A pattern in this plot suggests a problem with the simple linear regression model.

ENCORE

We again give the data first introduced in the Chapter Preview on $x =$ image quality of a CRT display and $y =$ reading time for certain passages (in seconds, averaged over a group of subjects). The accompanying scatter plot is quite consistent with the simple linear regression model.

x	4.30	4.55	5.55	5.65	5.95	6.30	6.45	6.45
y	8.0	8.3	7.8	7.25	7.7	7.5	7.6	7.2

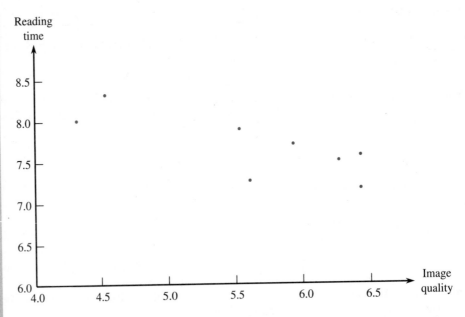

The summary statistics necessary for a simple linear regression analysis are as follows:

$$n = 8 \qquad \Sigma x = 45.20 \qquad \Sigma x^2 = 260.215$$
$$\Sigma y = 61.35 \qquad \Sigma y^2 = 471.4325 \qquad \Sigma xy = 344.9425$$

from which

$$b = -.348501 \qquad a = 9.637778 \qquad SSResid = .367626$$
$$s_e = .247530 \qquad r^2 = .615$$

Thus about 61.5% of observed variation in reading time can be explained by the simple linear regression model. It appears from this that there is a useful linear relation between the two variables, but a confirmation requires a formal test, the model utility test.

1. β = the true average change in reading time associated with a one-unit increase in image quality.
2. H_0: $\beta = 0$
3. H_a: $\beta \neq 0$
4. $t = \dfrac{b}{s_b}$
5. The calculation of t requires

$$s_b = \frac{s_e}{\sqrt{\Sigma x^2 - [(\Sigma x)^2/n]}} = \frac{.247530}{2.1989} = .11257$$

yielding

$$t = \frac{-.348501}{.11257} = -3.10$$

6. From the $6 = $ df row of our t table, since 3.10 is between 2.45 (tail area .025) and 3.14 (tail area .01), the two-tailed nature of the test gives

$$.02 < P\text{-value} < .05$$

(a more precise statement is P-value $\approx .02$).
7. For a significance level of .05, H_0 should be rejected (P-value $< .05$); we conclude that there is a useful linear relationship between image quality and reading time.

A 95% confidence interval for the change in true average reading time associated with a one-unit increase in image quality is

$$b \pm (t\,\text{critical value}) \cdot s_b = -.35 \pm (2.45)(.1126)$$
$$= -.35 \pm .28$$
$$= (-.63, -.07)$$

We can be highly confident that, on average, an improvement in reading time of between .07 and .63 s is associated with an increase of one unit in image quality.
At this point we could use formulas from the chapter to calculate a confidence interval for mean reading time when image quality is specified (for example, $x = 5$) or to obtain a prediction interval for reading time when image quality is specified.

SUPPLEMENTARY EXERCISES 13.62–13.80

13.62 Exercise 4.63 gave data on $x = $ bound rubber content (%) and $y = $ tensile modulus (MPa), a measure of coupling effectiveness. A scatter plot shows a substantial linear pattern. Summary quantities are

$$n = 11 \qquad \Sigma x = 292.9 \qquad \Sigma x^2 = 8141.75$$
$$\Sigma y = 69.03 \qquad \Sigma y^2 = 442.1903 \qquad \Sigma xy = 1890.200$$

a. Calculate point estimates for the slope and vertical intercept of the population regression line.
b. Calculate a point estimate for the standard deviation σ.

c. Using a .01 significance level, does the data suggest the existence of a useful linear relationship between x and y?

13.63 Return to the bound rubber content–tensile modulus data of Exercise 13.62.
a. Use a 95% confidence interval to estimate the true mean tensile modulus when the bound rubber content is 20%.
b. Use a 95% prediction interval to predict the value of the tensile modulus resulting from a single observation made when the rubber content is 20%.
c. What aspect of the problem description in part

(a) tells you that the requested confidence interval is not for β?

13.64 Data on x = depth of flooding and y = flood damage was given in Exercise 4.64. Summary quantities are

$$n = 13 \qquad \Sigma x = 91 \qquad \Sigma x^2 = 819$$
$$\Sigma y = 470 \qquad \Sigma y^2 = 19{,}118 \qquad \Sigma xy = 3867$$

a. Does the data suggest the existence of a *positive* linear relationship (one in which an increase in y tends to be associated with an increase in x)? Test using a .05 significance level.

b. Predict flood damage resulting from a claim made when depth of flooding is 3.5 ft, and do so in a way that conveys information about the precision of the prediction.

13.65 Eye weight (g) and cornea thickness (μm) were recorded for nine randomly selected calves, and the resulting data from the paper "The Collagens of the Developing Bovine Cornea" (*Exper. Eye Research* (1984):639–652) is given. Use this data and a .05 significance level to test the null hypothesis of no correlation between eye weight and cornea thickness against the alternative hypothesis of a positive correlation.

Eye weight	.2	1.4	2.2	2.7	4.9	5.3	8.0	8.8	9.6
Thickness	416	673	733	801	957	1035	883	736	567

13.66 Eight surface soil samples were analyzed to determine physiochemical properties. The following data on x = calcium–sodium exchange rate and y = percent of sodium in the soil was read from a scatter plot that appeared in the paper "Sodium–Calcium Exchange Equilibria in Soils as Affected by Calcium Carbonate and Organic Matter" (*Soil Science* (1984):109).

x	.641	.611	.463	.375	.260	.184	.182	.089
y	3.4	3.0	3.0	2.2	2.2	2.0	1.9	1.6

$$\Sigma x = 2.805 \qquad \Sigma x^2 = 1.281697 \qquad \Sigma y = 19.3$$
$$\Sigma y^2 = 49.41 \qquad \Sigma xy = 7.6546$$

a. Find the equation of the estimated regression line.

b. Compute the predicted values and the corresponding residuals. Use the residuals to calculate SSResid and s_e.

c. Using a significance level of .05, test to determine if the data suggests the existence of a linear relationship between the variables x and y.

d. Compute and interpret the values of r and r^2.

e. Predict the value of percent sodium for a future observation when exchange rate is .300, and do this in a way that conveys information about precision of the prediction.

13.67 A sample of n = 61 penguin burrows was selected and values of both y = trail length (m) and x = soil hardness (force required to penetrate the substrate to a depth of 12 cm with a certain gauge, in kg) were determined for each one ("Effects of Substrate on the Distribution of Magellanic Penguin Burrows," *The Auk* (1991):923–933). The equation of the least squares line was $\hat{y} = 11.607 - 1.4187x$, and $r^2 = .386$.

a. Does the relationship between soil hardness and trail length appear to be linear, with shorter trails associated with harder soil (as the paper asserted)? Carry out an appropriate test of hypotheses.

b. Using $s_e = 2.35$, $\bar{x} = 4.5$, and $\Sigma(x - \bar{x})^2 = 250$, predict trail length when soil hardness is 6.0 in a way that conveys information about the reliability and precision of the prediction.

c. Would you use the simple linear regression model to predict trail length when hardness is 10.0? Explain your reasoning.

13.68 The given observations on x = body weight (kg) and y = water intake (L/day) for n = 7 subjects appeared in the paper "Validation of a Metabolic Model for Tritium" (*Radiation Research* (1984):503–509). Calculate the correlation coefficient r and use it to test the null hypothesis of no correlation between body weight and water intake. Use a .01 significance level.

	Subject						
	1	2	3	4	5	6	7
x	95	52	73	50	82	68	60
y	3.94	1.03	1.71	1.75	1.76	2.01	.97

13.69 The paper "Photocharge Effects in Dye Sensitized Ag[Br,I] Emulsions at Millisecond Range Exposures" (*Photographic Science and Engr.* (1981):138–144) gave the accompanying data on x = % light absorption at 5800 A and y = peak photovoltage.

x	4.0	8.7	12.7	19.1	21.4	24.6	28.9	29.8	30.5
y	.12	.28	.55	.68	.85	1.02	1.15	1.34	1.29

$\Sigma x = 179.7 \qquad \Sigma y = 7.28 \qquad \Sigma x^2 = 4334.41$

$\Sigma y^2 = 7.4028 \qquad \Sigma xy = 178.683$

a. Construct a scatter plot of the data. What does it suggest?

b. Assuming that the simple linear regression model is appropriate, obtain the equation of the estimated regression line.

c. How much of the observed variation in peak photovoltage can be explained by the model relationship?

d. Predict peak photovoltage when percent absorption is 19.1, and compute the value of the corresponding residual.

e. The paper's authors claimed that there is a useful linear relationship between the two variables. Do you agree? Carry out a formal test.

f. Give an estimate of the average change in peak photovoltage associated with a 1% increase in light absorption. Your estimate should convey information about the precision of estimation.

g. Give an estimate of true average peak photovoltage when % light absorption is 20, and do so in a way that conveys information about precision.

13.70 Reduced visual performance with increasing age has been a much-studied phenomenon in recent years. This decline is due partly to changes in optical properties of the eye itself and partly to neural degeneration throughout the visual system.

As one aspect of this problem, the paper "Morphometry of Nerve Fiber Bundle Pores in the Optic Nerve Head of the Human" (*Exp. Eye Research* (1988):559–568) presented the accompanying data on x = age and y = percentage of the cribriform area of the lamina scleralis occupied by pores.

x	22	25	27	39	42	43	44	46	46
y	75	62	50	49	54	49	59	47	54

x	48	50	57	58	63	63	74	74
y	52	58	49	52	49	31	42	41

a. Suppose that the researchers had believed a priori that the average decrease in percentage area associated with a 1-year age increase was .5%. Does the data contradict this prior belief? State and test the appropriate hypotheses using a .10 significance level.

b. Estimate true average percent area covered by pores for all 50-year-olds in the population in a way that conveys information about the precision of estimation.

13.71 Occasionally an investigator may wish to compute a confidence interval for α, the y intercept of the true regression line, or test hypotheses about α. The estimated y intercept is just the height of the estimated line when $x = 0$, since $a + b(0) = a$. This implies that s_a, the estimated standard deviation of the statistic a, results from substituting $x^* = 0$ in the formula for s_{a+bx^*}. The desired confidence interval is then

$$a \pm (t \text{ crit. value})s_a$$

whereas a test statistic is

$$t = (a - \text{hyp. value})/s_a$$

a. The paper "Comparison of Winter-Nocturnal Geostationary Satellite Infrared-Surface Temperature with Shelter-Height Temperature in Florida" (*Remote Sensing of the Environ.* (1983):313–327) used the simple linear regression model to relate surface temperature as measured by a satellite (y) to actual air temperature (x) as determined from a thermocouple placed on a traversing vehicle. Selected data is given (read from a scatter plot in the paper).

x	−2	−1	0	1	2	3	4	5	6	7
y	−3.9	−2.1	−2.0	−1.2	0	1.9	.6	2.1	1.2	3.0

Estimate the true regression line.

b. Compute the estimated standard deviation s_a. Carry out a test at level of significance .05 to see whether the y intercept of the true regression line differs from zero.

c. Compute a 95% confidence interval for α. Does the result indicate that $\alpha = 0$ is plausible? Explain.

13.72 An experiment to measure y = magnetic relaxation time in crystals (μs) as a function of x = strength of the external magnetic field (KG) resulted in the following data ("An Optical Faraday Rotation Technique for the Determination of Magnetic Relaxation Times" *IEEE Trans. Magnetics* (1968):175–178).

x	11.0	12.5	15.2	17.2	19.0	20.8
y	187	225	305	318	367	365

x	22.0	24.2	25.3	27.0	29.0
y	400	435	450	506	558

Summary quantities are

$$\Sigma x = 223.2 \qquad \Sigma y = 4116$$
$$\Sigma(x - \bar{x})^2 = 348.569$$
$$\Sigma(y - \bar{y})^2 = 126{,}649.636$$
$$\Sigma(x - \bar{x})(y - \bar{y}) = 6578.718$$

a. Use the given information to compute the equation of the estimated regression line.

b. Is the simple linear regression model useful for predicting relaxation time from knowledge of the strength of the magnetic field?

c. Estimate the mean relaxation time when the field strength is 18 kg in a way that conveys information about the precision of estimation.

13.73 In some studies an investigator has n (x, y) pairs sampled from one population and m (x, y) pairs

from a second population. Let β and β' denote the slopes of the first and second population lines, respectively, and let b and b' denote the estimated slopes calculated from the first and second samples, respectively. The investigator may then wish to test the null hypothesis $H_0: \beta - \beta' = 0$ (that is, $\beta = \beta'$) against an appropriate alternative hypothesis. Suppose that σ^2, the variance about the population line, is the same for both populations. Then this common variance can be estimated by

$$s^2 = \frac{\text{SSResid} + \text{SSResid}'}{n + m - 4}$$

where SSResid and SSResid' are the residual sums of squares for the first and second samples, respectively. With SS_x and SS_x' denoting the quantity $\Sigma(x - \bar{x})^2$ for the first and second samples, respectively, the test statistic is

$$t = \frac{b - b'}{\sqrt{\dfrac{s^2}{SS_x} + \dfrac{s^2}{SS_x'}}}$$

When H_0 is true, this statistic has a t distribution based on $(n + m - 4)$ df.

The given data is a subset of the data in the paper "Diet and Foraging Mode of *Bufa marinus* and *Leptodactylus ocellatus*" (*J. of Herpetology* (1984):138–146). The independent variable x is body length (cm) and the dependent variable y is mouth width (cm), with $n = 9$ observations for one type of nocturnal frog and $m = 8$ observations for a second type. Test at level .05 to see whether or not the slopes of the true regression lines for the two different frog populations are identical (summary statistics appear on page 655).

Leptodactylus ocellatus

x	3.8	4.0	4.9	7.1	8.1	8.5	8.9	9.1	9.8
y	1.0	1.2	1.7	2.0	2.7	2.5	2.4	2.9	3.2

Bufa marinus

x	3.8	4.3	6.2	6.3	7.8	8.5	9.0	10.0
y	1.6	1.7	2.3	2.5	3.2	3.0	3.5	3.8

	Leptodactylus	Bufa
Sample size:	9	8
Σx	64.2	55.9
Σx^2	500.78	425.15
Σy	19.6	21.6
Σy^2	47.28	62.92
Σxy	153.36	163.36

13.74 Consider the following four (x, y) data sets: the first three have the same x values, so these values are listed only once (from Frank Anscombe, "Graphs in Statistical Analysis" *Amer. Statistician* (1973):17–21).

Data set	1–3	1	2	3	4	4
Variable	x	y	y	y	x	y
	10.0	8.04	9.14	7.46	8.0	6.58
	8.0	6.95	8.14	6.77	8.0	5.76
	13.0	7.58	8.74	12.74	8.0	7.71
	9.0	8.81	8.77	7.11	8.0	8.84
	11.0	8.33	9.26	7.81	8.0	8.47
	14.0	9.96	8.10	8.84	8.0	7.04
	6.0	7.24	6.13	6.08	8.0	5.25
	4.0	4.26	3.10	5.39	19.0	12.50
	12.0	10.84	9.13	8.15	8.0	5.56
	7.0	4.82	7.26	6.42	8.0	7.91
	5.0	5.68	4.74	5.73	8.0	6.89

For each of these data sets, the values of the summary quantities $\bar{x}$, $\bar{y}$, $\Sigma(x - \bar{x})^2$, $\Sigma(y - \bar{y})^2$, and $\Sigma(x - \bar{x})(y - \bar{y})$ are identical, so all quantities computed from these will be identical for the four sets—the estimated regression line, SSResid, s_e^2, r^2, and so on. The summary quantities provide no way of distinguishing among the four data sets. Based on a scatter plot for each set, comment on the appropriateness or inappropriateness of fitting the simple linear regression model.

13.75 The given scatter diagram, based on 34 sediment samples with $x =$ sediment depth (cm) and $y =$ oil and grease content (mg/kg), appeared in the paper "Mined Land Reclamation Using Polluted Urban Navigable Waterway Sediments" (*J. of Environ. Quality* (1984):415–422). Discuss the effect that the observation (20, 33,000) will have on the estimated regression line. If this point were omitted, what can you say about the slope of the estimated regression line? What do you think will happen to the slope if this observation is included in the computations?

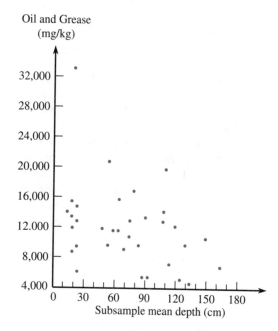

13.76 The paper "Improving Fermentation Productivity with Reverse Osmosis" (*Food Tech.* (1984):92–96) gave the following data (read from a scatter plot) on $y =$ glucose concentration (g/L) and $x =$ fermentation time (days) for a blend of malt liquor.

x	1	2	3	4	5	6	7	8
y	74	54	52	51	52	53	58	71

a. Use the data to calculate the estimated regression line.

b. Does the data indicate a linear relationship between y and x? Test using a .10 significance level.

c. Using the estimated regression line of part (a), compute the residuals and construct a plot of the residuals versus x (that is, of the $(x,$ residual) pairs).

d. Based on the plot in part (c), do you think that a linear model is appropriate for describing the relationship between y and x? Explain.

13.77 The employee relations manager of a large company was concerned that raises given to employees during a recent period might not have been based strictly on objective performance criteria. A sample of $n = 20$ employees was selected, and the values of x, a quantitative measure of productivity, and y, the percentage salary increase, were determined for each one. A computer package was used to fit the simple linear regression model, and the resulting output gave the P-value $= .0076$ for the model utility test. Does the percentage raise appear to be linearly related to productivity? Explain.

13.78 The paper "Statistical Comparison of Heavy Metal Concentrations in Various Louisiana Sediments" (*Environ. Monitoring and Assessment* (1984):163–170) gave the accompanying data on depth (m), zinc concentration (ppm), and iron concentration (%) for 17 core samples.

Core	Depth	Zinc	Iron
1	.2	86	3.4
2	2.0	77	2.9
3	5.8	91	3.1
4	6.5	86	3.4
5	7.6	81	3.2
6	12.2	87	2.9
7	16.4	94	3.2
8	20.8	92	3.4
9	22.5	90	3.1
10	29.0	108	4.0
11	31.7	112	3.4
12	38.0	101	3.6
13	41.5	88	3.7
14	60.0	99	3.5
15	61.5	90	3.4
16	72.0	98	3.5
17	104.0	70	4.8

a. Using a .05 significance level, test appropriate hypotheses to determine if a correlation exists between depth and zinc concentration.

b. Using a .05 significance level, does the data strongly suggest a correlation between depth and iron concentration?

c. Calculate the slope and intercept of the estimated regression line relating $y = $ iron concentration and $x = $ depth.

d. Use the estimated regression equation to construct a 95% prediction interval for the iron concentration of a single core sample taken at a depth of 50 m.

e. Compute and interpret a 95% interval estimate for the true average iron concentration of core samples taken at 70 m.

13.79 Give a brief answer, comment, or explanation for each of the following.

a. What is the difference between $e_1, e_2, \ldots, e_n$ and the n residuals?

b. The simple linear regression model states that $y = \alpha + \beta x$.

c. Does it make sense to test hypotheses about b?

d. SSResid is always positive.

e. A student reported that a data set consisting of $n = 6$ observations yielded residuals 2, 0, 5, 3, 0, and 1 from the least squares line.

f. A research report included the following summary quantities obtained from a simple linear regression analysis:

$$\Sigma(y - \bar{y})^2 = 615, \qquad \Sigma(y - \hat{y})^2 = 731$$

13.80 Some straightforward but slightly tedious algebra shows that

$$\text{SSResid} = (1 - r^2)\Sigma(y - \bar{y})^2,$$

from which it follows that

$$s_e = \sqrt{\frac{(n-1)}{(n-2)}}\sqrt{1 - r^2}\, s_y$$

Unless n is quite small, $(n - 1)/(n - 2) \approx 1$, so

$$s_e \approx \sqrt{1 - r^2}\, s_y$$

a. For what value of r is s_e as large as s_y? What is the least squares line in this case?

b. For what values of r will s_e be much smaller than s_y?

References

See the References at the end of Chapter 4.

14

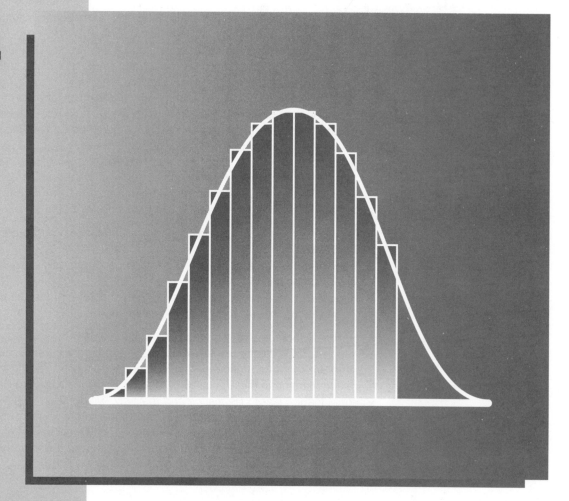

*Multiple Regression
Analysis*

PREVIEW

It has long been an article of faith in the education community that increasing resources will automatically improve the quality of education. This belief was called into question by a study that grew out of a court case in the state of Washington. Various school districts had banded together to sue the state on grounds that funding of K–12 education was inadequate to fulfill the obligation mandated in the constitution ("It is the paramount duty of the state to make ample provision for the education of all children within its borders."). The defense commissioned John Pincus and John E. Rolph, researchers employed by The Rand Corporation, to obtain and analyze relevant data, hoping that conclusions from the analysis would support their case. Data was gathered from Washington school districts on average student test scores and a number of potential "explanatory" (predictor) variables. These variables were of three different types (the value for each being an average over all families, teachers, and so on, in a district).

1. Background variables, such as parent's educational and income levels and family size
2. Peer group variables, including percentage of minority students and social class composition
3. School resource variables, comprising among others class size, teaching experience, teacher salary levels, and spending per pupil

The primary tool for analyzing the data was multiple regression, in which the dependent variable *test score* is related to the predictors by an equation similar in spirit to the model equation in simple linear regression. Results from the study were summarized in the article "How Much Is Enough? Applying Regression to a School Finance Case" (*Statistics and the Law,* Wiley, New York, 1986, pp. 257–287). The major conclusion reached by the investigators was that school resource variables did not appear to have much impact on test scores. After surveying the most important concepts and methods of multiple regression in this chapter, we shall return to this school finance study in the Chapter Encore.

Introduction

The general objective of regression analysis is to establish a useful relationship between a dependent variable y and one or more independent (predictor) variables. The simple linear regression model $y = \alpha + \beta x + e$ discussed in Chapter 13 has been used successfully by many investigators in a wide variety of disciplines to relate y to a single predictor variable x. However, in many situations there will not be a strong relationship between y and any single predictor variable, but knowing the values of several independent variables may considerably reduce uncertainty concerning the associated y value. For example, some variation in house prices in a large city can certainly be attributed to house size, but knowledge of size by itself would not usually enable a bank appraiser to accurately assess (predict) a home's value. Price is also determined to some extent by other variables such as age, lot size, number of bedrooms and bathrooms, distance from schools, and so on. As another example, let y denote a quantitative measure of wrinkle resistance in cotton cellulose fabric. Then the value of y may depend upon such variable quantities as curing temperature, curing time, concentration of formaldehyde, and concentration of the catalyst sulfur dioxide used in the production process.

In this chapter we extend the regression methodology developed in the previous chapter to *multiple regression models,* those models that include at least two predictor variables. Fortunately, many of the concepts developed in the context of simple linear regression carry over to multiple regression with little or no modification. The calculations required to fit such a model and make further inferences are *much* more tedious that those for simple linear regression, so a computer is an indispensable tool for doing multiple regression analysis. The computer's ability to perform a huge number of computations in a very short time has spurred the development of new methods for analyzing large data sets with many predictor variables. These include techniques for fitting numerous alternative models and choosing between them, tools for identifying influential observations, and both algebraic and graphical diagnostics designed to reveal potential violations of model assumptions. A single chapter can do little more than scratch the surface of this important and beautiful subject area. For more extensive expositions, refer to the sources listed in the Chapter 4 References.

14.1 Multiple Regression Models

The distinction between deterministic and probabilistic models when relating y to two or more independent variables is as important as it was in the case of a single predictor variable x. Generally speaking, the relationship is deterministic if the value of y is completely determined with no uncertainty once values of the independent variables have been specified. Consider, for example, a school district in which teachers with no prior teaching experience and no college credits beyond a bachelor's degree start at an annual salary of \$20,000. Suppose that for each year of teaching experience up to 20 years, a teacher receives an additional \$800 per year and that each unit of postcollege coursework up to a limit of 75 results in an extra \$60 per year. Define three variables by

y = salary of a teacher who has at most 20 years teaching experience
and at most 75 postcollege units

x_1 = number of years teaching experience

x_2 = number of postcollege units

Previously, x_1 and x_2 denoted the first two observations on the single variable x, but they now represent two different variables.

The value of y is entirely determined by values of x_1 and x_2 through the equation

$$y = 20{,}000 + 800x_1 + 60x_2$$

Thus if $x_1 = 10$ and $x_2 = 30$,

$$y = 20{,}000 + (800)(10) + (60)(30)$$
$$= 20{,}000 + 8000 + 1800$$
$$= 29{,}800$$

If two different teachers both have the same x_1 values and the same x_2 values, they will also have identical y values.

We previously discussed representing the equation $y = \alpha + \beta x$ geometrically as a straight line plotted on a two-dimensional coordinate system with a horizontal x axis and a vertical y axis. The equation for y given here can be visualized geometrically as a plane (flat surface) plotted on a three-dimensional coordinate system (see Figure 14.1). The point $(x_1, x_2, y) = (10, 30, 29{,}800)$ lies on the plane because $y = 29{,}800$ when $x_1 = 10$ and $x_2 = 30$. To locate this point, go out a distance 10 along the x_1 axis and then a distance 30 parallel to the x_2 axis to the point marked with an $\bigcirc$. Finally move up (off the ground, so to speak) from the point $\bigcirc$ a distance 29,800 parallel to the vertical axis to the point marked $\bullet$. Any other point on the pictured plane is located by first substituting values of x_1 and x_2 into the equation to obtain the height of the plane above the (x_1, x_2) point "on the ground." Thus $(5, 50, 27{,}000)$ is the point on the plane at height 27,000 above the ground point $(5, 50)$. Because $y = 20{,}000$ when $x_1 = 0$ and $x_2 = 0$, the constant 20,000 in the equation is the y intercept.

FIGURE 14.1
Geometric representation of the equation $y = 20{,}000 + 800x_1 + 60x_2$

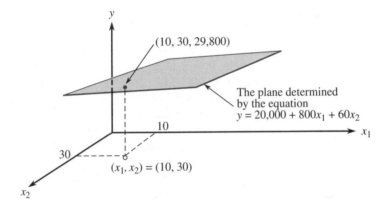

The equation relating the variables y, x_1, and x_2 just defined is a special case of the general deterministic relationship

$$y = \alpha + \beta_1 x_1 + \beta_2 x_2$$

The geometric representation of this equation is a plane in which the constant term α is the y intercept (the height of the plane when $x_1 = 0$ and $x_2 = 0$). The coefficient β_1 is the change in y when x_1 increases by 1 unit while x_2 is held fixed. Thus in the example involving teacher salaries, $\beta_1 = 800$, so salary increases by 800 when experience increases by 1 year while the number of postcollege units remains fixed. Similarly, β_2 gives the change in y when x_2 increases by one unit while x_1 is held fixed.

It is rarely the case that y can be deterministically related to independent variables x_1 and x_2. In the same way that the simple linear regression model generalizes the deterministic linear relationship $y = \alpha + \beta x$, the following probabilistic model generalizes the deterministic model $y = \alpha + \beta_1 x_1 + \beta_2 x_2$.

DEFINITION

The simplest **multiple regression model with two independent variables** x_1 and x_2 is given by the model equation

$$y = \alpha + \beta_1 x_1 + \beta_2 x_2 + e$$

The random deviation e is assumed to be normally distributed with mean value 0 and variance σ^2 regardless of the values of x_1 and x_2. This implies that for fixed x_1 and x_2 values, y itself has a normal distribution with variance σ^2 (standard deviation σ) and

$$\left(\begin{array}{c} \text{mean value of } y \text{ for} \\ \text{fixed } x_1 \text{ and } x_2 \text{ values} \end{array} \right) = \alpha + \beta_1 x_1 + \beta_2 x_2$$

This model equation has a geometric interpretation similar to that given for the simple linear regression model. Consider the plane whose height above the point (x_1, x_2) is $\alpha + \beta_1 x_1 + \beta_2 x_2$. This plane is called the *population* (or *true*) *regression plane*. Without the random deviation e, every observed point (x_1, x_2, y) would have to lie exactly on the plane. The presence of the random deviation in the model equation allows observed points to fall above or below the plane. The height of the plane above (x_1, x_2) is now the average, or expected, value of y for these values of the independent variables; the observed value will almost always deviate from the expected value by a random amount. This is illustrated in Figure 14.2. The coefficients β_1 and β_2 are often called *population regression coefficients*. The coefficient β_1 gives the average change in y associated with a 1-unit increase in x_1 when the value of x_2 is held constant, and β_2 has an analogous interpretation. Just as the value of σ described the amount of variability about the population regression line in simple linear regression, σ here reflects the amount of variability about the population regression plane. If σ is small, almost all observed points will lie on or close to the plane. When σ is large, it is quite likely that some observations will fall rather far above or below the plane. The value of σ indicates the amount by which an observation typically deviates from the plane.

FIGURE 14.2
Geometric representation of observations from the model
$y = \alpha + \beta_1 x_1 + \beta_2 x_2 + e$
■ = (x_1, x_2), a point on the ground
● = observation for which (x_1, x_2, y) lies above the regression plane
○ = observation for which (x_1, x_2, y) lies below the regression plane

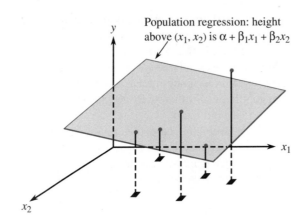

Population regression: height above (x_1, x_2) is $\alpha + \beta_1 x_1 + \beta_2 x_2$

EXAMPLE 14.1

Soil and sediment adsorption, the extent to which chemicals collect in a condensed form on the surface, is an important characteristic because it influences the effectiveness of pesticides and various agricultural chemicals. The paper "Adsorption of Phosphate, Arsenate, Methanearsonate, and Cacodylate by Lake and Stream Sediments: Comparisons with Soils" (*J. of Environ. Qual.* (1984):499–504) suggested the appropriateness of the previously defined regression model for relating the dependent variable

y = phosphate adsorption index

to

x_1 = amount of extractable iron

and

x_2 = amount of extractable aluminum

Suppose that $\alpha = -7.00$, $\beta_1 = .10$, $\beta_2 = .35$, and $\sigma = 4.5$, so that the model equation is

$$y = -7.00 + .10x_1 + .35x_2 + e$$

Then for any specified values of x_1 and x_2,

$$\left(\begin{array}{c}\text{mean value} \\ \text{of adsorption}\end{array}\right) = -7.00 + .10x_1 + .35x_2$$

For example,

$$\left(\begin{array}{c}\text{true average adsorption} \\ \text{when } x_1 = 150, x_2 = 40\end{array}\right) = -7.00 + (.10)(150) + (.35)(40)$$
$$= 22.00$$

An observation on adsorption made for these values of x_1 and x_2 may result in a y value less than 22 (an observed point below the regression plane, resulting from a negative deviation e) or one that exceeds 22.00 (a point above the plane, corresponding to $e > 0$). With $\sigma = 4.5$, it would not be very surprising to observe a y

value as small as 13.00 (2 standard deviations below the mean value) or as large as 31.00 when $x_1 = 150$ and $x_2 = 40$.

Because $\beta_1 = .10$, an increase of 1 μM/g in extractable iron while extractable aluminum remains fixed (at any value) is associated with an average increase of .10 in adsorption. Similarly, if extractable aluminum is increased by 1 μM/g while extractable iron is held fixed, the associated average increase in adsorption is .35.

The model involving two predictor variables, x_1 and x_2, can be extended to the case in which there are more than two predictor variables.

DEFINITION

A **general additive multiple regression model,** which relates a dependent variable y to k predictor variables $x_1, x_2, \ldots, x_k$, is given by the model equation

$$y = \alpha + \beta_1 x_1 + \beta_2 x_2 + \cdots + \beta_k x_k + e$$

The random deviation e is assumed to be normally distributed with mean value 0 and variance σ^2 for any values of $x_1, \ldots, x_k$. This implies that for fixed $x_1, x_2, \ldots, x_k$ values, y has a normal distribution with variance σ^2 and

$$\left(\begin{matrix} \text{mean } y \text{ value for fixed} \\ x_1, \ldots, x_k \text{ values} \end{matrix} \right) = \alpha + \beta_1 x_1 + \beta_2 x_2 + \cdots + \beta_k x_k$$

The β_i's are called **population regression coefficients,** and $\alpha + \beta_1 x_1 + \cdots + \beta_k x_k$ is often referred to as the **population regression function.**

A simple geometric interpretation of this k-predictor model is no longer possible except in certain special cases, but algebraic properties are analogous to those for the two-predictor model. In particular, the value of β_i gives the average change in y when x_i increases by 1 unit while the values of all other predictors are held fixed.

EXAMPLE 14.2

The paper "The Value of Information for Selected Appliances" (*J. of Marketing Research* (1980):14–25) suggests the plausibility of the general multiple regression model for relating the dependent variable y = the price of an air conditioner to $k = 3$ independent variables: x_1 = Btu-per-hour rating, x_2 = energy efficiency ratio, and x_3 = number of settings. Suppose that the model equation is

$$y = -70 + .025x_1 + 20x_2 + 7.5x_3 + e$$

and that $\sigma = 20$. Then the regression function is

$$\left(\begin{matrix} \text{mean value of } y \text{ for} \\ \text{fixed values of } x_1, x_2, x_3 \end{matrix} \right) = -70 + .025x_1 + 20x_2 + 7.5x_3$$

When $x_1 = 6000$, $x_2 = 8.0$, and $x_3 = 5$,

$$\left(\begin{array}{c}\text{mean value} \\ \text{of price}\end{array}\right) = -70 + (.025)(6000) + (20)(8.0) + (7.5)(5)$$
$$= \$277.50$$

With $2\sigma = 40$, a y observation for these values of x_1, x_2, and x_3 is quite likely to be between \$237.50 and \$317.50. Because $\beta_2 = 20$, the average price increase associated with a 1-unit increase in energy efficiency ratio x_2 while both Btu rating x_1 and number of settings x_3 remain fixed is \$20. Similar interpretations apply to the regression coefficients $\beta_1 = .025$ and $\beta_3 = 7.5$.

A Special Case: Polynomial Regression

Consider again the case of a single independent variable x, and suppose that a scatter plot of the n sample (x, y) pairs has the appearance of Figure 14.3. The simple linear regression model is clearly not appropriate, but it does look as though a parabola (quadratic function) with equation $y = \alpha + \beta_1 x + \beta_2 x^2$ would provide a very good, though not perfect, fit to the data for appropriately chosen values of α, β_1, and β_2. Just as the inclusion of the random deviation e in simple linear regression allowed an observation to deviate from the population regression line by a random amount, adding e to this quadratic function yields a probabilistic model in which an observation is allowed to fall above or below the parabola. The model equation is

$$y = \alpha + \beta_1 x + \beta_2 x^2 + e$$

FIGURE 14.3
A scatter plot that suggests the appropriateness of a quadratic probabilistic model

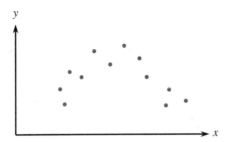

Let's rewrite the model equation by using x_1 to denote x and x_2 to denote x^2. The model equation then becomes

$$y = \alpha + \beta_1 x_1 + \beta_2 x_2 + e$$

This is a special case of the general multiple regression model with $k = 2$. You may wonder about the legitimacy of allowing one predictor variable to be a mathematical function of another predictor—here $x_2 = (x_1)^2$. However, there is absolutely nothing in the general multiple regression model that prevents this. *In the* *model $y = \alpha + \beta_1 x_1 + \cdots + \beta_k x_k + e$, it is permissible to have several predictors that are mathematical functions of other predictors.* For example, starting with the two independent variables x_1 and x_2, we could create a model with $k = 4$ predictors in which x_1 and x_2 themselves are the first two predictor variables and $x_3 = (x_1)^2$, $x_4 = x_1 x_2$ (we shortly discuss the consequences of using a predictor such as x_4). In particular, the general polynomial regression model begins with a single independent variable x and creates predictors $x_1 = x$, $x_2 = x^2$, $x_3 = x^3$, ..., $x_k = x^k$ for some specified value of k.

DEFINITION

The kth-degree polynomial regression model

$$y = \alpha + \beta_1 x + \beta_2 x^2 + \cdots + \beta_k x^k + e$$

is a special case of the general multiple regression model with $x_1 = x$, $x_2 = x^2$, ..., $x_k = x^k$. The **regression function** (mean value of y for fixed values of the predictors) is $\alpha + \beta_1 x + \cdots + \beta_k x^k$. The most important special case other than simple linear regression ($k = 1$) is the **quadratic regression model**

$$y = \alpha + \beta_1 x + \beta_2 x^2 + e$$

This model replaces the line of mean values $\alpha + \beta x$ in simple linear regression with a parabolic curve of mean values $\alpha + \beta_1 x + \beta_2 x^2$. If $\beta_2 > 0$, the curve opens upward, whereas if $\beta_2 < 0$, the curve opens downward (see Figure 14.4). A less frequently encountered special case is that of cubic regression, in which $k = 3$.

FIGURE 14.4
Graphs of polynomial regression functions
(a) quadratic regression model with $\beta_2 < 0$
(b) quadratic regression model with $\beta_2 > 0$
(c) cubic regression model with $\beta_3 > 0$

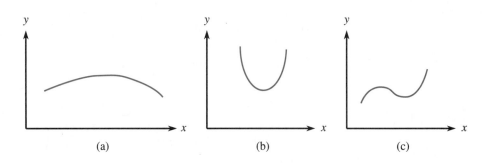

(a) (b) (c)

EXAMPLE 14.3

A variety of climatic variables have been examined by researchers in an attempt to gain an understanding of the mechanisms that govern rainfall runoff. The paper "The Applicability of Morton's and Penman's Evapotranspiration Estimates in Rainfall-Runoff Modeling" (*Water Resources Bull.* (1991):611–620) reported on a study in which data on $x = $ cloud cover and $y = $ daily sunshine (h) was gathered from a number of different locations. The authors used a cubic regression model to relate these variables. Suppose that the actual model equation for a particular location is

$$y = 11 - .400x - .250x^2 + .005x^3 + e$$

Then the regression function is

$$\left(\begin{array}{l}\text{mean daily sunshine} \\ \text{for given cloud cover } x\end{array}\right) = 11 - .400x - .250x^2 + .005x^3$$

For example

$$\left(\begin{array}{l}\text{mean daily sunshine} \\ \text{when cloud cover is } 4\end{array}\right) = 11 - (.400)(4) - (.250)(4)^2 + (.005)(4)^3$$
$$= 5.72$$

If $\sigma = 1$, it is quite likely that an observation on daily sunshine made when $x = 4$ would be between 3.72 and 7.72 h.

Notice that the interpretation of β_i previously given for the general multiple regression model cannot be applied in polynomial regression. This is because all predictors are functions of the single variable x, so $x_i = (x)^i$ cannot be increased by 1 unit without changing the values of all the other predictor variables as well. *In general, the interpretation of regression coefficients requires extra care when some predictor variables are mathematical functions of other variables.*

Interaction between Variables

Suppose that an industrial chemist is interested in the relationship between product yield (y) from a certain chemical reaction and two independent variables, $x_1 =$ reaction temperature and $x_2 =$ pressure at which the reaction is carried out. The chemist initially suggests that for temperature values between 80 and 110 in combination with pressure values ranging from 50 to 70, the relationship can be well described by the probabilistic model

$$y = 1200 + 15x_1 - 35x_2 + e$$

The regression function, which gives the mean y value for any specified values of x_1 and x_2, is then $1200 + 15x_1 - 35x_2$. Consider this mean y value for three different particular temperature values:

When $x_1 = 90$, mean y value $= 1200 + (15)(90) - 35x_2 = 2550 - 35x_2$.

When $x_1 = 95$, mean y value $= 2625 - 35x_2$.

When $x_1 = 100$, mean y value $= 2700 - 35x_2$.

Graphs of these three mean value functions (each a function only of pressure x_2, since the temperature value has been specified) are shown in Figure 14.5(a). Each

FIGURE 14.5
Graphs of mean value functions
(a) mean y values for the model $y = 1200 + 15x_1 - 35x_2 + e$
(b) mean y values for the model $y = -4500 + 75x_1 + 60x_2 - x_1x_2 + e$

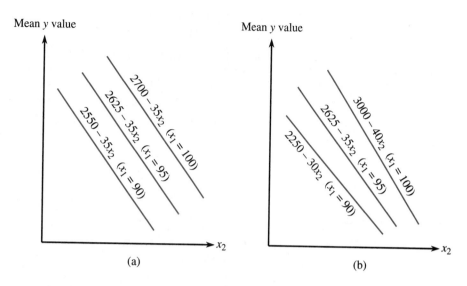

graph is a straight line, and the three lines are parallel, each one having slope -35. Because of this, the average change in yield when pressure x_2 is increased by 1 unit is -35 irrespective of the fixed temperature value.

Since chemical theory suggests that the decline in average yield when pressure x_2 increases should be more rapid for a high temperature than for a low temperature, the chemist now has reason to doubt the appropriateness of the proposed model. Rather than the lines being parallel, the line for temperature 100 should be steeper than the line for temperature 95, and that line in turn should be steeper than the one for $x_1 = 90$. A model that has this property includes, in addition to predictors x_1 and x_2 separately, a third predictor variable $x_3 = x_1x_2$. One such model is

$$y = -4500 + 75x_1 + 60x_2 - x_1x_2 + e$$

which has regression function $-4500 + 75x_1 + 60x_2 - x_1x_2$. Then

$$\binom{\text{mean } y \text{ value}}{\text{when } x_1 = 100} = -4500 + (75)(100) + 60x_2 - 100x_2$$
$$= 3000 - 40x_2$$

whereas

$$\binom{\text{mean } y \text{ value}}{\text{when } x_1 = 95} = 2625 - 35x_2$$

$$\binom{\text{mean } y \text{ value}}{\text{when } x_1 = 90} = 2250 - 30x_2$$

These are graphed in Figure 14.5(b), where it is clear that the three slopes are different. In fact, each different value of x_1 yields a different slope, so the average change in yield associated with a 1-unit increase in x_2 depends on the value of x_1. When this is the case, the two variables are said to *interact*.

> **DEFINITION**
>
> If the change in the mean y value associated with a one-unit increase in one independent variable depends on the value of a second independent variable, there is **interaction** between these two variables. When the variables are denoted by x_1 and x_2, such interaction can be modeled by including x_1x_2, the product of the variables that interact, as a predictor variable.

The general equation for a multiple regression model based on two independent variables x_1 and x_2 that also includes an interaction predictor is

$$y = \alpha + \beta_1 x_1 + \beta_2 x_2 + \beta_3 x_1 x_2 + e$$

This model has a geometric interpretation similar to the regression plane for the simpler model involving x_1 and x_2 alone ($\alpha + \beta_1 x_1 + \beta_2 x_2 + \beta_3 x_1 x_2$ specifies a surface, more complicated than a plane, such that observations fall above or below the surface by random amounts), but the details are beyond the scope of our discussion. The important point is that when x_1 and x_2 do interact, this model will usually give a much better fit to resulting sample data—and thus explain more variation in y—than would the no-interaction model. Failure to consider a model with interaction too often leads an investigator to conclude incorrectly that there is no strong relationship between y and a set of independent variables.

More than a single interaction predictor can be included in the model when more than two independent variables are available. If, for example, there are three independent variables x_1, x_2, and x_3, one possible model is

$$y = \alpha + \beta_1 x_1 + \beta_2 x_2 + \beta_3 x_3 + \beta_4 x_4 + \beta_5 x_5 + \beta_6 x_6 + e$$

where

$$x_4 = x_1 x_2 \qquad x_5 = x_1 x_3 \qquad x_6 = x_2 x_3$$

One could even include a three-way interaction predictor $x_7 = x_1 x_2 x_3$ (the product of all three independent variables), although in practice this is rarely done. In applied work, quadratic terms, such as x_1^2 and x_2^2, are often included to model a curved relationship between y and several independent variables. For example, a frequently used model involving just two independent variables x_1 and x_2 but $k = 5$ predictors is the *full quadratic model*

$$y = \alpha + \beta_1 x_1 + \beta_2 x_2 + \beta_3 x_1 x_2 + \beta_4 x_1^2 + \beta_5 x_2^2 + e$$

This model replaces the straight lines of Figure 14.5 with parabolas (each one is the graph of the regression function for different values of x_2 when x_1 has a fixed value). With four independent variables, one could examine a model containing four quadratic predictors and six two-way interaction predictor variables. Clearly, with just a few independent variables, one could examine a great many different multiple regression models. In the last section of this chapter we briefly discuss methods for selecting one model from a number of competing models.

Qualitative Predictor Variables

Up to this point we have explicitly considered the inclusion of only quantitative (numerical) predictor variables in a multiple regression model. Using a simple numerical coding, qualitative (categorical) variables can also be incorporated into a model. Let's focus first on a dichotomous variable, one with just two possible categories—male or female, U.S. or foreign manufacture, a house with or without a view, and so on. With any such variable we associate a numerical variable x whose possible values are 0 and 1, where 0 is identified with one category (for example, married) and $x = 1$ with the other possible category (not married). This 0-1 variable is often called a **dummy variable** or **indicator variable.**

EXAMPLE 14.4

The paper "Estimating Urban Travel Times: A Comparative Study" (*Transportation Research* (1980):173–175) considered relating the dependent variable $y = $ *travel time between locations* in a certain city and the independent variable *distance between locations* for two types of vehicles, passenger cars and trucks. Let

$$x_1 = \begin{cases} 1 & \text{if the vehicle is a truck} \\ 0 & \text{if the vehicle is a passenger car} \end{cases}$$

$x_2 = $ distance between locations

One possible multiple regression model is

$$y = \alpha + \beta_1 x_1 + \beta_2 x_2 + e$$

whereas a second possibility is a model with an interaction term,

$$y = \alpha + \beta_1 x_1 + \beta_2 x_2 + \beta_3 x_1 x_2 + e$$

The regression function for the no-interaction model is $\alpha + \beta_1 x_1 + \beta_2 x_2$, and for the interaction model it is $\alpha + \beta_1 x_1 + \beta_2 x_2 + \beta_3 x_3$, where $x_3 = x_1 x_2$. Considering separately the cases $x_1 = 0$ and $x_1 = 1$ yields

No interaction: $\begin{cases} \text{average time} = \alpha + \beta_2 x_2 & \text{when } x_1 = 0 \text{ (cars)} \\ \text{average time} = \alpha + \beta_1 + \beta_2 x_2 & \text{when } x_1 = 1 \text{ (trucks)} \end{cases}$

Interaction: $\begin{cases} \text{average time} = \alpha + \beta_2 x_2 & \text{when } x_1 = 0 \\ \text{average time} = \alpha + \beta_1 + (\beta_2 + \beta_3) x_2 & \text{when } x_1 = 1 \end{cases}$

For each model, the graph of the average time, when regarded as a function of distance, is a line for either type of vehicle (Figure 14.6). In the no-interaction model, the coefficient on x_2 is β_2 both when $x_1 = 0$ and when $x_1 = 1$, so the two lines are parallel, although their intercepts are different (unless $\beta_1 = 0$). With interaction, the lines not only have different intercepts but also different slopes (unless $\beta_3 = 0$). For this latter model, the change in average travel time when distance increases by one unit depends on which type of vehicle is involved—the

FIGURE 14.6
Regression functions for
models with one qualitative
variable (x_1) and one
quantitative variable (x_2)
(a) no interaction
(b) interaction

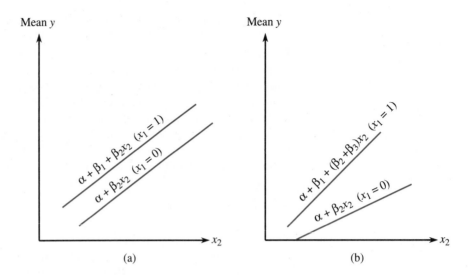

two variables *vehicle type* and *travel time* interact. Indeed, data collected by the authors of the paper suggested the presence of interaction.

You might think that the way to handle a three-category situation is to define a single numerical variable with coded values such as 0, 1, and 2 corresponding to the three categories. This is incorrect because it imposes an ordering on the categories that is not necessarily implied by the problem context. The correct approach to modeling a categorical variable with three categories is to define *two* different 0-1 variables.

EXAMPLE 14.5

The paper "The Effect of Ownership on the Organization Structure in Small Firms" (*Admin. Sci. Quarterly* (1984):232–237) considers three different management status categories—owner-successors, professional managers, and owner-founders—in relating degree of horizontal differentiation (y) to firm size. Let

$$x_1 = \begin{cases} 1 & \text{if the firm is managed by owner-successors} \\ 0 & \text{otherwise} \end{cases}$$

$$x_2 = \begin{cases} 1 & \text{if the firm is managed by professional managers} \\ 0 & \text{otherwise} \end{cases}$$

x_3 = firm size

Thus $x_1 = 1$, $x_2 = 0$ indicates owner-successors, $x_1 = 0$, $x_2 = 1$, professional managers, and $x_1 = x_2 = 0$, owner-founders ($x_1 = x_2 = 1$ is not allowed). The author suggests an interaction model of the form

$$y = \alpha + \beta_1 x_1 + \beta_2 x_2 + \beta_3 x_3 + \beta_4 x_1 x_3 + \beta_5 x_2 x_3 + e$$

This model allows the change in mean differentiation when size increases by 1 to be different for all three management status categories.

In general, incorporating a categorical variable with c possible categories into a regression model requires the use of $c - 1$ indicator variables. Thus even one such categorical variable can add many predictors to a model.

Nonlinear Multiple Regression Models

Many nonlinear relationships can be put in the form $y = \alpha + \beta_1 x_1 + \cdots + \beta_k x_k + e$ by transforming one or more of the variables. An appropriate transformation could be suggested by theory or by various plots of the data (for example, residual plots after fitting a particular model). There are also relationships that cannot be linearized by transformations, in which case more complicated methods of analysis must be used. A general discussion of nonlinear regression is beyond the scope of this text, but you can learn more by consulting one of the sources listed in the Chapter 4 References.

EXERCISES 14.1–14.13   SECTION 14.1

14.1   Explain the difference between a deterministic and a probabilistic model. Give an example of a dependent variable y and two or more independent variables that might be related to y deterministically. Give an example of a dependent variable y and two or more independent variables that might be related to y in a probabilistic fashion.

14.2   The paper "The Influence of Temperature and Sunshine on the Alpha-Acid Contents of Hops" (*Ag. Meteorology* (1974):375–382) used a multiple regression model to relate y = yield of hops to x_1 = mean temperature between date of coming into hop and date of picking and x_2 = mean percentage of sunshine during the same period. The model equation proposed is

$$y = 415.11 - 6.60x_1 - 4.50x_2 + e$$

a. Suppose that this equation does indeed describe the true relationship. What mean yield corresponds to a temperature of 20 and a sunshine percentage of 40?

b. What is the mean yield when the mean temperature and percentage of sunshine are 18.9 and 43, respectively?

14.3   The multiple regression model $y = \alpha + \beta_1 x_1 + \beta_2 x_2 + e$ can be used to describe the relationship between y = profit margin of savings and loan companies in a given year and x_1 = net revenues in that year and x_2 = number of branch offices. Based on data given in the paper "Entry and Profitability in a Rate-Free Savings and Loan Market" (*Quarterly Review of Econ. and Business* (1978):87–95) a reasonable model equation is

$$y = 1.565 + .237x_1 - .0002x_2 + e$$

a. How would you interpret the values of β_1 and β_2?

b. If the number of branch offices remains fixed and net revenue increases by 1, what is the average change in profit margin?

c. What would the mean profit margin be for a year in which net revenue is 4.0 and there are 6500 branch offices?

14.4   The paper "Readability of Liquid Crystal Displays: A Response Surface" (*Human Factors* (1983):185–190) used a multiple regression model with four independent variables, where

y = error percentage for subjects reading a four-digit liquid crystal display

x_1 = level of backlight (ranging from 0 to 122 cd/m^2)

x_2 = character subtense (ranging from .025° to 1.34°)

x_3 = viewing angle (ranging from 0° to 60°)

x_4 = level of ambient light (ranging from 20 to 1500 lx)

The model equation suggested in the paper is

$$y = 1.52 + .02x_1 - 1.40x_2 + .02x_3 - .0006x_4 + e$$

a. Assume that this is the correct equation. What is the mean value of y when $x_1 = 10$, $x_2 = .5$, $x_3 = 50$, and $x_4 = 100$?

b. What mean error percentage is associated with a backlight level of 20, character subtense of .5, viewing angle of 10, and ambient light level of 30?

14.5   The multiple regression model

$$y = .69 + 4.70x_1 + .00041x_2 - .72x_3 + .023x_4 + e$$

where

y = stock purchase tender premium (as a percentage of closing market price one week prior to offer date)

x_1 = fee per share (as a percentage of price)

x_2 = percentage of shares sought

x_3 = relative change in Dow Jones industrial average

x_4 = volume of shares traded (as a percentage of those outstanding)

is based on data appearing in the paper "Factors Influencing the Pricing of Stock Repurchase Tenders" (*Quarterly Rev. of Econ. and Business* (1978):31–39).

a. What is the mean stock tender premium when $x_1 = 2$, $x_2 = .1$, $x_3 = 1.2$, and $x_4 = 6$?

b. If the variables x_1, x_3, and x_4 are held fixed, would the mean tender premium increase or decrease as the percentage of shares sought increases? Explain.

14.6   The article "Pulp Brightness Reversion: Influence of Residual Lignin on the Brightness Reversion of Bleached Sulfite and Kraft Pulps" (*TAPPI* (1964):653–662) proposed a quadratic regression model to describe the relationship between

x = degree of delignification during the processing of wood pulp for paper and y = total chlorine content. Suppose that the actual model is

$$y = 220 + 75x - 4x^2 + e$$

a. Graph the regression function $220 + 75x - 4x^2$ over x values ranging between 2 and 12 (substitute $x = 2, 4, 6, 8, 10,$ and 12 to find points on the graph, and connect them with a smooth curve).

b. Would mean chlorine content be higher for a degree of delignification value of 8 or 10?

c. What is the change in mean chlorine content when the degree of delignification increases from 8 to 9? From 9 to 10?

14.7 The relationship between yield of maize, date of planting, and planting density was investigated in the article "Development of a Model for Use in Maize Replant Decisions" (*Agronomy J.* (1980):459–464). Letting

y = percent maize yield

x_1 = planting date (days after April 20)

x_2 = planting density (plants/ha),

the regression model with both quadratic terms ($y = \alpha + \beta_1 x_1 + \beta_2 x_2 + \beta_3 x_3 + \beta_4 x_4 + e$, where $x_3 = x_1^2$ and $x_4 = x_2^2$) provides a good description of the relationship between y and the independent variables.

a. If $\alpha = 21.09$, $\beta_1 = .653$, $\beta_2 = .0022$, $\beta_3 = -.0206$, and $\beta_4 = .00004$, write out the regression function.

b. Use the regression function in (a) to determine the mean yield for a plot planted on May 6 with a density of 41,180 plants/ha.

c. Would the mean yield be higher for a planting date of May 6 or May 22 (for the same density)?

14.8 Consider a regression analysis with two independent variables.

a. Explain what is meant by the statement "there is no interaction between the independent variables."

b. Explain what is accomplished by including an interaction term in a regression model.

14.9 Suppose that the variables y, x_1, and x_2 are related by the regression model

$$y = 1.8 + .1x_1 + .8x_2 + e$$

Then

$$\text{mean } y \text{ value} = 1.8 + .1x_1 + .8x_2$$

a. Construct a graph (similar to that of Figure 14.5) showing the relationship between y and x_2 for fixed values 10, 20, and 30 of x_1.

b. Construct a graph depicting the relationship between y and x_1 for fixed values 50, 55, and 60 of x_2.

c. What aspect of the graphs in (a) and (b) can be attributed to the lack of an interaction between x_1 and x_2?

14.10 Suppose the interaction term $.03x_3$, where $x_3 = x_1 x_2$, is added to the regression equation in Exercise 14.9. Using this new model, construct the graphs described in 14.9(a) and 14.9(b). How do they differ from those obtained in Exercise 14.9?

14.11   Consider a regression analysis with three independent variables x_1, x_2, and x_3. Write out the following regression models.

a. The model that includes all independent variables but no quadratic or interaction terms

b. The model that includes all independent variables and all quadratic terms

c. All models that include all independent variables, no quadratic terms, and exactly one interaction term

d. The model that includes all independent variables, all quadratic terms, and all interaction terms

14.12   The paper "The Value and the Limitations of High-Speed Turbo-Exhausters for the Removal of Tar-Fog from Carburetted Water-Gas" (*Soc. Chem. Industry J.* (1946):166–168) presented data on y = tar content (grains/100 ft^3) of a gas stream as a function of x_1 = rotor speed (rev/min) and x_2 = gas inlet temperature ($^\circ$ F). A regression model using x_1, x_2, $x_3 = x_2^2$, and $x_4 = x_1 x_2$ was suggested:

$$\text{mean } y \text{ value} = 86.8 - .123x_1 + 5.09x_2 - .0709x_3 + .001x_4$$

a. According to this model, what is the mean y value if $x_1 = 3200$ and $x_2 = 57$?

b. For this particular model, does it make sense to interpret the value of any individual β_i (β_1, β_2, β_3, or β_4) in the way we have previously suggested? Explain.

14.13   How many dummy variables would be needed to incorporate a nonnumerical variable with four categories? Suppose that you wanted to incorporate size class of car with four categories (subcompact, compact, midsize, and luxury) into a regression equation where y = gas mileage, x_1 = age of car, and x_2 = engine size. Define the necessary dummy variables and write out the complete model equation.

14.2   Fitting a Model and Assessing Its Utility

In Section 14.1 we discussed and contrasted multiple regression models containing several different types of predictors. Let's now suppose that a particular set of k predictor variables x_1, x_2, . . . , x_k has been selected for inclusion in the model

$$y = \alpha + \beta_1 x_1 + \beta_2 x_2 + \cdots + \beta_k x_k + e$$

It is then necessary to estimate the model coefficients α, β_1, . . . , β_k and the regression function $\alpha + \beta_1 x_1 + \cdots + \beta_k x_k$ (mean y value for specified values of the predictors), assess the model's utility, and perhaps use the estimated model to make further inferences. All this, of course, requires sample data. As before, n denotes the number of observations in the sample. With just one predictor variable, the sample consisted of n (x, y) pairs. Now each observation consists of $k + 1$ numbers: a value of x_1, a value of x_2, . . . , a value of x_k, and the associated value of y. The n observations are assumed to have been selected independently of one another.

EXAMPLE 14.6

(*Example 14.1 continued*) Example 14.1 cited an article that reported on a regression analysis with dependent variable y = phosphate adsorption index of a sediment and $k = 2$ predictor variables, x_1 = amount of extractable iron, and x_2 = amount of extractable aluminum. The analysis was based on the following sample of $n = 13$ observations, each one consisting of a triple (x_1, x_2, y):

Observation	x_1 = extractable iron	x_2 = extractable aluminum	y = adsorption index
1	61	13	4
2	175	21	18
3	111	24	14
4	124	23	18
5	130	64	26
6	173	38	26
7	169	33	21
8	169	61	30
9	160	39	28
10	244	71	36
11	257	112	65
12	333	88	62
13	199	54	40

The principle of least squares is used as in simple linear regression to estimate the coefficients $\alpha, \beta_1, \ldots, \beta_k$. For specified estimates $a, b_1, \ldots, b_k$,

$$y - (a + b_1x_1 + b_2x_2 + \cdots + b_kx_k)$$

is the deviation between the observed y value for a particular observation and the prediction of this value using the estimated regression function $a + b_1x_1 + \cdots + b_kx_k$. For example, the first observation in the data set of Example 14.6 is $(x_1, x_2, y) = (61, 13, 4)$. The resulting deviation between observed and predicted y values is

$$4 - [a + b_1(61) + b_2(13)]$$

Deviations corresponding to other observations are expressed in a similar manner. The principle of least squares then says to use as estimates of α, β_1, and β_2 the values of a, b_1, and b_2 that minimize the sum of these squared deviations.

DEFINITION

According to the principle of least squares, the fit of a particular estimated regression function $a + b_1x_1 + \cdots + b_kx_k$ to the observed data is measured by the sum of squared deviations between the observed y values and the y values predicted by the estimated function:

$$\Sigma[y - (a + b_1x_1 + \cdots + b_kx_k)]^2$$

The **least squares estimates** of $\alpha, \beta_1, \ldots, \beta_k$ are those values of $a, b_1, \ldots, b_k$ that make this sum of squared deviations as small as possible.

The least squares estimates for a given data set are obtained by solving a system of $k + 1$ equations in the $k + 1$ unknowns $a, b_1, \ldots, b_k$ (called the *normal equations*). In the case $k = 1$, simple linear regression, there are only two equations, and we gave their general solution—the expressions for b and a—in Chapter 4. For $k \geq 2$, it is not as easy to write general expressions for the estimates without using advanced mathematical methods. Fortunately, the computer saves us! Formulas for the estimates have been programmed into all the commonly used statistical computer packages.

EXAMPLE 14.7

Figure 14.7 displays MINITAB output from a regression command requesting that the model $y = \alpha + \beta_1 x_1 + \beta_2 x_2 + e$ be fit to the phosphate adsorption data of Example 14.6 (we named the dependent variable HPO, an abbreviation for the chlorate H_2PO_4 (dihydrogen phosphate), and the two predictor variables x_1 and x_2

FIGURE 14.7
MINITAB output for the regression analysis of Example 14.7

THE REGRESSION EQUATION is
HPO = -7.35 + 0.113 FE + 0.349 AL

Predictor	Coef	Stdev	t-ratio	p
Constant	-7.351	3.485	-2.11	0.061
FE	0.11273	0.02969	3.80	0.004
AL	0.34900	0.07131	4.89	0.000

s = 4.379   R-sq = 94.8%   R-sq(adj) = 93.8%

Analysis of Variance

SOURCE	DF	SS	MS	F	p
Regression	2	3529.9	1765.0	92.03	0.000
Error	10	191.8	19.2		
Total	12	3721.7			

Obs.	FE	HPO	Fit	Stdev.Fit	Residual	St.Resid
1	61	4.00	4.06	2.43	-0.06	-0.02
2	175	18.00	19.71	2.31	-1.71	-0.46
3	111	14.00	13.54	1.72	0.46	0.11
4	124	18.00	14.66	1.67	3.34	0.83
5	130	26.00	29.64	2.62	-3.64	-1.04
6	173	26.00	25.41	1.41	0.59	0.14
7	169	21.00	23.22	1.56	-2.22	-0.54
8	169	30.00	32.99	1.60	-2.99	-0.73
9	160	28.00	24.30	1.30	3.70	0.89
10	244	36.00	44.94	1.71	-8.94	-2.22R
11	257	65.00	60.71	3.20	4.29	1.44
12	333	62.00	60.90	3.19	1.10	0.37
13	199	40.00	33.93	1.29	6.07	1.45

R denotes an obs. with a large st. resid.

Fit	Stdev.Fit	95% C.I.	95% P.I.
23.52	1.31	(20.60, 26.44)	(13.33, 33.71)

were named FE and AL, abbreviations for iron and aluminum, respectively). In the remainder of this section and in the next one, we discuss many aspects of this output. For now, focus on the column labeled Coef in the table near the top of the figure. The three numbers in this column are the estimated model coefficients: $a = -7.351$ (the estimate of the constant term α), $b_1 = .11273$ (the estimate of the coefficient β_1), and $b_2 = .34900$ (the estimate of the coefficient β_2). Thus the estimated regression function is

$$\left(\begin{array}{c} \text{estimated mean value of } y \\ \text{for specified } x_1 \text{ and } x_2 \text{ values} \end{array}\right) = -7.351 + .11273x_1 + .34900x_2$$

This equation is given (with coefficients rounded slightly) using the named variables at the very top of the MINITAB output.

EXAMPLE 14.8

In Section 14.1 we pointed out that the quadratic regression model $y = \alpha + \beta_1 x + \beta_2 x^2 + e$ based on a single independent variable x can be regarded as a special case of the general additive multiple regression model with $k = 2$ and predictor variables $x_1 = x$ and $x_2 = x^2$. The accompanying data appeared in the paper "Determination of Biological Maturity and Effect of Harvesting and Drying Conditions on Milling Quality of Paddy" (*J. of Ag. Engr. Research* (1975):353–361). The dependent variable y is yield (kg/ha) of paddy, a grain farmed in India, and x is the number of days after flowering at which harvesting took place.

	$x_1 = x$	$x_2 = x^2$	y		$x_1 = x$	$x_2 = x^2$	y
1	16	256	2508	9	32	1024	3823
2	18	324	2518	10	34	1156	3646
3	20	400	3304	11	36	1296	3708
4	22	484	3423	12	38	1444	3333
5	24	576	3057	13	40	1600	3517
6	26	676	3190	14	42	1764	3241
7	28	784	3500	15	44	1936	3103
8	30	900	3883	16	46	2116	2776

A scatter plot of the 16 (x, y) observations given in Figure 14.8 shows curvature resembling the downward-opening parabola of Figure 14.4(a) (Section 14.1). On the basis of this plot, we agreed with the paper's authors that a quadratic regression model was appropriate for relating y to x. Figure 14.8 also gives MINITAB output resulting from first entering x and y values, then requesting that the x^2 values be computed, and finally using a regression command with $x_1 = x$ and $x_2 = x^2$ as the two predictor variables. The resulting estimated model coefficients are $a = -1070.4$, $b_1 = 293.48$ (the estimated coefficient on the linear term), and $b_2 = -4.5358$ (the estimated coefficient on the quadratic term).

FIGURE 14.8
MINITAB output for the data
and model of Example 14.8

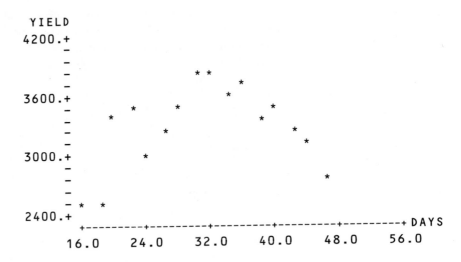

THE REGRESSION EQUATION is
YIELD = −1070 + 293 DAYS − 4.54 DAYSSQD

Predictor	Coef	Stdev	t-ratio	p
Constant	−1070.4	617.3	−1.73	0.107
DAYS	293.48	42.18	6.96	0.000
DAYSSQD	−4.5358	0.6744	−6.73	0.000

s = 203.9   R-sq = 79.4%   R-sq(adj) = 76.2%

Analysis of Variance

SOURCE	DF	SS	MS	F	p
Regression	2	2084779	1042389	25.08	0.000
Error	13	540388	41568		
Total	15	2625167			

SOURCE	DF	SEQ SS
DAYS	1	204526
DAYSSQD	1	1880253

Obs.	DAYS	YIELD	Fit	Stdev.Fit	Residual	St.Resid
1	16.0	2508.0	2464.2	135.6	43.8	0.29
2	18.0	2518.0	2742.7	104.8	−224.7	−1.28
3	20.0	3304.0	2984.9	83.0	319.1	1.71
4	22.0	3423.0	3190.9	71.3	232.1	1.22
5	24.0	3057.0	3360.6	68.4	−303.6	−1.58
6	26.0	3190.0	3494.0	70.7	−304.0	−1.59
7	28.0	3500.0	3591.1	74.2	−91.1	−0.48
8	30.0	3883.0	3651.9	76.4	231.1	1.22
9	32.0	3823.0	3676.4	76.4	146.6	0.78
10	34.0	3646.0	3664.6	74.2	−18.6	−0.10
11	36.0	3708.0	3616.6	70.7	91.4	0.48
12	38.0	3333.0	3532.3	68.4	−199.3	−1.04
13	40.0	3517.0	3411.6	71.3	105.4	0.55

(continued)

Obs.	DAYS	YIELD	Fit	Stdev.Fit	Residual	St.Resid
14	42.0	3241.0	3254.7	83.0	−13.7	−0.07
15	44.0	3103.0	3061.5	104.8	41.5	0.24
16	46.0	2776.0	2832.1	135.6	−56.1	−0.37

Fit	Stdev.Fit	95% C.I.	95% P.I.
3431.8	69.2	(3282.2, 3581.4)	(2966.5, 3897.1)

This gives as the equation of the estimated regression function

$$\left(\begin{array}{c}\text{estimated mean } y \text{ value}\\\text{for a specified value of } x\end{array}\right) = -1070.4 + 293.48x - 4.5358x^2$$

The negative value of b_2 implies that a graph of the estimated regression function opens downward.

Is the Model Useful?

The utility of an estimated model can be assessed by examining the extent to which predicted y values based on the estimated regression function are close to the y values actually observed.

DEFINITION

The first predicted value $\hat{y}_1$ is obtained by taking the values of the predictor variables $x_1, x_2, \ldots, x_k$ for the first sample observation and substituting these values into the estimated regression function. Doing this successively for the remaining observations yields the **predicted values** $\hat{y}_2, \ldots, \hat{y}_n$. The **residuals** are then the differences $y_1 - \hat{y}_1, y_2 - \hat{y}_2, \ldots, y_n - \hat{y}_n$ between the observed and predicted y values.

The predicted values and residuals are defined here exactly as they were in simple linear regression, but computation of the $\hat{y}$'s is more tedious because there is more than one predictor. Fortunately, the $\hat{y}$'s and $y - \hat{y}$'s are automatically computed and displayed on output by all good statistical computer packages. Consider Figure 14.7, which contains MINITAB output for the phosphate adsorption data. Since the first y observation, $y_1 = 4$, was made with $x_1 = 61$ and $x_2 = 13$, the first predicted value is

$$\hat{y}_1 = -7.351 + .11273(61) + .34900(13) \approx 4.06$$

as given in the output. The first residual is then

$$y_1 - \hat{y}_1 = 4 - 4.06 = -.06$$

The other predicted values and residuals are computed in a similar fashion. The sum of residuals from a least squares fit should, except for rounding effects, be zero. The sum in Example 14.7 is $-.01$.

As in simple linear regression, the sum of squared residuals is the basis for several important summary quantities that are indicative of a model's utility.

DEFINITION

The **residual (or error) sum of squares, SSResid,** and **total sum of squares, SSTo,** are given by

$$\text{SSResid} = \Sigma(y - \hat{y})^2 \qquad \text{SSTo} = \Sigma(y - \bar{y})^2$$

where $\bar{y}$ is the mean of the y observations in the sample. The number of degrees of freedom associated with SSResid is $n - (k + 1)$, because $k + 1$ df are lost in estimating the $k + 1$ coefficients $\alpha, \beta_1, \ldots, \beta_k$. An estimate of the random deviation variance σ^2 is given by

$$s_e^2 = \frac{\text{SSResid}}{n - (k + 1)}$$

and s_e is the estimate of σ. The **coefficient of multiple determination, R^2,** interpreted as the proportion of variation in observed y values that is explained by the fitted model, is

$$R^2 = 1 - \frac{\text{SSResid}}{\text{SSTo}}$$

EXAMPLE 14.9

(*Example 14.7 continued*) Looking again at Example 14.7, which contains MINITAB output for the adsorption data fit by a two-predictor model, residual sum of squares is

$$\text{SSResid} = (-.06)^2 + (-1.71)^2 + (.46)^2 + \cdots + (6.07)^2 = 191.8337$$

This value also appears in rounded form in the Error row and SS column of the table headed Analysis of Variance. The associated number of degrees of freedom is $n - (k + 1) = 13 - (2 + 1) = 10$, which appears in the DF column just to the left of SSResid. The sample average y value is $\bar{y} = 29.85$, so

$$\begin{aligned} \text{SSTo} &= \Sigma(y - \bar{y})^2 \\ &= (4 - 29.85)^2 + (18 - 29.85)^2 + \cdots + (40 - 29.85)^2 \\ &= 3721.6923 \end{aligned}$$

This value, rounded to one decimal place, appears in the Total row and SS column of the Analysis of Variance table just under the value of SSResid. The values of s_e^2, s_e, and R^2 are then

$$s_e^2 = \frac{\text{SSResid}}{n - (k + 1)} = \frac{191.83}{10} = 19.18 \approx 19.2$$

(in the MS column of the MINITAB output)

$$s_e = \sqrt{s_e^2} = \sqrt{19.18} = 4.379$$

($s = 4.379$ appears just above the Analysis of Variance table)

$$R^2 = 1 - \frac{\text{SSResid}}{\text{SSTo}} = 1 - \frac{191.83}{3721.69} = 1 - .052 = .948$$

Thus the percentage of variation explained is $100R^2 = 94.8\%$, which appears on the output as R-sq $= 94.8\%$. The values of R^2 and s_e suggest that the chosen model has been very successful in relating y to the predictors.

Generally speaking, a desirable model is one that results in both a large R^2 value and a small s_e value. However, there is a catch: These two conditions can be achieved by fitting a model that contains a large number of predictors. Such a model may be successful in explaining y variation, but it almost always specifies a relationship that is unrealistic and difficult to interpret. What we really want is a simple model, one with relatively few predictors whose roles are easily interpreted, which also does a good job of explaining variation in y.

All statistical computer packages include R^2 and s_e in their output, and most give SSResid also. In addition, some packages compute the quantity called *adjusted* R^2, which involves a downward adjustment of R^2. If a large R^2 has been achieved through using just a few model predictors, adjusted R^2 will differ little from R^2. However, the adjustment can be substantial when either a great many predictors (relative to the number of observations) have been used or when R^2 itself is small to moderate (which could happen even when there is no relationship between y and the predictors). In Example 14.9, adjusted $R^2 = .938$, not much less than R^2, since the model included only two predictor variables.

F Distributions

The model utility test in simple linear regression was based on the fact that when $H_0: \beta = 0$ is true, the test statistic $t = b/s_b$ has a t distribution. The model utility test for multiple regression employs a new type of probability distribution called an F distribution, so we first digress briefly to describe some general properties of F distributions.

An F distribution always arises in connection with a ratio in which the numerator involves one sum of squares and the denominator involves a second sum of squares. Each sum of squares has associated with it a specified number of degrees of freedom, so a particular F distribution is determined by fixing values of numerator df and denominator df. There is a different F distribution for each different numerator df–denominator df combination (each df must be a whole number). For

FIGURE 14.9
F distribution curves and
critical values

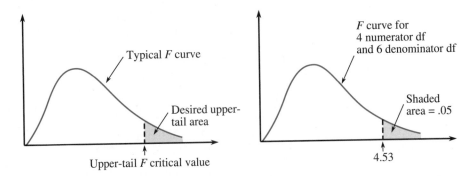

example, there is an *F* distribution based on 4 numerator df and 12 denominator df, another *F* distribution based on 3 numerator df and 20 denominator df, and so on. A typical *F* curve for fixed numerator and denominator df appears in Figure 14.9.

All *F* tests presented in this book are upper-tailed, so associated rejection regions require only upper-tail *F* critical values, those values that capture specified areas in the upper tail of the appropriate *F* curves. A particular *F* critical value depends on the desired tail area *and* on both numerator and denominator df. A tabulation of *F* critical values therefore consumes much more space than was the case for *t* critical values, which depended on only a single number of degrees of freedom. Appendix Table X(a) gives the critical values for upper tail area .05 and Appendix Table X(b) gives those for tail area .01. Different columns of the tables are identified with different numerator df and different rows are associated with different denominator df. For example, the .05 critical value for the *F* distribution with 4 numerator df and 6 denominator df is found in the column of Table X labeled 4 and the row labeled 6 to be 4.53. The .05 critical value for 6 numerator and 4 denominator df is 6.16 (so don't accidentally interchange numerator and denominator df!).

The *F* Test for Model Utility

In the simple linear model with regression function $\alpha + \beta x$, if $\beta = 0$, there is no useful linear relationship between *y* and the single predictor variable *x*. Similarly, if all *k* coefficients $\beta_1, \beta_2, \ldots, \beta_k$ are zero in the general *k*-predictor multiple regression model, there is no useful linear relationship between *y* and *any* of the predictor variables $x_1, x_2, \ldots, x_k$ included in the model. Before using an estimated model to make further inferences (for example, predictions and estimates of mean values), it is desirable to confirm the model's utility through a formal test procedure.

Recall that SSTo is a measure of total variation in the sample data and that SSResid measures the amount of total variation that has not been explained by the fitted model. The difference between total and error sums of squares is itself a sum of squares, called **regression sum of squares** and denoted by SSRegr:

$$\text{SSRegr} = \text{SSTo} - \text{SSResid}$$

SSRegr is interpreted as the amount of total variation that *has* been explained by the model. Intuitively, the model should be judged useful if SSRegr is large relative to SSResid, and this is achieved by using a small number of predictors relative to the sample size. The number of degrees of freedom associated with SSRegr is k, the number of model predictors, and df for SSResid is $n - (k + 1)$. The model utility F test is based on the following distributional result.

When all k β_i's are zero in the model $y = \alpha + \beta_1 x_1 + \cdots + \beta_k x_k + e$, the statistic

$$F = \frac{\text{SSRegr}/k}{\text{SSResid}/[n - (k + 1)]}$$

has an F probability distribution based on k numerator df and $n - (k + 1)$ denominator df.

The value of F tends to be larger when at least one β_i is not zero than when all the β_i's are zero, since more variation is typically explained by the model in the former case than in the latter. An F statistic value far out in the upper tail of the associated F distribution can be more plausibly attributed to at least one nonzero β_i than to something very unusual having occurred when all β_i's are zero. This is why the model utility F test is upper-tailed.

THE *F* TEST FOR UTILITY OF THE MODEL
$y = \alpha + \beta_1 x_1 + \cdots + \beta_k x_k + e$

Null hypothesis:
H_0: $\beta_1 = \beta_2 = \cdots = \beta_k = 0$. (There is no useful linear relationship between y and *any* of the predictors.)

Alternative hypothesis:
H_a: At least one among $\beta_1, \ldots, \beta_k$ is not zero. (There is a useful linear relationship between y and *at least one* of the predictors.)

Test statistic:

$$F = \frac{\text{SSRegr}/k}{\text{SSResid}/[n - (k + 1)]}$$

where SSRegr = SSTo − SSResid. An equivalent formula is

$$F = \frac{R^2/k}{(1 - R^2)/[n - (k + 1)]}$$

Rejection region:
$F > F$ critical value. The F critical value is based on k numerator df and $n - (k + 1)$ denominator df, respectively. Table X(a) gives critical values corresponding to level of significance .05 and Table X(b) gives level .01 critical values.

The null hypothesis is the claim that the model is not useful. Unless H_0 can be rejected at a small level of significance, the model has not demonstrated its utility, in which case the investigator must search further for a model that can be judged useful. The alternative formula for F allows the test to be carried out when only R^2, k, and n are available, as is frequently the case in published articles.

EXAMPLE 14.10

The model fit to the phosphate adsorption data introduced in Example 14.7 involved $k = 2$ predictors. Let's carry out the model utility test at level .05 using information from the MINITAB output displayed in Figure 14.7.

1. The model is $y = \alpha + \beta_1 x_1 + \beta_2 x_2 + e$, where y = phosphate adsorption, x_1 = extractable Fe, and x_2 = extractable Al.

2. $H_0: \beta_1 = \beta_2 = 0$

3. H_a: At least one of the two β_i's is not zero.

4. Test statistic:

$$F = \frac{\text{SSRegr}/k}{\text{SSResid}/[n - (k + 1)]}$$

5. Rejection region: $F > F$ critical value. With numerator df $= k = 2$ and denominator df $= n - (k + 1) = 13 - 3 = 10$, Table X(a) gives the level .05 critical value as 4.10. Thus H_0 will be rejected if $F > 4.10$.

6. Directly from the Analysis of Variance table in Figure 14.7, the SS column gives SSRegr $= 3529.9$ and SSResid $= 191.8$. Thus

$$F = \frac{3529.9/2}{191.8/10} = \frac{1764.95}{19.18} = 92.02 \quad \text{(92.03 in Figure 14.7)}$$

7. Since $92.02 > 4.10$, H_0 can be decisively rejected. The utility of the fitted model has been confirmed. This conclusion also follows from the P-value .000 given to the right of F on MINITAB output.

EXAMPLE 14.11

A multiple regression analysis presented in the paper "The Politics of Bureaucratic Discretion: Educational Access as an Urban Service" (*Amer. J. Political Sci.* (1991):155–177) considered a model in which the dependent variable was

y = percent of school board members in a school district who are black

and the predictors were

x_1 = black-to-white income ratio in the district

x_2 = percent whites in the district below the poverty line

x_3 = indicator for whether or not the district was in the south

x_4 = percent blacks in the district with high-school education

x_5 = black population percentage in the district

Summary quantities included $n = 140$ and $R^2 = .749$. Let's carry out the model utility test at the .01 significance level.

1. The fitted model was $y = \alpha + \beta_1 x_1 + \cdots + \beta_5 x_5 + e$

2. H_0: $\beta_1 = \beta_2 = \beta_3 = \beta_4 = \beta_5 = 0$

3. H_a: at least one among $\beta_1, \ldots, \beta_5$ is not zero

4. Test statistic:

$$F = \frac{R^2/k}{(1 - R^2)/[n - (k + 1)]}$$

5. Rejection region: $F > F$ critical value. With numerator df $= k = 5$ and denominator df $= 140 - (5 + 1) = 134$, Table X(b) gives the level .01 F critical value as approximately 3.15.

6. The test statistic value is

$$F = \frac{.749/5}{.251/134} = 80.0$$

7. Since $80.0 > 3.15$, H_0 is rejected. There appears to be a useful linear relationship between y and at least one of the five predictors.

In the next section we presume that a model has been judged useful by the F test and then show how the estimated coefficients and regression function can be used to draw further conclusions. However, you should realize that in many applications, there will be more than one model whose utility could be confirmed by the F test. Suppose, for example, that data has been collected on six independent variables $x_1, x_2, \ldots, x_6$. Then a model with all six of these as predictors might be judged useful, another useful model might have only x_1, x_3, x_5, and x_6 as predictors, and yet another useful model might incorporate the six predictors $x_1, x_4, x_6, x_7 = x_1 x_4$, $x_8 = x_1^2$, and $x_9 = x_6^2$. In the last section of this chapter we briefly consider strategies for selecting a model.

EXERCISES 14.14–14.28   SECTION 14.2

14.14   The paper "The Influence of Mount St. Helens Ash on Wheat Growth and Phosphorous, Sulfur, Calcium, and Magnesium Uptake" (*J. Envir. Quality* (1984):91–96) used a quadratic regression model ($y = \alpha + \beta_1 x_1 + \beta_2 x_2 + e$, where $x_1 = x$ and $x_2 = x^2$) to describe the relationship between y = biomass production of wheat (g/pot) and x = percent volcanic ash in the soil. Data from a greenhouse experiment in which x ranged between 0 and 75 was used to estimate α, β_1, and β_2. The resulting least squares estimates a, b_1, and b_2 were .067, .054, and $-.00052$, respectively.

a. Write out the estimated regression equation.

b. What would you predict biomass to be when the percent of volcanic ash is 20? When it is 40?

c. Graph the parabola $\hat{y}$ = .067 + .054x_1 $-$ .00052x_2. Use values of x ranging between 0 and 75. Based on this graph, at approximately what point does an increasing percent of volcanic ash begin to have a detrimental effect on average biomass?

14.15 In order to predict the demand for imports in Jamaica, the coefficients α, β_1, and β_2 in a multiple regression model with

y = import volume

x_1 = expenditures on personal consumption

x_2 = price of import/domestic price

were estimated using 19 years of data. The resulting estimated regression equation, $\hat{y}$ = -58.9 + .20x_1 $-$ .10x_2, appeared in the article "Devaluation and the Balance of Payments Adjustment in a Developing Economy: An Analysis Relating to Jamaica" (*Appl. Econ.* (1981):151–165).

a. How would you interpret the value b_1 = .20?

b. If personal consumption and import prices remain stable, would the predicted import volume increase or decrease with a reduction in domestic price?

c. The paper reported that the value of R^2 associated with this regression equation was .96. How would you interpret this value?

14.16 When coastal power stations take in large quantities of cooling water, it is inevitable that a number of fish are drawn in with the water. Various methods have been designed to screen out the fish. The paper "Multiple Regression Analysis for Forecasting Critical Fish Influxes at Power Station Intakes" (*J. Appl. Ecol.* (1983):33–42) examined intake fish catch at an English power plant and several other variables thought to affect fish intake:

y = fish intake (number of fish)

x_1 = water temperature (°C)

x_2 = number of pumps running

x_3 = sea state (taking values 0, 1, 2, or 3)

x_4 = speed (knots)

Part of the data given in the paper was used to obtain the estimated regression equation

$$\hat{y} = 92 - 2.18x_1 - 19.20x_2 - 9.38x_3 + 2.32x_4 \qquad \text{(based on } n = 26)$$

a. SSRegr = 1486.9 and SSResid = 2230.2 were also calculated. Use this information to carry out the model utility test with a significance level of .05.

b. What information (in addition to the result of the model utility test in (a)) would you need in order to decide whether the estimated regression equation should be used to predict fish catch? Explain how you would use the requested information.

14.17 The paper "Microbial Ecology of the Soils of the Indian Desert" (*Ag. Ecosystems and Environ.* (1983):361–369) reported data on characteristics of Indian desert soils. The following variables were included: y = soil pH, x_1 = electrical conductivity (mho/cm), x_2 = organic carbon (%), x_3 = nitrogen (%), x_4 = phosphorus (ppm), and x_5 = annual rainfall (mm). The n = 10 observations were used to compute SSRegr = .170368 and SSResid = .213632. Use the model utility test and a significance level of .05 to decide if the independent variables as a group provide any information that is useful for predicting soil pH.

14.18 The article "The Undrained Strength of Some Thawed Permafrost Soils" (*Canad. Geotech. J.* (1979):420–427) contained the accompanying data on y = shear strength of sandy soil (kPa), x_1 = depth (m), and x_2 = water content (%). The predicted values and residuals were computed using the estimated regression equation $\hat{y} = -151.36 - 16.22x_1 + 13.48x_2 + .094x_3 - .253x_4 + .492x_5$, where $x_3 = x_1^2$, $x_4 = x_2^2$, and $x_5 = x_1x_2$.

y	x_1	x_2	Predicted y	Residual
14.7	8.9	31.5	23.35	− 8.65
48.0	36.6	27.0	46.38	1.62
25.6	36.8	25.9	27.13	− 1.53
10.0	6.1	39.1	10.99	− .99
16.0	6.9	39.2	14.10	1.90
16.8	6.9	38.3	16.54	.26
20.7	7.3	33.9	23.34	− 2.64
38.8	8.4	33.8	25.43	13.37
16.9	6.5	27.9	15.63	1.27
27.0	8.0	33.1	24.29	2.71
16.0	4.5	26.3	15.36	.64
24.9	9.9	37.8	29.61	− 4.71
7.3	2.9	34.6	15.38	− 8.08
12.8	2.0	36.4	7.96	4.84

a. Use the given information to compute SSResid, SSTo, and SSRegr.

b. Calculate R^2 for this regression model. How would you interpret this value?

c. Use the value of R^2 from (b) and a .05 level of significance to conduct the appropriate model utility test.

14.19 **a.** The paper cited in Example 14.11 reported that $b_3 = -4.60$ and $b_5 = 1.07$. How would you interpret these values?

b. The authors also fit the model with just x_4 and x_5 as predictors and found that $R^2 = .730$. Is this a useful model?

14.20 Partial MINITAB output for the data and variables described in Exercise 14.12 is given here.

```
Predictor          Coef        Stdev    t-ratio
Constant          86.85        85.39       1.02
      X1        -0.12297      0.03276      -3.75
      X2          5.090        1.969       2.58
      X3        -0.07092      0.01799      -3.94
      X4       0.0015380    0.0005560      2.77

s = 4.784    R-sq = 90.8%    R-sq(adj) = 89.4%
```

ANALYSIS OF VARIANCE

```
                 DF        SS        MS
Regression        4     5896.6    1474.2
Error            26      595.1      22.9
Total            30     6491.7
```

a. What is the estimated regression equation?

b. Using a .01 significance level, perform the model utility test (for explanation of the MINITAB output, see Example 14.9).

c. Interpret the values of R^2 and s_e given in the output.

14.21 The paper "The Caseload Controversy and the Study of Criminal Courts" (*J. Criminal Law and Criminology* (1979):89–101) used a multiple regression analysis to help assess the impact of judicial caseload on the processing of criminal court cases. Data was collected in the Chicago criminal courts on the following variables:

y = number of indictments

x_1 = number of cases on the docket

x_2 = number of cases pending in criminal court trial system

The estimated regression equation (based on $n = 367$ observations) was

$$\hat{y} = 28 - .05x_1 - .003x_2 + .00002x_3, \text{ where } x_3 = x_1x_2$$

a. The reported value of R^2 was .16. Conduct the model utility test. Use a .05 significance level.

b. Given the results of the test in (a), does it surprise you that the R^2 value is so low? Can you think of a possible explanation for this?

14.22 The paper "Readability of Liquid Crystal Displays: A Response Surface" (*Human Factors* (1983):185–190) used the estimated regression equation

$$\hat{y} = 1.52 + .02x_1 - 1.40x_2 + .02x_3 - .0006x_4$$

to describe the relationship between y = error percentage for subjects reading a four-digit liquid crystal display and the independent variables x_1 = level of backlight, x_2 = character subtense, x_3 = viewing angle, and x_4 = level of ambient light. From a table given in the paper, SSRegr = 19.2, SSResid = 20, and $n = 30$.

a. Does the estimated regression equation specify a useful relationship between y and the independent variables? Use the model utility test with a .05 significance level.

b. Calculate R^2 and s_e for this model. Interpret these values.

c. Do you think that the estimated regression equation would provide reasonably accurate predictions of error rate? Explain.

14.23 Factors affecting breeding success of puffins were examined in the paper "Breeding Success of the Common Puffin on Different Habitats at Great Island, Newfoundland" (*Ecol. Monographs* (1972):239–266). Data given in the paper was used to estimate the regression model

$$y = \alpha + \beta_1 x_1 + \beta_2 x_2 + \beta_3 x_3 + \beta_4 x_4 + e$$

where y = puffin nest density (number per 9m^2), x_1 = grass cover (%), x_2 = mean soil depth (cm), x_3 = angle of slope (degrees), and x_4 = distance from cliff edge (m). The estimated regression equation (using least squares) was

$$\hat{y} = 12.3 - .0186x_1 - .043x_2 + .224x_3 - .182x_4$$

and SSRegr = 1650.02, SSResid = 264.19, and n = 38.
   a. Do the independent variables provide information that is useful for predicting y? Use the model utility test with a significance level of .01.
   b. What quantities would you want to calculate in order to assess the accuracy of predictions based on the estimated regression equation? Explain your choices.
   c. Calculate R^2 and s_e and interpret these values.
   d. For this data set, would the equation $\hat{y} = 12 - .02x_1 - .05x_2 + .2x_3 - .2x_4$ result in a larger or smaller sum of squared residuals than the estimated regression equation given? Explain.

14.24 The paper "Effect of Manual Defoliation on Pole Bean Yield" (*J. Econ. Ent.* (1984):1019–1023) used a quadratic regression model to describe the relationship between y = yield (kg/plot) and x = defoliation level (a proportion between zero and one). The estimated regression equation based on n = 24 was $\hat{y}$ = 12.39 + 6.67x_1 − 15.25x_2, where $x_1 = x$ and $x_2 = x^2$. The paper also reported that R^2 for this model was .902. Does the quadratic model specify a useful relationship between y and x? Carry out the appropriate test using a .01 level of significance.

14.25 Suppose that a multiple regression data set consists of n = 15 observations. For what values of k, the number of model predictors, would the corresponding model with R^2 = .90 be judged useful at significance level .05? Does such a large R^2 value necessarily imply a useful model? Explain.

14.26 *This exercise requires the use of a computer package.* Use the data given in Exercise 14.18 to verify that the true regression equation

$$\text{mean } y \text{ value} = \alpha + \beta_1 x_1 + \beta_2 x_2 + \beta_3 x_3 + \beta_4 x_4 + \beta_5 x_5$$

is estimated by

$$\hat{y} = -151.36 - 16.22x_1 + 13.48x_2 + .094x_3 - .253x_4 + .492x_5$$

14.27 *This exercise requires the use of a computer package.* The accompanying data resulted from a study of the relationship between y = brightness of finished paper and the independent variables x_1 = hydrogen peroxide (% by weight), x_2 = sodium hydroxide (% by weight), x_3 = silicate (% by weight), and x_4 = process temperature ("Advantages of CE-HDP Bleaching for High Brightness Kraft Pulp Production" *TAPPI* (1964):170A–173A).

x_1	x_2	x_3	x_4	y	x_1	x_2	x_3	x_4	y
.2	.2	1.5	145	83.9	.1	.3	2.5	160	82.9
.4	.2	1.5	145	84.9	.5	.3	2.5	160	85.5
.2	.4	1.5	145	83.4	.3	.1	2.5	160	85.2
.4	.4	1.5	145	84.2	.3	.5	2.5	160	84.5
.2	.2	3.5	145	83.8	.3	.3	.5	160	84.7
.4	.2	3.5	145	84.7	.3	.3	4.5	160	85.0
.2	.4	3.5	145	84.0	.3	.3	2.5	130	84.9
.4	.4	3.5	145	84.8	.3	.3	2.5	190	84.0
.2	.2	1.5	175	84.5	.3	.3	2.5	160	84.5
.4	.2	1.5	175	86.0	.3	.3	2.5	160	84.7
.2	.4	1.5	175	82.6	.3	.3	2.5	160	84.6
.4	.4	1.5	175	85.1	.3	.3	2.5	160	84.9
.2	.2	3.5	175	84.5	.3	.3	2.5	160	84.9
.4	.2	3.5	175	86.0	.3	.3	2.5	160	84.5
.2	.4	3.5	175	84.0	.3	.3	2.5	160	84.6
.4	.4	3.5	175	85.4					

a. Find the estimated regression equation for the model that includes all independent variables, all quadratic terms, and all interaction terms.

b. Using a .05 significance level, perform the model utility test.

c. Interpret the values of the following quantities: SSResid, R^2, s_e.

14.28   *This exercise requires the use of a computer package.* The cotton aphid poses a threat to cotton crops in Iraq. The accompanying data on

y = infestation rate (aphids/100 leaves)

x_1 = mean temperature (°C)

x_2 = mean relative humidity

appeared in the paper "Estimation of the Economic Threshold of Infestation for Cotton Aphid" (*Mesopotamia J. Ag.* (1982):71–75). Use the data to find the estimated regression equation and asses the utility of the multiple regression model

$$y = \alpha + \beta_1 x_1 + \beta_2 x_2 + e$$

y	x_1	x_2	y	x_1	x_2
61	21.0	57.0	77	24.8	48.0
87	28.3	41.5	93	26.0	56.0
98	27.5	58.0	100	27.1	31.0
104	26.8	36.5	118	29.0	41.0
102	28.3	40.0	74	34.0	25.0
63	30.5	34.0	43	28.3	13.0
27	30.8	37.0	19	31.0	19.0
14	33.6	20.0	23	31.8	17.0
30	31.3	21.0	25	33.5	18.5
67	33.0	24.5	40	34.5	16.0

(continued)

y	x_1	x_2	y	x_1	x_2
6	34.3	6.0	21	34.3	26.0
18	33.0	21.0	23	26.5	26.0
42	32.0	28.0	56	27.3	24.5
60	27.8	39.0	59	25.8	29.0
82	25.0	41.0	89	18.5	53.5
77	26.0	51.0	102	19.0	48.0
108	18.0	70.0	97	16.3	79.5

14.3 Inferences Based on an Estimated Model

In the previous section we discussed estimating the coefficients α, β_1, ..., β_k in the model $y = \alpha + \beta_1 x_1 + \cdots + \beta_k x_k + e$ (using the principle of least squares) and then showed how the utility of the model could be confirmed by application of the model utility F test. If H_0: $\beta_1 = \cdots = \beta_k = 0$ cannot be rejected at a reasonably small level of significance, it must be concluded that the model does not specify a useful relationship between y and any of the predictor variables x_1, ..., x_k. The investigator must search further for a model that does describe a useful relationship, perhaps by introducing different predictors or making variable transformations. Only if H_0 can be rejected is it appropriate to proceed further with the chosen model and make inferences based on the estimated coefficients a, b_1, ..., b_k and the estimated regression function $a + b_1 x_1 + \cdots + b_k x_k$. Here we shall consider two different types of inferential problems. One type involves drawing a conclusion about an individual regression coefficient β_i—either computing a confidence interval for β_i or testing a hypothesis concerning β_i. The second type of problem involves first fixing values of x_1, ..., x_k and then computing either a point estimate or confidence interval for the corresponding mean y value, testing a hypothesis about this mean value, or predicting a future y value (using a single number or a prediction interval).

Inferences about Regression Coefficients

A confidence interval for and hypothesis test concerning the slope coefficient β in simple linear regression were based on facts about the sampling distribution of the statistic b used to obtain a point estimate of β. Similarly, in multiple regression, procedures for making inferences about β_i are derived from properties of the sampling distribution of b_i. The difficulty is that formulas for b_i and its standard deviation σ_{b_i} are quite complicated and cannot be stated concisely except by using some advanced mathematical notation.

PROPERTIES OF THE SAMPLING DISTRIBUTION OF b_i

Let b_i denote the statistic for estimating (via the principle of least squares) the coefficient β_i in the model $y = \alpha + \beta_1 x_1 + \cdots + \beta_k x_k + e$. Assumptions about this model given in Section 14.1 imply that

1. b_i has a normal distribution.
2. b_i is an unbiased statistic for estimating β_i ($\mu_{b_i} = \beta_i$).
3. The standard deviation of b_i, σ_{b_i}, involves σ^2 and a complicated function of all the values of $x_1, x_2, \ldots, x_k$ in the sample. The estimated standard deviation s_{b_i} results from replacing σ^2 by s_e^2 in the formula for σ_{b_i}.

The standardized variable

$$t = \frac{b_i - \beta_i}{s_{b_i}}$$

then has a t distribution with $n - (k + 1)$ df.

Because the formula for s_{b_i} is quite complicated (as is the formula for b_i itself), we won't give it here. However, a good statistical computer package will provide both the estimated coefficients $a, b_1, \ldots, b_k$ and their estimated standard deviations s_a, $s_{b_1}, \ldots, s_{b_k}$. These values can then be used to compute a confidence interval for β_i or to test a hypothesis about β_i.

INFERENCES CONCERNING A SINGLE β_i

A **confidence interval for β_i is**

$$b_i \pm (t \text{ critical value}) \cdot s_{b_i}$$

A **procedure for testing hypotheses about β_i is** given by

Null hypothesis: $H_0: \beta_i = $ hypothesized value

Test statistic: $t = \dfrac{b_i - \text{hypothesized value}}{s_{b_i}}$

Alternative hypothesis	Rejection region
$H_a: \beta_i > $ hypothesized value	$t > t$ critical value
$H_a: \beta_i < $ hypothesized value	$t < -t$ critical value
$H_a: \beta_i \neq $ hypothesized value	Either $t > t$ critical value or $t < -t$ critical value

The t critical value is based on $n - (k + 1)$ df and is selected from Table IV to yield the desired confidence level or level of significance. When the hypothesized value is 0, the test statistic $t = b_i/s_{b_i}$ is often called a **t ratio.**

MINITAB displays the b_i's in the Coef column near the top of the output, and the s_{b_i}'s appear right next to them in the column headed Stdev (see Figure 14.7 or Figure 14.8). The value of each ratio b_i/s_{b_i} appropriate for testing H_0: $\beta_i = 0$ appears in the t-ratio column, and the P-value for this test is given in the column on the far right labeled p.

EXAMPLE 14.12

Reconsider the regression of phosphate adsorption (y) against extractable iron (x_1) and extractable aluminum (x_2), with the sample data given in Example 14.6 and MINITAB output displayed in Figure 14.7. Suppose that the investigator had requested a 95% confidence interval for β_1, the average change in phosphate adsorption when extractable iron increases by one unit and extractable aluminum is held fixed. The necessary quantities are

$$b_1 = .11273 \qquad s_{b_1} = .02969$$
$$df = n - (k + 1) = 13 - (2 + 1) = 10$$
$$t \text{ critical value} = 2.23$$

The resulting confidence interval is

$$.11273 \pm (2.23)(.02969) = .11273 \pm .06621 \approx (.047, .179)$$

EXAMPLE 14.13

After fitting a quadratic model (one involving predictors x and x^2) to sample data, it is often of interest to see whether the inclusion of the quadratic predictor is important. That is, one often wishes to test H_0: $\beta_2 = 0$ versus H_a: $\beta_2 \neq 0$. If H_0 cannot be rejected, the fit of the simple linear regression model (the model when $\beta_2 = 0$) is not much improved upon by including the quadratic term. Let's carry out this test at level of significance .01 for the paddy yield data introduced in Example 14.8. MINITAB output appears in Figure 14.8, from which we see that

$$b_2 = -4.5358 \qquad s_{b_2} = .6744$$
$$t\text{-ratio} = -6.73 \qquad P\text{-value} = .000$$

1. The model is $y = \beta_0 + \beta_1 x + \beta_2 x^2 + e$

2. H_0: $\beta_2 = 0$

3. H_a: $\beta_2 \neq 0$

4. Test statistic: $t = b_2/s_{b_2}$, the t ratio for β_2

5. Rejection region: $n = 16$ and $k = 2$, so $df = 16 - 3 = 13$. From Table IV, the t critical value for a two-tailed level .01 test based on 13 df is 3.01. H_0 will be rejected at this level of significance either if $t > 3.01$ or if $t < -3.01$.

6. The computed value of t is the t ratio -6.73.

7. Since $-6.73 < -3.01$, H_0 is rejected. This conclusion also follows from the P-value .000, which is clearly much smaller than the significance level .01. The data strongly suggests that $\beta_2 \neq 0$, so it is important to retain the quadratic predictor in the model.

EXAMPLE 14.14

Our analysis of the phosphate adsorption data introduced in Example 14.6 has so far focused on the model $y = \alpha + \beta_1 x_1 + \beta_2 x_2 + e$ in which x_1 (extractable iron) and x_2 (extractable aluminum) affect the response separately. Suppose that the researcher wishes to investigate the possibility of interaction between x_1 and x_2 through fitting the model with predictors x_1, x_2, and $x_3 = x_1 x_2$. We list a few of the sample values of y, x_1, and x_2, along with the corresponding values of x_3. In practice, a statistical computer package would automatically compute x_3 values upon request once x_1 and x_2 values had been entered, so hand computations would not be necessary. Figure 14.10 displays partial MINITAB output resulting from a request to fit this model. Let's use the output to see whether inclusion of the interaction predictor is justified.

Observation	y	x_1	x_2	$x_3 = x_1 x_2$
1	4	61	13	793
2	18	175	21	3,675
3	14	111	24	2,664
⋮	⋮	⋮	⋮	⋮
13	40	199	54	10,746

FIGURE 14.10
MINITAB output for model with interaction fit to the phosphate adsorption data ($x_1 = $ FE, $x_2 = $ AL, $x_3 = x_1 x_2 = $ FEAL)

```
THE REGRESSION EQUATION is
HPO = -2.37 + 0.0828 FE + 0.246 AL + 0.000528 FEAL

Predictor        Coef        Stdev     t-ratio
Constant       -2.368        7.179       -0.33
FE             0.08279       0.04818      1.72
AL             0.2460        0.1481       1.66
FEAL           0.0005278     0.0006610    0.80

s = 4.461   R-sq = 95.2%   R-sq(adj) = 93.6%
```

1. The model is $y = \alpha + \beta_1 x_1 + \beta_2 x_2 + \beta_3 x_3 + e$, where $x_3 = x_1 x_2$

2. $H_0: \beta_3 = 0$ (the interaction predictor does not belong in the model)

3. $H_a: \beta_3 \neq 0$

4. Test statistic: $t = b_3 / s_{b_3}$, the t ratio for β_3

5. Rejection region: $n = 13$ and $k = 3$ for this model, so $n - (k + 1) = 9$. Using level of significance .05, the t critical value for a two-tailed test is 2.26. H_0 will be rejected, justifying inclusion of the interaction predictor variable, only if either $t > 2.26$ or $t < -2.26$.

6. Directly from the t-ratio column in Figure 14.10, $t = .80$.

7. Since .80 is not in the rejection region, H_0 cannot be rejected at level of significance .05. In fact, P-value $> .20$ (since $t = .80$ does not exceed the smallest t critical value in the 9 df row of Table IV). So sample evidence suggests that the interaction predictor should be eliminated from the model.

An interesting aspect of the computer output for the interaction model in the foregoing example is that the t ratios for β_1, for β_2, and for β_3 (1.72, 1.66, and .80) are all relatively small, yet $R^2 = .952$ is quite large. The high R^2 value suggests a useful model (this can be confirmed by the model utility test), yet the smallness of each t ratio might tempt us to conclude that all three β_i's are zero. This sounds like a contradiction, but it involves a misinterpretation of the t ratios. For example, the t ratio for β_3—that is, b_3/s_{b_3}—tests H_0: $\beta_3 = 0$ *when x_1 and x_2 are included in the model.* The smallness of a given t ratio suggests that the associated predictor can be dropped from the model *as long as the other predictors are retained.* The fact that all t ratios are small in this example does not, therefore, allow us simultaneously to delete all predictors. The data does suggest deleting x_3 because the model that includes x_1 and x_2 has already been found to give a very good fit to the data and is simple to interpret. In Section 14.4 we comment further on why it might happen that all t ratios are small even when the model seems very useful.

The model utility test amounts to testing a simultaneous claim about the values of all β_i's—that they are all zero. There is also an F test for testing a hypothesis involving a specified subset consisting of at least two β_i's. For example, we might fit the model

$$y = \alpha + \beta_1 x_1 + \beta_2 x_2 + \beta_3 x_1 x_2 + \beta_4 x_1^2 + \beta_5 x_2^2 + e$$

and then wish to test H_0: $\beta_3 = \beta_4 = \beta_5 = 0$ (which says that the second-order predictors contribute nothing to the model). Please see the Chapter References for Chapter 4 for further details.

Inferences Based on the Estimated Regression Function

The estimated regression line $\hat{y} = a + bx$ in simple linear regression was used both to estimate the mean y value when x had a specified value and to predict the associated y value for a single observation made at a particular x value. The estimated regression function for the model $y = \alpha + \beta_1 x_1 + \cdots + \beta_k x_k + e$ can be used in the same two ways. When fixed values of the predictor variables $x_1, x_2, \ldots,$ x_k are substituted into the estimated regression function

$$a + b_1x_1 + b_2x_2 + \cdots + b_kx_k$$

the result can be used either as a point estimate of the corresponding mean y value or as a prediction of the y value that will result from a single observation when the x_i's have the specified values.

EXAMPLE 14.15

Precise information concerning bus transit times is important when making transportation planning decisions. The paper "Factors Affecting Running Time on Transit Routes" (*Transportation Research* (1983):107–113) reported on an empirical study based on data gathered in Cincinnati, Ohio. The variables of interest were

y = running time per mile during the morning peak period (s)

x_1 = number of passenger boardings per mile

x_2 = number of passenger alightings per mile

x_3 = number of signalized intersections per mile

x_4 = proportion of a route on which parking is allowed

The values of x_1 and x_2 were not necessarily equal because observations were made over partial segments of routes (so not all passengers entered or exited on the segments). The estimated regression function was

$$169.50 + 5.07x_1 + 4.53x_2 + 6.61x_3 + 67.70x_4$$

Consider the predictor variable values $x_1 = 4.5$, $x_2 = 5.5$, $x_3 = 5$, and $x_4 = .1$. Then a point estimate for true average running time per mile when the x_i's have these values is

$$169.50 + (5.07)(4.5) + (4.53)(5.5) + (6.61)(5) + (67.70)(.1) = 257.05$$

This value 257.05 is also the predicted running time per mile for a single trip when $x_1, x_2, x_3,$ and x_4 have the given values.

Remember that before the sample observations $y_1, y_2, \ldots, y_n$ are obtained, a and all b_i's are statistics (because they all involve the y_i's). This implies that for fixed values of $x_1, x_2, \ldots, x_k$, the estimated regression function $a + b_1x_1 + \cdots + b_k x_k$ is a statistic (its value varies from sample to sample). To obtain a confidence interval for the mean y value or test a hypothesis about this mean y value for specified $x_1, \ldots, x_k$ values, we need some facts about the sampling distribution of this statistic.

PROPERTIES OF THE SAMPLING DISTRIBUTION OF
$a + b_1x_1 + \cdots + b_kx_k$

Assumptions about the model $y = \alpha + \beta_1x_1 + \cdots + \beta_kx_k + e$ given in Section 14.1 imply that for fixed values of the predictors $x_1, x_2, \ldots, x_k$, the statistic $a + b_1x_1 + \cdots + b_kx_k$ satisfies the following properties:

1. It has a normal distribution.
2. Its mean value is $\alpha + \beta_1x_1 + \cdots + \beta_kx_k$. That is, the statistic is unbiased for estimating the mean y value when $x_1, \ldots, x_k$ are fixed.
3. The standard deviation of this statistic involves σ^2 and a very complicated function of all the sample predictor variable values. The estimated standard deviation of the statistic results from replacing σ^2 by s_e^2 in this function.

The standardized variable

$$t = \frac{a + b_1x_1 + \cdots + b_kx_k - (\alpha + \beta_1x_1 + \cdots + \beta_kx_k)}{(\text{estimated standard deviation of } a + b_1x_1 + \cdots + b_kx_k)}$$

then has a t distribution with $n - (k + 1)$ df.

The formula for the estimated standard deviation of $a + b_1x_1 + \cdots + b_kx_k$ is complicated, but fortunately it has been programmed into the most widely used statistical computer packages, and its value for specified $x_1, \ldots, x_k$ is available upon request. Manipulation of the t variable as before gives the following confidence interval formula.

For fixed values of $x_1, x_2, \ldots, x_k$, a **confidence interval for the mean y value**—that is, for $\alpha + \beta_1x_1 + \cdots + \beta_kx_k$—is

$$a + b_1x_1 + \cdots + b_kx_k \pm \binom{t \text{ critical}}{\text{value}}\binom{\text{estimated standard deviation}}{\text{of } a + b_1x_1 + \cdots + b_kx_k}$$

where the t critical value is based on $n - (k + 1)$ df.

EXAMPLE 14.16

The last row of MINITAB output in Figure 14.7 gives the following results from fitting the model $y = \alpha + \beta_1x_1 + \beta_2x_2 + e$ to the phosphate data.

```
  Fit   Stdev.Fit        95% C.I.          95% P.I.
23.52        1.31    (20.60, 26.44)    (13.33, 33.71)
```

This was in response to a request for estimation information when Fe $= x_1 = 150$ and AL $= x_2 = 40$. In particular,

$$\begin{pmatrix} \text{point estimate of mean } y \\ \text{when } x_1 = 150, x_2 = 40 \end{pmatrix} = a + b_1(150) + b_2(40)$$

$$= -7.351 + (.11273)(150) + (.34900)(40)$$

$$= 23.52 \quad \text{(Fit)}$$

$$\begin{pmatrix} \text{standard deviation of the} \\ \text{statistic } a + b_1(150) + b_2(40) \end{pmatrix} = 1.31 \quad \text{(Stdev. Fit)}$$

The t critical value for a 95% confidence level when df $= 10$ is 2.23. A confidence interval for the mean value of phosphate adsorption when extractable iron $= 150$ and extractable aluminum $= 40$ is

$$23.52 \pm (2.23)(1.31) = 23.52 \pm 2.92$$

$$= (20.60, 26.44)$$

This interval also appears on the output (in the current version of MINITAB, a confidence level other than 95% cannot be requested).

Recall that the prediction interval formula for a single y observation in simple linear regression was similar to the confidence interval formula for a mean y value. However, while both intervals were centered at the same place—$a + bx$—the prediction interval was typically much wider because of the extra uncertainty associated with prediction. These properties carry over to the prediction interval and confidence interval in multiple regression.

A prediction interval for a single y observation is

$$a + b_1x_1 + \cdots + b_kx_k \pm \begin{pmatrix} t \text{ critical} \\ \text{value} \end{pmatrix} \cdot \sqrt{s_e^2 + \left[\begin{matrix} \text{estimated standard} \\ \text{deviation of} \\ a + b_1x_1 + \cdots + b_kx_k \end{matrix} \right]^2}$$

EXAMPLE 14.17

Reconsider the data on paddy yield (y) and time between flowering and harvesting (x) presented in Example 14.8. MINITAB output from fitting the quadratic regression model $y = \alpha + \beta_1x + \beta_2x^2 + e$ (so $x_1 = x$, $x_2 = x^2$) appeared in Figure 14.8; the last row of output gives estimation and prediction information when $x_1 = 25$ and $x_2 = 625$:

```
   Fit   Stdev.Fit         95% C.I.              95% P. I.
 3431.8        69.2   (3282.2, 3581.4)    (2966.5, 3897.1)
```

The t critical value for a 95% prediction level when df $= 16 - (2 + 1) = 13$ is 2.16. With $s_e = 203.9$, a prediction interval for yield when harvesting occurs 25 days after flowering is

$$3431.8 \pm (2.16) \sqrt{(203.9)^2 + (69.2)^2} = 3431.8 \pm 465.1$$
$$= (2966.7, 3896.9)$$

The small discrepancy between this interval and the one given on the output is due to our use of the rounded values 203.9 and 69.2.

The danger of extrapolation in simple linear regression is that if the x value of interest is much outside the interval of x values in the sample, the postulated model might no longer be valid, and even if it were, $\alpha + \beta x$ could still be quite poorly estimated (s_{a+bx} could be large). There is a similar danger in multiple regression, but it is not always obvious when the x_i values of interest involve an extrapolation from sample data. As an example, suppose that a single y observation is made for each of the following 13 (x_1, x_2) pairs:

Observation	1	2	3	4	5	6	7	8	9	10	11	12	13
x_1	0	0	0	0	0	0	5	5	5	10	-5	-5	-10
x_2	10	5	0	-5	-10	-5	0	5	0	-5	0	5	0

The x_1 values range between -10 and 10, as do the x_2 values. After fitting the model $y = \alpha + \beta_1 x_1 + \beta_2 x_2 + e$, we might then want a confidence interval for the mean y value when $x_1 = 10$ and $x_2 = 10$. However, whereas each of these values separately is within the range of sample x_i values, Figure 14.11 shows that the point $(x_1, x_2) = (10, 10)$ is actually far from (x_1, x_2) pairs in the sample. Thus a conclusion about y when $x_1 = 10$ and $x_2 = 10$ involves a substantial extrapolation. In particular, the estimated standard deviation of $a + b_1(10) + b_2(10)$ would probably be quite large even if the model were valid near this point.

FIGURE 14.11
The Danger of extrapolation
● denotes an (x_1, x_2) pair for which the sample contains a y observation
○ denotes an (x_1, x_2) pair well outside the sample region, although the individual values $x_1 = 10$ and $x_2 = 10$ are within x_1 and x_2 sample ranges separately

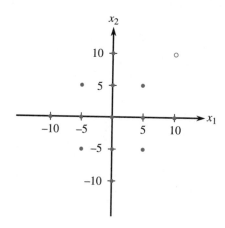

When more than two predictor variables are included in the model, we cannot see from a plot like that of Figure 14.11 whether the $x_1, x_2, \ldots, x_k$ values of interest involve an extrapolation. It is then best to compare the estimated standard deviation of $a + b_1x_1 + \cdots + b_kx_k$ for the values of interest with the estimated standard deviations corresponding to $x_1, x_2, \ldots, x_k$ values in the sample (those in the Stdev. Fit column of the MINITAB output). Extrapolation is indicated by a value of the former standard deviation (at the x_i values of interest) that is much larger than the standard deviations for sampled values.

EXERCISES 14.29–14.44   SECTION 14.3

14.29   Explain why it is preferable to perform a model utility test before using an estimated regression model to make predictions or to estimate the mean y value for specified values of the independent variables.

14.30   The article "Zoning and Industrial Land Values: The Case of Philadelphia" (*AREUEA J.* (1991):154–159) considered a regression model to relate the value of a vacant lot in Philadelphia to a number of different predictor variables.
   a. One of the predictors was x_3 = the distance from the city's major east-west thoroughfare, for which $b_3 = -.489$ and $s_{b_3} = .1044$. The model contained seven predictors, and the coefficients were estimated from a sample of 100 vacant lots. Calculate a confidence interval for β_3 using a confidence level of 95%.
   b. Another predictor was x_1, an indicator variable for whether or not the lot was zoned for residential use, for which $b_1 = -.183$ and $s_{b_1} = .3055$. Carry out a test of $H_0: \beta_1 = 0$ versus $H_a: \beta_1 \neq 0$ and interpret the conclusion in the context of the problem situation.

14.31   Twenty-six observations appearing in the paper "Multiple Regression Analysis for Forecasting Critical Fish Influxes at Power Station Intakes" (see Exercise 14.16) were used to fit a multiple regression model relating y = number of fish at intake to the independent variables x_1 = water temperature (° C), x_2 = number of pumps running, x_3 = sea state (taking values 0, 1, 2, or 3), and x_4 = speed (knots). Partial MINITAB output is given.

```
THE REGRESSION EQUATION is
Y = 92.0 − 2.18 X1 − 19.2 X2 − 9.38 X3 + 2.32 X4

Predictor        Coef      Stdev     t-ratio
Constant        91.98      42.07        2.19
X1             −2.179      1.087       −2.00
X2            −19.189      9.215       −2.08
X3             −9.378      4.356       −2.15
X4             2.3205     0.7686        3.02

s = 10.53    R-sq = 39.0%    R-sq(adj) = 27.3%
```

Analysis of Variance

SOURCE	DF	SS	MS
Regression	4	1486.9	371.7
Error	21	2330.2	111.0
Total	25	3817.1	

a. Construct a 95% confidence interval for β_3, the coefficient of x_3 = number of pumps running. Interpret the resulting interval.

b. Construct a 90% confidence interval for the mean change in y associated with a $1°$ increase in temperature when number of pumps, sea state, and speed remain fixed.

14.32   A study reported in the paper "Leakage of Intracellular Substances from Alfalfa Roots at Various Subfreezing Temperatures" (*Crop Sci.* (1991):1575–1578) considered a quadratic regression model to relate y = MDH activity (a measure of the extent to which cellular membranes suffer extensive damage from freezing) to x = electrical conductivity (which describes the damage in the early stages of freezing). The estimated regression function was

$$\hat{y} = -.1838 + .0272x + .0446x^2$$

with $R^2 = .860$.

a. Supposing that $n = 50$, does the quadratic model appear to be useful? Test the appropriate hypotheses.

b. Using $s_{b_2} = .0103$, carry out a test at significance level .01 to decide whether the predictor x^2 is important.

c. If the standard deviation of the statistic $a + b_1(40) + b_2(1600)$ is .120, calculate a confidence interval with confidence level 90% for true average MDH activity when conductivity is 40.

14.33   Data from a random sample of 107 students taking a managerial accounting course was used to obtain the estimated regression equation

$$\hat{y} = 2.178 + .469x_1 + 3.369x_2 + 3.054x_3$$

where y = student's exam score, x_1 = student's expected score on the exam, x_2 = time spent studying (h/week), and x_3 = student's grade point average or GPA ("Effort, Expectation and Academic Performance in Managerial Cost Accounting," *J. Acctg. Educ.* (1989):57–68). The value of R^2 was .686, and the estimated standard deviations of the statistics b_1, b_2, and b_3 were .090, .456, and 1.457, respectively.

a. How would you interpret the estimated coefficient .469?

b. Does there appear to be a useful linear relationship between exam score and at least one of the three predictors?

c. Calculate a confidence interval for the mean change in exam score associated with a one-hour increase in study time when expected score and GPA remain fixed.

d. Obtain a point prediction of the exam score for a student who expects a 75, has studied 8 hours per week, and has a GPA of 2.8.

e. If the standard deviation of the statistic on which the prediction of (d) is based is 1.2 and SSTo = 10,200, calculate a 95% prediction interval for the score of the student described in (d).

14.34   The paper "Assessing the Effects of Industrial Relations Systems and Efforts to Improve the Quality of Working Life on Organizational Effectiveness" (*Acad. Mgmt. J.* (1985):509–526) reported the result of a multiple regression analysis in which the dependent variable was y = labor efficiency index. A sample of $n = 64$ industrial plants was available, a model with $k = 8$ predictors was fit, and the fitted model explained 46.7% of the observed variation in y. Does the model appear to be a useful one?

   a. State and test the appropriate hypothesis using a significance level of .01.

   b. The F critical value that captures an upper-tail area of .001 under the F curve with 8 numerator and 55 denominator df is 3.92. What does this say about the P-value of the test conducted in (a)?

14.35   The estimated regression equation

$$\hat{y} = 28 - .05x_1 - .003x_2 + .00002x_3$$

where

> y = number of indictments disposed of in a given month
>
> x_1 = number of cases on judge's docket
>
> x_2 = number of cases pending in the criminal trial court
>
> $x_3 = x_1 x_2$

appeared in the paper "The Caseload Controversy and the Study of Criminal Courts" (*J. Criminal Law and Criminology* (1979):89–101). This equation was based on $n = 367$ observations. The b_i's and their associated standard deviations are given in the accompanying table.

i	b_i	Estimated standard deviation of b_i
1	−.05	.03
2	−.003	.0024
3	.00002	.000009

Is inclusion of the interaction term important? Test $H_0: \beta_3 = 0$ using a .05 level of significance.

14.36   Does exposure to air pollution result in decreased life expectancy? This question was examined in the paper "Does Air Pollution Shorten Lives?" (*Statistics and Public Policy*, Reading, Mass.: Addison-Wesley, 1977). Data on

> y = total mortality rate (deaths per 10,000)
>
> x_1 = mean suspended particle reading ($\mu g/m^3$)
>
> x_2 = smallest sulfate reading ($[\mu g/m^3] \times 10$)
>
> x_3 = population density (people/mi^2)
>
> x_4 = (percent nonwhite) $\times$ 10
>
> x_5 = (percent over 65) $\times$ 10

for the year 1960 was recorded for $n = 117$ randomly selected standard metropolitan statistical areas. The estimated regression equation was

$$\hat{y} = 19.607 + .041x_1 + .071x_2 + .001x_3 + .041x_4 + .687x_5$$

a. For this model, $R^2 = .827$. Using a .05 significance level, perform a model utility test.

b. The estimated standard deviation of b_1 was .016. Calculate and interpret a 90% confidence interval for β_1.

c. Given that the estimated standard deviation of b_4 is .007, determine if percent nonwhite is an important variable in the model. Use a .01 significance level.

d. In 1960, the values of x_1, x_2, x_3, x_4, and x_5 for Pittsburgh were 166, 60, 788, 68, and 95, respectively. Use the given regression equation to predict Pittsburgh's mortality rate. How does your prediction compare with the actual 1960 value of 103 deaths per 10,000?

14.37   The accompanying data was obtained from a study of a certain method for preparing pure alcohol from refinery streams ("Direct Hydration of Olefins" *Indus. and Engr. Chem.* (1961):209–211). The independent variable x is volume hourly space velocity and the dependent variable y is amount of isobutylene converted.

x	1	1	2	4	4	4	6
y	23.0	24.5	28.0	30.9	32.0	33.6	20.0

MINITAB output—the result of fitting a quadratic regression model where $x_1 = x$ and $x_2 = x^2$—is given. Would a linear regression have sufficed? That is, is the quadratic term important? Use a level .05 test.

```
THE REGRESSION EQUATION is
Y = 13.6 + 11.4 X1 − 1.72 X2

Predictor        Coef      Stdev     t-ratio
Constant       13.636      1.896        7.19
X1             11.406      1.356        8.41
X2            −1.7155     0.2036       −8.42

s = 1.428     R-sq = 94.7%     R-sq(adj) = 92.1%
```

14.38   The paper "Bank Full Discharge of Rivers" (*Water Resources J.* (1978):1141–1154) reported data on $y =$ discharge amount (m²/s), $x_1 =$ flow area (m²), and $x_2 =$ slope of the water surface (m/m) obtained at $n = 10$ floodplain stations. A multiple regression model using x_1, x_2, and $x_3 = x_1x_2$ was fit to this data, and partial MINITAB output appears here.

```
THE REGRESSION EQUATION is
Y = −3.14 + 1.70 X1 + 96.1 X2 + 8.38 X3

Predictor        Coef      Stdev     t-ratio
Constant        −3.14     14.54       −0.22
X1              1.697      1.431        1.19
X2               96.1      702.7        0.14
X3                8.4      199.0        0.04

s = 17.58     R-sq = 73.2%     R-sq(adj) = 59.9%
```

Analysis of Variance

SOURCE	DF	SS	MS
Regression	3	5073.4	1691.1
Error	6	1854.1	309.0
Total	9	6927.5	

a. Perform the model utility test using a significance level of .05.

b. Is the interaction term important? Test using a .05 significance level.

c. Does it bother you that the model utility test indicates a useful model but all values in the t-ratio column of the output are small? Explain.

14.39 If an estimated regression equation results in a large R^2 value, must all independent variables (the x_i's) have large t ratios (those appropriate for testing H_0: $\beta_i = 0$) associated with them? Explain.

14.40 In the paper "An Ultracentrifuge Flour Absorption Method" (*Cereal Chem.* (1978):96–101), the authors discussed the relationship between water absorption for wheat flour and various characteristics of the flour. A multiple regression model was used to relate y = absorption (%) to x_1 = flour protein (%) and x_2 = starch damage (Farrand units). MINITAB output based on $n = 28$ observations is given. Use a significance level of .05 for all tests requested.

THE REGRESSION EQUATION is
Y = 19.4 + 1.44 X1 + .336 X2

Predictor	Coef	Stdev	t-ratio	p
Constant	19.440	2.188	8.88	.000
X1	1.4423	0.2076	6.95	.000
X2	0.33563	0.01814	18.51	.000

s = 1.094   R-sq = 96.4%   R-sq(adj) = 96.2%

Analysis of Variance

SOURCE	DF	SS	MS	F	p
Regression	2	812.380	406.190	339.3	.000
Error	25	29.928	1.197		
Total	27	842.307			

a. Using the model utility test, determine if the regression equation specifies a useful relationship between y and the independent variables.

b. Conduct tests for each of the following pairs of hypotheses.

  i. H_0: $\beta_1 = 0$ versus H_a: $\beta_1 \neq 0$

  ii. H_0: $\beta_2 = 0$ versus H_a: $\beta_2 \neq 0$

c. Based on the results of (b), would you conclude that both independent variables are important? Explain.

d. An estimate of the mean water absorption for wheat with 10.2% protein and a starch damage of 20 is desired. The estimated standard deviation of the statistic $a + b_1(10.2) + b_2(20)$ is .318. Use this to compute a 95% confidence interval for $\alpha + \beta_1(10.2) + \beta_2(20)$.

e. Compute a 90% confidence interval for $\alpha + \beta_1(11.7) + \beta_2(57)$ if the estimated standard deviation of $a + b_1(11.7) + b_2(57)$ is .522. Interpret the resulting interval.

f. A single shipment of wheat is received. For this particular shipment, $x_1 = 11.7$ and $x_2 = 57$. Predict the water absorption for this shipment (a single y value) using a 90% interval.

14.41 When the model with $k = 2$ predictors was fit to the phosphate data ($n = 13$) of Example 14.6, MINITAB reported (21.40, 27.20) as a 95% confidence interval for mean phosphate adsorption when $x_1 = 160$ and $x_2 = 39$. Obtain a 99% confidence interval for mean adsorption in this case.

14.42 The paper "Predicting Marathon Time from Anaerobic Threshold Measurements" (*The Physician and Sportsmed.* (1984):95–98) gave data on $y = $ maximum heart rate (beats/min), $x_1 = $ age, and $x_2 = $ weight (kg) for $n = 18$ marathon runners. The estimated regression equation for the model $y = \alpha + \beta_1 x_1 + \beta_2 x_2 + e$ was $\hat{y} = 179 - .8x_1 + .5x_2$ and SSRegr $= 649.75$, SSResid $= 538.03$.

a. Is the model useful for predicting maximum heart rate? Use a significance level of .10.

b. Predict the maximum heart rate of a particular runner who is 43 years old and weighs 65 kg using a 99% interval. The estimated standard deviation of the statistic $a + b_1(43) + b_2(65)$ is 3.52.

c. Use a 90% interval to estimate the average maximum heart rate for all marathon runners who are 30 years old and weigh 77.2 kg. The estimated standard deviation of $a + b_1(30) + b_2(77.2)$ is 2.97.

d. Would a 90% prediction interval for a single 30-year-old runner weighing 77.2 kg be wider or narrower than the interval computed in (c)? Explain. (You need not compute the interval.)

14.43 The effect of manganese (Mn) on wheat growth is examined in the article "Manganese Deficiency and Toxicity Effects on Growth, Development and Nutrient Composition in Wheat" (*Agronomy J.* (1984):213–217). A quadratic regression model was used to relate $y = $ plant height (cm) to $x = $ log (added Mn), with μM as the units for added Mn. The accompanying data was read from a scatter diagram appearing in the paper. Also given is MINITAB output, where $x_1 = x$ and $x_2 = x^2$. Use a .05 significance level for any hypothesis tests needed to answer the questions that follow.

x	-1	$-.4$	0	.2	1	2	2.8	3.2	3.4	4
y	32	37	44	45	46	42	42	40	37	30

```
THE REGRESSION EQUATION is
Y = 41.7 + 6.58 X1 − 2.36 X2

Predictor        Coef      Stdev     t-ratio
Constant       41.7422    0.8522       48.98
X1              6.581     1.002        6.57
X2            − 2.3621    0.3073      − 7.69

s = 1.963     R-sq = 89.8%     R-sq(adj) = 86.9%
```

Analysis of Variance

SOURCE	DF	SS	MS
Regression	2	237.520	118.760
Error	7	26.980	3.854
Total	9	264.500	

a. Is the quadratic model useful for describing the relationship between y and x?

b. Are both the linear and quadratic terms important? Could either one be eliminated from the model? Explain.

c. Give a 95% confidence interval for the mean y value when $x = 2$. The estimated standard deviation of $a + b_1(2) + b_2(4)$ is 1.037. Interpret the resulting interval.

d. Estimate the mean height for wheat treated with 10 μM of Mn using a 90% interval. (Note: The estimated standard deviation of $a + b_1(1) + b_2(1)$ is 1.031 and log $(10) = 1$.)

14.44   *This exercise requires the use of a computer package.* A study on the effect of applying fertilizer in bands is described in the paper "Fertilizer Placement Effects on Growth, Yield, and Chemical Composition of Burley Tobacco" (*Agronomy J.* (1984):183–188). The accompanying data was taken from a scatter diagram appearing in the paper, with y = plant Mn (μg/g dry weight) and x = distance from the fertilizer band (cm). The authors suggest a quadratic regression model.

x	0	10	20	30	40
y	110	90	76	72	70

a. Use a suitable computer package to find the estimated quadratic regression equation.

b. Perform the model utility test.

c. Interpret the values of R^2 and s_e.

d. Are both the linear and quadratic terms important? Carry out the necessary hypothesis tests and interpret the results.

e. Find a 90% confidence interval for the mean plant Mn for plants that are 30 cm from the fertilizer band.

14.4   Other Issues in Multiple Regression

Primary objectives in multiple regression include the estimation of a mean y value, prediction of an individual y value, and gaining insight into how changes in predictor variable values impact y. Often an investigator has data on a number of predictor variables that might be incorporated into a model to be used for such purposes. Some of these may actually be unrelated or only very weakly related to y or may contain information that duplicates information provided by other predictors. If all these predictor variables are included in the model, many model coefficients have to be estimated. This reduces the number of degrees of freedom associated with SSResid, leading to a deterioration in the degree of precision associated with other inferences (for example, wide confidence and prediction intervals). A model with many predictors can also be cumbersome to use and difficult to interpret.

In this section we first introduce some guidelines and procedures for selecting a set of useful predictors. Before a model is decided upon, the analyst should examine the data carefully for evidence of unusual observations or potentially troublesome patterns. It is important to identify unusually deviant or influential observations and to look for possible inconsistencies with model assumptions. Our discussion of multiple regression closes with a brief mention of some diagnostic methods that facilitate such an examination.

Variable Selection

Suppose that an investigator has data on p predictor variables $x_1, x_2, \ldots, x_p$, which are candidates for use in building a model. Some of these variables might be specified functions of others—for example, $x_3 = x_1 x_2$, $x_4 = x_1^2$, and so on. The objective is then to select a set of these predictors that in some sense specifies a best model (of the general additive form considered in the two previous sections). Fitting a model that consists of a specified k predictors requires that $k + 1$ model coefficients (α and the k corresponding β's) be estimated. Generally speaking, the number of observations, n, should be at least twice the number of predictors in the largest model under consideration in order to ensure reasonably accurate coefficient estimates and a sufficient number of degrees of freedom associated with SSResid.

If p is not too large, a good statistical computer package can rather quickly fit a model based on each different subset of the p predictors. Consider as an example the case $p = 4$. There are two possibilities for each predictor—it could be included or not included in a model—so the number of possible models in this case is $2 \cdot 2 \cdot 2 \cdot 2 = 2^4 = 16$ (including the model with all four predictors and the model with only the constant term and none of the four predictors). These 16 possibilities are displayed in the accompanying table.

Predictors included	None	x_1	x_2	x_3	x_4	x_1,x_2	x_1,x_3	x_1,x_4	x_2,x_3	x_2,x_4
Number of predictors in model	0	1	1	1	1	2	2	2	2	2

Predictors included	x_3,x_4	x_1,x_2,x_3	x_1,x_2,x_4	x_1,x_3,x_4	x_2,x_3,x_4	x_1,x_2,x_3,x_4
Number of predictors in model	2	3	3	3	3	4

More generally, when there are p candidate predictor variables, the number of possible models is 2^p. The number of possible models is, therefore, substantial if p is even moderately large—for example, 1024 possible models when $p = 10$ and 32,768 possibilities when $p = 15$.

Model selection methods can be divided into two types. There are those based on fitting every possible model, computing one or more summary quantities from each fit, and comparing these quantities to identify the most satisfactory models. Several of the most powerful statistical computer packages have an **all-subsets** option, which will give limited output from fitting each possible model. Methods of the second type are appropriate when p is so large that it is not feasible to examine all subsets. These methods are often referred to as **automatic selection, or stepwise, procedures.** The general idea is to either begin with the p predictor model and delete variables one by one until all remaining predictors are judged important, or begin with no predictors and add predictors until no predictor not in the model seems important. With modern-day computing power, the value of p for which examination of all subsets is feasible is surprisingly large, so automatic selection procedures are not as important as they once were.

Suppose then that p is small enough so that all subsets can be fit. What characteristic(s) of the estimated models should be examined in the search for a best model? An obvious and appealing candidate is the coefficient of multiple determination, R^2, which measures the proportion of observed y variation explained by the model. Certainly a model with a large R^2 value is preferable to another model containing the same number of predictors but which has a much smaller R^2 value. Thus if the model with predictors x_1 and x_2 has $R^2 = .765$ and the model with predictors x_1 and x_3 has $R^2 = .626$, the latter model would almost surely be eliminated from further consideration.

However, using R^2 to choose between models containing different numbers of predictors is not so straightforward because adding a predictor to a model can never decrease the value of R^2. In particular, the model containing all p candidate predictors is guaranteed to have an R^2 value at least as large as R^2 for any model that includes some but not all of these predictors. More generally, let

$R^2_{(1)} =$ the largest R^2 for any one-predictor model

$R^2_{(2)} =$ the largest R^2 for any two-predictor model

$\vdots$ $\vdots$

Then $R^2_{(1)} \leq R^2_{(2)} \leq \cdots \leq R^2_{(p-1)} \leq R^2_{(p)}$. When statisticians base model selection on R^2, the objective is not simply to find the model with the largest R^2 value—the model with p predictors does that. Instead we should look for a model containing relatively few predictors but which has a large R^2 value and is such that no other model containing more predictors gives much of an improvement in R^2. Suppose, for example, that $p = 5$ and that

$$R^2_{(1)} = .427, \qquad R^2_{(2)} = .733, \qquad R^2_{(3)} = .885, \qquad R^2_{(4)} = .898, \qquad R^2_{(5)} = .901$$

Then the best three-predictor model appears to be a good choice, since it substantially improves on the best one- and two-predictor models, whereas very little is gained by using the best four-predictor model or all five predictors.

A small increase in R^2 resulting from the addition of a predictor to a model may be offset by the increased complexity of the new model and the reduction in degrees of freedom associated with SSResid. This has led statisticians to introduce a quantity called **adjusted R^2**, which can either decrease or increase when a predictor is added to a model.[1] It follows that adjusted R^2 for the best k-predictor model (the one with coefficient of multiple determination $R^2_{(k)}$) may be larger than adjusted R^2 for the best model based on $k + 1$ predictors. Adjusted R^2 formalizes the notion of diminishing returns as more predictors are added—small increases in R^2 are outweighed by corresponding decreases in degrees of freedom associated with SSResid. A reasonable strategy in model selection is to identify the model with the largest value of adjusted R^2 (the corresponding number of predictors k is often much smaller than p) and then consider only that model and any others whose adjusted R^2 values are nearly as large.

EXAMPLE 14.18

The paper "Anatomical Factors Influencing Wood Specific Gravity of Slash Pines and the Implications for the Development of a High-Quality Pulpwood" (*TAPPI* (1964):401–404) reported the results of an experiment in which 20 samples of slash pine wood were analyzed. A primary objective was to relate wood specific gravity (y) to various other wood characteristics. The independent variables on which observations were made were

x_1 = number of fibers/mm^2 in springwood

x_2 = number of fibers/mm^2 in summerwood

x_3 = springwood %

x_4 = % springwood light absorption

x_5 = % summerwood light absorption

The data is displayed in the accompanying table. Consider $x_1, x_2, \ldots, x_5$ as the set of potential predictors ($p = 5$, with no derived predictors such as squares or interaction terms as candidates for inclusion). Then there are $2^5 = 32$ possible models, among which 5 consist of a single predictor, 10 involve two predictors, 10 others involve three predictors, and 5 include four predictor variables. We used a statistical computer package to fit each possible model and extracted both R^2 and adjusted R^2 from the output. To save space, results appear for all one- and four-predictor models but only for the five best two- and three-predictor models.

---

[1] When n observations are used to fit a model that contains k predictors,

$$\text{adjusted } R^2 = 1 - \left[\frac{n - 1}{n - (k + 1)} \right] \cdot \frac{\text{SSResid}}{\text{SSTo}}$$

Since the quantity in square brackets exceeds 1, the number subtracted from 1 is larger than SSResid/SSTo, so adjusted R^2 is smaller than R^2. R^2 itself must be between 0 and 1, but adjusted R^2 can be negative.

	x_1	x_2	x_3	x_4	x_5	y
1	573	1059	46.5	53.8	84.1	.534
2	651	1356	52.7	54.5	88.7	.535
3	606	1273	49.4	52.1	92.0	.570
4	630	1151	48.9	50.3	87.9	.528
5	547	1135	53.1	51.9	91.5	.548
6	557	1236	54.9	55.2	91.4	.555
7	489	1231	56.2	45.5	82.4	.481
8	685	1564	56.6	44.3	91.3	.516
9	536	1182	59.2	46.4	85.4	.475
10	685	1564	63.1	56.4	91.4	.486
11	664	1588	50.6	48.1	86.7	.554
12	703	1335	51.9	48.4	81.2	.519
13	653	1395	62.5	51.9	89.2	.492
14	586	1114	50.5	56.5	88.9	.517
15	534	1143	52.1	57.0	88.9	.502
16	523	1320	50.5	61.2	91.9	.508
17	580	1249	54.6	60.8	95.4	.520
18	448	1028	52.2	53.4	91.8	.506
19	476	1057	42.9	53.2	92.9	.595
20	528	1057	42.4	56.6	90.0	.568

It is immediately clear that the best three-predictor models offer considerable improvement with respect to both R^2 and adjusted R^2 over any model containing one or two predictors and that the model with all five predictors is inferior to the best four-predictor model. The best four-predictor model has the largest value of adjusted R^2 (.709), but the best three-predictor model is not far behind. The five models that seem most appealing to us are color-tinted in the display of results. The selection of a single model would have to be based on a more detailed comparison of these five models, with special attention given to residuals and other diagnostics (to be mentioned shortly) that bear on model adequacy. In particular, it is dangerous to embrace the model with the largest adjusted R^2 value automatically and reject all other models out of hand.

	Models with one predictor				
Predictor	x_3	x_5	x_2	x_4	x_1
R^2	$R^2_{(1)} = .564$	.106	.053	.020	.008
Adjusted R^2	.539	.057	.001	−.034	−.047

	Models with two predictors				
Predictors	x_3, x_5	x_2, x_3	x_1, x_3	x_3, x_4	x_2, x_5
R^2	$R^2_{(2)} = .655$	.621	.603	.564	.158
Adjusted R^2	.614	.576	.556	.513	.059

Models with three predictors

Predictors	X_1, X_3, X_5	X_3, X_4, X_5	X_2, X_3, X_5	X_1, X_2, X_3	X_2, X_3, X_4
R^2	$R_{(3)}^2 = .723$	.712	.711	.622	.611
Adjusted R^2	.671	.659	.657	.551	.550

Models with four predictors

Predictors	X_1, X_3, X_4, X_5	X_2, X_3, X_4, X_5	X_1, X_2, X_3, X_5	X_1, X_2, X_3, X_4	X_1, X_2, X_4, X_5
R^2	$R_{(4)}^2 = .770$	.748	.727	.622	.239
Adjusted R^2	.709	.681	.654	.522	.036

The model with all five predictors included has $R_{(5)}^2 = .770$, adjusted $R^2 = .689$.

There are various other criteria that have been proposed and used for model selection after fitting all subsets. A chapter reference can be consulted for more details.

When using particular criteria as a basis for model selection, many of the 2^p possible subset models are not serious candidates because of poor criteria values. For example, if $p = 15$ there are 5005 different models consisting of six predictor variables, many of which typically have small R^2 and adjusted R^2 values. An investigator usually wishes to consider only a few of the best models of each different size (a model whose criteria value is close to the best one may be easier to interpret than the best model or may include a predictor that the investigator thinks should be in the selected model). In recent years statisticians have developed computer programs to achieve this without actually fitting all possible models. One version of such a program has been implemented in the BMDP statistical computer package and can be used as long as $p \le 26$ (there are roughly 67 million possible models when $p = 26$, so fitting them all would be out of the question). The user specifies a number between 1 and 10 as the number of models of each given size for which output will be provided. Output includes R^2, adjusted R^2, estimated model coefficients, and a few other quantities. After the choice of models is narrowed down, the analyst can request more detail on each finalist.

EXAMPLE 14.19

The accompanying data was taken from the paper "Applying Stepwise Multiple Regression Analysis to the Reaction of Formaldehyde with Cotton Cellulose" (*Textile Research J.* (1984):157–165). The dependent variable

y = durable press rating

is a quantitative measure of wrinkle resistance. The four independent variables used in the model building process are

x_1 = HCHO (formaldehyde) concentration
x_2 = catalyst ratio

x_3 = curing temperature

x_4 = curing time

In addition to these, the investigators considered as potential predictors x_1^2, x_2^2, x_3^2, x_4^2, and all six cross products $x_1 x_2$, . . . , $x_3 x_4$, a total of $p = 14$ candidates. We display BMDP output for the best three subset models of each size from $k = 4$ predictor variables up to $k = 9$ predictor variables. In addition to R^2 and adjusted R^2, values of another criterion, called *Mallow's CP,* are included. A good model according to this criterion is one that has small CP (for accurate predictions) and CP $\approx k + 1$ (for unbiasedness in estimating model coefficients).

The choice of a best model here is, as often happens, not clear-cut. We certainly don't see the benefit of including more than $k = 8$ predictor variables (after that, adjusted R^2 begins to decrease), nor would we suggest a model with fewer than five predictors (adjusted R^2 is still increasing and CP is large). Based just on this output, the best six-predictor model is a reasonable choice. The corresponding estimated regression function is

$$-1.218 + .9599x_2 - .0373x_1^2 - .0389x_2^2 + .0037x_1 x_3$$
$$+ .019x_1 x_4 - .0013x_2 x_3$$

Another good candidate is the best seven-predictor model. Although it includes one more predictor than the model just suggested, only one of the seven predictors is a cross-product term ($x_1 x_3$), so model interpretation is somewhat easier (notice, though, that none of the best three models with seven predictors results simply from adding a single predictor to the best six-predictor model). Since every good model includes $x_1, x_2, x_3,$ and x_4 in some predictor, it appears that HCHO concentration, catalyst ratio, curing time, and curing temperature are all important determinants of durable press rating.

Observation	x_1	x_2	x_3	x_4	y	Observation	x_1	x_2	x_3	x_4	y
1	8	4	100	1	1.4	16	4	10	160	5	4.6
2	2	4	180	7	2.2	17	4	13	100	7	4.3
3	7	4	180	1	4.6	18	10	10	120	7	4.9
4	10	7	120	5	4.9	19	5	4	100	1	1.7
5	7	4	180	5	4.6	20	8	13	140	1	4.6
6	7	7	180	1	4.7	21	10	1	180	1	2.6
7	7	13	140	1	4.6	22	2	13	140	1	3.1
8	5	4	160	7	4.5	23	6	13	180	7	4.7
9	4	7	140	3	4.8	24	7	1	120	7	2.5
10	5	1	100	7	1.4	25	5	13	140	1	4.5
11	8	10	140	3	4.7	26	8	1	160	7	2.1
12	2	4	100	3	1.6	27	4	1	180	7	1.8
13	4	10	180	3	4.5	28	6	1	160	1	1.5
14	6	7	120	7	4.7	29	4	1	100	1	1.3
15	10	13	180	3	4.8	30	7	10	100	7	4.6

R-SQUARED	ADJUSTED R-SQUARED	CP	VARIABLE	COEFFICIENT	T-STATISTIC
.822152	.793697	13.88	X2	.719972	6.34
			X4	.100399	2.23
			X2SQ	−.0353810	−4.50
			X1X3	.00136851	4.67
			INTERCEPT	−.567677	
.820829	.792161	14.13	X2	.739574	6.48
			X2SQ	−.0366689	−4.66
			X4SQ	.0120970	2.18
			X1X3	.00137952	4.68
			INTERCEPT	−.500064	
.817380	.788160	14.79	X2	.725317	6.30
			X2SQ	−.0357036	−4.49
			X1X3	.00129562	4.39
			X3X4	.000620500	2.05
			INTERCEPT	−.469898	

R-SQUARED	ADJUSTED R-SQUARED	CP	VARIABLE	COEFFICIENT	T-STATISTIC
.866735	.838971	7.39	X2	.755757	7.42
			X1SQ	−.0249950	−3.24
			X2SQ	−.0377513	−5.37
			X1X3	.00261758	4.97
			X1X4	.0194928	3.11
			INTERCEPT	−.751386	
.855228	.825068	9.58	X2	.760646	7.17
			X4	.109915	2.64
			X1SQ	−.0173769	−2.34
			X2SQ	−.0379611	−5.19
			X1X3	.00246978	4.56
			INTERCEPT	−.936857	
.855015	.824810	9.62	X2	.783083	7.36
			X1SQ	−.0176972	−2.38
			X2SQ	−.0394252	−5.39
			X4SQ	.0134874	2.63
			X1X3	.00250377	4.60
			INTERCEPT	−.876926	

SUBSETS WITH _6_VARIABLES

R-SQUARED	ADJUSTED R-SQUARED	CP	VARIABLE	COEFFICIENT	T-STATISTIC
.884952	.854939	5.92	X2	.959914	6.66
			X1SQ	−.0372760	−3.82
			X2SQ	−.0389469	−5.82
			X1X3	.00368402	4.91
			X1X4	.0192505	3.23
			X2X3	−.00128271	−1.91
			INTERCEPT	−1.21835	
.881662	.850791	6.54	X2	.779668	7.93
			X4	.408872	2.98
			X1SQ	−.0313804	−3.40
			X2SQ	−.0394407	−5.81
			X1X3	.00356717	5.12
			X3X4	−.00208494	−2.27
			INTERCEPT	−1.34754	
.880382	.849177	6.79	X2	.760472	7.71
			X1SQ	−.0380752	−3.46
			X2SQ	−.0383770	−5.64
			X1X3	.00319522	5.13
			X1X4	.0384039	2.92
			X3X4	−.000908222	−1.62
			INTERCEPT	−.632344	

SUBSETS WITH _7_VARIABLES

R-SQUARED	ADJUSTED R-SQUARED	CP	VARIABLE	COEFFICIENT	T-STATISTIC
.899208	.867138	5.20	X2	.800294	8.40
			X3	.0966644	2.41
			X4	.129477	3.49
			X1SQ	−.0392306	−3.13
			X2SQ	−.0416758	−6.35
			X3SQ	−.000388272	−2.70
			X1X3	.00435437	4.08
			INTERCEPT	−7.27515	
.898832	.866643	5.27	X2	.825845	8.60
			X3	.0974167	2.42
			X1SQ	−.0392516	−3.12
			X2SQ	−.0433512	−6.57
			X3SQ	−.000390110	−2.71
			X4SQ	.0158501	3.47
			X1X3	.00436212	4.08
			INTERCEPT	−7.25606	

.896670	.863792	5.68	VARIABLE	COEFFICIENT	T-STATISTIC
			X2	.786050	8.15
			X3	.0820370	2.02
			X1SQ	−.0413732	−3.21
			X2SQ	−.0407510	−6.13
			X3SQ	−.000325208	−2.24
			X1X3	.00401885	3.79
			X1X4	.0195025	3.36
			INTERCEPT	−6.06342	

SUBSETS WITH 8 VARIABLES

R-SQUARED	ADJUSTED R-SQUARED	CP	VARIABLE	COEFFICIENT	T-STATISTIC
.915161	.882841	4.16	VARIABLE	COEFFICIENT	T-STATISTIC
			X2	.775486	8.58
			X3	.109369	2.86
			X4	.455906	2.71
			X1SQ	−.0340476	−2.82
			X2SQ	−.0404306	−6.52
			X3SQ	−.000385008	−2.85
			X1X3	.00371235	3.53
			X3X4	−.00237915	−1.99
			INTERCEPT	−8.68827	
.905701	.869777	5.96	VARIABLE	COEFFICIENT	T-STATISTIC
			X2	.845585	8.79
			X3	.104772	2.61
			X1SQ	−.0364813	−2.89
			X2SQ	−.0448477	−6.76
			X3SQ	−.000390164	−2.74
			X4SQ	.0360597	2.13
			X1X3	.00403009	3.69
			X3X4	−.00121700	−1.24
			INTERCEPT	−7.93925	
.904737	.868446	6.15	VARIABLE	COEFFICIENT	T-STATISTIC
			X2	.923957	6.59
			X3	.0788275	1.97
			X1SQ	−.0432398	−3.40
			X2SQ	−.0405590	−6.20
			X3SQ	−.000297392	−2.06
			X1X3	.00417478	3.98
			X1X4	.0190484	3.34
			X2X3	−.000964844	−1.33
			INTERCEPT	−6.25679	

SUBSETS WITH 9 VARIABLES

R-SQUARED	ADJUSTED R-SQUARED	CP	VARIABLE	COEFFICIENT	T-STATISTIC
.916768	.879313	5.86	VARIABLE	COEFFICIENT	T-STATISTIC
			X1	.169779	.62
			X2	.761409	8.06
			X3	.106348	2.72
			X4	.464198	2.72

			VARIABLE	COEFFICIENT	T-STATISTIC
			X1SQ	−.0395106	−2.62
			X2SQ	−.0394067	−6.06
			X3SQ	−.000358450	−2.50
			X1X3	.00301598	1.95
			X3X4	−.00248516	−2.03
			INTERCEPT	−8.96140	
.916069	.878301	5.99	VARIABLE	COEFFICIENT	T-STATISTIC
			X2	.826844	5.75
			X3	.106946	2.72
			X4	.425886	2.33
			X1SQ	−.0350603	−2.81
			X2SQ	−.0404567	−6.40
			X3SQ	−.000374296	−2.68
			X1X3	.00380925	3.48
			X2X3	−.000346329	−.47
			X3X4	−.00217879	−1.68
			INTERCEPT	−8.61679	
.916046	.878267	5.99	VARIABLE	COEFFICIENT	T-STATISTIC
			X2	.769047	8.25
			X3	.103502	2.52
			X4	.410687	2.08
			X1SQ	−.0351573	−2.81
			X2SQ	−.0400069	−6.27
			X3SQ	−.000358782	−2.41
			X1X3	.00357947	3.22
			X1X4	.00847361	.46
			X3X4	−.00243189	−1.98
			INTERCEPT	−8.22400	

The most easily understood and implemented automatic selection procedure is referred to as **backward elimination.** It involves starting with the model that contains all p potential predictors and then deleting them one by one until all remaining predictors seem important. The first step is to specify the value of a positive constant t_{out}, which is used to decide whether deletion should be continued. After fitting the p predictor model, the t ratios $b_1/s_{b_1}, b_2/s_{b_2}, \ldots, b_p/s_{b_p}$ are examined. The predictor variable whose t ratio is closest to zero, whether positive or negative, is the obvious candidate for deletion. If this t ratio satisfies the inequalities $-t_{out} \leq t$ ratio $\leq t_{out}$, the corresponding predictor is eliminated from the model. Suppose that this is the case. The model with the remaining $p - 1$ predictors is then fit, and again the predictor with the t ratio closest to zero is eliminated, provided that it satisfies $-t_{out} \leq t$ ratio $\leq t_{out}$. The procedure continues until, at some stage, no t ratio satisfies $-t_{out} \leq t$ ratio $\leq t_{out}$ (all are either greater than t_{out} or less than $-t_{out}$). The chosen model is then the last one fit (though some analysts recommend examining other models of the same size). It is customary to use $t_{out} = 2$, since many t critical values for a two-tailed test with level of significance .05 are close to this value.[2]

---

[2]Some computer packages base the procedure on the squares of the t ratios, which are F ratios, and continue to delete as long as F ratio $\leq F_{out}$ for at least one predictor. The predictor with the smallest F ratio is eliminated. $F_{out} = 4$ corresponds to $t_{out} = 2$.

EXAMPLE 14.20

We display MINITAB output resulting from the application of the backward elimination procedure with $t_{out} = 2$ to the specific gravity data introduced in Example 14.18. The t ratio closest to zero when the model with all five predictors was fit was .12, so the corresponding predictor x_2 was deleted from the model. When the model with the four remaining predictors was fit, the t ratio closest to zero was -1.76, which satisfied $-2 \leq -1.76 \leq 2$. Thus the corresponding predictor, x_4, was eliminated, leaving x_1, x_3, and x_5 still in the model. The next predictor to be dropped was x_1 because its t ratio, 1.98, was the one closest to zero and (barely) satisfied $-2 \leq 1.98 \leq 2$. When the model with predictors x_3 and x_5 was fit, neither t ratio satisfied $-2 \leq t$ ratio ≤ 2, so the procedure terminated. Looking back to Example 14.18, this is actually the best model containing just two predictors. However, x_1 just barely met the elimination criterion, so the model with predictors x_1, x_3, and x_5 should also be given serious consideration.

STEP	1	2	3	4
CONSTANT	0.4421	0.4384	0.4381	0.5179
X1	0.00011	0.00011	0.00012	
T-RATIO	1.17	1.95	1.98	
X2	0.00001			
T-RATIO	0.12			
X3	−0.00531	−0.00526	−0.00498	−0.00438
T-RATIO	−5.70	−6.56	−5.96	−5.20
X4	−0.0018	−0.0019		
T-RATIO	−1.63	−1.76		
X5	0.0044	0.0044	0.0031	0.0027
T-RATIO	3.01	3.31	2.63	2.12
S	0.0180	0.0174	0.0185	0.0200
R-SQ	77.05	77.03	72.27	65.50

Unfortunately, the backward elimination method does not always terminate with a model that is the best of its size, and this is also true of other automatic selection procedures. For example, the authors of the paper mentioned in Example 14.19 used an automatic procedure to obtain a six-predictor model with $R^2 = .77$, whereas all of the 10 best six-predictor models have R^2 values of at least .87. Because of this, we recommend using a statistical computer package which will identify best subsets of different sizes whenever possible.

Checks on Model Adequacy

In Chapter 13 we discussed some informal techniques for checking the adequacy of the simple linear regression model. Most of these were based on plots involving the standardized residuals. The formula for standardizing residuals in multiple regression is quite complicated, but again it has been programmed into many statistical computer packages. Once the standardized residuals resulting from the fit of a particular model have been computed, plots similar to those discussed earlier are useful in diagnosing model defects. A normal probability plot of the standardized residuals that departs too much from a straight line casts doubt on the assumption that the random deviation e has a normal distribution. Plots of the standardized residuals against each predictor variable in the model—that is, a plot of (x_1, standardized residual) pairs, another of (x_2, standardized residual) pairs, and so on— are analogous to the standardized residual versus x plot discussed and illustrated in the previous chapter. The appearance of any discernible pattern in these plots (for example, curvature or increasing spread from left to right) points to the need for model modification. If observations have been made over time, a periodic pattern when the standardized residuals are plotted in time order suggests that successive observations were not independent. Models that incorporate dependence of successive observations are substantially more complicated than those we have presented here. They are especially important in econometrics, which involves using statistical methodology to model economic data. Please consult one of the references in Chapter 4 for more information.

One other aspect of model adequacy that has received much attention from statisticians in recent years is the identification of any observations in the data set that may have been highly influential in estimating model coefficients. Recall that in simple linear regression, an observation with potentially high influence was one whose x value placed it far to the right or left of the other points in the scatter plot or standardized residual plot. If a multiple regression model involves only two predictor variables x_1 and x_2, an observation with potentially large influence can be revealed by examining a plot of (x_1, x_2) pairs. Any point in this plot that is far away from the others corresponds to an observation which, if deleted from the sample, may cause coefficient estimates and other quantities to change considerably. The detection of influential observations when the model contains at least three predictors is more difficult. Recent research has yielded several helpful diagnostic quantities. One of these has been implemented in MINITAB, and a large value of this quantity automatically results in the corresponding observation being identified as one that might have great influence. Deleting the observation and refitting the model will reveal the extent of actual influence (which depends on how consistent the corresponding y observation is with the rest of the data).

Multicollinearity

When the simple linear regression model is fit using sample data in which the x values are all close to one another, small changes in observed y's can cause the values of the estimated coefficients a and b to change considerably. This may well result in standard deviations σ_b and σ_a that are quite large, so that estimates of β and α from any given sample are likely to differ greatly from the true values. There is an analogous condition that leads to this same type of behavior in multiple regression—a configuration of predictor variable values that is likely to result in poorly estimated model coefficients.

Consider first the case in which a model involving just two predictor variables x_1 and x_2 is to be fit. Suppose that the sample (x_1, x_2) pairs are those displayed in the scatter plot of Figure 14.12(a) and on the ground in the three-dimensional representation of Figure 14.12(b). An obvious characteristic of the (x_1, x_2) plot is the strong linear relationship between x_1 and x_2. Each sample observation (x_1, x_2, y) is a point in three dimensions, as pictured in Figure 14.12(b). Recall that the principle of least squares to estimate coefficients α, β_1, and β_2 amounts to finding the plane (flat surface) that has the smallest sum of squared deviations between it and the given points—the best-fit plane. Now suppose that the y observations made at the three points falling above the straight line in Figure 14.12(a)—the colored points in Figure 14.12(b)—are increased a bit and the y values at the other three points are decreased somewhat. Such small changes in y considerably change the tilt of the least squares plane and thus the values of a, b_1 and b_2. That is, even a small amount of variability in y (small σ^2 in the model) translates into a considerable amount of variability in a, b_1, and b_2. Trying to fit a plane here is like trying to rest a cardboard sheet on a picket fence—the result is very unstable.

FIGURE 14.12
An illustration of multicollinearity
(a) a scatter plot of predictor variable values that shows a strong linear relationship (multicollinearity)
(b) y observations made at (x_1, x_2) pairs shown in (a)

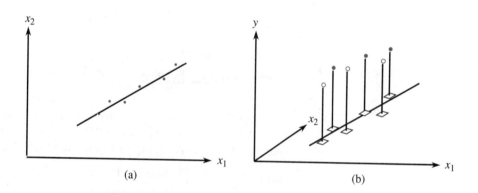

(a)

(b)

This instability would not have occurred had the sample (x_1, x_2) points been more spread out and not fallen so close to a straight line (try to visualize in this case how small changes in y would not have much effect on the best-fit plane). More generally, when the model to be fit includes k predictors $x_1, x_2, \ldots, x_k$, there is said to be **multicollinearity** if there is a strong linear relationship between values of the predictors. Severe multicollinearity leads to instability of estimated coefficients as well as various other problems. Such a relationship is difficult to visualize when $k > 2$, so statisticians have developed various quantitative indicators to measure the extent of multicollinearity in a data set. The most straightforward approach involves computing R^2 values for regressions in which the dependent variable is taken to be one of the k x's and the predictors are the remaining $k - 1$ x's. For example, when $k = 3$ there are three relevant regressions:

1. Dependent variable $= x_1$, predictor variables $= x_2$ and x_3
2. Dependent variable $= x_2$, predictor variables $= x_1$ and x_3
3. Dependent variable $= x_3$, predictor variables $= x_1$ and x_2

Each regression yields an R^2 value. In general, there are k such regressions and, therefore, k resulting R^2 values. If one or more of these R^2 values is large (close to one), multicollinearity is present. MINITAB will print a message saying that the predictors are highly correlated when at least one of the k R^2 values exceeds .99 and will refuse to include a predictor in the model if the corresponding R^2 value is larger than .9999. Other analysts are more conservative and would judge multicollinearity to be a potential problem if any of these R^2 values exceeded .9.

When predictor variable values are under the control of the investigator, which often happens in scientific experimentation, a careful choice of values will preclude multicollinearity from arising. Multicollinearity does frequently occur in social science and business applications of regression analysis, where data results simply from observation rather than from intervention by an experimenter. Statisticians have proposed various remedies for the problems associated with multicollinearity in such situations, but a discussion would take us beyond the scope of this book. (After all, we want to leave something for your next statistics course!)

EXERCISES 14.45–14.55   SECTION 14.4

14.45   The paper "The Caseload Controversy and the Study of Criminal Courts" (*J. Criminal Law and Criminology* (1979):89–101) used multiple regression to analyze a data set consisting of observations on the variables

y = length of sentence in trial case (months)

x_1 = seriousness of first offense

x_2 = dummy variable indicating type of trial (bench or jury)

x_3 = number of legal motions

x_4 = measure of delay for confined defendants (0 for those not confined)

x_5 = measure of judge's caseload

The estimated regression equation proposed by the authors is

$$\hat{y} = 12.6 + .59x_1 - 70.8x_2 - 33.6x_3 - 15.5x_5 + .0007x_6 + 3x_7 - 41.5x_8$$

where $x_6 = x_4^2$, $x_7 = x_1x_2$, and $x_8 = x_3x_5$. How do you think the authors might have arrived at this particular model?

14.46   The paper "Histologic Estimation of Age at Death Using the Anterior Cortex of the Femur" (*Amer. J. Phys. Anthro.* (1991):171–179) developed multiple regression models to relate y = age at death to a number of different histologic predictor variables. Stepwise regression (an automatic selection procedure favored over the backward elimination method by many statisticians) was used to identify the following models for the case of females.

Predictors	R^2	Adjusted R^2
x_6	.60	.60
x_3, x_6	.66	.66
x_3, x_5	.68	.68
$x_2, x_3, x_5,$	.69	.68
x_2, x_3, x_5, x_6	.70	.69
x_2, x_3, x_4, x_5, x_6	.71	.70
$x_1, x_2, x_3, x_4, x_5, x_6$	.71	.70
$x_1, x_2, x_3, x_4, x_5, x_6, x_7$	.71	.70
$x_1, x_2, x_3, x_5, x_6, x_7, x_8$	.72	.71
$x_1, x_2, x_3, x_4, x_5, x_6, x_7, x_8$	.72	.70

Based on the given information, which of these models would you recommend using, and why?

14.47 The article "The Analysis and Selection of Variables in Linear Regression" (*Biometrics* (1976):1–49) reports on an analysis of data taken from the 1974 issues of *Motor Trend* magazine. The dependent variable y was gas mileage, there were $n = 32$ observations, and the independent variables were

x_1 = engine type (1 = straight, 0 = V)

x_2 = number of cylinders

x_3 = transmission type (1 = manual, 0 = automatic)

x_4 = number of transmission speeds

x_5 = engine size

x_6 = horsepower

x_7 = number of carburetor barrels

x_8 = final drive ratio

x_9 = weight

x_{10} = quarter-mile time

The R^2 and adjusted R^2 values are given for the best model using k predictors for $k = 1, \ldots, 10$.

k	Variables included	R^2	Adjusted R^2
1	x_9	.756	.748
2	x_2, x_9	.833	.821
3	x_3, x_9, x_{10}	.852	.836
4	x_3, x_6, x_9, x_{10}	.860	.839
5	$x_3, x_5, x_6, x_9, x_{10}$	.866	.840
6	$x_3, x_5, x_6, x_8, x_9, x_{10}$	.869	.837
7	$x_3, x_4, x_5, x_6, x_8, x_9, x_{10}$	.870	.832
8	$x_3, x_4, x_5, x_6, x_7, x_8, x_9, x_{10}$	.871	.826
9	$x_1, x_3, x_4, x_5, x_6, x_7, x_8, x_9, x_{10}$	.871	.818
10	All independent variables	.871	.809

What model would you select? Explain your choice and the criteria used to reach your decision.

14.48   The paper "Estimation of the Economic Threshold of Infestation for Cotton Aphid" (*Mesopotamia J. Ag.* (1982):71–75) gave $n = 34$ observations on

$y =$ infestation rate (number of aphids per 100 leaves)

$x_1 =$ mean temperature (°C)

$x_2 =$ mean relative humidity

Partial SAS computer output resulting from fitting the model $y = \alpha + \beta_1 x_1 + \beta_2 x_2 + e$ to the data given in the paper is shown. If the method of backward elimination is to be employed, which variable would be the first candidate for elimination? Using the criteria of eliminating a variable if its t ratio satisfies $-2 \le t$ ratio ≤ 2, can it be eliminated from the model?

| | | | R-SQUARE | 0.5008 |
| | | | ADJ R-SQ | 0.4533 |

VARIABLE	DF	PARAMETER ESTIMATE	STANDARD ERROR	T FOR HO: PARAMETER = 0
INTERCEP	1	15.667014	84.157420	0.186
TEMP	1	−0.360928	2.330835	−0.155
RH	1	1.959715	0.576946	2.877

14.49   The accompanying data appeared in the paper "Breeding Success of the Common Puffin on Different Habitats at Great Island, Newfoundland" (*Ecol. Monographs* (1972):246–252). The variables considered are $y =$ nesting frequency (burrows per 9 m²), $x_1 =$ grass cover (%), $x_2 =$ mean soil depth (cm), $x_3 =$ angle of slope (degrees), and $x_4 =$ distance from cliff edge (m).

y	x_1	x_2	x_3	x_4	y	x_1	x_2	x_3	x_4
16	45	39.2	38	3	16	60	37.1	35	6
15	65	47.0	36	12	25	60	47.1	35	12
10	40	24.3	14	18	13	85	34.0	23	18
7	20	30.0	16	21	13	90	43.6	12	21
11	40	47.6	6	27	11	20	30.8	9	27
7	80	47.6	9	36	3	85	34.6	6	33
4	80	45.6	7	39	0	30	37.7	8	42
0	15	27.8	8	45	0	75	45.5	5	48
0	0	41.9	8	54	0	15	51.4	8	54
0	20	36.8	5	60	18	40	32.1	36	6
15	40	34.9	31	3	19	40	35.4	37	9
21	60	45.2	37	12	8	90	30.2	11	18
12	95	32.9	24	18	12	80	33.9	9	24
8	50	26.6	11	24	10	80	40.2	11	30
9	80	32.7	10	30	3	75	33.5	7	36
6	80	38.1	5	36	0	65	40.3	10	42

(continued)

y	x_1	x_2	x_3	x_4	y	x_1	x_2	x_3	x_4
0	60	31.4	5	39	0	80	40.3	12	45
0	70	32.7	2	48	0	50	43.1	13	51
0	35	38.1	8	51	0	50	42.0	3	57

MINITAB output resulting from application of the backward elimination procedure is given. Explain what action was taken at each step and why.

```
      STEP          1          2          3
   CONSTANT       12.29      11.45      13.96

   X1            -0.019
   T-RATIO       -0.70

   X2            -0.043     -0.043
   T-RATIO       -1.42      -1.42

   X3             0.224      0.225      0.176
   T-RATIO        2.91       2.94       2.54

   X4            -0.182     -0.203     -0.293
   T-RATIO       -2.12      -2.55      -6.01

   S              2.83       2.81       2.85
   R-SQ          86.20      85.99      85.16
```

14.50 *This exercise requires use of a computer package.* Using a statistical computer package, compare the best one-, two-, three-, and four-predictor models for the data given in Exercise 14.49. Does this variable-selection procedure lead you to the same choice of model as the backward elimination employed in Exercise 14.49?

14.51 The formulas for R^2 and adjusted R^2 are

$$R^2 = 1 - \frac{\text{SSResid}}{\text{SSTo}}$$

$$\text{adjusted } R^2 = 1 - \left(\frac{n-1}{n-(k+1)}\right) \cdot \frac{\text{SSResid}}{\text{SSTo}}$$

When would adjusted R^2 be substantially smaller than R^2?

14.52 Referring to the formula given in Exercise 14.51, if $n = 21$ and $k = 10$, for what values of R^2 would adjusted R^2 be negative?

14.53 Suppose you were considering a multiple regression analysis with y = house price, x_1 = number of bedrooms, x_2 = number of bathrooms, and x_3 = total number of rooms. Do you think that multicollinearity might be a problem? Explain.

14.54 *This exercise requires use of a computer package.* The accompanying $n = 25$ observations on y = catch at intake (number of fish), x_1 = water temperature (°C), x_2 = minimum tide height (m), x_3 = number of pumps running, x_4 = speed (knots), x_5 = wind–range of direction (degrees) constitute a subset of the data that appeared in the paper "Multiple Regression Analysis for Forecasting Critical Fish

Influxes at Power Station Intakes" (*J. Applied Ecol.* (1983):33–42). Use the variable-selection procedures discussed in this section to formulate a model.

y	x_1	x_2	x_3	x_4	x_5	y	x_1	x_2	x_3	x_4	x_5
17	6.7	.5	4	10	50	3	15.8	1.6	3	7	120
42	7.8	1.0	4	24	30	7	16.2	.4	3	10	50
1	9.9	1.2	4	17	120	9	15.8	1.2	3	9	60
11	10.1	.5	4	23	30	10	16.0	.8	3	12	90
8	10.0	.9	4	18	20	7	16.2	1.2	3	5	160
30	8.7	.8	4	9	160	12	17.1	.7	3	10	90
2	10.3	1.5	4	13	40	12	17.5	.8	3	12	110
6	10.5	.3	4	10	150	26	17.5	1.2	3	18	130
11	11.0	1.2	3	9	50	14	17.4	.8	3	9	60
14	11.2	.6	3	7	100	18	17.4	1.1	3	13	30
53	12.9	1.8	3	10	90	14	17.8	.5	3	8	160
9	13.2	.2	3	12	50	5	18.0	1.6	3	10	40
4	16.2	.7	3	6	80						

14.55 Given that $R^2 = .723$ for the model containing predictors x_1, x_4, x_5, and x_8 and $R^2 = .689$ for the model with predictors x_1, x_3, x_5, and x_6,

a. What can you say about R^2 for the model containing predictors x_1, x_3, x_4, x_5, x_6, and x_8? Explain.

b. What can you say about R^2 for the model containing predictors x_1 and x_4? Explain.

CHAPTER FOURTEEN SUMMARY OF KEY CONCEPTS AND FORMULAS

Term or Formula	Comment
Additive multiple regression model, $y = \alpha + \beta_1 x_1 + \cdots + \beta_k x_k + e$	This equation specifies a general probabilistic relationship between y and k predictor variables $x_1, x_2, \ldots, x_k$, where $\beta_1, \ldots, \beta_k$ are population regression coefficients and $\alpha + \beta_1 x_1 + \cdots + \beta_k x_k$ is the population regression function (the mean value of y for fixed values of $x_1, \ldots, x_k$).
Estimated regression function, $\hat{y} = a + b_1 x_1 + \cdots + b_k x_k$	The estimates $a, b_1, \ldots, b_k$ of $\alpha, \beta_1, \ldots, \beta_k$ result from applying the principle of least squares.
Coefficient of multiple determination, $R^2 = 1 - \dfrac{\text{SSResid}}{\text{SSTo}}$	The proportion of observed y variation that can be explained by the model relationship, where SSResid is defined as in simple linear regression but is now based on $n - (k + 1)$ degrees of freedom.
Adjusted R^2	A downward adjustment of R^2 that depends on the number of predictors k relative to the sample size n.

Term or Formula	Comment
F distribution	A type of probability distribution used in many different inferential procedures. A particular F distribution results from specifying both numerator df and denominator df.
$$F = \frac{R^2/k}{(1 - R^2)/[n - (k + 1)]}$$	The test statistic for testing $H_0: \beta_1 = \beta_2 = \cdots = \beta_k = 0$, which asserts that there is no useful linear relationship between y and any of the model predictors. The statistic F is compared to an F critical value which is based on k numerator df and $n - (k + 1)$ denominator df.
$b_i \pm (t \text{ crit. val.}) \cdot s_{b_i}$	A confidence interval for the regression coefficient β_i (based on $n - (k + 1)$ df).
$$t = \frac{b_i - \text{hyp. val.}}{s_{b_i}}$$	The test statistic for testing hypotheses about β_i (based on $n - (k + 1)$ df).
$\hat{y} \pm (t \text{ crit. val.}) \cdot s_{\hat{y}}$ $\hat{y} \pm (t \text{ crit. val.}) \cdot \sqrt{s_e^2 + s_{\hat{y}}^2}$	A confidence interval for a mean y value and a prediction interval for a single y value when $x_1, \ldots, x_k$ have specified values, where $\hat{y} = a + b_1 x_1 + \cdots + b_k x_k$ and $s_{\hat{y}}$ denotes the estimated standard deviation of $\hat{y}$.
Model selection	An investigator may have data on many predictors that could be included in a model. There are two different approaches to choosing a model: (1) Use an *all-subsets procedure* to identify the best models of each different size (one-predictor models, two-predictor models, etc.) and then compare these according to criteria such as R^2 and adjusted R^2; (2) employ an *automatic selection procedure*, which either successively eliminates predictors until a stopping point is reached (backward elimination) or starts with no predictors and adds them successively until the inclusion of additional predictors cannot be justified.

ENCORE

The study introduced in the Chapter Preview was based on data from 88 school districts throughout the state of Washington. Relevant variables for the regression analysis are as follows:

y = average language score for fourth-grade students

Background variables:

x_1 = occupational index (% managerial and professional workers in the community)

x_2 = median income

Peer group variables:

x_3 = % Title I enrollment

x_4 = Hispanic enrollment ($= 1$ if $> 5\%$ and $= 0$ otherwise)

x_5 = logarithm of fourth-grade enrollment •

x_6 = prior test score (from 4 years previous to year under study)

School variables:

x_7 = administrator-teacher ratio

x_8 = pupil-teacher ratio

x_9 = certificated staff–pupil ratio

x_{10}, x_{11} = indicator variables for average teaching
experience (x_{10} = 1 if less than 3 years and 0 otherwise;
x_{11} = 1 if more than 6 years and 0 otherwise)

The accompanying table gives estimated coefficients, values of t ratios (b_1/s_{b_1}, b_2/s_{b_2}, and so on), and other relevant information.

Variable	Estimated coefficient	t-ratio
Constant	70.67	6.08
x_1	0.458	3.08
x_2	−0.000141	−0.59
x_3	−58.47	−4.02
x_4	−3.668	−1.73
x_5	−2.942	−2.34
x_6	0.200	3.60
x_7	17.93	0.42
x_8	0.689	0.42
x_9	−0.403	−0.27
x_{10}	−0.614	−1.30
x_{11}	−0.382	−0.58

$s_e = 5.57$ $R^2 = .64$

The value of the F statistic for testing model utility is

$$F = \frac{R^2/k}{(1 - R^2)/[n - (k + 1)]} = \frac{.64/11}{.36/(88 - 12)} = 12.28$$

The corresponding F critical value for a significance level of .01 is roughly 2.5 (the P-value is essentially 0), so there is clearly a useful linear relationship between y and at least one of the predictors.

The article cited in the Chapter Preview discussed a number of different aspects of this regression analysis, including a commentary on why certain predictors were included and others excluded in the chosen model. Mention was made of a residual analysis carried out to make sure that no single observation (especially that for Seattle, by far the largest of the districts) was overly influential in the estimated model (presumably examination of the residuals also led to use of the logarithm of enrollment rather than enrollment itself). The most interesting and relevant aspect of the analysis was that none of the school variables appeared to be an important determinant of test score; the t-ratio for each of these variables is quite close to zero. Sometimes the individual t-ratios can be misleading in this respect. There is an F test for testing $H_0: \beta_7 = \beta_8 = \beta_9 = \beta_{10} = \beta_{11} = 0$, which says that the school variables as a group don't provide useful information about y; although not mentioned, the investigators undoubtedly used this test to support their conclusions.

The regression that we reported on here was not the only one considered by the investigators. They also looked at fourth-grade math scores and eleventh-grade language and math scores and for each one considered a set of "expenditure" variables as an alternative to the school resource variables discussed here. This gave an additional seven different regressions, all of which resulted in essentially the same conclusion as that just presented: More money and/or other school resources do not seem to substantially impact school performance measures. This conclusion is certainly controversial. The opposing side attempted in various ways to discredit the analysis. The authors of *Statistics for Lawyers* (New York: Springer-Verlag, 1990), Michael Finkelstein and Bruce Levin, comment that the inclusion of prior test score as a predictor results in the importance of school variables being understated because predictions from the model then involve changes in scores rather than scores on some absolute scale. Clearly the issues raised in this investigation are far from being resolved.

SUPPLEMENTARY EXERCISES 14.56–14.63

14.56 The accompanying data on y = glucose concentration (g/L) and x = fermentation time (days) for a particular blend of malt liquor was read from a scatter plot appearing in the paper "Improving Fermentation Productivity with Reverse Osmosis" (*Food Tech.* (1984):92–96).

x	1	2	3	4	5	6	7	8
y	74	54	52	51	52	53	58	71

a. Construct a scatter plot for this data. Based on the scatter plot, what type of model would you suggest?

b. MINITAB output resulting from fitting a multiple regression model with $x_1 = x$ and $x_2 = x^2$ is given. Does this quadratic model specify a useful relationship between y and x?

```
THE REGRESSION EQUATION is
Y = 84.5 - 15.9 X1 + 1.77 X2

Predictor      Coef     Stdev    t-ratio
Constant     84.482     4.904     17.23
X1          -15.875     2.500     -6.35
X2           1.7679    0.2712      6.52

s = 3.515      R-sq = 89.5%
R-sq(adj) = 85.3%
```

c. Could the quadratic term have been eliminated? That is, would a simple linear model have sufficed? Test using a .05 significance level.

14.57 Much interest in management circles has recently focused on how employee compensation is related to various company characteristics. The paper "Determinants of R and D Compensation Strategies" (*Personnel Psych.* (1984):635–650) proposed a quantitative scale for y = base salary for employees of high-tech companies. The following estimated multiple regression equation was then presented:

$$\hat{y} = 2.60 + .125x_1 + .893x_2 + .057x_3 - .014x_4$$

where x_1 = sales volume (in millions of dollars), x_2 = stage in product life cycles (1 = growth, 0 = mature), x_3 = profitability (%), and x_4 = attrition rate (%).

a. There were $n = 33$ firms in the sample and R^2 = .69. Is the fitted model useful?

b. Predict base compensation for a growth stage firm with sales volume $50 million, profitability 8%, and attrition rate 12%.

c. The estimated standard deviations for the coefficient estimates were .064, .141, .014, and .005 for b_1, b_2, b_3, and b_4, respectively. Should any of the predictors be deleted from the model? Explain.

d. β_3 is the difference between average base compensation for growth stage and mature stage firms when all other predictors are held fixed. Use the information in (c) to calculate a 95% confidence interval for β_3.

14.58 A study of total body electrical conductivity was described in the article "Measurement of Total Body Electrical Conductivity: A New Method for Estimation of Body Composition" (*Amer. J. Clinical Nutr.* (1983):735–739). Nineteen observations were given for the variables y = total body electrical conductivity, x_1 = age (years), x_2 = sex (0 = male, 1 = female), x_3 = body mass (kg/m^2), x_4 = body fat (kg), x_5 = lean body mass (kg).

a. The backward elimination method of variable selection was employed, and MINITAB output is given. Explain what occurred at each step in the process.

```
STEPWISE REGRESSION OF Y ON 5
PREDICTORS, WITH N = 19

STEP            1        2        3
CONSTANT    -6.193  -13.285  -15.175

X1            0.31     0.36     0.38
T-RATIO       1.90     2.36     2.96
```

X2	-7.9	-7.5	-7.0
T-RATIO	-1.93	-1.89	-2.04
X3	-0.43		
T-RATIO	-0.72		
X4	0.22	0.03	
T-RATIO	0.78	0.29	
X5	0.365	0.339	0.378
T-RATIO	2.16	2.09	4.18
S	5.16	5.07	4.91
R-SQ	79.53	78.70	78.57

b. MINITAB output for the multiple regression model relating y to x_1, x_2, and x_5 is given. Interpret the values of R^2 and s_e.

```
THE REGRESSION EQUATION is
Y = - 15.2 + 0.377 X1 - 6.99 X2 +
0.378 X5

Predictor      Coef     Stdev   t-ratio
Constant    -15.175     9.620    -1.58
X1           0.3771    0.1273     2.96
X2           -6.988     3.425    -2.04
X5          0.37779   0.09047     4.18

s = 4.914    R-sq = 78.6%
R-sq(adj) = 74.3%
```

c. Interpret the value of b_2 in the estimated regression equation.

d. If the estimated standard deviation of the statistic $a + b_1(31) + b_2(1) + b_5(52.7)$ is 1.42, give a 95% confidence interval for the true mean total body electrical conductivity of all 31-year-old females whose lean body mass is 52.7 kg.

14.59 The paper "Creep and Fatigue Characteristics of Ferrocement Slabs" (*J. Ferrocement* (1984):309–322) reported data on y = tensile strength (MPa), x_1 = slab thickness (cm), x_2 = load (kg), x_3 = age at loading (days), and x_4 = time under test (days) resulting from stress tests of $n = 9$ reinforced concrete slabs. The backward elimination method of variable selection was applied. Given here is partial MINITAB output. Explain what action was taken at each step in the process. MINITAB output for the selected model is also given. Use the estimated regression equation to predict tensile strength for a slab that is 25 cm thick, 150 days old, and is subjected to a load of 200 kg for 50 days.

STEP	1	2	3
CONSTANT	8.496	12.670	12.989
X1	−0.29	−0.42	−0.49
T-RATIO	−1.33	−2.89	−3.14
X2	0.0104	0.0110	0.0116
T-RATIO	6.30	7.40	7.33
X3	0.0059		
T-RATIO	0.83		
X4	−0.023	−0.023	
T-RATIO	−1.48	−1.53	
S	0.533	0.516	0.570
R-SQ	95.81	95.10	92.82

THE REGRESSION EQUATION is
Y = 13.0 − .487 X1 + .0116 X2

Predictor	Coef	Stdev	t-ratio
Constant	12.989	3.640	3.57
X1	−0.4867	0.1549	−3.14
X2	0.011569	0.001579	7.33

s = 0.5698   R-sq = 92.8%
R-sq(adj) = 90.4%

14.60 A study of pregnant grey seals involved $n = 25$ observations on the variables y = fetus progesterone level (μg), x_1 = fetus sex (0 = male, 1 = female), x_2 = fetus length (cm), and x_3 = fetus weight (g). MINITAB output for the model using all three independent variables is given ("Gonadothrophin and Progesterone Concentration in Placenta of Grey Seals" *J. Repro. and Fertility* (1984):521–528).

THE REGRESSION EQUATION is
Y = −1.98 − 1.87 X1 + .234 X2 + .0001 X3

Predictor	Coef	Stdev	t-ratio
Constant	−1.982	4.290	−0.46
X1	−1.871	1.709	−1.09
X2	0.2340	0.1906	1.23
X3	0.000060	0.002020	0.03

s = 4.189   R-sq = 55.2%
R-sq(adj) = 48.8%

Analysis of Variance

SOURCE	DF	SS	MS	F	p
Regression	3	454.63	151.54	8.63	.001
Error	21	368.51	17.55		
Total	24	823.15			

a. Use information from the MINITAB output to test the hypothesis $H_0: \beta_1 = \beta_2 = \beta_3 = 0$.
b. Using an elimination criteria of $-2 \le t$ ratio ≤ 2, should any variable be eliminated? If so, which one?
c. MINITAB output for the regression using only x_1 = sex and x_2 = length is given. Would you recommend keeping both x_1 and x_2 in the model? Explain.

THE REGRESSION EQUATION is
Y = − 2.09 − 1.87 X1 + .240 X2

Predictor	Coef	Stdev	t-ratio
Constant	−2.090	2.212	−0.94
X1	−1.865	1.661	−1.12
X2	0.23952	0.04604	5.20

s = 4.093   R-sq = 55.2%
R-sq(adj) = 51.2%

d. After elimination of both x_3 and x_1, the estimated regression equation is $\hat{y} = -2.61 + .231x_2$. The corresponding values of R^2 and s_e are .527 and 4.116, respectively. Interpret these values.
e. Referring to (d), how would you interpret the value of $b_2 = .231$? Does it make sense to interpret the value of a as the estimate of average progesterone level when length is zero? Explain.

14.61 The authors of the paper "Influence of Temperature and Salinity on Development of White Perch Eggs" (*Trans. Amer. Fisheries Soc.* (1982):396–398) used a quadratic regression model to describe the relationship between y = percent hatch of white perch eggs and x = water temperature (°C). The estimated regression equation was given as $\hat{y} = -41.0 + 14.6x - .55x^2$.

a. Graph the curve corresponding to this equation by plotting the (x, y) pairs using x values of 10, 12, 14, 16, 18, 20, 22, and 24 (these are the temperatures used in the paper). Draw a smooth curve through the points in your plot.

b. The authors make the claim that the optimal temperature for hatch is 14° C. Based on your graph in (a), does this statement seem reasonable? Explain.

14.62 A sample of $n = 20$ companies was selected, and the values of $y =$ stock price and $k = 15$ predictor variables (such as quarterly dividend, previous year's earnings, debt ratio, and so on) were determined. When the multiple regression model with these 15 predictors was fit to the data, $R^2 = .90$ resulted.

a. Does the model appear to specify a useful relationship between y and the predictor variables? Carry out a test using significance level .05. (The F critical value for 15 numerator and 4 denominator df is 5.86.)

b. Based on the result of (a), does a high R^2 value by itself imply that a model is useful? Under what circumstances might you be suspicious of a model with a high R^2 value?

c. With n and k as given here, how large would R^2 have to be for the model to be judged useful at the .05 level of significance?

14.63 *This exercise requires the use of a computer package.* The paper "Entry and Profitability in a Rate-Free Savings and Loan Market" (*Quarterly Review of Econ. and Business* (1978):87–95) gave the accompanying data on $y =$ profit margin of savings and loan companies in a given year, $x_1 =$ net revenues in that year, and $x_2 =$ number of savings and loan branch offices.

x_1	x_2	y
3.92	7298	.75
3.61	6855	.71

x_1	x_2	y
3.32	6636	.66
3.07	6506	.61
3.06	6450	.70
3.11	6402	.72
3.21	6368	.77
3.26	6340	.74
3.42	6349	.90
3.42	6352	.82
3.45	6361	.75
3.58	6369	.77
3.66	6546	.78
3.78	6672	.84
3.82	6890	.79
3.97	7115	.70
4.07	7327	.68
4.25	7546	.72
4.41	7931	.55
4.49	8097	.63
4.70	8468	.56
4.58	8717	.41
4.69	8991	.51
4.71	9179	.47
4.78	9318	.32

a. Fit a multiple regression model using both independent variables.

b. Use the F test to determine if the model provides useful information for predicting profit margin.

c. Interpret the values of R^2 and s_e.

d. Would a regression model using a single independent variable (x_1 alone or x_2 alone) have sufficed? Explain.

e. Plot the (x_1, x_2) pairs. Does the plot indicate any sample observation that may have been highly influential in estimating the model coefficients? Explain. Do you see any evidence of multicollinearity? Explain.

References

See the References at the end of Chapter 4.

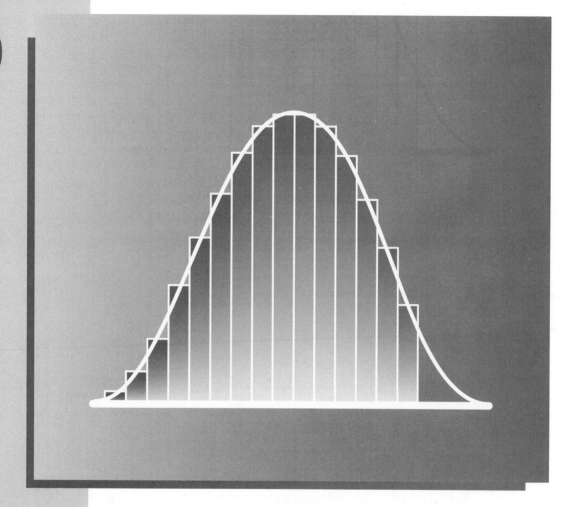

The Analysis of Variance

PREVIEW

M
uch controversy has surrounded the advertising of tobacco products in recent years. One aspect of this controversy relates to the identity of targeted audiences. Tobacco companies have denied engaging in any youth-directed marketing efforts, yet critics have observed that adolescents are attracted by the images portrayed in many advertisements. The paper "Perceived Age and Attractiveness of Models in Cigarette Advertisements" (*J. of Marketing* (1992):22–37) reported on the results of a study that focused on certain aspects of this issue. Consider the accompanying data on average median audience ages for readers of magazines in which a sample of cigarette advertisements appeared (obtained from marketing data). In addition, each individual in a sample was asked to guess the ages of models in certain advertisements. The resulting average perceived ages appear next to audiences ages.

Brand	Sample size	Average audience age	Average perceived model age
Lucky Strike Lights	3	28.5	20.4
Newport Lights	5	31.1	25.5
Camel Lights	21	31.3	36.6
Kool Milds	24	31.3	24.8
Newport	12	31.3	26.9
Winston Lights	15	31.3	26.2
Winston	8	31.6	27.8
Virginia Slims Lights	32	33.9	24.3
Marlboro	26	34.3	38.6
More	17	34.8	29.1
Benson Hedges Lights	23	35.1	31.9
Carlton	1	41.0	27.0
	187		

The investigators hypothesized that average audience age varies by brand of cigarette. We shall see how this hypothesis can be tested using single-factor analysis of variance. It was also conjectured that audience age and perceived model age are associated (not independent); a correlation analysis was used to confirm this assertion.

Introduction

Methods for testing $H_0: \mu_1 - \mu_2 = 0$ (that is, $\mu_1 = \mu_2$), where μ_1 and μ_2 are the means of two different populations or the true average responses when two different treatments are applied, were discussed in Chapter 11. Many investigations involve a comparison of more than two population or treatment means. For example, let μ_1,

μ_2, μ_3, and μ_4 denote true average burn times under specified conditions for four different fabrics used in children's sleepwear. Data from an appropriate experiment could be used to test the null hypothesis that $\mu_1 = \mu_2 = \mu_3 = \mu_4$ (no difference in true average burn times) against the alternative hypothesis that there are differences among the values of the μ's.

The characteristic that distinguishes the populations or treatments from one another is called the **factor** under investigation. In this example, the factor is fabric type. An experiment might be carried out to compare three different methods for teaching reading (three different treatments), in which case the factor of interest is teaching method. Both fabric type and teaching methods are qualitative factors. If growth of fish raised in waters having different salinity levels—0%, 10%, 20%, and 30%—is of interest, the factor *salinity level* is quantitative.

A **single-factor analysis of variance (ANOVA)** problem involves a comparison of k population or treatment means $\mu_1, \mu_2, \ldots, \mu_k$. The objective is to test

$$H_0\text{: } \mu_1 = \mu_2 = \cdots = \mu_k$$

against

H_a: at least two of the means are different

The analysis is based on k independently selected random samples, one from each population or for each treatment. That is, in the case of populations, the sample from any particular population is selected independently of that from any other population. When comparing treatments, the experimental units (subjects or objects) that receive any particular treatment are chosen independently of the units that receive any other treatment. A comparison of treatments based on independently selected experimental units is often referred to as a **completely randomized design.** Sections 15.1, 15.2, 15.3, and 15.6 discuss various aspects of single-factor ANOVA. In Section 15.4 we present an alternative to a completely randomized design, called a **randomized block design,** which controls for extraneous variation among experimental units in order to obtain a more precise assessment of treatment effects.

Researchers frequently carry out experiments to study the effects of two or more factors on some response variable. For example, a testing organization might wish to investigate whether average coverage (square feet) by a single gallon of paint depends either on which of four brands (factor A) is used or on which of three colors (factor B) is applied. Some concepts and methods for the analysis of data from two-factor experiments are introduced in Section 15.5.

15.1 Single-Factor ANOVA and the *F* Test

The decision concerning whether or not the null hypothesis of single-factor ANOVA should be rejected depends on how substantially the samples from the different populations or treatments differ from one another. Figure 15.1 displays two possible data sets that might arise when observations are selected from each

FIGURE 15.1
Two possible ANOVA data sets
when three populations are
under investigation
● = observation from population 1
x = observation from population 2
○ = observation from population 3

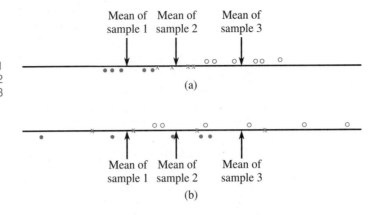

(a)

(b)

of three populations under study. Each data set consists of five observations from the first population, four from the second, and six observations from the third. For both data sets the three resulting sample means are located by vertical line segments. The means of the two samples from population 1 are identical, and a similar statement holds for the two samples from population 2 and those from population 3.

Almost anyone, after looking at the data set in Figure 15.1(a), would readily agree that the claim $\mu_1 = \mu_2 = \mu_3$ is false. Not only are the three sample means different, but there is very clear separation between the samples. Put another way, differences between the three sample means are quite large relative to variability within each sample. (If all data sets gave such clear-cut messages, statisticians would not be in such great demand.) The situation pictured in Figure 15.1(b) is much less clear-cut. While the sample means are as different as they were in the first data set, there is now considerable overlap among the three samples. The separation between sample means here can plausibly be attributed to substantial variability in the populations (and therefore the samples) rather than to differences between μ_1, μ_2, and μ_3. The phrase *analysis of variance* springs from the idea of analyzing variability in the data to see how much can be attributed to differences in the μ's and how much is due to variability in the individual populations. In Figure 15.1(a) there is little within-sample variability relative to the amount of between-samples variability, whereas in Figure 15.1(b), a great deal more of the total variability is due to variation within each sample. If differences between the sample means can be explained by within-sample variability, there is no compelling reason for rejecting H_0.

Notation and Assumptions

Notation in single-factor ANOVA is a natural extension of the notation used in Chapter 11 for comparing two population or treatment means.

ANOVA NOTATION AND HYPOTHESES

k = the number of populations or treatments being compared

	1	2	$\cdots$	k
Population or treatment				
Population or treatment mean	μ_1	μ_2	$\cdots$	μ_k
Population or treatment variance	σ_1^2	σ_2^2	$\cdots$	σ_k^2
Sample size	n_1	n_2	$\cdots$	n_k
Sample mean	$\bar{x}_1$	$\bar{x}_2$	$\cdots$	$\bar{x}_k$
Sample variance	s_1^2	s_2^2	$\cdots$	s_k^2

In addition, let $N = n_1 + n_2 + \cdots + n_k$ be the total number of observations in the data set, and let $\bar{\bar{x}}$ denote the average of all N observations ($\bar{\bar{x}}$ is the "grand mean").

The hypotheses to be tested are

$$H_0: \mu_1 = \mu_2 = \cdots = \mu_k$$

versus

$$H_a: \text{at least two of the } \mu\text{'s are different}$$

A decision between H_0 and H_a will be based on examining the $\bar{x}$'s to see whether observed discrepancies are small enough to be attributable simply to sampling variability or whether an alternative explanation for the differences is necessary.

EXAMPLE 15.1

After water, tea is the world's most widely consumed beverage, yet little is known about its nutritional value. The only B vitamin present in any significant amount in tea is folacin, and recent advances in assay methods have made accurate determination of folacin content feasible. Consider the four leading brands of green tea ($k = 4$ populations), and let μ_1, μ_2, μ_3, and μ_4 denote true average folacin content for brewed tea of these brands. The four population variances are denoted by σ_1^2, σ_2^2, σ_3^2, and σ_4^2. Suppose that seven specimens of the first brand are obtained, five of the second, six of the third, and six of the fourth brand. The folacin content of each specimen is then determined, yielding the following data (based on "Folacin Content of Tea" *J. Amer. Dietetic Assoc.* (1983):627–632; the authors do not give raw data, but their summary values are quite close to those given here).

Brand	Observations						
1	7.9	6.2	6.6	8.6	8.9	10.1	9.6
2	5.7	7.5	9.8	6.1	8.4		
3	6.4	7.1	7.9	4.5	5.0	4.0	
4	6.8	7.5	5.0	5.3	6.1	7.4	

The summary quantities appear in the accompanying table.

Brand	Sample size	Sample total	Sample mean	Sample variance
1	$n_1 = 7$	57.9	$\bar{x}_1 = 8.27$	$s_1^2 = 2.14$
2	$n_2 = 5$	37.5	$\bar{x}_2 = 7.50$	$s_2^2 = 2.83$
3	$n_3 = 6$	34.9	$\bar{x}_3 = 5.82$	$s_3^2 = 2.41$
4	$n_4 = 6$	38.1	$\bar{x}_4 = 6.35$	$s_4^2 = 1.12$

$\Sigma n_i = N = 24 \quad \Sigma ST = 168.4$

Since the sum of all 24 observations (the *grand total*) is 168.4, the grand mean is

$$\bar{\bar{x}} = \frac{\text{grand total}}{N} = \frac{168.4}{24} = 7.02 \quad \frac{\Sigma ST}{N}$$

The hypotheses of interest are

$$H_0: \mu_1 = \mu_2 = \mu_3 = \mu_4$$

versus

$$H_a: \text{at least two among the four } \mu\text{'s are different}$$

Notice that there are differences among the four $\bar{x}$'s. Are these differences small enough to be explained solely by sampling variability? Or are they of sufficient magnitude so that a more plausible explanation is that the μ's are not all equal? Our conclusion will depend on how variation among the $\bar{x}$'s (based on their deviations from the grand mean, $\bar{\bar{x}}$) compares to variation within the four samples.

Assumptions about the population or treatment response distributions and the resulting samples are analogous to those on which the two-sample (pooled) t test for testing $H_0: \mu_1 = \mu_2$ were based.

ASSUMPTIONS FOR THE ANOVA *F* TEST

1. Each of the k population or treatment response distributions is normal.

2. $\sigma_1^2 = \sigma_2^2 = \cdots = \sigma_k^2$
   (The k normal distributions have identical variances.)

3. The observations in the sample from any particular one of the k populations or treatments are selected independently of one another. (Each sample is a random sample.)

4. The k random samples are selected independently of one another.

In practice, the test based on these assumptions will work well as long as the assumptions are not too badly violated. Typically, sample sizes are so small that a separate normal probability plot for each sample is of little value in checking normality. A single combined plot results from first subtracting $\bar{x}_1$ from each observation in the first sample, $\bar{x}_2$ from each value in the second sample, and so on, and then constructing a normal probability plot of all N deviations. The plot should be reasonably straight. There are formal procedures for testing the equality of population variances, but for reasons discussed in Chapter 11, we do not favor them. Provided that the largest of the k sample variances is not too many times larger than the smallest, the F test can safely be used. In Example 15.1, the largest variance (2.83) is less than three times the smallest (1.12). For small sample sizes, this is not at all surprising when all four σ^2's are equal. More on checking assumptions and alternative methods of analysis when these assumptions are judged implausible can be found in the excellent book *Beyond ANOVA: Basics of Applied Statistics,* listed in the chapter references.

Mean Squares and the *F* Test

The standard measure of variation among the $\bar{x}$'s—*between-samples variation*—is based on the deviations from the grand mean, $\bar{x}_1 - \bar{\bar{x}}, \bar{x}_2 - \bar{\bar{x}}, \ldots, \bar{x}_k - \bar{\bar{x}}$. The larger these deviations, the more doubt is cast on H_0. Our benchmark for comparison is a measure of *within-samples variation* obtained by forming a weighted average of the individual sample variances $s_1^2, \ldots, s_k^2$.

DEFINITION

A measure of disparity among the sample means is the **mean square for treatments,** denoted by **MSTr** and given by

$$\text{MSTr} = \frac{n_1(\bar{x}_1 - \bar{\bar{x}})^2 + n_2(\bar{x}_2 - \bar{\bar{x}})^2 + \cdots + n_k(\bar{x}_k - \bar{\bar{x}})^2}{k - 1}$$

The number of degrees of freedom associated with MSTr is $k - 1$.

A measure of variation within the k samples, called **mean square for error** and denoted by **MSE**, is given by

$$\text{MSE} = \frac{(n_1 - 1)s_1^2 + (n_2 - 1)s_2^2 + \cdots + (n_k - 1)s_k^2}{N - k}$$

where $N = n_1 + n_2 + \cdots + n_k$. MSE has $N - k$ degrees of freedom associated with it.

The terminology "mean square" will be explained in the next section when we discuss ANOVA computations. The fact that MSTr is based on the k deviations $\bar{x}_1 - \bar{\bar{x}}, \ldots, \bar{x}_k - \bar{\bar{x}}$ might initially suggest k degrees of freedom. However, there is a restriction on these deviations, namely $\Sigma n(\bar{x} - \bar{\bar{x}}) = 0$. Thus once any $k - 1$ of the deviations are known, the remaining one is completely determined, so MSTr has $(k - 1)$ df. Now consider MSE. The first sample contributes $(n_1 - 1)$ df to MSE (df for s_1^2), the second sample $(n_2 - 1)$ df, and so on. Because the samples are independent, the df's can be added, to yield

$$\begin{aligned} \text{df for MSE} &= (n_1 - 1) + (n_2 - 1) + \cdots + (n_k - 1) \\ &= n_1 + n_2 + \cdots + n_k - (1 + 1 + \cdots + 1) \\ &= N - k \end{aligned}$$

Notice also that specializing MSE to the case $k = 2$ gives s_p^2, the pooled estimate of variance used in the two-sample t test, with df $= n_1 + n_2 - 2$.

EXAMPLE 15.2

(*Example 15.1 continued*) Let's return to the folacin-content data of Example 15.1. With $\bar{x}_1 = 8.27$, $\bar{x}_2 = 7.50$, $\bar{x}_3 = 5.82$, $\bar{x}_4 = 6.35$, $\bar{\bar{x}} = 7.02$, and sample sizes 7, 5, 6, and 6, respectively,

$$\text{MSTr} = \frac{n_1(\bar{x}_1 - \bar{\bar{x}})^2 + \cdots + n_k(\bar{x}_k - \bar{\bar{x}})^2}{k - 1}$$

$$= \frac{7(8.27 - 7.02)^2 + 5(7.50 - 7.02)^2 + 6(5.82 - 7.02)^2 + 6(6.35 - 7.02)^2}{4 - 1}$$

$$= \frac{10.9375 + 1.1520 + 8.6400 + 2.6934}{3}$$

$$\approx 7.81$$

Since $s_1^2 = 2.14$, $s_2^2 = 2.83$, $s_3^2 = 2.41$, and $s_4^2 = 1.12$,

$$\text{MSE} = \frac{(n_1 - 1)s_1^2 + \cdots + (n_k - 1)s_k^2}{N - k}$$

$$= \frac{(7 - 1)(2.14) + (5 - 1)(2.83) + (6 - 1)(2.41) + (6 - 1)(1.12)}{(7 + 5 + 6 + 6) - 4}$$

$$= \frac{41.81}{20}$$

$$\approx 2.09$$

Both MSTr and MSE are quantities whose values can be calculated once sample data is available; that is, they are statistics. Each of these statistics will vary in value from data set to data set. For example, repeating the experiment of Example

15.1 with the same sample sizes might yield $\bar{x}_1 = 7.85, \bar{x}_2 = 8.03, \bar{x}_3 = 6.40$, and $\bar{x}_4 = 6.52$, giving MSTr ≈ 3.14. If these samples also yielded $s_1^2 = 1.83, s_2^2 = 3.05, s_3^2 = 2.70$, and $s_4^2 = 1.82$, then MSE ≈ 2.29. Both MSTr and MSE have sampling distributions and, in particular, mean (expected) values. The following box describes the key relationship between $E(\text{MSTr})$, the *expected value of the mean square for treatments,* and $E(\text{MSE})$, *the expected value of the mean square for error.*

When H_0 is true ($\mu_1 = \mu_2 = \cdots = \mu_k$),

$$E(\text{MSTr}) = E(\text{MSE})$$

However, when H_0 is false,

$$E(\text{MSTr}) > E(\text{MSE}),$$

and the greater the differences among the μ's, the larger $E(\text{MSTr})$ will be relative to $E(\text{MSE})$.

According to this result, when H_0 is true we expect the two mean squares to be close to one another, whereas we expect MSTr to substantially exceed MSE when some μ's differ greatly from others. Thus a calculated MSTr that is much larger than MSE casts doubt on H_0. In Example 15.2, MSTr $= 7.81$ and MSE $= 2.09$, so MSTr is about 3.7 times as large as MSE. Can this be attributed just to sampling variability, or is the ratio MSTr/MSE of sufficient magnitude to suggest that H_0 is false? Before we can describe a formal test procedure, it is necessary to introduce a new type of probability distribution.

Many ANOVA test procedures are based on sampling distributions called F distributions.[1] An F distribution is characterized by a number of degrees of freedom associated with the numerator and a number of df associated with the denominator. Thus a particular F distribution may have 3 numerator df and 20 denominator df or 5 numerator df and 18 denominator df.

Figure 15.2 pictures a typical F curve obtained by specifying both numerator and denominator df's. The numerator and denominator of an F ratio are never negative, so an F curve has positive height only for positive values of an F variable. We need critical values for different F distributions; that is, values that capture specified tail areas underneath F curves. Notice that an F curve is not symmetric, so knowledge of an upper-tail critical value does not immediately yield the corresponding lower-tail value. However, ANOVA F tests will always be upper-tailed (we reject H_0 if the F ratio exceeds a specified critical value), so only upper-tailed values need be tabulated.

---

[1]F distributions were introduced in Chapter 14 as a basis for the model utility test in multiple regression. Since you may not have covered that material, our discussion here presumes that this is your first confrontation with these distributions. The use of an uppercase F is traditional.

FIGURE 15.2
An *F* curve and *F* critical value

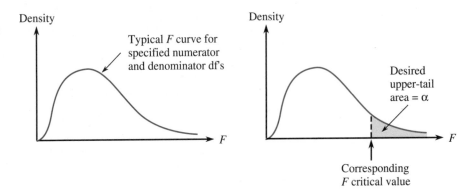

Table X(a) in the appendix gives *F* critical values that capture an upper-tail area of .05, and Table X(b) gives values for area .01. To obtain a critical value for a particular *F* distribution, go to Table X(a) or X(b), depending on the desired tail area. Then locate the column corresponding to the numerator df, the row corresponding to the denominator df, and finally the critical value at the intersection of this column and row. For example, the critical value for tail area .05, numerator df = 3, and denominator df = 20 is 3.10, the number at the intersection of the column marked 3 and the row marked 20. Similarly the 1% critical value for numerator df = 3 and denominator df = 8 is 7.59, whereas that for numerator df = 8 and denominator df = 3 is 27.49. Do not accidentally reverse numerator and denominator df!

The single-factor ANOVA *F* test uses the *F* ratio MSTr/MSE as the test statistic. The theoretical result that underlies the test procedure is this: when H_0 is true, this *F* ratio has an *F* sampling distribution with a numerator df of $k - 1$ and a denominator df of $N - k$. The hypothesis H_0 should be rejected when *F* exceeds an appropriate *F* critical value, since when this happens the value of MSTr exceeds that of MSE by enough to cast considerable doubt on H_0.

THE SINGLE-FACTOR ANOVA *F* TEST

Test statistic: $F = \dfrac{\text{MSTr}}{\text{MSE}}$

Rejection region: F > *F* critical value, where the *F* critical value is based on $k - 1$ numerator df and $N - k$ denominator df. The critical value is taken from Table X(a) when a significance level of .05 is desired and from Table X(b) when a significance level of .01 is appropriate.

EXAMPLE 15.3

The calculations for the folacin-content data were done in Example 15.2. The value of *F* is

$$F = \frac{\text{MSTr}}{\text{MSE}} = \frac{7.81}{2.09} = 3.74$$

The test is based on $k - 1 = 3$ numerator df and $N - k = 20$ denominator df. For $\alpha = .05$, Table X(a) gives *F* critical value 3.10. Since $3.74 > 3.10$, the calculated *F* falls in the rejection region. We reject H_0 in favor of the conclusion that there are differences among μ_1, μ_2, μ_3, and μ_4.

EXAMPLE 15.4

An individual's *critical flicker frequency* (cff) is the highest frequency (in cps) at which the flicker in a flickering light source can be detected. At frequencies above the cff, the light source appears to be continuous even though it is actually flickering. An investigation carried out to see if true average cff depends on iris color yielded the following data (based on the article "The Effect of Iris Color on Critical Flicker Frequency" *J. of Gen. Psych.* (1973):91–95).

Iris color	Data					*n*	$\bar{x}$	s^2
1. Brown	26.8	27.9	23.7	25.0	⟩204.7	8	25.59	1.86
	26.3	24.8	25.7	24.5				
2. Green	26.4	24.2	28.0	26.9	⟩134.6	5	26.92	3.40
	29.1							
3. Blue	25.7	27.2	29.9	28.5	⟩169	6	28.17	2.33
	29.4	28.3						

EST·508.3 N= 19

Also, $N = 19$, grand total $= 508.30$, and $\bar{\bar{x}} = 508.30/19 = 26.75$.

Let's perform a level .05 test to see if true average cff does vary with iris color.

1. Let μ_1, μ_2, and μ_3 denote the true mean cff for individuals having brown, green, and blue iris colors, respectively.

2. H_0: $\mu_1 = \mu_2 = \mu_3$

3. H_a: at least two among μ_1, μ_2, μ_3 are different

4. Test statistic: $F = \dfrac{\text{MSTr}}{\text{MSE}}$

5. Rejection region: Numerator df $= k - 1 = 2$ and denominator df $= N - k$ $= 19 - 3 = 16$. For $\alpha = .05$, Table X(a) gives 3.63 as the desired critical value. The hypothesis H_0 will now be rejected in favor of H_a if $F > 3.63$.

6. Computations:

$$\text{MSTr} = \frac{8(25.59 - 26.75)^2 + 5(26.92 - 26.75)^2 + 6(28.17 - 26.75)^2}{3 - 1}$$

$$= 11.50$$

$$\text{MSE} = \frac{(8 - 1)(1.86) + (5 - 1)(3.40) + (6 - 1)(2.33)}{19 - 3}$$

$$= 2.39$$

Thus

$$F = \frac{\text{MSTr}}{\text{MSE}} = \frac{11.50}{2.39} = 4.81$$

7. Since $4.81 > 3.63$, we reject H_0 in favor of H_a at level .05. The data does suggest that true average cff varies with iris color, a conclusion agreeing with that given in the paper cited.

The F test was introduced to test the equality of $\mu_1, \mu_2, \ldots, \mu_k$ for $k > 2$. However, the test can also be used when $k = 2$ (that is, to test the hypothesis $H_0: \mu_1 = \mu_2$). The formulas for MSTr and MSE remain valid in this case, and Table X gives F critical values for a numerator df of $k - 1 = 1$ and various denominator df's. The pooled t test can also be used to test $H_0: \mu_1 = \mu_2$. It doesn't matter which test is used when the alternative hypothesis is $H_a: \mu_1 \neq \mu_2$. Irrespective of what samples happen to result, the two test procedures yield exactly the same conclusion—reject H_0 or don't reject H_0—when used at the same level of significance. However, the F test can be used only for $H_a: \mu_1 \neq \mu_2$, while a one-tailed t test can also be used for $H_a: \mu_1 > \mu_2$ or $H_a: \mu_1 < \mu_2$. For this reason, the t test is more flexible when $k = 2$.

EXERCISES 15.1–15.13   SECTION 15.1

15.1   What assumptions about the k population or treatment response distributions must you be willing to make in order for the ANOVA F test to be an appropriate method of analysis?

15.2   State the rejection region for the ANOVA F test in each case.
a. Numerator df $= 5$ and denominator df $= 18$.
b. There are three populations and six observations from each.
c. There are six treatments and each is applied to three subjects.
d. Six observations are made on each of the first two treatments and seven observations are made on each of the last three treatments.

15.3   Employees of a certain state university system can choose from among four different health plans. Each plan differs somewhat from the others in terms of hospitalization coverage. Four samples of recently hospitalized individuals were selected, each sample consisting of people covered by a different one of the health plans. The length of the hospital stay (number of days) was determined for each individual selected.

a. What hypotheses would you test to decide whether average length of stay was related to health plan? (Note: Be sure to define carefully the population characteristics of interest.)

b. If each sample consisted of eight individuals and the value of the ANOVA *F* statistic was $F = 4.37$, what conclusion would be appropriate for a test with $\alpha = .01$?

c. Answer the question posed in part (b) if the *F* value given there resulted from sample sizes $n_1 = 9$, $n_2 = 8$, $n_3 = 7$, and $n_4 = 8$.

15.4 The paper "An Analysis of Job Sharing, Full-Time, and Part-Time Arrangements" (*Amer. Business Review* (1989):34–40) reported on a study of hospital employees from three different groups. Each employee reported a level of satisfaction with his or her work schedule (1 = very dissatisfied to 7 = very satisfied).

Group	Sample size	Sample mean	
1. Job sharers	24	6.60	158.4
2. Full-time employees	24	5.37	128.88
3. Part-time employees	20	5.20	104

H=3 N=68   391.28

a. What are numerator and denominator df's for the *F* test? 2, 65
b. The test statistic value is $F = 6.62$. Use a test with significance level .05 to decide whether it is plausible that true average satisfaction levels are identical for the three groups.
c. What is the value of MSE?

15.5 High productivity and carbohydrate storage ability of the Jerusalem artichoke make it a promising agricultural crop. The paper "Leaf Gas Exchange and Tuber Yield in Jerusalem Artichoke Cultivars" (*Field Crops Research* (1991):241–252) reported on various plant characteristics. Consider the accompanying data on chlorophyll concentration (gm/m^2) for four varieties.

Variety	BI	RO	WA	TO
Sample mean	.30	.24	.41	.33

Suppose that the sample sizes were 5, 5, 4, and 6, respectively, and also that MSE = .0130. Does the data suggest that true average chlorophyll concentration depends on the variety? State and test the appropriate hypotheses using a significance level of .05.

15.6 A study was carried out to see whether brands of rollerball pens differed with respect to writing lifetime. Five different brands were used in the study. A sample of six pens of each brand was selected, and the pens were inserted in a machine that applied constant pressure on a certain writing surface. The number of hours of use was determined for each pen.

a. What are the hypotheses of interest?

b. If MSTr = 237.5 and MSE = 44.3, carry out a test at significance level .05.

15.7   The paper "Utilizing Feedback and Goal Setting to Increase Performance Skills of Managers" (*Academy of Mgmt. J.* (1979):516–526) reported the results of an experiment to compare three different interviewing techniques for employee evaluations. One method allowed the employee being evaluated to discuss previous evaluations, the second involved setting goals for the employee, and the third did not allow either feedback or goal setting. After the interviews were concluded, the evaluated employee was asked to indicate how satisfied he or she was with the interview. (A numerical scale was used to quantify level of satisfaction.) The authors used ANOVA to compare the three interview techniques. An *F* statistic value of 4.12 was reported.

a. Suppose that a total of 33 subjects were used, with each technique applied to 11 of them. Use this information to conduct a level .05 test of the null hypothesis of no difference in mean satisfaction level for the three interview techniques.

b. The actual number of subjects on which each technique was used was 45. After studying the *F* table, explain why the conclusion in part (a) still holds.

15.8   Mercury is a very hazardous pollutant, and many studies have been carried out in an attempt to assess its toxic effects. One such study is described in the paper "Comparative Responses of the Action of Different Mercury Compounds on Barley" (*Intl. J. of Environ. Studies* (1983):323–327). Ten different concentrations of mercury (0, 1, 5, 10, 50, 100, 200, 300, 400, and 500 mg/L) were compared with respect to their effects on average dry weight (per 100 seven-day-old seedlings). The basic experiment was replicated four times for a total of 40 dry-weight observations (four for each treatment level). The paper reported an ANOVA *F* statistic value of 1.895. Using a significance level .05 and the usual seven-step procedure, test the null hypothesis that the true mean dry weight is the same for all ten concentration levels.

15.9   In an experiment to compare tensile strength of five different types of wire, four specimens of each type were tested. MSTr and MSE were computed to be 2573.3 and 1394.2, respectively. Use the ANOVA *F* test with significance level .01 to test $H_0: \mu_1 = \mu_2 = \mu_3 = \mu_4 = \mu_5$ versus H_a: at least two of the μ's are different.

15.10   Measurement of athletes' body characteristics have been used to establish optimal playing weights for use in training programs. The paper "Prediction of Body Composition in Female Athletes" (*J. of Sports Med.* (1983):333–341) compared average lean body mass (kg) for female basketball players, cross-country runners, and swimmers. From summary quantities given in the paper, MSTr and MSE were calculated to be 803.9 and 27.5, respectively. These figures were based on three random samples, each of size 10. Does this data suggest that the true average lean body mass differs by sport for female athletes? Use a .01 significance level.

15.11   The paper "Computer-Assisted Instruction Augmented with Planned Teacher Student Contacts" (*J. of Exp. Educ.* (Winter 1980/1981):120–126) compared five different methods for teaching descriptive statistics. The five methods were traditional lecture and discussion (L/D), programmed textbook instruction (R), programmed text with lectures (R/L), computer instruction (C), and computer instruction with lectures (C/L). Forty-five students were randomly assigned, nine to each method. After completion of the course, a 1-h exam was given. In addition, a 10-min retention test was administered 6 weeks later. Summary quantities are given.

Method	n	Exam $\overline{x}$	s	Retention test $\overline{x}$	s
L/D	9	29.3	4.99	30.20	3.82
R	9	28.0	5.33	28.80	5.26
R/L	9	30.2	3.33	26.20	4.66
C	9	32.4	2.94	31.10	4.91
C/L	9	34.2	2.74	30.20	3.53

$N = 45$ $\overline{\overline{x}} = 30.82$ $\overline{\overline{y}} = 29.30$

The grand mean for the exam was 30.82 and the grand mean for the retention test was 29.30.

a. Does the data suggest that there is a difference between the five teaching methods with respect to true mean exam score? Use $\alpha = .05$.

b. Using a .05 significance level, test the null hypothesis of no difference between the true mean retention test scores for the five different teaching methods.

15.12   Growing interest in trout farming has prompted a number of experiments designed to compare various growing conditions. One factor of interest is the salinity of the water. The effect of salinity on the growth of rainbow trout (measured by increase in weight) was examined in the paper "Growth, Training and Swimming Ability of Young Trout Maintained under Different Salinity Conditions." (*J. of Marine Biological Assoc. of U.K.* (1982):699–708). Full-strength seawater (32% salinity), brackish water (18% salinity), and fresh water (.5% salinity) were used, and the following summary quantities were obtained.

Salinity	Number of fish	Mean weight gain	s
Fresh	12	8.078	1.786
18%	12	7.863	1.756
32%	8	6.468	1.339

Does the data provide sufficient evidence to conclude that the mean weight gain is not the same for the three salinity levels? Use a significance level of .01.

15.13   The *fog index* is a measure of reading difficulty based on the average number of words per sentence and the percentage of words with three or more syllables. High values of the fog index are associated with difficult reading levels. Independent random samples of six advertisements were taken from three different magazines and fog indices were computed to obtain the given data ("Readability Levels of Magazine Advertisements" *J. of Ad. Research* (1981):45–50).

Scientific American	15.75	11.55	11.16	9.92	9.23	8.20
Fortune	12.63	11.46	10.77	9.93	9.87	9.42
New Yorker	9.27	8.28	8.15	6.37	6.37	5.66

Use a significance level of .01 to test the null hypothesis of no difference between the mean fog index levels for advertisements appearing in the three magazines.

15.2 ANOVA Computations

The formulas for MSTr and MSE given in Section 15.1 are somewhat cumbersome. An alternative method for efficiently computing F involves introducing quantities called *sums of squares*. The accompanying box gives the defining formula, computational formula, and associated df for each of the three sums of squares for single-factor ANOVA.

SUMS OF SQUARES IN SINGLE-FACTOR ANOVA

1. *Total Sum of Squares* (SSTo)

   Defining formula: $\sum_{\substack{\text{all } N \\ \text{obs.}}} (x - \bar{\bar{x}})^2$

   Computing formula:

   $$\sum_{\substack{\text{all } N \\ \text{obs.}}} x^2 - \frac{T^2}{N}$$

   where T is the grand total (sum of all N observations)

   Associated df: $N - 1$

2. *Treatment Sum of Squares* (SSTr)

   Defining formula: $n_1(\bar{x}_1 - \bar{\bar{x}})^2 + \cdots + n_k(\bar{x}_k - \bar{\bar{x}})^2$

   Computing formula:

   $$\frac{T_1^2}{n_1} + \cdots + \frac{T_k^2}{n_k} - \frac{T^2}{N}$$

   where $T_1, T_2, \ldots, T_k$ are the individual sample totals

   Associated df: $k - 1$

(continued)

---

3. *Error Sum of Squares* (SSE)

Defining formula:

$$\sum_{\substack{\text{1st} \\ \text{sample}}} (x - \bar{x}_1)^2 + \cdots + \sum_{\substack{kth \\ \text{sample}}} (x - \bar{x}_k)^2$$

Computing formula: $\text{SSE} = \text{SSTo} - \text{SSTr}$

Associated df: $N - k$ (total df − treatment df)

Before indicating how F is related to these sums of squares, several preliminary observations are in order. First of all, the defining formula for each SS shows quite clearly that $\text{SSTo} \geq 0$, $\text{SSTr} \geq 0$, and $\text{SSE} \geq 0$. More generally, it is impossible for any sum of squares to have a negative value. The defining formulas are burdensome for hand calculation because in each case many subtractions are necessary to obtain the deviations that are then squared and summed. This preliminary subtraction is avoided in the computational formulas. In both SSTo and SSTr, the single subtraction of T^2/N is done as the last step in the computation.

Once SSTo and SSTr have been obtained, the latter is subtracted from the former to give SSE. Since $\text{SSE} \geq 0$, this implies that $\text{SSTo} \geq \text{SSTr}$. As we will see shortly, SSTr and SSE are the two SS's needed for F; SSTo is introduced to give an efficient method for calculating SSE. An additional benefit lies in interpreting the relationship between the three sums of squares. Since $\text{SSTo} - \text{SSTr} = \text{SSE}$, we can write

$$\text{SSTo} = \text{SSTr} + \text{SSE}$$

This is often called the *fundamental identity for single-factor ANOVA*. The quantity SSTo, the sum of squared deviations about the grand mean, is a measure of total variability in the data set consisting of all k samples. The quantity SSE results from measuring variability separately within each sample and then combining. Such within-sample variability is present regardless of whether or not H_0 is true. The magnitude of SSTr, on the other hand, has much to do with the status of H_0 (whether it's true or false). The more the μ's differ from one another, the larger SSTr will tend to be. Thus SSTr represents variation that can (at least to some extent) be explained by any differences between means. An informal paraphrase of the fundamental identity is

total variation = explained variation + unexplained variation

The F statistic is the ratio of two mean squares. A mean square is an "average square," namely, the sum of squares divided by its associated df. In particular,

$$\text{MSTr} = \frac{\text{SSTr}}{k - 1} \qquad \text{MSE} = \frac{\text{SSE}}{N - k}$$

Thus to carry out the F test, SSTo and SSTr are obtained from the computing formulas, SSE is calculated by subtraction, then the two mean squares are computed, and finally $F = \text{MSTr}/\text{MSE}$.

The ANOVA computations are frequently summarized in a tabular format called an **ANOVA table.** The general form of such a table is displayed in Table 15.1.

TABLE 15.1   General format for a single-factor ANOVA table

Source of variation	df	Sum of squares	Mean square	F
Treatments	$k - 1$	SSTr	$MSTr = \dfrac{SSTr}{k - 1}$	$F = \dfrac{MSTr}{MSE}$
Error	$N - k$	SSE	$MSE = \dfrac{SSE}{N - k}$	
Total	$N - 1$	SSTo		

EXAMPLE 15.5

Parents are frequently concerned when their child seems slow to begin walking (although when the child finally walks, the resulting havoc sometimes has the parents wishing they could turn back the clock!). The paper "Walking in the Newborn" (*Science* 176 (1972):314–315) reported on an experiment in which the effects of several different treatments on the age at which a child first walks were compared. Children in the first group were given special walking exercises for 12 min per day beginning at age 1 week and lasting 7 weeks. The second group of children received daily exercises but not the walking exercises administered to the first group. The third and fourth groups were control groups—they received no special treatment and differed only in that the third group's progress was checked weekly, whereas the fourth group's progress was checked just once at the end of the study. Observations on age (in months) when the children first walked are given.

Treatment	Age						n	Total
1	9.00	9.50	9.75	10.00	13.00	9.50	6	60.75
2	11.00	10.00	10.00	11.75	10.50	15.00	6	68.25
3	11.50	12.00	9.00	11.50	13.25	13.00	6	70.25
4	13.25	11.50	12.00	13.50	11.50		5	61.75
							$N = 23$	$T = 261.00$

Let's carry out a level .05 test to see whether true average age at which a child first walks depends on which treatment is given.

1. $\mu_1, \mu_2, \mu_3, \mu_4$ are the true average ages of first walking for the four treatments.

2. $H_0: \mu_1 = \mu_2 = \mu_3 = \mu_4$

3. H_a: at least two among the four μ's are different

4. Test statistic: $F = MSTr/MSE$

5. Rejection region: $F > F$ critical value; with $\alpha = .05$, treatment df $= k - 1 = 3$, and error df $= N - k = 23 - 4 = 19$, Table X(a) gives an F critical value of 3.13.

6. Computations: first

$$\Sigma x^2 = (9.00)^2 + (9.50)^2 + \cdots + (11.50)^2 = 3020.25$$

and

$$\frac{T^2}{N} = \frac{(261.00)^2}{23} = 2961.78$$

Thus

$$SSTo = 3020.25 - 2961.78 = 58.47$$

$$SSTr = \frac{T_1^2}{n_1} + \frac{T_2^2}{n_2} + \frac{T_3^2}{n_3} + \frac{T_4^2}{n_4} - \frac{T^2}{N}$$

$$= \frac{(60.75)^2}{6} + \frac{(68.25)^2}{6} + \frac{(70.25)^2}{6} + \frac{(61.75)^2}{5} - \frac{(261.00)^2}{23}$$

$$= 2976.56 - 2961.78$$

$$= 14.78$$

$$SSE = 58.47 - 14.78 = 43.69$$

The remaining computations are summarized in the accompanying ANOVA table.

Source of variation	df	Sum of squares	Mean square	F
Treatments	3	14.78	4.93	$\frac{4.93}{2.30} = 2.14$
Error	19	43.69	2.30	
Total	22	58.47		

7. The computed F ratio, 2.14, does not exceed the critical value 3.13, so H_0 is not rejected at level of significance .05. The data does not suggest that there are differences in true average responses among the treatments.

All of the commonly used statistical computer packages will perform a single-factor ANOVA upon request and summarize the results in an ANOVA table. As an example, Table 15.2 resulted from the use of MINITAB to analyze the data of Example 15.5.

TABLE 15.2   An ANOVA table from MINITAB

Analysis of Variance

Due to	df	SS	MS	F	P
Factor	3	14.78	4.93	2.14	0.129
Error	19	43.69	2.30		
Total	22	58.47			

P-Values

As with other test procedures, the P-value for an F test is the smallest level of significance at which H_0 can be rejected. Because our F table contains F critical values only for levels .05 and .01, information from these tables about the P-value is limited to one of the following three statements:

1. P-value > .05 (if F < critical value for α = .05);

2. .01 < P-value < .05 (if F falls between the two critical values);

3. P-value < .01 (if F > critical value for α = .01).

However, several of the most widely available statistical computer packages will provide an exact P-value for the test. Table 15.3 displays output from the package SPSS for the data of Example 15.5. The P-value appears in the far right column under F PROB as .129. This is consistent with our earlier decision not to reject H_0 at level .05. Even at level of significance .10, we would not reject H_0 because P-value = .129 > .10.

TABLE 15.3   ANOVA table with P-value from SPSS

Analysis of Variance

Source	df	Sum of sq.	Mean sq.	F Ratio	F Prob
Between Groups	3	14.778	4.926	2.142	.129
Within Groups	19	43.690	2.299		
Total	22	58.467			

EXERCISES 15.14–15.21   SECTION 15.2

15.14   In an experiment to investigate the performance of four different brands of spark-plugs intended for use on a 125 cm^3 motorcycle, five plugs of each brand were tested and the number of miles (at a constant speed) until failure was observed. A partially completed ANOVA table is given. Fill in the missing entries and test the relevant hypotheses using a .05 level of significance.

$k = 4$ $N = 20$

Source of variation	df	Sum of squares	Mean square	F
Treatments				
Error		235,419.04		
Total		310,500.76		

15.15 The partially completed ANOVA table given in this problem is taken from the article "Perception of Spatial Incongruity" (*J. of Nervous and Mental Disease* (1961):222) in which the abilities of three different groups to identify a perceptual incongruity were assessed and compared. All individuals in the experiment had been hospitalized to undergo psychiatric treatment. There were 21 individuals in the depressive group, 32 individuals in the functional "other" group, and 21 individuals in the brain-damaged group. Complete the ANOVA table. Carry out the appropriate test of hypotheses (use $\alpha = .01$) and interpret your results.

Source of variation	df	Sum of squares	Mean square	F
Treatments		152.18		
Error				
Total		1123.14		

15.16 Research carried out to investigate the relationship between smoking status of workers and short-term absenteeism rate (h/month) yielded the following summary information ("Work-Related Consequences of Smoking Cessation," *Academy of Mgmt. J.* (1989):606–621).

Status	Sample size	Sample mean
Continuous smoker	96	2.15
Recent ex-smoker	34	2.21
Long-term ex-smoker	86	1.47
Never smoked	206	1.69

In addition, $F = 2.56$.
a. Construct an ANOVA table, and then state and test the appropriate hypotheses using a .01 significance level.
b. What can be said about the *P*-value of the test carried out in (a)?

15.17 The paper "Effect of Transcendental Meditation on Breathing and Respiratory Control" (*J. of Appl. Physiology* (1984):607–611) reported on an experiment to compare four different groups—alert nonmeditators, relaxed nonmeditators, alert meditators, and meditators while meditating—with respect to breathing characteristics. Sixteen observations (breaths/min) were made for each condition. Data compatible with summary values given in the paper was used to compute SSTr = 136.14 and SSE = 532.26. Construct an ANOVA table. State and test the relevant hypotheses using a .01 level of significance.

15.18   The accompanying summary quantities are representative of data on professional productivity given in the article "Research Productivity in Academia: A Comparative Study of the Sciences, Social Sciences and Humanities" (*Soc. of Educ.* (1981):238–253). Randomly selected faculty members in each of the three disciplines were asked to indicate the number of years that they had been teaching. Suppose that 30 faculty members from each subject area were included in the study. Construct an ANOVA table. Is there sufficient evidence to indicate that the true mean number of years of teaching experience is not the same for the three subject areas? Use a .05 significance level.

Natural sciences	Social sciences	Humanities	
$\Sigma(x - \bar{x}_1)^2 = 4468.92$	$\Sigma(x - \bar{x}_2)^2 = 4138.34$	$\Sigma(x - \bar{x}_3)^2 = 4629.44$	
$\bar{x}_1 = 12.65$	$\bar{x}_2 = 10.41$	$\bar{x}_3 = 10.93$	$\bar{\bar{x}} = 11.33$

15.19   An article in the British scientific journal *Nature* ("Sucrose Induction of Hepatic Hyperplasis in the Rat" (August 25, 1972):461) reported on an experiment in which five groups, each consisting of six rats, were put on diets with different carbohydrates. At the conclusion of the experiment, liver DNA content (mg/g) was determined, with the following results:

$$\Sigma (x - \bar{\bar{x}})^2 = 3.61 \qquad \bar{\bar{x}} = 2.448$$
$$\bar{x}_1 = 2.58 \qquad \bar{x}_2 = 2.63 \qquad \bar{x}_3 = 2.13 \qquad \bar{x}_4 = 2.41 \qquad \bar{x}_5 = 2.49$$

Does the data indicate that the true average DNA content is affected by the type of carbohydrate in the diet? Construct an ANOVA table and use a .05 level of significance.

15.20   College students were assigned to various study methods in an experiment to determine the effect of study technique on learning. The given data was generated to be consistent with summary quantities found in the paper "The Effect of Study Techniques, Study Preferences and Familiarity on Later Recall" (*J. of Exper. Educ.* (1979):92–95). The study methods compared were reading only, reading and underlining, and reading and taking notes. One week after studying the paper "Love in Infant Monkeys" by Harlow, students were given an exam on the article. Test scores are given in the accompanying table.

Technique	Test score					
Read only	15	14	16	13	11	14
Read and underline	15	14	25	10	12	14
Read and take notes	18	18	18	16	18	20

a. Compute SSTo, SSTr, and SSE.

b. Construct an ANOVA table.

c. Use a .05 level of significance to test the null hypothesis of no difference between the true mean exam scores for the three study methods.

d. Which of the following statements can be made about the P-value associated with the computed value of the ANOVA F statistic?

   i. P-value $> .05$

   ii. $.01 < P$-value $< .05$

   iii. P-value $< .01$

e. Based on your answer in part (d), would the conclusion of the hypothesis test of part (c) have been any different if a .01 significance level had been used? Explain.

15.21 Some investigators think that the concentration (μg/mL) of a particular antigen in supernatant fluids could be related to onset of meningitis in infants. The accompanying data is typical of that given in plots appearing in the paper "Type-Specific Capsular Antigen Is Associated with Virulence in Late-Onset Group B Streptococcal Type III Disease" (*Infection and Immunity* (1984):124–129).

Asymptomatic infants	1.56	1.06	.87	1.39	.71	.87	.95	1.51
Infants with late-onset sepsis	1.51	1.78	1.45	1.13	1.87	1.89	1.07	1.72
Infants with late-onset meningitis	1.21	1.34	1.95	2.00	2.27	.88	1.67	2.57

Construct an ANOVA table and use it to test the null hypothesis of no difference in mean antigen concentrations for the three groups.

15.3 Multiple Comparisons

When H_0: $\mu_1 = \mu_2 = \cdots = \mu_k$ is rejected by the F test, we believe that there are differences among the k population means. A natural question to ask at this point is "Which means differ?" For example, with $k = 4$, it might be the case that $\mu_1 = \mu_2 = \mu_4$ with μ_3 different from the other three. Another possibility is that $\mu_1 = \mu_4$ and $\mu_2 = \mu_3$. Still another possibility is that all four means are different from one another. A **multiple comparison procedure** is a method for identifying differences among the μ's once the hypothesis of overall equality has been rejected. We will present one such method, called the **Bonferroni multiple comparison procedure.**

The Bonferroni procedure is based on computing confidence intervals for the difference between each possible pair of μ's. In the case $k = 3$, there are three differences to consider: $\mu_1 - \mu_2$, $\mu_1 - \mu_3$, and $\mu_2 - \mu_3$. (The difference $\mu_2 - \mu_1$ is not considered since the interval for $\mu_1 - \mu_2$ provides the same information. Similarly, intervals for $\mu_3 - \mu_1$ and $\mu_3 - \mu_2$ are not necessary.) Once all confidence intervals have been computed, each is examined to determine whether the interval includes zero. If a particular interval does not include zero, the two means are declared to be "significantly different" from one another. An interval that does include zero supports the conclusion that there is no significant difference between the means involved.

Suppose, for example, that $k = 3$ and the three Bonferroni confidence intervals are:

Difference	Bonferroni interval
$\mu_1 - \mu_2$	$(-0.9, 3.5)$
$\mu_1 - \mu_3$	$(2.6, 7.0)$
$\mu_2 - \mu_3$	$(1.2, 5.7)$

Since the interval for $\mu_1 - \mu_2$ includes zero, we judge that μ_1 and μ_2 do not differ significantly. The other two intervals don't include zero, so we conclude $\mu_1 \neq \mu_3$ and $\mu_2 \neq \mu_3$.

The following box provides the formulas for constructing the Bonferroni intervals.

THE BONFERRONI MULTIPLE COMPARISON PROCEDURE

When there are k populations to be compared, $k(k - 1)/2$ Bonferroni 95% confidence intervals are computed:

$$\text{For } \mu_1 - \mu_2: \quad (\bar{x}_1 - \bar{x}_2) \pm \left(\begin{array}{c} \text{Bonferroni } t \\ \text{critical value} \end{array} \right) \sqrt{\frac{\text{MSE}}{n_1} + \frac{\text{MSE}}{n_2}}$$

$$\vdots$$

$$\text{For } \mu_{k-1} - \mu_k: \quad (\bar{x}_{k-1} - \bar{x}_k) \pm \left(\begin{array}{c} \text{Bonferroni } t \\ \text{critical value} \end{array} \right) \sqrt{\frac{\text{MSE}}{n_{k-1}} + \frac{\text{MSE}}{n_k}}$$

where MSE is from the analysis of variance, and the Bonferroni t critical value comes from Appendix Table XI (using error df).

Two means are judged to differ significantly if the corresponding interval does not include zero.

The Bonferroni confidence intervals are similar in form to the independent-samples confidence interval for $\mu_1 - \mu_2$ introduced in Chapter 11. That interval had the form

$$\bar{x}_1 - \bar{x}_2 \pm (t \text{ critical value}) \sqrt{\frac{s_p^2}{n_1} + \frac{s_p^2}{n_2}}$$

where s_p^2 was the pooled estimate of the common variance σ^2, obtained by combining the two sample variances s_1^2 and s_2^2. In the Bonferroni intervals, s_p^2 is replaced by MSE, a combined estimate of the common population variance based on all k samples. A second difference is the use of a Bonferroni t critical value from Table XI rather than a t critical value from the t table. This is done in order to achieve a *simultaneous confidence level* of at least 95% for all intervals computed. This means that the Bonferroni multiple comparison procedure has an overall error rate of at most 5%. That is, if the procedure is used on many different data sets, at most 5% of the time at least one pair of means will incorrectly be declared significantly different. If separate 95% t confidence intervals were used (each constructed using a method that has a 5% error rate), the chance that at least one incorrectly identifies a difference between two sample means increases dramatically with the number of intervals computed.

EXAMPLE 15.6

Most large companies have established grievance procedures for their employees. One question of interest to employers is why certain groups within a company have higher grievance rates than others. The study described in the paper "Grievance Rates and Technology" (*Academy of Mgmt. J.* (1979):810–815) distinguished four types of jobs. These types were labeled apathetic, erratic, strategic, and conservative. Suppose that a total of 52 work groups were selected (13 of each type) and a measure of grievance rate was determined for each one. The resulting sample means and analysis of variance table follow.

Group:	Apathetic	Erratic	Strategic	Conservative
Sample mean:	2.96	5.05	8.74	4.91

ANOVA Table

Source of variation	df	Sum of squares	Mean square	F
Treatments	3	175.9034	58.6344	5.56
Error	48	506.1936	10.5457	
Total	51	682.0970		

The F critical value for $\alpha = .05$, numerator df $= 3$, and denominator df $= 48$ is approximately 2.84, so $H_0: \mu_1 = \mu_2 = \mu_3 = \mu_4$ is rejected at the .05 level of significance.

To determine which means differ, we compute $4(3)/2 = 6$ Bonferroni intervals using MSE $= 10.5457$ and the Bonferroni t critical value of 2.78 (from the column labeled 6 and the row labeled 40—the closest entry to 48 error df—in Table XI). The interval for $\mu_1 - \mu_2$ is computed to be

$$(\bar{x}_1 - \bar{x}_2) \pm \left(\begin{array}{c}\text{Bonferroni } t \\ \text{critical value}\end{array}\right) \sqrt{\frac{\text{MSE}}{n_1} + \frac{\text{MSE}}{n_2}}$$

$$= (2.96 - 5.05) \pm (2.78) \sqrt{\frac{10.5457}{13} + \frac{10.5457}{13}}$$

$$= -2.09 \pm 3.54$$

$$= (-5.63, 1.45)$$

The other five intervals follow.

Difference	Interval	Conclusion
$\mu_1 - \mu_2$	$(-5.63, \quad 1.45)$	Not significantly different
$\mu_1 - \mu_3$	$(-9.32, -2.24)$	$\mu_1 \neq \mu_3$
$\mu_1 - \mu_4$	$(-5.49, \quad 1.59)$	Not significantly different
$\mu_2 - \mu_3$	$(-7.23, -0.15)$	$\mu_2 \neq \mu_3$
$\mu_2 - \mu_4$	$(-3.40, \quad 3.68)$	Not significantly different
$\mu_3 - \mu_4$	$(\quad 0.29, \quad 7.37)$	$\mu_3 \neq \mu_4$

Based on these intervals, we conclude that the mean grievance rate for the strategic group (μ_3) is significantly different from the other three groups. None of the other means differ significantly from one another.

An effective display for summarizing the results of the Bonferroni multiple comparison procedure involves listing the $\bar{x}$'s and underscoring pairs judged not significantly different. The details of the construction of such a display are described in the accompanying box.

SUMMARIZING THE RESULTS OF THE BONFERRONI PROCEDURE

1. List the sample means in increasing order, identifying the corresponding population just above the value of each $\bar{x}$.
2. Use the Bonferroni intervals to determine the group of means that do not differ significantly from the first in the list. Draw a horizontal line extending from the smallest mean to the last mean in the group identified. For example, if there are five means, arranged in order,

Population	3	2	1	4	5
Sample mean	$\bar{x}_3$	$\bar{x}_2$	$\bar{x}_1$	$\bar{x}_4$	$\bar{x}_5$

and μ_3 is judged not significantly different from μ_2 or μ_1 but is judged significantly different from μ_4 and μ_5, draw the following line:

Population	3	2	1	4	5
Sample mean	$\bar{x}_3$	$\bar{x}_2$	$\bar{x}_1$	$\bar{x}_4$	$\bar{x}_5$

(continued)

3. Use the Bonferroni intervals to determine the group of means that are not significantly different from the second smallest. (You need consider only means that appear to the right of the mean under consideration.) If there is already a line connecting the second smallest mean with all means in the new group identified, no new line need be drawn. If this entire group of means is not underscored with a single line, draw a line extending from the second smallest to the last mean in the new group. Continuing with our example, if μ_2 is not significantly different from μ_1 but is significantly different from μ_4 and μ_5, no new line need be drawn. However, if μ_2 was not significantly different from either μ_1 or μ_4 but was judged different from μ_5, a second line is drawn as shown:

Population	3	2	1	4	5
Sample mean	$\bar{x}_3$	$\bar{x}_2$	$\bar{x}_1$	$\bar{x}_4$	$\bar{x}_5$

4. Continue considering the means in the order listed, adding new lines as needed.

To illustrate this summary procedure, suppose that four samples with $\bar{x}_1 = 19$, $\bar{x}_2 = 27$, $\bar{x}_3 = 24$, and $\bar{x}_4 = 10$ are used to test $H_0: \mu_1 = \mu_2 = \mu_3 = \mu_4$, and that this hypothesis is rejected. Suppose that the Bonferroni confidence intervals indicate that μ_4 is significantly different from μ_1, μ_2, and μ_3, that μ_1 is significantly different from μ_2, and that there are no other significant differences. The resulting summary display would then be

Population	4	1	3	2
Sample mean	10	19	24	27

EXAMPLE 15.7

(*Example 15.6 continued*) For the grievance data of Example 15.6, the resulting summary display is

	(1)	(4)	(2)	(3)
Group	Apathetic	Conservative	Erratic	Strategic
Sample mean	2.96	4.91	5.05	8.74

A line is drawn below the means of samples 1, 4, and 2 because these μ's were judged by the Bonferroni procedure to be not significantly different.

EXERCISES 15.22–15.30 SECTION 15.3

15.22 Leaf surface area is an important variable in plant gas-exchange rates. The paper "Fluidized Bed Coating of Conifer Needles with Glass Beads for Determination of Leaf Surface Area" (*Forest Sci.* (1980):29–32) included an analysis of dry matter per unit surface area (mg/cm^2) for trees raised under three different growing conditions. Let μ_1, μ_2, and μ_3 represent the true mean dry matter per unit surface area for the growing conditions 1, 2, and 3, respectively. The given 95% simultaneous confidence intervals are based on summary quantities that appear in the paper.

Difference	Confidence interval
$\mu_1 - \mu_2$	$(-3.11, -1.11)$
$\mu_1 - \mu_3$	$(-4.06, -2.06)$
$\mu_2 - \mu_3$	$(-1.95, \quad 0.05)$

Which of the following four statements do you think describes the relationship between μ_1, μ_2, and μ_3? Explain your choice.
  i. $\mu_1 = \mu_2$ and μ_3 differs from μ_1 and μ_2.
  ii. $\mu_1 = \mu_3$ and μ_2 differs from μ_1 and μ_3.
  iii. $\mu_2 = \mu_3$ and μ_1 differs from μ_2 and μ_3.
  iv. All three μ's are different from one another.

15.23 Exercise 15.4 presented the accompanying summary information on satisfaction levels for employees on one of three different work schedules:

$$n_1 = 24 \qquad n_2 = 24 \qquad n_3 = 20$$
$$\bar{x}_1 = 6.60 \qquad \bar{x}_2 = 5.37 \qquad \bar{x}_3 = 5.20 \qquad \text{MSE} = 2.028$$

Calculate the Bonferroni intervals and identify any significant differences.

15.24 Sample mean chlorophyll concentrations for the four artichoke varieties introduced in Exercise 15.5 were .30, .24, .41, and .33, with corresponding sample sizes of 5, 5, 4, and 6, respectively. In addition, MSE = .0130. Calculate the Bonferroni intervals and then use the underscoring procedure described in this section to identify significant differences among the varieties.

15.25 The paper "Growth Response in Radish to Sequential and Simultaneous Exposures of NO$_2$ and SO$_2$" (*Environ. Pollution* (1984):303–325) compared a control group (no exposure), a sequential exposure group (plants exposed to one pollutant followed by exposure to the second 4 weeks later), and a simultaneous-exposure group (plants exposed to both pollutants at the same time). The paper states: "Sequential exposure to the two pollutants had no effect on growth compared to the control. Simultaneous exposure to the gases significantly reduced plant growth." Let $\bar{x}_1, \bar{x}_2$, and $\bar{x}_3$ represent the sample means for the control, sequential, and simultaneous groups, respectively. Suppose that $\bar{x}_1 > \bar{x}_2 > \bar{x}_3$. Use the given information to construct a table where the sample means are listed in increasing order, with those that are not judged to be significantly different underscored.

15.26   The nutritional quality of shrubs commonly used for feed by rabbits was the focus of a study summarized in the paper "Estimation of Browse by Size Classes for Snowshoe Hare" (*J Wildlife Mgmt.* (1980):34–40). The energy content (cal/g) of three sizes (4 mm or less, 5–7 mm, and 8–10 mm) of serviceberries was studied. Let μ_1, μ_2, and μ_3 denote the true energy content for the three size classes. Suppose that 95% simultaneous confidence intervals for $\mu_1 - \mu_2$, $\mu_1 - \mu_3$, and $\mu_2 - \mu_3$ are (-10, 290), (150, 450), and (10, 310), respectively. How would you interpret these intervals?

15.27   The accompanying table appeared in the paper "Effect of SO_2 on Transpiration, Chlorophyll Content, Growth and Injury in Young Seedlings of Woody Angiosperms" (*Canadian J. Forest Research* (1980):78–81). Water loss of plants (species: *Acer saccharinum*) exposed to 0, 2, 4, 8, and 16 hours of fumigation was recorded, and a multiple comparison procedure was used to detect differences among the mean water losses for the different fumigation durations. How would you interpret this table?

Duration of fumigation	16	0	8	2	4
Sample mean water loss	27.57	28.23	30.21	31.16	36.21

15.28   The paper of Exercise 15.27 also included the accompanying underscoring pattern for plants of species *Robinia pseudoacacia*. How would you interpret this pattern?

Duration of fumigation	0	8	16	4	2
Sample mean water loss	23.52	28.39	32.49	36.54	39.26

15.29   Samples of six different brands of diet or imitation margarine were analyzed to determine the level of physiologically active polyunsaturated fatty acids (PAPFUA, in percent), resulting in the following data:

Imperial	14.1	13.6	14.4	14.3	
Parkay	12.8	12.5	13.4	13.0	12.3
Blue Bonnet	13.5	13.4	14.1	14.3	
Chiffon	13.2	12.7	12.6	13.9	
Mazola	16.8	17.2	16.4	17.3	18.0
Fleischmann's	18.1	17.2	18.7	18.4	

(The above data is fictitious, but the sample means agree with data reported in the January 1975 issue of *Consumer Reports*.)

   a. Test for differences among the true average PAPFUA percentages for the different brands. Use $\alpha = .05$.

   b. Use the Bonferroni procedure to compute 95% simultaneous confidence intervals for all differences between means.

c. Summarize the confidence intervals of (b) by listing the sample means in increasing order and then underscoring those that are not significantly different. Interpret the resulting display.

15.30   Scores of 24 hard-of-hearing children on a test of basic concepts are given in the accompanying table ("Performance of Young Hearing-Impaired Children on a Test of Basic Concepts" *J. Speech and Hearing Research* (1974):342–351).

Age 6	17	20	24	34	34	38						
Age 7	23	25	27	34	38	47						
Age 8	22	23	26	32	34	34	36	38	38	42	48	50

a. Use an ANOVA F test with significance level .05 to determine if true mean score depends on age.

b. Let μ_1, μ_2, and μ_3 represent the true mean score for 6-, 7-, and 8-year-olds, respectively. A reasonable theory is that the true mean score increases with age ($\mu_1 < \mu_2 < \mu_3$). Use the Bonferroni procedure to compute simultaneous confidence intervals for $\mu_1 - \mu_2$, $\mu_1 - \mu_3$, and $\mu_2 - \mu_3$. Based on these intervals, would you conclude that $\mu_1 < \mu_2 < \mu_3$? Explain.

15.4   The *F* Test for a Randomized Block Experiment

In Chapter 12 we saw that when two treatments are to be compared, a paired experiment is often more effective than one involving two independent samples. This is because pairing can considerably reduce the extraneous variation in subjects or experimental units. A similar result can be achieved when more than two treatments are to be compared. Suppose that four different pesticides (the treatments) are being considered for application to a particular crop. There are 20 plots of land available for planting. If 5 of these plots are randomly selected to receive pesticide 1, 5 of the remaining 15 randomly selected for 2, and so on, the result is a *completely randomized* experiment and the data should be analyzed using single-factor ANOVA. The disadvantage of this experiment is that if there are any substantial differences in characteristics of the plots that could affect yield, a separate assessment of any differences between treatments won't be possible.

Here is an alternative experiment. Consider separating the 20 plots into five groups, each consisting of 4 plots. Within each group, the plots are as alike as possible with respect to characteristics affecting yield. Then within each group, one plot is randomly selected for pesticide 1, a second plot is randomly chosen to receive pesticide 2, and so on. The homogeneous groups are called *blocks* and the random allocation of treatments within each block as described gives a *randomized block experiment*.

> **DEFINITION**
>
> Suppose that experimental units (individuals or objects to which the treatments are applied) are first separated into groups consisting of *k* units in such a way that the units within each group are as similar as possible. Each unit in a group then receives a different treatment. The groups are often called **blocks,** and the experimental design is referred to as a **randomized block design.**

EXAMPLE 15.8

High energy costs have made consumers and home builders increasingly conscious of whether or not household appliances are energy efficient. A large developer carried out a study to compare electricity usage for four different residential air-conditioning systems being considered for tract homes. Each system was installed in five homes, and the resulting electricity usage (in KWh) was monitored for a 1-month period. Because the developer realized that many characteristics of a home could affect usage (for example, floor space, type of insulation, directional orientation, and type of roof and exterior), care was taken to ensure that extraneous variation in such characteristics did not influence the conclusions. Homes selected for the experiment were grouped into five blocks consisting of four homes each so that the four homes within any given block were as similar as possible. Resulting data is displayed in the accompanying rectangular table, in which rows correspond to the different treatments (air-conditioning systems) and columns correspond to the different blocks.

		Block = *group*					Treatment average
		1	2	3	4	5	
	1	116	118	97	101	115	109.40
Treatment = K	2	171	131	105	107	129	128.60
ac system	3	138	131	115	93	110	117.40
	4	144	141	115	93	99	118.40
Block average		142.25	130.25	108.00	98.50	113.25	Grand mean 118.45

We analyze this data shortly to see whether electricity usage depends on which system is used.

The hypotheses of interest and assumptions underlying the analysis are similar to those for a completely randomized design.

ASSUMPTIONS AND HYPOTHESES

The single observation made on any particular treatment in a given block is assumed to be selected from a normal distribution. The variance of the distribution is σ^2, the same for each block-treatment combination. However, the mean value may depend separately both on the treatment applied and on the block.[2] The hypotheses of interest[3] are

H_0: the mean value does not depend on which treatment is applied

versus

H_a: the mean value does depend on which treatment is applied

The F Test

The key to analyzing data from an experiment such as the one described is to represent SSTo, which measures total variation, as a sum of three pieces: SSTr, SSE, and a block sum of squares SSB*l*. The latter SS incorporates any variation due to differences between the blocks, which will be substantial if there was great heterogeneity in experimental units (for example, plots) prior to creating the blocks. Once the four sums of squares have been computed, the test statistic is again an F ratio MSTr/MSE, but error df is no longer $N - k$, as in single-factor ANOVA.

SUMMARY OF THE RANDOMIZED BLOCK F TEST

Notation:

Let k = number of treatments

l = number of blocks

$\bar{x}_1$ = the average of all observations on the first treatment

$\vdots$

$\bar{x}_k$ = the average of all observations on the kth treatment

$\bar{b}_1$ = the average of all observations in the first block

$\vdots$

$\bar{b}_l$ = the average of all observations in the lth block

(continued)

---

[2]More specifically, it is assumed that there is no interaction between treatment effects and block effects. The concept of interaction is explored further in Section 13.5.

[3]An observation's mean value now depends both on the treatment and block utilized, so our previous notation $\mu_1, \mu_2, \ldots, \mu_k$ is no longer appropriate for stating hypotheses. In more advanced sources, hypotheses are stated using more complex notation.

$\bar{\bar{x}}$ = the average of all bl observations in the experiment (the grand mean)

Sums of squares and associated df are as follows.[4]

Sum of squares	Symbol	df	Formula
Total	SSTo	$kl - 1$	$\displaystyle\sum_{\substack{\text{all } kl \\ \text{observations}}} (x - \bar{\bar{x}})^2 = \sum_{\substack{\text{all } kl \\ \text{observations}}} x^2 - \frac{T^2}{kl}$
Treatments	SSTr	$k - 1$	$l[(\bar{x}_1 - \bar{\bar{x}})^2 + (\bar{x}_2 - \bar{\bar{x}})^2 + \cdots + (\bar{x}_k - \bar{\bar{x}})^2]$
Blocks	SSBl	$l - 1$	$k[(\bar{b}_1 - \bar{\bar{x}})^2 + (\bar{b}_2 - \bar{\bar{x}})^2 + \cdots + (\bar{b}_l - \bar{\bar{x}})^2]$
Error	SSE	$(k - 1)(l - 1)$	By subtraction

SSE is most easily obtained through the use of the fundamental identity

$$\text{SSTo} = \text{SSTr} + \text{SSB}l + \text{SSE}$$

Thus $\text{SSE} = \text{SSTo} - \text{SSTr} - \text{SSB}l$
Also, error df = total df − treatment df − block df.

Test statistic: $F = \dfrac{\text{MSTr}}{\text{MSE}}$

where $\text{MSTr} = \dfrac{\text{SSTr}}{k - 1}$ and $\text{MSE} = \dfrac{\text{SSE}}{(k - 1)(l - 1)}$

Rejection region: $F > F$ critical value, where the F critical value is based on $k - 1$ numerator df and $(k - 1)(l - 1)$ denominator df.

Calculations for this F test are usually summarized in an ANOVA table. The table is similar to the one for single-factor ANOVA except that blocks are an extra source of variation, so four rows are included rather than just three.

[4]Calculations can be expedited a bit by using the computational formulas

$$\text{SSTr} = \left(\frac{T_1^2 + T_2^2 + \cdots + T_k^2}{l}\right) - \frac{T^2}{kl}$$

$$\text{SSB}l = \left(\frac{B_1^2 + B_2^2 + \cdots + B_l^2}{k}\right) - \frac{T^2}{kl}$$

where $T_1, \ldots, T_k$ are the treatment totals, $B_1, \ldots, B_l$ are the block totals, and T is the grand total.

TABLE 15.4   The ANOVA table for a randomized block experiment

Source of variation	df	Sum of squares	Mean square	F
Treatments	$k - 1$	SSTr	$\text{MSTr} = \dfrac{\text{SSTr}}{k - 1}$	$F = \dfrac{\text{MSTr}}{\text{MSE}}$
Blocks	$l - 1$	SSBl	$\text{MSB}l = \dfrac{\text{SSB}l}{l - 1}$	
Error	$(k - 1)(l - 1)$	SSE	$\text{MSE} = \dfrac{\text{SSE}}{(k - 1)(l - 1)}$	
Total	$kl - 1$	SSTo		

Table 15.4 shows a mean square for blocks as well as for treatments and error. Sometimes the F ratio MSBl/MSE is also computed. A large value of this ratio suggests that blocking was effective in filtering out extraneous variation.

EXAMPLE 15.9

Let's reconsider the electricity usage data given in Example 15.8 and test at level .05 for the presence of any treatment effects.

H_0: the mean electricity usage does not depend on which air conditioning system is used

H_a: the mean electricity usage does depend on which system is used

Test statistic: $F = \dfrac{\text{MSTr}}{\text{MSE}}$

Rejection region: $F > F$ critical value, where the F critical value is based on $k - 1$ numerator and $(k - 1)(l - 1)$ denominator df. Since $k = 4$ and $l = 5$, $k - 1 = 3$, and $(k - 1)(l - 1) = 12$. Table X then gives the F critical value for $\alpha = .05$ as 3.49.

Computations: From Example 15.8,

$T = 2369 \qquad \overline{\overline{x}} = 118.45$

$\overline{x}_1 = 109.40 \qquad \overline{x}_2 = 128.60 \qquad \overline{x}_3 = 117.40 \qquad \overline{x}_4 = 118.40$
(these are the four row averages)

$\overline{b}_1 = 142.25 \quad \overline{b}_2 = 130.25 \quad \overline{b}_3 = 108.00 \quad \overline{b}_4 = 98.50 \quad \overline{b}_5 = 113.25$
(the five column averages)

Using the individual observations given earlier,

$$\text{SSTo} = \sum_{\substack{\text{all 20} \\ \text{observations}}} x^2 - \frac{T^2}{kl} = (116)^2 + (118)^2 + \cdots + (99)^2 - \frac{(2369)^2}{20}$$

$$= 288{,}203 - 280{,}608.05$$
$$= 7594.95$$

The other sums of squares are

$$\text{SSTr} = l[(\bar{x}_1 - \bar{\bar{x}})^2 + \cdots + (\bar{x}_4 - \bar{\bar{x}})^2]$$
$$= 5[(109.4 - 118.45)^2 + (128.6 - 118.45)^2$$
$$+ (117.4 - 118.45)^2 + (118.4 - 118.45)^2]$$
$$= 930.15$$

$$\text{SSBl} = k[(\bar{b}_1 - \bar{\bar{x}})^2 + \cdots + (\bar{b}_5 - \bar{\bar{x}})^2]$$
$$= 4[(142.25 - 118.45)^2 + (130.25 - 118.45)^2$$
$$+ \cdots + (113.25 - 118.45)^2]$$
$$= 4959.70$$

$$\text{SSE} = \text{SSTo} - \text{SSTr} - \text{SSBl}$$
$$= 7594.95 - 930.15 - 4959.70$$
$$= 1705.10.$$

The remaining calculations are displayed in the accompanying ANOVA table.

Source of variation	df	Sum of squares	Mean square	F
Treatments	3	930.15	310.05	$\dfrac{310.05}{142.09} = 2.18$
Blocks	4	4959.70	1239.93	
Error	12	1705.10	142.09	
Total	19	7594.95		

Conclusion: $F = 2.18$ does not exceed the critical value 3.49, so H_0 should not be rejected at level .05. Mean electricity usage does not seem to depend on which of the four air-conditioning systems is used.

In many studies, all k of the treatments can be applied to the same experimental unit, so there is no need to group different experimental units to form blocks. For example, an experiment to compare effects of four different gasoline additives on automobile engine efficiency could be carried out by selecting just 5 engines and using all four treatments on each one rather than using 20 engines and blocking them. Each engine by itself then constitutes a block. As another example, a manufacturing company might wish to compare outputs for three different packaging machines. Because output could be affected by which machine operator is used, a design that controls for the effects of operator variation is desirable. One possibility is to use 15 operators grouped into homogeneous blocks of 5 operators each, but such homogeneity within each block may be difficult to achieve. An alternative approach is to use only 5 operators and have each one operate all three machines. There are then three observations in each block, all three with the same operator.

EXAMPLE 15.10

The accompanying data resulted from a study of assembly and implementation times for four different packaged injection systems used to give shots ("An Assessment of Unit Dose Injection Systems" *Amer. J. of Hospital Pharmacy* (1972):61). Ten subjects, all pharmacists and nurses, were selected, and each was timed while using all four systems.

					Block (subject)							Treatment average
Treatment	1	2	3	4	5	6	7	8	9	10	
1. Standard	35.6	31.3	36.2	31.1	39.4	34.7	34.1	36.5	32.2	40.7	35.18
2. Vari-Ject	17.3	16.4	18.1	17.8	18.8	17.0	14.5	17.9	14.6	16.4	16.88
3. Unimatic	24.4	22.4	22.8	21.5	23.3	21.8	23.0	24.1	23.5	31.3	23.81
4. Tubex	25.0	26.0	25.3	24.0	24.2	26.2	24.0	20.9	23.5	36.9	25.60
Block average	25.575	24.025	25.600	23.600	26.425	24.925	23.900	24.850	23.450	31.325	$\bar{\bar{x}} = 25.3675$

H_0: mean implementation time does not depend on which injection system is used

H_a: mean implementation time does depend on which system is used

Test statistic: $F = \text{MSTr/MSE}$.

Rejection region: For a level .01 test based on $k - 1 = 3$ numerator df and $(k - 1)(l - 1) = (3)(9) = 27$ denominator df, the required F critical value is 4.60, so H_0 will be rejected if $F > 4.60$.

Computations: These are summarized in the accompanying ANOVA table.

Source of variation	df	Sum of squares	Mean square	F
Treatments	3	1708.03	569.34	100.95
Blocks	9	191.71	21.30	
Error	27	152.25	5.64	
Total	39	2051.99		

Conclusion: Because $F = 100.95 > 4.60 = F$ critical value, H_0 should be rejected at level of significance .01. The data very strongly suggests that average implementation time depends on which injection system is used.

Experiments such as the one described in Example 15.10, in which repeated observations are made on the same experimental unit, are sometimes called *repeated measures designs*. Such designs should not be used when application of the first several treatments somehow affects responses to later treatments. This would be the case if treatments were different methods for learning the same skill, so that if all treatments were given to the same subject, the response to the treatment given last would presumably be much better than the response to the treatment initially applied.

A randomized block experiment is a special case of a two-factor experiment in which one factor, blocks, is created solely to control for extraneous variation. Many statistical computer packages will perform a two-factor ANOVA on request, so data from a randomized block experiment can be analyzed by any such package. If H_0 is rejected by the *F* test, a multiple comparison procedure can be used to identify significant differences between treatments. In particular, the only modification to the Bonferroni procedure described in the previous section is that the Bonferroni *t* critical value now comes from the $(k - 1)(l - 1)$ df row of Table XI (because this is now error df). Finally, when $k = 2$, the randomized block *F* test and two-tailed paired *t* test are equivalent test procedures.

EXERCISES 15.31–15.41   SECTION 15.4

15.31 A particular county employs three assessors who are responsible for determining the value of residential property in the county. To see whether or not these assessors differ systematically in their appraisals, 5 houses are selected and each assessor is asked to determine the market value of each house. Explain why a randomized block experiment (with blocks corresponding to the 5 houses) was used rather than a completely randomized experiment involving a total of 15 houses with each assessor asked to appraise 5 different houses (a different group of 5 for each assessor).

15.32 A partially completed ANOVA table for the experiment described in Exercise 15.31 (with houses representing blocks and assessors representing treatments) is given.

Source of variation	df	Sum of squares	Mean square	F
Treatments		11.7		
Blocks		113.5		
Error				
Total		250.8		

a. Fill in the missing entries in the ANOVA table.

b. Use the ANOVA *F* statistic and a .05 level of significance to test the null hypothesis of no difference between assessors.

15.33 Land-treatment wastewater-processing systems work by removing nutrients and thereby discharging water of better quality. The land used is often planted with a crop such as corn because plant uptake removes nitrogen from the water and sale of the crop helps reduce the costs of wastewater treatment. The concentration of nitrogen in treated water was observed from 1975 to 1979 under wastewater application rates of none, .05 m/week, and .1 m/week. A randomized block ANOVA was performed with the 5 years serving as blocks. A partially completed ANOVA table is given ("Quality of Percolate Water After Treatment of a Municipal Wastewater Effluent by a Crop Irrigation System" *J. Environ. Quality* (1984):256–264).

Source of variation	df	Sum of squares	Mean square	F
Treatments		1835.2		
Blocks				
Error		206.1		
Total	14	2134.1		

    a. Complete the ANOVA table.

    b. Is there sufficient evidence to reject the null hypothesis of no difference between the true mean nitrogen concentrations for the three application rates? Use $\alpha = .05$.

15.34 In a comparison of the energy efficiency of three types of ovens—conventional, biradiant, and convection—the energy used in cooking was measured for eight different foods (one-layer cake, two-layer cake, biscuits, bread, frozen pie, baked potatoes, lasagna, and meat loaf). Since a comparison between the three types of ovens is desired, a randomized block (with the eight foods serving as blocks) ANOVA will be used. Suppose calculations result in the quantities $SSTo = 4.57$, $SSTr = 3.97$, and $SSBl = .2503$ (a similar study is described in the paper "Optimizing Oven Radiant Energy Use" *Home Ec. Res. J.* (1980):242–251). Construct an ANOVA table and test the null hypothesis of no difference in mean energy use for the three types of ovens. Use a .01 significance level.

15.35 The article "Rate of Stuttering Adaptation Under Two Electro-Shock Conditions" (*Behavior Res. Therapy* (1967):49–54) gave adaptation scores for three different treatments: no shock (treatment 1), shock following each stuttered word (treatment 2), and shock during each moment of stuttering (treatment 3). These treatments were used on each of 18 stutterers. The 18 subjects were viewed as blocks and the data analyzed using a randomized block ANOVA. Summary quantities are $SSTr = 28.78$, $SSBl = 2977.67$, and $SSE = 469.55$. Construct the ANOVA table and test at significance level .05 to see whether true average adaptation score depends on the treatment given.

15.36 The given table shows average height of cotton plants during 1978–1980 under three different effluent application rates (350, 440, and 515 mm). ("Drip Irrigation of Cotton with Treated Municipal Effluents: Yield Response" *J. Environ. Quality* (1984):231–238)

	Application rate		
Year	350	440	515
1978	166	176	177
1979	109	126	136
1980	140	155	156

a. This data was analyzed using a randomized block ANOVA with years serving as blocks. Explain why this would be better for comparing treatments than a completely randomized ANOVA.

b. With treatments 1, 2, and 3 denoting the application rates 350, 440, and 515, respectively, summary quantities are:

$$\Sigma(x - \bar{\bar{x}})^2 = 4266.0 \qquad \bar{\bar{x}} = 149.00$$

$$\bar{x}_1 = 138.33 \qquad \bar{x}_2 = 152.33 \qquad \bar{x}_3 = 156.33$$

$$\bar{b}_1 = 173.00 \qquad \bar{b}_2 = 123.67 \qquad \bar{b}_3 = 150.33$$

Construct an ANOVA table. Use a .01 significance level to determine if the true mean height differs for the three effluent rates.

15.37 The paper "Cardiac Output in Preadolescent Competitive Swimmers and in Untrained Normal Children" (*J. Sports Med.* (1983):291–299) gives the accompanying data on heart rate at rest for eight trained and eight untrained swimmers. The trained and untrained swimmers were paired on the basis of physical characteristics so that the members of each pair were as similar as possible.

Subject pair	1	2	3	4	5	6	7	8
Trained	90	85	75	120	95	105	85	75
Untrained	95	75	80	65	82	80	100	85

To determine whether there is a difference in true mean resting heart rate, the data can be analyzed using a randomized block ANOVA with subjects serving as blocks. Summary quantities include $\bar{\bar{x}} = 87$ and $\Sigma(x - \bar{\bar{x}})^2 = 2770$.

a. Construct an ANOVA table and test the null hypothesis of no difference between true mean heart rate of trained and untrained swimmers. Use $\alpha = .05$.

b. A paired t test can be used to test H_0: $\mu_1 - \mu_2 = 0$, where μ_1 and μ_2 denote the true mean heart rate for trained and untrained swimmers, respectively. Verify that a paired t test with significance level .05 leads you to the same conclusion as the test in (a). (Also note that $t^2 = F$.)

15.38 The paper "Responsiveness of Food Sales to Shelf Space Changes in Supermarkets" (*J. Mktg. Research* (1964):63–67) described an experiment to assess the effect of allotted shelf space on product sales. Two of the products studied were baking soda (a staple product) and Tang (considered to be an impulse product). Six stores (blocks) were used in the experiment and six different shelf-space allotments were tried for one week each. Space allotments of 2, 4, 6, 8, 10, and 12 ft were used for baking soda and 6, 9, 12, 15, 18, and 21 ft were used for Tang. The author speculated that sales of staple goods would not be sensitive to changes in shelf space, whereas sales of impulse products would be affected by changes in shelf space.

a. Data on number of boxes of baking soda sold during a 1-week period is given. Construct an ANOVA table and test the appropriate hypotheses. Use a significance level of .05.

		\multicolumn{6}{c}{Shelf space}
		2	4	6	8	10	12
	1	36	42	36	40	30	22
	2	74	61	65	67	83	84
Store	3	40	58	42	73	69	63
	4	43	65	65	41	43	47
	5	27	33	35	17	40	26
	6	23	31	36	38	42	37

b. Data for Tang sales is also given. Construct an ANOVA table and test the appropriate hypotheses using a .05 significance level.

		\multicolumn{6}{c}{Shelf space}
		6	9	12	15	18	21
	1	30	35	25	25	38	31
	2	47	59	43	62	65	48
Store	3	47	55	48	54	36	54
	4	29	19	41	27	33	39
	5	17	11	25	23	24	26
	6	22	9	19	18	25	22

c. Was the author correct in his speculation that sales of the staple product would not be affected by shelf space allocation, whereas sales of the impulse product would be affected? Explain.

15.39   Four plots were available for an experiment to compare clover accumulation (kg DM/ha) for four different sowing rates ("Performance of Overdrilled Red Clover with Different Sowing Rates and Initial Grazing Managements" *N. Zeal. J. Exp. Ag.* (1984):71–81). Since the four plots had been grazed differently prior to the experiment and it was thought that this might affect clover accumulation, a randomized block experiment was used with all four sowing rates tried on a section of each plot. Use the given data to test the null hypothesis of no difference in true mean clover accumulation for the different sowing rates.

		Sowing rate (kg/ha)			
		3.6	6.6	10.2	13.5
Plot	1	1155	2255	3505	4632
	2	123	406	564	416
	3	68	416	662	379
	4	62	75	362	564

15.40   The paper "Measuring Treatment Effects Through Comparisons Along Plot Boundaries" (*Forest Sci.* (1980):704–709) reported the results of a randomized block experiment. Five different sources of pine seed were used in each of four blocks. Data is given for plant height (m) and plant diameter (cm).

		Height				Diameter			
	Block	I	II	III	IV	I	II	III	IV
Source	1	7.1	5.8	7.2	6.9	9.4	7.9	9.4	9.4
	2	6.2	5.3	7.7	4.7	8.9	7.9	10.7	7.6
	3	7.9	5.4	8.6	6.2	10.4	7.9	12.2	9.1
	4	9.0	5.9	5.7	7.3	12.2	8.4	7.6	9.4
	5	7.0	6.3	4.4	6.1	9.9	8.6	6.6	8.6

a. Does the data provide sufficient evidence to conclude that the true mean height is not the same for all five seed sources? Use a .05 level of significance.

b. Does the data strongly suggest that the true mean diameter is not the same for all seed sources? Use a .05 level of significance.

→15.41   The paper of Exercise 15.40 also gave the accompanying data on survival rate for five different seed sources.

Block	I	II	III	IV
Source				
1	62.5	87.5	50.0	70.3
2	50.0	50.0	54.7	59.4
3	93.8	92.2	87.5	87.5
4	96.9	76.6	70.3	65.6
5	56.3	50.0	45.3	56.3

a. Construct an ANOVA table and test the null hypothesis of no difference in true mean survival rates for the five seed sources. Use $\alpha = .05$.

b. Use the Bonferroni procedure (described in Section 15.3) to identify significant differences among the seed sources.

15.5 Two-Factor ANOVA

An investigator will often be interested in assessing the effects of two different factors on a response variable. Consider the following examples.

1. A physical education researcher wishes to know how body density of football players varies with position played (a categorical factor with categories defensive back, offensive back, defensive lineman, and offensive lineman) and level of play (a second categorical factor with categories professional, college division I, college division II, and college division III).

2. An agricultural scientist is interested in seeing how yield of tomatoes is affected by choice of variety planted (a categorical factor with each category corresponding to a different variety) and planting density (a quantitative factor with a level corresponding to each planting density being considered).

3. An applied chemist might wish to investigate how shear strength of a particular adhesive varies with application temperature (a quantitative factor with levels 250°F, 260°F, and 270°F) and application pressure (a quantitative factor with levels 110 lb/in.^{2}, 120 lb/in.^{2}, 130 lb/in.^{2}, and 140 lb/in.^{2}).

Let's call the two factors under study factor A and factor B. Even when a factor is categorical, it simplifies terminology to refer to the categories as levels. Thus in the first example, the categorical factor *position played* has four levels. The number of levels of factor A is denoted by k, and l denotes the number of levels of factor B. The rectangular table displayed contains a row corresponding to each level of factor A and a column corresponding to each level of factor B. Each cell in this table corresponds to a particular level of factor A in combination with a particular level of factor B. Because there are l cells in each row and k rows, there are kl cells in the table. The kl different combinations of factor A and factor B levels are often referred to as **treatments.** In the second example, if there are three tomato varieties and four different planting densities under consideration, the number of treatments is 12.

Suppose that an experiment is carried out, resulting in a data set that contains some number of observations for each of the kl treatments. In general, there could be more observations on some treatments than on others, and there may even be a few treatments for which no observations are available. An experimenter may set out to make the same number of observations on each treatment, but on occasion forces beyond the experimenter's control—the death of an experimental subject, malfunctioning equipment, and so on—result in different sample sizes for some treatments. However, such imbalance in sample sizes makes analysis of the data rather difficult. We will restrict consideration to data sets containing the same number of observations on each treatment and let m denote this number.

NOTATION

k = number of levels of factor A

l = number of levels of factor B

kl = number of treatments (each one a combination of a factor A level and a factor B level)

m = number of observations on each treatment

EXAMPLE 15.11

An experiment was carried out to assess the effects of tomato variety (factor A, with $k = 3$ levels) and planting density (factor B, with $l = 4$ levels—10, 20, 30, and 40 thousand plants per hectare) on yield. Each of the $kl = 12$ treatments was used on $m = 3$ plots, resulting in the accompanying data set, which consists of $klm = 36$ observations (adapted from "Effects of Plant Density on Tomato Yields in Western Nigeria" *Exper. Ag.* (1976):43–47).

		Density (B)			
		1	2	3	4
Variety (A)	1	7.9, 9.2, 10.5	11.2, 12.8, 13.3	12.1, 12.6, 14.0	9.1, 10.8, 12.5
	2	8.1, 8.6, 10.1	11.5, 12.7, 13.7	13.7, 14.4, 15.4	11.3, 12.5, 14.5
	3	15.3, 16.1, 17.5	16.6, 18.5, 19.2	18.0, 20.8, 21.0	17.2, 18.4, 18.9

Sample average yields for each treatment, each level of factor A, and each level of factor B are important summary quantities. These are displayed in the given rectangular table.

Sample average yield for each treatment		Factor B				Sample average yield for each level of factor A
		1	2	3	4	
Factor A	1	9.20	12.43	12.90	10.80	11.33 $\bar{x}_1$
	2	8.93	12.63	14.50	12.77	12.21 $\bar{x}_2$
	3	16.30	18.10	19.93	18.17	18.13 $\bar{x}_k$
Sample average yield for each level of factor B		11.48 $\bar{x}_1$	14.39 $\bar{x}_2$	15.78 $\bar{x}_3$	13.91 $\bar{x}_l$	Grand mean 13.89

A plot of these <u>sample averages</u> is also quite informative. First construct horizontal and vertical axes, and scale the vertical axis in units of the response variable (yield). Then mark a point on the horizontal axis for each level of one of the factors (either A or B can be chosen). Now above each such mark, plot a point for the sample average response for each level of the other factor. Finally, connect all points corresponding to the same level of the other factor by straight line segments. Figure 15.3 displays one such plot for which factor A levels mark the horizontal axis and another plot for which factor B levels mark this axis; usually only one of the two plots is constructed.

FIGURE 15.3
Graphs of treatment sample average responses for the data of Example 15.11

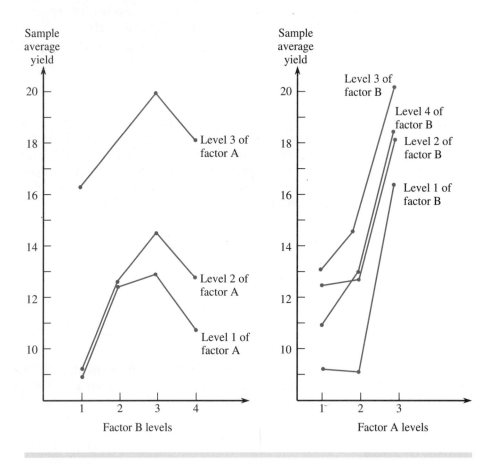

Interaction

An important aspect of two-factor studies involves assessing how simultaneous changes in the levels of both factors affect the response. As a simple example, suppose that an automobile manufacturer is studying engine efficiency (miles per gallon) for two different engine sizes (factor A, with $k = 2$ levels) in combination with two different carburetor designs (factor B, with $l = 2$ levels). Consider the two possible sets of true average responses displayed in Table 15.5. In Table 15.5(a), when factor A changes from level 1 to level 2 and factor B remains at level 1 (the change within the first column), the true average response increases by 2. Similarly, when factor B changes from level 1 to level 2 and factor A is fixed at level 1 (the change within the first row), the true average response increases by 3. And when the levels of both factors are changed from 1 to 2, the true average response increases by 5, which is the sum of the two "one-at-a-time" increases. This is because the change in true average response when the level of either factor changes from 1 to 2 is the same for each level of the other factor—the change within either row is 3 and the change within either column is 2. In this case, changes in levels of the two factors affect the true average response separately, or in an additive manner.

TABLE 15.5 Two possible sets of true average responses when $k = 2$ and $l = 2$

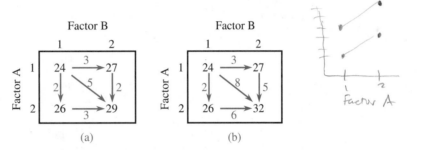

(a)   (b)

The changes in true average responses in the first row and in the first column of Table 15.5(b) are 3 and 2, respectively, exactly as in Table 15.5(a). However, the change in true average response when the levels of both factors change simultaneously from 1 to 2 is 8, which is much larger than the separate changes suggest. In this case there is interaction between the two factors, so that the effect of simultaneous changes cannot be determined from the individual effects of separate changes. This is because in Table 15.5(b), the change in going from the first to the second column is different for the two rows, and the change in going from the first to the second row is different for the two columns. That is, *the change in true average response when the level of one factor changes depends on the level of the other factor.* This is not true in Table 15.5(a).

When there are more than two levels of either factor, a graph of true average responses, similar to that for sample average responses in Figure 15.3, provides insight into how changes in the level of one factor depend on the level of the other factor. Figure 15.4 shows several possible such graphs when $k = 4$ and $l = 3$. The most general situation is pictured in Figure 15.4(a). There the change in true average response when the level of B is changed (a vertical distance) depends on the level of A. An analogous property would hold if the picture were redrawn so that levels of B were marked on the horizontal axis. This is a prototypical picture suggesting **interaction** between the factors—the change in true average response when the level of one factor changes depends on the level of the other factor.

FIGURE 15.4
Some graphs of
true average responses

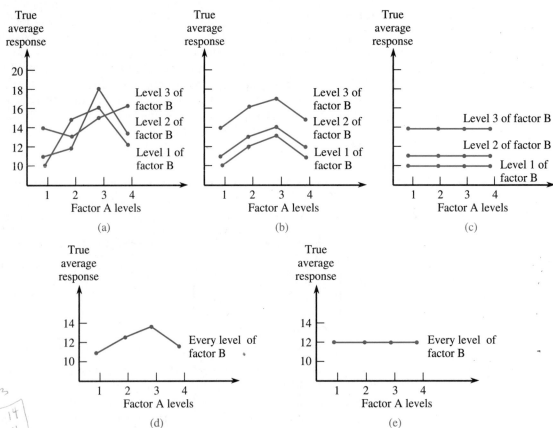

(a)

(b)

(c)

(d)

(e)

There is no interaction between the factors when the connected line segments are parallel, as in Figure 15.4(b). Then the change in true average response when the level of one factor changes is the same for each level of the other factor (the vertical distances are the same for each level of factor A). Figure 15.4(c) illustrates an even more restrictive situation—there is no interaction between factors, and, in addition, the true average response does not depend on the level of factor A. Only when the graph looks like this can it be said that factor A has no effect on the responses. Similarly, the graph in Figure 15.4(d) indicates no interaction and no dependence on the level of factor B. A final case, pictured in Figure 15.4(e), shows a single set of four points connected by horizontal line segments, which indicates that the true average response is identical for every level of either factor.

> If the graphs of true average responses are connected line segments that are parallel, there is no interaction between the factors. In this case the change in true average response when the level of one factor is changed is the same for each level of the other factor. Special cases of no interaction are
>
> 1. The true average response is the same for each level of factor A (no factor A main effects);
> 2. The true average response is the same for each level of factor B (absence of factor B main effects).

The graphs of Figure 15.4 picture true average responses, quantities whose values are fixed but unknown to an investigator. Figure 15.3 contains graphs of the sample average responses based on data resulting from an experiment. These sample averages are, of course, subject to variability because there is sampling variation in the individual observations. If the experiment discussed in Example 15.11 were repeated, the resulting graphs of sample averages would probably look somewhat different from the graph in Figure 15.3 and perhaps a great deal different if there were substantial underlying variability in responses. Even when there is no interaction among factors, the connected line segments in the sample mean picture will not typically be exactly parallel and may deviate quite a bit from parallelism in the presence of substantial underlying variability. Similarly, there might actually be no factor A effects (Figure 15.4(c)), yet the sample graphs would not usually be exactly horizontal. The sample pictures give us insight, but formal inferential procedures are needed in order to draw sound conclusions about the nature of the true average responses for different factor levels.

Hypotheses and F Tests

> **BASIC ASSUMPTION**
>
> The observations on any particular treatment are independently selected from a normal distribution with variance σ^2 (the same variance for each treatment), and samples from different treatments are independent of one another.

Because of the normality assumption, tests based on F statistics and F critical values are appropriate. The necessary sums of squares result from breaking up $\text{SSTo} = \Sigma(x - \bar{\bar{x}})^2$ into four parts, which reflect random variation and variation attributable to various factor effects:

$$\text{SSTo} = \text{SSA} + \text{SSB} + \text{SSAB} + \text{SSE}$$

where

1. SSTo is total sum of squares, with associated df $klm - 1$
2. SSA is the factor A main effect sum of squares, with associated df $k - 1$
3. SSB is the factor B main effect sum of squares, with associated df $l - 1$
4. SSAB is the interaction sum of squares, with associated df $(k - 1)(l - 1)$
5. SSE is error sum of squares, with associated df $kl(m - 1)$

The formulas for these sums of squares are similar to those given in previous sections, but for our purposes it is not necessary to give them. The standard statistical computer packages will calculate all sums of squares and other necessary quantities. As before, the magnitude of SSE is related entirely to the amount of underlying variability (as specified by σ^2) in the distributions being sampled. It has nothing to do with values of the various true average responses. SSAB reflects in part underlying variability, but its value is also affected by whether or not there is interaction between the factors. Generally speaking, the more extensive the amount of interaction (that is, the further the graphs of true average responses are from being parallel), the larger the value of SSAB tends to be. The test statistic for testing the null hypothesis that there is no interaction between factors is the ratio MSAB/MSE. A large value of this statistic suggests that interaction effects are present.

The absence of factor A effects and of factor B effects are both special cases of no-interaction situations. If the data suggests that interaction is present, it doesn't make sense to investigate effects of one factor without reference to the other factor. Our recommendation is that hypotheses concerning the presence or absence of separate factor effects be tested only if the hypothesis of no interaction is not rejected. Then the factor A main effect sum of squares SSA will reflect random variation and, in addition, any differences between true average responses for different levels of factor A. A similar comment applies to SSB.

TWO-FACTOR ANOVA HYPOTHESES AND TESTS

1. H_0: there is no interaction between factors
   H_a: there is interaction between factors
   Test statistic: $F_{AB} = $ MSAB/MSE
   Rejection region: $F_{AB} > F$ critical value, where the test statistic and critical value are based on $(k - 1)(l - 1)$ numerator df and $kl(m - 1)$ denominator df.

The following two hypotheses should be tested only if H_0 in (1) is not rejected.

2. H_0: there are no factor A main effects (true average response is the same for each level of factor A)
   H_a: H_0 is not true
   Test statistic: $F_A = $ MSA/MSE.
   Rejection region: $F_A > F$ critical value, where the test statistic and criti-

(continued)

cal value are based on $k - 1$ numerator and $kl(m - 1)$ denominator df, respectively.

3. H_0: there are no factor B main effects
   H_a: H_0 is not true
   Test statistic: $F_B = $ MSB/MSE
   Rejection region: $F_B > F$ critical value, where the test statistic and critical value are based on $l - 1$ numerator and $kl(m - 1)$ denominator df, respectively.

Computations are typically summarized in an ANOVA table, as shown.

Source of variation	df	Sum of squares	Mean square	F
A Main Effects	$k - 1$	SSA	$\text{MSA} = \dfrac{\text{SSA}}{k - 1}$	$F_A = \dfrac{\text{MSA}}{\text{MSE}}$
B Main Effects	$l - 1$	SSB	$\text{MSB} = \dfrac{\text{SSB}}{l - 1}$	$F_B = \dfrac{\text{MSB}}{\text{MSE}}$
AB Interaction	$(k - 1)(l - 1)$	SSAB	$\text{MSAB} = \dfrac{\text{SSAB}}{(k - 1)(l - 1)}$	$F_{AB} = \dfrac{\text{MSAB}}{\text{MSE}}$
Error	$kl(m - 1)$	SSE	$\text{MSE} = \dfrac{\text{SSE}}{kl(m - 1)}$	
Total	$klm - 1$	SSTo		

EXAMPLE 15.12

The accompanying ANOVA table resulted from using MINITAB's two-factor ANOVA command on the tomato-yield data of Example 15.11.

ANALYSIS OF VARIANCE ON YIELD

```
SOURCE        DF        SS        MS
VARIETY        2    327.60    163.80
DENSITY        3     86.69     28.90
INTERACTION    6      8.03      1.34
ERROR         24     38.04      1.58
TOTAL         35    460.36
```

1. Test of H_0: no interaction between variety and density:

   Test statistic: $F_{AB} = \dfrac{\text{MSAB}}{\text{MSE}}$

   Numerator df $= (k - 1)(l - 1) = 6$
   Denominator df $= kl(m - 1) = 24$

F critical value for level .05 test $= 2.51$

Calculated $F_{AB} = \dfrac{1.34}{1.58} = .85$

Since $.85 < 2.51$, H_0 should not be rejected. There is no evidence of interaction, so it is appropriate to carry out further tests concerning the presence of main effects.

2. Test of H_0: factor A (variety) main effects are absent:

Test statistic: $F_A = \dfrac{MSA}{MSE}$

Numerator df $= k - 1 = 2$
Denominator df $= kl(m - 1) = 24$
F critical value for level .05 test $= 3.40$

Calculated $F_A = \dfrac{163.80}{1.58} = 103.7$

Since $103.7 > 3.40$, reject H_0 and conclude that true average yield does depend on which variety is used.

3. Test of H_0: factor B (density) main effects are absent:

Test statistic: $F_B = \dfrac{MSB}{MSE}$

Numerator df $= l - 1 = 3$
Denominator df $= kl(m - 1) = 24$
F critical value for level .05 test $= 3.01$

Calculated $F_B = \dfrac{28.90}{1.58} = 18.3$

Since $18.3 > 3.01$, reject H_0 and conclude that true average yield does depend on which planting density is used.

After the null hypothesis of no factor A main effects has been rejected, significant differences in factor A levels can be identified by using a multiple comparisons procedure. In particular, the Bonferroni method described earlier can be applied. The quantities $\bar{x}_1, \bar{x}_2, \ldots, \bar{x}_k$ are now the sample average responses for levels $1, \ldots, k$ of factor A, and error df is $kl(m - 1)$. A similar comment applies to factor B main effects and significant differences in factor B levels.

The Case $m = 1$

There is a problem with the foregoing analysis when $m = 1$ (one observation on each treatment). Although we did not give the formula, MSE is an estimate of σ^2

obtained by computing a separate sample variance s^2 for the m observations on each treatment and then averaging these kl sample variances. With only one observation on each treatment, there is no way to estimate σ^2 separately from each of the treatments.

One way out of this dilemma is to assume a priori that there is no interaction between factors. This should, of course, be done only when the investigator has sound reasons, based on a thorough understanding of the problem, for believing that the factors contribute separately to the response. Having made this assumption, what would otherwise be interaction sum of squares can then be used for SSE. The fundamental identity becomes

$$\text{SSTo} = \text{SSA} + \text{SSB} + \text{SSE}$$

with the four associated df $kl - 1, k - 1, l - 1$, and $(k - 1)(l - 1)$.

The analysis of data from a randomized block experiment in fact assumed no interaction between treatments and blocks. If SSTr is relabeled SSA and SSBl is relabeled SSB, the formulas for all sums of squares given in Section 15.4 are valid here ($\bar{x}_1, \ldots, \bar{x}_k$ and $\bar{b}_1, \ldots, \bar{b}_l$ are now the sample average responses for factor A levels and factor B levels, respectively). The corresponding ANOVA table is given. F_A is the test statistic for testing the null hypothesis that true average responses are identical for all factor A levels. F_B plays a similar role for factor B main effects.

Source of variation	df	Sum of squares	Mean square	F
Factor A	$k - 1$	SSA	$\text{MSA} = \dfrac{\text{SSA}}{k - 1}$	$F_A = \text{MSA/MSE}$
Factor B	$l - 1$	SSB	$\text{MSB} = \dfrac{\text{SSB}}{l - 1}$	$F_B = \text{MSB/MSE}$
Error	$(k - 1)(l - 1)$	SSE	$\text{MSE} = \dfrac{\text{SSE}}{(k - 1)(l - 1)}$	
Total	$kl - 1$	SSTo		

EXAMPLE 15.13

When metal pipe is buried in soil, it is desirable to apply a coating to retard corrosion. Four different coatings are under consideration for use with pipe that will ultimately be buried in three types of soil. An experiment to investigate the effects of these coatings and soils was carried out by first selecting 12 pipe segments and applying each coating to three segments. The segments were then buried in soil for a specified period in such a way that each soil type received one piece with each coating. The resulting data (depth of corrosion) and ANOVA table are given. Assuming that there is no interaction between coating type and soil type, let's test at level .05 for the presence of separate factor A (coating) and factor B (soil) effects.

	Factor B (soil)			
	1	2	3	Sample average
Factor A 1	64	49	50	54.33
(coating) 2	53	51	48	50.67
3	47	45	50	47.33
4	51	43	52	48.67
Sample average	53.75	47.00	50.00	$\bar{\bar{x}} = 50.25$

Source of variation	df	Sum of squares	Mean square	F
Factor A	3	83.5	27.8	$F_A = \dfrac{27.8}{20.6} = 1.3$
Factor B	2	91.5	45.8	$F_B = \dfrac{45.8}{20.6} = 2.2$
Error	6	123.3	20.6	
Total	11	298.3		

The number of denominator df for each F test is 6, and the level .05 F critical values for 3 and 2 numerator df are 4.76 and 5.14, respectively. Neither computed F ratio exceeds the corresponding critical value, so it appears that the true average response (amount of corrosion) depends neither on the coating used nor on the type of soil in which pipe is buried.

EXERCISES 15.42–15.51   SECTION 15.5

15.42   Many students report that test anxiety affects their performance on exams. A study of the effect of anxiety and instructional mode (lecture versus independent study) on test performance was described in the paper "Interactive Effects of Achievement Anxiety, Academic Achievement, and Instructional Mode on Performance and Course Attitudes" (*Home Ec. Research J.* (1980):216–227). Students classified as either belonging to high- or low-achievement anxiety groups (factor A) were assigned to one of the two instructional modes (factor B). Mean test scores for the four treatments (factor level combinations) are given. Use these means to construct a graph (similar to those of Figure 15.3) of the treatment sample averages. Does the picture suggest the existence of an interaction between factors? Explain.

Anxiety group	Instructional mode	
	Lecture	Independent study
High	145.8	144.3
Low	142.9	144.8

15.43 The accompanying plot appeared in the paper "Group Process—Work Outcome Relationships: A Note on the Moderating Impact of Self-Esteem" (*Academy of Mgmt. J.* (1982):575–585). The response variable was tension, a measure of job strain. The two factors of interest were peer-group interactions (with two levels— high and low) and self-esteem (also with two levels—high and low)

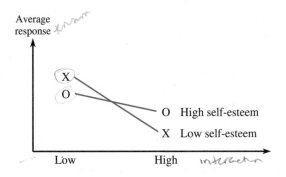

a. Does this plot suggest an interaction between peer-group interaction and self-esteem? Explain.

b. The authors of the paper state: "Peer group interaction had a stronger effect on individuals with lower self-esteem than on those with higher self-esteem." Do you agree with this statement? Explain.

15.44 Explain why the individual effects of factor A or factor B can't be interpreted when an AB interaction is present.

15.45 The paper "Experimental Analysis of Prey Selection by Largemouth Bass" (*Trans. Amer. Fisheries Soc.* (1991):500–508) gave an ANOVA summary in which the response variable was a certain preference index, there were three sizes of bass, and there were two different species of prey. Three observations were made for each size-species combination. Sums of squares for size, species, and interaction were reported as .088, .048, and .048, respectively, and SSTo = .316. Test the relevant hypotheses using a significance level of .01.

15.46 Three ultrasonic devices (factor A, with levels 20, 30, and 40 kHz) were tested for effectiveness under two test conditions (factor B, with levels *plentiful food supply* and *restricted food supply*). Daily food consumption was recorded for three rats under each factor level combination for a total of 18 observations. Data compatible with summary values given in the paper "Variables Affecting Ultrasound Repellency in Philippine Rats" (*J. Wildlife Mgmt.* (1982):148–155) was used to obtain the sums of squares given in the following ANOVA table. Complete the table and use it to test the relevant hypotheses.

Source of variation	df	Sum of squares	Mean square	F
A main effects		4206		
B main effects		1782		
AB interaction				
Error		2911		
Total		10,846		

15.47 The paper "Learning, Opportunity to Cheat, and Amount of Reward" (*J. Exper. Educ.* (1977):30–40) described a study to determine the effects of expectations concerning cheating during a test and perceived payoff on test performance. Subjects, students at UCLA, were randomly assigned to a particular factor-level combination. Factor A was expectation of opportunity to cheat, with levels high, medium, and low. Those in the high group were asked to study and then recall a list of words. For the first four lists, they were left alone in a room with the door closed and so could look at the original list of words if desired. The medium group was asked to study and recall the list while left alone but with the door open. For the low group, the experimenter remained in the room. For study and recall of a fifth list, the experimenter stayed in the room for all three groups, thus precluding any cheating on the fifth list. Score on the fifth test was the response variable. The second factor (B) under study was the perceived payoff, with a high and a low level. The high payoff group was told that if they scored above average on the test, they would receive 2 h of credit rather than just 1 h (subjects were fulfilling a course requirement by participating in experiments). The low group was not given any extra incentive for scoring above the average. The paper gave the following statistics: $F_A = 4.99$, $F_B = 4.81$, $F_{AB} < 1$, error df ≈ 120. Test the null hypothesis of no interaction between the factors. If appropriate, test the null hypotheses of no factor A and no factor B effects. Use $\alpha = .05$.

15.48 The accompanying (slightly modified) ANOVA table appeared in the paper "An Experimental Test of Mate Defense in an Iguanid Lizard" (*Ecology* (1991):1218–1224). The response variable was territory size.

Source of variation	df	SS
Age	1	.614
Sex	1	1.754
Interaction	1	.146
Error	80	5.624

a. How many age classes were there?

b. How many observations were made for each age-sex combination?

c. What conclusions can be drawn about how the factors affect the response variable?

15.49 Identification of sex in human skeletons is an important part of many anthropological studies. An experiment conducted to determine if measurements of the sacrum could be used to determine sex was described in the paper "Univariate and Multivariate Methods for Sexing the Sacrum" (*Am. J. Phys. Anthro.* (1978):103–110). Sacra from skeletons of individuals whose race (factor A, with two levels—Caucasian and Black) and sex (factor B, with two levels—male and female) were known were measured and the lengths recorded. Data compatible with summary quantities given in the paper was used to compute the following: SSA = 857, SSB = 291, SSAB = 32, SSE = 5541, and error df = 36.

a. Use a significance level of .01 to test the null hypothesis of no interaction between race and sex.

b. Using a .01 significance level, test to determine if the true average length differs for the two races.

c. Using a .01 significance level, test to determine if the true average length differs for males and females.

15.50 The paper "Food Consumption and Energy Requirements of Captive Bald Eagles" (*J. Wildlife Mgmt.* (1982):646–654) investigated mean gross daily energy intake (the response variable) for different diet types (factor A, with three levels—fish, rabbit, and mallard) and temperatures (factor B, with three levels). Summary quantities given in the paper were used to generate data, resulting in SSA = 18,138, SSB = 5182, SSAB = 1737, SSE = 11,291, and error df = 36. Construct an ANOVA table and test the relevant hypotheses.

15.51 The effect of three different soil types and three phosphate application rates on total phosphorus uptake (mg) of white clover was examined in the paper "A Glasshouse Comparison of Six Phosphate Fertilisers" (*N. Zeal. J. Exp. Ag.* (1984):131–140). Only one observation was obtained for each factor–level combination. Assuming there is no interaction between soil type and application rate, use the data below to construct an ANOVA table and to test the null hypotheses of no main effects due to soil type and of no main effects due to application rate.

Application rate (kgP/ha)	Soil type		
	Ramiha	Konini	Wainui
0	1.29	10.42	17.10
75	11.73	21.08	23.69
150	17.63	31.37	32.88

15.6 Distribution-Free ANOVA

The validity of the F tests presented in earlier sections is based on the assumption that observations are selected from normal distributions, all of which have the same variance, σ^2. When this is the case, the type I error probability is controlled at the desired level of significance α by using an appropriate F critical value. Additionally, the test has good ability to detect departures from the null hypothesis—its type II error probabilities are smaller than those for any other test.

There are two potential difficulties in using the F test when the basic assumptions are violated. One is that the actual level of significance may be different from what the investigator desires. This is because the test statistic will no longer have an F distribution, so an F critical value won't capture the desired tail area (for example, .05 or .01) under the actual sampling distribution curve. A second problem is that the test may have rather large type II error probabilities, so that substantial departures from H_0 are likely to go undetected.

Studies have shown that when population or treatment distributions are only mildly nonnormal, neither problem alluded to above is serious enough to warrant abandoning the F test. Statisticians say that the test is *robust* to small departures from normality. However, distributions that are either very skewed or have much heavier tails than the normal distribution do adversely affect the performance of the F test. Here we present test procedures that are valid (have a guaranteed type I error probability) when underlying population or treatment distributions are nonnormal, as long as they have the same shape and spread. These procedures are distribution-free because their validity is guaranteed for a very wide class of distributions rather than just for a particular type of distribution, such as the normal. As was the case with the distribution-free rank-sum test discussed in Chapter 11, the distribution-free ANOVA procedures are based on ranks of the observations.

The Kruskal-Wallis Test for a Completely Randomized Design

As before, k denotes the number of populations or treatments being compared, and $\mu_1, \mu_2, \ldots, \mu_k$ represent the population means or average responses when treatments are administered. The hypotheses to be tested are still H_0: $\mu_1 = \mu_2 = \cdots = \mu_k$ versus H_a: at least two among the k means are different.

> **BASIC ASSUMPTION**
>
> The k population or treatment distributions all have the same shape and spread.

The distribution-free test to be described here is called the **Kruskal-Wallis (K-W) test** after the two statisticians who developed it. Suppose that k independent random samples are available, one from each population or treatment. Again let n_1, $n_2, \ldots, n_k$ denote the sample sizes, with $N = n_1 + n_2 + \cdots + n_k$. When H_0 is true, observations in all samples are selected from the same population or treatment-response distribution. Observations in the different samples should then be quite comparable in magnitude. However, when some μ's are different, some samples will consist mostly of relatively small values, whereas others will contain a preponderance of large values.

Let the smallest observation among all N in the k samples be assigned rank 1, the next smallest rank 2, and so on (for the moment let's assume that there are no tied observations). The average of all ranks assigned is

$$\frac{1 + 2 + 3 + \cdots + N}{N} = \frac{N + 1}{2}$$

If all μ's are equal, the average of the ranks for each of the k samples should be reasonably close to $(N + 1)/2$ (since observations will typically be intermingled, their ranks will be also). On the other hand, large differences between some of the μ's will usually result in some samples having average ranks much below $(N + 1)/2$ (those samples that contain mostly small observations), whereas others will have average ranks considerably exceeding $(N + 1)/2$. The K-W statistic measures the discrepancy between the average rank in each of the k samples and the overall average $(N + 1)/2$.

DEFINITION

Let $\bar{r}_1$ denote the average of the ranks for observations in the first sample, $\bar{r}_2$ denote the average rank for observations in the second sample, and let $\bar{r}_3, \ldots, \bar{r}_k$ denote the analogous rank averages for samples $3, \ldots, k$. Then the K-W statistic is

$$KW = \frac{12}{N(N + 1)} \left[n_1 \left(\bar{r}_1 - \frac{N + 1}{2} \right)^2 + n_2 \left(\bar{r}_2 - \frac{N + 1}{2} \right)^2 \right.$$
$$\left. + \cdots + n_k \left(\bar{r}_k - \frac{N + 1}{2} \right)^2 \right]$$

EXAMPLE 15.14

A *Newsweek* article (September 24, 1984) reported that average starting salaries for graduating seniors in four business disciplines were ranked as follows: (1) finance, (2) accounting, (3) marketing, and (4) business administration. To gain information on salaries for its own graduates, suppose that a business school selected a random sample of students from each discipline and obtained the accompanying starting salary data. Within each sample, values are listed in increasing order, and the corresponding rank among all $N = 22$ reported salaries appears below each observation.

1. Finance salary:	19.4	19.8	20.3	22.3	23.9	
rank:	10	12	14	19	22	

2. Accounting salary:	18.7	18.9	19.5	20.1	21.8	22.9
rank:	6	8	11	13	18	20

3. Marketing salary:	16.7	17.6	18.2	20.4	21.4	23.4
rank:	1	4	5	15	17	21

4. Business administration salary: 16.9   17.3   18.8   19.1   21.0
                               rank: 2   3   7   9   16

The average rank in the first sample is

$$\bar{r}_1 = \frac{10 + 12 + 14 + 19 + 22}{5} = 15.4$$

and the other rank averages are $\bar{r}_2 = 12.7$, $\bar{r}_3 = 10.5$, and $\bar{r}_4 = 7.4$. The average of all ranks assigned is $(N + 1)/2 = 23/2 = 11.5$, so

$$
\begin{aligned}
KW &= \frac{12}{(22)(23)} [5(15.4 - 11.5)^2 + 6(12.7 - 11.5)^2 + 6(10.5 - 11.5)^2 \\
&\quad + 5(7.4 - 11.5)^2] \\
&= \frac{12}{(22)(23)} (174.74) = 4.14
\end{aligned}
$$

H_0 will be rejected when the value of KW is sufficiently large. To specify a critical value that controls the type I error probability, it is necessary to know how KW behaves when H_0 is true. That is, we need information about the sampling distribution of KW when H_0 is true.

There are only a finite number of ways to assign the N ranks, and these all have the same chance of occurring when H_0 is true. Suppose all possibilities are enumerated, KW is computed for each one, and the 5% with the largest KW values are separated out. Rejecting H_0 when the observed allocation of ranks to samples falls within this 5% set then results in a level .05 test. The difficulty with this procedure is that unless N is small, the number of possibilities is quite large, and so enumeration is really out of the question. Fortunately, as long as no n_i is too small, there is an approximate result that saves the day. The approximation is based on a type of probability distribution called a *chi-squared distribution*. As with t distributions, there is a different chi-squared distribution for each different number of df. Unlike a t curve, a chi-squared curve is not symmetric but instead looks rather like an F curve. Table XII gives upper-tail critical values for various chi-squared distributions.

THE KRUSKAL-WALLIS TEST

When H_0 is true and either

1. $k = 3$ and each n_i is at least 6 or
2. $k \geq 4$ and each n_i is at least 5,

the statistic KW has approximately a chi-squared distribution based on $k - 1$ df. A test with (approximate) level of significance α results from using KW as the test statistic and rejecting H_0 if KW > chi-squared critical value. The chi-squared critical value is obtained from the $k - 1$ df row of Table XII in the column headed by the desired α.

EXAMPLE 15.15

Let's use the K-W test at level .05 to analyze the salary data introduced in Example 15.14.

1. Let μ_1, μ_2, μ_3, and μ_4 denote the true average starting salaries for all graduates in each of the four disciplines, respectively.
2. $H_0: \mu_1 = \mu_2 = \mu_3 = \mu_4$
3. H_a: at least two of the four μ's are different
4. Test statistic:

$$\text{KW} = \frac{12}{N(N+1)} \left[n_1 \left(\bar{r}_1 - \frac{N+1}{2} \right)^2 + \cdots + n_4 \left(\bar{r}_4 - \frac{N+1}{2} \right)^2 \right]$$

5. Rejection region: The number of df for the chi-squared approximation is $k - 1 = 3$. For $\alpha = .05$, Table XII gives 7.82 as the critical value. H_0 will be rejected if $\text{KW} > 7.82$.
6. We previously computed KW as 4.14.
7. The computed KW value 4.14 does not exceed the critical value 7.82, so H_0 should not be rejected. The data does not provide enough evidence to conclude that the true average starting salaries for the four disciplines are different.

When there are tied values in the data set, ranks are determined as they were for the rank-sum test—by assigning each tied observation in a group the average of the ranks they would receive if they all differed slightly from one another. Rejection of H_0 by the K-W test can be followed by the use of an appropriate multiple comparison procedure (although not the Bonferroni method described earlier). Also, the most widely used statistical computer packages will perform a K-W test on request.

The K-W test does not require normality, but it does require equal population or treatment-response distribution variances (all distributions must have the same spread). If you encounter a data set in which variances appear to be quite different, you should consult a statistician for advice.

Friedman's Test for a Randomized Block Design

The validity of the randomized block F test rested on the assumption that every observation in the experiment was drawn from a normal distribution with the same variance. The test described here, called Friedman's test, does not require normality.

> **BASIC ASSUMPTION**
>
> Every observation in the experiment is assumed to have been selected from a distribution having exactly the same shape and spread, but the mean value may depend separately both on the treatment applied and on the block.

Again, the hypotheses are

H_0: the mean value does not depend on which treatment is applied

versus

H_a: the mean value does depend on which treatment is applied

The rationale for Friedman's test is quite straightforward. The observations in each block are first ranked separately from 1 to k (since every treatment appears once, there are k observations in any block). Then the rank averages $\bar{r}_1, \bar{r}_2, \ldots, \bar{r}_k$ for treatments 1, 2, . . . , k, respectively, are computed. When H_0 is false, some treatments will tend to receive small ranks in most blocks, whereas other treatments will tend to receive mostly large ranks. In this case the $\bar{r}$'s will tend to be rather different. On the other hand, when H_0 is true, all the $\bar{r}$'s will tend to be close to the same value $(k + 1)/2$, the average of ranks 1, 2, . . . , k. The test statistic measures the discrepancy between the $\bar{r}$'s and $(k + 1)/2$; a large discrepancy suggests that H_0 is false.

FRIEDMAN'S TEST

After ranking observations separately from 1 to k within each of the l blocks, let $\bar{r}_1, \bar{r}_2, \ldots, \bar{r}_k$ denote the resulting rank averages for the k treatments. The test statistic is

$$F_r = \frac{12l}{k(k + 1)}\left[\left(\bar{r}_1 - \frac{k + 1}{2}\right)^2 + \left(\bar{r}_2 - \frac{k + 1}{2}\right)^2 \right.$$
$$\left. + \cdots + \left(\bar{r}_k - \frac{k + 1}{2}\right)^2\right]$$

As long as l is not too small, when H_0 is true F_r has approximately a chi-squared distribution based on $k - 1$ df. The rejection region for a test that has approximate level of significance α is then $F_r >$ chi-squared critical value.

EXAMPLE 15.16

High-pressure sales tactics of door-to-door salespeople can be quite offensive. Many people succumb to such tactics, sign a purchase agreement, and later regret their actions. In the mid-1970s the Federal Trade Commission implemented regulations clarifying and extending rights of purchasers to cancel such agreements. The accompanying data is a subset of that given in the paper "Evaluating the FTC Cooling-Off Rule" (*J. Consumer Affairs* (1977):101–106). Individual observations are cancellation rates for each of nine salespeople (the blocks) during each of 4 years. Let's use Friedman's test at level .05 to see if true average cancellation rate depends on the year.

Emotion	Subject (block)							
	1	2	3	4	5	6	7	8
Fear	23.1	57.6	10.5	23.6	11.9	54.6	21.0	20.3
Happiness	22.7	53.2	9.7	19.6	13.8	47.1	13.6	23.6
Depression	22.5	53.7	10.8	21.1	13.7	39.2	13.7	16.3
Calmness	22.6	53.1	8.3	21.6	13.3	37.0	14.8	14.8

Does the data suggest that the true mean skin potential differs for the emotions tested? Use a significance level of .05.

15.56 In a test to determine if soil pretreated with small amounts of Basic-H makes the soil more permeable to water, soil samples were divided into blocks and each block received all four treatments under study. The treatments were (1) water with .001% Basic-H on untreated soil, (2) water without Basic-H on untreated soil, (3) water with Basic-H on soil pretreated with Basic-H, and (4) water without Basic-H on soil pretreated with Basic-H. Using a significance level of .01, determine if mean permeability differs for the four treatments.

Block	Treatment				Block	Treatment			
	1	2	3	4		1	2	3	4
1	37.1	33.2	58.9	56.7	6	25.3	19.3	48.8	37.1
2	31.8	25.3	54.2	49.6	7	23.7	17.3	47.8	37.5
3	28.0	20.2	49.2	46.4	8	24.4	17.0	40.2	39.6
4	25.9	20.3	47.9	40.9	9	21.7	16.7	44.0	35.1
5	25.5	18.3	38.2	39.4	10	26.2	18.3	46.4	36.5

15.57 The following data on amount of food consumed (g) by eight rats after 0, 24, and 72 h of food deprivation appeared in the paper "The Relation Between Differences in Level of Food Deprivation and Dominance in Food Getting in the Rat" (*Psych. Sci.* (1972):297–298). Does the data indicate a difference in the true mean food consumption for the three experimental conditions? Use $\alpha = .01$.

Hours	Rat							
	1	2	3	4	5	6	7	8
0	3.5	3.7	1.6	2.5	2.8	2.0	5.9	2.5
24	5.9	8.1	8.1	8.6	8.1	5.9	9.5	7.9
72	13.9	12.6	8.1	6.8	14.3	4.2	14.5	7.9

15.58 The article "Effect of Storage Temperature on the Viability and Fertility of Bovine Sperm Diluted and Stored in Caprogen" (*N. Zeal. J. Ag. Res.* (1984):173–177) examined the effect of temperature on sperm survival. Survival data for various storage times is given below. Use Friedman's test with a .05 significance level to determine if storage temperature affects survival (regard time as the blocking factor).

Storage Temperature °C	Storage time (h)				
	6	24	48	120	168
15.6	61.9	59.6	57.0	58.8	53.7
21.1	62.5	60.0	57.4	59.3	54.9
26.7	60.7	55.5	54.5	53.3	45.3
32.2	59.9	48.6	42.6	36.6	24.8

CHAPTER FIFTEEN SUMMARY OF KEY CONCEPTS AND FORMULAS

Term or Formula	Comment

Single-factor analysis of variance (ANOVA)

A test procedure for determining if there are significant differences among k population or treatment means. The hypotheses tested are $H_0: \mu_1 = \cdots = \mu_k$ versus H_a: at least two μ's differ.

Mean square for treatments,
$$\text{MSTr} = \frac{n_1(\bar{x}_1 - \bar{\bar{x}})^2 + \cdots + n_k(\bar{x}_k - \bar{\bar{x}})^2}{k - 1}$$

A measure of how different the k sample means $\bar{x}_1, \bar{x}_2, \ldots, \bar{x}_k$ are from one another.

Mean square for error
$$\text{MSE} = \frac{(n_1 - 1)s_1^2 + \cdots + (n_k - 1)s_k^2}{N - k}$$

A measure of the amount of variability within the individual samples.

$$F = \frac{\text{MSTr}}{\text{MSE}}$$

The test statistic for testing $H_0: \mu_1 = \mu_2 = \cdots = \mu_k$ in a single-factor ANOVA. When H_0 is true, F has an F distribution with a numerator df of $k - 1$ and a denominator df of $N - k$.

Sums of squares in single factor ANOVA: SSTo, SSTr, SSE

SSTr and SSE are the basis for the computational formulas for the mean squares. The sums of squares satisfy the fundamental identity SSTo = SSTr + SSE.

$$\text{SSTo} = \Sigma(x - \bar{\bar{x}})^2$$
$$= \Sigma x^2 - \frac{T^2}{N}$$

The defining and computational formulas for the total sum of squares.

$$\text{SSTr} = \Sigma n(\bar{x} - \bar{\bar{x}})^2$$
$$= \frac{T_1^2}{n_1} + \cdots + \frac{T_k^2}{n_k} - \frac{T^2}{N}$$

The defining and computational formulas for the treatment sum of squares.

Term or Formula	Comment
$SSE = SSTo - SSTr$	A computational formula for the error sum of squares.
$MSTr = \dfrac{SSTr}{k-1}$	The formula for the mean square for treatments.
$MSE = \dfrac{SSE}{N-k}$	The formula for the mean square for error.
Bonferroni multiple comparison procedure	A procedure for identifying significant differences among the μ's once the hypothesis $H_0: \mu_1 = \mu_2 = \cdots = \mu_k$ has been rejected by the ANOVA F test.
Randomized block design	An experimental design that controls for extraneous variation when comparing treatments. The experimental units are grouped into homogeneous *blocks* so that within each block, the units are as similar as possible. Then each treatment is used on exactly one experimental unit in every block (each treatment appears once in every block).
Randomized block F test	The four sums of squares for a randomized block design, SSTo, SSTr, SSBl, and SSE (with df $kl - 1$, $k - 1$, $l - 1$, and $(k - 1)(l - 1)$, respectively), are related by SSTo $=$ SSTr $+$ SSBl $+$ SSE. Usually SSE is obtained by subtraction once the other three have been calculated using computing formulas. The null hypothesis is that the true average response does not depend on which treatment is applied. With MSTr $=$ SSTr/$(k - 1)$ and MSE $=$ SSE/$(k - 1)(l - 1)$, the test statistic is $F =$ MSTr/MSE. H_0 is rejected if $F > F$ critical value (based on $k - 1$ numerator df and $(k - 1)(l - 1)$ denominator df).
Interaction between factors	Two factors are said to interact if the average change in response associated with changing the level of one factor depends on the level of the other factor.
Two-factor ANOVA	When there are k levels of factor A and l levels of factor B, and $m\ (> 1)$ observations made for each combination of A–B levels, total sum of squares SSTo can be decomposed into SSA (sum of squares for A main effects), SSB, SSAB (interaction sum of squares) and SSE. Associated df are $klm - 1$, $k - 1$, $l - 1$, $(k - 1) \cdot (l - 1)$, and $kl(m - 1)$, respectively. The null hypothesis of no interaction between the two factors is tested using $F_{AB} =$ MSAB/MSE, where MSAB $=$ SSAB/$(k - 1)(l - 1)$ and MSE $=$ SSE/$kl(m - 1)$. If this null hypothesis cannot be rejected, tests for A and B main effects are based on $F_A =$ MSA/MSE and $F_B =$ MSB/MSE, respectively.
Distribution-free ANOVA	The Kruskal-Wallis test and Friedman's test are appropriate for completely a randomized design and a randomized block design, respectively. Both tests are based on ranks of the observations. Whereas the F tests require normal population or treatment distributions, these tests require only that the distributions have the same shape and spread.

ENCORE

W̶e reproduce here the data given in the Chapter Preview on average audience ages and average perceived model ages for various advertisements promoting particular brands of cigarettes.

Brand	Sample size	Average audience age	Average perceived model age
1	3	28.5	20.4
2	5	31.1	25.5
3	21	31.3	36.6
4	24	31.3	24.8
5	12	31.3	26.9
6	15	31.3	26.2
7	8	31.6	27.8
8	32	33.9	24.3
9	26	34.3	38.6
10	17	34.8	29.1
11	23	35.1	31.9
12	1	41.0	27.0
	187		

Let μ_1, μ_2, . . . , μ_{12} denote the average audience ages for magazines in which advertisements for the various brands appeared. We wish to test

$$H_0\colon \mu_1 = \mu_2 = \cdots = \mu_{12} \quad \text{versus} \quad H_a\colon \text{At least two } \mu\text{'s are different}$$

The grand mean is

$$\overline{\overline{x}} = \frac{(3)(28.5) + (5)(31.1) + \cdots + (1)(41.0)}{187} = 32.96$$

from which

$$\begin{aligned} \text{SSTr} &= n_1(\overline{x}_1 - \overline{\overline{x}})^2 + \cdots + n_{12}(\overline{x}_{12} - \overline{\overline{x}})^2 \\ &= 3(28.5 - 32.96)^2 + \cdots + 1(41.0 - 32.96)^2 \\ &= 592.66 \end{aligned}$$

In addition, SSE = 2282.98, giving the following ANOVA table.

Source	df	SS	MS	F
Treatments (brands)	11	592.66	53.88	4.13
Error	175	2282.98	13.05	
Total	186	2875.64		

The F critical value for 11 numerator df, 175 denominator df, and a significance level of .01 is approximately 2.35. Since 4.13 > 2.35, H_0 is rejected. This lends strong support to one of the hypotheses conjectured by the investigators: that average audience age of cigarette advertisements differs across brands. At this point a multiple comparisons procedure could be used to identify significant differences among brands, although this was not done in the paper cited in the Chapter Preview.

To explore the relation between audience age and perceived model age, the investigators calculated Pearson's sample correlation coefficient for the 12 (audience age, model age) pairs. The result was $r = .263$, which is positive and differs significantly from zero (see the discussion of correlation in Chapter 13). This led to the intuitively reasonable conclusion that there is a positive correlation between perceived model age in cigarette advertisements and the average audience age for the magazines in which the models appear.

SUPPLEMENTARY EXERCISES 15.59–15.77

15.59 Are some methods of cooking more economical than others? The paper "Cookery Methods for Vegetables: Influence on Sensory Quality, Nutrient Retention, and Energy Consumption" (*Home Ec. Res. J.* (1984):61–79) gave the energy usage (W–h) required to cook a potato for five different cooking methods. Data compatible with summary quantities given in the paper is given below.

Cooking method	Energy usage		
Microwave	201	199	219
Pressure cooker	394	375	381
Electric pressure cooker	359	405	419
Boiling	583	584	553
Baking	1281	1242	1248

a. Construct an ANOVA table. Using a .05 significance level, test to determine if the mean energy use is the same for all cooking methods.

b. Construct appropriate confidence intervals in order to determine which methods differ with respect to mean energy usage.

15.60 The results of a study on the effectiveness of line drying on the smoothness and stiffness of fabric was summarized in the paper "Line-Dried vs.

Machine-Dried Fabrics: Comparison of Appearance, Hand, and Consumer Acceptance" (*Home Ec. Res. J.* (1984):27–35). Smoothness scores were given for nine different types of fabric and five different drying methods ((1) machine dry, (2) line dry, (3) line dry followed by 15–min tumble, (4) line dry with softener, and (5) line dry with air movement). Regarding the different types of fabric as blocks, construct an ANOVA table. Using a .05 significance level, test to see if there is a difference in the true mean smoothness scores for the drying methods.

Fabric	Drying method				
	1	2	3	4	5
Crepe	3.3	2.5	2.8	2.5	1.9
Double knit	3.6	2.0	3.6	2.4	2.3
Twill	4.2	3.4	3.8	3.1	3.1
Twill mix	3.4	2.4	2.9	1.6	1.7
Terry	3.8	1.3	2.8	2.0	1.6
Broadcloth	2.2	1.5	2.7	1.5	1.9
Sheeting	3.5	2.1	2.8	2.1	2.2
Corduroy	3.6	1.3	2.8	1.7	1.8
Denim	2.6	1.4	2.4	1.3	1.6

15.61 A study to determine whether use of concentrated milk proteins affected cheese production was described in the paper "Membrane Processing of Milk on the Dairy Farm" (*Food Technology* (1984):88–90). Samples of size 5 were analyzed to determine the bacteria count for each of four concentration levels (1× concentrate, 1.16× concentrate, 1.48× concentrate, and 1.79× concentrate). The resulting data is given. Construct the appropriate ANOVA table. Does the data suggest that the mean bacteria count is not the same for the four concentrations? Test the relevant hypotheses using a .05 significance level.

Concentration		Bacteria count			
1×	39	21	48	58	63
1.16×	24	19	34	28	50
1.48×	22	12	54	16	59
1.79×	29	13	36	30	63

15.62 Controlling a filling operation with multiple fillers requires adjustment of the individual units. Data resulting from a sample of size 5 from each pocket of a 12-pocket filler was given in the paper "Evaluating Variability of Filling Operations" (*Food Technology* (1984):51–55). Data for the first 5 pockets is given.

Pocket		Fill (oz)			
1	10.2	10.0	9.8	10.4	10.0
2	9.9	10.0	9.9	10.1	10.0
3	10.1	9.9	9.8	9.9	9.7
4	10.0	9.7	9.9	9.7	9.6
5	10.2	9.8	9.9	9.7	9.8

Use the ANOVA *F* test to determine if the null hypothesis of no difference in the mean fill weight of the 5 pockets can be rejected. If so, use an appropriate technique to determine where the differences lie.

15.63 *This problem requires the use of a computer package.* The effect of oxygen concentration on fermentation end products was examined in the article "Effects of Oxygen on Pyruvate FormateLyase in Situ and Sugar Metabolism of Streptococcusmutans and *Streptococcus sam-*

guis" (*Infection and Immunity* (1985):129–134). Four oxygen concentrations (0, 46, 92, and 138 μM) and two types of sugar (galactose and glucose) were used. Below are two observations on amount of ethanol (μmol/mg) for each sugar-oxygen concentration combination. Construct an ANOVA table and test the relevant hypotheses.

Oxygen concentration	Galactose	Glucose
0	.59, .30	.25, .03
46	.44, .18	.13, .02
92	.22, .23	.07, .00
138	.12, .13	.00, .01

15.64 Eye inflammation can be induced by the endotoxin lipopolysaccharide (LPS). A random sample of 35 rats was randomly divided into five groups of seven rats each (a completely randomized design). Rats within each group received the same dose of LPS. The accompanying data on vascular permeability was read from plots that appeared in the paper "Endotoxin-Induced Uveitis in the Rat: Observations on Altered Vascular Permeability, Clinical Findings, and Histology" (*Exper. Eye Res.* (1984):665–676). Use analysis of variance with $\alpha = .05$ to test the null hypothesis of no difference between the five treatment means.

Treatment dose (μg)	Vascular permeability (ocular to serum fluorescence ratio)						
0	8	3	2	1	0	0	0
1	4.5	4	4	3.5	3	2	0
10	5	5	4	3.5	1	0	0
100	13	12	12	9	8	4	2
500	13	12	9	7.5	7	5	4

15.65 Four types of mortars—ordinary cement mortar (OCM), polymer impregnated mortar (PIM), resin mortar (RM), and polymer cement mortar (PCM)—were subjected to a compression test to measure strength. Three strength observations for each mortar type appeared in the paper "Polymer Mortar Composite Matrices for Maintenance-Free

Highly Durable Ferrocement" (*J. Ferrocement* (1984):337–345) and are reproduced here. Construct an ANOVA table. Using a .05 significance level, determine whether the data suggests that the true mean strength is not the same for all four mortar types. If you determine that the true mean strengths are not all equal, use the Bonferroni method to identify the significant differences.

Mortar type	Strength (MPa)		
OCM	32.15	35.53	34.20
PIM	126.32	126.80	134.79
RM	117.91	115.02	114.58
PCM	29.09	30.87	29.80

15.66 Referring to Exercise 15.65, use a distribution-free procedure with a .05 significance level to test the null hypothesis of no differences between the true mean strengths of the four mortars.

15.67 The paper "Clothing Symbolism and the Changing Role of Nurses" (*Home Ec. Res. J.* (1980): 294–301) reported on a comparison of five groups of nurses (those who wore their caps (1) all the time, (2) 75% of the time, (3) 50% of the time, (4) 25% of the time, or (5) none of the time) with respect to attitudes toward role symbols. Attitude was measured using the Role Symbol Scale (RSS). A partially completed ANOVA table is given.

Source	df	Sum of squares	Mean square	F
Treatments	4	62,222		
Error				
Total	299	4,772,243		

a. Complete the ANOVA table and use it to test the null hypothesis of no difference in true mean RSS scores for the five groups.

b. The paper states "Further analysis . . . indicated that nurses who wore their caps all of the time or 75% of the time had a significantly more favorable attitude (lower mean RSS scores) than nurses who never wore their caps

or wore their caps only 25% of the time." Group means and standard deviations are given. Assuming five equal sample sizes of 60 each, does the application of the Bonferroni method yield conclusions that agree with the statement in the paper?

Group	Sample mean	Sample standard deviation
1	82.17	20.00
2	85.19	19.20
3	98.09	11.71
4	102.26	20.10
5	117.05	20.96

15.68 The effect of nitrogen application on pasture yield was examined in the paper "Response of Pastures to Nitrogen Fertiliser Applied in Autumn and Spring on the West Coast of South Island" (*N. Zeal. J. Exper. Ag.* (1983):247–250). Four levels of nitrogen application were used (0, 25, 50, and 100 kg/ha) and the dry-matter production (kg/ha) was recorded on three different cutting dates. Viewing the three cutting dates as blocks, analyze the data below to determine if the mean dry matter production is the same for the four nitrogen levels. Construct an ANOVA table and test the appropriate hypotheses using a .05 level of significance.

Nitrogen	Cut date		
	I	II	III
0	210	1030	1680
25	390	1130	1570
50	540	1410	1560
100	770	1840	1530

15.69 The accompanying ANOVA table appeared in the paper "Bacteriological and Chemical Variations and Their Inter-Relationships in a Slightly Polluted Water-Body" (*Inter. J. Environ. Studies* (1984):121–129). A water specimen was taken every month for a year at each of 15 designated locations on the Lago di Piediluco in Italy. The ammonia-nitrogen concentration was determined for each specimen and the resulting data analyzed using a two-way ANOVA. The researchers were willing to assume that there was no interaction between the two factors *location* and *month*. Complete the given ANOVA table, and use it to perform the tests required to determine if the true mean concentration differs by location or by month of year. Use a .05 significance level for both tests.

Source	df	Sum of squares	Mean square	F
Location	14	.6		
Month	11	2.3		
Error	154			
Total	179	6.4		

15.70 The paper "The Effect of Sewage with Special Reference to Aquatic Insects in the River Kshipra (India)" (*Inter. J. Environ. Studies* (1984):191–208) describes a randomized block experiment designed to evaluate chemical conditions at three sampling stations along the river Kshipra. Water specimens at each station were taken each month for 12 months and chemical oxygen demand was determined. Data for four of the months appears here. Viewing the months as blocks, use a distribution-free procedure to test the null hypothesis of no difference in true mean oxygen demand for the three stations.

	Station		
Month	A	B	C
January	78.9	56.0	113.6
February	51.2	86.4	208.0
March	62.4	73.6	108.8
April	41.6	126.4	133.6

15.71 The concentration of cadmium (Cd) in sediments from lakes around a coal-powered electric plant in Texas appeared in the article "The Analysis of Aqueous Sediments for Heavy Metals" (*J. Environ. Sci. and Health* (1984):911–924). At each lake, one measurement was taken at each of five different depths. Does the mean concentration of Cd vary with depth? Viewing the four lakes as blocks, construct an ANOVA table and test the appropriate hypotheses using a .01 significance level.

	Depth				
Lake	1	2	3	4	5
Oyster Creek (O)	1.0	0.5	1.0	1.0	2.0
Herman (He)	1.0	3.0	0.5	1.0	1.0
Gannoway (G)	3.0	3.0	2.0	1.0	2.0
Horseshoe (Ho)	2.0	1.0	2.0	1.0	2.0

15.72 The water absorption of two types of mortar used to repair damaged cement was discussed in the paper "Polymer Mortar Composite Matrices for Maintenance-Free, Highly Durable Ferrocement" (*J. Ferrocement* (1984):337–345). Specimens of ordinary cement mortar (OCM) and polymer cement mortar (PCM) were submerged for varying lengths of time (5, 9, 24, or 48 h) and water absorption (% by weight) was recorded. With mortar type as factor A (with two levels) and submersion period as factor B (with four levels), three observations were made for each factor-level combination. Data included in the paper was used to compute the given sums of squares. Use this information to construct an ANOVA table, and then use a .05 significance level to test the appropriate hypotheses.

Sum of squares for factor A: 322.667
Sum of squares for factor B: 35.623
Sum of squares for AB interaction: 8.557
Total sum of squares: 372.113

15.73 Suppose that each observation in a single-factor ANOVA data set is multiplied by a constant c (a change in units; for example, $c = 2.54$ changes observations from inches to centimeters). How does this affect MSTr, MSE, and the test statistic F? Is this reasonable? Explain.

15.74 Is it true that the grand mean $\bar{\bar{x}}$ is the ordinary average of $\bar{x}_1, \bar{x}_2, \ldots, \bar{x}_k$, that is, that

$$\bar{\bar{x}} = \frac{\bar{x}_1 + \cdots + \bar{x}_k}{k}$$

Under what conditions on $n_1, n_2, \ldots, n_k$ will the preceding relationship be true?

15.75 Three different brands of automobile batteries, each one having a 42-month warranty, were included in a study of battery lifetime. A random sample of batteries of each brand was selected and lifetime (in months) was determined, resulting in the following data.

Brand 1	45	38	52	47	45	42	43
Brand 2	39	44	50	54	48	46	40
Brand 3	50	46	43	48	57	44	48

State and test the appropriate hypotheses using a significance level of .05. Be sure to summarize your calculations in an ANOVA table.

15.76 Let $c_1, c_2, \ldots, c_k$ denote k specified numbers, and consider the quantity θ defined by

$$\theta = c_1\mu_1 + c_2\mu_2 + \cdots + c_k\mu_k$$

A confidence interval for θ is then

$$c_1\bar{x}_1 + \cdots + c_k\bar{x}_k \pm$$

$$(t \text{ critical value}) \cdot \sqrt{\text{MSE}\left(\frac{c_1^2}{n_1} + \cdots + \frac{c_k^2}{n_k}\right)}$$

where the t critical value is based on an error df of $N - k$.

For example, in a study carried out to compare pain relievers with respect to true average time to relief, suppose that brands 1, 2, and 3 are nationally available whereas brands 4 and 5 are sold only by two large chains of drug stores. An investigator might then wish to consider

$$\theta = \tfrac{1}{3}\mu_1 + \tfrac{1}{3}\mu_2 + \tfrac{1}{3}\mu_3 - \tfrac{1}{2}\mu_4 - \tfrac{1}{2}\mu_5$$

which, in essence, compares the average effect of the national brands to the average for the house brands.

Refer to Exercise 15.75, and suppose that brand 1 is a store brand and 2 and 3 are national brands. Obtain a 95% confidence interval for $\theta = \mu_1 - \tfrac{1}{2}\mu_2 - \tfrac{1}{2}\mu_3$.

15.77 One of the assumptions that underlies the validity of the ANOVA F test is that the population or treatment response variances $\sigma_1^2, \sigma_2^2, \ldots, \sigma_k^2$ should be identical whether or not H_0 is true—the assumption of constant variance across populations or treatments. In some situations the x values themselves may not satisfy this assumption, yet a transformation using some specified mathematical function (for example, taking the logarithm or the square root) will give observations that have (approximately) constant variance. The ANOVA F test can then be applied to the transformed data. When observations are made on a counting variable (x = number of something), statisticians have found that taking the square root will frequently "stabilize the variance." In an experiment to compare the quality of four different brands of videotape, cassettes of a specified length were selected and the number of flaws in each was determined.

Brand 1	10	14	5	12	8
Brand 2	17	14	8	9	12
Brand 3	13	18	15	18	10
Brand 4	14	22	12	16	17

Make a square root transformation and analyze the resulting data by using the ANOVA F test at significance level .01.

References

Hicks, Charles. *Fundamental Concepts in the Design of Experiments.* New York: Holt, Rinehart & Winston, 1982. (Discusses the analysis of data arising from many different types of designed experiments; the focus is more on methods than concepts.)

Miller, Rupert. *Beyond ANOVA: Basics of Applied Statistics.* New York: John Wiley and Sons, 1986. (A wealth of information concerning violations of basic assumptions and alternative methods of analysis.)

Neter, John, William Wasserman, and Michael Kutner. *Applied Linear Statistical Models.* Homewood, Ill.: Richard D. Irwin, Inc., 1990. (The latter half of the book contains a readable survey of ANOVA and experimental design.)

Ott, Lyman. *Introduction to Statistical Methods and Data Analysis.* Boston: Duxbury Press, 1988. (A good source for learning more about the methods most frequently employed to analyze experimental data, including various multiple comparison techniques.)

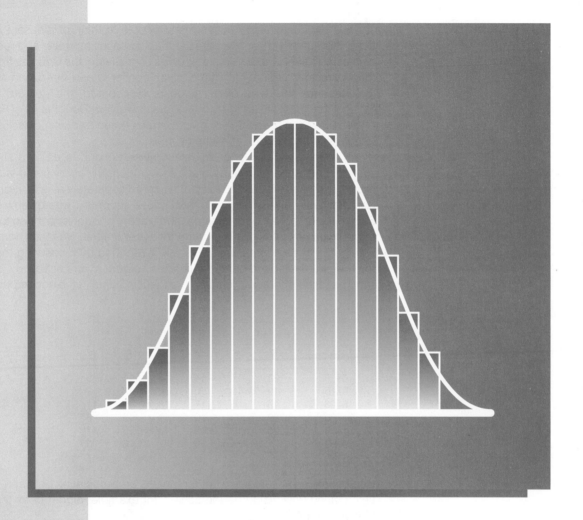

The Analysis of Categorical Data and Goodness-of-Fit Methods

Although mistletoe causes many people to think of pleasant holiday traditions, it is actually a serious parasite that increases mortality and reduces growth of infested trees. One particular species of mistletoe, the Douglas fir dwarf mistletoe, is present in about half of the mixed conifer forests in Arizona and New Mexico. Because this type of mistletoe is widespread, the authors of the paper "Intensification of Dwarf Mistletoe on Southwestern Douglas Fir" (*Forest Science* (1990):955–969) studied 445 infected trees. Each tree was classified according to both size and degree of mistletoe infestation.

The degree of mistletoe infestation was described using a six-class rating system. The rating for a particular tree was determined by first dividing the tree's crown into thirds. Each third was then scored separately as a 0, 1, or 2. A score of 0 was given when there was no mistletoe, a score of 1 was given when less than 50% of the branches were infested, and a score of 2 corresponded to 50% or more of the branches infested. The rating for the entire tree was then computed as the sum of the three scores. Tree size was described by measuring the diameter of the tree at 1.4 m above ground. Six size categories were used.

The researchers summarized the resulting data in the accompanying table.

	Mistletoe rating					
Diameter (cm)	1	2	3	4	5	6
0– 8	21	17	14	15	11	9
9–15	10	10	20	8	13	12
16–23	15	6	17	18	10	11
24–30	9	17	10	14	13	8
31–58	20	18	22	19	22	17
59–89	1	4	4	7	3	0

One question of interest is whether there is an association between size and mistletoe rating (this would be the case if, for example, bigger trees tended to have higher ratings).

The chi-squared test for association, to be introduced in this chapter, can be used to determine if there is evidence of such an association.

Introduction

Most of the techniques presented in earlier chapters are designed for numerical data. Different methods must be used when information has been collected on categorical variables. As with numerical data, categorical data sets can be univariate (consisting of observations on a single categorical variable), bivariate (observations on two categorical variables), or even multivariate. In this chapter we first consider inferential methods for analyzing univariate categorical data sets and then turn to techniques appropriate for use with bivariate data. In the last section, we look at how the methods of this chapter can be applied to determine if it is plausible that a population distribution is normal in shape.

16.1 Chi-Squared Tests for Univariate Categorical Data

Univariate categorical data sets arise in a variety of different settings. If each printed circuit board in a sample of 50 is classified as either defective or nondefective, data on a categorical variable with two categories results. If specifications require that the thickness of the boards be between .055 and .065 inches, boards might be classified into three categories—undersized, meeting specification, and oversized. Each registered voter in a sample of 100 selected from those registered in a particular city might be asked which of five city council members he or she favors for mayor. This would yield observations on a categorical variable with five categories.

Univariate categorical data is most conveniently summarized in a **one-way frequency table.** Suppose, for example, that each item returned to a department store is classified according to disposition—cash refund, credit to charge account, merchandise exchange, or return refused. Records of 100 randomly selected returns are examined and each disposition recorded. The first few observations might be

Cash refund   Return refused
Exchange   Cash refund
Exchange   Credit to account

Counting the number of observations of each type might then result in the accompanying one-way table.

	Disposition			
	Cash	Credit	Exchange	Refused
Frequency	34	18	31	17

For a categorical variable with k possible values (k different levels or categories), sample data is summarized in a one-way frequency table consisting of k cells displayed horizontally or vertically. (This is really nothing more than a frequency distribution, as discussed in Chapter 2.)

In this section, we consider testing hypotheses about the proportion of the population falling into each of the possible categories. For example, the customer relations manager for a department store might be interested in determining whether the four possible dispositions for a return request occur with equal frequency. If this is indeed the case, the long-run proportion of returns falling into each of the four categories is ¼, or .25. The test procedure presented shortly would allow the manager to decide whether this hypothesis is plausible.

NOTATION

$$k = \text{number of categories of a categorical variable}$$
$$\pi_1 = \text{true proportion for category 1}$$
$$\pi_2 = \text{true proportion for category 2}$$
$$\vdots$$
$$\pi_k = \text{true proportion for category } k$$
(Note: $\pi_1 + \pi_2 + \ldots + \pi_k = 1$)

The hypotheses to be tested are

$$H_0: \pi_1 = \text{hypothesized proportion for category 1}$$
$$\pi_2 = \text{hypothesized proportion for category 2}$$
$$\vdots$$
$$\pi_k = \text{hypothesized proportion for category } k$$

H_a: H_0 is not true, so at least one of the true category proportions differs from the corresponding hypothesized value

---

For the example involving department store returns,

π_1 = proportion of all returns that result in a cash refund
π_2 = proportion of all returns that result in an account credit
π_3 = proportion of all returns that result in an exchange
π_4 = proportion of all returns that are refused

The null hypothesis of interest is then

$$H_0: \pi_1 = .25, \qquad \pi_2 = .25, \qquad \pi_3 = .25, \qquad \pi_4 = .25$$

A null hypothesis of the type just described will be tested by first selecting a random sample of size n and then classifying each sample response into one of the k possible categories. In order to decide whether the sample data is compatible with the null hypothesis, the observed cell counts (frequencies) are compared to the cell counts that would have been expected when the null hypothesis is true. In general, the expected cell counts are $n\pi_1$ for category 1, $n\pi_2$ for category 2, and so on. The expected cell counts when H_0 is true result from substituting the corresponding hypothesized proportion for each π.

EXAMPLE 16.1

The paper "Birth Order and Political Success" (*Psych. Reports* (1971):239–242) reported that in a sample of 31 candidates for political office, 12 were firstborn children, 11 were middleborn, and 8 were lastborn. Since birth position is related to family size, all 31 candidates considered were from families with exactly four children. The author of this paper was interested in ascertaining whether any ordinal position was overrepresented, as this would indicate that those with certain birth orders are more likely to enter political life. In fact, the author thought that first- and lastborns would be overrepresented. Let's suppose that first-, middle-, and lastborns are equally likely to run for political office. In this case, 25% of the candidates from families with four children should be firstborn, 25% lastborn, and 50% middleborn. With π_1, π_2, and π_3 representing the true proportion of candidates for political office from families with four children who are first-, middle-, and lastborn, respectively, the hypotheses of interest are

$$H_0: \pi_1 = .25, \quad \pi_2 = .50, \quad \pi_3 = .25$$

$$H_a: H_0 \text{ is not true}$$

When H_0 is true, the expected counts are

$$\left(\begin{array}{c}\text{expected count}\\\text{for category 1}\end{array}\right) = n\left(\begin{array}{c}\text{hypothesized proportion}\\\text{for category 1}\end{array}\right) = 31(.25) = 7.75$$

$$\left(\begin{array}{c}\text{expected count}\\\text{for category 2}\end{array}\right) = n\left(\begin{array}{c}\text{hypothesized proportion}\\\text{for category 2}\end{array}\right) = 31(.5) = 15.50$$

$$\left(\begin{array}{c}\text{expected count}\\\text{for category 3}\end{array}\right) = n\left(\begin{array}{c}\text{hypothesized proportion}\\\text{for category 3}\end{array}\right) = 31(.25) = 7.75$$

Observed and expected cell counts are given in the accompanying table.

Category	Observed cell count	Expected cell count
(1) Firstborn	12	7.75
(2) Middleborn	11	15.50
(3) Lastborn	8	7.75

Since the observed cell counts are based on a sample of candidates from families with four children, we would typically not observe exactly 25% falling in the first cell, 50% in the second, and 25% in the third cell, even when H_0 is true. If the differences between the observed and expected cell counts can reasonably be attributed to sampling variation, the data would be considered compatible with H_0. On the other hand, if the discrepancy between the observed and expected cell counts is too large to be attributed solely to chance differences from one sample to another, H_0 should be rejected in favor of H_a. Thus we need an assessment of how different the observed and expected counts are.

The goodness-of-fit statistic, denoted by X^2, is a quantitative measure of the extent to which the observed counts differ from those expected when H_0 is true.[1]

The **goodness-of-fit statistic, X^2,** results from first computing the quantity

$$\frac{(\text{observed cell count} - \text{expected cell count})^2}{\text{expected cell count}}$$

for each cell, where, for a sample of size n,

$$\left(\begin{array}{c}\text{expected cell} \\ \text{count}\end{array}\right) = n\left(\begin{array}{c}\text{hypothesized value of corresponding} \\ \text{population proportion}\end{array}\right)$$

Then X^2 is the sum of these quantities for all k cells:

$$X^2 = \sum_{\substack{\text{all} \\ \text{cells}}} \frac{(\text{observed cell count} - \text{expected cell count})^2}{\text{expected cell count}}$$

The value of the X^2 statistic reflects the magnitude of the discrepancies between observed and expected cell counts. When the differences are sizable, the value of X^2 tends to be large. Therefore, large values of X^2 suggest rejection of H_0. A small value of X^2 (it can never be negative) occurs when the observed cell counts are quite similar to those expected when H_0 is true and so would lend support to H_0.

In general, H_0 will be rejected when X^2 exceeds a specified critical value (so the test is upper-tailed). As with previous test procedures, the critical value is chosen to control the probability of a type I error (rejecting H_0 when H_0 is true). This requires information concerning the sampling distribution of X^2 when H_0 is true. A key result is that when the null hypothesis is correct and the sample size is sufficiently large, the behavior of X^2 is described approximately by what statisticians call a **chi-squared distribution.** A chi-squared curve has no area associated with negative values and is asymmetric, with a longer tail on the right. There are actually many chi-squared distributions, each one identified with a different number of degrees of freedom. Curves corresponding to several chi-squared distributions are shown in Figure 16.1.

---

[1]The Greek letter χ (chi) is often used in place of X. The symbol X^2 is referred to as the *chi-squared (χ^2)* statistic. In using X^2 rather than χ^2, we are adhering to our convention of denoting sample quantities by Roman letters.

FIGURE 16.1
Chi-squared curves and an
upper-tailed critical value

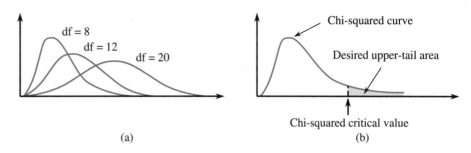

(a)   (b)

Upper-tailed chi-squared critical values, which capture specified upper-tail areas under the corresponding chi-squared curves, are given in Appendix Table XII. The columns of this table are headed by various areas captured in the upper tail. For example, the critical value 5.99 captures an upper-tail area of .05 for the chi-squared distribution with 2 df, as shown in the accompanying figure.

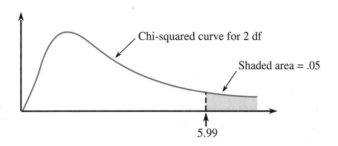

The critical value 5.99 is found by looking in the 2-df row and the column labeled .05 in Appendix Table XII.

Goodness-of-Fit Test

As long as none of the expected cell counts are too small, when H_0 is true, the X^2 goodness-of-fit statistic has approximately a chi-squared distribution with $k - 1$ degrees of freedom. *It is generally agreed that use of the chi-squared distribution is appropriate when the sample size is large enough so that every expected cell count is at least 5.* If any of the expected cell frequencies are less than 5, categories may be combined in a sensible way to create acceptable expected cell counts. Just remember to compute df based on the reduced number of categories.

> **GOODNESS-OF-FIT TEST PROCEDURE**
> H_0: π_1 = hypothesized proportion for category 1
> $\vdots$
> π_k = hypothesized proportion for category k
> H_a: H_0 is not true
>
> *(continued)*

> **Test statistic:** $X^2 = \sum \dfrac{(\text{observed count} - \text{expected count})^2}{\text{expected count}}$
>
> **Rejection region:** When H_0 is true and all expected counts are at least 5, X^2 has approximately a chi-squared distribution with df $= k - 1$. Therefore, we reject H_0 if $X^2 >$ chi-squared critical value. The chi-squared critical value is obtained from Table XII.

EXAMPLE 16.2

(*Example 16.1 continued*) We will use the birth-order data of Example 16.1 to test the researcher's hypothesis. Let's employ a .05 level of significance and use the seven-step hypothesis-testing procedure illustrated in earlier chapters.

1. Let π_1, π_2, and π_3 denote the true proportions of political candidates who are first-, middle-, and lastborn, respectively (in families with four children).

2. H_0: $\pi_1 = .25$, $\pi_2 = .50$, $\pi_3 = .25$

3. H_a: H_0 is not true

4. Test statistic: X^2

5. Rejection region: Since all expected cell counts are at least 5, the chi-squared critical value that specifies the appropriate rejection region is 5.99 (from the .05 column and the $k - 1 = 3 - 1 = 2$ df row of Table XII). The null hypothesis, H_0, will be rejected if $X^2 > 5.99$.

6. $X^2 = \dfrac{(12 - 7.75)^2}{7.75} + \dfrac{(11 - 15.50)^2}{15.50} + \dfrac{(8 - 7.75)^2}{7.75}$

   $= 2.33 + 1.31 + .01$

   $= 3.65$

7. Since 3.65 is less than 5.99, the hypothesis H_0 is not rejected. There is not enough evidence to suggest that any birth position is overrepresented among political candidates. The data does not support the researcher's premise that first- and lastborn children would be more likely to enter politics than those who are middleborn.

EXAMPLE 16.3

The paper "Environmentalism, Values, and Social Change" (*Brit. J. of Soc.* (1981):103) investigated characteristics that distinguish environmentalists from the general public. Each member of a sample of 437 environmentalists was classified into one of nine occupational categories. The resulting data appears in the accompanying table. With the nine categories ordered as in the table, the proportions of the general public falling in the nine categories were given as .140, .116, .031, .117, .311, .088, .155, .022, and .020. If the same proportions hold for environmentalists, the corresponding expected cell counts will be

$$\begin{pmatrix} \text{first expected} \\ \text{count} \end{pmatrix} = 437(.140) = 61.18$$

$$\begin{pmatrix} \text{second expected} \\ \text{count} \end{pmatrix} = 437(.116) = 50.69$$

$$\vdots$$

$$\begin{pmatrix} \text{ninth expected} \\ \text{count} \end{pmatrix} = 437(.020) = 8.74$$

These expected cell counts have been entered in the accompanying table.

Cell	Occupation	Observed cell count	Expected cell count
1	Professional	67	61.18
2	Clerical	31	50.69
3	Self-employed	42	13.55
4	Service, welfare	190	51.13
5	Manual	23	135.91
6	Retired	11	38.46
7	Housewife	33	67.74
8	Unemployed	6	9.61
9	Student	34	8.74

The X^2 goodness-of-fit test and a .01 level of significance will be used to test the null hypothesis that the true proportion of environmentalists falling into each of the nine categories is the same as that for the general population.

1. Let $\pi_1, \pi_2, \ldots, \pi_9$ denote the true proportions of all environmentalists falling into the nine occupational categories.

2. H_0: $\pi_1 = .140$, $\quad \pi_2 = .116$, $\quad \pi_3 = .031$, $\quad \pi_4 = .117$, $\quad \pi_5 = .311$, $\quad \pi_6 = .088$, $\quad \pi_7 = .155$, $\quad \pi_8 = .022$, $\quad \pi_9 = .020$

3. H_a: H_0 is not true

4. Test statistic:
$$X^2 = \sum \frac{(\text{observed count} - \text{expected count})^2}{\text{expected count}}$$

5. Rejection region: All expected cell counts exceed 5, so the rejection region can be based on a chi-squared distribution with $9 - 1 = 8$ df. With a .01 significance level, the appropriate critical value is obtained from Table XII as 20.09. Therefore, H_0 will be rejected if $X^2 > 20.09$.

6. Computations:

$$X^2 = \frac{(67 - 61.18)^2}{61.18} + \frac{(31 - 50.69)^2}{50.69} + \cdots + \frac{(34 - 8.74)^2}{8.74}$$

$$= .554 + 7.648 + \cdots + 73.005$$

$$= 650.696$$

7. Since $650.696 > 20.09$, the hypothesis H_0 is rejected. There is strong evidence to indicate that at least one of the true occupation proportions for environmentalists differs from that of the general public.

P-Values

Bounds on the P-value associated with a chi-squared test can be obtained from the appropriate df row of Appendix Table XII. Since the chi-squared test is upper-tailed, there are three possible cases:

1. If the computed value of X^2 falls between two consecutive critical values, the P-value lies between the corresponding significance levels.
2. If the computed value of X^2 is larger than the critical value for significance level .001, P-value $< .001$.
3. If the computed value of X^2 is smaller than the critical value for significance level .10, P-value $> .10$.

The chi-squared test in Example 16.2 was based on 2 df. The calculated value of X^2 was 3.65. Since 3.65 is smaller than the critical value for significance level .10 (critical value $= 4.61$),

P-value $> .10$

Based on the P-value, we would be unable to reject H_0 when $\alpha = .01, .05$, or even .10.

EXERCISES 16.1–16.9   SECTION 16.1

16.1   What is the rejection region for a chi-squared test based on
   a. Five categories carried out at significance level .05?
   b. Five categories carried out at significance level .01?
   c. Ten categories carried out at significance level .01?

16.2   A particular paperback book is published in a choice of four different covers. A certain bookstore keeps copies of each cover on its racks. To test the hypothesis that sales are equally divided among the four choices, a random sample of 100 purchases is identified.

a. If the resulting X^2 value is 6.4, what conclusion would you reach when using a test with significance level .05?

b. What conclusion would be appropriate at significance level .01 if $X^2 = 15.3$?

c. If there were six different covers rather than just four, what would you conclude if $X^2 = 13.7$ and a test with $\alpha = .05$ is used?

16.3   Packages of mixed nuts made by a certain company contain four types of nuts. The percentages of nuts of types 1, 2, 3, and 4 are supposed to be 40%, 30%, 20%, and 10%, respectively. A random sample of nuts is selected and each one is categorized by type.

a. If the sample size is 200 and the resulting test statistic value is $X^2 = 19.0$, what conclusion would be appropriate for a significance level of .001?

b. If the random sample had consisted of only 40 nuts, would you use the chi-squared test here? Explain your reasoning.

16.4   Each person in a 1989 random sample of prison inmates was classified according to the type of offense committed, resulting in the following one-way frequency table. (These values are based on information in the article "Profile of Jail Inmates," *USA Today*, April 25, 1991). In 1983, it was reported that 30.7% of inmates had been convicted of violent crimes, 38.6% of crimes against property, 9.3% of drug-related crimes, 20.6% of public-order offenses, and .8% of other types of crimes. Does this data provide sufficient evidence to conclude that the true 1989 proportions falling into the various offense categories are not all the same as in 1983? Test the relevant hypotheses using $\alpha = .05$.

	Type of offense				
	Violent crime	Crimes against property	Drug-related crimes	Public-order offense	Other
Frequency	225	300	230	228	16

16.5   Criminologists have long debated whether there is a relationship between weather and violent crime. The author of the paper "Is There a Season for Homicide?" (*Criminology* (1988):287–296) classified 1361 homicides according to season, resulting in the following data. Does this data support the theory that the homicide rate is not the same over the four seasons?

Season			
Winter	Spring	Summer	Fall
328	334	372	327

a. Test the relevant hypotheses using a significance level of .05.

b. What can be said about the *P*-value associated with the test in part (a)?

16.6   When public opinion surveys are conducted by mail, a cover letter explaining the purpose of the survey is usually included. To determine if the wording of the cover letter influences the response rate, three different cover letters were used in a survey of students at a Midwestern university ("The Effectiveness of Cover-Letter Appeals" (*J. of Soc. Psych.* (1984):85–91). Suppose that each of the three cover letters accompanied questionnaires sent to an equal number of students. Returned questionnaires were then classified according to the type of cover letter (I, II, or III). Use the given data to test the hypothesis that $\pi_1 = \frac{1}{3}$, $\pi_2 = \frac{1}{3}$, and $\pi_3 = \frac{1}{3}$, where π_1, π_2, and π_3 are the true proportions of all returned questionnaires accompanied by cover letters I, II, and III, respectively. Use a .05 significance level.

	Cover-letter type		
	I	II	III
Frequency	48	44	39

16.7   A certain genetic characteristic of a particular plant can appear in one of three forms (phenotypes). A researcher has developed a theory, according to which the hypothesized proportions are $\pi_1 = .25$, $\pi_2 = .50$, and $\pi_3 = .25$. A sample of 200 plants yields $X^2 = 4.63$.
   a.   Carry out a test of the null hypothesis that the theory is correct using level of significance $\alpha = .05$.
   b.   What can be said about the *P*-value associated with the test in (a)?
   c.   Suppose that a sample of 300 plants had resulted in the same value of X^2. How would your analysis and conclusion differ from the analysis and conclusion in part (a)?

16.8   The paper "Linkage Studies of the Tomato" (*Trans. Royal Canad. Inst.* (1931): 1–19) reported the accompanying data on phenotypes resulting from crossing tall cut-leaf tomatoes with dwarf potato-leaf tomatoes. There are four possible phenotypes: (1) tall cut-leaf, (2) tall potato-leaf, (3) dwarf cut-leaf, and (4) dwarf potato-leaf. Mendel's laws of inheritance imply that $\pi_1 = \frac{9}{16}$, $\pi_2 = \frac{3}{16}$, $\pi_3 = \frac{3}{16}$, and $\pi_4 = \frac{1}{16}$. Is the data from this experiment consistent with Mendel's laws? Use a .01 significance level.

	Phenotype			
	1	2	3	4
Frequency	926	288	293	104

16.9   It is hypothesized that when homing pigeons are disoriented in a certain manner, they will exhibit no preference for any direction of flight after takeoff. To test this, 120 pigeons are disoriented, let loose, and the direction of flight of each is recorded. The resulting data is given. Use the goodness-of-fit test with significance level .10 to determine if the data supports the hypothesis.

Direction	0°–45°	45°–90°	90°–135°	135°–180°
Frequency	12	16	17	15

Direction	180°–225°	225°–270°	270°–315°	315°–360°
Frequency	13	20	17	10

16.2   Tests for Homogeneity and Independence in a Two-Way Table

Data resulting from observations made on two different categorical variables can also be summarized using a tabular format. As an example, suppose that residents of a particular city can watch national news on ABC, CBS, NBC, or PBS (the public television network) affiliate stations. A researcher wishes to know whether there is any relationship between political philosophy (liberal, moderate, or conservative) and preferred news program among those residents who regularly watch the national news. Let x denote the variable *political philosophy* and y the variable *preferred network*. A random sample of 300 regular watchers is to be selected, and each one will be asked for his or her x and y values. The data set is bivariate and might initially be displayed as follows:

Observation	x value	y value
1	Liberal	CBS
2	Conservative	ABC
3	Conservative	PBS
⋮	⋮	⋮
299	Moderate	NBC
300	Liberal	PBS

Bivariate categorical data of this sort can most easily be summarized by constructing a **two-way frequency table,** or **contingency table.** This is a rectangular table that consists of a row for each possible value of x (each category specified by this variable) and a column for each possible value of y. There is then a cell in the table for each possible (x, y) combination. Once such a table has been constructed, the number of times each particular (x, y) combination occurs in the data set is determined and these numbers (frequencies) are entered in the corresponding cells of the table. The resulting numbers are called **observed cell counts.** The table for the *political philosophy–preferred news program* example discussed earlier contains 3 rows and 4 columns (because x and y have 3 and 4 possible values, respectively). Table 16.1 is one possible table, with the rows and columns labeled with the possible x and y "values." These are often referred to as the *row* and *column categories.*

TABLE 16.1   An example of a 3 × 4 frequency table

	ABC	CBS	NBC	PBS	Row marginal total
Liberal	20	20	25	15	80
Moderate	45	35	50	20	150
Conservative	15	40	10	5	70
Column marginal total	80	95	85	40	300

Marginal totals are obtained by adding the observed cell counts in each row and also in each column of the table. The row and column marginal totals, along with the total of all observed cell counts in the table—the **grand total**—have been included in Table 16.1. The marginal totals provide information on the distribution of observed values for each variable separately. In this example, the row marginal totals reveal that the sample consisted of 80 liberals, 150 moderates, and 70 conservatives. Similarly, column marginal totals indicated how often each of the preferred program categories occurred: 80 preferred ABC news, 95 preferred CBS, and so on. The grand total, 300, is the number of observations in the bivariate data set, in this case the sample size (although occasionally such a table results from a census of the entire population).

Two-way frequency tables are often characterized by the number of rows and columns in the table (specified in that order: rows first, then columns). Table 16.1 is called a 3 × 4 table. The smallest two-way frequency table is a 2 × 2 table, which has only two rows and two columns and thus four cells.

Bivariate categorical data arises naturally in two different types of investigations. A researcher may be interested in comparing two or more groups on the basis of a categorical variable and so may obtain a sample separately from each group. For example, data could be collected at a university in order to compare students, faculty, and staff on the basis of primary mode of transportation to campus (car, bicycle, motorcycle, bus, or by foot). One random sample of 200 students, another of 100 faculty, and a third of 150 staff might be chosen, and the selected individuals could be interviewed in order to obtain the needed transportation information. Data from such a study could easily be summarized in a 3 × 5 two-way frequency table with row categories of student, faculty, and staff and column categories corresponding to the five possible modes of transportation. The observed cell counts could then be used to gain insight into differences and similarities among the three groups with respect to the means of transportation. This type of bivariate categorical data is characterized by having one set of marginal totals fixed (the sample sizes from the different groups), whereas each total in the other set is random. In the 3 × 5 situation just discussed, the row totals would be fixed at 200, 100, and 150, respectively.

Bivariate data also arises when the values of two different variables are observed for all individuals or items in a single sample. For example, a sample of 500 registered voters might be selected. Each voter could then be asked both if he or she favored a particular property tax initiative and if he or she was a registered Democrat, Republican, or Independent. This would result in a bivariate data set with *x* representing *political affiliation* (with categories Democrat, Republican, and Independent) and *y* representing *response* (favor initiative or oppose initiative). The corresponding 3 × 2 frequency table could then be used to investigate any association between position on the tax initiative and political affiliation. This type of bivariate categorical data is characterized by having both sets of marginal totals random and only the grand total fixed.

Comparing Two or More Populations

When the value of a categorical variable is recorded for members of separate random samples obtained from each population under study, the central issue is whether the category proportions are the same for all of the populations. As in Section 16.1, the test procedure uses a chi-squared statistic that compares the observed counts to those that would be expected if there were no differences between the populations.

EXAMPLE 16.4

Until recently, a number of professions were prohibited from advertising. In 1977, the U.S. Supreme Court ruled that prohibiting doctors and lawyers from advertising violated their right to free speech. The paper "Should Dentists Advertise?" (*J. of Ad. Research* (June 1982):33–38) compared the attitudes of consumers and dentists toward the advertising of dental services. Separate samples of 101 consumers and 124 dentists were asked to respond to the following statement: I favor the use of advertising by dentists to attract new patients. Possible responses were: strongly agree, agree, neutral, disagree, and strongly disagree. The data presented in the paper appears in the accompanying 2 × 5 frequency table. The authors were interested in determining whether the two groups—consumers and dentists—differed in their attitudes toward advertising.

	Response					
Group	Strongly agree	Agree	Neutral	Disagree	Strongly disagree	Row marg. total
Consumers	34	49	9	4	5	101
Dentists	9	18	23	28	46	124
Col. marg. total	43	67	32	32	51	225
Col. % of total	19.11	29.78	14.22	14.22	22.67	

Estimates of expected cell counts can be reasoned out in the following manner: There were 225 responses, of which 43 were "strongly agree." The proportion of the total responding "strongly agree" is then

$$\frac{43}{225} = .1911$$

If there were no difference in response for consumers and dentists, we would then expect about 19.11% of the consumers and 19.11% of the dentists to have strongly agreed. Therefore, the *expected cell counts*[2] for the two cells in the "strongly agree" column are

$$\left(\begin{array}{c}\text{expected count for}\\\text{consumer–strongly agree cell}\end{array}\right) = .1911(101) = 19.30$$

$$\left(\begin{array}{c}\text{expected count for}\\\text{dentist–strongly agree cell}\end{array}\right) = .1911(124) = 23.70$$

Note that the expected cell counts need not be whole numbers. The expected cell counts for the remaining cells can be computed in a similar manner. For example,

$$\frac{67}{225} = .2978$$

of all responses were in the agree category, so

$$\left(\begin{array}{c}\text{expected count for}\\\text{consumer–agree cell}\end{array}\right) = .2978(101) = 30.08$$

$$\left(\begin{array}{c}\text{expected count for}\\\text{dentist–agree cell}\end{array}\right) = .2978(124) = 36.93$$

It is common practice to display the observed cell counts and the corresponding estimated expected cell counts in the same table, with the estimated expected cell counts enclosed in parentheses. Expected cell counts for the remaining six cells have been computed and entered into the table that follows. Except for small differences due to rounding, each marginal total for expected cell counts is identical to that of the corresponding observed counts.

---

[2]In this section, all expected cell counts will be estimated from sample data. All references to "expected counts" should be interpreted as *estimated* expected counts.

Group	Observed and expected cell counts					
	Strongly agree	Agree	Neutral	Disagree	Strongly disagree	Row marg. total
Consumers	34 (19.30)	49 (30.08)	9 (14.36)	4 (14.36)	5 (22.89)	101
Dentists	9 (23.70)	18 (36.92)	23 (17.64)	28 (17.64)	46 (28.11)	124
Col. marg. total	43	67	32	32	51	225

A quick comparison of the observed and expected cell counts reveals large discrepancies. It appears that most consumers are more favorable toward advertising since the observed counts in the consumer–strongly agree and consumer–agree cells are substantially higher than expected, whereas the observed cell counts for consumers in the disagree and strongly disagree cells are lower than expected (when no difference exists). The opposite relationship between observed and expected counts is exhibited by the dentists.

In Example 16.4, the expected count for a cell corresponding to a particular group-response combination was computed in two steps. First the response *marginal proportion* was computed (for example, 43/225 for the strongly agree response). This proportion was then multiplied by a marginal group total (for example, 101(43/225) for the consumer group). This is equivalent to first multiplying the row and column marginal totals and then dividing by the grand total:

$$\frac{(101)(43)}{225}$$

To compare two or more groups on the basis of a categorical variable, calculate an **expected cell count** for each cell by selecting the corresponding row and column marginal totals and then computing

$$\begin{pmatrix} \text{expected} \\ \text{cell count} \end{pmatrix} = \frac{(\text{column marginal total})(\text{row marginal total})}{\text{grand total}}$$

These quantities represent what would be expected when there is no difference between the groups under study.

The X^2 statistic, introduced in Section 16.1, can now be used to compare the observed cell counts to the expected cell counts. A large value of X^2 results when there are substantial discrepancies between the observed and expected counts, and suggest that the hypothesis of no differences between the populations should be rejected. A formal test procedure is described in the accompanying box.

COMPARING TWO OR MORE POPULATIONS USING THE X^2 STATISTIC

Null hypothesis: H_0: the true category proportions are the same for all the populations (homogeneity of populations)

Alternative hypothesis: H_a: the true category proportions are not the same for all the populations

Test statistic:

$$X^2 = \sum_{\substack{\text{all} \\ \text{cells}}} \frac{(\text{observed cell count} - \text{expected cell count})^2}{\text{expected cell count}}$$

The expected cell counts are estimated from the sample data (assuming that H_0 is true) using the formula

$$\left(\begin{array}{c} \text{expected} \\ \text{cell count} \end{array} \right) = \frac{(\text{row marginal total})(\text{column marginal total})}{\text{grand total}}$$

Rejection region: When H_0 is true and all expected cell counts are at least 5, X^2 has approximately a chi-squared distribution with

$$df = (\text{number of rows} - 1)(\text{number of columns} - 1)$$

Therefore, H_0 should be rejected if $X^2 >$ chi-squared critical value. (If some expected cell counts are less than 5, rows or columns of the table may be combined to achieve a table with satisfactory expected counts.) The critical value comes from the column of Table XII corresponding to the desired level of significance.

EXAMPLE 16.5

(*Example 16.4 continued*) The following table of observed and expected cell counts appeared in Example 16.4.

	Response				
Group	Strongly agree	Agree	Neutral	Disagree	Strongly disagree
Consumers	34 (19.30)	49 (30.08)	9 (14.36)	4 (14.36)	5 (22.89)
Dentists	9 (23.70)	18 (36.92)	23 (17.64)	28 (17.64)	46 (28.11)

The hypotheses to be tested are:

H_0: proportions in each response category are the same for consumers and dentists

H_a: H_0 is not true

A significance level of .05 will be used. All expected cell counts exceed 5, so use of the X^2 test statistic is appropriate.

The critical value comes from the .05 column and the row corresponding to df $= (2 - 1)(5 - 1) = 4$ of Table XII. H_0 will be rejected if $X^2 > 9.49$. In fact,

$$X^2 = \frac{(34 - 19.30)^2}{19.30} + \cdots + \frac{(46 - 28.11)^2}{28.11} = 84.47$$

and since $84.47 > 9.49$, the hypothesis H_0 is rejected. There is strong evidence to support the claim that the proportions in the response categories are not the same for dentists and consumers.

EXAMPLE 16.6

What factors influence people to respond to mail surveys? Researchers have found that the appearance of the survey and the nature of the first question have an influence on the overall response rate, but do they affect the speed of response? The paper "The Impact of Cover Design and First Questions on Responses for a Mail Survey of Skydivers" (*Leisure Science* (1991):67–76) presents the results of an experiment to investigate rate of response. Surveys with a plain cover were mailed to a sample of 427 skydivers. Surveys with a cover graphic of a skydiver were mailed to a separate random sample of 414 skydivers. The postmark on the returned survey was used to classify each person who received a survey into one of the following response categories: returned in 1–7 days, returned in 8–14 days, returned in 15–31 days, returned in 32–60 days, and not returned. The resulting data is summarized in the following two-way table.

		Response category					
		1–7	8–14	15–31	32–60	Not returned	
Cover design	Graphic	70	76	51	19	198	414
	Plain	84	53	51	32	207	427
		154	129	102	51	405	841

Does the data support the theory that the proportions falling into the various response categories are not identical for the two cover designs? We will use a significance level of .05 to test the relevant hypotheses.

The hypotheses are

H_0: the response category proportions are the same for the two cover designs

H_a: the proportions are not the same for all response categories for the two cover designs

Expected cell counts are computed using

$$\text{expected count} = \frac{(\text{column total})(\text{row total})}{\text{grand total}}$$

For example, the expected count for the cell in row 1 and column 2 of the table (graphic cover, 8–14-day response) is

$$\text{expected count} = \frac{(129)(414)}{841} = 63.5$$

The other expected cell counts appear in parentheses in the following table.

		Response category					
		1–7	8–14	15–31	32–60	Not returned	
Cover design	Graphic	70 (75.8)	76 (63.5)	51 (50.2)	19 (25.1)	198 (199.4)	414
	Plain	84 (78.2)	53 (65.5)	51 (51.8)	32 (25.9)	207 (205.6)	427
		154	129	102	51	405	841

Since all expected cell counts are at least 5, the X^2 statistic can be used. The appropriate rejection region will be based on the chi-squared distribution with

$$df = (\text{rows} - 1)(\text{columns} - 1) = (2 - 1)(5 - 1) = 4$$

From Appendix Table XII, with $\alpha = .05$ the appropriate critical value is 9.49. We will reject H_0 if $X^2 > 9.49$. The calculated value of X^2 is

$$X^2 = \frac{(70 - 75.8)^2}{75.8} + \cdots + \frac{(207 - 205.6)^2}{205.6}$$
$$= .444 + \cdots + .010 = 8.68$$

Since 8.68 is not greater than 9.49, we fail to reject H_0. The data does not support the theory that the proportions falling in the various response categories differ for the two cover designs. There is no evidence that the cover design affects speed of response.

Testing for Independence of Two Categorical Variables

The X^2 test statistic and test procedure can also be used to investigate association between two categorical variables in a single population. Suppose that each population member has a value of a first categorical variable and also of a second such variable. As an example, television viewers in a particular city might be categorized both with respect to preferred network (ABC, CBS, NBC, or PBS) and with respect to favorite type of programming (comedy, drama, or information-news). The question of interest is often whether knowledge of one variable's value provides any information about the value of the other variable—that is, are the two variables independent? Continuing the example, suppose that those who favor ABC prefer the three types of programming in proportions .4, .5, and .1 and that these proportions are also correct for individuals favoring any of the other three networks. Then learning an individual's preferred network provides no extra information concerning that individual's favorite type of programming. The categorical variables *preferred network* and *favorite program type* are independent.

To see how the expected counts are obtained in this situation, first recall from our probability discussion in Chapter 5 the condition for independence of two events. The events A and B are said to be independent if

$$P(A \text{ and } B) = P(A) \cdot P(B)$$

so that the proportion of time that they occur together in the long run is the product of the two individual long-run relative frequencies. Similarly, two categorical variables are independent in a population if for *any* particular category of the first variable and *any* particular category of the second variable,

$$\begin{pmatrix} \text{proportion} \\ \text{of individuals} \\ \text{in both categories} \end{pmatrix} = \begin{pmatrix} \text{proportion in} \\ \text{specified category} \\ \text{of 1st variable} \end{pmatrix} \cdot \begin{pmatrix} \text{proportion in} \\ \text{specified category} \\ \text{of 2nd variable} \end{pmatrix}$$

Thus if 30% of all viewers prefer ABC and the proportion of program type preferences are as previously given, assuming the two variables are independent, the proportion of individuals who both favor ABC and prefer comedy is $(.3)(.4) = .12$ (or 12%).

Multiplying the right-hand side of this expression by the sample size gives us the expected number of individuals in the sample who are in both specified categories of the two variables when the variables are independent. However, these expected counts cannot be calculated because the individual population proportions are not known. The resolution of this dilemma is to estimate each population proportion by the corresponding sample proportion:

$$\begin{pmatrix} \text{estimated expected no.} \\ \text{in specified categories} \\ \text{of the two variables} \end{pmatrix} = \begin{pmatrix} \text{sample} \\ \text{size} \end{pmatrix} \cdot \left(\frac{\text{obs. no. in categ. of 1st var.}}{\text{sample size}} \right) \cdot \left(\frac{\text{obs. no. in categ. of 2nd var.}}{\text{sample size}} \right)$$

$$= \frac{\left(\begin{array}{c} \text{obs. no. in categ. of} \\ \text{1st var.} \end{array}\right) \cdot \left(\begin{array}{c} \text{obs. no. in categ. of} \\ \text{2nd var.} \end{array}\right)}{\text{sample size}}$$

Suppose that the observed counts are displayed in a rectangular table in which rows correspond to the different categories of the first variable and columns to the categories of the second variable. Then the numerator in the preceding expression for estimated expected counts is just the product of the row and column marginal totals. This is exactly how estimated expected counts were computed in the test for homogeneity of several populations.

TESTING FOR INDEPENDENCE OF TWO CATEGORICAL VARIABLES

Null hypothesis: H_0: The two variables are independent
Alternative hypothesis: H_a: The two variables are not independent
Test statistic:

$$X^2 = \sum_{\substack{\text{all} \\ \text{cells}}} \frac{(\text{observed cell count} - \text{expected cell count})^2}{\text{expected cell count}}$$

The expected cell counts are estimated (assuming H_0 is true) by the formula

$$\left(\begin{array}{c} \text{expected} \\ \text{cell count} \end{array}\right) = \frac{(\text{row marginal total})(\text{column marginal total})}{\text{grand total}}$$

Rejection region: When H_0 is true and all expected cell counts are at least 5, then X^2 has approximately a chi-squared distribution, with

$$df = (\text{number of rows} - 1)(\text{number of columns} - 1)$$

The hypothesis H_0 should be rejected if $X^2 >$ chi-squared critical value where chi-squared critical values are given in Table XII.

EXAMPLE 16.7

The paper "Impulsive and Premeditated Homicide: An Analysis of Subsequent Parole Risk of the Murderer" (*J. of Criminal Law and Criminology* (1978):108–114) investigated the relationship between the circumstances surrounding a murder and subsequent parole success of the murderer. A sample of 82 convicted murderers was selected, and each murderer was categorized according to type of murder (impulsive, premeditated) and parole outcome (success, failure). The resulting data is given in the accompanying 2×2 table.

	Success	Failure	Row marg. total
Impulsive	13	29	42
Premeditated	22	18	40
Col. marg. total	35	47	82

The authors were interested in determining whether there is an association between type of murder and parole outcome. Using a .05 level of significance, we will test

H_0: type of murder and parole outcome are independent

H_a: the two variables are not independent

Expected cell counts are as follows:

Cell		
Row	Column	Expected cell count
1	1	$\dfrac{(35)(42)}{82} = 17.93$
1	2	$\dfrac{(47)(42)}{82} = 24.07$
2	1	$\dfrac{(35)(40)}{82} = 17.07$
2	2	$\dfrac{(47)(40)}{82} = 22.93$

The observed and expected counts are given together in the accompanying table.

	Success	Failure	Row marg. total
Impulsive	13 (17.93)	29 (24.07)	42
Premeditated	22 (17.07)	18 (22.93)	40
Col. marg. total	35	47	82

Since all expected cell counts exceed 5, the X^2 statistic can be used. With level of significance $\alpha = .05$ and df $= (2 - 1)(2 - 1) = 1$, the chi-squared critical value is 3.84. Thus H_0 will be rejected if $X^2 > 3.84$.

$$X^2 = \frac{(13 - 17.93)^2}{17.93} + \cdots + \frac{(18 - 22.93)^2}{22.93} = 4.85$$

Since $4.85 > 3.84$, the hypothesis H_0 is rejected. The data supports the existence of an association between type of murder and parole outcomes.

EXAMPLE 16.8

The accompanying two-way table was constructed using data in the paper "Television Viewing and Physical Fitness in Adults" (*Research Quarterly for Exercise and Sport* (1990):315–320). The author hoped to determine whether time spent watching television is associated with cardiovascular fitness. Subjects were asked about their television-viewing time (per day, rounded to the nearest hour) and were classified as physically fit if they scored in the excellent or very good category on a step test. Expected cell counts (computed under the assumption of no association between TV viewing and fitness) appear in parentheses in the table.

		Fitness		
		Physically fit	Not physically fit	
TV group	0	35 (25.5)	147 (156.5)	182
	1–2	101 (102.2)	629 (627.8)	730
	3–4	28 (35.0)	222 (215.0)	250
	5 or more	4 (5.3)	34 (32.7)	38
		168	1032	1200

The X^2 test with a significance level of .01 will be used to test the relevant hypotheses:

H_0: Fitness and TV viewing are independent

H_a: Fitness and TV viewing are not independent

Since all expected cell counts are greater than 5, the X^2 test can be used. With significance level $\alpha = .01$ and

$$df = (\text{rows} - 1)(\text{cols} - 1) = (4 - 1)(2 - 1) = 3$$

Appendix Table XII gives 11.34 as the appropriate chi-squared critical value. H_0 will be rejected if $X^2 > 11.34$. The computed value of X^2 is

$$X^2 = \frac{(35 - 25.5)^2}{25.5} + \cdots + \frac{(34 - 32.7)^2}{32.7} = 6.13$$

Since 6.13 is not in the rejection region, we fail to reject H_0. There is not sufficient evidence to conclude that an association exists between TV viewing and fitness.

Most statistical computer packages will calculate both estimated expected cell counts and the value of the X^2 test statistic. MINITAB output for the data of Example 16.8 follows. (The discrepancy between $X^2 = 6.13$ and $X^2 = 6.161$ is due to rounding.)

Expected counts are printed below observed counts

		1	2	Total
1		35	147	182
		25.48	156.52	
2		101	629	730
		102.20	627.80	
3		28	222	250
		35.00	215.00	
4		4	34	38
		5.32	32.68	
Total		168	1032	1200

```
ChiSq =     3.557   + 0.579   +
            0.014   + 0.002   +
            1.400   + 0.228   +
            0.328   + 0.053   = 6.161
   df = 3
```

In some investigations, values of more than two categorical variables are recorded for each individual in the sample. For example, in addition to the variables *TV viewing time* and *fitness level,* the researchers in the study referenced in Example 16.8 might also have recorded age group (with categories under 21, 21–30, 31–40, and so on) for each subject. A number of interesting questions could then be explored: Are all three variables independent of one another? Is it possible that age and fitness level are dependent but that the relationship between them does not depend on TV viewing time? For a particular age group, are TV viewing time and fitness independent?

The X^2 test procedure described in this section for analysis of bivariate categorical data can be extended for use with *multivariate categorical data.* Appropriate hypothesis tests can then be used to provide insight into the relationships between variables. However, the computations required to calculate estimated expected cell counts and to compute the value of X^2 are quite tedious and so are seldom done without the aid of a computer. Several statistical computer packages (including BMDP and SAS) can perform this type of analysis. The chapter references can be consulted for further information on the analysis of categorical data.

EXERCISES 16.10–16.27   SECTION 16.2

16.10   A particular state university system has six campuses. On each campus, a random sample of students will be selected and each student will be categorized with respect to political philosophy as liberal, moderate, or conservative. The null hypothesis of interest is that the proportion of students falling in these three categories is the same at all six campuses.

a. On how many degrees of freedom will the resulting X^2 test be based, and what is the rejection region for significance level .01?

b. How do your answers in part (a) change if there are seven campuses rather than six?

c. How do your answers in part (a) change if there are four rather than three categories for political philosophy?

16.11   A random sample of 1000 registered voters in a certain county is selected and each voter is categorized with respect to both educational level (four categories) and preferred candidate in an upcoming supervisorial election (five possibilities). The hypothesis of interest is that educational level and preferred candidate are independent factors.

a. If it is decided to use a test with significance level .05, what is the rejection region?

b. If $X^2 = 7.2$, what would you conclude at significance level .10?

c. If there were only four candidates vying for election, what would you conclude if $X^2 = 14.5$ and a test with $\alpha = .05$ is appropriate?

16.12   Jail inmates can be classified into one of the following four categories according to the type of crime committed: violent crime, crime against property, drug offenses, and public-order offenses. Suppose that random samples of 500 male inmates and 500 female inmates are selected and each inmate is classified according to type of offense. The data in the accompanying table is based on summary values given in the article " Profile of Jail Inmates" (*USA Today,* April 25, 1991). We would like to know if male and female inmates differ with respect to type of offense.

a. Is this a test of homogeneity or a test of association?

b. Test the relevant hypotheses using a significance level of .05.

		Sex	
		Male	Female
Type of Crime	Violent	117	66
	Property	150	160
	Drug	109	168
	Public-order	124	106

16.13   Job satisfaction of professionals was examined in the paper "Psychology of the Scientist: Work Related Attitudes of U.S. Scientists" (*Psychological Reports* (1991):443–450). Each person in a sample of 778 teachers was classified according to a job satisfaction variable and also by teaching level, resulting in the accompanying two-way table. Can we conclude that there is an association between job satisfaction and teaching level? Test the relevant hypotheses using $\alpha = .05$.

		Job satisfaction	
		Satisfied	Unsatisfied
Teaching level	College	74	43
	High school	224	171
	Elementary	126	140

16.14   The paper on job satisfaction cited in Exercise 16.13 also gave job-satisfaction data for a sample of professionals consisting of doctors, lawyers, and engineers. Use the accompanying data to determine if there is an association between profession and job satisfaction. Use a significance level of .01.

		Job satisfaction	
		Satisfied	Unsatisfied
Profession	Doctors	62	38
	Lawyers	46	36
	Engineers	106	96

16.15   Qualifications of male and female head and assistant college athletic coaches were compared in the paper "Sex Bias and the Validity of Believed Differences Between Male and Female Interscholastic Athletic Coaches" (*Research Quarterly for Exercise and Sport* (1990):259–267). Each person in random samples of 2225 male coaches and 1141 female coaches was classified according to number of years of coaching experience to obtain the accompanying two-way table. Is there enough evidence to conclude that the proportions falling into the experience categories are different for males and females? Use $\alpha = .01$.

Sex	Years of experience				
	1–3	4–6	7–9	10–12	13+
Males	202	369	482	361	811
Females	230	251	238	164	258

16.16   The results of an experiment to assess the effects of crude oil on fish parasites were described in the paper "Effects of Crude Oils on the Gastrointestinal Parasites of Two Species of Marine Fish" (*J. of Wildlife Diseases* (1983):253–258). Three treatments (corresponding to three populations) were compared: (1) no contamination, (2) contamination by 1-year-old weathered oil, and (3) contamination by new oil. For each treatment condition, a sample of fish was taken and then each fish was classified as either parasitized or not parasitized.

a. Data compatible with that in the paper is given in the accompanying table. Can we conclude that the three treatments differ with respect to the true proportion of parasitized and nonparasitized fish? Test the relevant hypotheses using a significance level of .01.

Treatment	Parasitized	Nonparasitized
Control	30	3
Old oil	16	8
New oil	16	16

b. What can be said about the *P*-value associated with the hypothesis test in part (a)?

16.17   The accompanying two-way frequency table appeared in the paper "Marijuana Use in College" (*Youth and Society* (1979):323–334). Four hundred forty-five college students were classified according to both frequency of marijuana use and parental use of alcohol and psychoactive drugs.

Parental use of alcohol and drugs	Student level of marijuana use			Row marg. total
	Never	Occasional	Regular	
Neither	141	54	40	235
One	68	44	51	163
Both	17	11	19	47
Col marg. total	226	109	110	445

a. Use an X^2 test with a significance level of .01 to determine if there is an association between marijuana use and parental use of drugs and alcohol.

b. What can be said regarding the *P*-value associated with the hypothesis test in part (a)?

16.18   An increasing number of people are spending their working hours in front of a video display terminal (VDT). The paper "VDT Workstation Design: Preferred Settings and Their Effects" (*Human Factors* (1983):161–175) summarized a study of adjustable VDT screens. Sixty-five workers using nonadjustable screens and 66 workers using adjustable screens were asked if they experienced annoying reflections from the screens. The resulting data is given in the accompanying table.

	Annoying reflection	
Screen type	No	Yes
Nonadjustable	15	50
Adjustable	28	38

a. The investigators were interested in whether the proportion experiencing annoying reflections was the same for both types of VDT screens. Does this problem situation involve comparing two populations or testing for independence? Explain.

b. Use a .05 significance level and the X^2 statistic to test the appropriate hypotheses.

c. Can you think of another test statistic that could be used to answer the researchers' question? (Hint: See Chapter 11.) If the researchers were interested in determining whether the proportion experiencing annoying reflection was smaller for the adjustable VDT screens, which test statistic would you recommend? Explain. (Hint: Look at the alternative hypothesis for the X^2 test.)

16.19   The paper "The Liking and Viewing of Regular TV Series" (*J. of Consumer Research* (1987):63–70) raised the issue of the extent to which people actually like the TV programs they watch. Viewers of two comedy series were asked to respond to the question "How interesting do you find this show?" Data in the accompanying table is compatible with percentages given in the paper. Using a significance level of .05, test the null hypothesis

H_0: the true proportions of responses in the five response categories are the same for regular viewers of the two programs

	Response				
Series	Extremely interesting	Very interesting	Fairly interesting	Not very interesting	Not at all interesting
Three's Company	19	24	30	10	17
Hello Larry	9	22	46	37	36

16.20   The paper "Color Associations of Male and Female Fourth-Grade School Children" (*J. of Psych.* (1988):383–388) asked children to indicate what emotion they associated with the color red. The response and the sex of the child were noted, and the data is summarized in the accompanying two-way table. Is there strong evidence of an association between response and gender? Use a .01 level of significance.

Emotion	Gender	
	Male	Female
Anger	34	27
Pain	28	17
Happiness	12	19
Love	38	39

16.21 The U.S. Census Bureau contends "... the American people are the most educated people in the world" ("Ticket to Success," *Washington Post,* Oct. 17, 1985). Suppose that a random sample of 1000 adults in each of the United States, East Germany, Canada, Sweden, and Japan resulted in the data in the accompanying table. (These figures are based on summary values given in the article.) Use the test for homogeneity of proportions to determine whether the proportion of the adult population with some college education is the same for the five countries compared.

Country	Education	
	Some college	No college
United States	320	680
East Germany	173	827
Canada	172	828
Sweden	155	845
Japan	145	855

16.22 An experiment to determine the response of soybeans to long-term ozone exposure was described in the paper "Injury and Yield Response of Soybean to Chronic Doses of Ozone and Soil Moisture Deficit" (*Crop Science* (1987):1016–1024). Soybean seeds were exposed to one of seven different ozone treatments and the number of exposed seeds that produced normal seedlings was noted. The resulting data appears in the accompanying table. Is there evidence that the proportion of normal seedlings is not the same for all seven treatments? Test the relevant hypotheses using a level .05 test.

Treatment	Seedling type		
	Normal seedlings	Abnormal seedlings	Total
1	1747	410	2157
2	2099	526	2625
3	1292	386	1678
4	1676	446	2122
5	1238	413	1651
6	863	678	1541
7	1364	408	1772

16.23   A study financed by the U.S. Dept. of Justice (*Los Angeles Times* (September 7, 1986)) looked at the records of convicts released from prison in 1978 in three states—California, Michigan, and Texas. The number who had been rearrested within 3 years of release was noted, resulting in the accompanying table. Is there evidence that the proportions of those rearrested differs for the three states? Test the relevant hypotheses using a .01 level of significance.

| | Arrest status | | |
State	Rearrested	Not rearrested	Total
California	217	69	286
Texas	278	185	463
Michigan	145	129	274

16.24   Are the educational aspirations of students related to family income? This question was investigated in the article "Aspirations and Expectations of High School Youth" (*Int. J. of Comp. Soc.* (1975):25). The given 4 × 3 table resulted from classifying 273 high school students according to expected level of education and family income. Does the data indicate that educational aspirations and family income are not independent? Use a .10 level of significance.

| | Income | | |
Aspired level	Low	Middle	High
Some high school	9	11	9
High school graduate	44	52	41
Some college	13	23	12
College graduate	10	22	27

16.25   The effect of copper on earthworms was investigated in the paper "Sublethal Toxic Effects of Copper on Growth, Reproduction and Litter Breakdown Activity in the Earthworm *Lumbricus rubellus,* with Observations on the Influence of Temperature and Soil pH" (*Environ. Pollution* (1984):207–219). Each of four concentrations of copper (14, 54, 131, and 372 mg/kg soil) was applied to a sandy soil containing a known number of worms. After six weeks, the number of surviving worms was recorded. Data compatible with that given in the paper appears in the accompanying table. Does this data strongly suggest that the mortality rate (proportion not surviving) differs for the four concentrations? Use a .01 significance level.

| | Concentration level | | | |
Status	I	II	III	IV
Survived	80	74	78	66
Died	0	6	2	14

16.26   The accompanying frequency table appeared in the paper "Commitment to Work in Immigrants: Its Functions and Peculiarities" (*J. of Vocational Behavior* (1984):329–339). The data resulted from classifying 175 workers according to two variables: *job type* (with three categories: immigrant (I), white-collar nonimmigrant (W), and executive nonimmigrant (E)) and *attitude toward authority* (with two categories: positive (P) and negative (N)). Does the data support the theory that there is an association between attitude toward authority and job type? Use a significance level of .01.

	Attitude	
Job type	P	N
I	51	23
W	34	32
E	25	10

16.27   In a study of 2989 cancer deaths, the location of death (home, acute-care hospital, or chronic-care facility) and age at death were recorded, resulting in the given two-way frequency table ("Where Cancer Patients Die" *Public Health Reports* (1983): 173). Using a .01 significance level, test the null hypothesis that age at death and location of death are independent.

	Location		
Age	Home	Acute-care	Chronic-care
15–54	94	418	23
55–64	116	524	34
65–74	156	581	109
Over 74	138	558	238

16.3   Goodness-of-Fit Test for Normality

Many of the small-sample inferential procedures introduced in earlier chapters required the assumption of a normal population distribution. Normal probability plots provided one way of assessing the reasonableness of this assumption. The chi-squared goodness-of-fit test can also be used to decide whether it is plausible that the population distribution is normal. The X^2 test statistic again compares observed and expected cell counts for a specified set of categories. Since a variable with a normal distribution is numerical, we begin by constructing a frequency distribution whose class intervals and corresponding frequencies serve as categories and observed cell counts, respectively.

The expected counts are particularly easy to compute when H_0 specifies the values of μ and σ for the normal population, so we consider this case first.

X^2 GOODNESS-OF-FIT TEST FOR A NORMAL DISTRIBUTION WITH SPECIFIED MEAN μ AND STANDARD DEVIATION σ

Null hypothesis: H_0: The population distribution is normal with specified values of μ and σ.

Alternative hypothesis: H_a: The population distribution is not the specified normal distribution.

Test statistic: X^2 goodness-of-fit statistic.

Rejection region: As long as all of the expected counts are at least 5, reject H_0 if $X^2 >$ chi-squared critical value. If some expected counts are smaller than 5, adjacent class intervals can be combined. The chi-squared critical value is obtained from the appropriate column of Table XII and the row corresponding to

$$df = \text{number of class intervals} - 1$$

EXAMPLE 16.9

The article "A Probabilistic Analysis of Dissolved Oxygen—Biochemical Oxygen Demand Relationship in Streams" (*J. Water Resources Control Fed.* (1969):73–90) reported data on the rate of oxygenation in streams at 20°C in a certain region. Based on the accompanying frequency distribution, can we conclude that the true distribution of oxygenation rates is normal with $\mu = .2$ and $\sigma = .05$? A .01 significance level has been selected.

Rate (per day)	Frequency
Below .100	12
.100–<.150	20
.150–<.200	23
.200–<.250	15
At least .250	13
	83

The appropriate hypotheses are:

H_0: the oxygenation rate distribution is normal with $\mu = .2$ and $\sigma = .05$

H_a: the oxygenation rate distribution is not normal with $\mu = .2$ and $\sigma = .05$ (H_0 is not true)

If H_0 is rejected, we will have ruled out only this one particular normal distribution as a population model. It is possible that a different normal distribution (different μ and/or σ) might be appropriate.

The next step in the analysis is to compute the expected cell counts for the five categories. When H_0 is true, the population distribution is normal with $\mu = .2$ and $\sigma = .05$. The proportion of oxygenation rates below .100 is the area under the corresponding normal curve to the left of .100, as pictured.

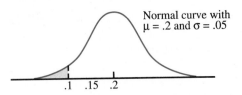

Normal curve with
$\mu = .2$ and $\sigma = .05$

To find this area, we compute

$$z = \frac{.1 - .2}{.05} = -2$$

From Appendix Table II, the area to the left of -2 under the standard normal (z) curve is .0228. The proportion of oxygenation rates below .100 when H_0 is true is .0228.

Since the sample size was 83, the expected cell count for the first category (below .100) is

$$83(.0228) = 1.89$$

The proportion of oxygenation rates for category 2 ($.100 - <.150$) is the shaded area in the accompanying figure.

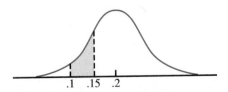

This is equal to the area above the interval from

$$\frac{.1 - .2}{.05} = -2$$

to

$$\frac{.15 - .2}{.05} = -1$$

under the standard normal (z) curve. From Appendix Table II, this area is

$$.1587 - .0228 = .1359$$

and so the corresponding expected category count is

$$83(.1359) = 11.28$$

Expected counts for the remaining three categories are computed in a similar manner.

Cell	Interval	Observed cell count	Expected cell count
1	Below .100	12 }32	1.89 }13.17
2	.100–<.150	20	11.28
3	.150–<.200	23	28.33
4	.200–<.250	15	28.33
5	At least .250	13	13.17

Since the expected count for the first cell is less than 5, let's combine the first two cells. The subsequent analysis is based on 4 cells and, therefore,

$$\text{df} = \text{number of class intervals} - 1 = 3$$

The X^2 goodness-of-fit statistic will be used. With a significance level of .01, the chi-squared critical value in the 3-df row of Table XII is 11.34. H_0 will be rejected if $X^2 > 11.34$. Otherwise, H_0 will not be rejected.
The computed value of X^2 is

$$X^2 = \frac{(32 - 13.17)^2}{13.17} + \cdots + \frac{(13 - 13.17)^2}{13.17} = 34.20$$

Since $34.20 > 11.34$, H_0 is rejected. The data strongly indicates that the true distribution of oxygenation rate is not normal with $\mu = .2$ and $\sigma = .05$.

In Example 16.9, the null hypothesis specified a particular normal distribution ($\mu = .2$ and $\sigma = .05$). Much more frequently, an investigator is interested in whether the population distribution is normal in shape but doesn't have a specific normal distribution in mind. In this case, μ and σ are estimated from the data by $\bar{x}$ and s. The estimation of the population characteristics μ and σ results in a loss of 2 df, so the test is now based on

$$\text{df} = \text{number of class intervals} - 3$$

> ## X^2 GOODNESS-OF-FIT TEST FOR NORMALITY (μ AND σ NOT SPECIFIED)
>
> When the X^2 goodness-of-fit test is used to test
>
> H_0: the population distribution is normal
>
> versus
>
> H_a: the population distribution is not normal
>
> the sample mean, $\bar{x}$, and sample standard deviation, s, are used in place of μ and σ to compute (estimated) expected cell counts. The chi-squared critical value for the rejection region is based on
>
> $$\text{df} = \text{number of intervals} - 3$$

EXAMPLE 16.10

The paper discussed in Example 16.9 reported the values $\bar{x} = .173$ and $s = .066$. Is it reasonable to think that the true distribution of oxygenation rate is normal? A .05 significance level will be used.

H_0: the oxygenation rate distribution is normal

H_a: the oxygenation rate distribution is not normal

Expected category counts are computed in a manner analogous to that of Example 16.9. The expected proportion of oxygenation rates less than .100 is the area to the left of .1 under the normal curve with mean .173 and standard deviation .066. The corresponding z value is

$$z = \frac{.1 - .173}{.066} = -1.1$$

From Appendix Table II, the desired area is .1357. The expected count for the first category is then

$$83(.1357) = 11.26$$

The remaining expected counts have been computed in a similar fashion and appear in the accompanying table.

Cell	Interval	Observed cell count	Expected cell count
1	Below .100	12	11.26
2	.100–<.150	20	20.45
3	.150–<.200	23	22.68
4	.200–<.250	15	19.05
5	At least .250	13	9.55

All expected category counts are greater than 5, so there is no need to combine cells. With $5 - 3 = 2$ df and a .05 significance level, the chi-squared critical value (from Table XII) is 5.99. Therefore, H_0 will be rejected if $X^2 > 5.99$.

The computed value of X^2 is

$$X^2 = \frac{(12 - 11.26)^2}{11.26} + \cdots + \frac{(13 - 9.55)^2}{9.55} = 2.17$$

Since $2.17 < 5.99$, H_0 is not rejected. The data supports the hypothesis of normality.

The goodness-of-fit procedure can also be used to compare observed category counts to those expected under hypothesized population distributions other than the normal. Several examples are included in the exercises.

EXERCISES 16.28–16.34   SECTION 16.3

16.28   The accompanying frequency distribution of protein level in alfalfa clones appeared in the paper "Variability of Fraction I Protein and Total Phenolic Constituents in Alfalfa" (*Agronomy J.* (1974):384–386). Use the goodness-of-fit test with a .05 significance level to test the null hypothesis that the true distribution of protein level in alfalfa clones is normal with mean 4.3 and standard deviation .8.

Protein level (% of oven-dry weight)	Frequency
Less than 2.4	8
2.4–<3.0	65
3.0–<3.6	180
3.6–<4.2	328
4.2–<4.8	408
4.8–<5.4	284
5.4–<6.0	83
6.0–<6.6	13
At least 6.6	3

16.29   The Institute of Central America and Panama has carried out extensive dietary studies and research projects in Central America. In one study, reported in "The Blood Viscosity of Various Socioeconomic Groups in Guatemala" (*Amer. J. of Clin. Nutrition* (November 1964)), serum total cholesterol measurements for a sample of 49 rural low-income Indians were reported as follows (in mg/L):

204	108	140	152	158	129	175	146	157	174	192	194	144
152	135	223	145	231	115	131	129	142	114	173	226	155
166	220	180	172	143	148	171	143	124	158	144	108	189
136	136	197	131	95	139	181	165	142	162			

a. Use the cholesterol data to construct a frequency distribution. (Note: The sample mean and sample standard deviation are 157.02 and 31.75, respectively.)

b. Using the frequency distribution in (a), conduct a goodness-of-fit test to determine if it is plausible that the population distribution of total serum cholesterol is normal. Use a .05 significance level.

16.30   In a study similar to that of Exercise 16.29, the blood cholesterol measurements of 500 American males were recorded and summarized in the accompanying frequency distribution (*Primer for the Biomedical Sciences* by O. J. Dunn (New York: John Wiley, 1977)). The corresponding sample mean and standard deviation were calculated to be 275 and 47, respectively.

Cholesterol level	Frequency
Less than 189.5	17
189.5–<219.5	41
219.5–<249.5	80
249.5–<279.5	134
279.5–<309.5	118
309.5–<339.5	71
339.5–<369.5	24
369.5–<399.5	13
At least 399.5	2

a. Use the X^2 test to determine whether a normal distribution provides an adequate description of the population. Use a .05 level of significance.

b. Do you think the same normal distribution could be used to describe the population of cholesterol measurements of Guatemalan Indians (see Exercise 16.29) and American males? Explain.

16.31   In a Swedish study, the number of males among the first seven children was recorded for each of 1334 families with seven or more children. The accompanying observed counts appeared in the article "Distribution and Sequences of Sexes in a Selected Sample of Swedish Families" (*Ann. Human Genetics* (1960):245–252). The expected counts have been computed under the assumption that the variable x = *number of males in first seven children* has a binomial distribution with $n = 7$ and $\pi = .5$ (for a discussion of the binomial distribution, see Chapter 6). Use the goodness-of-fit test and a .01 level of significance to test the hypotheses

H_0: x has a binomial distribution with $n = 7$ and $\pi = .5$

H_a: H_0 is not true

	Number of males							
	0	1	2	3	4	5	6	7
Observed count	6	57	206	362	365	256	69	13
Expected count	10.4	73.0	218.8	364.8	364.8	218.8	73.0	10.4

16.32   The paper "Some Studies on Tuft Weight Distribution in the Opening Room" (*Textile Res. J.* (1976):567–573) reported the accompanying observed counts for output tuft weight (mg) of cotton fibers. The authors hypothesized that the true distribution of tuft weights was described by a distribution called a *truncated exponential distribution* and computed the given expected counts in order to test

H_0: tuft weight has a particular truncated exponential distribution

H_a: H_0 is not true

Use the goodness-of-fit test with a .01 significance level to test these hypotheses.

Tuft weight	0–<8	8–<16	16–<24	≥24
Observed count	20	8	7	5
Expected count	18.0	9.9	5.5	6.6

16.33   The authors of the paper "Some Sampling Characteristics of Plants and Arthropods of the Arizona Desert" (*Ecology* (1962):567–571) hypothesized that an important type of probability distribution called a *Poisson distribution* could be used to describe the distribution of a number of *Larrea divaricata* plants found in sampling regions of fixed size. The Poisson distribution has a single characteristic, whose value was estimated from the sample data, resulting in the loss of 1 df. Use a .05 significance level and the observed and expected counts given to test

H_0: number of *Larrea divaricata* plants follows a Poisson distribution

H_a: H_0 is not true

Number of plants	0	1	2	3	4 or more
Observed count	9	9	10	14	6
Expected count	5.9	12.3	13.0	9.0	7.8

16.34   A certain vision test involves marking a measurement scale on a horizontal axis, placing a point at some distance above the axis, and asking the subject to locate the point on the marked scale. Suppose it is hypothesized that errors in location have a normal distribution with mean 0 and standard deviation 1 (a standard normal distribution). A goodness-of-fit test is to be based on the following six class intervals $(-\infty, -b), (-b, -a), (-a, 0), (0, a), (a, b),$ and (b, ∞). What values of a and *b* result in these class intervals having equal probability when the null hypothesis is true?

CHAPTER SIXTEEN SUMMARY OF KEY CONCEPTS AND FORMULAS

Term or Formula	Comment
One-way frequency table	A compact way of summarizing data on a categorical variable; it gives the number of times each of the possible categories in the data set occurs (the frequencies).
Goodness-of-fit statistic, $$X^2 = \sum_{\substack{\text{all} \\ \text{cells}}} \frac{\left(\begin{array}{c}\text{observed} \\ \text{cell count}\end{array} - \begin{array}{c}\text{expected} \\ \text{cell count}\end{array}\right)^2}{\text{expected cell count}}$$	A statistic used to provide a comparison between observed counts and those expected when a given hypothesis is true. When none of the expected counts are too small, X^2 has approximately a *chi-squared distribution*.
X^2 test in a one-way frequency table: H_0: π_1 = **hypothesized proportion for category 1** $\vdots$ π_k = **hypothesized proportion for category k**	A hypothesis test performed to determine whether the true category proportions are different from those specified by the given null hypothesis.
Two-way frequency table	A rectangular table used to summarize a bivariate categorical data set; two-way tables are used to compare several populations on the basis of a categorical variable or to identify whether an association exists between two categorical variables.
X^2 test for comparing two or more populations: H_0: **the true category proportions are the same for all of the populations**	The hypothesis test performed to determine whether the true category proportions are the same for all of the populations to be compared.
X^2 test for independence: H_0: **the two variables defining the table are independent**	A hypothesis test performed to determine whether an association exists between two categorical variables.

Term or Formula	Comment
X^2 **test for normality**	A hypothesis test performed to determine whether a sample comes from a normal population distribution.

ENCORE

The authors of the paper "Intensification of Dwarf Mistletoe on Southwestern Douglas Fir" cited in the Chapter Preview were interested in determining whether there was evidence of an association between tree size and degree of mistletoe infestation. Let's use the chi-squared test for association to test the hypotheses

> H_0: no association between tree size and degree of mistletoe infestation
>
> H_a: there is an association between tree size and degree of mistletoe infestation

The two-way table presented in the Chapter Preview is shown with expected cell counts appearing in parentheses.

	Mistletoe rating						
Diameter	1	2	3	4	5	6	Total
0–8	21 (14.86)	17 (14.08)	14 (17.01)	15 (15.84)	11 (14.08)	9 (11.14)	87
9–15	10 (12.47)	10 (11.81)	20 (14.27)	8 (13.29)	13 (11.81)	12 (9.35)	73
16–23	15 (13.15)	6 (12.46)	17 (15.05)	18 (14.02)	10 (12.46)	11 (9.86)	77
24–30	9 (12.13)	17 (11.49)	10 (13.88)	14 (12.92)	13 (11.49)	8 (9.09)	71
31–58	20 (20.15)	18 (19.09)	22 (23.07)	19 (21.48)	22 (19.09)	17 (15.11)	118
59–89	1 (3.24)	4 (3.07)	4 (3.71)	7 (3.46)	3 (3.07)	0 (2.43)	19
Total	76	72	87	81	72	57	445

Since the expected cell counts in the last row of the table (tree diameter category 59–89 cm) are less than 5, we have chosen to combine the last two rows of the table. The resulting table, including expected values in parentheses, is given. Since all expected cell counts are now greater than 5, the use of the chi-squared test is appropriate.

Diameter	Mistletoe rating						Total
	1	2	3	4	5	6	
0–8	21 (14.86)	17 (14.08)	14 (17.01)	15 (15.84)	11 (14.08)	9 (11.14)	87
9–15	10 (12.47)	10 (11.81)	20 (14.27)	8 (13.29)	13 (11.81)	12 (9.35)	73
16–23	15 (13.15)	6 (12.46)	17 (15.05)	18 (14.02)	10 (12.46)	11 (9.86)	77
24–30	9 (12.13)	17 (11.49)	10 (13.88)	14 (12.92)	13 (11.49)	8 (9.09)	71
31–89	21 (23.40)	22 (22.17)	26 (26.78)	26 (24.94)	25 (22.17)	17 (17.55)	137
Total	76	72	87	81	72	57	445

With $\alpha = .05$ and

$$df = (\text{rows} - 1)(\text{cols} - 1) = (4)(5) = 20$$

the appropriate chi-squared critical value is 31.41. The null hypothesis will be rejected if $X^2 > 31.41$. Computing the value of X^2 gives

$$X^2 = \frac{(21 - 14.86)^2}{14.86} + \cdots + \frac{(17 - 17.55)^2}{17.55} = 22.1$$

The null hypothesis cannot be rejected. We cannot conclude that there is an association between tree size and mistletoe rating.

SUPPLEMENTARY EXERCISES 16.35–16.46

16.35 Each driver in a sample of size 1024 was classified according to both seat-belt usage and sex to obtain the accompanying 2 × 2 frequency table ("What Kinds of People Do Not Use Seat Belts" *Amer. J. of Public Health* (1977):1043–1049). Does the data strongly suggest an association between sex and seat-belt usage? Use a .05 significance level.

Sex	Seat-belt usage	
	Don't use	Use
Male	192	272
Female	284	276

16.36 The *Los Angeles Times* (July 29, 1983) conducted a survey to find out why some Californians don't register to vote. Random samples of 100 Latinos, 100 Anglos, and 100 Blacks who were not registered to vote were selected. The resulting data is summarized in the accompanying table. Does the data suggest that the true proportion falling into each response category is not the same for Latinos, Anglos, and Blacks? Use a .05 significance level.

	Race		
Reason for not registering	Latino	Anglo	Black
Not a citizen	45	8	0
Not interested	19	33	19
Can't meet residency requirements	9	35	23
Distrust of politics	5	10	8
Too difficult to register	10	10	27
Other reason	12	4	23

16.37 The relative importance attached to work and home life by high-school students was examined in "Work Role Salience as a Determinant of Career Maturity in High School Students" (*J. Vocational Behavior* (1984):30–44). Does the data summarized in the accompanying two-way frequency table suggest that sex and relative importance assigned to work and home are not independent? Test using a .05 level of significance.

	Relative importance		
Sex	Work > Home	Work = Home	Work < Home
Female	68	26	94
Male	75	19	57

16.38 One important factor that affects the quality of sorghum, a major world cereal crop, is presence of pigmentation. The paper "A Genetic and Biochemical Study on Pericarp Pigments in a Cross between Two Cultivars of Grain Sorghum, Sorghum Bicolor" (*Heredity* (1976):413–416) reported on a genetic experiment in which three different pigmentations—red, yellow, or white—were possible. A particular genetic model predicted that these colors would appear in the ratios 9:3:4, (that is, proportions $9/16$, $3/16$, and $4/16$). The experiments yielded 195 seeds with red pigmentation, 73 with yellow, and 100 with white. Does this data cast doubt on the appropriateness of this genetic theory? Carry out a goodness-of-fit test at significance level .10.

16.39 The Japanese farming community of Achihara was the focus of a study described in the article "Part-Time Farming: A Japanese Example" (*J. of Anthro. Research* (1984):293–305). A random sample of farms for which the head of household was between 45 and 72 years old was selected, and each member of the sample was classified according to size of farm and residence of the farmer's oldest child. Data compatible with that given in the paper is summarized in the given two-way table. Using a .05 significance level, test the null hypothesis of no association between farm size and child's residence.

	Oldest child's residence	
Size (ha)	With parents	Separate residence
0–<.3	28	8
.3–<1.0	10	8
1.0–<9.0	18	20

16.40 The accompanying 2 × 2 frequency table is the result of classifying random samples of 112 librarians and 108 faculty members of the California State University system with respect to sex ("Job Satisfaction among Faculty and Librarians: A Study of Gender, Autonomy, and Decision Making Opportunities" *J. of Library Admin.* (1984): 43–56). Does the data strongly suggest that librarians and faculty members differ with respect to the proportion of males and females? Test using a .05 level of significance.

	Faculty	Librarians
Male	56	59
Female	52	53

16.41 Is there any relationship between the age of an investor and the rate of return that the investor expects from an investment? A sample of 972 common stock investors was selected and each was placed in one of four age categories and in one of four *rate believed attainable* categories ("Patterns of Investment Strategy and Behavior among Individual Investors" *J. of Business* (1977):296–333). The resulting data is given. Does there appear to be an association between age and rate believed attainable? Test the appropriate hypotheses using a .01 significance level.

Investor age	Rate believed attainable			
	0–5%	6–10%	11–15%	Over 15%
Under 45	15	51	51	29
45–54	31	133	70	48
55–64	59	139	35	20
65 or over	84	157	32	18

16.42 The paper "Participation of Senior Citizens in the Swine Flu Inoculation Program" (*J. of Gerontology* (1979):201–208) described a study of the factors thought to influence a person's decision to obtain a flu vaccination. Each member of a sample of 122 senior citizens was classified according to belief about the likelihood of getting the flu and vaccine status to obtain the given two-way frequency table. Using a .05 significance level, test to determine if there is an association between belief and vaccine status.

Belief	Vaccine status	
	Received vaccine	Didn't receive vaccine
Very unlikely	25	24
Unlikely	30	11
Likely	6	8
Don't know	5	13

16.43 The paper "An Instant Shot of 'Ah': Cocaine Use among Methadone Clients" (*J. of Psychoactive Drugs* (1984):217–227) reported the accompanying data on frequency of cocaine use for individuals in three different treatment groups. Does the data suggest that the true proportion of individuals in each of the different cocaine-use categories differs for the three treatments? Carry out an appropriate test at level .05.

Cocaine use	Treatment		
	A	B	C
None	149	75	8
1–2 times	26	27	15
3–6 times	6	20	11
At least 7 times	4	10	10

16.44 The paper "Identification of Cola Beverages" (*J. of Appl. Psych.* (1962):356–360) reported on an experiment in which each of 79 subjects was presented with glasses of cola in pairs and asked to identify which glass contained a specific brand of cola. The accompanying data appeared in the paper. Does this data suggest that individuals' abilities to make correct identification differ for the different brands of cola?

Cola	Number of correct identifications			
	0	1	2	3 or 4
Coca-Cola	13	23	24	19
Pepsi Cola	12	20	26	21
Royal Crown	18	28	19	14

16.45 Many shoppers have expressed unhappiness because grocers do not put prices on individual grocery items. The paper "The Impact of Item Price Removal on Grocery Shopping Behavior" (*J. of Marketing* (1980):73–93) reported on a study in which each shopper in a sample was classified by age and by whether he or she felt the need for item pricing. Based on the accompanying data, does the need for item pricing appear to be independent of age? (Hint: Construct the appropriate two-way frequency table.)

	Age				
	<30	30–39	40–49	50–59	≥60
Number in sample	150	141	82	63	49
Number who want item pricing	127	118	77	61	41

16.46 A variety of different probability distributions have been fit to data sets consisting of scores of games in various sports (this is what statisticians do for recreation). The paper "Collegiate Football Scores and the Negative Binomial Distribution" (*J. Amer. Stat. Assoc.* (1973):351–352) proposed a probability distribution called the *negative binomial distribution* for describing the points scored per game by an individual team. Observed and expected counts taken from the paper are given. The expected counts were computed by first estimating two population characteristics (analogous to estimation of μ and σ for the normal distribution); this reduces the number of df for the goodness-of-fit test by 2. Does this distribution provide a good fit to the data?

Points	Observed	Expected
0–5	272	278.7
6–11	485	490.2
12–17	537	509.1
18–24	407	406.6
25–31	258	275.9
32–38	157	167.3
39–45	101	93.5
46–52	57	49.0
53–59	23	24.4
60–66	8	11.7
Over 66	11	9.7

References

Agresti, Alan, and Barbara Agresti. *Statistical Methods for the Social Sciences* 2nd ed. New York: Dellen-Macmillan, 1986. (This book includes a good discussion of measures of association for two-way frequency tables.)

Everitt, B. S. *The Analysis of Contingency Tables.* New York: Halstead Press, 1977. (A compact but informative survey of methods for analyzing categorical data.)

Mosteller, Frederick, and Robert Rourke. *Sturdy Statistics.* Reading, Mass.: Addison-Wesley, 1973. (Contains several very readable chapters on the varied uses of the chi-squared statistic.)

A P P E N D I X   *Statistical Tables*

TABLE I Binomial probabilities

n = 5

							π						
x	0.05	0.1	0.2	0.25	0.3	0.4	0.5	0.6	0.7	0.75	0.8	0.9	0.95
0	.774	.590	.328	.237	.168	.078	.031	.010	.002	.001	.000	.000	.000
1	.203	.329	.409	.396	.360	.259	.157	.077	.029	.015	.007	.000	.000
2	.022	.072	.205	.263	.309	.346	.312	.230	.132	.088	.051	.009	.001
3	.001	.009	.051	.088	.132	.230	.312	.346	.309	.263	.205	.072	.022
4	.000	.000	.007	.015	.029	.077	.157	.259	.360	.396	.409	.329	.203
5	.000	.000	.000	.001	.002	.010	.031	.078	.168	.237	.328	.590	.774

n = 10

							π						
x	0.05	0.1	0.2	0.25	0.3	0.4	0.5	0.6	0.7	0.75	0.8	0.9	0.95
0	.599	.349	.107	.056	.028	.006	.001	.000	.000	.000	.000	.000	.000
1	.315	.387	.268	.188	.121	.040	.010	.002	.000	.000	.000	.000	.000
2	.075	.194	.302	.282	.233	.121	.044	.011	.001	.000	.000	.000	.000
3	.010	.057	.201	.250	.267	.215	.117	.042	.009	.003	.001	.000	.000
4	.001	.011	.088	.146	.200	.251	.205	.111	.037	.016	.006	.000	.000
5	.000	.001	.026	.058	.103	.201	.246	.201	.103	.058	.026	.001	.000
6	.000	.000	.006	.016	.037	.111	.205	.251	.200	.146	.088	.011	.001
7	.000	.000	.001	.003	.009	.042	.117	.215	.267	.250	.201	.057	.010
8	.000	.000	.000	.000	.001	.011	.044	.121	.233	.282	.302	.194	.075
9	.000	.000	.000	.000	.000	.002	.010	.040	.121	.188	.268	.387	.315
10	.000	.000	.000	.000	.000	.000	.001	.006	.028	.056	.107	.349	.599

TABLE I   (continued)

n = 15

x						π							
	0.05	0.1	0.2	0.25	0.3	0.4	0.5	0.6	0.7	0.75	0.8	0.9	0.95
0	.463	.206	.035	.013	.005	.000	.000	.000	.000	.000	.000	.000	.000
1	.366	.343	.132	.067	.030	.005	.000	.000	.000	.000	.000	.000	.000
2	.135	.267	.231	.156	.092	.022	.004	.000	.000	.000	.000	.000	.000
3	.031	.128	.250	.225	.170	.064	.014	.002	.000	.000	.000	.000	.000
4	.004	.043	.188	.225	.218	.126	.041	.007	.001	.000	.000	.000	.000
5	.001	.011	.103	.166	.207	.196	.092	.025	.003	.001	.000	.000	.000
6	.000	.002	.043	.091	.147	.207	.153	.061	.011	.003	.001	.000	.000
7	.000	.000	.014	.040	.081	.177	.196	.118	.035	.013	.003	.000	.000
8	.000	.000	.003	.013	.035	.118	.196	.177	.081	.040	.014	.000	.000
9	.000	.000	.001	.003	.011	.061	.153	.207	.147	.091	.043	.002	.000
10	.000	.000	.000	.001	.003	.025	.092	.196	.207	.166	.103	.011	.001
11	.000	.000	.000	.000	.001	.007	.041	.126	.218	.225	.188	.043	.004
12	.000	.000	.000	.000	.000	.002	.014	.064	.170	.225	.250	.128	.031
13	.000	.000	.000	.000	.000	.000	.004	.022	.092	.156	.231	.267	.135
14	.000	.000	.000	.000	.000	.000	.000	.005	.030	.067	.132	.343	.366
15	.000	.000	.000	.000	.000	.000	.000	.000	.005	.013	.035	.206	.463

n = 20

x						π							
	0.05	0.1	0.2	0.25	0.3	0.4	0.5	0.6	0.7	0.75	0.8	0.9	0.95
0	.358	.122	.012	.003	.001	.000	.000	.000	.000	.000	.000	.000	.000
1	.377	.270	.058	.021	.007	.000	.000	.000	.000	.000	.000	.000	.000
2	.189	.285	.137	.067	.028	.003	.000	.000	.000	.000	.000	.000	.000
3	.060	.190	.205	.134	.072	.012	.001	.000	.000	.000	.000	.000	.000
4	.013	.090	.218	.190	.130	.035	.005	.000	.000	.000	.000	.000	.000
5	.002	.032	.175	.202	.179	.075	.015	.001	.000	.000	.000	.000	.000
6	.000	.009	.109	.169	.192	.124	.037	.005	.000	.000	.000	.000	.000
7	.000	.002	.055	.112	.164	.166	.074	.015	.001	.000	.000	.000	.000
8	.000	.000	.022	.061	.114	.180	.120	.035	.004	.001	.000	.000	.000
9	.000	.000	.007	.027	.065	.160	.160	.071	.012	.003	.000	.000	.000
10	.000	.000	.002	.010	.031	.117	.176	.117	.031	.010	.002	.000	.000
11	.000	.000	.000	.003	.012	.071	.160	.160	.065	.027	.007	.000	.000
12	.000	.000	.000	.001	.004	.035	.120	.180	.114	.061	.022	.000	.000
13	.000	.000	.000	.000	.001	.015	.074	.166	.164	.112	.055	.002	.000
14	.000	.000	.000	.000	.000	.005	.037	.124	.192	.169	.109	.009	.000
15	.000	.000	.000	.000	.000	.001	.015	.075	.179	.202	.175	.032	.002
16	.000	.000	.000	.000	.000	.000	.005	.035	.130	.190	.218	.090	.013
17	.000	.000	.000	.000	.000	.000	.001	.012	.072	.134	.205	.190	.060
18	.000	.000	.000	.000	.000	.000	.000	.003	.028	.067	.137	.285	.189
19	.000	.000	.000	.000	.000	.000	.000	.000	.007	.021	.058	.270	.377
20	.000	.000	.000	.000	.000	.000	.000	.000	.001	.003	.012	.122	.358

TABLE I   *(continued)*

$n = 25$

							π						
x	0.05	0.1	0.2	0.25	0.3	0.4	0.5	0.6	0.7	0.75	0.8	0.9	0.95
0	.277	.072	.004	.001	.000	.000	.000	.000	.000	.000	.000	.000	.000
1	.365	.199	.023	.006	.002	.000	.000	.000	.000	.000	.000	.000	.000
2	.231	.266	.071	.025	.007	.000	.000	.000	.000	.000	.000	.000	.000
3	.093	.227	.136	.064	.024	.002	.000	.000	.000	.000	.000	.000	.000
4	.027	.138	.187	.118	.057	.007	.000	.000	.000	.000	.000	.000	.000
5	.006	.065	.196	.164	.103	.020	.002	.000	.000	.000	.000	.000	.000
6	.001	.024	.163	.183	.148	.045	.005	.000	.000	.000	.000	.000	.000
7	.000	.007	.111	.166	.171	.080	.015	.001	.000	.000	.000	.000	.000
8	.000	.002	.062	.124	.165	.120	.032	.003	.000	.000	.000	.000	.000
9	.000	.000	.030	.078	.134	.151	.061	.009	.000	.000	.000	.000	.000
10	.000	.000	.011	.042	.091	.161	.097	.021	.002	.000	.000	.000	.000
11	.000	.000	.004	.019	.054	.146	.133	.044	.004	.001	.000	.000	.000
12	.000	.000	.002	.007	.027	.114	.155	.076	.011	.002	.000	.000	.000
13	.000	.000	.000	.002	.011	.076	.155	.114	.027	.007	.002	.000	.000
14	.000	.000	.000	.001	.004	.044	.133	.146	.054	.019	.004	.000	.000
15	.000	.000	.000	.000	.002	.021	.097	.161	.091	.042	.011	.000	.000
16	.000	.000	.000	.000	.000	.009	.061	.151	.134	.078	.030	.000	.000
17	.000	.000	.000	.000	.000	.003	.032	.120	.165	.124	.062	.002	.000
18	.000	.000	.000	.000	.000	.001	.015	.080	.171	.166	.111	.007	.000
19	.000	.000	.000	.000	.000	.000	.005	.045	.148	.183	.163	.024	.001
20	.000	.000	.000	.000	.000	.000	.002	.020	.103	.164	.196	.065	.006
21	.000	.000	.000	.000	.000	.000	.000	.007	.057	.118	.187	.138	.027
22	.000	.000	.000	.000	.000	.000	.000	.002	.024	.064	.136	.227	.093
22	.000	.000	.000	.000	.000	.000	.000	.000	.007	.025	.071	.266	.231
24	.000	.000	.000	.000	.000	.000	.000	.000	.002	.006	.023	.199	.365
25	.000	.000	.000	.000	.000	.000	.000	.000	.000	.001	.004	.072	.277

TABLE II   Standard normal (z) curve areas

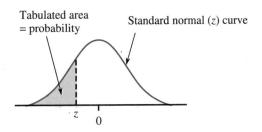

Tabulated area = probability

Standard normal (z) curve

z 0

z	.00	.01	.02	.03	.04	.05	.06	.07	.08	.09
−3.4	.0003	.0003	.0003	.0003	.0003	.0003	.0003	.0003	.0003	.0002
−3.3	.0005	.0005	.0005	.0004	.0004	.0004	.0004	.0004	.0004	.0003
−3.2	.0007	.0007	.0006	.0006	.0006	.0006	.0006	.0005	.0005	.0005
−3.1	.0010	.0009	.0009	.0009	.0008	.0008	.0008	.0008	.0007	.0007
−3.0	.0013	.0013	.0013	.0012	.0012	.0011	.0011	.0011	.0010	.0010
−2.9	.0019	.0018	.0018	.0017	.0016	.0016	.0015	.0015	.0014	.0014
−2.8	.0026	.0025	.0024	.0023	.0023	.0022	.0021	.0021	.0020	.0019
−2.7	.0035	.0034	.0033	.0032	.0031	.0030	.0029	.0028	.0027	.0026
−2.6	.0047	.0045	.0044	.0043	.0041	.0040	.0039	.0038	.0037	.0036
−2.5	.0062	.0060	.0059	.0057	.0055	.0054	.0052	.0051	.0049	.0048
−2.4	.0082	.0080	.0078	.0075	.0073	.0071	.0069	.0068	.0066	.0064
−2.3	.0107	.0104	.0102	.0099	.0096	.0094	.0091	.0089	.0087	.0084
−2.2	.0139	.0136	.0132	.0129	.0125	.0122	.0119	.0116	.0113	.0110
−2.1	.0179	.0174	.0170	.0166	.0162	.0158	.0154	.0150	.0146	.0143
−2.0	.0228	.0222	.0217	.0212	.0207	.0202	.0197	.0192	.0188	.0183
−1.9	.0287	.0281	.0274	.0268	.0262	.0256	.0250	.0244	.0239	.0233
−1.8	.0359	.0351	.0344	.0336	.0329	.0322	.0314	.0307	.0301	.0294
−1.7	.0446	.0436	.0427	.0418	.0409	.0401	.0392	.0384	.0375	.0367
−1.6	.0548	.0537	.0526	.0516	.0505	.0495	.0485	.0475	.0465	.0455
−1.5	.0668	.0655	.0643	.0630	.0618	.0606	.0594	.0582	.0571	.0559
−1.4	.0808	.0793	.0778	.0764	.0749	.0735	.0721	.0708	.0694	.0681
−1.3	.0968	.0951	.0934	.0918	.0901	.0885	.0869	.0853	.0838	.0823
−1.2	.1151	.1131	.1112	.1093	.1075	.1056	.1038	.1020	.1003	.0985
−1.1	.1357	.1335	.1314	.1292	.1271	.1251	.1230	.1210	.1190	.1170
−1.0	.1587	.1562	.1539	.1515	.1492	.1469	.1446	.1423	.1401	.1379
−0.9	.1841	.1814	.1788	.1762	.1736	.1711	.1685	.1660	.1635	.1611
−0.8	.2119	.2090	.2061	.2033	.2005	.1977	.1949	.1922	.1894	.1867
−0.7	.2420	.2389	.2358	.2327	.2296	.2266	.2236	.2206	.2177	.2148
−0.6	.2743	.2709	.2676	.2643	.2611	.2578	.2546	.2514	.2483	.2451
−0.5	.3085	.3050	.3015	.2981	.2946	.2912	.2877	.2843	.2810	.2776
−0.4	.3446	.3409	.3372	.3336	.3300	.3264	.3228	.3192	.3156	.3121
−0.3	.3821	.3783	.3745	.3707	.3669	.3632	.3594	.3557	.3520	.3483
−0.2	.4207	.4168	.4129	.4090	.4052	.4013	.3974	.3936	.3897	.3859
−0.1	.4602	.4562	.4522	.4483	.4443	.4404	.4364	.4325	.4286	.4247
−0.0	.5000	.4960	.4920	.4880	.4840	.4801	.4761	.4721	.4681	.4641

TABLE II   *(continued)*

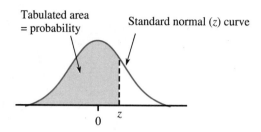

Tabulated area = probability

Standard normal (z) curve

z	.00	.01	.02	.03	.04	.05	.06	.07	.08	.09
0.0	.5000	.5040	.5080	.5120	.5160	.5199	.5239	.5279	.5319	.5359
0.1	.5398	.5438	.5478	.5517	.5557	.5596	.5636	.5675	.5714	.5753
0.2	.5793	.5832	.5871	.5910	.5948	.5987	.6026	.6064	.6103	.6141
0.3	.6179	.6217	.6255	.6293	.6331	.6368	.6406	.6443	.6480	.6517
0.4	.6554	.6591	.6628	.6664	.6700	.6736	.6772	.6808	.6844	.6879
0.5	.6915	.6950	.6985	.7019	.7054	.7088	.7123	.7157	.7190	.7224
0.6	.7257	.7291	.7324	.7357	.7389	.7422	.7454	.7486	.7517	.7549
0.7	.7580	.7611	.7642	.7673	.7704	.7734	.7764	.7794	.7823	.7852
0.8	.7881	.7910	.7939	.7967	.7995	.8023	.8051	.8078	.8106	.8133
0.9	.8159	.8186	.8212	.8238	.8264	.8289	.8315	.8340	.8365	.8389
1.0	.8413	.8438	.8461	.8485	.8508	.8531	.8554	.8577	.8599	.8621
1.1	.8643	.8665	.8686	.8708	.8729	.8749	.8770	.8790	.8810	.8830
1.2	.8849	.8869	.8888	.8907	.8925	.8944	.8962	.8980	.8997	.9015
1.3	.9032	.9049	.9066	.9082	.9099	.9115	.9131	.9147	.9162	.9177
1.4	.9192	.9207	.9222	.9236	.9251	.9265	.9279	.9292	.9306	.9319
1.5	.9332	.9345	.9357	.9370	.9382	.9394	.9406	.9418	.9429	.9441
1.6	.9452	.9463	.9474	.9484	.9495	.9505	.9515	.9525	.9535	.9545
1.7	.9554	.9564	.9573	.9582	.9591	.9599	.9608	.9616	.9625	.9633
1.8	.9641	.9649	.9656	.9664	.9671	.9678	.9686	.9693	.9699	.9706
1.9	.9713	.9719	.9726	.9732	.9738	.9744	.9750	.9756	.9761	.9767
2.0	.9772	.9778	.9783	.9788	.9793	.9798	.9803	.9808	.9812	.9817
2.1	.9821	.9826	.9830	.9834	.9838	.9842	.9846	.9850	.9854	.9857
2.2	.9861	.9864	.9868	.9871	.9875	.9878	.9881	.9884	.9887	.9890
2.3	.9893	.9896	.9898	.9901	.9904	.9906	.9909	.9911	.9913	.9916
2.4	.9918	.9920	.9922	.9925	.9927	.9929	.9931	.9932	.9934	.9936
2.5	.9938	.9940	.9941	.9943	.9945	.9946	.9948	.9949	.9951	.9952
2.6	.9953	.9955	.9956	.9957	.9959	.9960	.9961	.9962	.9963	.9964
2.7	.9965	.9966	.9967	.9968	.9969	.9970	.9971	.9972	.9973	.9974
2.8	.9974	.9975	.9976	.9977	.9977	.9978	.9979	.9979	.9980	.9981
2.9	.9981	.9982	.9982	.9983	.9984	.9984	.9985	.9985	.9986	.9986
3.0	.9987	.9987	.9987	.9988	.9988	.9989	.9989	.9989	.9990	.9990
3.1	.9990	.9991	.9991	.9991	.9992	.9992	.9992	.9992	.9993	.9993
3.2	.9993	.9993	.9994	.9994	.9994	.9994	.9994	.9995	.9995	.9995
3.3	.9995	.9995	.9995	.9996	.9996	.9996	.9996	.9996	.9996	.9997
3.4	.9997	.9997	.9997	.9997	.9997	.9997	.9997	.9997	.9997	.9998

TABLE III   Normal scores ($\mu = 0$, $\sigma = 1$)

Ordered position	n			
	10	20	25	30
1	− 1.539	− 1.867	− 1.965	− 2.043
2	− 1.001	− 1.408	− 1.524	− 1.616
3	− .656	− 1.131	− 1.263	− 1.365
4	− .376	− .921	− 1.067	− 1.179
5	− .123	− .745	− .905	− 1.026
6	.123	− .590	− .764	− .894
7	.376	− .448	− .637	− .777
8	.656	− .315	− .519	− .669
9	1.001	− .187	− .409	− .568
10	1.539	− .062	− .303	− .473
11		.062	− .200	− .382
12		.187	− .100	− .294
13		.315	.000	− .209
14		.448	.100	− .125
15		.590	.200	− .041
16		.745	.303	.041
17		.921	.409	.125
18		1.131	.519	.209
19		1.408	.637	.294
20		1.867	.764	.382
21			.905	.473
22			1.067	.568
23			1.263	.669
24			1.524	.777
25			1.965	.894
26				1.026
27				1.179
28				1.365
29				1.616
30				2.043

TABLE IV   *t* critical values

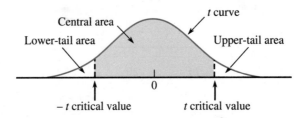

Central area
Lower-tail area
t curve
Upper-tail area

0

− *t* critical value   *t* critical value

Central area captured Confidence level		.80 80%	.90 90%	.95 95%	.98 98%	.99 99%	.998 99.8%	.999 99.9%
	1	3.08	6.31	12.71	31.82	63.66	318.31	636.62
	2	1.89	2.92	4.30	6.97	9.93	23.33	31.60
	3	1.64	2.35	3.18	4.54	5.84	10.21	12.92
	4	1.53	2.13	2.78	3.75	4.60	7.17	8.61
	5	1.48	2.02	2.57	3.37	4.03	5.89	6.86
	6	1.44	1.94	2.45	3.14	3.71	5.21	5.96
	7	1.42	1.90	2.37	3.00	3.50	4.79	5.41
	8	1.40	1.86	2.31	2.90	3.36	4.50	5.04
	9	1.38	1.83	2.26	2.82	3.25	4.30	4.78
	10	1.37	1.81	2.23	2.76	3.17	4.14	4.59
	11	1.36	1.80	2.20	2.72	3.11	4.03	4.44
	12	1.36	1.78	2.18	2.68	3.06	3.93	4.32
	13	1.35	1.77	2.16	2.65	3.01	3.85	4.22
	14	1.35	1.76	2.15	2.62	2.98	3.79	4.14
	15	1.34	1.75	2.13	2.60	2.95	3.73	4.07
	16	1.34	1.75	2.12	2.58	2.92	3.69	4.02
Degrees of freedom	17	1.33	1.74	2.11	2.57	2.90	3.65	3.97
	18	1.33	1.73	2.10	2.55	2.88	3.61	3.92
	19	1.33	1.73	2.09	2.54	2.86	3.58	3.88
	20	1.33	1.73	2.09	2.53	2.85	3.55	3.85
	21	1.32	1.72	2.08	2.52	2.83	3.53	3.82
	22	1.32	1.72	2.07	2.51	2.82	3.51	3.79
	23	1.32	1.71	2.07	2.50	2.81	3.49	3.77
	24	1.32	1.71	2.06	2.49	2.80	3.47	3.75
	25	1.32	1.71	2.06	2.49	2.79	3.45	3.73
	26	1.32	1.71	2.06	2.48	2.78	3.44	3.71
	27	1.31	1.70	2.05	2.47	2.77	3.42	3.69
	28	1.31	1.70	2.05	2.47	2.76	3.41	3.67
	29	1.31	1.70	2.05	2.46	2.76	3.40	3.66
	30	1.31	1.70	2.04	2.46	2.75	3.39	3.65
	40	1.30	1.68	2.02	2.42	2.70	3.31	3.55
	60	1.30	1.67	2.00	2.39	2.66	3.23	3.46
	120	1.29	1.66	1.98	2.36	2.62	3.16	3.37
z critical values		1.28	1.645	1.96	2.33	2.58	3.09	3.29
Level of significance for a *two*-tailed test		.20	.10	.05	.02	.01	.002	.001
Level of significance for a *one*-tailed test		.10	.05	.025	.01	.005	.001	.0005

TABLE V   Curves of $\beta = P$ (type II error) for t tests

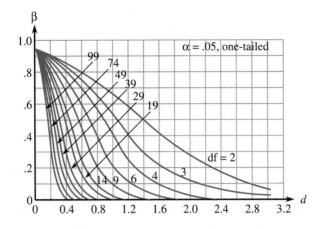

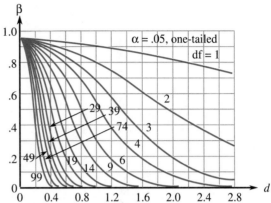

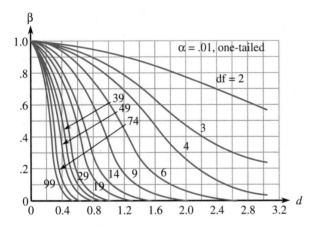

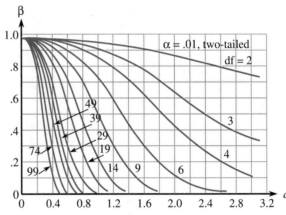

TABLE VI   Critical values for the rank sum test[1]

		Upper-tailed test		Lower-tailed test		Two-tailed test	
n_1	n_2	$\alpha = .05$	$\alpha = .01$	$\alpha = .05$	$\alpha = .01$	$\alpha = .05$	$\alpha = .01$
3	3	15	—	6	—	—	—
3	4	17	—	7	—	18,6	—
3	5	20	21	7	6	21,6	—
3	6	22	24	8	6	23,7	—
3	7	24	27	9	6	26,7	27,6
3	8	27	29	9	7	28,8	30,6
4	3	21	—	11	—	—	—
4	4	24	26	12	10	25,11	—
4	5	27	30	13	10	29,11	30,10
4	6	30	33	14	11	32,12	34,10
4	7	33	36	15	12	35,13	37,11
4	8	36	40	16	12	38,14	41,11
5	3	29	30	16	15	30,15	—
5	4	32	35	18	15	34,16	35,15
5	5	36	39	19	16	37,18	39,16
5	6	40	43	20	17	41,19	44,16
5	7	43	47	22	18	45,20	48,17
5	8	47	51	23	19	49,21	52,18
6	3	37	39	23	21	38,22	—
6	4	41	44	25	22	43,23	45,21
6	5	46	49	26	23	47,25	50,22
6	6	50	54	28	24	52,26	55,23
6	7	54	58	30	26	56,28	60,24
6	8	58	63	32	27	61,29	65,25
7	3	46	49	31	28	48,29	49,28
7	4	51	54	33	30	53,31	55,29
7	5	56	60	35	31	58,33	61,30
7	6	61	65	37	33	63,35	67,31
7	7	66	71	39	34	68,37	72,33
7	8	71	76	41	36	73,39	78,34
8	3	57	59	39	37	58,38	60,36
8	4	62	66	42	38	64,40	67,37
8	5	68	72	44	40	70,42	73,39
8	6	73	78	47	42	76,44	80,40
8	7	79	84	49	44	81,47	86,42
8	8	84	90	52	46	87,49	92,44

[1]As explained in Chapter 11, the significance levels .05 and .01 cannot be achieved exactly for most sample sizes. For example, in the case $n_1 = 3$, $n_2 = 6$, the actual significance level for the test that rejects H_0 if *rank* sum ≥ 24 is .012, as close to .01 as can be achieved. Whenever a critical value is missing (for example, $n_1 = 3$, $n_2 = 4$, $\alpha = .01$), it is not possible to get close to the desired α.

TABLE VII   Values of *d* for the rank sum confidence interval
(*d*th smallest difference, *d*th largest difference)

Sample sizes[1]	*d* for 90% confidence	*d* for 95% confidence	*d* for 99% confidence
5, 5	5	4	1
5, 6	6	5	2
5, 7	8	6	3
5, 8	9	7	4
5, 9	11	8	5
5, 10	12	10	5
5, 11	13	11	6
5, 12	15	12	7
6, 6	8	6	3
6, 7	10	8	4
6, 8	12	9	5
6, 9	13	11	6
6, 10	15	13	8
6, 11	17	14	9
6, 12	19	16	10
7, 7	12	10	6
7, 8	14	12	7
7, 9	16	14	8
7, 10	19	16	10
7, 11	21	17	12
7, 12	23	19	13
8, 8	17	14	9
8, 9	19	16	11
8, 10	22	19	12
8, 11	24	21	14
8, 12	27	23	16
9, 9	22	19	13
9, 10	25	22	15
9, 11	28	24	17
9, 12	31	27	19
10, 10	29	25	17
10, 11	32	28	20
10, 12	35	31	22
11, 11	36	31	23
11, 12	40	35	25
12, 12	44	39	29

[1]When $n_1 \neq n_2$, the smaller sample size is listed first.

TABLE VIII Critical values for the signed-rank test

n	Significance level for one-tailed test	Significance level for two-tailed test	Critical value
5	.031	.062	15
	.062	.124	13
	.094	.188	11
6	.016	.032	21
	.031	.062	19
	.047	.094	17
	.109	.218	13
7	.008	.016	28
	.023	.046	24
	.055	.110	20
	.109	.218	16
8	.012	.024	32
	.027	.054	28
	.055	.110	24
	.098	.196	20
9	.010	.020	39
	.027	.054	33
	.049	.098	29
	.102	.204	23
10	.010	.020	45
	.024	.048	39
	.053	.106	33
	.097	.194	27
11	.009	.018	52
	.027	.054	44
	.051	.102	38
	.103	.206	30
12	.010	.020	58
	.026	.052	50
	.046	.092	44
	.102	.204	34
13	.011	.022	65
	.024	.048	57
	.047	.094	49
	.095	.190	39
14	.010	.020	73
	.025	.050	63
	.052	.104	53
	.097	.194	43

(continued)

TABLE VIII   *(continued)*

n	Significance level for one-tailed test	Significance level for two-tailed test	Critical value
15	.011	.022	80
	.024	.048	70
	.047	.094	60
	.104	.208	46
16	.011	.022	88
	.025	.054	76
	.052	.104	64
	.096	.192	52
17	.010	.020	97
	.025	.050	83
	.049	.098	71
	.103	.206	55
18	.010	.020	105
	.025	.048	91
	.049	.098	77
	.098	.196	61
19	.010	.020	114
	.025	.050	98
	.052	.104	82
	.098	.196	66
20	.010	.020	124
	.024	.048	106
	.049	.098	90
	.101	.202	70

TABLE IX   Values of *d* for the signed-rank confidence interval

n	Confidence level	d	n	Confidence level	d
5	93.8	1	14	99.1	13
	87.5	2		95.1	22
				89.6	27
6	96.9	1			
	90.6	3	15	99.0	17
				95.2	26
7	98.4	1		90.5	31
	96.9	2			
	89.1	5	16	99.1	20
				94.9	31
8	99.2	1		89.5	37
	94.5	5			
	89.1	7	17	99.1	25
				94.9	36
9	99.2	2		90.2	42
	94.5	7			
	90.2	9	18	99.0	29
				95.2	41
10	99.0	4		90.1	48
	95.1	9			
	89.5	12	19	99.1	33
				95.1	47
11	99.0	6		90.4	54
	94.6	12			
	89.8	15	20	99.1	38
				95.2	53
12	99.1	8		90.3	61
	94.8	15			
	90.8	18			
13	99.0	11			
	95.2	18			
	90.6	22			

TABLE X (a)   *F* distribution critical values for tests with significance level .05

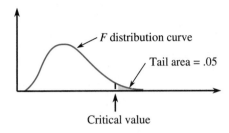

		Numerator degrees of freedom								
	1	**2**	**3**	**4**	**5**	**6**	**7**	**8**	**9**	**10**
1	161.4	199.5	215.7	224.6	230.2	234.0	236.8	238.9	240.5	241.9
2	18.51	19.00	19.16	19.25	19.30	19.33	19.35	19.37	19.38	19.40
3	10.13	9.55	9.28	9.12	9.01	8.94	8.89	8.85	8.81	8.79
4	7.71	6.94	6.59	6.39	6.26	6.16	6.09	6.04	6.00	5.96
5	6.61	5.79	5.41	5.19	5.05	4.95	4.88	4.82	4.77	4.74
6	5.99	5.14	4.76	4.53	4.39	4.28	4.21	4.15	4.10	4.06
7	5.59	4.74	4.35	4.12	3.97	3.87	3.79	3.73	3.68	3.64
8	5.32	4.46	4.07	3.84	3.69	3.58	3.50	3.44	3.39	3.35
9	5.12	4.26	3.86	3.63	3.48	3.37	3.29	3.23	3.18	3.14
10	4.96	4.10	3.71	3.48	3.33	3.22	3.14	3.07	3.02	2.98
11	4.84	3.98	3.59	3.36	3.20	3.09	3.01	2.95	2.90	2.85
12	4.75	3.89	3.49	3.26	3.11	3.00	2.91	2.85	2.80	2.75
13	4.67	3.81	3.41	3.18	3.03	2.92	2.83	2.77	2.71	2.67
14	4.60	3.74	3.34	3.11	2.96	2.85	2.76	2.70	2.65	2.60
15	4.54	3.68	3.29	3.06	2.90	2.79	2.71	2.64	2.59	2.54
16	4.49	3.63	3.24	3.01	2.85	2.74	2.66	2.59	2.54	2.49
17	4.45	3.59	3.20	2.96	2.81	2.70	2.61	2.55	2.49	2.45
18	4.41	3.55	3.16	2.93	2.77	2.66	2.58	2.51	2.46	2.41
19	4.38	3.52	3.13	2.90	2.74	2.63	2.54	2.48	2.42	2.38
20	4.35	3.49	3.10	2.87	2.71	2.60	2.51	2.45	2.39	2.35
21	4.32	3.47	3.07	2.84	2.68	2.57	2.49	2.42	2.37	2.32
22	4.30	3.44	3.05	2.82	2.66	2.55	2.46	2.40	2.34	2.30
23	4.28	3.42	3.03	2.80	2.64	2.53	2.44	2.37	2.32	2.27
24	4.26	3.40	3.01	2.78	2.62	2.51	2.42	2.36	2.30	2.25
25	4.24	3.39	2.99	2.76	2.60	2.49	2.40	2.34	2.28	2.24
26	4.23	3.37	2.98	2.74	2.59	2.47	2.39	2.32	2.27	2.22
27	4.21	3.35	2.96	2.73	2.57	2.46	2.37	2.31	2.25	2.20
28	4.20	3.34	2.95	2.71	2.56	2.45	2.36	2.29	2.24	2.19
29	4.18	3.33	2.93	2.70	2.55	2.43	2.35	2.28	2.22	2.18
30	4.17	3.32	2.92	2.69	2.53	2.42	2.33	2.27	2.21	2.16
40	4.08	3.23	2.84	2.61	2.45	2.34	2.25	2.18	2.12	2.08
60	4.00	3.15	2.76	2.53	2.37	2.25	2.17	2.10	2.04	1.99
120	3.92	3.07	2.68	2.45	2.29	2.17	2.09	2.02	1.96	1.91
∞	3.84	3.00	2.60	2.37	2.21	2.10	2.01	1.94	1.88	1.83

Denominator degrees of freedom

TABLE X (b)   *F* distribution critical values for tests with significance level .01

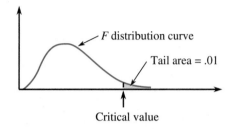

	Numerator degrees of freedom									
	1	2	3	4	5	6	7	8	9	10
1	4,052	4,999.5	5,403	5,625	5,764	5,859	5,928	5,982	6,022	6,056
2	98.50	99.00	99.17	99.25	99.30	99.33	99.36	99.37	99.39	99.40
3	34.12	30.82	29.46	28.71	28.24	27.91	27.67	27.49	27.35	27.23
4	21.20	18.00	16.69	15.98	15.52	15.21	14.98	14.80	14.66	14.55
5	16.26	13.27	12.06	11.39	10.97	10.67	10.46	10.29	10.16	10.05
6	13.75	10.92	9.78	9.15	8.75	8.47	8.26	8.10	7.98	7.87
7	12.25	9.55	8.45	7.85	7.46	7.19	6.99	6.84	6.72	6.62
8	11.26	8.65	7.59	7.01	6.63	6.37	6.18	6.03	5.91	5.81
9	10.56	8.02	6.99	6.42	6.06	5.80	5.61	5.47	5.35	5.26
10	10.04	7.56	6.55	5.99	5.64	5.39	5.20	5.06	4.94	4.85
11	9.65	7.21	6.22	5.67	5.32	5.07	4.89	4.74	4.63	4.54
12	9.33	6.93	5.95	5.41	5.06	4.82	4.64	4.50	4.39	4.30
13	9.07	6.70	5.74	5.21	4.86	4.62	4.44	4.30	4.19	4.10
14	8.86	6.51	5.56	5.04	4.69	4.46	4.28	4.14	4.03	3.94
15	8.68	6.36	5.42	4.89	4.56	4.32	4.14	4.00	3.89	3.80
16	8.53	6.23	5.29	4.77	4.44	4.20	4.03	3.89	3.78	3.69
17	8.40	6.11	5.18	4.67	4.34	4.10	3.93	3.79	3.68	3.59
18	8.29	6.01	5.09	4.58	4.25	4.01	3.84	3.71	3.60	3.51
19	8.18	5.93	5.01	4.50	4.17	3.94	3.77	3.63	3.52	3.43
20	8.10	5.85	4.94	4.43	4.10	3.87	3.70	3.56	3.46	3.37
21	8.02	5.78	4.87	4.37	4.04	3.81	3.64	3.51	3.40	3.31
22	7.95	5.72	4.82	4.31	3.99	3.76	3.59	3.45	3.35	3.26
23	7.88	5.66	4.76	4.26	3.94	3.71	3.54	3.41	3.30	3.21
24	7.82	5.61	4.72	4.22	3.90	3.67	3.50	3.36	3.26	3.17
25	7.77	5.57	4.68	4.18	3.85	3.63	3.46	3.32	3.22	3.13
26	7.72	5.53	4.64	4.14	3.82	3.59	3.42	3.29	3.18	3.09
27	7.68	5.49	4.60	4.11	3.78	3.56	3.39	3.26	3.15	3.06
28	7.64	5.45	4.57	4.07	3.75	3.53	3.36	3.23	3.12	3.03
29	7.60	5.42	4.54	4.04	3.73	3.50	3.33	3.20	3.09	3.00
30	7.56	5.39	4.51	4.02	3.70	3.47	3.30	3.17	3.07	2.98
40	7.31	5.18	4.31	3.83	3.51	3.29	3.12	2.99	2.89	2.80
60	7.08	4.98	4.13	3.65	3.34	3.12	2.95	2.82	2.72	2.63
120	6.85	4.79	3.95	3.48	3.17	2.96	2.79	2.66	2.56	2.47
∞	6.63	4.61	3.78	3.32	3.02	2.80	2.64	2.51	2.41	2.32

Denominator degrees of freedom

TABLE XI   Bonferroni 95% *t* critical values

Number of df	Number of intervals						
	2	3	4	5	6	10	15
2	6.21	7.65	8.86	9.92	10.89	14.09	17.28
3	4.18	4.86	5.39	5.84	6.23	7.45	8.58
4	3.50	3.96	4.31	4.60	4.85	5.60	6.25
5	3.16	3.53	3.81	4.03	4.22	4.77	5.25
6	2.97	3.29	3.52	3.71	3.86	4.32	4.70
7	2.84	3.13	3.34	3.50	3.64	4.03	4.36
8	2.75	3.02	3.21	3.36	3.48	3.83	4.12
9	2.69	2.93	3.11	3.25	3.36	3.69	3.95
10	2.63	2.87	3.04	3.17	3.28	3.58	3.83
11	2.59	2.82	2.98	3.11	3.21	3.50	3.73
12	2.56	2.78	2.93	3.05	3.15	3.43	3.65
13	2.53	2.75	2.90	3.01	3.11	3.37	3.58
14	2.51	2.72	2.86	2.98	3.07	3.33	3.53
15	2.49	2.69	2.84	2.95	3.04	3.29	3.48
16	2.47	2.67	2.81	2.92	3.01	3.25	3.44
17	2.46	2.66	2.79	2.90	2.98	3.22	3.41
18	2.45	2.64	2.77	2.88	2.96	3.20	3.38
19	2.43	2.63	2.76	2.86	2.94	3.17	3.35
20	2.42	2.61	2.74	2.85	2.93	3.15	3.33
21	2.41	2.60	2.73	2.83	2.91	3.14	3.31
22	2.41	2.59	2.72	2.82	2.90	3.12	3.29
23	2.40	2.58	2.71	2.81	2.89	3.10	3.27
24	2.39	2.57	2.70	2.80	2.88	3.09	3.26
25	2.38	2.57	2.69	2.79	2.86	3.08	3.24
26	2.38	2.56	2.68	2.78	2.86	3.07	3.23
27	2.37	2.55	2.68	2.77	2.85	3.06	3.22
28	2.37	2.55	2.67	2.76	2.84	3.05	3.21
29	2.36	2.54	2.66	2.76	2.83	3.04	3.20
30	2.36	2.54	2.66	2.75	2.82	3.03	3.19
40	2.33	2.50	2.62	2.70	2.78	2.97	3.12
60	2.30	2.46	2.58	2.66	2.73	2.91	3.06
120	2.27	2.43	2.54	2.62	2.68	2.86	3.00
∞	2.24	2.39	2.50	2.58	2.64	2.81	2.94

TABLE XII   Chi-squared distribution critical values

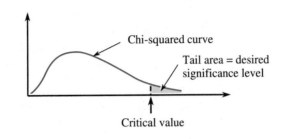

		Significance level			
		.10	.05	.01	.001
	1	2.71	3.84	6.64	10.83
	2	4.61	5.99	9.21	13.82
	3	6.25	7.82	11.34	16.27
	4	7.78	9.49	13.28	18.47
	5	9.24	11.07	15.09	20.52
	6	10.64	12.59	16.81	22.46
	7	12.02	14.07	18.48	24.32
	8	13.36	15.51	20.09	26.12
Degrees of	9	14.68	16.92	21.67	27.88
freedom	10	15.99	18.31	23.21	29.59
	11	17.28	19.68	24.72	31.26
	12	18.55	21.03	26.22	32.91
	13	19.81	22.36	27.69	34.53
	14	21.06	23.68	29.14	36.12
	15	22.31	25.00	30.58	37.70
	16	23.54	26.30	32.00	39.25
	17	24.77	27.59	33.41	40.79
	18	25.99	28.87	34.81	42.31
	19	27.20	30.14	36.19	43.82
	20	28.41	31.41	37.57	45.31

TABLE XIII   Random numbers

74970	06996	11136	26428	23607	97462
74077	63454	45058	20708	42772	61311
13557	72942	59693	42635	69187	17870
66824	77092	51315	11910	91362	85877
36135	62333	37762	06766	52006	48746
06176	37697	40726	66014	78540	03503
17371	29089	26149	86755	36502	45455
21223	60124	07325	61085	61663	93814
31842	75317	58670	07821	75722	75152
20516	27594	21126	21262	14847	85513
99277	64548	70107	01059	34794	89863
01991	83000	27894	43577	82087	71504
54377	90482	39785	75722	20978	72511
20121	24555	25752	35312	85403	46189
11571	25668	34005	60874	72564	27470
93725	16472	21779	22432	71132	58118
65299	19900	21083	77915	20234	57314
36671	66533	86361	01327	80226	67405
49870	72912	20126	71728	86130	22113
50647	27134	56117	08650	91732	56189
17834	90311	00470	25024	20604	55526
27421	59467	69163	36665	26139	59445
26586	93561	52994	91112	74191	53986
51769	19891	46105	60143	63230	43817
41635	22882	85301	06875	58116	90778
04382	75863	37867	86246	58449	47432
48736	95362	21908	86094	43262	82826
49226	85080	33783	98388	62526	04014
20854	80874	15061	24566	72654	83590
50093	79411	58243	12538	16000	81354
32746	91894	87531	03933	08670	35011
45655	67247	49062	80256	21828	70217
96268	69668	23518	85192	81640	19832
43792	70776	17047	10233	44527	40725
66726	38354	88229	52784	48167	43464
00305	60732	03985	83552	83744	33572
47203	23522	41528	72453	88184	97289
94417	00980	76255	09103	55746	57149
28492	27329	28987	08292	22457	27594
15068	78906	13085	52751	42272	10144
86628	62686	03694	38080	35208	10638
70099	52095	34944	74139	92323	24202
59642	03751	88891	73720	90197	48857
21373	68891	89516	31394	29618	13531
62249	55787	68112	51338	09111	84084
15068	28465	20985	64222	79260	22767
35078	08613	30709	07408	99171	30553
19643	91937	12828	53404	07541	10589
75025	72481	37200	27222	92688	11164
71553	58597	83573	12991	32797	24758

Answers to Selected Odd-Numbered Exercises

CHAPTER 1

1.1 Descriptive statistics is made up of those methods whose purpose is to organize and summarize a data set. Inferential statistics refers to those procedures whose purpose is to generalize to or make an inference about the population based on the information in the sample. **1.3** The population of interest is the entire student body (the 15,000 students). The sample consists of the 200 students interviewed. **1.5** The population consists of all single-family homes in Pasadena. The sample consists of the 100 homes selected for inspection. **1.7** The population consists of all 5000 bricks in the lot. The sample consists of the 100 bricks selected for inspection.

CHAPTER 2

2.1 a. numerical (discrete) **b.** categorical **c.** numerical (continuous) **d.** numerical (continuous) **e.** categorical **2.3 a.** discrete **b.** continuous **c.** discrete **d.** discrete **e.** continuous **f.** continuous **g.** continuous **h.** ~~discrete~~ continuous

2.5

4	48, 01, 50, 19, 58, 17, 05, 40, 02, 07, 33, 92, 00, 84, 24, 17, 68
5	12, 01, 69, 09, 99, 59, 54, 53, 65, 24
6	44, 47, 24, 03, 34
7	30, 92, 55, 91, 77, 23
8	85, 56

stems: hundreds
leaves: ones

2.7

64	64, 70, 35, 33
65	26, 83, 06, 27
66	14, 05, 94
67	70, 70, 90, 00, 98, 45, 13
68	50, 73, 70, 90
69	36, 27, 00, 04
70	05, 40, 22, 11, 51, 50
71	31, 69, 68, 05, 65, 13
72	09, 80

stems: hundreds
leaves: ones

2.9

	4l	35
50	4h	50, 50, 60, 70, 75, 95
30	5l	00, 00, 20, 40
60, 95	5h	50
00, 27, 37, 45, 49	6l	00, 00, 00
60, 60, 64, 82, 82, 96	6h	50
04, 05, 05, 16	7l	
	7h	
	8l	stems: dollars
	8h	75 leaves: cents

The rental rates for Marina del Rey are higher than for the Los Angeles–Long Beach Harbor. Most of the marinas in Marina del Rey charge $6 or more per foot, while those in the Los Angeles–Long Beach Harbor charge $6 or less per foot. The $8.75 value in the Los Angeles–Long Beach data set is unusually large. It would be considered an outlier.

2.11

	0L	334
889	0H	6789
000223344	1L	23344444
55555667777889	1H	55567778888
0111134	2L	02344
677899	2H	555899
	3L	0444
556779	3H	8
0	4L	4
	4H	588
	5L	2

Based on the stem and leaf displays, there does not seem to be any evidence that the proportion of students disqualified is smaller for nonathletes than for athletes. There appears to be slightly more variation in the nonathletes.

2.13 a.

Number of times	Frequency	Relative frequency
0	5	.227
1	4	.182
2	3	.136
3	3	.136
4	1	.045
5	1	.045
6	0	.000
7	0	.000
8	2	.091
9	3	.136

b. .227 or 22.7% **c.** .272 or 27.2%, .136 or 13.6% **2.15 a.** .9354, .1705 **b.** .7883

2.17 b.

Concentration	Frequency
20–<30	1
30–<40	8
40–<50	8
50–<60	6
60–<70	16
70–<80	7
80–<90	2
90–<100	2

c. .34, .54

2.19 a.

Class Interval	Frequency	Relative frequency
0–<100	21	.21
100–<200	32	.32
200–<300	26	.26
300–<400	12	.12
400–<500	4	.04
500–<600	3	.03
600–<700	1	.01
700–<800	0	.00
800–<900	1	.01

b. .242

2.21 a.

Class Interval	Freq.	Rel. freq.	Cum. rel. freq.
0–< 6	2	.0225	.0225
6–<12	10	.1124	.1349
12–<18	21	.2360	.3709
18–<24	28	.3146	.6855
24–<30	22	.2472	.9327
30–<36	6	.0674	1.0001

c. .2360 **d.** .8651 **e.** .5506 **f.** 20.46 months **g.** 29.21 months **2.23** The cumulative relative frequencies can't decrease **2.29 b.** No, since there would not be any way of determining the largest observation, the right side boundary point of the rectangle for the class "≥ 15" could not be determined. **c.** Yes, because now you know the largest observation is 17 and the right side boundary point would be placed at 17.5. **2.31 b.** .518 **c.** .635 **2.35 a.** negatively skewed **b.** positively skewed **c.** bimodal **2.37 a.** symmetric **b.** negatively skewed **c.** positively skewed **d.** bimodal **2.39 b.** This histogram is not very skewed. **c.** There appears to be little skewness. Transforming this data set would probably not be productive. **2.41 a.** positively skewed **b.** still positively skewed **2.45 b.** .0908 **c.** .2382 **2.49** The histogram for the nondiabetics suggests that sodium concentration is bimodal, whereas the histogram for the diabetics suggests that sodium concentration is unimodal and quite symmetric. **2.55** The histogram is skewed slightly in the positive direction. The majority of the observations are in the center. **2.57** The transformation on Mn has been very successful in obtaining a symmetric distribution. The transformation on Zn appears to have produced a bimodal distribution. It is not as symmetric as the transformed Mn. The transformation on Cu has been reasonably successful, but not as much as for Mn.

CHAPTER 3

3.1 a. 54.59 **b.** 55 **c.** 91.18 **3.3** 122.57 **3.5 a.** 13.875 **b.** 14 **c.** 14.07 **d.** 11.5, 12 **3.7** This statement could be correct if there were a small group of residents with very high wages. **3.9** Average for diet 1 is larger than that for diet 2. **3.11** median = 31, mean will be larger than the median. **3.13** median = 68, 20% trimmed mean = 66.17 **3.15 a.** 60 **b.** 86.67 **3.17** 1.143 **3.19 a.** 7, 4.528 **b.** 7, 1.581 **c.** 4, 1.581 **d.** 6, 1.581 **3.21** .2098 **3.23** The standard deviation of the new data set is 10 times larger than the standard deviation of the original data set. **3.25 a.** 2.74, 3.88 **b.** 1.14 **c.** no effect **d.** The observation 2.34 could be increased to as much as 2.74 without affecting the iqr. **e.** lq = 2.74, uq = 3.93, iqr = 1.19 **3.27 a.** sample 1: 7.81, .39847 sample 2: 49.68, 1.73897 **b.** sample 1: 5.10 sample 2: 3.50 **3.29 a.** approx. 68% **b.** approx. 16% **3.31 a.** approx. 68% **b.** approx. 5% **c.** approx. 13.5% **3.33 a.** lq = 3.59, uq = 4.65, iqr = 1.06 **b.** There are two mild outliers (6.49 and 6.79) and no extreme outliers. **3.35** Performance was better on the second exam. **3.37 b. i.** 21 **ii.** 18 **iii.** 21.67 **iv.** 25.375 **v.** 17.615 **3.39** at most 16% **3.41** at most 10.6% **3.43 a.** −1.86 **b.** 0.36 **c.** −0.43 **d.** 2.29 **3.47** $\bar{x}$ = 1.6681, median = 1.285, s^2 = 1.1936, s = 1.0925 **3.49 a.** $\bar{x}$ = 103.83, median = 82.5, s^2 = 3497.8091, s = 59.14 **b.** lq = 58.0, uq = 137.5, iqr = 79.5 **3.51 a.** $\bar{x}$ = 8.006, s = .287 **b.** 10% trimmed mean = 7.976, median = 7.91 **c.** uq = 8.01, lq = 7.82, iqr = 0.19 **3.53 a.** $\bar{x}$ = 22.15, s = 11.366 **b.** 19.4375 **c.** uq = 20.5, lq = 18.0, iqr = 2.5 **d.** 25 and 28 are mild outliers, 69 is an extreme outlier **3.55 a.** 6.67%, 13.33% **b.** 10.66, 10.58 **c.** 10.62 **3.61** 248 **3.63 a.** 120 **b.** 20 **c.** −.5 **d.** The 97.5th percentile **e.** approx .15%

CHAPTER 4

4.3 a. Not deterministic since there are two observations with the same x value but different y values. **c.** There appears to be a tendency for oxygen consumption rate to increase as plasma cortisol concentration increases. **4.7 a.** positive **b.** negative **c.** positive **d.** no correlation **e.** positive **f.** weak positive **g.** negative **h.** no correlation **4.11** .355 **4.13 a.** .966 **4.15** No, because *artist* is not a numerical variable. **4.17** $\Sigma(x'y') = (n - 1)r$ **4.21** .7765 **4.23 a. i.** .821 **ii.** −.714 **iii.** .964 **b.** ganging prevalence **4.25** .7 **4.27 b.** a = −4.546, b = 0.1123 **c.** .1123, 1.123 **d.** 5.0055 **e.** no **4.29 b.** $\hat{y}$ = 321.2413 − 5.2027x **d.** 165.16 **e.** 10 is well outside the range of the x values in the data set. **4.31 a.** $\hat{y}$ = 124.6729 + 1.3606x **b.** 1.3606 **c.** 192.70 **4.33 a.** $\hat{y}$ = 4027.083 − 577.895x **b.** −577.895 **c.** $\hat{y}$ = −596.077; No way! **4.35** It is dangerous to use the least squares line to obtain predictions of x values outside the range of those contained in the sample, because there is no information in the sample about the relationship that exists between x and y outside that range. **4.37** b and r will always have the same signs. **4.39** .6561, 13.27 **4.41 a.** $\hat{y}$ = −89.08722 + .72907x; the residual at x = 375 is −19.311403. **b.** .96283 **4.43 b.** After deletion of the observation (143, .3), $\hat{y}$ = 5.1151 − .0333x. **c.** For full data set, r^2 = .8829; for data set with the observation removed, r^2 = .6789. **4.45 a.** 827.019 **b.** .9012 **c.** 893.08 **4.47 c.** 666.4937 **d.** 692.72 **e.** .4997 **4.53** The plot looks like segment 3 of Figure 4.26. This suggests going down the ladder on y or x. One possible transformation would be 1/y. **4.55 b.** .9565 **d.** For the transformed data, $\hat{y}$ = .7565 + 1.5940x, r^2 = .9718 **e.** 74.2506 **4.57 a.** −.717 **b.** −.835 **4.63 b.** $\hat{y}$ = 2.2255 + .1521x **c.** r = .93875, r^2 = .881 **4.65 a.** $\hat{y}$ = 1.6932 + .0805x **b.** $\hat{y}$ = −20.0514 + 12.1149x **c.** both have r^2 = .9748 **4.67 c.** $\hat{y}$ = 4.8615 − .3466x **d.** $\hat{y}$ = 2.2620, residual = .0380 **e.** .7286 **4.69** r = .132

CHAPTER 5

5.1 a. S = {AA, AM, MA, MM} **c.** B = {MA, AM, AA}; C = {AM, MA}; D = {MM} **d.** (B and C) = {AM, MA}; (B or C) = {MA, AM, AA} **5.3 b.** A = {(1, 2), (1, 4), (2, 1), (2, 3), (2, 4), (3, 2), (3, 4), (4, 1), (4, 2), (4, 3)} **c.** B = {(1, 3), (1, 4), (2, 3), (2, 4), (3, 1), (3, 2), (4, 1), (4, 2)} **5.5 a.** N, DN, DDN, DDDN, DDDDN **b.** There are an infinite number **c.** E = {DN, DDDN, DDDDDN, . . .} **5.7 b.** A = {(1, 1, 1), (2, 2, 2), (3, 3, 3)} **c.** B = {(1, 2, 3), (1, 3, 2), (2, 1, 3), (2, 3, 1), (3, 1, 2), (3, 2, 1)} **d.** C = {(1, 1, 1), (1, 1, 3), (1, 3, 1), (1, 3, 3), (3, 1, 1), (3, 1, 3), (3, 3, 1), (3, 3, 3)} **e.** (not B) = {(1, 1, 1), (1, 1, 2), (1, 1, 3), (1, 2, 1), (1, 2, 2), (1, 3, 1), (1, 3, 3), (2, 1, 1), (2, 1, 2), (2, 2, 1), (2, 2, 2), (2, 2, 3), (2, 3, 2), (2, 3, 3), (3, 1, 1), (3, 1, 3), (3, 2, 2), (3, 2, 3), (3, 3, 1), (3, 3, 2), (3, 3, 3)} (A or B) = {(1, 1, 1), (2, 2, 2), (3, 3, 3), (1, 2, 3), (1, 3, 2), (2, 1, 3), (2, 3, 1), (3, 1, 2), (3, 2, 1)} (A and B) contains no outcomes (A and C) = {(1, 1, 1), (3, 3, 3)}

5.11 a. .0119 **b.** .00000238 **c.** .012 **5.13 a.** .40 **b.** .81 **c.** .94 **d.** .21 **5.15 a.** 52 **b.** $\frac{1}{52}$ **c.** $P(\text{heart}) = \frac14$, $P(\text{face card}) = \frac{3}{13}$ **d.** $\frac{3}{52}$ **e.** $\frac{11}{26}$ **5.17 b.** .2500 **c.** .3333 **d.** 0 **e.** .2917 **5.19 b.** .1 **c.** .4 **d.** .3 **5.21 a.** $\frac{1}{10}$ **b.** $\frac{3}{10}$ **c.** $\frac{7}{10}$
5.37 a. .55 **b.** .45 **c.** .40 **d.** .25 **5.39 a.** .10 **b.** .18, .19 **c.** .41 **d.** .59 **e.** .31 **f.** .69 **5.41 b.** .00095 **c.** .10085
d. .00942 **5.43** .008 **5.45** 1107 **5.47 a.** 120 **b.** 455 **c.** .2637 **5.49** 240 **5.51 a.** 1,816,214,400 **b.** .011 **5.53** .4 **5.55** .6
5.57 .49 **5.61 a.** .533 **b.** .444, .556 **5.63 b.** E_1 and E_3 are independent, E_2 and E_3 are independent **5.63 a.** .32 **b.** .032768
5.67 a. .0286 **b.** .324 **5.69 a.** $P(B_1 \text{ and } S) = .10$; $P(B_2 \text{ and } S) = .06$; $P(B_3 \text{ and } S) = .04$ **b.** .5625 **5.71 a.** .0129 **b.** .0518
c. .000495 **5.73 a.** .512 **b.** .608 **5.75** .0547

CHAPTER 6

6.1 a. discrete **b.** continuous **c.** discrete **d.** discrete **e.** continuous **6.3** Possible y values are the positive integers. **6.5** y is a
continuous variable with values from 0 to 100 ft. **6.9 a.** .82 **b.** .18 **c.** .65, .27

6.13 a.

x	0	1	2	3	4
$p(x)$	.4096	.4096	.1536	.0256	.0016

b. 0 and 1 **c.** .1808

6.15

w	1	10	25
$p(w)$	.3	.3	.4

6.17

x	1	2	3	4	5	6
$p(x)$	$\frac{1}{12}$	$\frac{1}{12}$	$\frac{1}{12}$	$\frac14$	$\frac14$	$\frac14$

6.19

x	0	1	2	3
$p(x)$	.16	.33	.32	.19

6.21 a. $\sigma^2 = 1.9456$, $\sigma = 1.3948$ **b.** .72 **c.** .07 **6.23** For the royalty plan, $\mu = 10,550$ **6.25.** 98.9813 **6.27 a.** discrete
b. .40, .86 **c.** $\mu = 126.760$, $\sigma^2 = 178.0885$, $\sigma = 13.345$

6.29 b.

y	80	85	90	95
$p(y)$	.1	.3	.4	.2

c. 88.5 **6.31** 10 **6.33 a.** .2637 **b.** .6328 **c.** .3672 **d.** .7363 **6.35** .03125, .15625, .31250, .31250, .15625, .03125 **6.37 a.** .735
b. .392 **c.** .070 **6.39** 200, 13.42 **6.41 a.** x has a binomial distribution with $n = 100$ and $\pi = .2$. **b.** 20 **c.** $\sigma^2 = 16$, $\sigma = 4$
6.43 a. .044 **b.** .002 **c.** .845 **6.45 a.** .902 **b.** .967 **c.** $\mu = 22.5$, $\sigma = 1.5$ **d.** .033 **6.47** .784 **6.49 a.** $\mu = 2.64$, $\sigma^2 = 2.3704$,
$\sigma = 1.54$ **b.** 0

6.51

w	-10	-8	-6	-4	-2	0	2	4	6	8	10
$p(w)$	$\frac{1}{16}$	$\frac{1}{16}$	$\frac{1}{16}$	$\frac{2}{16}$	$\frac{2}{16}$	$\frac{2}{16}$	$\frac{2}{16}$	$\frac{2}{16}$	$\frac{1}{16}$	$\frac{1}{16}$	$\frac{1}{16}$

6.53

x	1	2	3
$p(x)$	$\frac12$	$\frac13$	$\frac16$

6.55

x	4	5	6	7
y	0	1	2	3
$p(y)$	.1152	.2688	.29952	.27648

6.57 a.

y	.25	1.25	2.25
$p(y)$	$\frac{1}{15}$	$\frac{2}{15}$	$\frac{12}{15}$

$\mu_y = 1.983$

b.

y	0	1	2	3
$p(y)$	$\frac{1}{15}$	$\frac{2}{15}$	$\frac{3}{15}$	$\frac{9}{15}$

$\mu_y = 2.33$

6.59 c. When $n = 10$, $\mu = 5.5$, $\sigma^2 = \frac{99}{12}$, and $\sigma = 2.87$
6.61 a. .4 **b.** .1, .433

c.

x	0	1	2	3
$p(x)$	$\frac{24}{60}$	$\frac{26}{60}$	$\frac{9}{60}$	$\frac{1}{60}$

6.63 a. .1804 **b.** .594 **c.** .15629 **d.** 60

6.65 c.

x	1	2	3
$p(x)$	$\frac{1}{6}$	$\frac{4}{6}$	$\frac{1}{6}$

$\mu = 2$ **d.** 24

CHAPTER 7

7.1 a. .5 **b.** .2 **c.** 5   **7.3 b.** .08   **c.** .36   **d.** .40, .40   **e.** 13.75   **f.** 3.608   **7.5 a.** .5, .25   **b.** .25   **c.** $c = 18$ **7.7 a.** 1   **b.** .84375
c. .6875   **d.** 0   **7.9 a.** .9599   **b.** .2483   **c.** .1151   **d.** .9976   **e.** .6887   **f.** .6826   **g.** 1   **7.11 a.** .9909   **b.** .9909   **c.** .1093
d. .1267   **e.** .0706   **f.** .8730   **g.** .0228   **h.** .9996   **i.** 1   **7.13 a.** $c = .23$ **b.** $c = -.23$ $c = 2.75$ **d.** $c = 1.16$ **7.15 a.** $c = 1.96$
b. $c = 1.28$ **c.** $c = -1.28$ **d.** $c = 2.58$ **e.** $c = 2.58$ **f.** $c = 3.10$ **7.17 a.** .5   **b.** .9772   **c.** .9772   **d.** .8185   **e.** .9938   **f.** 1
7.19 a. .0228   **b.** .8400   **7.21 a.** .9452   **b.** .9452   **c.** .9370   **d.** .0456   **7.23 a.** $c = 28.602$ **b.** $c = 1.176$ **7.25 a.** .9938
b. .9876, 1   **c.** .0013, .0052   **7.27** .073   **7.29 a.** .9901   **b.** 31.466   **c.** 31.256   **d.** 30.534   **7.31 a.** .0016   **b.** .9946   **c.** .7925
7.33 a. .1114   **b.** .0409   **c.** .0968   **d.** .9429   **e.** .9001   **7.35 a.** .7960   **b.** .7016   **c.** .0143   **d.** .05   **7.37 b.** .8708   **7.39** The plot
is quite straight; it is reasonable to conclude that the normal distribution provides an adequate description.   **7.41** Not normal.   **7.43** Normality
is plausible.   **7.45 a.** .1359   **b.** .0228   **c.** .5955   **7.47 a.** .9332   **b.** $c = 72.8$ **c.** 60   **7.49** .0228, 0   **7.51 a.** Only about 69% of all
women are shorter than 5'7".   **7.53 a.** .7745   **b.** .1587   **c.** .3085   **d.** 6.1645   **7.55 a.** $\mu = 32, \sigma = 5.1846$ **b.** .8760   **7.57** .3174
7.59 a. 88th percentile   **b.** 98th percentile   **c.** 628   **7.61** $w = 15.66$ **7.63 a.** .8647   **b.** .6321   **c.** .4712

CHAPTER 8

8.3 a. population characteristic   **b.** statistic   **c.** population characteristic   **d.** statistic   **e.** statistic

8.9 a.

t value	6	11	15	21	25	30
probability	$\frac{1}{6}$	$\frac{1}{6}$	$\frac{1}{6}$	$\frac{1}{6}$	$\frac{1}{6}$	$\frac{1}{6}$

b. population mean $= 9$, mean value of $t = 18$

8.11

$\bar{x}$ value	2.67	3.00	3.33	3.67
probability	.1	.4	.3	.2

statistic 2 value	3	4	
probability	.7	.3	

statistic 3 value	2.5	3.0	3.5
probability	.1	.5	.4

8.13 a.

$\bar{x}$ value	281.0	295.5	364.5	393.5	462.5	477.0
probability	$\frac{1}{6}$	$\frac{1}{6}$	$\frac{1}{6}$	$\frac{1}{6}$	$\frac{1}{6}$	$\frac{1}{6}$

$\mu_{\bar{x}} = 379$

b.

$\bar{x}$ value	281.0	364.5	393.5	477.0
probability	.25	.25	.25	.25

$\mu_{\bar{x}} = 379$

8.15 a. 8.16   **8.17** The histograms would be centered in the same place, but would have less variability.   **8.19** 36, 50, and 400
8.21 a. approximately normal with mean 40 and standard deviation .625   **b.** .5762   **c.** .2628   **8.23 a.** $\mu_{\bar{x}} = 2, \sigma_{\bar{x}} = .267$ **b.** for $n = 20$,
$\mu_{\bar{x}} = 2, \sigma_{\bar{x}} = .179$ for $n = 100, \mu_{\bar{x}} = 2, \sigma_{\bar{x}} = .08$ **8.25 a.** .9544   **8.27 b.** $\mu_{\bar{x}} = 22.0, \sigma_{\bar{x}} = 1.65$ **c.** .1131, .0344   **8.29 a.** $\mu_{\bar{x}} = 3$,
$\sigma_{\bar{x}} = .0125$, normal (since the population is normal)   **b.** 2.9625, 3.0375   **c.** .0026   **d.** .8413   **8.31 a.** When $\pi = .65, n = 20, 30, 50, 100$,
and 200. When $\pi = .2, n = 30, 50, 100$, and 200.   **8.33 a.** $n(1 - \pi) < 5$, binomial not well approximated by normal   **b.** 400, .0249
c. .9556   **d.** 0   **8.35** .1841   **8.37** .1587, .0013   **8.39** .1056   **8.41 a.** .8185   **b.** .8357, .9993   **8.43** .0793

CHAPTER 9

9.1 Statistic II   **9.3** .7541   **9.5 a.** .484   **b.** .3   **9.7** .70   **9.9** 73.2   **9.11 a.** As the confidence level increases, interval width increases.
b. As the sample size increases, interval width decreases.   **c.** As σ increases, interval width increases.   **9.13 a.** narrower   **b.** Statement is
incorrect.   **c.** Statement is incorrect.   **9.15** (6.73, 9.67)   **9.17** (349.42, 354.58) for time in min., (5.8237, 5.9097) for time in hours; this
interval does not include 6 hr., so the true average time appears to be less than 6 hr.   **9.19** 1015   **9.21** 62   **9.23** (68.52, 79.48)   **9.25 a.** for
boys: (99.486, 103.914)   for girls: (99.423, 104.177)   **b.** (83.05, 90.35)   **9.27** 385   **9.29 a.** yes   **b.** no   **c.** yes   **d.** no   **e.** yes   **f.** yes
g. yes   **h.** yes   **9.31** (.741, .799)   **9.33** (.625, .807)   **9.35** (.1612, .1836)   **9.37 a.** (.492, .608)   **b.** (.411, .549)   **9.39** (.3941, .7171)

9.41 (.35, .51)   **9.43 a.** (.411, .549)   **b.** No, use confidence interval for a population mean.   **9.45** 97   **9.47** Use 2.58 in place of 1.96 in sample size formula.   **9.49 a.** 2.12   **b.** 1.80   **c.** 2.81   **d.** 1.71   **e.** 1.78   **f.** 2.26   **9.51** (19.51, 24.29)   **9.53 a.** (5.2, 8.0)   **b.** (31.78, 48.82)   **9.55 a.** (394.66, 461.34)   **b.** narrower   **c.** convection oven: (2074.67, 2323.33); food dehydrator: (3708.65, 4131.35); microwave: (1393.7, 1468.3)   **9.57 a.** (232.45, 294.95)   **b.** (51.2, 65.8)   **c.** The distribution of the number of operations must be normal for each of the two populations.   **9.59** (5.77, 28.23)   **9.61** (9.976, 11.824)   **9.63** (.6218, .6782)   **9.65** (.4702, .5382)   **9.67** (91.55, 184.45)   **9.69** (.38, .42)   **9.71** (.6898, .9232)   **9.73** Width of text interval $= 3.92s/\sqrt{n}$, width of interval given here $= 4.08s/\sqrt{n}$.   **9.75** mean per unit statistic: 1,703,000; difference statistic: 1,591,300; ratio statistic: 1,601,438.28

CHAPTER 10

10.3 $H_0: \mu = 100$ $H_a: \mu > 100$ **10.5** $H_0: \pi = .6$ $H_a: \pi > .6$ **10.9** $H_0: \mu = 40$ $H_a: \mu \neq 40$ **10.11 a.** failed to reject H_0 **b.** type II error   **10.17 a.** $H_0: \mu = 5$ $H_a: \mu > 5$ **b.** $\alpha = .1$ **10.19 a.** $z > 2.33$ **b.** $z > 1.645$ **c.** $z > 1.28$ **d.** $z > 1.13$ **10.21 a.** $z < -2.33$ **b.** $z < -1.645$ **c.** $z < -1.28$ **10.23** $z = 3.328$, reject H_0 **10.25** $z = 4.84$, reject H_0 **10.27** $z = 5.39$, reject H_0 **10.29** $z = -8.6898$, reject H_0 **10.31** $z = 2.96$, reject H_0 **10.33** $z = -1.13$, fail to reject H_0 **10.35** $z = -5$, reject H_0 **10.37 a.** fail to reject H_0 **b.** fail to reject H_0 **c.** fail to reject H_0 **d.** reject H_0 **10.39 a.** .0358   **b.** .0892   **c.** .6170   **d.** .1616   **e.** 0   **10.41 a.** $z = 3.0$ **b.** .0013   **c.** reject H_0 **10.43** $z = -6.91$, P-value < .0002, reject H_0 **10.45 a.** $z = 1.04$, fail to reject H_0 **b.** P-value = .1492, so reject H_0 if $\alpha \geq .1492$.   **10.47 a.** reject H_0 if either $t < -2.26$ or $t > 2.26$ **b.** reject H_0 if either $t < -2.90$ or $t > 2.90$ **c.** reject H_0 if either $t < -3.75$ or $t > 3.75$ **d.** reject H_0 if either $t < -1.67$ or $t > 1.67$ **10.49** $t = 1.875$, reject H_0; we assume that activation time has a normal distribution.   **10.51** $t = .77$, fail to reject H_0 **10.53** $t = -.59$, fail to reject H_0 **10.55** $t = -0.816$, fail to reject H_0 **10.57 a.** .05 < P-value < .10   **b.** .002 < P-value < .01   **c.** P-value < .001   **d.** P-value > .20   **10.59** .025 < P-value < .05, fail to reject H_0 **10.61** $z = 1.41$, reject H_0 **10.63** $z = 3.55$, reject H_0 **10.65** $z = 1.78$, fail to reject H_0 **10.67** $z = 7.58$, reject H_0 **10.69** $z = 2.73$, reject H_0 **10.71** $z = -1.26$, fail to reject H_0 **10.73 a.** $z = 4.91$, reject H_0 **b.** No, a causal relationship can not be inferred.   **10.75 c.** .0359   **e.** .3745   **f.** 0   **10.77 a.** $z = 1.71$, reject H_0 **b.** .6480   **10.79 a.** $t > 1.83$ **b. i.** .85   **ii.** .55   **iii.** .10   **iv.** 0   **10.81** $z = .2$, fail to reject H_0 **10.83 a.** $z = 4.19$, reject H_0 **b.** P-value < .0002, reject H_0 **10.85** $z = -6.62$, reject H_0 **10.87** $t = .16$, fail to reject H_0 **10.89** $z = -21.6$, reject H_0 **10.91 a.** $z = 6.43$, reject H_0 **b.** P-value < .0002, reject H_0

CHAPTER 11

11.1 Approximately normal, mean 5, standard deviation .529.   **11.3** $z = -7.91$, reject H_0 **11.5** $z = 9.58$, reject H_0 **11.7** $z = 15.78$, reject H_0 **11.9 a.** $(-1.32, 3.32)$ **b.** $z = -2.00$, reject H_0 **c.** $z = -2.58$, reject H_0 **11.11** $(-2.176, -1.804)$; no assumptions about the two salinity distributions are necessary.   **11.13 a.** $z = -2.98$, reject H_0 **b.** $(-4.71, -.097)$ **11.15 a.** $z = 4.63$, reject H_0 **b.** P-value < .0002   **c.** $(-0.9, 4.26)$ **11.17** $z = -.41$, fail to reject H_0 **11.19** $t = -1.20$, fail to reject H_0 **11.21** $t = -0.1965$, fail to reject H_0 **11.25** $t = 3.01$, reject H_0 **11.27** $t = 10.21$, reject H_0 **11.29** $t = 3.13$, reject H_0 **11.31** $t = 4.10$, reject H_0 **11.33 a.** $t = 1.55$, fail to reject H_0 **b.** $t = 1.10$, fail to reject H_0 **c.** (1164.27, 1835.73)   **d.** (1009.34, 1904.66)   **11.35 a.** $t = -2.81$, reject H_0 **b.** $t = -2.43$, reject H_0 **c.** .01 < P-value < .02   **11.37 b.** $t = 2.39$, reject H_0 **c.** .01 < P-value < .025, so at significance level .01 H_0 should not be rejected   **11.39 b.** $t = -2.64$, reject H_0 **11.41 a.** 4897.4275   **b.** $t = 4.058$, reject H_0 **c.** P-value < .0005   **11.43 a.** $z = 2.62$, reject H_0 **b.** (.028, .202)   **11.45** $z = -.1906$, fail to reject H_0 **11.47** $z = -3.195$, reject H_0 **11.49** (.0544, .2456)   **11.51** $z = 6.83$, reject H_0 **11.53** $z = 4.17$, reject H_0 **11.55** $z = -.88$, fail to reject H_0 **11.57** $z = 13.19$, reject H_0 **11.59 a.** $z = 3.49$, reject H_0 **b.** P-value = .0002   **11.61** rank sum = 53, fail to reject H_0 **11.63 a.** rank sum = 43, fail to reject H_0 **b.** $(-.41, .29)$ **11.65** $z = 3.61$, reject H_0 **11.67** rank sum = 53, fail to reject H_0 **11.69** $z = 2.04$, fail to reject H_0 **11.71** $(-.50, .57)$ **11.73** $t = 4.92$, reject H_0 **11.75** $z = 1.79$, fail to reject H_0 **11.77** $(-42.18, 69.98)$ **11.79** For glucose, $z = .95$, fail to reject H_0. For potassium, $z = 1.60$, fail to reject H_0. For total protein, $z = -.31$, fail to reject H_0. For cholesterol, $z = -.55$, fail to reject H_0.   **11.81 a.** $z = 3.41$, reject H_0 **b.** P-value = .0003   **11.83** $z = 5.59$, reject H_0

CHAPTER 12

12.9 $t = 9.91$, reject H_0 **12.11** $t = -1.34$, fail to reject H_0 **12.13** $t = 2.68$, reject H_0 **12.15** $t = .36$, fail to reject H_0 **12.17 a.** $t = 3.95$, reject H_0 **b.** $t = -1.17$, fail to reject H_0 **12.19** $t = .86$, fail to reject H_0 **12.21** signed-rank sum = 55, reject H_0 **12.23** signed-rank sum = 1, fail to reject H_0 **12.25** $(-1.1, 3.9)$ **12.27 a.** signed-rank sum = -6, fail to reject H_0 **b.** signed-rank sum = -33, reject H_0 **12.29** $z = 3.75$, reject H_0 **12.31** signed-rank sum = 9, fail to reject H_0 **12.33** $t = -1.698$, fail to reject H_0 **12.35 a.** $t = 1.04$, fail to reject H_0 **b.** $t = 1.71$, fail to reject H_0 **12.37** $t = 0.51$, fail to reject H_0

CHAPTER 13

13.1 a. $y = -5.0 + .017x$ **c.** 30.7 **d.** .017 **e.** 1.7 **f.** There is no information to suggest that the model is adequate for houses of this size. **13.3 a.** 3.6, 4.3 **b.** .121 **c.** .5, .1587 **13.7 a.** .6228 **b.** $s_e = 1.5923$ **c.** 3.4307 **d.** 3.4426 **13.9 a.** .883 **b.** 13.682 **13.11 b.** $\hat{y} = -.002274 + 1.246712x$; when $x = .09$, $\hat{y} = .10993$ **c.** .436 **d.** .0263 **13.15** It would be better to use the x values given in this problem rather than the ones given in Exercise 4.32, since $\Sigma(x - \bar{x})^2$ is smaller for the former than for the latter. **13.17 a.** .766 **b.** $s_e = 6.5719$, $s_b = 8.0529$ **c.** (38.313, 66.821) **13.19 a.** P-value $= .000$, reject H_0 **b.** $(-0.161365, .092055)$ **13.21** $(-.069, -.043)$ **13.23 a.** $b = -.77782$, $a = 100.79116$ **b.** $t = -2.8$, reject H_0 **c.** 77.45 **d.** $(-1.306, -0.250)$ **13.25** $t = -18.07$, reject H_0 **13.27** $t = 0.45$, fail to reject H_0 **13.31 a.** 4.038 **b.** 4.038 **c.** 3.817 **d.** $x^* = \bar{x} = 2.5$ **13.33 a.** (6.4722, 6.6300) **b.** (6,4779, 6.6973) **c.** Yes, because 60 is further from $\bar{x}$ than is 40 or 35. **13.35 a.** $\hat{y} = 30.019 + .1109x$ **b.** (38.354, 43.864) **c.** (30.311, 51.907) **13.37 a.** $\hat{y} = 2.78551 + .04462x$ **b.** $t = 10.85$, reject H_0 **c.** (3.671, 4.577) **13.39 a.** $\hat{y} = 40.31024 - .44256x$ **b.** (30.108, 34.580) **c.** (28.32, 32.83) **13.14 a.** (3.2416, 3.7624) **b.** (3.467, 4.217) **13.43** $t = -2.80$, fail to reject H_0 **13.47** $r = .5778$, $t = 3.32$, reject H_0 **13.49 a.** $r = .574$, $t = 1.85$, fail to reject H_0 **b.** $.10 < P$-value $< .20$ **13.51** $r = .728$, $t = 3.52$, reject H_0 **13.53 a.** .8777 **b.** $t = 6.07$, reject H_0 **c.** P-value $< .0005$ **d.** The change has no effect on the value of r. **13.55** $t = 2.2$, so reject H_0; however, the result appears to have no practical significance. **13.57 b.** The normal probability plot is reasonably straight. **c.** There are two residuals that are unusually large. **d.** The negative residuals tend to be associated with small x values and the positive residuals tend to be associated with large x values. This would cause us to question the appropriateness of the simple linear regression model. **13.61** The residual plot exhibits a pattern that casts doubt on the appropriateness of the linear regression model. **13.63 a.** (4.903, 5.632) **b.** (4.4078, 6.1272) **13.65** $r = .2645$, $t = .73$, fail to reject H_0 **13.67 a.** $t = -6.09$, reject H_0 **b.** (2.3376, 3.8520) **c.** Do not use the simple linear regression model to predict for $x = 10$. **13.69 b.** $\hat{y} = -.08259 + .044649x$ **c.** .983 **d.** $\hat{y} = .7702$, residual $= -.0902$ **e.** $t = 20.0$, reject H_0 **f.** a 95% confidence interval is (.039359, .049939) **g.** (.7621, .8587) **13.71 a.** $\hat{y} = -1.7521 + .68485x$ **b.** $t = -5.20$, reject H_0 **c.** $(-2.5306, -.9736)$ **13.73** $t = -1.03$, fail to reject H_0 **13.77** P-value $= .0076$, reject H_0

CHAPTER 14

14.3 a. $\beta_1 = .237$, $\beta_2 = -.0002$ **b.** .237 **c.** 1.213 **14.5 a.** 9.364 **b.** It would increase. **14.7 a.** mean $y = 21.09 + .653x_1 + .0022x_2 - .0206x_1^2 + .00004x_2^2$ **b.** 67,948.5564 **c.** It is smaller. **14.13** Three dummy variables are needed. **14.17** $F = .638$, fail to reject H_0 **14.19 b.** $F = 185.2$, reject H_0 **14.21 a.** $F = 23.05$, reject H_0 **14.23 a.** $F = 51.53$, reject H_0 **b.** R^2, s_e, and the residuals **c.** .862, 2.83 **d.** Larger, since the estimated regression equation minimizes SSResid **14.25** The model is judged useful if $k \le 9$ but not if $k = 10$. **14.27 b.** $F = 8.76$, reject H_0 **c.** $R^2 = .885$, SSResid $= 1.9926$, $s_e = .3529$ **14.31 a.** $(-18.438, -.318)$ **b.** $(-4.049, -.309)$ **14.33 a.** .469 **b.** $F = 75.01$, reject H_0 **c.** (2.466, 4.272) **d.** 72.856 **e.** (61.562, 84.150) **14.35** $t = 2.22$, reject H_0 **14.37** $t = -8.42$, reject H_0 **14.39** no **14.41** (20.179, 28.421) **14.43 a.** $F = 30.81$, reject H_0; $t = -7.69$, reject H_0 **b.** $t = 6.57$, reject H_0 **c.** (43.00, 47.92) **d.** (44.00, 47.92) **14.51** Adjusted R^2 will be substantially smaller than R^2 when the number of predictors is large compared to the number of observations in the data set. **14.53** Multicollinearity might be a problem. **14.55 a.** $\ge .723$ **b.** $\le .723$ **14.57 a.** $F = 15.58$, reject H_0 **b.** 10.031 **c.** x_1 can be deleted **d.** (.0283, .0857) **14.63 b.** $F = 70.67$, reject H_0 **c.** $R^2 = .865$, $s_e = .0533$ **d.** no

CHAPTER 15

15.3 b. Fail to reject H_0 **c.** Fail to reject H_0 **15.5** $F = 1.71$, fail to reject H_0 **15.7 a.** $F = 4.12$, reject H_0 **b.** reject H_0 **15.9** $F = 1.85$, fail to reject H_0 **15.11 a.** $F = 3.43$, reject H_0 **b.** $F = 1.65$, fail to reject H_0 **15.13** $F = 6.97$, reject H_0

15.15

Source	df	Sum of Squares	Mean Square	F
Treatments	2	152.18	76.09	5.56
Error	71	970.96	13.675	
Total	73	1123.14		

$F = 5.56$, reject H_0

15.17

Source	df	Sum of Squares	Mean Square	F
Treatments	3	136.14	45.38	5.12
Error	60	532.26	8.871	
Total	63	668.40		

$F = 5.12$, reject H_0

15.19

Source	df	Sum of Squares	Mean Square	F
Treatments	4	.92928	.23232	2.17
Error	25	2.68072	.10723	
Total	29	3.61		

$F = 2.17$, fail to reject H_0

15.21

Source	df	Sum of Squares	Mean Square	F
Treatments	2	1.6297	.8148	4.589
Error	21	3.7289	.1776	
Total	23	5.3586		

$F = 4.589$, reject H_0

15.23 For $\mu_1 - \mu_2$: (.22, 2.24); for $\mu_1 - \mu_3$: (.34, 2.46); for $\mu_2 - \mu_3$: (−.89, 1.23). μ_1 differs from μ_2 and μ_3, but μ_2 and μ_3 do not differ.

15.25 $\bar{x}_3 \quad \bar{x}_2 \quad \bar{x}_1$

15.29 a. $F = 79.264$, reject H_0

c.

Brand	1	2	3	4	5	6
Mean	12.8	13.1	13.825	14.1	17.14	18.1

15.33 a.

Source	df	Sum of Squares	Mean Square	F
Treatments	2	1835.2	917.60	35.62
Blocks	4	93.1	23.28	
Error	8	206.1	25.76	
Total	14	2134.4		

b. $F = 35.62$, reject H_0

15.35

Source	df	Sum of Squares	Mean Square	F
Treatments	2	28.78	14.39	1.04
Blocks	17	2977.67	175.16	
Error	34	469.55	13.81	
Total	53	3476.00		

fail to reject H_0

15.37 a.

Source	df	Sum of Squares	Mean Square	F
Treatments	1	289.00	289.00	1.09
Blocks	7	623.00	89.00	
Error	7	1858.00	265.43	
Total	15	2770.00		

fail to reject H_0

b. $t = 1.04$, fail to reject H_0

15.39

Source	df	Sum of Squares	Mean Square	F
Treatments	3	3141153.5	1040751.17	2.276
Blocks	3	19470550.0	6490183.33	
Error	9	4141165.5	460129.50	
Total	15	26752869.0		

$F = 2.276$, fail to reject H_0

15.41 a.

Source	df	Sum of Squares	Mean Square	F
Treatments	4	4195.603	1048.901	10.932
Blocks	3	336.354	112.118	
Error	12	1151.389	95.949	
Total	19	5683.348		

$F = 10.932$, reject H_0

b.

Source	5	2	1	4	3
Mean	51.975	53.525	67.575	77.35	90.25

15.45

Source	df	Sum of Squares	Mean Square	F
Size (A)	1	.088	.088	8.00
Species (B)	2	.048	.024	2.18
Interaction (AB)	2	.048	.024	2.18
Error	12	.132	.011	
Total	17	.316		

$F_{AB} = 2.18$, fail to reject H_0; $F_A = 8.00$, fail to reject H_0; $F_B = 2.18$, fail to reject H_0

15.47 $F_{AB} < 1$, fail to reject H_0; $F_A = 4.99$, reject H_0; $F_B = 4.81$, reject H_0

15.49

Source	df	Sum of Squares	Mean Square	F
Race (A)	1	857	857	5.57
Sex (B)	1	291	291	1.89
Interaction (AB)	1	32	32	.21
Error	36	5541	153.92	
Total	39	6721		

a. $F_{AB} = .21$, fail to reject H_0 **b.** $F_A = 5.57$, fail to reject H_0 **c.** $F_B = 1.89$, fail to reject H_0
15.51 $F_{RATE} = 76.14$, reject H_0; $F_{SOILTYPE} = 54.14$, reject H_0 **15.53** $KW = 23.11$, reject H_0
15.55 $F_r = 6.45$, fail to reject H_0 **15.57** $F_r = 12.25$, reject H_0
15.59 a. $F = 1286.312$, reject H_0

b.

Method	1	2	3	4	5
Mean	206.33	383.33	394.33	573.33	1257.00

15.61 $F = .73$, fail to reject H_0 **15.63** $F_{AB} = .44$, fail to reject H_0; $F_A = 2.76$, fail to reject H_0; $F_B = 13.28$, reject H_0
15.65 $F = 1117.28$, reject H_0

Mortar	PCM	OCM	RM	PIM
Mean	29.92	33.96	115.84	129.30

15.67 a. $F = .97$, fail to reject H_0 **b.** The Bonferoni intervals do not reveal any significant differences.   **15.69** $F_{LOCATION} = 1.89$, fail to reject H_0; $F_{MONTHS} = 9.20$, reject H_0 **15.71** $F = .90$, fail to reject H_0 **15.75** $F = .907$, fail to reject H_0 **15.77** $F = 3.22$, fail to reject H_0

CHAPTER 16

16.1 a. Reject H_0 if $X^2 > 9.49$ **b.** Reject H_0 if $X^2 > 13.28$ **c.** Reject H_0 if $X^2 > 21.67$ **16.3 a.** reject H_0 **b.** The Chi-square test should not be used since one of the expected counts is less than 5.   **16.5 a.** $X^2 = 4.03$, fail to reject H_0 **b.** P-value $> .10$ **16.7 a.** $X^2 = 4.63$, fail to reject H_0 **b.** $.05 < P$-value $< .10$ **c.** The analysis and conclusion would be the same.   **16.9** $X^2 = 4.8$, fail to reject H_0
16.11 a. df $= 12$, reject H_0 if $X^2 > 21.03$ **b.** $X^2 = 7.2$, fail to reject H_0 **c.** $X^2 = 14.5$, fail to reject H_0 **16.13** $X^2 = 9.844$, reject H_0
16.15 $X^2 = 131.496$, reject H_0 **16.17 a.** $X^2 = 22.45$, reject H_0 **b.** P-value $< .001$ **16.19** $X^2 = 20.155$, reject H_0
16.21 $X^2 = 133.02$, reject H_0 **16.23** $X^2 = 33.769$, reject H_0 **16.25** $X^2 = 22.45$, reject H_0 **16.27** $X^2 = 197.62$, reject H_0
16.29 b. $X^2 = 2.97$, fail to reject H_0 **16.31** $X^2 = 13.33$, fail to reject H_0 **16.33** $X^2 = 6.41$, fail to reject H_0 **16.35** $X^2 = 8.89$, reject H_0
16.37 $X^2 = 6.54$, reject H_0 **16.39** $X^2 = 7.44$, reject H_0 **16.41** $X^2 = 103.87$, reject H_0 **16.43** Combining the two usage categories of 3–6 and 7 or more (because some expected cell counts are less than 5) results in $X^2 = 73.03$, reject H_0.   **16.45** $X^2 = 11.65$, reject H_0

Index